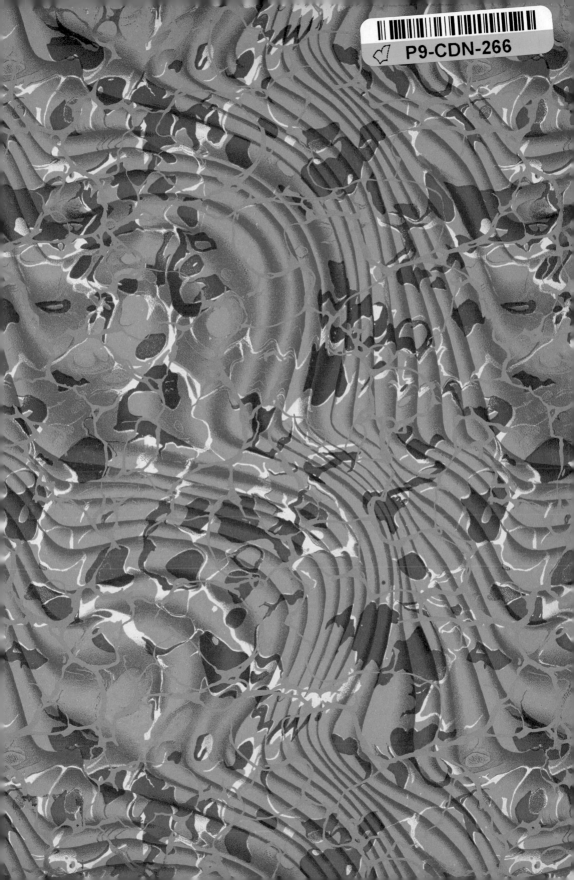
P9-CDN-266

Holy Ghost College,

Pittsburg, Pa

Duquèsne University
of the Holy Ghost
Pittsburgh Pa.

UNIVERSAL CLASSICS LIBRARY

APPLETON PRENTISS CLARK GRIFFIN
LIBRARY OF CONGRESS
EDITORIAL DIRECTOR

ILLUSTRATED
WITH PHOTOGRAVURES ON
JAPAN VELLUM, ETCHINGS
HAND PAINTED INDIA-PLATE
REPRODUCTIONS, AND
FULL PAGE PORTRAITS
OF AUTHORS.

M. WALTER DUNNE, PUBLISHER

MDV

WASHINGTON & LONDON

Copyright, 1901,
BY
M. WALTER DUNNE,
PUBLISHER

Jacobi 1901

CATHARINE II., EMPRESS OF RUSSIA

Hand-painted photogravure after Rosselin

CATHARINE II., EMPRESS OF RUSSIA

Hand-painted photogravure after Rosslin

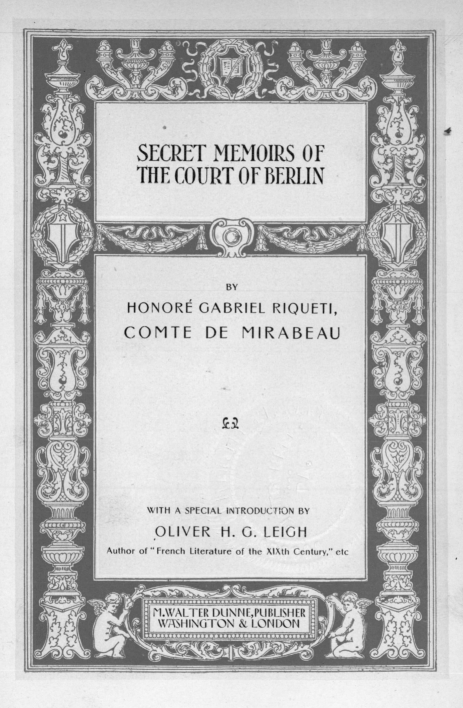

SECRET MEMOIRS OF THE COURT OF BERLIN

BY

HONORÉ GABRIEL RIQUETI,
COMTE DE MIRABEAU

WITH A SPECIAL INTRODUCTION BY

OLIVER H. G. LEIGH

Author of "French Literature of the XIXth Century," etc

M. WALTER DUNNE, PUBLISHER
WASHINGTON & LONDON

DD414
M643
1901 +
r92   cp 4
M671

COPYRIGHT, 1901,

BY

M. WALTER DUNNE,

PUBLISHER

ILLUSTRATIONS

(vii)

14188   JUN 27 1934

INTRODUCTION

PIQUANT entertainment used to be found by our grand-sires and dames in "secret memoirs" and "Mysteries" of high life. London and Paris each maintained its school for scandal, with an organ department in which the merest snatch of table-tattle was worked up into a fine fantasia of delicious mischief. In those antediluvian days there was a great gulf fixed between People who were People, and the people who were not. "Middle" and "Upper-Middle"—class scientific culture had not yet extended much beyond the musical glasses and a pious craze to explore the polar region of the court circle. The conscious nether world revelled in envious awe as it got these glimpses of distant spheres and gloried as it found their denizens frail. It was the day of a Paul Pry press, before the advent of the instrument with telescopic range and microscopic penetration, which could not but slacken interest in one constellation by revealing so much of so many.

There has been too pharisaical a view taken of the old-fashioned secret memoir. The gathering of facts known to the *entourage* of great personages, which throw even the fiercest glare upon those whose prominence challenges it, is not strictly a scandalous act though it may include scandals. The strong man bade his artist paint "warts and all." If society's head is sufficiently important to be portrayed for posterity, as it assuredly is, better it should be a portrait than a picture. Court chronicles were historical counterfeits. The demi-godded folk whose diplomatic marriages were deftly contrived to keep the business in the family, were by these veracious records of personal observations shown to be really humans. Rummage collections of faded letters with fadeless memories completed the Garlands which Friendship placed on the brow of the Great. The only corrective of pseudo-historical biography was the "secret" memoir, to which posterity owes more substantial acknowledgements than its affected blush fully expresses or hides.

Frederick the uniquely great is one of the few about whom we cannot know too much. Mirabeau came late on the scene, but brought with him such qualifications as a chronicler of royal and courtly and plebeian every-day passion-play acting as have seldom been so handily combined under one hat. He had passed the stiffest courses in the university of the world with honors and dishonors. A stranger career was never run to a sadder and more momentous ending. The wine may drink as lusciously out of a pipkin as a golden goblet, but only an exceptionally gifted observer is competent to make a study of outlandish men, manners, or movements.

Mirabeau's father was of the very last type that should have been chosen to pose, or rather impose, paternally over such a son. Born with a giant's capacity for public service and private mischief the young Count's unfortunate physiognomy won him the positive hatred of his Marquis father, who printed himself for the world to admire as "The Friend of Humanity," though he dropped the r in the case of his brilliant son. Young Mirabeau early became an expert in prison life, although not a legal prisoner. His boy-amours were the excuse for the father's lavish use of *lettres-de-cachet*, by means of which convenient rod he chastised the lad with years of prison odium. Philosopher though the Marquis supposed himself to be it was beyond him to perceive that thrashing a flour-sack or a boy is an excellent way to waste the fine and retain the course. The sorely handicapped youth lost his army chance by one escapade. Next, to facilitate affairs with a somewhat reluctant heiress, he used her maid, by arrangement, to hasten the gainful marriage. His income was small, but his debts did honor to his rank and talent. For this a paternal *lettre-de-cachet* placed him again in limbo, which was not cheered by the quarreling that accompanied his wife's visits. Three years after the marriage Mirabeau's confessedly forbidding face did not hinder a romantic attachment with Sophie de Ruffey, the eighteen-year-old wife of a rich man of sixty. Once again a *lettre* caged him but he escaped to

Holland, where the adoring Sophie followed him. This was in 1776, Gabriel in his twenty-seventh year. He dwelt in the Dutch Grub Street for a year, expert and diligent at all pen-work, solaced by the news that only his effigy had been duly executed under the death sentence his parent had secured. The confiscation also pronounced did not add to his poverty. By and by both were spied out, arrested, and brought back, the result being three years and a half in Vincennes Castle, apart from his Sophie. The outcome of his confinement was a batch of books, the "*Erotica Biblion*," and such like effusions of a genius, goaded like Burns's, when its tottery steps should have been gently led.

Being free once more in 1780 Mirabeau made his first effort in forensic pleading, urging the annulment of the extreme sentence. This his eloquence won, but not his repeated pleas for the restitution of conjugal rights with Sophie, now enjoying a separate income from her divorced husband. In 1784 Mirabeau went to England, accompanied by the daughter of a well-to-do citizen of Holland. He was received into distinguished society, and justice was done to his great talents, without condonation of his least pardonable faults. On returning to Paris he fell into the toils of a shameless creature who had ulterior schemes in view. His desertion of the devoted Madame de Nehra is still inexplicable.

He had established a certain claim to statesmanship by some writings, and Franklin had moved him to write his famous plea for the order of the Cincinnati, which was translated into English. In 1786 he went on a secret mission to the Prussian Court. Events in France were leading up to the breach between King and commoners. Mirabeau never sold a principle nor advocated for a fee a cause in which he had no faith, but it is true that his impecuniosity, at mid-age and at the turning point between drifting and leadership, led him to accept from the King's friends the wherewithal to clear his debts and take up the patriotic work which he alone had the sagacity, opportunity, and the genius effectively to do. The rest is familiar. He saw where the nation was being whirled, his eloquence and experience of the English compromise

government devolved on him the high duty of guiding
the helm of state. His hour had come, but the ripened
statesman found it was also his hour of doom for the
sins of a defiant physique. Strong and tall, bulldog
mien, Goethe's eyes, sensual, ambitious, vain of person,
and of an eloquence that could have saved his country
one indelible reproach, he died when supremely needed
by his people, and was only forty-two. The picture recalls Gambetta.

Mirabeau conversed with Frederick in the old man's last
illness. His report went up to the French King through
M. Calonne and the Duke de Lauzun. It led to nothing
in the way of definite assistance for the monarchy. He
gathered materials for his masterly work on the Prussian
monarchy, and the Prussian and Saxon States, published
in four volumes in 1788. Next year Mirabeau issued the
present work, in two volumes, "*Histoire Secrète et Anecdotes de la cour de Berlin*," in two octavo volumes. A
little reign of terror was inaugurated in royalty circles
by this startling work. Some sort of demonstration had
to be made, so, in cousinly affection as between King
and King poor Mirabeau's rich book was condemned by
the Parliament of Paris to be publicly burned by the common hangman, an honor once appreciated by Voltaire.
Its offense was the disrespectful treatment of the reigning King and other great personages in the course of its
exposure of intrigues by princes and courtesans in the
shadow of the Court.

As for the great Frederick himself, even scandals took
on a greatness to which they had no claim, by flickering
around his crown. The religious world was scandalized
by his anticipation of Huxleyan agnosticism, which was then,
too, dubbed "atheism." Goody-goodyism languished into
fits at his masculine toleration of fancy faiths. A man so
bad must be a worse King. His training, temperament,
and ascetic habits in all but eating were well known, but
the peccadilloes of any youthful lordling must necessarily
magnify into unspeakable vices if stumbled into by wearers
of purple, who are the wicked world's mark for temptation.

Frederick married to please his father, who out-Mira-
beaued Mirabeau *père* in outrageous misrule of his son.

He married at twenty-two and took the crown at twenty-eight. Thenceforward his heart went out to strong men, to men of genius, men of his own stamp, men and not women. For the last half of his reign Frederick dined with his amiable consort; when they met at table the King bowed to the Queen and the Queen to the King, but they never conversed. He paid her the customary pretty gift courtesies on anniversary days, and once went to her room to tell his regrets over her gouty seizure, but converse they never did all those years, and she survived him by eleven.

The Court of Frederick had its full sheaf of eighteenth century scandals. His relations, his henchmen, the distinguished writers, musicians, philosophers (alas!) had their foibles and met their fascinating fates in that once upon a time Liberty Hall. As already observed, even these small-beer chronicles have their legitimate and even admirable historical uses. The flamboyant schools always paint "personages" posing as sublimities, and it requires the faithful pencil of the old Dutch realist to complete the *vraisemblance* to life. Frederick, as King at least, was no voluptuary. Indeed it was thought an act of pious duty to vindicate his memory from a slander of the most unlikely kind, by making a *post-mortem* examination akin to that decreed to be made prior to the election of each Pope. He was first and last a soldier and a martinet, afflicted with a weakness for mistaking feminine grace for insipidity and womanliness as either wanton or prudish extremes. He showered alternate contempt and ferocious hatred on men he had thought were proof to sparkling eyes. And yet, no court more than his was swayed by the mysterious influence that blows where it listeth and is not seen until its work is virtually done. These secret memoirs are, of course, excellent reading, racy of the temper of the writer and of his subject and the times.

Oliver H. Leigh.

CONTENTS

EDITOR'S PREFACE

MIRABEAU, exiled to Prussia on a secret mission, has left behind him, in the following work, a curious account of his sojourn at the Court of Frederick the Great. It is generally supposed that these letters were addressed to Calonne.

The last moments of Frederick are therein depicted in a vivid and lifelike manner, and every portrait that Mirabeau essayed to paint bears the mark of a master's hand. However, Frederick dies, and the writer has no longer anything but low intrigues to depict, as he is now surrounded only by little men and little interests.

If he is reproached with including in this work several scandalous revelations, it must be remembered that " The Secret History " was never intended to see the light of day, and that it was quite contrary to the author's wishes that it was published. It was also in direct opposition to his wishes that the " *Lettres à Sophie*," and others of his productions, were issued.

The manuscript of " The Secret History " was stolen, sold to Malassis, a printer of Alençon, and published by him as a work by an unknown traveler who had died about a year previously in a village in Germany. Twenty thousand copies of the book were speedily disposed of.

The original manuscript, in Mirabeau's handwriting, remained in the printer's possession, and great care was taken that, in every edition issued by him, all the names and certain passages were suppressed and indicated by asterisks only. Unfortunately, the manuscript was subsequently burned. M. Dubois-du-Desert, who had the privilege of inspecting this manuscript before its destruction, has communicated to us all the names, of which he had taken a note. This it is that is known as the " Key "

I

to "The Secret History." A very small number of the
names have been lost, and it is impossible for us, after
this long interval, to repair these omissions.

The following are some appropriate reflections included
in the Preface, written by M. Brissot-Thivars, for the
edition of 1821:

"The ministerial modesty, which so easily reconciled
itself to the secret picture of the licentiousness of a
neighboring Court, grew much alarmed at the prospect
of a similar picture of their own Court being exhibited
to the public gaze. The Government received orders to
confiscate the book, and to prosecute the author, who
had disappeared under an anonymous name. Meanwhile
the public were much rejoiced at the ill humor displayed
by the Court.

"The *Etats-Généraux* were convoked, the nobility repulsed Mirabeau, the Commons welcomed him with open
arms, and the privileged classes heaped insults and abuse
upon the author of 'The Secret History.'"

Among the most noticeable pamphlets issued at this
period, was one entitled "*L' Examen politique et critique
de l' Histoire secrète de la Cour de Berlin,*" *par Frédéric,
Baron de Trenck.**

"The Baron de Trenck was a Prussian, and had, therefore, some right to enter the lists. It was also to his
interest to do so, as for some time he had been in bad
odor with his Government, and he was only too rejoiced to purchase his pardon by breaking a lance in
honor of his country.

"Mirabeau pretends that the Prussians are a dull people.
The Baron de Trenck admits that this is the case; but,
he adds, they are so systematically.

"Mirabeau hints that the two sons of Prince Ferdinand are really the sons of the Comte de Schmettau. The
Baron de Trenck replies that he has closely examined
the children of Princess Ferdinand. 'They are,' he says,
'destined to occupy glorious positions in the House of

---

* "Political and Critical Examination of the Secret History of the
Court of Berlin," by Frédéric, Baron de Trenck. A thick 8vo volume.
The Baron de Trenck was known by his misfortunes and by his sundry
writings.

Brandenburg. I would never guarantee,' he adds, 'the birth of any man; all that I can certify is that he is the son of a man. It is to be hoped that, in certain European royal families, they will act as they do in England toward the race horses. It is unnecessary and absurd to try and discover who are the fathers of the kings who rule over us. It is often much better that they owe their existence to wise and vigorous plebeians than to a self-styled "noble" race, which is in no way superior to others, save by an opinion based upon absurd prejudices. I heartily congratulate Prince Ferdinand on being the head of so interesting a family.'

"Mirabeau, having related some amorous scenes of Frederick William, the Baron gravely examines the two following questions:

"1. Is it true that the King of Prussia is fond of women? Nobody doubts it.

"2. Is this a crime in a king? William, in love, is capable of a tender attachment. He understands how to value his mistress. Refined and sensitive, it is by the personal interest that he inspires, that he endeavors to find favor in the eyes of the woman he loves. He puts aside all rank and power. It is solely for himself that he would win the lady's affection. Mademoiselle de Voss resisted his wooing during twenty months. The tardy gratification of his desires did not cool his passion. In the present condition of Prussia the King may prefer the myrtles of Cupid to the laurels of Mars.

"Did the reputation of Baron de Trenck re-establish Frederick William and the Prince Ferdinand — the one in his paternal rights, and the other in the respect and veneration which a virtuous monarch has the right to expect from his subjects? We do not think it did. It appears to us, on the contrary, that it will remain proved that Mirabeau had correctly observed, and that he stated the truth, since his adversary is reduced to representing concubinage and adultery as the accustomed pastime of the nobility and as the legitimate resource of a monarch. Mirabeau's statements, therefore, must have been based largely on facts, since there did not exist any other means of extenuating the scandal.

"In the absence of logic and reason, Baron de Trenck had recourse to abuse of Mirabeau, whom he vilified as an impostor and a spy. Such insults, however, proved nothing; and, even at the present time, there are those who firmly believe in the truth of Mirabeau's assertions.*

"At the date of the publication of 'The Secret History,' time had strongly confirmed nearly all of Mirabeau's predictions — the invasion of Holland, the ridiculous combinations of the French Cabinet, etc., at the present day — after a lapse of thirty years. Some personages who are still living are attacked; for instance, he says, 'The Duke of York arrived here this evening. This Duke is a great sportsman, fond of laughter, but without grace, deportment, or politeness; and, judging from external appearances, he possesses many of the moral and physical features of the Duc de Luynes. I do not think that there is any question of his marriage with Princess Caroline of Brunswick, who is very amiable, intellectual, handsome, and vivacious.'"

The Princess Caroline, who was married in 1759 to the Prince of Wales, was divorced after he had become King of England.

"It must be admitted, however, that Mirabeau was sometimes mistaken in his judgments. He judged mankind; and, for good or for evil, the human species is subject to variations. Time and education modify the character, and alter the inclinations. The horoscope that Mirabeau cast of the Prince Royal of Prussia, the present reigning monarch, was it realized? Did that Prince resuscitate the great Frederick?"

Mirabeau recommends l'Abbé de Périgord to M. de Calonne. "L'Abbé de Périgord," he says, "combines a talent of a rare order and great experience with a profound circumspection and an unfailing secrecy. It would be impossible for you to choose a man who is more

---

* In all matters apart from the Prussian monarchy, or Ministry, and any facts relating to either, Baron de Trenck renders full justice to Mirabeau; he even admits the accuracy of Mirabeau's estimate of political affairs, and of his profound knowledge of the actual state of Europe.

anxious to do good, and who would be more eager to show his gratitude." Prince de Talleyrand, before the Revolution, bore the name of *l'Abbé de Périgord*.

Among the curious facts relating to this work, we should not omit to give a copy of the Decree ordering it to be burned. We reproduce this document as an example of the jurisprudence of the period.

"Decree of the Court of Parliament, the Chambers assembled, the Peers being present, condemning a printed book entitled: 'The Secret History of the Court of Berlin; or, the Correspondence of a French Traveler' (Comte de Mirabeau, *Député de la Sénéchaussée d' Aix aux États-Généraux*), to be torn and burned by the Public Executioner."

EXTRACT FROM THE PARLIAMENTARY REGISTER OF THE
10TH OF FEBRUARY, 1789.

"This day the Court, the Chambers assembled, the Peers being present, and the King's representatives being admitted, M. Antoine Louis Séguier, Advocate to the King, opened the proceedings in the following words:—

"'GENTLEMEN, — Justly indignant at the impression produced by a libel as surprising as it is atrocious, the King, in placing in our hands the two printed works which we have brought before you, relies upon the vigilance of the Ministry to denounce and condemn them.

"'This libel, which has spread itself through the Capital, has already caused the greatest sensation. It has been received with a cry of indignation, the public verdict has been given, and this work of darkness has already been stamped with the seal of universal reprobation.

"'It is within the rights of Justice to proscribe, with the strongest qualifications, a correspondence which the author seeks to disown by announcing it as the secret agent of a minister who wishes to remain unknown. In denouncing this clandestine work, therefore, we propose to proceed against both the author and the printer, if it is possible to discover them.

"'You will doubtless feel some surprise that our Ministry, so long a dumb recipient of the complaints addressed to it by all the Orders of the State, was not to be awakened out of its voluntary inaction, excepting by the command of the King himself. But at this critical moment, when every day sees some fresh production, alternately extravagant and wise, violent and moderate, circumspect and licentious, dictated by party spirit and inspired by patriotism; in this universal madness, when the indefinite liberty of the Press distributes with equal profusion the fruits of knowledge, of ignorance, and of frenzy; in this total inversion of principles, it required nothing less than an order emanating from the Throne to decide us to fulfill those functions which would be indispensable under all other circumstances, but which it seemed to us prudent to suspend, in the midst of the fanaticism of opinions. There are moments when, by a kind of public discretion, or decency, the magistrate should not consult the oracle of the Law.

"'There is no need for dissimulation on our part, and we regard with an unfeeling eye the product of resentment and vengeance. The past is a guarantee for the future. We have no fear in making this avowal in the presence of magistrates who, while demanding the legitimate liberty of the Press, are very far from countenancing the publication of the deluge of anonymous sheets, and the seditious and scandalous pamphlets, with which France is inundated. Tolerance degenerates into abuse, impunity encourages license, and license has reached its last stage. Nothing is respected; rank, position, services rendered are forgotten; the nobles, and even crowned heads themselves, become objects of derision and satire. The evil is so widespread that one fears to augment the epidemic in attempting to stay its progress.

"'The slightest prohibition of a work is sufficient to make the author celebrated, to accelerate its sale, at double the original price, and to give a wider publicity to imposture and calumny.

"'The work which we are now denouncing was not written with the intention of still further fertilizing the germs of discord which are already too much scattered throughout the kingdom, but it is of a nature likely to influence the reception, and the mode of existence, of the

French nobility at foreign Courts; and far from confirming the high opinion which it has always gained for its generosity, far from being characterized by that frank and loyal spirit of ancient chivalry, which led it on to honor and glory, this vile and infamous production cannot but inspire the strongest prejudice against a people at once polite, natural, complaisant, and quick to familiarize itself wherever it finds an opportunity of displaying its wit, or of captivating hearts by the charm of that sociability which distinguishes it from the other European nations.

"'This work, in two volumes, is entitled: "The Secret History of the Court of Berlin; or, Correspondence of a French Traveler, from the month of July, 1786, until the 19th January, 1787. Posthumous work, 1789;" without the names of either author or printer, or the place where printed.

"'This title would seem to indicate that the author was no longer in existence, and that the work was therefore published without his knowledge or consent; but supposing, as the title-page states, that the Secret History is the result of observations made by a writer who had ceased to exist, if it has taken two entire years to print and distribute a work of this nature, is it not obvious that the publisher is even more culpable than the author, since he has given publicity to a correspondence written under the seal of confidence, and which, therefore, was never intended to become a means of defamation, or to supply food for the scandal mongers?

" 'The period at which this Secret History commences will be forever memorable in the annals of Germany. The short space of time which it includes was full of events likely to affect the policy of many a monarchy. Frederick II., whose name alone was sufficient to preserve that balance of power which assured to Europe general peace and happiness, Frederick still reigned; but this Prince was fast declining, and his power and fame, which did not abandon him during life, seemed to await him even at the tomb.

" 'It was at this moment that the self-styled " *Voyageur français* " endeavored to ingratiate himself with the greatest personages of the State, in order to gather any stray scraps of conversation, and to endeavor, in the midst of the trouble and commotion caused by the unforeseen changes of a new ruler to surprise ministerial secrets, to detect the aims and ambitions of the nobles, to expose the intrigues of courtesans, and to fathom the plots of the Court.

"'If one is to believe this disguised observer, his ability surmounts all obstacles. He is at once welcomed, and, far from being suspected, he seems to have obtained almost general confidence. Princes treat him with kindness; the Ministers put him in possession of State secrets; the nobles admit him into their society; the political veil is rent asunder for his benefit; Frederick dies; Frederick William succeeds him; the army has not yet taken the oath of allegiance, and yet this attentive politician is aware of the spirit, the character, and the resources of those in authority. The plan of administration is no longer a mystery, and even the King himself, who suspects his mission, does not take offense at his assiduity or his *liaisons*.

"'After having explained the system upon which the correspondence would be based; after having explained the sources from which he proposes to draw his information; in fact, after having exposed his relations and his intimacy with the principal members of the Royal Family, the first object with which the author has thought it his duty to concern himself is the panegyric on the King which Prussia has just lost. He eulogizes that great man, and he is nearly the only person of whom he speaks highly, or even of whom he does not speak ill, in a Secret History which has no other authenticity than that of the observations, estimates, and the combinations, true or false, of a writer who possessed neither title nor qualification.

"'And how was it that he did not render to Frederick II. the justice that was his due? Worthy of the admiration of his century, our soldiers were sent to be instructed in his schools, to study his manœuvers and his evolutions, and, above all, his military discipline, in the hope of transferring to France some portion of that genius which had founded a new school of tactics, and which had, in some sort, revolutionized the art of war. Amid the homage which truth sometimes forces from this mysterious correspondent, one discovers reproaches against the memory of the greatest man in Europe; but, notwithstanding this critical observer and his remarks, his reflections and his criticisms, Frederick, the friend of science and the protector of literature, legislator and philosopher, profound politician and indefatigable warrior, combined in his person, and displayed on his throne, all the gifts of a hero and a king. His name, even before his death, was inscribed in the temple of Immortality.

" 'Why did not the author of this correspondence show the same respect for a prince of the same blood, animated by the same spirit, and endowed with the same talents? Did not Prince Henry prove himself to be a general worthy of commanding his august brother, to second his views, and to execute his projects? Frederick himself, on learning of his success, could not suppress a feeling of rivalry. The greatest generals and the most famous captains are sometimes at fault; the ablest have their reverses. Alone exempt from the common destiny of mankind, fortune seems, in his case, to have renounced its natural inconsistency, or, rather, the experience of Prince Henry enabled him to control the caprices of fortune, and to fix the victory under his standard. Could we but examine here the witnesses of his brave deeds, the companions of his glory, the only true judges of his merit, they would say, with one voice, that, gentle and affable in the everyday affairs of life, intrepid and at ease in action, humane and compassionate after the combat, by a most happy accord of the most eminent qualities, he combined the activity of Hannibal, the prudence of Fabius, and the wisdom of Scipio.

" 'But is it necessary for us to call witnesses to prove the bravery and genius of a prince whose name is revered by both officers and soldiers? It is for the French army to avenge the insults. A magistrate, a friend of peace, is not the proper man to pronounce his eulogy; and the Minister of Justice would hardly dare to add his voice to the general acclamations of this celebrated Prince.

" 'One is tempted to believe that, from the midst of his "nebulous position," the author has taken upon himself to open the flood gates of his malice nnd animosity on all those whose positions and characters are above suspicion, and who are worthy of his respect. It is not enough to have showered invectives on the uncle of the new King, the King himself, his august family, the princesses of the blood, and the Ministry; in fact the whole Court is treated with such a criminal indecency, that we should blush to repeat the infamous expressions of which the author has made use.

" 'His "amphibious existence" enables him sometimes to wander from his native land; his imagination transports him to far distant countries, to Austria, to Poland, and to the northernmost lands; and it is always with the same culpable purpose of collecting fresh horrors, of filling his correspondence with untruthful statements, and to circulate with his discoveries the blackest calumnies.

" 'What opinion can one form of this Secret History, which is even more abominable than that of the historian, Procopius, who, when criticising an emperor, did at least refer to his merits as well as his demerits? It presents us with nothing but a collection of shameful impostures, highly improbable and easily invented, more for the purpose of gratifying the mania of the author, than for attracting the curiosity of the reader in search of knowledge.

" 'It is a collection of portraits in which the artist's imagination is largely predominant. His hand has mixed the colors with the bitter spleen with which his brush was already filled; and, if we are told that he painted his subjects as they appeared to him, it must be remembered that his prejudiced eye enveloped them in that shade in which he was himself obscured.

" 'It is an assemblage of reflections based indiscriminately upon malicious conversations, upon lying reports, upon fictitious secrets, and upon allegations which have since been proved untrue. All these have been written down without thought or hesitation, and the author has no fear in asserting that they are veritable facts, because

it was the only return he could make for the treatment
he received, of the mediocrity of which he is constantly
complaining.

" 'It is most unfortunate to possess great talent when
one has not sufficient force of character to apply it to
good purposes. If the corruption of the soul stifle the
sentiment of honor and the cry of conscience, genius is
a disastrous gift from Nature. What are we to think of
a writer who voluntarily adopts the rôle of anonymous
accuser; who settles himself in a foreign Court with that
frankness, that ease, that amenity, which leads to the
forming of *liaisons;* and who, ere long, abusing the sentiments which he had inspired, dares to reveal particulars which he has learned in the most intimate confidence;
who dares to slander all those who have received him with
kindness, dares to make insinuations and suggestions concerning them which are entirely unjustifiable; and who
even carries his audacity to the length of insulting, with
a brutal cynicism, those whose station is so greatly above
that of this "*agent subalterne*" (for so he styles himself)
that it is difficult to place any confidence in his assertions; because, if they were true, his relations with people of rank must have been most intimate — in fact, they
must have treated him as an equal? Again, what man
would wish to expose himself before his equal? The
nobles may lay aside their rank in their own households;
it is frequently necessary for them to do so. But a king,
or prince, or a man of dignity, always knows how to
respect himself before a stranger; should any familiari-
ties or confidences be accorded to him, it is done with
suspicion and is but temporary.

" 'What must have been the result, therefore, when this
stranger himself admits that he is regarded as a spy?
And if he is suspected of wishing to find out the secrets
of the Government, would not a wise circumspection suggest the advisability of deceiving him by making a pretense of that confidence which he is so eager to abuse?

" 'Let us suppose, nevertheless, that the author, deceived by false reports or by feigned contrivances,
believed that he was really a witness of all that he inserted in his correspondence: the entire work would still

be a violation of the Law of Nations, an abuse of hospitality, an infamy the more unpardonable in that familiarity was with him but the cloak of perfidiousness, and that the closest friendship became the instrument of treachery.

" ' These reflections lead necessarily to the pronouncement of judgment both upon the author of this pretended posthumous work and upon itself. And, in the first place, it is by simple and by sure rules that the author may be judged without error.

" ' Has he placed himself beyond the laws of honor and probity? Has he gone beyond the bounds of decency? Has he so far forgotten himself as to violate public morality? Has he been wanting in that respect of which the French are ever ready to accord the most touching proofs to their King,—respect impelled as much by love as by duty, but respect that every Frenchman owes to other nations, whether they are friends or enemies of France; which every man owes to other men, and which every one owes to himself? This writer has an unruly spirit. His natural perversity makes him rash, violent, and passionate; and, after having broken down all the barriers that prudence opposes to his license, he only brings trouble and remorse into the hearts of those who are unfortunate enough to allow themselves to be entrapped by his fables, his lies, and his calumnies.

" ' We are, nevertheless, bound to admit that, if this unknown author only fulfilled the particular mission which he pretends to have received; if the letters which compose this Secret History were written by him only to be sent direct to their destination; if he made no copies of them; if it was not by his act that they were made public; in fact, if he is entirely innocent of the printing of this work, however ignominious may be the obscure person who played this part, it is for him alone to reproach himself with his baseness and crime, and justice cannot hold as a crime the publication of his correspondence. The publisher only merits prosecution, and the printer, equally guilty, should share the punishment of an offense which is as contrary to public honesty as it is to the Law of Nations.

" ' With regard to the work itself, it is difficult to consider this " Correspondence " otherwise than as a defamatory libel worthy of all the rigor of the law. By a species of fatality, writings of this nature generally excite the curiosity; the more they are vicious, the more they are sought after. The human heart permits itself to be so easily attracted toward that which is evil. In censuring the writer, one gives publicity to his libels. The malicious smile, the honest man contents himself with a sigh, and the defamation remains unpunished; whereas general indignation should denounce and prosecute the slanderer. " The Secret History of the Court of Berlin " has not received the same indulgent treatment. Public opinion was shocked, and it measured the insult, not by the man who uttered it, but by the elevated position of those against whom it was directed. The disparity of rank seemed to add to the gravity of the outrage. The libel was regarded as sufficient to excite the indignation of all the Powers, should the law not hasten to proscribe the work.

" ' It is by the King's command that we have denounced this fictitious correspondence; it is in his name that we demand its condemnation; and, after having consigned it to the flames, we call upon the Ministry to employ every effort for the discovery of the author, publisher, and printer.

" ' This, then, is the conclusion of our indictment, which we place before the Court, together with the two volumes referred to, of which the following is a faithful description:

" ' A printed work, in two volumes, entitled: " The Secret History of the Court of Berlin; or, Correspondence of a French Traveler, from the month of July, 1786, until 19th January, 1787. A posthumous work, 1789;" without names of either the author or printer, containing — Vol. i., 318 pages; vol. ii., 376 pages.'

[*Conclusion of the indictment of the Procureur-général of the King. Follows the decision of the Court.*]

" The Court orders that the two volumes be destroyed and burned in the courtyard of the palace, at the foot of

the grand staircase, by the public executioner, the Court
being of the opinion that the volumes contain defamatory
and slanderous libels, which are contrary to the respect
due to other Powers, and in opposition to our laws and
those of other nations. The Court calls upon all those
who possess copies of this work to deliver them up to
the clerk of this Court in order that they may be destroyed. It also strictly prohibits all printers and booksellers from printing or selling copies of this work, and
all *colporteurs* and distributors from hawking or distribu-
ting it, under penalty of prosecution and punishment with
such rigor as the law may permit. And the Court further ordains that, at the request of the *Procureur-général*
of the King, information may be heard against the author,
printer, and publisher, before the *Conseilleur-rapporteur*
that the Court may appoint, for the witnesses at Paris;
and before the *Lieutenant-criminel des bailliages et sénéchaussées du ressort*, for such witnesses as may reside in
the provinces, having regard to the printing and distribu-
ting of this work. The Court ordains that the present
Decree be printed and posted up in all public places, and
that copies may be sent to all *bailliages et sénéchaussées
du ressort*, for a similar purpose. The Court enjoins upon
the deputies of the *Procureur-général du roi* to give this
matter their attention, and to report to the Court within
a month from this date. Given in Parliament, fully assembled, the Peers being present, the tenth day of
February, the year seventeen hundred and eighty-nine.

"(Verified) CLUTTON.

"(Signed) ISABEAU.

"And the same date (10th February, 1789), at the rising of the Court, the aforesaid work, entitled 'The
Secret History of the Court of Berlin; or, Correspondence of a French Traveler,' was destroyed and burned
by the Public Executioner, at the foot of the grand staircase in the Palace, in the presence of me, Dagobert
Étienne Isabeau, esquire, one of the clerks of the *Grande
Chambre*, assisted by two ushers of the Court.

"(Signed) ISABEAU."

At the end of the Secret History will be found a letter addressed by Mirabeau to Frederick William II., on the day of his ascension to the throne. He was the nephew of the great Frederick, and the father of the present King.

This Prince is not much known as a soldier, his only experience in the art of warfare being during the invasion of Champagne in 1792. He received Mirabeau's letter with kindness, but he did not foresee the destiny which the " *Voyageur français* " had traced for him.

C. Y.

SECRET COURT MEMOIRS

THE COURT OF BERLIN

LETTER I.*

July 5th, 1786.

SIR,—I have the honor to write to you by the first post, to inform you that the Berlin mail, for which I waited before I would enter my carriage, has brought me no letter. It is possible, but not probable, that the letter of my correspondent has been sent too late for the post. It is also possible, and very likely, nay, if the Comte de Vergennes has received no intelligence it is almost certain, that the great event either approaches or is past; for I hold it as infallible that, when death becomes inevitable, the couriers will be stopped. This, sir, deeply engages my attention, and I shall hasten with all expedition to Brunswick, where I shall gain certain information; there I shall remain several days if the King is living.

I have at present only to add, I shall think no labor, time, or trouble too great if I can but serve you, monsieur, and the cause of the public.

I shall not repeat any of our conversations, but shall take the liberty to offer you my advice, solely founded on my personal attachment; of which you cannot doubt,

---

* This letter is evidently addressed to a Minister, who had given the traveler some secret commission to execute. It seems evident to us that this Minister was M. de Calonne; and the following letter is extremely curious, as it leads to prove that, from the beginning of the year 1786, M. de Calonne was determined on the Assembly of the Notables; whom he convoked and directed, in 1787, with so much perilous and fatal precipitation.

since, independent of that amiable seduction which you exercise with power so irresistible, our interests are the same. The torrent of your affairs, the activity of cabals, the efforts of every kind which you so prodigally are obliged to make, render it impossible that you should yourself class and arrange the grand projects which your genius has brought to maturity, and which are ready to bud and bloom. You have testified some regret that I, for the present, declined performing this office for you. Permit me therefore, monsieur, to name a person who is, in every respect, worthy of this mark of your confidence.

The Abbé de Périgord, to consummate and practical abilities, joins profound circumspection and inviolable secrecy. You never can select a man more to be depended upon; or one who will with more fervent piety bow before the shrine of gratitude and friendship; who will be more anxiously active in good, less covetous of others' fame, or one with superior conviction that fame is justly due to him, only, who has the power to conceive and the fortitude to execute.

He possesses another advantage. His ascendency over Panchand represses the defects of the latter, which have been so described to you as to inspire fears, and sets all his great qualities and uncommon talents, which daily become more necessary to you, in action. There is no man who can guide and rule M. Panchand like the Abbé de Périgord, who will momentarily become more valuable to you the better to effect a grand money measure, without which no other measures can be effected. You may confide that delicate business to the Abbé de Périgord, which, especially in the present moment, ought not to be trusted to clerks. The noble, the enlightened, the civic project of drawing inferences from the numerous false statements that infest the accounts of Ministers (and which, being compared to the true statements, caused, or rather obliged, the King to determine that decisive measures should give France a national credit, and consequently a legal constitution) cannot be better realized than by the joint labors of these two persons. One of them has long been devoted to you; and the other will be, whenever any single act of benevolence shall excite his emulation. Condescend to believe, monsieur, that you cannot act more to your own interest.

I was desirous of writing thus to-night, because it would neither be delicate nor decent for the person interested to read what I have written; and this letter is the last you will receive that must not pass through the hands of a third person. My attachment, monsieur, to you, and your fame, induces me to hope you will place some confidence in this counsel, if I may so venture to call it; and that it will not be ranked among the least of the proofs of the most devoted respect with which I am, etc.

LETTER II.

BRUNSWICK, July 12th, 1786.

THAT the King is very ill is very certain; but he is
not at the point of death. Zimmermann, the famous
Hanoverian physician, whom he sent for, has declared that, if he would be careful, he might still live;
but he is incorrigible on the article of abstinence. He
still mounts his horse, and he even trotted fifty paces
some days since, with a man on each side of him; but
it is nevertheless true that he has the dropsy; and in
reality, he has not been any better since my departure.

I shall not see the reigning Duke of Brunswick before
this evening; he is in the country. He has powerfully
supported the election which the Chapters of Hildesheim
and Paderborn have lately made of a coadjutor. M.
Furstemberg has been elected. Vienna caballed exceedingly in favor of the Archduke Maximilian. It appears
that the Duke wishes to promote peace, since he endeavors, by every means, to strengthen the Germanic
confederation, which certainly has that only for its end,
though the means may give room for reflection. I have
my reasons for being of that opinion, which I shall explain on some other occasion. To-day I am at the mercy
of the courier.

Parties are very busy at Berlin; especially that of
Prince Henry, who is eternally eager, without well
knowing what he wishes. But all is silence in the King's
presence; he still is King, and so will remain to the
last moment.

As the immediate death of the King is not expected,
I shall continue at Brunswick some days, in order to
prepare him for my return (much more premature
than I had announced) and that I may more nearly
study the Duke.

(20)

The coinage continues to be an object of contention, and exaggerated discredit. I think it would be of use to publish apologetic reasons concerning the gold coin, confessing its too high rate (for wherefore deny that which is demonstrated?); and justificatory proofs, relative to the silver, the crowns of sixty-nine, and those since 1784, still remaining prohibited.

You no doubt know that the Duke, Louis of Brunswick,* has quitted Aix-la-Chapelle, and is retired to Eisenach. The troubles of that petty republic may perhaps explain his retreat; but these do not seem to me sufficient motives for his new abode, and for this single reason, that the Duchess of Weymar is his niece.

* Not the reigning Duke of Brunswick, just before mentioned, but his uncle, the late Prime Minister of the Stadtholder; or rather the late effective regent of the United Provinces.

LETTER III.

July 14th, 1786.

I DINED and supped yesterday with the Duke. When we
rose from table, after dinner, he took me aside to the
window, where we conversed for about two hours,
with much reserve at first, on his part, afterward with
more openness, and at last with an evident desire to be
thought sincere.

An expression of esteem for the Comte de Vergennes,
and fear for his approaching retreat, gave occasion to
this private conversation. The expression alluded to was
immediately followed by the question (which was asked
in a tone of affected indifference, and betrayed a very
strong degree of curiosity), "No doubt M. de Breteuil
will be his successor?" The Duchess was of our party.
I answered, lowering my voice, but articulating with
great firmness, "I hope and believe not." It was after
I had said this that he led me to the window, at the far
end of the apartment. He presently began to converse,
with all the energy which his slowness and native dignity
admit, of the inquietude which the Germanic body could
not avoid feeling, should M. de Breteuil, who was at the
head of the Austrian party, and who has long been a
servant and friend of the Cabinet of Vienna, succeed to
the place of first Minister.

I replied (speaking of the Comte de Vergennes with
every respect, and of the generous and pacific intentions
of the King with great confidence) that, should the Comte
de Vergennes retire, it would probably be of his own
free will; and that no one would have greater influence
than himself in the choice of his successor; that consequently, whether he remained in office or went out, the
first Minister would not be of the Austrian party; and,
though most assuredly the probity of the King, and the
morale of his politics, would continue to render the con-

nections between the Courts of Vienna and Versailles respected, as they would all others, yet, that the interest of Europe, and of France in particular, was so intimately united to the continuance of peace, that these connections, far from inciting war, could but contribute to render peace durable; that France was sufficiently puissant, from innate strength and from the state of her affairs, honorably to own that she dreaded war, which she would take every care to shun; that I did not think sudden war probable, especially when, studying the administration of the Duke of Brunswick, I perceived that he had performed his duties, of Prince and father, with so much assiduity and success; that, however natural it might be for man to seek that career, in which he was indubitably the first, I could not believe he (the Duke) would sacrifice to the desire of military renown, so much of which he had already acquired, his favorite work, his real enjoyments, and the inheritance of his children; that all circumstances called him to supreme influence over the affairs of Prussia after the death of the great King, and that, Prussia being at this time the pivot on which continental war or peace were balanced, he (the Duke of Brunswick) would almost singly decide which was to ensue; that he had formerly sufficiently shone the hero of war, and that I was convinced he would hereafter remain the angel of peace.

He then forcibly denied ever having been fond of war; even at the time when he had been most fortunate. He showed, independent of his principles, how ardently his family and personal interest would induce him to beware of war. "And if it were necessary," added he, "in an affair so important, to consult nothing further than the despicable gratification of self-love, do I not know how much war is the sport of chance? I have formerly not been unfortunate. I might hereafter be a better general, and yet might not have the same success. No prudent man, especially one who is advanced in life, will risk his reputation in so hazardous a pursuit, if it may be avoided."

This part of his discourse, which was long, animated, energetic, and evidently sincere, was preceded by a phrase of etiquette and remonstrance, in which he assured me that he never should possess, and was far from desiring to possess, any influence in Prussia. To this phrase I reverted; and, by a rapid sketch, proving to him that I was well acquainted with Berlin, the principal actors there, and the present state of men and things, I demonstrated (which he most certainly knows better than I do) that his interest, the interest of his house, of Germany, and of Europe, made it a duty in him to take the helm of State in Prussia; to preserve that kingdom from the hurricane most fatal to States, the strength of which principally depends upon opinion. I mean from petty intrigues, petty passions, and want of stability and consistency of system. "Your personal dignity," added I, "which is truly immense, and a thousand times more elevated than your rank, however eminent that may be, no doubt forbids you to tender your services; but it is your duty, I will not say not to refuse, no, I repeat, it is your duty to take measures, and employ all your abilities, all your powers, to gain an ascendency over the successor, and to seize the direction of affairs."

This mode of treatment greatly developed the man. He spoke with truth, and consequently with a degree of confidence, of Berlin. He told me Count Hertzberg had not let him remain ignorant of our intimacy; he depicted many of the persons who have influence, such as I know them to be. I clearly saw that there was a coolness, founded on some unknown subject, between him and the Prince of Prussia;* that he (the Duke of Brunswick) neither loved nor esteemed Prince Henry; and that his (the Duke's) party was as powerfully formed as it could be, in a country hitherto little in the habit of cabal, but which, perhaps, will presently be initiated. I purposely assumed much faith in the warlike dispositions of the Cabinet of Berlin. The Duke gave good proofs that, independent of the Heir Apparent, who, though personally brave, was not warlike, as well because of his manners and habits as of his prodigious stature, it would be madness to begin; that the moment of acquisition by arms, which, perhaps, still was neces-

* The Heir Apparent.

sary to Prussia, was not yet come; and that it was necessary to consolidate, etc., etc. All this was very serious, very sensible, and very circumstantial.

The Oriental system, Russia, Poland, Courland, all passed in review.

They still have their fears concerning the Oriental system; that is to say, concerning the part that we might take. They seem to believe that Russia will never powerfully second the Emperor, except in support of the Oriental system, and whatever may contribute to its success. Poland is to reconstruct. We remitted speaking of it, as well as of Courland. Suddenly, and by a very abrupt transition (it seems to me he employs transitions to surprise the secrets of those with whom he converses, and on whom he earnestly fixes his eyes while he listens), he asked what I meant to do at Berlin. " Complete my knowledge of the North," answered I, " which I have had little opportunity of studying, except at that city; since Vienna and Petersburg are to me forbidden places. And who knows? We always presume on our own powers. It may be hoped that, the subject being so grand, the soul may elevate the genius. I, perhaps, shall dare to snatch the portrait of Cæsar from the daubers who are so eager to besmear." This answer seemed satisfactory. I found it easy to interlard my discourse with agreeable compliments. I told him he had rather conquered than vanquished us; that we regarded the fate of Germany as resting on his shoulders, etc., etc.; and that, therefore, the design of writing the most brilliant history of the age in which I lived had placed me, even before I was acquainted with him, in the rank of one of his most ardent admirers. I know not whether he did or did not believe that I solely occupied myself with literature; but the supposition that I shall write history will perhaps render him more accessible to me, and acquire me more of his confidence; for he appears to possess the love, and even the jealousy, of fame to the utmost degree.

I am pressed by the courier because, not having quitted the Court all yesterday, I could not write before this morning; and the courier departs at eleven o'clock.

Writing in cipher is very tedious; I therefore omit a thousand particulars which lead me to believe —

1. That the English will not, by any means, be so quickly successful in their artifices in the North as might be feared; if the Court of Berlin may at all depend on the Court of Versailles.

2. That it is time to speak a little more openly to the former; and not to confound mystery and secrecy, finesse and prudence, ambiguity and policy.

3. That the Duke of Brunswick, whom I believe to be by much the most able Prince of Germany, is sincerely desirous of peace; and that he will inspire the Cabinet of Berlin with the same sentiments, if but the least restraint be laid on the Emperor; who, said he to me, has spoken in outrageous terms, in the presence of seven or eight witnesses besides myself, of the Prince of Prussia.

4. That the intention of the Duke is to govern Prussia, and to obtain great confidence and superior influence in Europe; that he would dread lest these would not be augmented by war, which he is convinced ought to be avoided, at Berlin; and that war is not really to be feared, except as far as France shall encourage the Emperor, who without us will not be anything.

I have not time to-day to give more than a sketch of the Duke such as he appears to me, who certainly will not be thought a common man even among men of merit. His person bespeaks depth and penetration, a desire to please tempered by fortitude, nay by severity. He is polite to affectation; speaks with precision, and with a degree of elegance; but he is somewhat too careful to speak thus, and the proper word sometimes escapes him. He understands the art of listening, and of interrogating according to the very spirit of reply. Praise, gracefully embellished and artfully concealed, he finds agreeable. He is prodigiously laborious, well informed, and perspicuous. However able his first Minister Feronce may be, the Duke superintends all affairs, and generally decides for himself. His correspondence is immense, for which he can only be indebted to his personal consideration; because he cannot be sufficiently wealthy to keep so many correspondents in pay; and few great Courts are so well informed as he is. All his affairs are in excellent order. He became the reigning Duke of Brunswick in 1780, and found his principality loaded with debts, to the amount of forty millions of livres. His administration has been such that, with a revenue of about one hundred thousand louis, and a sinking fund in which he has deposited the savings of the English subsidies, he will, in 1790, not only have perfectly liquidated the debts of the sovereignty, but, also, those of the State. His country is as free as it can be; and is happy and contented, except that the trading class regret the prodigality of his father. Not that the reigning Duke is less sensible to elegant pleasures than another; but, severely observant of decency, and religiously faithful to his duty as a Prince, he has perceived that economy was his only resource. His mistress, Madame Hartfeld, is the most reasonable woman at Court; and so proper is this attachment that, having a short time since discovered an inclination for another woman, the Duchess leagued with Madame Hartfeld to keep her at a distance. Truly an Alcibiades, he delights in the pleasures and the graces; but these never subtract anything from his labors or his duties, not even those of prudence. When he is to act as a Prussian general, no one is so early, so active, so minute as himself. It is a mark of superior character and understanding, in my opinion, that the labor of the day can be less properly said to be sufficient for him than he is for the labor of the day; his first ambition is that of executing it well. Intoxicated by military success, and universally pointed out as a great general (especially since the campaign of 1778, during which he all the winter maintained the feeble post of Troppau, to which the King of Prussia annexed a kind of vanity, against every effort of the Austrians), he appears effectually to have quitted military glory, to betake himself to the cares of government. Everywhere made welcome, possessed of unbounded curiosity, he still is capable of assiduously confining himself to Brunswick, and attaching himself to business. He is, in fine, a man of an uncommon stamp, but too wise to be formidable to the wise. He delights much in France, with which he is exceedingly well acquainted, and appears to be very fond of whatever comes from that country. His eldest son, returning from Lausanne, has passed through Franche-Comté, Languedoc, and Provence, and is very desirous to return to France. I shall soon know if he is to be sent back. In my opinion the son cannot be treated with too much respect there, so as to testify confidence in the father; which it seems to me would give the latter pleasure, by which he would certainly be sufficiently confirmed and flattered, to keep this treatment in memory.

I cannot at present speak of the supper, when the Duke removed me from the place of honor, opposite the Duchess, where I sat at dinner, to seat me beside himself, which is always at the far end of the table. The conversation was lively, and absolutely individual, but not political. (We had listeners.) He questioned me much concerning France. I am to dine with him to-day, and to sup with the Duchess Dowager, at Antoinetten-Ruh. I could not avoid this tax on propriety, which deprives me of an opportunity of supping with the Duke, — a favor he rarely grants, and which appeared to be much remarked here, yesterday, where I am observed with anxiety. Perhaps I am supposed a place hunter.

The continuance of Zimmermann at Potsdam is prolonged, more than it was supposed it would have been. He writes that the dropsy is not confirmed, and he again talks of an asthma. This is medical cant. He is the creature of the King, not of the public. Certain it is that he has gained no victory over eel pies and *polenta;* that there are no longer any wrinkles in the face; and that the parts are all inflated and œdematous.

Prince Henry, however, is returned to Rheinsberg, where the youthful and handsome R——, as it is said, occasions rain and fair weather.

I can warrant it as a fact that a Scotchman who is first physician to Catherine II. of Russia, being lately at Vienna, dined at the table of the Emperor, and was seated by his side. Indeed, this was avowed in the Gazettes; but it was not there avowed that, while this physician remained at Vienna, Cobenzl (the Austrian Ambassador to the Court of Petersburg, but then at Vienna) having been ordered to show the physician a pleasure house in the vicinity of the metropolis, the Emperor on horseback HAPPENED to meet the doctor on the road, and continued in conversation with him, at the coach window, for the space of more than two leagues.

LETTER IV.

July 16th, 1786.

TO-DAY I was three hours alone with the Duke, after rising from dinner. The conversation was animated, frank, and almost confidential: it confirmed me in most of the opinions I gave in my last letter (Number III.), but it has inspired me with much fear, concerning the situation of Prussia after the death of the King. The successor seems to have every symptom of the most incurable weakness; the most corrupt among the persons by whom he is surrounded, of whom the gloomy and visionary Bishopswerder may be ranked as first, daily increase in power. There is a coolness said to prevail between the Heir Apparent and his uncles. The coadjutorship of the Order of St. John, bestowed with great solemnity on Prince Henry, the eldest son of Prince Ferdinand, which deprives the successor of more than fifty thousand crowns per annum, is the most recent cause of this coolness. It should seem that there have been very powerful intrigues for the establishment of these two young Princes, whom both city and Court regard as the children of Count Schmettau. The measures taken to effect this were strengthened at the very moment when the King was supposed to be expiring, so as to bind the successor, of whom they consequently have testified their suspicion. To the King's brother, Prince Henry, the half at least of all this appertains; nor has the Heir Apparent attempted to conceal his dissatisfaction. Thence it results that all the subaltern parties, and their dirty cabals, become more active; so that the respect in which the Court of Berlin has been held, and in which consists its greatest power, depends, perhaps, but too much on the life of the King; unless the Duke of Brunswick should seize the reins of government, the burden of which he seriously appears to dread. In effect, a kingdom like this, which has no constituent foundation, will be cruelly agitated, should the winds of Court begin to blow; and should the Duke, who has formed himself without having studied in the school of adversity, and whose reason and sagacity it is impossible to speak too highly of, fear to reverse the whole system of his mode of life. But he does not start at difficulties; and he is too much interested in the prosperity of Prussia not to seek to obtain influence there.

It does not appear to me probable that the first six months, or even the first year, should produce any change, or do more than prepare for change. The Duke has repeatedly assured me that all the Protestant powers of Germany, and a great part of the Catholic, would incontrovertibly be in the interest of France, whenever the latter should fully convince the Germanic body of her amicable intentions; and when I asked what pledges should be given us that the high part with which the Elector of Hanover was invested, in the confederation of the Princes, should not sway the Cabinet of Berlin to the side of the English, and should not become an invincible impediment to any sincere union between Versailles and Prussia, he clearly showed me, so as not to admit of reply, that the Germanic league would never have existed, or at least would never have assumed its present form, had it not been for the ambiguity of our conduct, relative to the Schelde, to Bavaria, and to the Oriental system. He added that the Elector of Hanover, and the King of England, were two very distinct persons: and that the English and the Germans were great strangers to each other.

Here I ought to observe that, in my opinion, the Duke overacts his part, whenever he speaks of depressing England, which I well know he loves; and that perhaps because he feels his family connections may, in this respect, render him more liable to suspicion. In a word, I cannot too often repeat that they do not appear to have confidence in us, but that such confidence is very sincerely desired; and that the more because the Emperor, unsupported by France, is not held in the least dread,

and that there is a reigning conviction he will not dare
to take a single step, when the Cabinet of Versailles
shall say, " We will not suffer any infraction."

Be it however remarked that the incoherent conduct
of the Emperor, and his abrupt vagaries, often unhinge
all the combinations of reason. The Duke has to-day
learned a fact of this kind, which may well incite meditation.

The Baron of Gemmingen, some time since, wrote a
very violent pamphlet against the German confederacy.
Dohm, an excellent Prussian civilian, answered in a
strong and victorious manner. The Ministry of Vienna,
in consequence, requested our Ministry to entreat the
Court of Berlin to suffer wordy hostilities to cease. The
latter consented; but there has just appeared (printed
indeed at Munich, but indubitably coming from Vienna)
a satirical and bitter reply to Dohm. Verbal wars are
rarely insignificant at Vienna, where they are never begun
but under the auspices of Government.

The following is another fact of serious import, if
true. The Duke has received advice, from Vienna, that
between four and five thousand Russians have entered
Poland, where the Diet threatens to be very turbulent.
The Duke is desirous we should take a decisive part concerning and against all new arrangements tending to the
further dissolution or dismemberment of Poland. I have
not knowledge sufficient of this country to enter into any
circumstantial detail; but I spoke to him on the subject
of Courland, explaining my ideas, relative to the late
proceedings of Russia in this country, such as they will
be found in my Memorial; and I introduced my discourse
as if arising out of the conversation. He was ardently
attentive to what I said, and promised to write according
to my sense of the danger to Count Hertzberg. I well
comprehend that the circumstances of the moment are
nothing less than favorable; and the assent which was
warmly given by a most excellent politician emboldens
me to entreat that my Memorial may be taken into consideration, though it should only be practicable in future,
and that some instructions may be sent me, on the manner in which I may sound the Duke of Courland on this

head, whom I shall meet at Berlin, and the principal persons of Courland, with whom I may easily correspond; my trade of traveler being known, and my desire to collect facts and to deduce consequences giving great opportunities to inquire and speak concerning all subjects.

3

MEMORIAL.*

Sent to the Court of France, Concerning the Declaration Made by Russia to Courland, and Published in the «Leyden Gazettes,» from the 20th of May to the 3d of June, 1786.

COURLAND has lately been officially menaced with the indignation of the Sovereign of all the Russias, on the supposition that the report, relative to the abdication of the Duke of Courland in favor of the Prince of Wurtemberg, a general in the Prussian service, should be true.

The reigning Duke, Ernest John, a ferocious man, so much abhorred in his own country as not to be able to remain there, although he should not dread any violence from the Ministry of Petersburg, is known to be the son of the famous Biron, who was reinstated Duke of Courland, in 1760, by the influence, or rather through the fear of Russia, which power, with the aid of forty thousand men, expelled Prince Charles of Saxony, the uncle of the Elector and the legitimate Duke, to restore the former favorite of Elizabeth,† whom a Court faction had lately recalled from Siberia.

It is also known that this Ernest John has more than once felt the whole weight of the resentment of Catherine II.; that he has been near twenty years banished into Siberia; that he has no influence whatever in Courland; and that his abdication is universally wished.

* This is apparently the Memorial which is mentioned in the preceding letter.

† This is a mistake. Biron was the favorite of the Empress Anne Ivanowna; was banished to Siberia by Anne of Mecklenburg, the Princess Regent of Russia; was soon recalled from Schlusselburg and sent to Yaroslaf by the Empress Elizabeth; was restored to freedom by Peter III.; and after the assassination of the latter, to his duchy by Catherine II.; not to confer a favor on Biron, but to wrest the duchy from Poland, and to render it dependent on herself.

But it is not known, or rather it is kept secret, that he was enjoined, by a Ukase (or edict) six years ago, to resign his duchy to Prince Potemkin; and that, by the advice of the Chancellor Taubè, and of the Chamberlain Howen, he averted the storm by remitting to Prince Potemkin (whose affairs ever were and are in disorder) two hundred thousand ducats. Rason, the ministerial secretary of the Duke, was intrusted to carry him this sum.

Whether it be that Potemkin, while waiting for the execution of his grand projects, which perhaps relate to the Oriental system, or to circumstances that are yet immature, wishes to acquire this accession of power; whether it be that he is in want of money; or more especially whether it be that the Duke of Courland, since his situation has been so precarious is known in consequence of his avarice to have become one of the richest princes in Europe, and that, rendered effeminate by adversity, old age, and the daily importunities of his last wife, who has acquired some influence over him, he is endeavoring to place himself beyond the reach of ill fortune; be it which of these causes it may, a similar crisis is again returned.

The Cabinet of Petersburg is ignorant of none of these things. It doubtless fears that the Court of Berlin is speculating concerning the province of Courland; hoping, by the aid of a new Duke, to have it entirely at its disposal. The conditions which gave Poland a right of protection over Courland having ceased, when power became law, and at the moment the oppressed republic found it impossible to fulfill those conditions, it is not absurd to apprehend that Prussia will surreptitiously take the place of Poland, and thus to its own profit confirm the right by the deed.

Courland is in reality far from a contemptible country. Its climate, being in the 57th degree of latitude, though sufficiently is not insupportably cold. Its extent in length is eighty leagues, and in breadth fifty. Its soil is fertile, and its natural products are very necessary for all the commercial and maritime powers. Two principal and navigable rivers divide it, from east to west, the Aa and

the Windau; several brooks and canals intersect it in
every direction. It has two ports, Windau and Liebau
on the Baltic. In its present important and indolent
state its commerce, active and passive, does not employ
less than from six to seven hundred vessels, of three,
four, and as far as eight hundred tons burden. It contains seven or eight small towns, and its population is
estimated at more than a million and a half of inhabitants. The landholders may be supposed not to be in a
state of wretchedness, since the revenues of the reigning
Duke, whose influence in the republic is so small, annually amount to two hundred thousand pounds sterling.
Such is the outline of the situation of Courland.

It would be of little use to prove in this place that the
republic being a free State, the Prince of which is purely
elective, so that though he may abdicate he cannot transfer
his privileges, Russia cannot legally interfere in the affairs
of Courland, which ought to be as independent as are its
rights. This word RIGHTS is totally stripped of meaning
when opposed to the word POWER. Russia has long been
in the habit of vexing Courland, internally and exter-
nally; of dictating the choice of its Governors; of laying
its suffrages under restraint; and of extorting or forcibly
seizing on its money, its produce and its men. The
Monarchs of Petersburg have always made it a principle
to familiarize the Courts of Europe to the supposition that
Courland has no political existence except such as Russia shall please to bestow. All this is well known.

The points I should wish briefly here to examine are:

1. Whether it is not evidently our interest to introduce a new order of affairs; and—

2 Whether we have not the means so to do.

Courland, kept back and oppressed by every kind of
exterior and interior tyranny, possesses no one species
of manufacture. It abounds in naval stores; stores for
which reason there is an affinity, resulting from circumstances, between Courland and France, which latter holds
the first rank among industrial nations, or an affinity
between their mutual products, the direct barter of
which would give birth to the most advantageous kind of
trade.

In reality, there exists at present a species of barter between Courland and France; but in so indirect a manner that it is carried on at second or third hand, by the intervention of the English, the Dutch, the Swedes, the Danes, the Prussians, the Hanse Towns, etc.

This intervention absorbs and destroys all the benefit which a trade so advantageous would be of to France, and which certainly ought abundantly to procure us, and at a moderate price, a price unknown in our dockyards and markets, ship timber, masts, spokes, fellies, veneering wood, etc., grain, ship beef, saltfish, vegetables, etc. The natural returns for these would be the produce of our industry, from the coarsest to the finest articles (for nothing is manufactured in Courland), which the Courlanders (whose consumption is great, and who are very desirous of articles of luxury, and even of finery) would then obtain from us at a moderate price, still infinitely lucrative to our traders.

The advantage of this direct trade would not be confined merely to money ; for, besides the influence which such intimate connections with Courland would give us in the Baltic and the North, where we should become the mediators between Prussia, Russia, and Poland, which last State must necessarily soon undergo some new change, France, by a commercial treaty with Courland, would acquire two ports on the Baltic, which would at least remain neuter and almost exclusive to herself. These would be useful to us, both in war and peace, as depository places for stores, and most of the materials which are requisite for the royal and mercantile marine; and would highly compensate the disadvantage which continually increases, and which is preparing for us in the North, relative to our marine, in consequence of the strict connections between England and Russia.

To the attentive observer, England presents every symptom which can menace the possessions of the Dutch in the East, and which can forebode the desire of revenge. Russia can at any time rob France of a great part of the naval supplies of war in the European seas.

This order of affairs cannot too soon be reversed.

Let it be attentively observed that there is no question here of a new treaty, but the revival of an ancient
one; for the Cardinal de Richelieu made a treaty with
Courland, in 1643, which was registered by the Parliament of Paris, in 1647; so that, should we at present
treat with Courland, we can decisively affirm, and demonstrate, we are committing no innovation.

This seems to me to be a very important remark,
which ought not a little to influence the resolution that
may be taken, and the form given to that resolution,
when once it is taken.

The States of Courland desire this political affinity between the two countries.   The Chamberlain Howen, of
whom I have spoken, is a man of the greatest influence
in the republic, and, of all the Courlanders, the most
anti-Russian; because that, while an envoy from Courland to the Court of Warsaw, he was carried off, by order
of the Empress, and banished into Siberia.   His nephew
was indirectly, but formally, charged to question the Government of France on this subject.   I positively know he
has spoken to the Comte de Vergennes, and that the only
answer he received from the Minister was:

1. That, he being Minister for Foreign Affairs, this
was a subject that did not appertain to his department.

2. That it was requisite that the Duke of Courland
and the States, conjointly and officially, should make a
proposition to the King, concerning a treaty of commerce.

To this I reply:

1. That, most certainly, the Minister for Foreign Affairs
ought to consult with the Minister of Finance, on whatever relates to commercial treaties; but that this does
not therefore appear to me a sufficient reason to reject
either the project or the proposal.

2. That it would be absurd to suppose that Courland,
bowed as it is under the iron rod of present circumstances, would expose itself, by taking any open step,
without first being certain its propositions should be
favorably received, and that the country should be protected against that power which, possessed of strength
and in the habit of taking its will for law, should make
every effort to counteract and prevent whatever might

tend to impart solidity to the constitution of Courland, and to render its political independence respectable.

I see no hope that any power, except Prussia, should interest itself in the affairs of this province. And this is the second point which it is my intention to prove, in this Memorial.

1 Because the situation of the Prussian States is such that the stability and prosperity of Courland ought no less to influence the King of Prussia than if this country was one of his own provinces.

2. Because he cannot prudently covet Courland, which Russia would never leave him in peaceable possession of, and which would but increase the length of his provinces, already too much extended, without rendering his power more real or more compact.

This latter point is self-demonstrative; and, as to the advantages which Prussia might derive from the future stability of Courland, and from the increase of its energy and industry, these are evident from a mere view of the map. Between the States of Brandenburg and Russia there is only the dismemberment of Poland, which at present forms part of Prussian Lithuania and of Courland, of which the King of Prussia, politely speaking, would become the useful proprietor that very day on which he should become its guardian and protector. Russia, therefore, necessarily and indubitably is formidable to none of the powers of Europe, Prussia excepted, on which kingdom she can bring evil, and which can do her no injury.

On the other part, it is known that there is only a very narrow slip of Polish Lithuania between the States of Prussia and Courland, which barely extends from five to six leagues. Here Prussia might easily make legal and amicable acquisitions, sufficient to open a very advantageous transport trade on the Memel, and the canals that might be cut between that river and the rivers of Courland, descending to the ports of the Baltic, of which I have spoken.

Either I am much deceived or the Ministry of Berlin might easily be made to comprehend that, instead of forming projects of ambition on this republic, its real

interest would be to declare, in some manner, Prussia to
be the representative of Poland in her engagements
toward Courland, as stipulated by the *pacta conventa*
and the *pacta subjectionis*, which have been actually and
necessarily destroyed. Prussia might find a hundred
reasons of public right to allege, independent of her
dignity and safety. This proposition, and that of acced-
ing to our treaty of commerce with Courland, would
therefore contain nothing imprudent; it would perhaps
be a good means of depriving the House of Brandenburg
of all fears relative to our Northern politics. Nor does
it seem to be impossible but that the King of Prussia
would, on this condition, support the declaration we
might make to the Court of Petersburg, that it was our
determination to protect Courland; and not to suffer a
free country, allied to France by ancient treaties, to be
humbled, over which we would not permit any direct
and legislative influence to be exerted by any Court.

Such a declaration, softened by every diplomatic formality, which is so easily practiced, would at this time
be sufficient, in my opinion, especially if made in concert with the Court of Berlin, to repel the projects of
usurpation conceived by Russia over Courland.

Be these things as they may, this small country, too
little known, together with Poland and the Germanic
body, claims the serious attention of the King of France;
who, if my opinion be right, has no other general interest, on the continent, than that of maintaining peace
and the reciprocal safety of States.

LETTER V.

YESTERDAY morning, before my departure, the Duke granted me an audience for the space of about three hours; or rather, personally indicated a conference, under the pretense of remitting letters to Berlin, and which, indeed, he committed to my care. We again spoke of general affairs, and of the particular situation of Prussia; of the suspicions which he pretends it is impossible to avoid entertaining, concerning our intentions and our system (how should I answer him when such is the disorder of our finances that it is impossible we should have any system?); of the dread that daily increases, which the Emperor necessarily inspires, who does good awkwardly, but who does enough to acquire great power, the basis of which is magnificent, and highly disproportionate to that of any other monarchy, France excepted; of the impossibility of finding any counterpoise to this power, except in the prudence of the Cabinet of Versailles; of the little hope that the new regulations of Prussia should be wise; of the various directions which the various factions that were fermenting at Berlin might take; of the military vigor and the ambitious fumes which intoxicate the Duke of Weymar, who aspires to enter into the service of Prussia, and to embroil parties; of the necessity which there was that the Cabinet of Versailles should send a man of merit to Berlin, there to inspire awe and give advice, keep watch over the factious and the turbulent, etc., etc., etc.

At length, questioning me with an air of fearing what he was going to say was an absurdity, he asked whether I should think the project of an alliance between France, England, and Prussia an impracticable chimera; the end of which, solemnly avowed, should be to guarantee, throughout Europe, to each Prince his respective possessions; a measure in itself noble, and worthy of the two first powers, which should command all others to remain at peace; founded on the evident and combined interest of the two rivals, and the greatest obstacle to which would be that no one would dare to put it in execution.

The idea, on which I have for these seven years been ruminating, is too sublime not to be seductive. It would infallibly immortalize the Sovereign by whom it should be realized, and the Minister by whom it should be promoted. It would change the face of Europe, and totally to our advantage; for, once again, commercial treaties, however advantageous to England, would never make the English anything more than our carriers and our most useful factors.

The Duke has permitted me to correspond with him; he even desired me so to do, and I find I have obtained almost that very place in his opinion which I myself could have wished.

July 21st, 1786.

FIRST POSTSCRIPT.—I am arrived, and perhaps I shall learn but little to-day. The dropsy is in the stomach; nay, in the lungs. He was informed of it on Thursday. He heard it with great magnanimity, say some; others affirm he treated the physician, who was too sincere, very ill. He might drag on life, if he would take advice, Doctor Baylies says, another year; but I suspect he will never give up eel pies. Count Hertzberg has been at Sans Souci this week past; he had never before been sent for. Two days previous to that on which the King made him this kind of honorable reparation, if, however, it be anything else than the necessity of giving breath to those who are obliged to converse with him, and of enlivening his conversation, the Heir Apparent dined with the Count at his country seat, and passed the best part of the evening with him and the Prince of Dessau. This has bewildered the parties that are hotly animated against this estimable Minister, in and for whom, according to my opinion, our embassy has always testified too little confidence and respect.

Second Postscript.— I have intelligence, from what I believe to be a very certain and profound source, wholly independent of the Cabinet of Berlin, that the Emperor has made preparations which greatly menace those parts of Moldavia and Wallachia that would be convenient to him to possess; that he is immediately expected to repair to those frontiers in person; and that such motions cannot otherwise be explained than by reacting the conquest of the Crimea in those countries. This information, combined with the ultimatum which Russia has delivered in to the Porte, seems to me to be of sovereign importance. I do not know the precise intentions of the Court of France; but if the indefinite aggrandizement of the Emperor, and particularly the execution of the Oriental system, are as formidable to us as I suppose them to be, I entreat deliberations may be held whether it befits the dignity of the King to suffer the tragedy of Poland to recommence, the interest of the State to lose the Levant trade, or prudent policy to temporize, when the match is putting to the touch-hole. I cannot for my part doubt but that our inactivity, in such a case, must be gratuitous; because the Emperor would most certainly not brave us; and fatal also, since we are precisely the only power who have at once the interest and the strength to impede such attempts. England will trouble herself little concerning them, and without us Prussia is nothing.

LETTER VI.

July 21st, 1786.

* * * * * * *

A N ODD incident has happened to me. I am just returned from the French Ambassador's, who sent
me word he could not have the honor of receiving
my visit, because he was busy. To feel the whole import
of this act, it is necessary to know that there has lately
appeared an article in the "Hamburg Gazette," affirming in
express terms I had received orders to quit France.
You will further recollect that, in general, the Ambassador of France is eagerly desirous of receiving the visits
of French travelers. Such is the present combination of
circumstances that this, which would only, on any other
occasion, be an affair of rather serious impoliteness, is
at this moment a very embarrassing affectation. I believe I have no need to tell you I am far superior to
punctilio; but this is not mere form. The natural preponderance of France is such that the respect in which
a native of that country is held cannot be wholly independent of the reception he shall meet from the Ambassador. What, then, must be thought when he shall be
envied, suspected, and watched, and when pretenses are
sought to render his character equivocal? And what must
be his situation, when, far from seeking to quarrel with
the Ambassador, it is his duty and his wish, on all occasions, to preserve appearances, and to protect him from
becoming instead of making him ridiculous?

You will have no difficulty in comprehending that it
is an intricate affair, and that I must well reflect on the
part I have to take. At present I must dissemble, and
expose myself to a new refusal to-morrow; but it will
be impossible to suffer this new refusal to remain unnoticed. I write you word of this in order that, in any
case, and rather too soon than too late, you should inform M. d'Esterno it is not the intention of Government

that I should be treated in a disrespectful manner, and still less as a proscribed person. He is so much of a timid trembler, that he may have been imposed upon by the Hamburg paragraph. I do not think him sufficiently cunning to have written it himself. He certainly appeared ridiculously disturbed at my return, and entirely departed from his silent circumspection, that he might discover, by questioning those whom he supposed intimate with me, what were my intentions. Some of the numerous persons who do not love him, especially among the *corps diplomatique*, have amused themselves with inventing tales relative to my views, similar to those of the « Thousand and One Nights. » His brain is in a state of fermentation upon the subject; and the more so as he is acting out of character. I may in consequence of this be very ill-situated here. To prevent this you will take proper measures. I shall tell you more before I seal this letter; he is not a person who will oppose the least ministerial insinuation.

LETTER VII.

July 23d, 1786.

THERE is nobody here, consequently I shall for some days lead an inactive life. There is no Court, except that of Prince Ferdinand, which is always insignificant; he is at present on the recovery.* Prince Frederick of Brunswick knows nothing. The English Embassy caress and suspect me. Count Hertzberg still remains at Sans Souci; I must, therefore, satisfy myself with the sterility of the moment. I imagine I have discovered that the real occasion of the threatening declaration of Russia respecting Courland, was a secret proposal of marriage between the Countess of Wurtemberg, the natural daughter of the Duke, and a Prussian; and the increasing intimacy of the Duke with the Heir Apparent, who has found in the purse of this savage Scythian that pecuniary aid with which he ought long since to have been supplied by France. The Duke of Courland departed, soon after the menace of Petersburg appeared, with his wife, who is said to be pregnant, to drink the Pyrmont waters. According to all appearances, instead of remaining at Berlin on his return, he will go to Mittau. He still continues to make acquisitions in the Prussian dominions; he has lately bought the county of Sagan, in Silesia; and the King, who was not a little vexed to see the Prince of Lobkowitz spend the revenues of this fine estate at Vienna, treats the Duke of Courland with great favor. Besides remitting the manor fees, he consented to alienate or at least to entail the fief on female descendants, which before was revertible to the Crown on the want of male heirs; so that the Duke, who has no son, found that, by his carelessness, or a very strange kind of ignorance, he had risked six hundred thousand German crowns on a chance the most hazardous.

* Prince Ferdinand had just then escaped from a dangerous fit of sickness.

(46)

It is indubitable that Prince Potemkin is, or appears to be, more in favor than ever. It has been found necessary to approve his disobedience. There are reports that he has sought a reconciliation with the Grand Duke, which he has accomplished.

The new Minister of Petersburg (the son of Field-marshal Romanzow) is not successful here; intelligent people, however, affirm he possesses understanding and information. I know he has strong prejudices against me, which I shall endeavor to remove, and to gain his intimacy; for he is of such a nature that much may be derived from his acquaintance. But you must feel I stand in need of some instructions, or at least of a series of questions, which shall serve me as a compass, and by which I may obtain the customary intelligence. General politics have for some years been very incoherent, for want of possessing some fixed system. Which of the two alliances, that of the House of Austria, or that between the two Imperial Courts, Austria and Russia, ought to be regarded as stable, sacred, and subordinate to the other? Is France resolved to quit her natural train, I mean to say her continental system, for the maritime? If so, whether wisely or not, this will at least explain our extreme cautiousness, in what relates to the projects of the Court of Vienna.

The man who wants this knowledge can do little more than wander at a venture; he may, with more or less intelligence, write a gazette, but, not having a sufficient basis to build on, cannot be a negotiator. I entreat it may not be supposed I have the presumption to interrogate; I only mean to explain, in very few words, such of the reasons which, exclusive of my own want of capacity, and of the few means my situation affords me, infinitely circumscribe that utility which I wish and labor to be of to my country.

I hope I shall not be suspected of supposing any importance annexed to those extracts from the German newspapers, which I shall in future send by every courier. It is purely an object of curiosity, but which I thought might be agreeable in a country where, I believe, not a single German gazette is received; and into which so many Ambassadors send no other dispatches than those obtained on the authority of these gazettes. I shall only speak in my extracts of the news of the North.

FIRST POSTSCRIPT. — Advice yesterday arrived commanding Lord Dalrymple to depart, and bear the Order of the Garter to the Landgrave of Hesse Cassel.

SECOND POSTSCRIPT. — I have received a very friendly letter from Sans Souci. The King seems to hope he shall still live long; he appears, however, to be much more occupied concerning himself and his pineapples than by foreign affairs. Astonishment is testified (this is a surprising affair!) though in a very obliging manner, that the son of the Comte de Vergennes should pass through Hamburg, Dresden, Vienna, etc., without any hope of seeing him at Berlin. I have answered I was very grateful, in behalf of my nation, for the importance annexed to the topographical peregrination of the son of our Minister for Foreign Affairs, and that I imagined nothing could be more flattering to his father; but that, for my own part, I was wholly uninformed on the subject; though I was persuaded that, if the Court of Berlin was reserved as the last place to be visited, it would only be from a love of the *Crescendo*. I said the same to Count Goertz, by whom I was warmly questioned.

LETTER VIII.

BERLIN, July 26th, 1786.

THE fine weather supports the life of the King, but he is ill. On Wednesday he was for some minutes wheeled about in his chair, by which he was much incommoded, and suffered greatly during and after the exercise. His pains increased on Thursday, and yesterday he was no better. I persist in my opinion that the period of his existence will be toward the month of September.

The Heir Apparent does not quit Potsdam, where he keeps on the watch. Still the same respectful passion for Mademoiselle Voss.* During a short journey that she lately made with her brother, a confidential *valet de chambre* followed her carriage at a distance, and if the beauty, who in my opinion is very ordinary, testified the least desire (to eat white bread, for example), before she had proceeded half a league further she found everything she wished. It appears indubitable that she has not yet yielded. No great use can be made either of her uncle or her brothers. Frenchwomen arrive daily; but I doubt much whether there will be any great advantage derived from them, except to innkeepers and milliners.

The Duke of Courland has lent the Heir Apparent money to pay his debts at Berlin; they are supposed to be all discharged, except those of his Princess, which they are not very anxious to liquidate, from the fear of giving her bad habits.

I have spoken at large with Struensee. He supposes the project of the bank to be a grand and superb operation, which cannot but succeed. He asks timely information, and promises to place and cause to be placed in it a considerable sum; but the secret must only be known to him, and the subject treated only between ourselves.

*At present the Countess of Ingenheim.

4

LETTER IX.

July 31st, 1786.

*　　*　　*　　*　　*　　*　　*

I SUPPOSE in reality that, in this commencement of correspondence, my letters are waited for, in order to
write to me; however, if my letter of the 23d of
July (Number V.) has been well deciphered and considered, it cannot be disowned that I stand in need of instructions. Politics are at a crisis. I repeat, politics
are at a crisis. It is impossible they should continue as
they are, whether it be from endeavors to accelerate or
efforts to retard. Everything denotes the Oriental system to increase in vigor. I have no doubt but that,
soon or late, it will be destructive of that of the West;
and the danger is immediate, is instantaneous. If Turkey in Europe, speaking in political and commercial language, be one of our colonies, if we are not resolved to
leave it to its fate, is it not time to pay it some attention? and because that it is so, is the general system of
Europe out of the question? Were the King of Prussia
ten years younger, he would well know how to restore
the equilibrium, for he would take as much from Poland as others might take elsewhere; but he dies and has
no successor. For my own part, it is easy to conceive,
I shall consume my time in barren efforts; and, after
taking much more trouble, shall be much less useful
than if I knew what track to follow, and where to gain
information.

The King is in daily danger of death, though he may
live some months. I persist in my autumnal prognostics.
Prince Henry having sent for me to Rheinsberg by a
very formal and friendly letter, it would appear affectation in me not to go; and I shall set off on Wednesday,
after the departure of the courier. I shall not remain
there longer than a week, where I shall have good

(50)

opportunities of intelligence concerning the state of the King, and of gaining information on various matters.

POSTSCRIPT.— The King is sensibly worse; he has had a fever these two days; this may kill him, or prolong his life. Nature has continually done so much for this extraordinary man, that nothing more is wanting to restore him than a hemorrhoidal eruption. The muscular powers are very great.

The English Embassy has received advice from Vienna that the Emperor is in Transylvania, and that the world is ignorant of what he is doing, what he intends, or even to what place he is gone.

All the boats on the Danube are taken into his service.

The maritime company wished to monopolize the sale of snuff and tobacco in Sweden, offering to pay half a million annually to the King; but the Swedish States have totally refused to forbid the cultivation of tobacco in the kingdom, and this was the condition, *sine quâ non*. The actions of this Monarch decline greatly, on all occasions; another Diet like the present, and monarchical power would once more fall in Sweden. It appears to be undoubted that the rumor of his having turned Catholic, on his journey to Rome, has alienated the whole nation. But are we to impute nothing to the intrigues of Russia, in the present fermentation?

Struensee repeats that, if the bank be established, he and his friends are ready; that is to say, the most moneyed men in the kingdom, and probably, under a new reign, the Government itself. This man ought to be cherished. It would be of importance were I often empowered to give him good information respecting the state of the place. Meditate on this. His resources are in himself, and will probably survive his administration. He has gained immensely, by speculating in the English funds. He ought to be weaned of this, to which he is self-inclined, for he feels and owns that chances in the English funds are exhausted for the remainder of his life.

LETTER X.

August 2d, 1786.

Written before my departure for Rheinsberg.

*   *   *   *   *   *   *

THE King is evidently better, at least with respect to pain, when he does not move; he has even left off the use of the *taraxicum*, or dandelion, the only thing Zimmermann prescribed, who, consequently, is in despair. He simply takes a tincture of rhubarb mixed with diarrhœtics, which give him copious evacuations. His appetite is very good, which he indulges without restraint. The most unhealthy dishes are his greatest favorites. If indigestion be the consequence, as it frequently is, he takes a double aperitive dose.

Frese, his physician of Potsdam, still continues in disgrace, for having dared to whisper the word dropsy on the question being asked him, and an appeal made to his conscience, what was the name and character of the disease. The King is exceedingly chilly, and is continually enveloped in furs, and covered by feather beds. He has not entered his bed these six weeks, but is removed from one armchair to another, in which he takes tolerably long sleeps, turned on his right side. Inflation augments; the scrotum is exceedingly tumid. He perceives this, but will not persuade himself, or appear to believe, that it is anything more than the inflation of convalescence, and the result of great feebleness.

This information is minutely exact, and very recent. There is no doubt of his unwillingness to die. The people best informed think that, as soon as he believes himself really dropsical and at the point of death, he will submit to be tapped, and to the most violent

(52)

remedies, rather than peaceably resign himself to sleep with his fathers. He even desired, some time since, incisions might be made in his hams and thighs; but the physician feared to risk them. With respect to his understanding, it is still sound; and he even continues his labors.

LETTER XI.

August 8th, 1786.

THE King is dangerously ill; some affirm he has not many hours to live, but this probably partakes of exaggeration. On the fourth, the erysipelas with blisters on the legs made their appearance; this prognosticates bursting, and soon after gangrene. At present there is suffocation, and a most infectious smell. The smallest fever — and the curtain must drop.

(54)

LETTER XII.

August 12th, 1786.

THE King is apparently much better. The evacuation,
which was the consequence of the apertures in his
legs, has caused the swelling to abate, and given
ease; but has been followed by a dangerous excess of
appetite. He cannot continue in this state. You may
expect to receive a grand packet at my return from
Rheinsberg.

(55)

LETTER XIII.

I AM just returned from Rheinsberg, where I have lived in the utmost familiarity with Prince Henry.

I have numerous modes of communication, which will develop themselves as time and opportunity shall serve; at present I shall only state consequences.

Prince Henry is in the utmost incertitude, concerning what he shall or shall not be under the new reign. He greatly dreads, and more than he wishes to appear to dread, though his fears are very visible, the influence of Count Hertzberg, who is still detained at Sans Souci, but, as I think, only for the sake of his conversation, — at least, as far as respects the old King. This Count Hertzberg has openly espoused the English system; but, though the flatteries of Ewart* and his secret arts have much profited by the long contempt in which the French Embassy have held this Minister, I believe his principal reason for attaching himself to England is because Prince Henry, his implacable enemy, is the avowed and fanatical protector of the French system; and because the Count imagines he cannot otherwise make himself indispensably necessary to the opposite party; for which reason he clothes himself in the uniform of the Stadtholder.

In consequence of this, and persuaded as I am that Prince Henry has not sufficient influence over the successor (who is weary of avuncular despotism) to displace Hertzberg, who will continually batter his enemy in breach, by boasting, by meannesses, by a faithful portrait of the Prince's creatures, and by the jealousy with which he will inspire the new King against Prince Henry, who, if he be anything, will be master; con-

* Then Secretary to the Embassy, and later the English Ambassador at Berlin.

vinced also that he (Hertzberg) is useful to France, which is influenced by the uncle because he holds the English system in abhorrence I have exerted every effort to induce Prince Henry (who wants nothing but dissimulation) to reconcile himself with Count Hertzberg, and thus put his nephew out of fear. This he might with the greater security do, because Hertzberg, relative to him, could be nothing more than a first clerk, who, if he should act uprightly, would make as good a clerk as another; and who, should he endeavor to deceive, might be the more easily crushed, after having been admitted a colleague.

I have had much difficulty in persuading him, for Baron Knyphausen, the brother-in-law of Hertzberg, and his irreconcilable enemy, because that their interests clash, is possessed of the entire political confidence of the Prince, of which he is worthy, for he is a very able man, and perhaps the only able man in Prussia; but as he is in danger of a confirmed palsy as his mind and body both decay, and as the Prince himself perceives they do, I was able to effect my purpose by dwelling on all these circumstances, while I heaped exaggerated praise on Baron Knyphausen, and expressed infinite regret for his situation; so that I have prevailed on the Prince, and have personally received a commission to negotiate an accommodation between him and Hertzberg; for which purpose I shall go the day after to-morrow to Potsdam.

What may I augur from all this? Weakness only and incoherency. It appears indubitable that petty cabals, the fine arts, the blues, the subalterns, the wardrobe, and particularly the mystics, will engross the new King. I have anecdotes innumerable on this subject, by which I shall endeavor to profit, and which I shall communicate in good time. Has he any system? I believe not. Any understanding? Of that I doubt. Any character? I cannot tell; my present opinion is that no conclusions, for or against, ought yet to be drawn.

To memorials exceedingly well drawn up by Prince Henry and Baron Knyphausen, all tending to demonstrate that, should Prussia attach itself to the English system,

fifteen years hence Frederick William will be the Marquis
of Brandenburg, he gives replies which are slow, vague,
laconic, and hieroglyphic. He wrote the other day, for
example (I saw the letter), "THE PRINCE OF THE ASTURIAS
IS ALL ENGLISH." Baron Boden, however, who is his confidential correspondent, and who has lately remained shut
up with him a whole week in his garden at Potsdam,
has protested that the dispositions of the successor are
wholly French, and that he had charged him to endeavor
to convert Hertzberg. Remark this. Remark, still further,
that Boden is a man of low cunning, who may wish to
deceive Prince Henry, in whose service he formerly was,
with whom he quarreled, and to whom he is now reconciled,— Heaven knows by what means. Observe, once
again, that the Prince of Salm-Kirburg has also been
(nearly about the same time) a week concealed at Potsdam. What inconsistency?

It is the advice of Prince Henry that Boden, who is
returned to Paris, should be tampered with. He also
wishes (for your great men do not disdain little means)
that a lady should be sent hither, of a fair complexion,
rather fat, and with some musical talents, who should
pretend to come from Italy, or anywhere but France;
who shall have had no public amour; who should appear
rather disposed to grant favors than to display her poverty, etc., etc. Some elegant trifles would not be amiss,
but take care not to forget the man is avaricious. The
French letters, at least those which I shall show, ought
to speak well of him, and to report that the King has
spoken favorably of him; particularly that he has said:
"This Prince, like me, will be a worthy man." Repetition might be made of the success of Prince Henry in
France; but in this I would advise moderation, for I
believe Prince Henry has spoken too much himself on
that subject; he has pretended to prophesy concerning
the new reign, and predictions are disagreeable. Let me
add it is affirmed that, could the new King be gained,
he would become the most faithful and the most fervent
of allies; to this his uncle Henry pledges his honor and
his head; and, indeed, the Prince of Prussia has never
forfeited his word. It is added, as you may well believe,

that it is neither possible nor proper to require more, for in fine we are suspected, and with good reason, etc., etc.

You will imagine France has not been thus treated without any pleadings in the behalf of Prussia; and the advocates have pretended to prove (the map on the table), alike by military and political details, that the alliance of Prussia would be much more effectual to France, against England, than that of Austria. If it be requested, I will draw up a memorial, according to the grounds that have been given me. Nor is it at all required that we should quarrel with Vienna; nothing more is asked than a treaty of confraternity, agreeable to the guarantee of the treaty of Westphalia; a treaty well known at all Courts, and with this only secret article that, should there be any infringement of the peace, we then should go further; and if at the present a treaty should be refused, reciprocal letters between the two Kings, sealed and so left till some event should happen, would be deemed satisfactory. In short, a pledge is demanded against the Austrian system; and the written word of honor of the King of France will be accepted. No subsidies are or will in any case be asked; perhaps even Prussia will pay subsidies to Brunswick and Hesse. Great complaints are made of France for having permitted and even favored the German confederation. "For must not Germany, soon or late, assume some consistent form? Must not Prussia acquire a frontier? And what other means are there than those of secularization, which by this confederacy are interdicted? How otherwise arrange the affairs of Saxony than by Westphalia and Liège?" This latter phrase appeared to me very remarkable.

I do not nor cannot at present mean to send anything more than the great outlines. Prince Henry is French, and so will live and die. Will he have any influence? I know not. He is too pompous; and the Duke of Brunswick, of a very different complexion, is the man necessary to the King and the country, though he is not loved by the former. However, I am supplied with the secret means of correspondence, inquiry, and success;

and it could not be more made a common cause between us. I am promised that my services to my country shall be amply repaid on the day an alliance is concluded with France, etc., etc.

I forgot a curious fact. The Heir Apparent wrote to Boden, before his journey to Berlin, to inquire what the people of Paris thought of him. "That you will be feeble, indolent, and governed," was the substance of Boden's reply. The Prince, as he read the letter, stamped with his foot, and exclaimed: "I have suffered by myself and I will reign by myself."

POSTSCRIPT.— By the natural discharge of the water from the legs, which may be calculated at a pint *per diem*, the swelling of the scrotum has disappeared; the patient imagines the general inflation is diminished. It is probable he is feverish every night; but of this he endeavors to remain ignorant. His appetite is so extraordinary that he generally eats of ten or twelve of the highest dishes. His supper and breakfast consist of smoked tongues, bread, butter, and a large quantity of pepper. If he feel his stomach oppressed by its load, which is usually the case, he has recourse an hour or two after dinner to a dose of *anima rhei*. He wishes to have six or seven motions in the twenty-four hours, exclusive of clysters. From all this you may gather the result, which is that we are incontestibly at the last scene, more or less protracted.

LETTER XIV.

ALL is over! — Frederick William reigns — and one of the grandest characters that ever occupied the throne has burst one of the finest molds that nature ever organized!

The vanity of friendship was highly interested that you should be the first informed of this event; and my measures were all most carefully taken. On Wednesday, at eight in the morning, I knew he was as ill as possible; that the preceding day the hour of appointment for the day following was noon, instead of eleven o'clock, as was before customary; that he had not spoken to his secretaries till midday, who had been waiting from five in the morning; that, however, the dispatches had been clear and precise; and that he still had eaten excessively, and particularly a lobster. I further knew that the prodigious foulness of the sick chamber, and the damp clothes of the patient, which he wore without changing, appeared to have brought on a species of putrid fever; that the slumbers of this Wednesday approached lethargy; that every symptom foreboded an apoplectic dropsy, a dissolution of the brain; and that, in fine, the scene must close in a few hours.

At one o'clock I took an airing on horseback, on the road to Potsdam, impelled by I know not what foreboding, and also to observe the meanderings of the river, which is on the right, when a groom, riding full speed, came for the physician Zelle, who received orders to make all haste, and who instantly departed. I soon was informed that the groom had killed a horse.

I was thrown into some perplexity. That the city gates would be shut was certain; it was even possible that the drawbridges of the island of Potsdam would be raised the moment death should take place, and should this happen by uncertainty would continue as long as it

should please the new King. On the first supposition —
how send off a courier? There were no means of scaling
the ramparts or the palisades, without being exposed
to a fray, for there are sentinels at every forty paces
behind the palisades, and at every fifty behind the wall.
What was to be done? I had not received, could not
receive any orders; I could only use my own resources.
And ought I to expose myself to ridicule, by sending
intelligence already known, or concerning an event so
well foreseen? Was the loss or gain of a week worth
the expense of a courier? Had I been Ambassador, the
certain symptoms of mortality would have determined
me to have sent off an express before death. For what
addition was the word death? How was I to act in my
present situation? It certainly was most important to
serve, and not merely to appear to have served. I
hastened to the French Ambassador. He was not at
home; he dined at Charlottenburg. No means of joining
him at Berlin. I dressed myself, hurried to Schoenhausen, and arrived at the palace of the Queen as soon
as the Ambassador. He had not been informed of particulars, and did not imagine the King was so ill; not a
Minister believed it; the Queen had no suspicion of it;
she only spoke to me of my dress, of Rheinsberg, and of
the happiness she had there enjoyed when Princess
Royal. Lord Dalrymple, with whom I am too intimate
to admit of dissembling what my opinion was, assured
me I was deceived. "That may be," replied I; but I
whispered to our Ambassador that I had my intelligence
from the sick couch, and that he ought to believe stock-
jobbers had as good information as the diplomatic body.*
I know not whether he believed me; but, like me, he
would not sit down to play, and left the company soon
enough to send news of the approach of death.

I still had great reason to be diffident of the activity
of our Embassy. How did I act? I sent a man, on
whom I could depend, with a strong and swift horse to
a farm, four miles from Berlin, from the master of which
I had some days before received two pairs of pigeons, an

* It will here be perceived this was intended to give the French
Ambassador to understand that he had no competitor.

experiment on the flight of which had been made; so that, unless the bridges of the isle of Potsdam were raised, I acted with certainty; and, that I might not have a single chance against me, for I thought the news tardy in arriving, I sent M. de Noldé by the daily stage, with orders to wait at the bridges of the island. He was acquainted with the station of my other man; the raising of the bridges would speak plainly enough; he had money sufficient to push forward; there was no human power apparently that could counteract me, for my gentry had not a single Prussian post to pass, and were to proceed to Saxony, taking care not to go through any fortified place; and they had their route ready traced.

M. de Noldé was departing at half past six in the morning, with the stage, when General Goertz, aide-de-camp to the late King, arriving full speed, called aloud: «In the King's name, lower the portcullis,» and M. de Noldé was obliged to turn back! Five minutes after, I was on horseback; my horses had passed the night saddled; and, that I might omit nothing, I hastened to the French Ambassador. He was asleep. I wrote to him immediately that I knew a certain mode of conveyance, if he had anything to send. He answered, and I keep his note as a curious proof if, which, however, to me appears impossible, the Comte de Vergennes keeps no courier,* — «The Comte d'Esterno has the honor to return thanks to Mirabeau, but cannot profit by his obliging offer.»

I then reflected, either he had sent off a courier, who only could convey the news of the King's extreme danger, consequently there must be something to add, or he had received orders not to send any; otherwise his apathy was wholly inconceivable. I, moreover, knew that the Saxon envoy had sent off his chasseur on the eve, so that he was twenty hours and forty leagues in advance with me; it therefore was wholly improbable that M. de Vibraye at Dresden should not hear of the King's danger. The same might be conjectured of the aide-de-camp Wittinkoff, who bore the news to the Duchess Dowager of

---

* The Comte de Vergennes first read the news in the «Leyden Gazette.»

Brunswick, and would certainly spread it, so that nothing was left for me till absolute death should happen.
After considering, I did not find we were rich enough to
throw a hundred guineas away; I therefore renounced all
my fine projects, which had cost me some thought, some
trouble, and some guineas; and I let fly my pigeons to
my man with the word RETURN.

Have I done well, or ill? Of this I am ignorant; but
I had no express orders, and sometimes works of super-
erogation gain but little applause. I have thought it my
duty to send you this account; first, because it may be
of service (observe that several prizes have thus been
gained); and secondly, to prove that I wanted neither
zeal nor activity, but effrontery.

The new King remained all Thursday at Sans Souci,
in the apartment of General Moellendorf. His first act
of sovereignty was to bestow the order of the Black Eagle
on Count Hertzberg. At five in the morning, his Majesty
was busy with the secretaries of the late King. This
morning he was on horseback in the streets of Berlin,
accompanied by his eldest son. Thursday presented a
spectacle worthy of observation.

There were many wet eyes, even among the foreign
Ambassadors; for they were all present, the French excepted, when the troops took the oath of allegiance.

The ceremony is awful, and would be more so if the
oath, which the soldiers repeat word by word, were
not so long. Yet this vast military paraphernalia, that
multitude of soldiers, who all the morning swarmed in
the streets, and the precipitate administering of the legionary oath, seem but to me too exclusively to proclaim the
military power; seem but to say: I AM MORE ESPECIALLY
THE KING OF THE SOLDIERS. I COMMIT MYSELF TO MY ARMY,
BECAUSE I AM NOT CERTAIN OF POSSESSING A KINGDOM. I
am persuaded these military forms will be mitigated
under the new reign.

LETTER XV.

August 18th, 1786.

Pᴿɪɴᴄᴇ Hᴇɴʀʏ received information of the decease somewhat late; not till yesterday, the seventeenth, at midnight. But this, perhaps, was occasioned by their desire to send him one of his favorite officers, who was a very bad horseman. The letter of the King was a page and a half in length, written by his own hand, and inviting the Prince to come, who arrived to-day at three in the afternoon. As soon as it was dark, his aide-de-camp came for me; and what follows is the substance of the Prince's narrative.

He has had an interview of an hour and a half with the King, but is no further advanced in the knowledge of what he shall hereafter be. The King was devoid of ostentation in his behavior to his family; and was very much moved with the Prince, says the latter, but no way communicative. The uncle only attempted to speak of foreign politics. His request in behalf of his favorite, Tauensien, captain and aide-de-camp to his Royal Highness, was immediately granted.

"Resolved on the French system, but desirous of seeing—" "Why?" "Dignity, prudence, the alarming discontents of Holland." "Are you brother or King? as brother interest yourself; as King do not interfere, you will but have the greater influence." "Your father, whose name you cannot pronounce without weeping, was as much French as I am; this I will demonstrate by his letters." "Oh, I have seen proofs of that," replied the King, "in those of the Queen of Sweden."

"Vienna." "Advances it is supposed will be made; they will be accepted; the war of peace will actually be concluded."

5

" The English system ? "   " God preserve me from it! " *
" Russia ? "   " It has scarcely been thought on. "

The whole day passed in well-managed artifice. The
King was on horseback with his eldest son; he addressed
his generals with caresses of every kind: " If you serve
less faithfully than formerly, I, by being obliged to
punish, shall be the person punished. " He spoke a little more seriously to the Ministers, with whom, notwithstanding, he dined. Severely to the secretaries — " I
well know you have been guilty of indiscretions; I would
advise you to change your behavior. "

Hertzberg hitherto preserves all his consequence. The
King has not once pronounced his name to Prince Henry,
nor the Prince to the King. His Majesty, however,
tenderly embraced Count Finckenstein, a true French
knight-errant, and the only person, after Knyphausen,
in whom Prince Henry confides; that is to say, willingly.
" I thank you," said the King, " for the eminent services
you have been so indefatigable in rendering my uncle;
and I request you will act in the same manner for my
interest. " It is to be noted that Count Finckenstein is
the implacable enemy of Hertzberg, but the uncle of the
dearly beloved Mademoiselle Voss.

The will is to be opened to-morrow, in presence of
those interested. The King will not attempt to alter a
single line, one article excepted, the necessity of erasing
which he will submit to his uncles. The old Monarch
has been generous. He has bequeathed Prince Henry
two hundred thousand crowns and a handsome ring,
exclusive of what will revert to him by the family agreement. The rest are likewise well treated, but not so
magnificently.

The funeral ceremony afforded Prince Henry a proper
excuse for remaining; it is to be performed at Potsdam.
The King will depart thence to receive homage in Prussia and Silesia; this is an old custom of the country.
Prince Henry will come to an explanation previous to
his journey; but he is determined to wait as long as
possible, that the King may begin the subject himself.

* It is Hertzberg who debates warmly for Holland; and beneath
this mask the tip of the English ear appears.

Speaking of me, his Majesty said: "I suspect he is ordered to observe me; his love* for the Emperor probably will not expose him to the temptation of speaking ill of me, when there is nothing ill to be spoken."

Prince Henry fears that, the mode of life excepted, the method and especially the ceremonies of Government will be continued. He has charged me to mention that Comte d'Esterno is much too cold, too distant, too entirely an Ambassador, for the new King. He entreats our Ministry not to be tedious in bargaining concerning the pledges of confidence.

It is said, and I forgot to ask Prince Henry, who perhaps does not know, whether it be or be not true, that the King has sent for the Duke of Brunswick. The Minister, Schulemburg, is in danger. Prince Henry, by whom he has so long been hated and decried, is resolved to give him support. Schulemburg returned only this morning. He has composed, or rather made Struensee compose, an apologetic memorial, adroit and sophistical, in which he has imputed to the late King that order of affairs which he proposes to remedy. He declaims against monopolies,— he, who is himself at the head of all the monopolies; but he endeavors to prove they cannot be suddenly reformed, especially that of the maritime company.

* This is ironical.

LETTER XVI.

August, 22d, 1786.

PRINCE HENRY is singularly well satisfied with the new King, who the day before yesterday (Sunday) spent the greatest part of the afternoon with his uncle. The latter went to him in the morning to know the watchword. He pretends his nephew indicates an entire confidence in him; but I fear he interprets compliments into pledges of trust. He affirms the downfall of Hertzberg approaches; this I do not believe. "I and my nephew," said the Prince, "have been very explicit;" but I doubt the nephew has deceived the uncle. The conciliating temper of the King, and his good-nature, which induce him to receive all with kindness, may likewise lead to error, without intending deception; and these rather prove he possesses sensibility than strength of mind.

Prince Henry affirms that the King is entirely French. He requests that no attention may be paid to the sending of Colonel or Major Geysau to London, with accession compliments; these, he affirms, relate only to the family. The King has besides been deceived; he was told that the Court of St. James had sent compliments at the death of King George, which is not true. This, it is added, is an artifice of Count Hertzberg. Prince Henry did not arrive soon enough to prevent the thing being done; were it to do again it should be otherwise. (Remark, it is the Prince himself who speaks.) No one has been sent either to Vienna or to Petersburg. (Not to Vienna, to the chief of the Empire, who is almost as near a relation as the King of England. And as to Petersburg, Romanzow has made such bitter complaints that Count Finckenstein, moderate as he is, demanded whether he had received orders from his Court to speak in that style.) But it is singular enough that envoys have been sent everywhere else; and particularly Count

(68)

Charles Podewils (brother to him who is at Vienna) is gone to bear the news to Sweden. This is departing from the old system, to which, it is said, the King means, in other respects, to adhere; for the King of Sweden was held in aversion by the late King; nor is he less hated by Prince Henry. Count Stein, a kind of domestic favorite, is gone to Saxony, Weymar, Deux-Ponts, etc.

Prince Henry wishes the Minister for Foreign Affairs should write, and immediately, that the Court of France hopes the new King will confirm the friendship his predecessor began; and should give it to be understood that all the Prussian Ministers are not supposed to mean as well, toward France, as the King himself (I am not at all of this opinion; for this would be to distinguish Hertzberg, and to render the war against our Cabinet more inveterate. If the downfall of this Minister be necessary, it can be effected only by taxing him with governing the King), and that the reciprocity of good will and good offices may, and ought to, produce a more intimate connection. He wishes M. de Calonne might write soon to him (Prince Henry) a friendly and ostensible letter, but which ought to be sent by safe hands; that it should be recommended to Comte d'Esterno to smooth his brow; and he is particularly desirous a mode of somewhat calming the affairs of Holland should be found, and that this act should be much praised and insisted on.

The Duke of Brunswick has been sent for, and is to arrive on Thursday. It is said he brings another will, which was deposited in his hands. The first was not read before the family, but only in presence of the two uncles and the two Ministers. The legatees have all received their bequests. The date of this will is 1769. It is in a pompous style, and is written with labor and declamation. The King has been exceedingly attentive to specify that his legacies are made from the savings of his privy purse.

The following is a sketch of his donations: The Queen has an annual augmentation to her income of ten thousand crowns. Prince Henry has the gross sum of two hundred thousand crowns, a large green diamond, a luster of rock crystal estimated at fifteen thousand crowns, a set of eight coach horses, two led horses richly caparisoned, and fifty *anteaux*, or small casks of Hungarian wine. Prince Ferdinand the gross sum of fifty thousand crowns, and some Hungarian wine. Princess Ferdinand ten thousand crowns annually (the reason of this was that, in 1769, she was the only Princess of her house who had any children), and a box. Princess Henry six thousand crowns annually. The Duchess Dowager of Brunswick ten thousand crowns annually. The Princess Amelia ten thousand crowns annually, and all the personal plate of the late King. The Princess of Wurtemberg the gross sum of twenty thousand crowns. The Duke of Wurtemberg a ring. The Landgrave of Hesse the gross sum of ten thousand crowns. Prince Frederick of Brunswick the same. The reigning Duke of Brunswick the same, with eight horses (among others, the last that Frederick mounted) and a diamond ring, estimated at twenty-two thousand crowns, etc., etc., etc.

The King has confirmed all this with a very good grace. The only article that he will not agree to was a strange whim of the late King, relative to the interment of his body; he wished to be buried beside his dogs. Such is the last mark of contempt which he thought proper to cast upon mankind.* I know not whether the will that is coming will be equally respected with that

* The tongue of scandal VERY PUBLICLY, that is to say, in Prussia, gives a far different reason; but it is one so revolting, so atrocious, that not only charity but probability leads us to suspect the truth of SUCH an accusation. Still, his love for his dogs while living, his manner of treating them, and his last request to be buried by their side, are very strange, or, in a man like him, very whimsical facts. One of these favorites, a greyhound bitch, was taken at the battle of Sorr, when the baggage was plundered by Trenck and Nadasti. Regardless of inferior losses, the King was in the act of writing to Nadasti, to request his bitch might be restored, when the Austrian general, knowing his love for the animal, which was itself greatly attached to him, sent it back; the bitch, unperceived by the Monarch, leaped upon the table while he was writing, and, as usual, began to caress him, at which he was so affected that he shed tears. The day before he had cut off many thousands of men, and charged his DEAR CHILDREN to give no Saxon quarter.

already opened, even though they should not be contra-dictory.

As to the situation of the Court, I believe the truth to be that Prince Henry exaggerates his ascendency; and that he is in absolute ignorance of the King's intentions. They prattle much together, but there is no single point on which they have yet come to any stipulation. True it is that five days are scarcely yet elapsed. But where-fore presume? The Prince supports the Minister, Schu-lemburg; and I know that Schulemburg found the King dry and cold. He had one choice for the French Em-bassy; and I know the King has another, which he has not even concealed from the Prince. The Monarch hears all, but is in nothing explicit. Bishopswerder himself perhaps does not know what he is to be, and, if he be prudent, will not be in too great haste.

I have twice seen Count Hertzberg, and found him still the same, a small portion of dissimulation excepted. He very positively denied being English. He does not seem to me to think he has the least need of Prince Henry, whom he has not been to visit (which is very marked, or rather indecent behavior) since his promotion to the Order of the Black Eagle. I wished to insinuate to him that it would be easy to consult the uncle by the aid of the nephew; this he declined, but gave me an apologetic memorial for Prince Henry, relative to his personal dis-cussions with Baron Knyphausen. Either Prince Henry or Hertzberg, or both, are much deceived. Hertzberg certainly sups almost every night with the King; and the opinion of some well-informed people is that this Minister, and General Moellendorf, will be appointed to educate the Prince of Prussia.

The Marquis of Luchesini is continued in his place by the present King; but hitherto he has only been desired to write the poem for the funeral. The secretary of Prince Henry, it is said, is to compose the music; and this is one of the things which turn the uncle's brain.

I have sent the King my grand Memorial*; he has only acknowledged having received it, adding that I might remain persuaded whatever should come from me would

* The Memorial found at the end of this volume.

give him pleasure; and that, of all the obliging things that were said to him, none flattered him more highly than mine.

P. S.— The Ministers took the oath of allegiance yesterday, about three o'clock; hence, no probable changes for some time to come. Count Arnim Boytzemburg, sent for by the King, arrived with all haste, and passed the evening with his Majesty. I believe him proper for nothing but a place about Court; it may, however, have relation to the Embassy to France, but more probably to the place of Grand Marshal, or that of Minister of the Landschafft, a kind of president of the provinces, who greatly influences the assessments of the taxes, and other internal arrangements.

LETTER XVII.

August 26th, 1786.

I FEAR my prophecies will be accomplished. Prince Henry appears to me to have gained nothing but bows from his nephew. One article of the will of the King's grandfather disposed of the succession of certain *bailliages*, so as to bequeath an accession of income, of about forty or fifty thousand crowns, to Prince Henry, including an augmentation of the revenue of Prince Ferdinand. Circumstances not being exactly the same now as supposed by the testator, the Ministers (that is to say, Hertzberg) have pretended that this bequest no longer was legal; and the king, eluding to grant the legacy, has made a proposal to his uncle to have the suit determined either in Germany, France or Italy. The Prince has written an ingenious and noble letter to him, but in which he indicates the enemy. The King has redoubled his outward caresses for his uncle, and has submitted to three judges, who have been nominated by the Prince. I hence conclude that the uncle will gain the suit of the *bailliages*, but never that of the regency.

Hertzberg, however, has commissioned me to make some advances from himself to the Prince, and this I think is a sign that he is not in perfect security. I never could prevail on the Prince to comply; sometimes inflated, sometimes agitated, he neither could command his countenance nor his first emotions. He is deceitful, yet knows not how to dissemble; endowed with ideas, wit, and even a portion of understanding, but has not a single opinion of his own. Petty means, petty councils, petty passions, petty prospects; all is diminutive in the soul of that man. While he makes gigantic pretensions, he has a mind without method; is as haughty as an upstart, and as vain as a man who had no claim to respect; he can neither lead nor be led. He is one of too frequent examples that insignificance of character may stifle the greatest qualities.

The thing the new King fears the most is being thought to be governed; and in this respect Prince Henry, of all men, is the least adapted to the Monarch; who I believe would consent not to reign, provided he might only be supposed to reign.

Remarkable change! The general directory is restored to the footing on which it was under Frederick William I.* This is a wise act. The result of the madness of innovation, under Frederick II., was that, of all the Kings in Europe, he was the most deceived. The mania of expediting the whole affairs of a kingdom in one hour and a half was the cause that the Ministers were each of them absolute in their departments. At present, all must be determined in a committee; each will have occasion of the consent and sanction of all the rest. In a word, it is a kind of Council. This, no doubt, will have its inconveniences; but how are inconveniences to be avoided?

The edict for suppressing the Lotto is signed, as I am assured. I shall at least have done this much good to the country. But the King has permitted the last drawing, which is wrong; there ought to have been none under his reign. Perhaps it is only popular report.

The Duke of Brunswick arrived this evening. M. Ardenberg-Reventlau, a man of merit and his favorite Minister — though M. Feronce is the principal — preceded him, and was here at a quarter after four. The Duke was admitted to see his Majesty, who rises at four o'clock; at half after six he was on the parade. The King received him with neither distance nor ardor. Perhaps nothing more is meant by this journey than politeness. Necessity only could make such a man Prime Minister, who will not trouble himself with fruitless efforts, but who will be very tenacious in his grasp. I shall not converse with him till to-morrow. The will he brings will probably be burned; it is said to be of a much earlier date than the other, and as far back as 1755.

The Landgrave of Hesse Cassel, it is affirmed, is coming; also the Duke of Weymar, the Prince de Deux-

* The predecessor of the late King.

Ponts, and even the Duke of York. Of the latter I doubt.

Hertzberg pretends that the King, by becoming the pledge of the Stadtholder, ought to make us easy concerning Holland, but he has not told us who shall make the pledge respected.

Prince Henry wishes advice should be sent that Count Hertzberg, who has not the good word of the world, appears to have gained the entire confidence of the King, and even to act the master. This last imputation is probably the most effectual method to procure the downfall of any man, under the present sign.

There are many small Court favors granted, but no considerable place bestowed. I have attempted to reconcile Hertzberg and Knyphausen, which I was in a train to accomplish, by demonstrating to them that their coalition would erect a throne which could not be shaken. Knyphausen refused, because, alleged he, Hertzberg is so deceitful it can never be known whether the reconciliation is or is not sincere; "and it is better," said the Baron, "to be the open enemy than the equivocal friend of a man whose credit is superior to our own."

I am inclined to think Hertzberg must be displaced, if we wish the Prussians should become French. Three months are necessary to draw any conclusions that should be at all reasonable. I again repeat, if you have any grand political views, relative to this country and Germany, put an end to the democratical quarrels of Holland; which are only the disputes of cunning, profitable to those who have their fortunes to make, but not to those whose fortunes are made.

LETTER XVIII.

August 29th, 1786.

To PROPHESY here daily becomes more difficult; time only can afford any rational prognostics. The King apparently intends to renounce all his old habits; this is a proud undertaking. He has made three visits to Schoenhausen,* nor has he cast one look on Mademoiselle Voss; no semblance of an *orgia;* not one woman's bosom touched since he has sat on the throne. One of his confidants proposed a visit to Charlottenburg. "No," replied he; "all my former allurements are there." He retires before ten in the evening, and rises at four; he works excessively, and certainly with some difficulty. Should he persevere, he will afford a singular example of habits of thirty years being vanquished. This will be an indubitable proof of a grand character, and show how we have all been mistaken. But even, the supposition granted, which is so far from probable, how deficient are his understanding and his means. I say how deficient, since even his most ecstatic panegyrists begin by giving up his understanding. The last day that he exercised the troops he was ridiculously slow, heavy, and monotonous. The men were four times ranged in columns, and concluded with parading. This continued three hours, and in the presence of a general such as is the Duke of Brunswick. Everybody was dissatisfied. Yesterday, the first Court day, he was ill; he forgot some of the foreign Ministers, and uttered nothing but a few commonplace phrases, hasty, embarrassed, and ill-chosen; this scarcely continued five minutes. He immediately left us to go to church; for he does not miss church; and religious zeal, homilies, and pulpit flatteries already begin to be everywhere heard and seen.

Prince Henry has gained his suit, concerning the *bailliages*, as I had foreseen; in other respects, he has not

* The Queen's Palace.

(76)

advanced a step, consequently has gone backward. He dines every day with the King, and does wrong; he affects to whisper with him, and does wrong; he speaks to him of public affairs incessantly, and does wrong. The King goes alone to visit the Duke of Brunswick; and also goes in company with Hertzberg, or meets him at the Duke's. The latter pretends to interfere only with the army,—the sole thing which, according to him, he understands. I have never yet seen him in private, but he has appointed me an audience on Wednesday morning.

The English faction continues very active, and this proves there are difficulties to encounter. In reality, it is an alliance so unnatural, when compared to ours, that it seems to me we should not suffer ourselves, though the King should commit blunders, to be routed by his mistakes.

The Monarch becomes very difficult effectually to observe. He reverts to the severe ceremonies of German etiquette. It is imagined he will not receive foreigners, at least for some time. I know all that can be learned from subaltern spies; from valets, courtiers, secretaries, and the intemperate tongue of Prince Henry; but there are only two modes of influencing,—which are to give, or rather to give birth to, ideas in the master, or in his Ministers. In the master! How, since he is not to be approached? In the Ministers! It is neither very easy nor very prudent to speak to them on public affairs, I not being in a public character; and the discussions which chance affords are short, vague, and incomplete. If I am supposed capable of business, I ought to be sent to some place where I should have a public character. I am afraid I shall here cost more than I am worth.

Count Goertz goes to Holland; I know not whether instead of Thulemeyer or *ad tempus*. He is followed by the son of Count Arnim, who is a young shoot for the *corps diplomatique*. Goertz is not a man without talents: when sent into Russia, under every kind of disadvantage, he obtained a good knowledge of the country; he is cold, dry, and ungracious; but subtle, master of his temper, though violent, and a man of observation. That he is of

the English party is certain; he is loyal to Hertzberg,
and convinced that the alliance of Holland and France is
so unnatural it must soon end. I own I think as he
does, especially should we abuse our power.

A new Ambassador is appointed, *in petto*, for France.
I have not yet been able to discover who; but Hertzberg
supports the ridiculous Goltz with all his power.   Schulemburg daily declines in favor.   The maritime company
have already lost their monopoly of coffee, of which there
are four millions and a half pounds' weight consumed in
the various provinces of the Prussian monarchy.   Hence
we may observe that the free use of coffee, which daily
becomes general in Germany, is the cause that the consumption of beer is gradually and much less.   The same
company may be deprived of a prodigious profit on sugars;
but it will be in vain to destroy old monopolies only to
substitute new, though they should be for the profit of
the King.

The personal debts of his Majesty are paying off by
the Minister, Blumenthal; it is said there are tolerably
great reductions made, but not unjustly, as I imagine,
for there are no complaints on the subject.   Exclusive
of the Royal Treasury, Frederick II. has left savings so
great that they will scarcely be absorbed by the personal
debts of Frederick William II.   It is said he will pay off
his Italian opera, and everybody believes there will be a
French opera instead.   This certainly would be no trifling
means of support to intrigue.

The freedom of scrutiny is restored to the Academy,
and the Germans are henceforward to be admitted members.   I regard the curatorship of this body as a favor
conferred on, and a tolerable resource of power for,
Hertzberg, who will be curator by title, and president in
reality.   The presidency of the Academy is so truly ministerial that the late Frederick exercised it himself, after
the decease of the restless and morose De Maupertuis.
Count Hertzberg said to me, at Court, "You are a compliment in my debt."   "On what occasion?"   "I am
curator of the Academy; which title gives me greater
pleasure and, in my opinion, is more honorable than a
ribbon."   Forty persons heard our discourse.   "Cer-

tainly," replied I, "he who is the minister of knowledge
may well be called the Prime Minister."

The King will not ruin himself in gifts; he has hitherto bestowed only prebendaries, which cost him nothing, except a pension of three hundred crowns, on
General Levald. I am informed that he has just granted
one of eight hundred crowns — to the poet Rammler.
It would perhaps have been more delicate not to have
begun by pensioning fame, and her trumpet.

LETTER XIX.

September 2d, 1786.

ALL circumstances confirm my predictions. Prince Henry and his nephew have almost quarreled. The uncle is inconsolable, and thinks of retiring to Rheinsberg. He will almost certainly return during the journey of the King, through Prussia and Silesia. Probably we shall have no great changes before the Monarch has performed these journeys, if then. There is one, however, besides those I have before spoken of, which is remarkable; and that is, a commission to examine the administration of the customs,— what is to be abrogated, what preserved, and what qualified, especially in the excise.

M. Werder, a Minister of State, and the intimate friend of Hertzberg, the enemy of Schulemburg who brought him into place, and father-in-law to the secretary of the English Embassy, or perhaps to his wife, is at the head of this commission. The other members are ridiculously selected; but the very project of such a reform is most agreeable to the nation; as much so as the pension of eight hundred crowns granted to the poet Rammler, and the promise of admission of Germans into the Academy, is to the distributors of renown. It remains to be seen whether the people have not been led to hope too much; and whether it is not requisite to be certain of substitutes, previous to the promise of relief.

The King goes to Prussia attended by Messieurs Hertzberg (for the King to be attended by a Minister out of his department is unexampled), Goltz, surnamed the Tartar, Boulet, a French engineer, General Goertz, Gaudi, and Bishopswerder.

This Goltz the Tartar is he who, in the last campaign of the Seven Years' War, raised an insurrection of fifty thousand Tartars, in the Crimea and the neighboring countries; who were marching to make a diversion in

favor of the King of Prussia, and had arrived at Bender,
when peace was concluded. Notwithstanding this, Goltz
can boast of but little abilities; except that he is a good
officer, and ardently active. He was indebted for his
great and singular success to a Dutchman named Biskamp, whom he met with in the Crimea. He attached
himself to this very able and enterprising man, who understood the language, knew the country, and served Frederick II. according to his wishes; by whom, indeed, he
was well paid. This Biskamp is at Warsaw, and there
forgotten, which is very strange. I have supposed the
relating this anecdote, which is but little known, might
be interesting.

Boulet is an honest man, for whom the King shows
some affection, and to whom he is indebted for all he
knows concerning fortification.

General Goertz is the brother of the Goertz who is going to Holland, but not his equal; he is artful and subtle,
and his good faith is of a suspicious complexion.

Gaudi is the brother of the celebrated general of the
same name; little known hitherto as the Minister of the
Prussian department, but capable, well-informed, firm,
decided, and indubitably the man most proper to influence interior arrangements in reconstructing the grand
directory.

Bishopswerder you are acquainted with; he and Boulet
each lately received the commission of lieutenant colonel.

The King has told Schulemburg that, on his return
from Prussia, he will determine which of his nine departments he shall be deprived of. He and his wife are
the only ministerial family who are not invited to Court.
The probabilities all are that Schulemburg will demand
leave to resign, should his colleagues continue to humble
him, and the King to treat him with contempt. But
Struensee probably will keep his place, and he then proposes to act, in concert with us, in our public funds;
especially should the King, as is apparent, commit to his
charge the four millions of crowns which he means to
set apart for the operations of previous finance. Struensee is the only man who understands them. This is a

6

subject not to be neglected, as it hitherto has been, even
so far as to render it impossible for me to act with propriety. We might profit by him, during peace; but if
unfortunately the news which is whispered be true, concerning the increasing ill health of the Elector of Bavaria, depend upon war, for I then hold it inevitable. Is
this a time for us to exist from day to day, as we do,
when each month (for there is a probability, at any
time, that he should die within a month) menaces all
Europe with inextricable confusion?

M. de Larrey, sent from the Stadtholder to compliment
the King, openly affirms it is impossible the disputes of
Holland should be appeased without effusion of blood;
and the speculations of Hertzberg upon this subject are
boundless; but the secret is well kept by those who surround the King.

LETTER XX.

September 2d, 1786.

B<small>Y WHAT</small> fatality, monseigneur, has it happened that I have not received your letter, dated the sixteenth, till this day? And, still more especially, why was it not written some weeks sooner? The importance of the proposition with which it concludes will never be fully understood; and which, made at any other time, except when the King was dying, would have been willingly accepted. It will never be known, had it been presented soon enough, how much it might have effected, impeded, and indicated, relative to a Prince whose understanding perhaps is not great, but who possesses gratitude, and who will much more certainly be an honest man than a great King; so that his heart rather than his mind ought to have been appealed to; and that at a time when he was far otherwise accessible than at present,—walled in, as he is, by system and intrigue. How does it happen that you are the only person of the country you inhabit who conceived this plan? How could the Cabinet of Versailles give up the merit of offering trifling sums to Serilly? How could it permit the Duke of Courland to secure the claim of having hushed the loud cries of creditors to silence? How impolitic and disastrous are the sordid views, the confined plans, and short-sighted prudence of certain persons! In what a situation would such an act have placed us, as it would me personally, in his opinion! All things then would have been possible, would have been easy to me. But of this we must think no more; we must only remember this is a new proof that reason is always on your side.

Since the death of the King I have sent supplies of information to your Cabinet, respecting the *Aulic phases*,*

* Court changes, or appearances.

and my dispatch of to-day, a great part of which no
doubt our common friend will read to you, is a statement, according to the best of my abilities, of present
and future contingencies.   You will there perceive that
Prince Henry has accomplished his own destiny; that his
trifling character has, on this occasion, weighty as it
was, been stranded on the rock of his excessive vanity,
as it has before so often been; that he has at once displayed an excessive desire of power, disgusting haughtiness, insupportable pedantry, and a disdain of intrigue,
at the same time that his conduct was one continuation
of petty, low, dirty cabal; that he has despised the people in power, while he himself is surrounded only by
those who are evidently either foolish, knavish, or contemptible, — one sole man, Baron Knyphausen, excepted,
and he is in daily danger of being carried off by apoplexy; that, in fine, no man can be more out of favor,
and particularly out of confidence, or can have put himself into a situation in which confidence and favor will
be more difficult to regain.

I therefore persist in my opinion that the Duke of
Brunswick, who is master of himself, by no means
ostentatious, and who is possessed of profound talents,
will be the man, — not of the present moment, but of
the moment of necessity.   My reasons are numerous, and
so deduced as, in my opinion, not to admit of contradiction, the order of events and circumstances which I
see and foresee considered.   All this does but render the
execution of your project the more necessary, and which
I regard as very practicable, with some small exceptions,
if executed by the persons in whom you ought to confide,
— should you, with your natural dexterity, and irresistible seduction, pursue the plan of interesting the vanity
of the MASTER, so as to make it his own act, and, as you
have so well expressed it, that it shall be he himself
who shall inform his Ministers of his intentions.

I repeat, your project is the more immediately necessary because that England cabals, with great industry,
in her own behalf, under the pretense of the interests of
Holland, which are very much at heart, in the Cabinet
of Berlin.   I own that what I have often insinuated here,

namely, that the Prussian power is not sufficiently con-
solidated, and that, if opposed to stand the shock of
France and Austria combined, it must be reduced to
powder, is a proposition not so unanswerable but that,
thanks to Russia, there are many objections to be made;
and so there always will be, even in suppositions the
most unfavorable to Prussia.

1. Because this would but be commencing a deplorable career of sanguinary contentions, under the direction
of the Emperor, who is so little able to direct that he
may be affirmed to be the least military of men.

2. That the utmost success would leave a Prince without counterpoise in Europe, who has claims and preten-
tions of every kind.

Lastly, and more especially, this would be painfully to
seek that which the nature of events spontaneously offers;
like as spring makes the apparently dry and sapless tree
bud and bloom.

There are some errors in ciphering, which are the cause
that I do not perfectly understand the grounds of your
dissension with me, concerning the maritime system; but
I too well know the extreme justness of your mind, which
does not remain satisfied with phantoms, to imagine our
opinions are very opposite. And, for my own part, I have
never pretended to say that we ought not to maintain a
navy which should make our commerce respected. The
question to determine is, What ought the extent of this
commerce to be, which is to be effectually protected?
You, like me, perceive that no alliance with England can
be solidly established but by a commercial treaty, which
should have exact, clear, and distinct lines of demarca-
tion; for, were unlimited freedom of trade permitted, they
would be the sufferers. How might they support the rivalship? And, if we do not cut away the voracious suckers
from the root of the tree, how shall we prevent the Indies
and Antilles from eternally continuing the apple of discord?

Be this as it may, monseigneur, do not suffer yourself to be discouraged or disgusted by difficulties. Ascend
the height with a firm though measured step, and with
inflexible constancy. You have found the only unbeaten

track which, in these times, can lead to political fame, and which best may tend to the pacification of the earth. How admirable is it to unite the talents of the hero, the principles of the sage, and the projects of the philosopher! By a single diplomatic act to reverse all the obsolete forms, all pitiable rubrics, all the destructive arts of modern politics, would be to gain no vulgar crown; and a prospect so magnificent must be a most powerful support to your fortitude.

I need not repeat how much I am devoted to you, or how entirely you may dispose of me.

LETTER XXI.

September 5th, 1786.

IT IS impossible that I should send you intelligence more exact, concerning the situation of Prince Henry with the King, than that which my preceding letters contain. The Prince himself no longer conceals the truth, and, like all weak men, passing from one extreme to the other, he clamorously affirms the country is undone; that priests, blockheads, prostitutes, and Englishmen are hastening its destruction; and, by the intemperance of his language, confirms what the indiscretion of Chevalier d'Oraison, and the personal confidence of the uncle to the nephew, when he was only Prince of Prussia, probably before but too certainly told Frederick William II. I repeat, he has completed his disgrace, in the private estimation of the King. It is my opinion that, if he may be permitted, he will either quit this country, in which he has not one friend, one parasite, except in the most subaltern and abject class, or will become insane, or will die; such is my augury.

Not that I am convinced that the administration must always be committed to subalterns. The King has too much dread of seeming to be governed not to have the necessity of being governed. Why should he be the first man who should pretend to be what he is not? Frederick II., who by nature was so perfectly designed to govern, never testified a fear of being governed; he was certain of the contrary. The present King fears he shall, and therefore shall be. While public affairs are transacted separately, he will not seem to be; for nothing is more easy in this country than to receive and to pay. The machinery is so wound up that the surplus of revenue is great indeed. It is easy to pay some attention to detail, to keep watch over the police, to make some subordinate changes, and to coquette with the nation. And here be it said, by the way, there seems a determination of humbling the vanity of foreigners; so that, as I have always affirmed, the *gallomania* * of Prince Henry has been very prejudicial to us. Some good will be done; for it is not here as in other kingdoms, where the passing from evil to good is sometimes worse than evil itself, and where there is terror in resistance. All is here done *ad nutum*. Besides, the cords are so stretched they cannot but relax; the people have been so oppressed, have suffered such vexation, such extortion, that they must find ease. All will proceed, therefore, and almost without aid, while foreign politics shall continue calm and uniform; but, whenever a gun is fired, or even at the first lowering storm, with what a petty crash will this scaffolding of mediocrity come to the ground! How will these subaltern Ministers shrink, from the slave at the oar to the terrified steersman? How will they call for a pilot's aid?

Who must be this pilot? The Duke of Brunswick. Of this I have no doubt. Every little accident, in the day of trouble, is only an additional aptitude to fear. Besides that, the Prince is, of all men, he who best can conduct little vanity; he will satisfy himself with appearing the servant of servants; the most polite, the most humble, and indubitably the most adroit of courtiers; while, at the same time, his iron hand will fetter all paltry views, all trifling intrigues, all inferior factions. Such is the horoscope I draw; nor do I think, at present, one more rational can be erected.

Hertzberg is the man who must be managed in the State; and for this Comte d'Esterno is not qualified, because he formerly deserted him too much; and he well perceived it would have been indelicate and stupid to have veered too suddenly. Hertzberg, however, may ruin himself by his boasting, and even by his ostentation. This is a mode of effecting the fall of Ministers which the courtiers will not fail to employ because of the character of the King, and which may succeed.

But Holland and her convulsions are the subject of present consideration. There is a conviction that we can do what we please; and, though I am far from thinking

* Enthusiasm in favor of France.

this to be incontrovertible, I still think that, were we to
say to the party that has gained so much ground, probably from a conviction that we were ready to march up
to their support (for how would they have dared to make
themselves responsible if they had possessed no securities
for such future contingencies as may be expected?). I
repeat, were we to say, YOU MUST GO NO FURTHER, we
should be obeyed. It will be supposed, I neither pretend
nor wish to give advice. I am too far removed from
truth, which I can only inspect through the magnifying
glass of passion; and the Comte d'Esterno informs me
of nothing; but I can distinctly perceive that that hurricane, which is forming in those marshes, may extend to
other countries. The French Embassy of Berlin will not
say thus much to you, because they do not see things
in the same light, but are persuaded that the interest
of the brother will have no influence on the connections of
the King. Of this I doubt, and have good reason so to
doubt. Hertzberg is wholly Dutch, for it is the only
decent manner in which he can be English; and he may
greatly influence foreign politics, although he does not
understand them. As, the other day, he was rehearsing
his eternal repetition of — THE KING WILL BE THE PLEDGE
OF THE STADTHOLDER — I said to him, "I respect the
King too much to ask who shall be the pledge of the
pledge; but I dare venture to ask — HOW WILL THE KING
MAKE HIS PLEDGE RESPECTED? What shall happen when
France shall demonstrate that the Stadtholder has broken
engagements entered into under her sanction? The King
is not the brother-in-law of Holland; and the affair of
Naples is sufficient proof that family interventions may
be eluded? What can the King accomplish against Holland? And is he not too equitable to require us, who
cannot wish that the Dutch should become English, to
risk our alliance for the knight-errant of the English?"
To all this Hertzberg, who beholds nothing on this sub-
lunary earth but HERTZBERG and PRUSSIA, made vague
replies; but, at the words, "What can the King accomplish against Holland?" he muttered, with a gloomy air,
"HOLLAND WILL NOT DEFY HIM, I BELIEVE." Once again,
beware of Holland; where, by way of parenthesis the

English legation affirms that we have bought the town of Schiedam; that M. de Calonne, in particular, inundates the country with gold; and, in a word, that he is personally the brand of discord.

I have reserved the questions with which your letter begins, to conclude with; first, because they relate to affairs the least pressing, since it appears impossible that the Emperor should make any attempts on Turkey in Europe before the coming spring; and next, it was necessary I should previously recollect myself; the concurring circumstances of the death of the King, and the accession of Frederick William, being the subjects which have almost exclusively demanded my attention, and induced me to defer more distant objects to future consideration. Still, I fear mine is a barren harvest, Prussia not having any continued intercourse with these wide lying countries, which are more than four hundred leagues distant; for she has neither any great merchant, nor any system of politics, because the *corps diplomatique* of Prussia is extremely deficient.

As to those individuals that are met with in society, they are ignorant, and can afford no information. Buckholz, the Prussian envoy to Warsaw, a man of ordinary capacity, but active, and Huttel, who is in the same capacity at Petersburg, an intelligent person, write word that Russia is more pacific than Turkey, and that the internal Ottoman provinces call for war. The frontier provinces, appertaining to the Tartars, certainly are not friendly to Russia. Moldavia and Wallachia are governed by Hospodars, who, being Greeks, most certainly are sold to whoever will purchase them, consequently to Russia. The Emperor deceives them, and is hated there, as elsewhere. I shall speak further of this, and shall endeavor to give a sketch of a journey along the frontiers of these countries, which should be undertaken in the disguise of a trader, and kept rigidly secret, by which the state of the frontiers, the magazines, the propensities of the people, etc., etc., might be known, and what is to be hoped or feared, if it be found necessary to arm (in which case it is very probable Prussia would voluntarily aid us with all her powers),— that is to say if the Emperor should determine to pay no respect to our remonstrances, as he has twice done before.

Perhaps I might be more useful employed in such a journey than at Berlin, where at every step I tread on danger, and shall so continue to do, unless I have credentials, at least as an assistant; which perhaps would be the more proper, because it sometimes happens that such an interlocutor is spoken to with greater freedom than an Ambassador; for the refusals he meets, or the proposals he makes, have no ministerial consequences; and thus each party gains information, without either being offended.

Pay serious attention to this, I request. In vain you recommend me to act privately; permit me to inform you that, in despite of all my efforts, this is impracticable. I have too much celebrity, too much intercourse with Prince Henry, who is a true Joan of Arc, and who has no secrets of any kind. I am made to speak when I am silent; and when I say anything it is unfaithfully repeated. It is impossible to conceive all that has been attributed to me since the King's death; that is to say, since an epoch when I have taken advantage of the interruption of social meetings to keep myself recluse, and to labor only by mining. Comte d'Esterno discredits me all in his power. The English Embassy exclaims: "*Fœnum habet in cornu, longè fuge.*" The favorites keep me at a distance; the wits, the priests, and the mystics have formed a league, etc., etc. Each fears an invasion of his domains, because my real business is not known. I cannot remain and be of any utility, unless you shall find means to inform Count Finckenstein that I am only a good citizen and a good observer; but that these I am, and that I am authorized to give my opinion. I cannot doubt but that this Minister is very desirous these few words should be said. I am, however, in conscience obliged to repeat, the part I have to play daily becomes more difficult and more invidious; and that, in order to be truly useful, I must have some character given me, or be employed elsewhere.

Prince Henry at present reads his recantation; he again pretends Hertzberg has received his deathblow, and that

his downfall will be instantaneous.   He relates miracles of
the Duke of Brunswick, and flatters himself that he shall,
soon or late, have great influence — "He will be in no
haste.   He will ply to windward six months."   He affirms
the English projects are absolutely abortive.   Hertzberg,
he is confident, acts as if he had lost all understanding,
and precisely as if he, Prince Henry, had counseled
him, in order to render his fall more headlong, etc., etc.,
etc.   In fine, his discourse is a mixture of enthusiasm
and rodomontade, of presumption and anxiety; a flux of
words that confirm nothing; or of half phrases without
any determinate meaning, except of exaggeration and
tumor.   Hence, it is difficult to conjecture whether he
deceives himself or wishes to deceive; whether he maintains the cause of vanity, feasts on illusion, or if he has
recently any ray of hope; for, as I have said, it is not
impossible but that Hertzberg, by his boasting, should
effect his own ruin.   Prince Henry presses me to request
the Court to send me some credentials, while the King
shall be in Prussia and Silesia; or, at least, to write concerning me to Count Finckenstein, by whom the intelligence may be communicated to the King.

No change in the new habits of the Monarch. Madame Rietz has been but once to see him; but, on Saturday last, he wrote to his natural son by that woman,
and directed his letter: "To my son Alexander, Count
de la Marche."* He has ennobled, and even made a
Baroness of the mistress of the Margrave of Schwedt
(Baroness of Stoltzenberg, which is the title of a Barony,
worth about eight thousand crowns a year, given her by
the Margrave), who is nothing more than a tolerably
pretty German girl, formerly an actress, by whom the
Margrave has a son.   It was not thought proper to refuse
the only thing this old Prince of seventy-seven wished
or could request.   Perhaps, too, it was a pretext to do as
much for Madame Rietz. The husband of this lady is
erzkaemmerer, † a place nearly corresponding to that of
first *valet de chambre*, and treasurer of the privy purse;
but it is supposed he will do nothing more than get

* Meaning one of the Marches of Brandenburg.
† Archchamberlain.

rich; his wife hitherto has never had any serious influence.

The Court Marshal, Ritwitz, having suddenly become raving mad, after a quarrel with one of the provision officers, Marwitz, who is a totally insignificant person, has been proposed to the King. "He will do as well as another," replied the Monarch. Is this thoughtlessness, or is it fear of importance being annexed to a place which in reality but little merits importance? This question it is impossible to answer.

Lucchesini increases in his pretensions; he demands a place in the finance or commercial department; perhaps the direction of the maritime company, but this would be a very lofty stride. Annexed to wit and information, he has some qualities to which ambition is seldom allied; at most they will entitle him to become a member of the *corps diplomatique*, of which he is capable. I believe this Italian to be one of the most ardent in keeping me at a distance from the King, who will not indeed be easy of access before the winter.

The commission of regulations has hitherto rather appeared a caustic than a healing and paternal remedy. There is much more talk of the sums the employment of which cannot be justified than of easing the excise. Verder, the president, is besides known to be the personal enemy of some of the members of the tax administration. This, perhaps, has occasioned suspicions. Verder, however, was proposed by the Duke of Brunswick, who, in fact, had need of his aid in some affairs that relate to his country.

Hertzberg has certainly been in a storm, and the credit of Count Finckenstein appears to be augmented, though I confess the shade of increasing favor is scarcely perceptible. I persist in believing that Hertzberg is immovable, unless by his want of address.

LETTER XXII.

September 8th, 1786.

THE sixth, at a review of the artillery, I dismounted my horse to attend the King, in the front of the ranks. The Duke of Brunswick joined me; and, as we talked of mortars, bombs, and batteries, we gradually removed to a distance. As soon as we were alone, he began to speak to me of the prodigious knowledge I had of the country; giving me to understand he had read my memorial to the King. He then reverted to the new reign, and suddenly afterward to foreign politics. Having entered at length into the subject, and spoken more than is necessary here to repeat, he added, "In God's name, arrange affairs in Holland; free the King of his fears. Must the Stadtholder never be other than *ad honores?* You are in full credit there, and this credit you cannot lose; if you did, the party by which you obtained it would be too much exposed to danger. I repeat, put us at our ease, and I will answer on my head for everything else; but use dispatch, I conjure you. On Sunday I shall depart for Brunswick; come and visit me, while the King is gone into Silesia; we can converse freely there, and nowhere else. But write to your friends that they ought to exert all their influence to engage the French Ministry to use moderation with the Prince of Orange, who cannot be proscribed without State convulsions. Things are not ripe for his abolishment; give him protection. France cannot render a greater service to Europe. What, is your Court yet to learn those forms which effect no change, but which give every support?" Here we separated, because the subject began to be too interesting. But tell me — ought I not to go to Brunswick?

To this I should add that Count Goertz has taken eight chasseurs with him, who are to convey letters to the frontiers of the Prussian States, in order that no dispatches may be sent by land, nor pass through foreign hands. The Duke of Brunswick has repeated what Prince Henry had told me, and which I forgot to inform you of, that one of the principal motives for selecting Count Goertz was his former friendship with M. de Veyrac.

From my conversation with the Duke, I conclude that he is or soon will be master of affairs; and this explains the new fit of joy, hope, and presumption which has seized on Prince Henry, who has been persuaded by the cunning Duke that, if he will but have patience, the scepter will devolve on him; and that he, the Duke, will be no more than high constable. It is said Koenigsberg will be appointed Field Marshal. This, added to the smooth turn which the Duke has given discussions and pecuniary matters, has turned the Prince's brain, who told me the other day that " the Duke was the most loyal of men, and his best friend; that he owned a fortnight ago he was of a different opinion; but that," etc. So that the metamorphosis has been produced within this fortnight. In truth, there is no real difference between a fool and a man of understanding who thus can suffer himself to be deceived; as little is there between a fool and a man of understanding who can be persuaded that a fool is a man of understanding. Both these things daily happen to Prince Henry. On the thirteenth he departs for Rheinsberg and is to return the day before the King.

The fervor of the novice appears somewhat to abate. I have good reason to believe that Mademoiselle Voss is ready to capitulate,— ogling, frequent conversations (for the present assiduity at Schoenhausen is not paid to the Queen Dowager), presents accepted (a canonicate for her brother), and an attempt at influence. (It is she who placed Mademoiselle Vierey in the service of the Princess Frederica of Prussia.) To ask is to grant. Since the accession all circumstances denote how dazzling is the luster of a diadem; but so much the better, for her fall only can render her but little dangerous. She is wholly English, and is not incapable of intrigue. When we reflect that the credit of a Madame du Troussel had the power, under a Frederick II., to bestow places of importance, we may imagine what may happen under another

King, as soon as it shall be discovered that intrigue may be employed at the Court of Berlin, as well as at other Courts.

Madame Rietz yesterday received a diamond worth four thousand crowns; she will probably be put on the invalid list, with some money, and perhaps a title.

Her son, at present, has publicly the title of Count de la Marche (or Count Brandenburg), and has a separate establishment.

General Kalckstein, disgraced by the late King, and regretted by everybody, has received a regiment.

At present, and till I hear other news relative to Berlin, accept the following important anecdote, which I think it necessary to send in the now doubtful state of the health of the Empress of Russia: About six years ago, a young foreigner, and a gentleman, in the service of France, was presented to the Grand Duchess, by a lady who had been educated with her, and who has remained her intimate friend. It was the intention of this young gentleman to enter into the Russian service. He was presented to the Grand Duke by the Grand Duchess, who warmly solicited, and while he was present, a place for the youth in the service of her husband.

The young favorite, well-formed and handsome, often visited the Grand Duchess. Invited to her palace, feasted, distinguished, and continually receiving new favors, he fell in love; of which the Grand Duchess was informed by his extreme confusion. One grand Court day, at a masked ball, in the evening, she had him conducted by one of her women into an obscure apartment, and sufficiently distant from those where the Court was held. In a little time the conductress quitted him, and advised him to wait, and the Grand Duchess arrived in a black domino. She removed her mask, took the youth by the hand, led him to a sofa, and made him sit down by her side. The Grand Duchess then told him this was the moment for him to choose between the service of France and the service of Russia. A certain time, however, was allowed him to come to a decision. Coquetry and even caresses succeeded. Wavering, taken by surprise, distracted between love and fear, the youth behaved with excessive awkwardness at the beginning of the interview. The Grand Duchess, however, encouraged him, inspired him with audacity, and made him every advance, till at length he vanquished his timidity and indeed became very daring.

To this scene of transports, adieus suddenly succeeded, which partook as much of terror, and of despotism, as of love. The Grand Duchess commanded the youth, in the most tender but the most absolute tone, to inform the Grand Duke that he could not accept the rank of captain, which was intended to be given him. She added that he must depart, instantly depart; and that his head must answer should the least circumstance transpire. She, at the same time, pressed him to demand some mark of remembrance. The terrified youth, confused and trembling, requested a black ribbon, which she took from her domino. He received the pledge, and so totally lost all recollection that he left the ball, and quitted Petersburg, without contriving any means of correspondence, arrangements for the future, or precautions of any kind, in favor of his fortune. In a few days he left Russia, traveling day and night, and did not write to the Grand Duke till he had passed the frontiers. He received a very gracious answer; and here the affair ended.

This person is returned to, and is now in, the service of France. He has little firmness, but does not want understanding. Were he guided he might certainly be useful; at least, attempts might be made after so extraordinary an incident. But for this it would be necessary he should go to Russia before there is any change of monarch, and should tempt his fortune, now that the Grand Duchess has not so much fear. I am not personally acquainted with him, but I can dispose of his most intimate friend, in whom every dependence may be placed. I have not thought proper to name the hero of the romance, whom it is not necessary to know, unless it should be intended to afford him employment. If, on the contrary, it should be thought proper for him to pursue any such plan, I will name him instantly.

The Elector of Bavaria is certainly not in good health; he may not live to see winter; and it is scarcely proba-

7

ble he will reach the spring. I shall go from hence to
Dresden, that I may not appear to absent myself purposely for the Duke of Brunswick. I shall remain there
seven or eight days, as long at Brunswick, and three or
four weeks in the whole. My journey will be exactly of
the same duration as that of the King, in whose absence
there is nothing to be learned, and I shall certainly profit
by my peregrinations, and learn more at Brunswick in
a week than I should here divine in three months.

My letter is too long to speak of Turkey in Europe. I
doubt the Emperor cannot be prevented, if he is not
destitute of all capacity, from marching any day he shall
please to the mouth of the Danube; but on the same day
he must become the natural enemy of Russia, who will
find in his presence one too many on the Black Sea, and
this may render the combined projects abortive. I am
assured that Moldavia and Wallachia desire to be under
the Emperor's Government. This I cannot believe, since
his own peasants fly their country, and even go to Poland,
rather than remain in his power. But the before-mentioned
provinces are absolutely unprotected, and I think no opposition can be made, except in Roumelia and Bulgaria.
In fine, I believe we only, by promises or threats, are
able to prevent the Emperor from laboring at this grand
demolition. If we believe the rodomontadoes of Petersburg, Russia is singly capable of the work. But, were
she to attempt it, what would she be on the succeeding
day? You are not ignorant she has received some check;
that Prince Heraclius has been obliged to desert her
cause; that she is once again reduced to defend Mount
Caucasus as a frontier; that she cannot at present march
into the heart of the Ottoman territories; and that perhaps this would be the best moment for recovering the
Crimea. Should all these particulars be true, and these
conjectures well founded, it is impossible that I should
know any one of them so perfectly as you do yourself.

The dispute, relative to the *bailliage* of Wusterhausen,
has been very nobly ended by the King. He has retaken
it, but has made an annual grant of fifty thousand
crowns to Prince Henry, seventeen thousand of which
the latter is obliged to pay Prince Ferdinand. The *bail-*

liage does not produce more than about forty-three thousand.

Prince Ferdinand at present recants the renunciation to the Margraviate of Anspach. As it is known that Prince Ferdinand has no will of his own, it is evident he receives his impulse from Prince Henry, and the more so, because this is the *manet altâ mente repostum* against Count Hertzberg. It would be difficult to imagine anything more silly, or better calculated eternally to embroil him with the King.

I have always regarded the singularity of Romanzow, of not going into mourning, and his violence with Count Finckenstein concerning not sending a complimentary envoy to Petersburg, which occasioned the Count to demand whether he had orders from his Court to speak in such a style, as the effervescence of a young man; especially since Baron Reeden, the Dutch envoy, did not likewise go into mourning from economy, which shows it was not considered as a matter of any great importance. As these debates very ridiculously occupied the *corps diplomatique* for a week; and as the Comte d'Esterno, who has conducted himself well on the occasion, must have mentioned it, I thought it to no purpose to write on the subject. But as Romanzow, of all the foreign Ambassadors, did not attend the funeral at Potsdam, this mark, either of thoughtlessness or dissatisfaction, was felt; and, the time necessary to receive orders being past, I send information of the fact, to which I do not, however, pay so much attention as the good people in the pit, though it has greatly displeased the boxes. The Cabinet of Berlin must long have known that friendship, on the part of Russia, is hopeless till the accession of the Grand Duke; but it is impossible to butt with more force, or greater disrespect, than Romanzow has done.

LETTER XXIII.

September 10th, 1786.

THE following are some particulars concerning what happened, on the day of interment, at Potsdam.

The King arrived at seven o'clock. At half-past seven he went with the Princesses Frederica and Louisa of Brunswick, the young ladies Knisbec, Voss, etc., to see the chamber of Frederick. It was small, hung with violet-colored cloth, and loaded with ornaments of black and silver. At the far end was an alcove, in which the coffin was placed, under the portrait of the hero. This coffin was richly ornamented with cloth of silver, laced with gold. Toward the head was a casque of gold, the sword that Frederick wore, his military staff, the ribbon of the Black Eagle, and gold spurs. Round the coffin were eight stools, on which were placed eight golden cushions, meant to sustain:

1. The crown.
2. The golden globe and cross.
3. The gold box containing the seal.
4. The electoral cap.
5. The scepter.
6. The Order of the Golden Eagle, of diamonds and other precious stones.
7. The royal sword.
8. The royal hand.

The balustrade was hung with violet-colored velvet. A splendid glass chandelier was in the center, and on each side was a mutilated pyramid of white marble veined with black; that is to say, of white cloth, marbled with great art. The chamber appeared to me to want light.

His Majesty afterward passed into the canopy *salon*, hung with black, and adorned with plates of silver from the Berlin palace; and next into the grand hall, hung with black. Eight artificial black columns had been added to this immense hall. Its only embellishments were garlands of cypress, and here again there was too little light.

In about half an hour the King returned to his apartments; and, at half past eight, Prince Henry, Prince Ferdinand, and the Duke of Brunswick came to see the same apartments, where they only remained five minutes.

At a quarter past nine the King went to Prince Henry. The regiments of guards formed under their windows. The canopy was brought; it was of black velvet, surrounded by cloth of gold, and laced with a crape fringe On the cloth of gold were black eagles. Twelve posts, covered with velvet, supported the canopy; and over them were twelve silver eagles, each a foot high, which produced a good effect.

After the canopy came the state coach;* very large, very low, hung with white satin edged with gold fringe, and drawn by eight horses covered with black velvet.

To the state coach succeeded a chariot, in black velvet, on which was a black crown, drawn by eight cream-colored horses, in black velvet harness, on which were fixed black eagles, embroidered in gold. The livery servants, chamber lackeys, heydukes, running footmen, huntsmen, and pages followed.

The Princesses, ushered by Messieurs Goertz and Bishopswerder, were at church.

At ten o'clock the procession began. The place of assembly was the grand hall with the eight columns. A gentle descent had been made from the grand canopy to the door, to which the state coach was drawn up to receive the coffin. The road from the palace to the church was planked, and covered with black cloth. The procession was truly superb, and conducted with great order. The troops formed two lines.

The church was illuminated with wax candles and small lamps; and the coffin was deposited under a cupola, supported by six pillars of white marble. The organ began to play and the funeral service was performed, which continued half an hour. The return was not disorderly, but it was not made in procession.

* *Corbillard.* Perhaps the word is here used to signify a hearse.

When the guests came back to the palace, the tables
were ready spread, and the courses were served up at
noon. The guests rose from table at half past one. The
King, Prince Henry, the Duke of Brunswick, and the
Princesses, went to Sans Souci. Such was the manner in
which the morning was spent.

There was no comparison to be drawn between this
and the funerals of the Church of Notre Dame with respect to magnificence, taste, or splendor; but they did
everything that could be done, the country and the time
considered.

There was much order from the commencement to the
close. The music was indifferent, had no effect, no energy, no charm, and was ill executed,— not one good
voice, Concialini excepted, who did not sing well.

The tables were well supplied, the viands abundant and
select, the servants numerous and orderly. Each of the
aides-de-camp general did the honors of a table. French,
Rhenish, and Hungarian wines were served in profusion.

The King, going to table, led Prince Henry. On
every occasion his Majesty saluted with dignity. His
countenance was neither serious nor too cheerful.

He testified his satisfaction to Reck, who replied that
Captain Gonthard had regulated the whole; and that he
had no other merit except that of having procured him
everything of which he stood in need.

The King wore the grand uniform of the guards. The
Princes were booted. Prince Goethen had mourning
spurs, which was remarked.

The King went and returned in company only with
the Duke of Brunswick.

LETTER XXIV.

September 12th, 1786.

THE King departs to-morrow. The order of his journey has undergone no change. He will be back on the 28th, and again set out on the 2d for Silesia. I shall probably have a good opportunity, on his return, to speak of finance and of substitutes. Previous to this Panchaud must absolutely unite with me to form a good plan of speculating in our funds,—good for the finances, and in particular good for the King who is to be allured. Remember the importance of this Monarch.

Bishopswerder increases in credit, which he carefully conceals. Welner, a subaltern creature, endowed with understanding, management, and knowledge of interior affairs,—a mystic when mysticism was necessary to please, and cured of his visions since the King has required these should be kept secret,—active, industrious, and, what is more, sufficiently obscure to be employed without creating jealousy,—Welner, I say, appears to gain prodigious influence. He has the qualities necessary to succeed, and even to outwit all his competitors.*

I again repeat, Boden ought not to be neglected, by the way of insinuation. He is vain, and should be capable of corruption; for, always suspected of the most insatiable avarice and the basest means, he has lost a place of eight thousand German crowns by the death of the Landgrave of Hesse Cassel, and, it is said, is driven to expedients. He corresponds with the King, and rather intimately; that which he should often repeat must produce an effect. He is the hero to slay Hertzberg, who, I may add, has not been successful concerning Holland, and, in despite of whom, Thulemer may still be recalled.

Prince Henry still feeds on hopes. I have no doubt that he is cajoled by the Duke of Brunswick. But he is exactly at the same point, except that Hertzberg is not

---

* He is at present absolutely the principal Minister.

so powerful. The King intends Alvensleben for the French Embassy; a man of high birth, sense, and wisdom, as it is affirmed. He is at Dresden. I shall endeavor to study him and shall take him letters.

No person is satisfied; civil and military, courtiers and Ministers, all pout. I imagine they expected it would rain gold. I have nothing to add to my prognostics, which may be reduced to this alternative: the nation sacrificed, while affairs continue tranquil, that we may persuade ourselves we govern; the Duke of Brunswick, should perils intervene, and the storm begin to blow.

In the name of business and of friendship, do not forget a plan of operations for finance. Schulemburg is supported, and I have reasons to believe he will not be dismissed. Should I acquire influence in finance I would not be his enemy. He will be more serviceable than any other, Baron Knyphausen only excepted, who will never be anything while Hertzberg is in power.

Remember that you have an incapable envoy in Bavaria, and that this will become an embassy of importance at the death of the Elector. If it be meant to place me, which must be meant if I am to serve, had not I best make my first appearance here?

LETTER XXV.

DRESDEN, September 16th, 1786.

I SHALL say nothing particular to you yet of this country, as you may suppose, for who can run and read?

Besides, I find the inconvenience of having no credentials, and, consequently, have not been able to speak with propriety on affairs, except in very general and metaphorical terms.

Stuterheim, the Minister for Foreign Affairs, with whom I have dined, is said to be a very well, a labyrinth of secrecy, and it follows that his subalterns are exceedingly reserved. The Ministers here rather give in their REPORTS than act. "Give in their reports" is the consecrated phrase. But I have been so well convinced by what I have seen under Frederick II., that the King, who governs most himself, is so little the master, and is so infinitely deceived, that I am perfectly aware of the degree of credit which these Court *dicta* deserve.

I have seen Alvensleben. Should he go to France, I do not think he will live long. He is worn out, and only keeps himself alive by extreme abstinence, and an almost total sequestration from society. He is well acquainted with Germany, is said to act with prudence and propriety, is successful in what he undertakes, and has a good moral character. He is not, however, without art, and, perhaps, he wishes to be cunning. He is not precisely the man for France, but he is a specimen of the fruit of the country, and, for any other use, is some of the best it produces. I imagine you will find him agreeable.

I shall endeavor to get into the currency of the country, but, I repeat, while I shall have no credentials, and am left so much in ignorance concerning home affairs, I shall be much more proper to collect literary and written opinions than for any other business; and the thoughts of men are not written in their faces. Nor do you, for example, find in any book that a Prime Minister has confided his eldest son, on his travels, to such a blockhead as G——, or to a Chevalier du Vivier, who never utters a word that he does not utter an absurdity, and, perhaps, some that are dangerous. But why has he related that he waited at Hamburg five weeks for permission to take the Vicomte de Vergennes to Berlin, on occasion of the accession of the King, and that this was refused? Is he afraid that they should be insensible at Berlin of the affectation of having avoided that Court? I should never finish were I to cite all the incoherencies he utters, the least of which is ridiculous in the extreme.

In reality, if I am to commence as a subaltern in the diplomatic corps, I have no objection to Hamburg, where, exclusive of the great intercourse of the commerce of the North, with which we are unacquainted, and in which we do not sufficiently participate, since we wish to have an envoy there, we ought to have an active person, instead of one from whom nothing is so desirable as that he should be deaf and dumb.

The vast connections that are between the grand emporiums of trade are such that these posts are never things of indifference. Why do not they bestow a sinecure on M. du Vivier?

LETTER XXVI.

DRESDEN, September 19th, 1786.

THERE are few MEN here, yet is the machine tolerably well regulated; nothing can better prove that order and constancy are more necessary for good government than great talents.

The extreme credit of Marcolini is to be regarded as a popular rumor. He is a favorite without ascendency (as without merit) at least in the Cabinet; his influence does not extend beyond the Court. At present he is in Italy, and the routine of affairs is the same. Probably some favors which pass through his hands, and which the excessive devotion of the Elector rather bestows on Catholics than on Lutherans, are the real cause of these murmurs; which, however, are sufficiently believed to occasion the Emperor to make a stupid blunder. He has sent here one of the silliest of Ambassadors — one O'Kelly, an Irishman — because Marcolini had married his niece. He thought by this means to have governed everything; but the trap was so palpably gross that no one has taken the trouble to remove the bait.

The Ministers who have real influence are Stuterheim and Gudschmidt. The first is very infirm, but prudent, sage, and with understanding enough to know on what subjects he is ignorant, to ask information, and to consult others. He, however, draws near his end. The second does not show himself to the world. It is affirmed that he is a man of the greatest merit; that he has infinite knowledge; that not a single pamphlet in any language throughout Europe escapes him; that his judgment is sound, his understanding perspicuous and penetrating, and his temper communicative; which last quality is in him the more compatible with discretion because he possesses its piety without its superstitions. He ranks first in the confidence of the Elector; but it

must be added he is sixty years of age, and has ill
health.

Among the Ministers we must also enumerate M.
Worm, a well-informed man, who possesses some principles of political economy, with information not very
common on the general relations of commerce, together
with industry, activity, and great quickness of apprehension; but, as it is said, rarely with much justness of
understanding. His moral character is suspected. He is
accused of not keeping his hands pure from bribery; but
it is not the less true that he is of great service to internal government. He appeared to me to be artful,
communicative, ironical, subtle, satirical, and crafty, but
very proper for business in all countries.*

Of all the foreign Ambassadors, I believe M. Saftzing,
from Sweden, to be the only one above, or rather not
below, mediocrity. I except the English envoy, who has
the character of being an able man, but whom I have
not yet any proper opportunity for examining. He is
open and complaisant, even to affectation, considering
that his character is English. If we except Alvensleben,
not one of the remainder deserves the honor of being
mentioned.

The Elector is a man distinct from Princes in general,
yet he appears to partake of the character of the King
of England. The consistency of his mind, which is entire, has a small alloy of obstinacy. I spoke but little to
him, because of the confusion of the dinner. Etiquette
is observed at the table of the Elector; consequently I
paid every care and attention to seat M. de Vergennes
near the Prince. He speaks with intelligence and precision, but his voice is harsh, sharp, and shrill. His
dress and countenance seemed to indicate devout and
wheedling, but acute and implacable, jealousy. The very
ill education of the Electress, her noisy mode of speech,
and her unreserved freedom, greatly occupy this Prince
to his disadvantage; for, besides that such kind of vigilance ever bears somewhat of the stamp of ridicule, his

---

* No wonder governments, and consequently nations, are vicious,
when such are supposed, even by men of considerable abilities, to be the
proper qualities for governors.

crabbed figure, rendered more disagreeable by a paralytic affection of the eyes, becomes at such moments restless, disturbed, and hideous.

Such, and so ungracious, as he is here depicted, he is a Prince who, from many considerations, is worthy esteem and respect. Since the year 1763, his desire to do good, his economy, his indefatigable labors, his innumerable privations, his perseverance, and his industry, have not for a moment relaxed. He has paid all the personal debts of the Electors; and is advanced in the liquidation of the debts of the State. He pursues his plans with inflexible punctuality. Slow, but not irresolute, difficult in accomplishing, but intelligent, with few resources at a first view, but possessed of aptitude and the gift of meditation, his only weakness arises from his religion, which yet does not occasion him to exaggerate his rights, or to neglect his duties. One step further and he would have been a bigot, and one step backward and he would no longer be a devotee. It is much to be doubted whether his confessor, Hertz, has the least influence except in the distribution of some footmen's places. The Elector supports his Ministers with uncommon firmness, against all, and to all. In a word, but for him the country had been undone; and, should he have the good fortune to see a duration of peace, he will render it very flourishing. Population visibly increases; the annual surplus of births over deaths amounts to twenty thousand; and the number of the people is less than two millions. Trade, which might be better, is not bad. The army imitates that of Prussia, over which it has the advantage of being purely national; but, to say the truth, Saxony is the least military of all the provinces of Germany. Credit is good, and even great. The paper currency is at par, or nearly; and the interest of money at four per cent. The Cabinet of Dresden is the only one in Europe which has adopted the true principles of coinage. Agriculture is in a state of passable respectability. Manufactures are free; the rights of the people are uninfringed; justice is impartially administered; in a word, all things considered, it is the most happy country in Germany. Yet this is a remarkable circumstance, and excites admiration when we recollect the terrible scourges* which have successively, and sometimes collectively, laid this fine, but ill-situated country, desolate.

They are persuaded here that we instigate the Turk; that there is a coolness between the two imperial Courts; and that Russia is in want of men, money, and horses. It must be frankly owned that her bank operations have a gloomy appearance. It is supposed we shall endeavor, should it be absolutely necessary, to effect a diversion in Germany, without interfering, except by coming to the aid of those who should be too much exposed to danger. For no one imagines we shall suffer Germany to devolve on one single head, nor even to be divided between two. And, with respect to Turkey in Europe, it is thought that our interest, conjointly with that of England, will, by one means or other, avert the destruction with which it is menaced.

On inquiry, I find the Elector of Bavaria has not properly had an attack. He has only changed his mistress; and when he does so, he alters his regimen to excite venery. It happens on these occasions that he has nervous affections, which resemble false attacks, and which will some day bring on a paralytic stroke. His life is not depended upon.

The hostilities of the Stadtholder have produced an effect here greatly to his disadvantage. For my part, I do not think his affairs in so disastrous a state as they seem to be believed. Should we embroil province with province, we shall lose our advantages; it will in vain be urged that the Stadtholder is master of Guelderland; the nobility is numerous in that province, and they form A PUBLIC opinion.

I send you the state of the military in the Electorate of Saxony, which is no secret; but I shall also add, by

* The principal scourges to which the author alludes, by the epithet of «ill-situated,» are wars; by which its sufferings have indeed been dreadful. Charles V., the Thirty Years' War, Charles XII., and still more flagrantly the late Frederick, have been its tormentors. That it should recover, as it continually has recovered, from such periodical, such renovating destruction, is a fact remarkable in history, worthy the attention of the philosophers and the highest eulogium on the country.

the next courier, that of the public stores, which I procured by a singular accident, the particulars of which it
would be useless here to relate. I shall only remark
that the custom which the Elector has for several years
adopted in his offices, of employing supernumeraries
without salaries, might give place to discovery, however
well secrets may here be kept.

I shall commit to M. de Vibraye, who is returning to
Paris, all the minutes of my ciphers, well and duly sealed,
and addressed to you.

He does not expect to return hither, and has hopes of
the Swedish Embassy.

May not the changes which will take place in the
corps diplomatique, by the vacancy of M. d'Adhémard,
afford an opportunity of giving me something more
agreeable and less precarious than a secret commission,
which must end of course, with the life of a Minister
who is hastening toward the grave? I hope your friendship will not slumber. You must own others might act
with less diligence. If you will take the trouble again
to read my dispatches as they are here sent, not in
ciphers but correct, and will at the same time consider
all the difficulties of various kinds that I have had to
surmount, and the few means which my cloudy situation
can afford, you will not be dissatisfied with my correspondence. Since, for example, Zelle has published
the history of the King's disease, I have the satisfaction
to perceive the information I sent you was exact. True
it is that, under the late King, at the conclusion of so
long a reign, a man knew to whom to address himself;
whereas at present it is necessary to discover which are
the doors at which you must knock. Yet I think I have
given a passable picture of men and things. And what
could I not effect of this kind, what could I not discover, had I credentials?

LETTER XXVII.

I HAVE several times mentioned, and particularly in Numbers XI. and XIX., this Boden; I can only refer you to the circumstances you will there find.

As to the person named Dufour, whose real name is Chauvier, and who was a journeyman barber in France, had I thought it of any importance I should have spoken before and given his character at full; for he is one of the circuitous paths pointed out to me by Prince Henry. He certainly had influence over the Heir Apparent, which he obtained:

1. Because he was persecuted by the late King, by whom he had been expelled;* so that, in order to return, he was obliged to take the name of Dufour, which is that of a family of the French colonists. And —

2. That he might aid to banish the spleen. He often dined in private with the Prince, who was so familiar with him, some time before his accession, that when wearied with his discourse he would dryly bid him hold his tongue.† Dufour was one of those with whom I should have made myself intimate, had the King continued to live some time longer; and he was among the persons and things that occasioned me to project a journey to Potsdam. But death suddenly interposed, and I should have sought his intimacy too abruptly; not to mention that subaltern influence has, on the King's accession, totally disappeared.

The person named Chapuis is a man who is not deficient in understanding and address. He was born in French Switzerland. He is the governor of the natural son of

---

* The author does not say whether from the the Court or from the country.

† It is not very clear, from the original, whether it was the Prince who bade Dufour, or Dufour who bade the Prince, hold his tongue. The word *présomtif*, we believe, can only be applied to an Heir Apparent, or we should have reversed the reading.

the King, and the well-beloved of Madame Rietz. Thinking his acquaintance might be valuable in many respects, I consequently sought it, under the pretense of literature only; but at present Chapuis has not in himself any one point of contact. To run after such people, so circumstanced, would but be to render myself suspicious to no purpose. I mentioned to you, on my return from Rheinsberg (Number XI), "I have numerous modes of communication, which will develop themselves as time and opportunity shall serve." But these have been retarded by the accession. Applications of this secret kind can only be made in the depth of winter, and during the Carnival, with utility and safety.

These, generally, are rather TOOLS proper for a spy to work with than the engines of influence. Should such people ever have power over foreign politics, the puissance of Prussia must draw to a conclusion. This country must not be estimated by France; there is not here the same margin in which to insert follies, or to correct. And as in general man remains at that point where it is necessary he should be fixed, the King of Prussia will act with circumspection in what relates to foreign affairs.

Not that this should prevent us from recollecting that we ought to guard, with extreme caution, against a coalition between Prussia and Austria, for this system also is capable of defense. It is even the easiest of execution, and the most splendid; nor would Prince Henry be so averse to it as he himself supposes, should he perceive the least glimmering of hope. Hitherto, indeed, I have not noticed anything that could give suspicion, but I shall more carefully examine whatever might occasion such an event, on my return to Berlin. There can be little danger that I should become languid in the pursuit of this object, having four years ago published my fears of such an event, and having begun to send my static tables of Austria, only that you might attentively consider the immense basis of power which the Emperor possesses, and whose alliance with France I cannot but consider as the masterpiece of Prince Kaunitz, and the type of our indelible levity.

It may be that this power of the Emperor is as much

8

overrated elsewhere as it is the reverse in France; but even this is a reason which may lead to prefer, instead of the perilous honor of being the champion of the Germanic liberties, the easy and deceptive advantage of dividing the spoils. Therefore, delay appears to me more unseasonable than it has been, for it is probable that the King of Prussia, having once pledged himself, will not recede, which seems to be warranted by his personal probity, his hatred of the Emperor, the antipathy that exists between the two nations, and the universal opinion which prevails that the chief of the empire is a perfidious Prince.

Your project concerning Brunswick is certainly excellent, and I shall spare no labor that may tend to give it success. But the man is very circumspect, Hertzberg very vehement, and the crisis equally urgent.

I have conversed with several of the English who are returned from the Emperor's reviews; he behaved there with great affability, and was very talkative. He particularly distinguished a French officer, who had traveled on horseback, that not a single military position might escape him on his route. The Austrian troops, in general, manœuver well by companies, and even tolerably by regiments, but, collectively, their inferiority to the Prussian army is prodigious. Opinions on this point are unanimous. They were not capable of keeping their distances, even when filing off in the presence of the Emperor. This grand pivot, on which tactics turn, is unknown to the Austrians, whereas the Prussians so habitually, so religiously, observe their distances, that any failure of this kind is an error unheard of.

The inferiority of the Austrian army, compared to the Prussian, is attributed:

1. To the want of a sufficient number of officers and subalterns, compared to the number of soldiers.

2. To the economy, totally anti-military, of the Emperor, who, while the companies nominally consist of two hundred men, does not maintain more than fifty or sixty under arms, and sends the others home, even against their will, so that three-fourths of the soldiers are never disciplined.

3. To the troops being dispersed, kept in petty detachments, and never exercised as a whole, except when they are encamped, where, even then, they are disciplined by detail.

4. To the very great inferiority of the officers. The corps of captains forms the soul of the Prussian army, and, at the same time, is the disgrace of the Austrian, etc.

It is generally affirmed that, should the two nations go to war, there is little doubt concerning which would have the advantage; that there is no equality between them, even supposing their generals to be equal; and that the contest most certainly would be favorable to the Prussians, during the first campaign. But this equality of generals is not true. Laudon, though still vigorous, cannot wear much longer. Besides that, he has often said he never would command an army, unless at the distance of four hundred miles from the Emperor. The abilities of Lacy are suspected, though he enjoys the entire confidence of Joseph II., and, as it is rumored, has rendered himself singularly necessary, by the complication of the military machine. No commander in the Austrian army can contend against the Duke of Brunswick, nor even against Kalcreuth, or Moellendorf.

Persons who have come very lately from Russia affirm that the Empress is in good health and that ERMENOW has obliterated her long sorrows for the death of LANSKOI. It is also said that Belsborotko gains ground upon Potemkin, but of this I more than doubt.

I have no belief in the facility with which the fifth dispatch may be deciphered. I think that, in general, the ciphers have rather been conjectured than divined. The way by which they are commonly known is the official communication of writings, which is made from one Court to another, and, which the Minister has sometimes the ill address to send without his accustomed cipher, on a known day. This is a quicksand of which I am not in danger. It is necessary, however, to have a variety of ciphers, and I entreat you will not neglect any occasion of sending me some that are new and more complete.

LETTER XXVIII.

DRESDEN, September 24th, 1786.

YOUR letter of the fourth of September, which, by mistake, your secretaries have dated the fourth of August, came to hand very late, and I shall reply without written references and solely from memory, in the annexed sheet, to the principal points. I had, indeed, previously answered them; nor do I believe that anything has escaped me which it was in my power to learn, or that I have any reason to repent having sacrificed too much to respect and to probabilities, at the time of the death of the King. Had I pursued my plan, I should have been four days sooner than any of the diplomatic couriers; but I request you will answer me whether it was possible to divine the conduct of our embassy. I disregarded the minute circumstances of death, as I had done that of the news itself; nor could I divine that these, being no longer secret, and having become so easy to examine and describe, should yet have remained secrets to you. I suspected it the less because certain Ambassadors (indeed, most of them) appeared to me so embarrassed by the completing of their dispatches that I should not have imagined they would have disdained a supply which was to be obtained with so much facility. Satisfied also with having informed you, thanks to lucky circumstances, of the progress of the disease, in such a manner as few Ministers were informed, I despised those particulars that were become public. But there were some that were sufficiently interesting, relative to the last two days of the King, from which a banquet might be prepared at an easy expense; and the poignancy of which not death itself could destroy,—relating as they did to a mortal so extraordinary, both in body and mind.

His disease, which would have killed ten men, was of eleven months' continuance, without interruption, and almost without relaxation, after his first fit of an asphyxic apoplexy, from which he was recovered by emetics, and after which the first word he uttered, with an imperious gesture, was SILENCE. Nature made four different efforts to save this her rare composition,— twice by diarrhœas, and twice again by cuticular eruptions. Hence it might be said, by the worshipers of a God, that this his image was broken by the Creator himself; and that nature did not abandon one of the most beauteous of her works till the total destruction of the organs, exhausted by age, had been effected; nor till after a continual warfare between body and mind * during forty-six years; till after fatigues and agitations of every kind which signalized this fairy reign, and after the most ruinous disease.

This man died on the seventeenth of August, at twenty minutes past two in the morning; and on the fifteenth, when, contrary to his constant custom, he slept till eleven o'clock, he transacted his Cabinet business, though his feebleness was excessive, without any want of attention; and even with a conciseness scarcely perhaps to be found in any other Prince in good health. Thus when, on the sixteenth, the reigning Monarch sent orders to Zelle to repair instantaneously to Potsdam, because the King had remained insensible almost since the noon of the day before, and because he was in a lethargic sleep, the physician, arriving at three o'clock, and finding Frederick II. with animation in his eyes, sensibility in his organs, and so much recollection, not being called, dared not make his appearance. Zelle judged he was past recovery less from the cadaverous odor which exhaled from his wound than because he, for the first time during the whole course of his reign, did not recollect that he had not expedited the affairs of the Cabinet. The conclusion was sagely drawn: dying only could he forget his duty. . . . Two-thirds of Berlin at present are violently

---

* The French reads: "*Contention continuelle d'âme et d'esprit*"; or of SOUL and MIND; the translator has the misfortune not to understand the distinction.

declaiming in order to prove that Frederick II. was a man of common, and almost of mean capacity. Ah! could his large eyes, which obedient to his wishes seduced or terrified the human heart, could they but for a moment open, where would these idiot parasites find courage sufficient to expire with shame?

LETTER XXIX.

DRESDEN, September 26th, 1786.

CONVERSING with a well-informed man who is returned from Russia, I learned a fact totally strange to me, though no doubt known to the Comte de Vergennes; but, whether or no, one which appeared to me proper to make you acquainted with; and more especially because the project is pursued with greater ardor than ever.

When Hyder Ali, having advanced beyond the Orixa, was at the height of his prosperous success, the inhabitants of the north of Bengal, interrupted in their customary commerce by the conflict between the English and their enemies, brought their iron as far as the frontiers of Siberia, there to find a market. This extraordinary fact was the cause of a remarkable attempt made by Russia, in 1783. She sent a fleet to Astracan, to seize on Astrabat, there to form an establishment, on the northern coast of the Caspian Sea, and thence to penetrate into the interior parts of India. The enterprise failed; but is so far from being abandoned that, at this very moment, a plan may be seen in relief at Petersburg, of the works by which it is intended to fortify Astrabat.

Of all the gigantic projects of Russia this is, perhaps, the least unreasonable; since it is pointed out by the nature of things, and since there is already an inland navigation completely carried on from Astracan, on the Volga, the Mita, the Lake Jemen, the Wologda, the Canal of Ladoga, and the Neva, to Petersburg. Should this plan ever be pursued with activity and success, it must either happen that England will seriously think of an alliance with us, against the system of the North, or she must suffer every sort of an advantage to be obtained over her at Petersburg; for the interest of the Russians must then become totally opposite to those of the English; and hence may arise dreadful hurricanes, that may sweep away their puissance in the East.

How many revolutions, how much strife between men and things, shall be occasioned by the development of the destiny of that empire which successively overawes and enslaves all surrounding nations? It must, indeed, be owned that her influence in each place ought to decrease in an inverse proportion to the multiplicity of these places. But how great is the influence of these augmenting points of contact, relative to Europe! And, without prematurely divining the fate of Turkey in Europe, with an intent to overcharge the picture, should Russia seize on the Polish Ukraine, as the manner in which she is arming on the Black Sea, and disposing of her commerce, seem to indicate and to threaten, how much greater shall they still be? What species of understanding must the Emperor possess, if it be impossible to make him perceive that the Turks and the Poles are less dangerous neighbors than those strange people; who are susceptible of all, capable of all, who become the best soldiers in the world, and who, of all the men that inhabit the globe, are the most malleable?

The various ideas I have acquired here, where I have made a tolerable harvest, will be comprised in a particular memorial. They are not immediately necessary, and are too numerous to be inserted in my dispatches. But there was one temptation, which was rather expensive, that I could not resist. The Elector has employed his engineers in the topography of Saxony. Twenty-four maps have already been laid down; they are kept in great secrecy, and yet, by paying some louis for each map, I can have them copied. True it is I recollected that, since I COULD, M. de Vibraye perhaps HAS— but, as we rarely do all we may, or even all we ought to do, it is exceedingly possible this should not be so; and then I should have lost an opportunity that nevermore could be recovered. This reflection determined me, in the hope that the intent of the act would be its apology; and, as I have not put the Government to the least fruitless expense, or which did not appertain to the better execution of the office I have undertaken, my surplus accounts, I suppose, will be passed.

The Elector of Bavaria is not ill. His new mistress seems only to have been the whim of a day, and his favor again reverts to his former, Madame von Torring Seefeld, originally Minuzzi.

LETTER XXX.

You have been informed, no doubt, by the courier of Tuesday, of what happened on Monday, at the first Court held by the Queen; but, as I think it is proper I should add some reflections on this subject, I shall begin by relating what passed.

The Princess Frederica of Prussia, who imagined that, according to the very sensible custom of the country, the Queen would sit down to play with natives, and not with foreign ambassadors, had placed the Comte d'Esterno at her table; for it was she who arranged the parties. She asked the Queen whom she appointed for her own table. The Queen named Prince Reuss, the Austrian Ambassador, and the Prince of Goethe; but, this species of infantine elephant having, after some consideration, declared that he did not know any one game, the Queen substituted Romanzow, the Russian Ambassador. The Princess Frederica was exceedingly surprised, but either dared not, or would not make any remonstrances; and the Queen's party sitting down to play, the Comte d'Esterno, with great positiveness, energy, and emphasis, refused to sit down at the table of the Princess; declaring he certainly would not play. He immediately withdrew.

Everybody blames the Queen and the Count. The first for having committed an unexampled blunder, and the second, say the people of Berlin, ought not to have refused the daughter of the King. Perhaps this judgment is severe; though I own I should not myself have refused; because, in my opinion, we should not show we are insulted, except when we wish to be supposed insulted. And, as I think, it would have been very thoughtless to

* The scene of this and the two following letters, though dated at Dresden, is Berlin.

have taken serious notice of the absurd mistake of a
Princess who is the most awkward of all the Princesses
in Europe. Neither had Comte d'Esterno, rigorously
speaking, any greater cause for complaint than any other
of the royal ambassadors, among whom there is no claim
of precedency. Perhaps, too, it would be imprudent to
endeavor to establish any such claim; for this would be
very certainly to call that in question which tradition
and universal tolerance have granted to us. And here
let me observe that, as soon as Lord Dalrymple knew
Comte d'Esterno had been to complain to Count Finckenstein, he declared he made no demand of precedency
whatever; but neither would he suffer precedency from
anyone. I should, therefore, have accepted the party
of the Princess; but should have said aloud, and, pointing to the table of the Queen, "I see we are all here
without distinction of persons; and certainly fortune could
not have been more favorable to me." (The Princess
may really be called handsome.) Had I thought I still
owed more to my Sovereign, I should, on the next Court
day, have refused the nomination of the Queen; though
it must have been a violent and hazardous step, and
reparation must have become a public topic; instead of
which it is the insult only that is talked of, and that
considerably, in the world.

Will the Comte d'Esterno, or will he not, at present,
accept the first invitation he shall receive? Should he
comply, it will remain on record that, having resented
the procedure, he has acknowledged himself second.
Yet how may he refuse? I have proposed to Prince
Henry, who is the *mezzo termine*, that there should be a
Court held by the Queen Dowager, who, from her circumspection and native dignity, is more respected than
the reigning Queen; and that Comte d'Esterno should
be of her party, with the Emperor's Ambassador; which
distinction would be the more marked because that this
Queen never yet played with foreign ministers. If her
mourning for her husband does not counteract this project, it seems to me the best under the present circumstances. The Queen has written a letter to Count
Finckenstein, which must have been read to Comte d'Es-

terno, in which is inserted the word EXCUSE, and wherein she requires the King should not be informed of the affair. But it is answered the offense was public, and excuses are wished to be kept secret, since silence is required.

The most important and incontestably certain fact is, that there was no premeditation in the matter; that it was the silly giddiness of the Queen in which it originated; that Count Finckenstein and the whole Court are vexed at the affair; that should the King hear of it he will be very much offended with the Queen, whom he has not seen for these six weeks, and whom he thwarts on all occasions; that he has reversed all the arrangements which, in the rapture of accession, she had made with the Master of the Household; and that, in fine, never had Queen of Prussia, that is to say, the most insignificant of queens, less influence.

If, therefore, it be true, on the one part, that the place of every man in this world is that which he himself shall assign to himself, that our rank, already much on the decline in the public opinion, has no need to sink lower, and that Russian insolence, which takes indefatigable strides, has need of being watched and traversed, it is perfectly certain on the other, also, that the proceeding of Monday was distinct and unmeaning, which ought not to be regarded with a lowering brow, under circumstances which may lead from lowering to cold distance, and from the latter to great changes; or, at least, to decisively false steps, to which the Courts of Vienna and London are desirous of giving birth, and by which they will not fail to profit.

Such is my advice, since I have had the honor to have this advice asked. Permit me to add, that Berlin is not any longer an indifferent embassy, but that it is necessary there to be active, yet cautious; amiable, yet dignified; firm, yet pliant; faithful, yet subtle; in a word, to unite qualities which do not often meet. M. de Vibraye means to ask this embassy, should Comte d'Esterno retire, or be sent elsewhere. I speak uninterestedly, since I have no reason to presume that, should it be determined to send me on an embassy, I should begin

by one of so much consequence; but it is my duty to
say that M. de Vibraye, and particularly his lady, are
not the proper persons.   His understanding is heavy and
confined; rather turbulent than active; and timid than
prudent.   He is more the giver of dinners than the
representative of monarchy; he has neither manners,
elocution, nor eyes.   Madame de Vibraye, who does not
want understanding, would be too gay even for Paris,
and, to speak plainly, she has little propriety, and less
decency.   But as she is enterprising, she makes pretensions to dignity with all the behavior of thoughtlessness; and, as she molds her husband as she pleases,
by suffering him to believe he is absolute master, she
renders him morose, uncivil, and rude.   Besides which,
she sequesters him from the world; and such sequestration must everywhere, and particularly at Berlin, be
totally disadvantageous to an Ambassador of France.
This is one of the errors of Comte d'Esterno.

The following is the chief intelligence I hear concerning the King and his administration, relative either to
his absence or his return.   He is exceedingly dissatisfied
with the Stadtholder.   It is affirmed you ought to accept
the declaration of Count Goertz.   I repeat incessantly,
that this is the very time when our intentions ought no
longer to be suspected; since assuredly, if we wish the
destruction of the Stadtholdership, the Prince of Orange
has given us a fine opportunity.   Prince Henry affirms
that, provided he was restored to the right of maintaining order, and not of giving order, at the Hague,
and was in possession of a little money, the King would
be contented.   I believe he, the King, feels the necessity
of not making a false step at the beginning of his
political career.   One fact, I can assure you, is certain,
which is that it was the advice of Hertzberg to march
ten thousand men into Holland; and that there was on
this occasion a very warm contention between him and
General Moellendorf, in the King's presence.   By this
you may judge of what is to be expected from the violence of such a Minister.   Still, however, this has not
prevented him from being created a Count in Prussia;
and, if I am not mistaken, his influence continues.

With respect to domestic affairs, whatever Prince Henry may say to the contrary, the credit of Schulemburg is on the decline; were it only that he no longer appears in the transaction of public business. It is, however, affirmed that he, with many others, is soon to be made a Count, for they are not economists of their titles. The commission for the regulation of the customs begins to strike bold strokes; but they alight on individuals, and are not aimed at general reformation. Launay has received information that the King henceforth can give him only six thousand crowns per annum, in lieu of twenty thousand, the sum he before had; and that he must accept this or resign. Launay, enraged, and the more so because he has long since demanded his dismissal, loudly declares he will print an estimate,* which will prove not only that, in justification of each of his acts, he has a letter from the late King, the fiscal temper of whom he has moderated much oftener than he has provoked, but that he likewise has refused twenty bargains, offered him by Frederick II., which would have acquired him tons of gold. The scandal of this estimate, should he dare to publish it, will be very great; and the analyzing of it will rather be a commission of inquiry into the conduct of the late King than of the present state of the customs, which might easily have been foreseen were thus regulated. The commissioners have dismissed Roux, the only able man among the collectors, with a pension of five hundred crowns; and Groddard, a person of insignificance, with a like sum. They have bestowed their places on Koepke and Beyer, with a salary of three thousand crowns, neither of whom know anything,—with this difference, that the last is exact, assiduous, and laborious; but both of them are without information, and devoid of principles. Generally speaking, the commissioners themselves have none; nor have they the least knowledge of how they ought to act. Commissions here will all be the same; for, exclusive of the inconveniences that are annexed to them in every country, there is in this the additional one that men of knowledge are very scarce, and they must, therefore,

* *Compte rendu.*

long continue ill-sorted. But the King wishes to satisfy
some, bestow places on those who have protectors, and
particularly not to have any Prime Minister. There
must be an embargo on business while it remains in
this state; and I have many reasons for supposing that
no person will, for some months to come, have found
his true place, or that which he is destined to keep; we
must not, therefore, be in haste to judge.

But we may affirm that the King has exceedingly displeased the people,—less in refusing to partake of the
festival prepared for his return than in avoiding the
street where the citizens had assembled to see him pass.
« He treats us as his uncle did, on his return from the
Seven Years' War,» say the mob; «but, before imitating
him in this, he ought to have imitated the great actions
of his uncle.» It must be owned good sense is sometimes on the side of the multitude.

With respect to the domestic affairs of the palace, anyone may remark at the first glance that they are totally
in disorder. No master, no one to give directions, no
funds assigned; footmen and the household officers govern all. Dufour, or Chauvier (I before explained to you
that this was one and the same person), like all the
other subordinate confidants without any influence whatever, is rather ill, than well treated. Colonel Vartensle-
ben, formerly banished into Prussia because of his
intimacy with the hereditary Prince, is supposed to increase in favor. But the two men to be observed are—
Welner, to whom it is affirmed are communicated all
ministerial papers, the reports on all projects, and the
revisal of all decisions; and Bishopswerder, who, besides
universal suspicion, talks with too much affectation of
having no influence over the King not to betray himself,
in a country where people are not artful enough to say
they do not possess a thing which they really do not
possess in order that it may be supposed they do.

With respect to pleasures, they are improved upon.
One very remarkable arrangement is, that a cook has
been appointed for the Princess Frederica of Prussia,
the King's daughter by his first Queen; thus she is to
have a kind of household; which, if I am not mistaken,

is nothing more than a mode, and none of the most moral, of procuring frequent and decent interviews with Mademoiselle Voss, who is capitulating; for she has declared that no hopes of success must be entertained as long as Madame Rietz shall continue to be visited. The latter went to meet the King on his return; then, passing through the city with an arrow's speed, she flew to Charlottenburg, whither the King came, and where she lives. She acts the prudent part of taking charge herself of the pleasures of his Majesty; who apparently sets a great price on any new enjoyment, be it of what kind it may.

It is secretly rumored, though I cannot warrant its truth, that England is prodigal in caresses, and reiterated offers of a treaty of commerce, on the most advantageous terms; and that Russia itself spares no advances. Certain it is that our enemies and their partisans loudly proclaim that we have lately disbanded ten thousand men; which is sufficient proof, say they, that we have no thoughts of holding the two imperial Courts in awe.

I can also certify that the Grand Duke and the Grand Duchess, who long had afforded no signs of existence to Prince Henry, have lately written him very charming letters, but these are no impediments to the licentious discourse of Romanzow, who, on the eve of the King's funeral, asked, in a public company, whether there would not be rejoicings on the morrow; and who has bestowed the epithet of THE ILLUMINATION OF THE FIVE CANDLES on the night of the second, on which homage was paid to the new King, and when a general illumination was ordered. Apropos of homage, Prince Henry is permitted to make written oath, and this favor has not a little redoubled his fumes; he still wagers that Hertzberg will be disgraced. This Hertzberg yesterday read a pompous account to the Academy of his journey into Prussia, and he was suffocated with incense by all the candidates. Nothing could be more completely silly.

I shall conclude with a word concerning Saxony. I do not believe the health of the Elector to be good, he withers visibly; and this is promoted by the violent exercise which he takes, from system, and in which he perseveres with all his invincible obstinacy. He will leave no sons, and there is no imagining the hypocritic imbecility of his brothers, who are not married; the result of which is that this fine country is dangerously menaced by future contingencies. Marcolini, as I have said, is on his journey through Italy; and it is supposed that one of his commissions is to seek a wife for Prince Anthony. Prince Henry, who fears lest choice should be made of a Tuscan Princess, or some other of the Austrian alliances, has conceived the project of bestowing the hand of the Princess de Condé on him, by which we should secure the Electorate and the Elector. I give this as I received it.

FIRST POSTSCRIPT.— Let me add that, with respect to the map I determined to have secretly copied, it is the map of the most important part of Saxony; and one which all the foreign ambassadors, without exception, with M. de Vibraye at their head, are convinced the Elector will not permit his brother to see. I have had a windfall much more valuable,— that of the land survey of 1783, made with great exactitude, and containing a circumstantial division of territorial wealth. I shall have it copied in haste, for which I do not imagine I shall be blamed. M. de Vibraye is quitting Dresden, whither he does not wish to return. It is a pleasant post, and a very excellent one from which to observe the Emperor and the King of Prussia.

Boden is on the road hither; he is imagined to be presumptuous enough to solicit the French Embassy. Either he will be disappointed or the Court of Berlin will act improperly. The King still continues in the intention of sending you Alvensleben. I spoke to you of him when at Dresden, where I conversed much with him; he is certainly a man of information and understanding. M. d'Entragues was intimately acquainted with him, and this friendship has continued. It would be very easy to send for M. d'Entragues, who is at Montpellier; whether it were to conduct or to watch his entrance on the scene of action.

9

SECOND POSTSCRIPT.— Prince Henry was sent for by the
King this morning, on business, and invited to go and
dine at Charlottenburg. This he has acquainted me with,
and desired me to come to him at five o'clock. I can
add nothing to this enormous length of ciphering, except
that I wish to repeat that the intelligence of the ten
thousand men proposed by Hertzberg is fact. It has
appeared so important to me, when combined with the
affairs of Hattem and Elburg, which seemed to give invincible demonstration that Count Hertzberg had long
promised, in the secret correspondence of which I have
spoken, the aid of the army of the new King. I say this
information appeared so important that I thought it my
duty to make it known to the Comte d'Esterno, by a
channel which he cannot suspect is derived from me.

With respect to Court intrigues here, I have proof that
Prince Henry tells everything to Prince Ferdinand, who
tells everything to his wife, who, lured by the tempting
bribes she receives in ready money, betrays Prince Henry.
Luckily, the excessive stupidity of this Princess deadens
her influence, and congeals the good-will which the King
wishes to entertain for her.

LETTER XXXI.

I HAVE had very little time for the courier of to-day, having spent all day yesterday, from six o'clock in the morning till night, at, and in the affairs of, the Court. The ceremony of rendering homage was awful, notwithstanding the narrowness of the place in which the States were received. As moral ideas have a great influence, even unperceived by us, on our physical sensations, this tribute of respect, paid by armed despotism to the nation it governs, this species of paternal colloquy between the Monarch and the deputies, here called the States, establishing in some manner a correlative engagement, — to which only a little more dignity on the part of the deputies, and at least the appearance of deliberation, are wanting to give pleasure to the heart, — fill the mind with sublime and affecting reveries. To a Prince capable of reflection, I would only wish this ceremony to be contrasted with the military oath, and the different emotions they excite to be analyzed, in order to lead him to examine whether it be true that a monarchy depends wholly upon force, and whether the pyramid ought to rest upon its basis or upon its point.

After the discourse of the Minister of Justice (Reek) to the States, after the harangue of the first order (the ecclesiastics), conducted by Prince Frederick of Brunswick, Provost of the Chapter of Brandenburg, and after the oath of the nobility, the declaration and confirmation of privileges, the enumeration of titles to be bestowed, made by the Minister Hertzberg (the Minister Schulemburg is one among the number of new Counts), the King advanced, on a projecting balcony, over which a very fine canopy had been raised, to receive the oaths and the homage of the people. The citizens were assembled, by companies, wards, and trades, in the square opposite the palace. The symptoms of tumultuous joy are here, as elsewhere, the effects of sympathy (I had almost said contagious) between a great multitude of men, assembled to behold one elevated superior to them all, whom they called their Monarch and their Master, and on whom, in reality, depends the greatest part of the blessings or the woes that await them.

It must, however, be remarked that the order was much greater all the day, and at night, than could have been hoped in any other large metropolis. It is true that they distribute here neither wine, *cervelats,** nor money. The largesses are distributed to each quarter, and pass through the hands of the pastor and the magistrate. It is equally true that the passions of this are scarcely so strong as the emotions of other nations.

The King dined upward of six hundred people. All who were noble were invited. When the proposal was made to me to remain, I replied that, apparently, only the national nobility was meant; and that, had it been intended to admit foreigners to that favor, they no doubt would have had the honor of receiving such an intimation. All the English, and almost all the French, like me, and with me, retired.

The illuminations were not very great. One was remarked where all the small lamps were covered over by crape, so that the light appeared dim, gloomy, and truly funereal. This was the invention of a Jew, and it was in the front of his own house that it took place. It calls to my mind a beautiful passage in the sermon which preceded the ceremony, and which was preached in the Lutheran church. The minister of the prevailing religion long invoked, and with considerable pathos and energy, the blessings of toleration, — "That happy and holy harvest, for which the Prussian provinces are indebted to the family by which they are governed."

I send you the best medals that were struck on the occasion. They are your own. Others are to be distributed among the foreign ambassadors, who, no doubt, will send them home. There are some in gold, but I thought them too dear, the workmanship considered. Each general in the service was presented with a large

* A species of large sausage.

medal, the price of which is forty crowns. Each commander of a regiment received a small one, of the price of six ducats. The large are good, the small very indifferent. I speak of those that were distributed yesterday; and only of the likeness.

October 4th, 1786.

THE day of homage and its preparations have wholly consumed the time, and obstructed all society, since the last courier; for which reason I have at present little to say. Prince Henry was invited, the other day, principally, as I believe, let him say what he will, because M. de Custine, the father, dined with the King. However, his Majesty, before dinner, spoke to the Prince concerning Holland, and complained that the discourse of M. de Veyrac, who had informed Goertz he could not interfere, was in exact contradiction to the promises of the Cabinet of Versailles. The subject of Holland puts him out of temper, as it naturally must; and yet, as I have incessantly repeated, "When could we find a better opportunity of acting disinterestedly than at present; now that the Stadtholder, contrary to reason and all propriety, has taken a violent and decisive part, a few days before the arrival of the advice which was intended to be sent him by the King?"

I have had a very impassioned scene, concerning Holland, with Count Hertzberg: patience, firmness, and something of cunning, on my part; violence, passion, and want of reason, on his. It is evident to me that he is pursuing some secret project concerning Holland.

Apropos of M. de Custine; he made the King wait an hour for him at dinner. It is a melancholy circumstance for France that she should continually be, in some measure, represented by certain travelers, when political affairs are in a delicate state. Our Duc de la F——, amid an assembly of our enemies, said to the Duke of Brunswick, "Apropos; pray has your Highness ever served?" At Dresden, a ceremonious and circumspect place, where our embassy has given much dissatisfaction, this same pitiable interrogator, having been shown a collection of precious stones, the most magnificent that exists in Europe, said to the Elector at high dinner, "Very good! Yes, indeed, very good! Pray how much did the collection cost your Highness?" A certain M. de P——, a week before the death of the King, dining at Potsdam with the Prince of Prussia, hearing the name of M. de H—— mentioned, exclaimed, "Apropos; I forgot that I have a letter from him, which I am to give you." And this letter he threw to the Prince across the table. He no doubt imagined such familiarity was exceedingly natural — he who, at Prague, taking leave of the Emperor, seized and shook him by the hand, testifying the great satisfaction he had received at having seen his manœuvers, and renewed his acquaintance with him. And, what is better, it is M. de —— who relates this anecdote here; which there are Englishmen enough would take care should not have been forgotten, had he not with so much precaution treasured it up in his memory. Wherefore permit such people to travel, whom, by means of the places they enjoy, it is easy to detain at home? There is no possibility of exaggerating the evil which such ridiculous pasquinades produce, at a moment when the ill-designing are so numerous, and who wish that the nation should be judged by such specimens.

Suffer me further to remark, of Messieurs de Custine, that, foolish as the father is, physically a fool, a fool unmeasurable and disgusting, equally is the son a man of great hopes, and appears in all companies with universal success. Not any man so young, with whom I am acquainted, unites so much modesty, so much reason, and such decent timidity, to so great a talent for observation, or to manners so agreeable and mild, so much caution and wise activity. There is no doubt but that the extravagances of the father display these qualities to advantage in the son, but they exist, and on the most solid basis, for, in all probability, he has taken an aversion for, by being a continual spectator of, the follies of his father. He is a scion who, of all the young men I have known, is most proper to be transplanted into the diplomatic nursery.

The King, all yesterday, was cold and taciturn; not an emotion, not a gracious word, not a smile. The

Minister Reek, who harangued the States in the name of the Sovereign, promised, in his discourse, that no new tax should be imposed during the present reign, but that, on the contrary, those that existed should be diminished. Was he commanded to make this promise, or did he venture to make it uncommanded? Of this I am ignorant, and it is a matter of doubt.

The day before yesterday, the King had some domestic brawls and a scene of jealousy, at Charlottenburg, to support from Madame Rietz. The remembrance perhaps remained with him yesterday; whether or no, the discourse of his Minister of Justice spoke more pleasingly than his countenance, however agreeable it may in reality be. He is to depart on the fourth for Silesia, and does not return till the seventeenth.

A part of the palace is at present furnishing, but in a simple style.

Public notice has been given that those persons who had been promised reversions of fiefs should appear, that their reversions were annulled, and that they were not allowed to solicit till first there should be a vacant fief, and not for the reversion of fiefs.

I have seen a narrative of what passed in Prussia. The person who wrote it has employed very sounding expressions to depict the enthusiasm of the public, and among them, the following phrase of the King: "I have found Prussia very ill, but I will cure her."

Count Katzerling, who had suffered great losses during the Seven Years' War, and met with very ill treatment from the late Monarch, after having been very graciously received by him, had accepted a loan of one hundred and fifty thousand crowns, for thirty years, without interest.

It is said the Bishop of Warmia will be here within three weeks. He is a very amiable man, with the levity of a Pole, and was much in the favor of the Prince of Prussia. The King seems to remember this; he has been treated with much greater kindness than any other person in Prussia.

In November, the King is to balance the statements of expense and receipt.

First Postscript.— I forgot to inform you that, for so cloudy a day, Prince Henry was yesterday highly caressed. He dined and supped with his Majesty, and singly attended him to see the illuminations.

Second Postscript.— I return from Court, the Ambassadors were mingled promiscuously, but, as the Ministers of the two Imperial Courts were together, the King proceeded in rather a singularly retrograde manner. It so happened (because of the number of Englishmen that were to be presented) that Lord Dalrymple was the nearest to the King's door, and preceded the Imperial Ambassadors. The King began with the latter. He then returned to Lord Dalrymple, after which he descended much lower toward Comte d'Esterno, and spoke no further to him than by thanking, in general, the foreign Ambassadors for their illuminations. Should this neglect of customary forms continue, I think it would be right to let it be understood that it gives displeasure, for the rumor of the hatred of the King for the French is daily strengthened, and rumor, sometimes, in reality produces the event it proclaims.

LETTER XXXII.

IT APPEARS extremely probable that habit will be the conqueror, and that Frederick William will never be more than what his penetrating uncle had foreboded. No terms are too hyperbolical to express the excessive negligence of his domestic affairs, their disorder, and his waste of time. The valets dread his violence; but they are the first to turn his incapacity to derision. Not a paper in its place; not a word written at the bottom of any of the memorials; not a letter personally opened; no human power could induce him to read forty lines together. It is at once the tumult of vehemence and the torpor of inanity. His natural son, the Count of Brandenburg, is the only one who can rouse him from his lethargy; he loves the boy to adoration. His countenance brightens the moment he appears, and he amuses himself, every morning, a considerable time with this child, and this, even of his pleasures, is the only one in which he is regular; for the remaining hours are wasted in inexplicable confusion. His ill humor the other day, for example, which I had supposed was occasioned by the quarrel at Charlottenburg, induced me to inquire into particulars. It was nothing more than a musical dispute. The King would have a chamber concert. He ordered two-and-twenty musicians to be assembled. It was his intention to have performed himself; his violoncello was uncased and tuned. Fourteen musicians only came; and passions, threats, intemperance succeeded. The *valets de chambre* laid the blame on Kalikan, whose business it was to summon the musicians. Kalikan was thrown into prison. Duport, the famous violoncello player, and consequently the favorite musician, came to the aid of Kalikan, and gave the King the letter which the *valets de chambre* had intercepted. His choler then became outrageous; everybody fled; but no further effects have followed this subaltern prevarication. Poor King! Poor country!

I am persuaded by two particulars: the one, that his Majesty has conceived the idea and the hope of becoming a great man, by making himself wholly and purely German, and by hectoring French superiority; the other, that he is already in his heart determined to resign business to a principal Minister. He has not, perhaps, yet owned the fact to himself; but at least he is inwardly convinced it must be so. In this case his last resource will be to call in the aid of the Duke of Brunswick, or of MY UNCLE.

The first of these plans is the work and the masterpiece of Count Hertzberg. He has said, and justly said: "There is only one mode of acquiring reputation; which is to impart an impulse to your nation, that under your reign a new kind of glory may take date. This impulse you can only give by acting determinately. What can you ever effect as the partisan of France? You can only be the feeble imitator of Frederick II. As a German you will be an original, personally revered throughout Germany, adored by your people, vaunted by men of letters, respected by Europe, etc., etc." The explication of the enigma is, that Count Hertzberg imagined this to be the shortest road to make himself Prime Minister.

But the necessities of accident demand, or will soon demand, a different person. Servile as the country is, it is not habituated to ministerial slavery; and Hertzberg, long a subaltern, rather crafty than able, deceitful than cunning, violent than determined, vain than ambitious, old, infirm, and not promising any long duration of life, will not bend the people to this servility. They must have (though this Welner, who is so much attended to at present, and whose influence near spectators only can discover, may push his pretensions), I repeat, they must have a man whose rank can quell subordinate candidates; and the number of such men is not great. I can discover but two men of this kind, — Prince Henry and the Duke of Brunswick. To the disadvantage of not living in the country, the latter adds that of being necessarily formidable to a feeble and indolent, but vain and jealous,

Prince; who may imagine that Prince Henry will not commit the same injury on his, the Sovereign's, reputation as a Prince who cannot leave his own country, and reside here constantly as Prime Minister, without being undoubtedly and conspicuously such. For which reason the credit of Prince Henry daily strengthens, in spite of his ill address. However, he has boasted less within some few weeks; and, instead of not returning from Rheinsberg, whither he again goes during the absence of the King, till the middle of December, as was his intention, he will be here on the same day as his nephew.

Yet, exclusive of the personal defects of Prince Henry, and the errors of which he will indubitably be guilty, how shall we reconcile the German system and the Monarch's hatred of the French to the confidence granted this Prince? The symptoms of such hatred, whether systematic or natural, continually increase and correspond. The King, when he dismissed Roux and Groddart, said: "*Voilà donc de ces B—— dont je me suis défait.*"* The real crime of Roux, perhaps, was that he kept a Jewess whom the Prince of Russia wished to possess, and obstinately refused to listen to any kind of accommodation. A French merchant brought some toys† to show him, to whom he harshly replied: "I have baubles already of this kind to the amount of seven millions." He then turned his back, and did not utter another word, except to bid him not go to the Queen, for if he did, he should not be paid. The action was far from blamable; it is the manner only that I notice. Boden was passably well received, except that the only consolation he found for his fever was, "Go to Berlin, and keep yourself quiet, for you have a companion that will stay by you these three months." Boden said to him, "I should have had thousands of messages to your Majesty, had I dared to take charge of them." "You did well to refuse," replied the King; and in so rough a

---

* "I have rid myself of these——." The epithet must be left with the reader; there is no danger he should be more indelicate than the original.

† *Des gentillesses*, probably jewels,

tone that Boden dared not even given him the letters of Dusaulx and Bitaubé.

Launay is treated with severity, and even with tyranny. He was confined to his chamber while his papers were examined, independent of a general prohibition not to leave Berlin. One Délâtre, his personal enemy, has been opposed to him on all occasions, and has been sent for to become an informer against him,—a man devoid of faith or honor; suspected of great crimes; a dissipator of the King's money; an unbridled libelist, and as such denounced by our Court to that of Berlin, which officially returned thanks, two years ago, for our behavior on that subject. I say he was sent for; because owing, as he does, eighty thousand crowns to the King, would he have ventured to come without a passport, or being asked? It is evident that Launay is persecuted as a farmer of the taxes, and as a Frenchman.

It is believed that the collectors and farmers-general will all be dismissed * at the festival of the Trinity, the time when those accounts that shall actually be settled are to be examined. This is the grand sacrifice that is to be offered up to the nation. But what is to supply the deficiency in the revenue? For in fine, the farmers, last year, paid six millions eight hundred thousand German crowns; and it is not only impossible to replace this immense sum, but, knowing the country, it is easy to foresee that the German farmers of finance will scarcely collect the half of the amount.

Of what will the convocation of the provincial and finance counselors, and the deputies of the merchants, be productive? Of complaints, and not one project which will not be distinct, partial, and in contradiction to the general system,— or such as the nature of things presents as a system; for in reality not any as yet exists.

*Congédier la régie.—The late King introduced the French into Prussia, to farm and collect the taxes, at the beginning of his reign. It was one of the most odious of the acts of his internal administration; in which whenever his own revenues were out of the question, he endeavored to act for the good of the people. ENDEAVORED, but most frequently did not; of this, his innumerable monopolies are proofs incontestable.

I return, and say, all these projects are contrary to the personal hopes of Prince Henry. Will he make all his passions subservient to his ambition? (He is far from possessing that degree of fortitude.) Or, does he dissemble that he may obtain power? Of this I do not believe him uniformly capable. I rather fear he is once again the dupe of caresses; which, however, it must be confessed, are more substantial and more marked than they ever had been before. I particularly fear he should be in too great haste, and too eager to gather the harvest before it be ripe; neglecting the care of providing seed for futurity.

The King has given the Minister of Justice, Reek, a box of petrified shells, splendidly enriched with diamonds, estimated to be worth twelve thousand crowns; a similar box to the Minister Gaudi, and ten thousand crowns; another of the same kind to General Moellendorf; a fine solitaire to the Marquis di Luchesini; and a diamond ring to Philippi, the lieutenant of the police. He has further broken up three boxes set with diamonds, of which thirty rings have been made; these he has taken with him to distribute in Silesia.

Take good note, that Launay has not had the alternative of accepting a salary of six thousand crowns, or his dismission; he has merely received information, under the form of an order, that his salary was reduced to six thousand crowns.

Count Hertzberg this day gave a grand dinner to foreigners, to which the new Spanish Ambassador was invited, but neither Comte d'Esterno nor any Frenchman; which affectation was the more remarkable since all the English, Piedmontese, Swedish, and not only foreign Ambassadors but complimentary envoys, were there assembled. Comte d'Esterno takes a proper revenge; he gives a grand dinner to-morrow, to which Count Hertzberg is invited.

POSTSCRIPT.— Mr. Ewart, the secretary of the English Embassy, said to me yesterday, in the presence of fifteen people, Count Hertzberg supporting him with voice and gesture, in these precise terms, "The Stadtholder is, by the constitution, the executive power in Holland; or to speak more intelligibly, he is precisely in Holland what the King is in England." I replied, in the most ironical and dry tone, " It is to be hoped he will not be beheaded by his subjects." The laughers were not with Mr. Ewart.

Boden has sent your packets. The extracts from the pleadings of Linguet, which are excellent (I speak of the extracts), have been perfectly successful. I entreat you will not fail to send me the continuation. You cannot find a better means of procuring me customers than by things of this kind.

There is a demur concerning Alvensleben. It is Hertzberg who supports Goltz.

Number LXXVIII. of the " Courier of the Lower Rhine " is so insolent, relative to the King of France and his Ambassador, that I imagine it would be proper to make a formal complaint. This might somewhat curb Hertzberg, who is the accomplice of Manson, and who may do us many other favors of a like nature, should this pass with impunity. You are not aware of the influence these gazettes have in Germany.

LETTER XXXIII.

L EAVING Berlin, I by chance discovered the person who
has remained four days shut up in the apartment
of the Prince of Hesse (of Rothembourg), who is no
other than that Croisy, formerly St. Huberty, and once
the husband of our celebrated St. Huberty,* whose marriage was annulled, Counselor Bonneau† of the Prince of
Prussia, and relative to his own wife a bankrupt, a forger,— in a word, a knight of industry, of the most despicable order, and concerning whom all foreigners ask,
"Is it possible such a man can be an officer in the
French service?" I am no longer astonished that the
Prince of Hesse should be coldly received by the King.
To come expressly to lay the train to the mine of corruption; and to depend upon it as a certainty that the
combustibles should catch fire, from a knowledge of the
errors of the Sovereign; to found hopes of success on
the ill opinion we have of him, and in a manner to proclaim this knowledge, by a rapid journey from Paris to
Berlin, destitute of all other pretext, since the Prince of
Hesse and his minion have stayed only five days, and
are already gone back to Paris,— this is at once to display foolish cunning and contemptible conduct. I imagine it is of importance that we should tell the King
aloud, and with the strongly marked, ironical tone of
disdain, which shall make him feel, without debasing
ourselves to speak more openly, that this manœuver was
totally unknown to our Cabinet; for I am persuaded,
from some half-phrases which I have heard those who
wish us ill drop, that they do not desire anything better
than to fix this blot upon us.

* The first singer at the French opera.

† Bonneau is a sea term, in the French language, and signifies buoy.
But the word was chosen by Voltaire, because it was an apt metaphor,
as the name of a Pandar. From him it is here borrowed, and is several times so applied in this work.

I have traveled through Brandenburg to Magdeburg with Count Hatzfeldt, who had been sent by the Elector of Mayence to compliment the King on his accession, and Baron Geilling, sent for the same purpose by the Duc de Deux-Ponts. The latter, formerly a captain of hussars in our service, is a handsome blockhead, who could only have been chosen because he is the brother of Madame Eixbeck, the Duke's mistress. Count Hatzfeldt is a man of great urbanity, and whose knowledge and understanding are deserving of esteem. It seems he will remain some time at Berlin, that he may discover what shall be created out of the chaos. I conversed much on Mayence; the Elector is better, but does not promise any length of life. The two persons who, in all appearance, are most likely to succeed him are Feckenberg and Alberg. The first is wholly Austrian, the latter a man of abilities, of whom the highest opinion is entertained, whose political inclinations are little known, and who dissembles, like Sixtus V., while yet a monk.

That Court at present seems to be exceedingly averse to the Emperor, who every day, indeed, by a multitude of traits, both private and public, and which are really inconceivable, increases universal hatred. It is impossible to depict the effect which his answer to the request of the Hungarians produced — (*Pueri sunt pueri: pueri puerilia tractant*) — together with the violent abolition of all their privileges. But, on the one hand, the great landholders are at Vienna, there enchained by their places, and almost kept under a guard, so that they are in truth the hostages of the slavery of the Hungarians; and, on the other, the aristocracy being excessively odious to the people, there is in this superb and formidable country neither unity of interest, nor center of concord. The regular troops are, besides, posted, and provided with artillery, supported by veterans, colonists, etc., etc.

An Englishman, very much my friend, and a man of excellent observation, whom I have happened to meet with here, and who has visited all the camps of the Emperor, while speaking in raptures of those formidable pillars of his power, Hungary, Moravia, Bohemia, Galicia, etc., confesses that the inferiority of his troops, compared with the Prussian army, has infinitely surpassed his expectation. He affirms it is impossible, either relative to the individual or collective information of the officers or to the military talents of the Emperor, which are in reality null, insomuch that he appears incapable of conceiving such complicated evolutions,—he affirms, I say, it is impossible to compare the two nations: with this difference, that the Emperor, like Cadmus, can make men spring out of the earth; and that the Prussian army, once annihilated, will be incapable of renovation, except from its treasury. Should A MAN once be seated upon the Austrian throne, there will be an end to the liberties of Europe. The health of the Emperor is supposed not to be good; his activity gradually decreases; he still, however, surpasses his real strength, but his projects seem like the wishes of an expiring patient who raves on recovery. He is supposed at present to be on very cool terms with the Empress of Russia.

10

LETTER XXXIV.

THOUGH I ride post, you perceive it is not in the spirit of dissipation. Alas! what mode of life in reality less corresponds with my natural inclination than that indolent activity, if so I may call it, which hurries me into every tumult, and among the proud and fastidious, to the utter loss of time! For such is the general consequence of the confusion of society. among the Germans, who converse as they call it AMONG THEMSELVES although thirty persons should be present. Thus am I robbed of study, deprived of my favorite pursuits, my own thoughts, and forced incessantly to comply with forms so foreign, not to say odious, to my nature. You yourself, who lead a life so full of hurry, but who, however, associate with the chosen few, in despite of all the gifts of nature, you must feel how difficult it is abruptly to pass from the buzz of men to the meditations of the closet. Yet is this indispensably necessary, in order to manage the ASIDE speeches, by which the current news of the day is acquired and consequences are divined. We must gallop five days with the Prince, and pursue all the physical and moral meanderings of the man, in public and in private, before we can obtain the right, or the opportunity, to ask him a question; or, which is better, to catch a word, which may be equivalent both to question and answer.

But who knows this better than you? I only wish you to understand my excursions are not the effect of chance, and still less of whim. Let me add that each of my journeys improves my local knowledge, a subject on which I have made it a law not to be easily satisfied. I hope that, among others, you will perceive by my memorial on Saxony, and by that on the Prussian States, which are, in reality, works of labor, and which you will not have a sight of for months to come, that I have profoundly studied the countries which I wished to understand, and as ardently in men as in books; with this difference, however, that I scarcely dare confide in the mere assertion of the best-informed man, unless he brings written proofs.* The necessity of that species of superstitious conscientiousness, with which I am almost mechanically impressed, whenever I take up the pen, has been demonstrated to my own mind too often for it ever to forsake me.

Yet whither am I traveling in this painful road? If I may depend on the few reports which your friendship has deigned to make me of the sensation which my dispatches have produced, when corrected, arranged, and embellished by you (for how is it possible for me to correct that which I write at the moment, by snatches, with lightning-like rapidity, and without having time to read?), they have given satisfaction. If I judge by the reiterated symptoms of the extreme inattention which long silence supposes, on questions the most important, on requests the most instantaneous, and sometimes of absolute forgetfulness of the greatest part of these things, I should be induced to believe that my letters are read, at the most, with as much interest as a packet would be, the materials of which are tolerably clear and orderly, and that the reading produces not the least ultimate effect. Should this be so, is it worth the trouble (I put the question to you, whose energetic sentiments and high thoughts so often escape, notwithstanding all the contagion of levity, carelessness, egotism and inconsistency which exhale out of every door in the country which you inhabit), is it right, I say, that I should sacrifice, to an interest so subordinate as that of curiosity, my inclinations, my talents, my time and my powers? I believe you know me to be no quack, you know it is not my custom to speak of my pains, and of my labors, in fustian terms. Permit me, then, my good and dear friend, to protest that they both are great. I keep three men totally occupied in mechanically copying the materials I have arranged. I am assisted by the labor and

* Are there not, *cæteris paribus*, as many written as related lies?

the knowledge of several; all my moments, all my thoughts are there, thence depart, and thither return. Should the product be no greater (and I may say to you that you cannot yet estimate the whole product, for the greatest of my labors are still in my desk),* it must either be the fault of my own incapacity or of my situation; perhaps of both, and perhaps also of the latter only. But here I am wholly, and, as a man of thirty-seven, ought not to be wholly, devoted to nullities; for nullities they are if nothing be produced, nothing effected, either in behalf of myself or others.

If, therefore, anything BE produced, afford me some proof of it; and when, for example, I ask any question, for the purpose of more effectually executing my trust, let it be answered. When I say it is necessary I should have a plan of operations of such or such a kind to propose, because I shall be immediately questioned on the subject, and shall lose an opportunity which probably may never be recovered should I be caught unprovided, let such a plan of operations be sent me.

If all this is to have any good effect in my favor, let me be told so; for in my present situation I have great need of encouragement, if it were but to empower me to yield without madness to the impulses of my zeal. I say without madness; for, to speak only of the vilest, but, notwithstanding, the most palpable of wants, when I perceive that I am very unable to make my accounts balance with my present appointments, ought I not to clog the down-hill wheel? And what have I to hope from these appointments, when I recollect how much they are in arrear; and that a change of Ministry may increase my personal debts with the sums which my friends have advanced me, for the service of those who cannot be ignorant I am myself incapable of making such advances? Yet, should I stop, is there not an end to all utility from what I have hitherto effected? Shall I then have anything remaining except regret for time lost, and the deep, the rankling affliction of having attached people to

---

* The author no doubt refers to his "*Histoire de la Monarchie prussienne.*"

my fortunes for whom I can do nothing but what must be an ill compensation, and at my own expense, for all which they have done for me?

Pardon these expansions of the heart. To whom may I confide my anxieties, if not to you, my friend, my consolation, my guide, and my support? To whom may I say, what is all this to me, since it does not produce me even money? For that I expend in the business I have undertaken, and not in private gratifications. In truth, I should be susceptible of no other, were the hoped futurity come, and I had no dependents. You well know that money to me is nothing, at least when I have any. Where am I going, whither leading others? Have I made a good bargain by bartering my life, stormy as it was, but so mingled with enjoyments of which it was not in human power to deprive me, for a sterile activity, which snatches me even from the frequent and delightful effusions of your friendship? You are to me but a statesman; you, for the pressure of whose hand I would relinquish all the thrones on earth. Alas, I am much better formed for friendship than for politics.

Post Scriptum, began at Helmstadt, and finished at Brunswick, October 14th, 1786.

They write from Silberberg, in Silesia, that the King's carriage has been overturned, and that he has received contusions on the head and on the arm. The coachman, it is added, expired on the place. The news reached me yesterday, at Magdeburg, and the same has been written to General Prittwitz; it probably exceeds the truth, but is not wholly without foundation. The extreme agitation of the Duke of Brunswick, and my own emotions, made me profoundly feel the fortunes that rest on this Monarch's head. The Duke immediately sent off a courier, and, as I shall follow him to Brunswick, where he wishes to speak to me at large concerning Holland, I shall learn more circumstantial intelligence, and such as will be indubitable. I have not time to add a single word; I write while the horses are changed.

Duquesne University of the Holy Ghost. Pittsburgh, Pa.

From Brunswick, October 14th, 1786.

Not having found an opportunity of sending off these few lines, I continue.

I arrived here two hours before the Duke. As soon as he came to Brunswick, he wrote to me with a pencil, on a slip of paper:

"I spoke yesterday evening, before I departed, with the Minister Count Schulemberg, who had left Berlin on the eleventh. He is in absolute ignorance of the alarming intelligence by which we were so much affected, and, as I have heard nothing on the subject since, I begin to have better hopes. I expect my courier will arrive early in the morning. I write you this, Monsieur le Comte, from my mother's, and I hope you will do me the favor to come to me early to-morrow morning and dine with us."

It appears to be very probable that no material harm has happened to the Sovereign.

The splendor of the talents and urbanity of the Duke appeared perfect at Magdeburg. Nothing could be more awful than his manœuvers, nothing so instructive as his school, nothing so finished, so connected, so perfect, as his conduct in every respect. He was the subject of admiration to a great number of foreigners, who had crowded to Magdeburg, and he certainly stood in no need of the contrast which the Duke of Weimar and the Prince of Dessau afforded, the latter the weakest of men, the former industriously laboring to be something, but ill-provided with requisites, if we are to judge him by appearances. He might and ought to become a Prince of importance. According to all probabilities, however, Saxony will devolve on him for want of children in the Electoral branch, and it is an afflicting perspective to contemplate the destruction of all the labors of the worthy Prince who at present governs the country, and who, tormented in his childhood, unhappy in youth, and truly respectable in manhood, will, perhaps, descend to the tomb with the bitter affliction of feeling that all the good he has done will be rendered ineffectual.

I have learned a fact, which will afford some pleasure to M. de Segur, if he be still living. A foundry has been built at Hanover, at a great expense, which has cost the King of England near one hundred thousand livres. The Duke of Brunswick, not being satisfied with his own foundry, had two cannons cast at Hanover, and they were so ill-cast that they were soon obliged to be laid aside. It is not to be supposed, when we recollect the connections between the Duke and the King of England, that this was occasioned by any trick in the founders; the fact, therefore, is a proof that they are bad workmen.

By the next courier I hope to send you the exact result of the dispositions of Berlin, and the Duke, relative to Holland. He has promised me a precise statement of the propositions which appear to him necessary, and he did not conceal the extreme desire he had that they should be accepted by France. These Dutch disturbances daily present a more threatening aspect for the repose of Europe — if not at the present moment, at least from future contingencies, and the coolness and distrust to which they will give rise.

LETTER XXXV.

BRUNSWICK, October 16th, 1786.

THE two conversations I have had with the Duke have
hitherto been but vague respecting Holland, and
indeed almost foreign to the subject. His courier,
having brought him the news of hopes of an accommodation, and of the retreat of the person who of all those
concerned with M. de Veyrac was supposed to be the
chief firebrand, having, in fine, brought him details
which led him to imagine that his interference will not
be necessary, or not yet wanted in Holland, he passed
rapidly over the country to come to one which is of infinitely greater importance to him; I mean to say Prussia.
He only discovered himself to be greatly averse to the
party of the Stadtholder, and well convinced that the
right of presentation ought to remain such as it was in
its origin; that the constitution of Gueldres, Frieseland,
and Utrecht evidently was in want of reformation, with
respect to the inconceivable regulation of the magistrates,
who are revocable *ad nutum;* that, in a word, the Prince,
who from absolute monarchical authority, which he in
reality possessed, was sunken into absolute discredit, by
conduct the most abject, and the folly of having claimed
that as a right, in contempt of all law, all decency, and
all popular prejudice, which he effectually possessed, was
not deserving of the least support; but that, from respect to Prussia, and particularly to retard commotions,
it was requisite to restore him the decorum of pageantry,
—except that watch should be kept over his connections. And here he explained himself on the subject of
Harris, and even concerning Prince Louis of Brunswick,
nearly in the manner I should have done myself. In
conclusion, however, he not only did not inform me of
anything on the subject, but he imperceptibly declined
that debate which a few days before he had provoked.

I repeat, there is some news arrived of which I am
ignorant, that has occasioned this change in his proceedings. My information is in general much too confined.
Thus, for example, it is very singular, nor is it less
embarrassing, and to speak plainly, it is tolerably ridiculous, that it should be the Duke who should inform me
of the treaty of commerce signed between France and
England, not one of the articles of which I am acquainted
with, and on which occasion I knew not what face to
wear. As my usual method is not to conceal myself
behind any veil of mystery, which hides the insignificance
of certain Ambassadors, the part I had to act was not a
little difficult. I should learn a thousand times more
were I myself better informed. In this, as in everything
else, fortune follows the successful.

Returning to Prussia, it was quite a different affair,
for of this I know as much as the Duke. His confidence
was the less limited, and the more profuse, because I
presently set him at his ease with respect to Prince
Henry, whom he neither loves nor esteems. I perceived
with inquietude that his opinions and fears are similar
to my own. He is dissatisfied with most of the proceedings and public acts of the King, with that crowd of
titles, and that mass of nobility, which has been added
so prodigally; insomuch that it will be henceforward
much more difficult to find a man than a nobleman in
the Prussian States; with the promise made to the Prince
of Dessau (whose only merit is such an excess of enthusiasm for mysticism and visionaries that, when Lavater
came to Bremen, he addressed the most earnest supplications to him to come and pay him a visit, in order
that he might adore him), and perhaps with that given
to the Duke of Weimar (who to the same inclinations,
and more lively passions, adds greater understanding;
but who is too much in debt for his military projects
to be otherwise regarded than as a money speculation),
to restore the one and to admit the other into the Prussian service; by which rank in the army will be violated,
and the army discouraged and vitiated,— a system very
opposite to that of Frederick II., who said of the few
grandees who were employed in his time, "In the name

of God, my dear Moellendorf, rid me of THESE PRINCES."
The Duke is equally dissatisfied with that fluctuation
which occasions essays to be made on twenty systems at
once; with the most of the persons chosen; with domestic
disorder; with nocturnal rites, and with the anecdotes the
augury of which from day to day becomes more inaus-
piciously characteristic, etc., etc. In a word, should I
transcribe our conversation, I should but send new copies
of old dispatches.

"Believe me," said he, "I may, in a certain degree,
serve you as a thermometer, for if I perceive there are
no hopes of a firm and noble regimen, and that therefore
the day of the House of Brandenburg is come, I shall
not be the last to sound a retreat. I never received
money from the King of Prussia, and I am well determined never to accept anything from him, though I mean
to remain in the service. It has, as you have seen, been
a dear service to me. I am independent. I wish to pay
a tribute of respect to the memory of the great man
who is no more, and am ready to shed my blood, if that
might cement his work; but I will not, even by my presence, become the accomplice of its demolition. Our
debts never exceed our abilities. I shall provide in the
best manner in my power for my country and my children; these I shall leave in great order. I keep up my
family connections. We perhaps shall be the last who
will be smitten by the overthrow of the Germanic body,
because of the confraternity which unites us to the Elector of Hanover. I, therefore, shall no further follow the
destiny of the Prussian monarchy than as its Government shall maintain its wisdom, its dignity, etc., etc."

At present the Duke despairs of nothing; and in this
he is right. He supposes that no person has yet found
his proper place. I think like him, and I perceive he
hopes his turn will come; of this neither can I doubt,
unless the annihilation of the Prussian power has been
decreed by fate.

He has informed me of the very singular fact that M.
de Custine, the father, has demanded to be admitted into
the service of the King of Prussia, and has pretended to
disclose all the hostile plans of the Emperor, whose

alliance, nevertheless, this same M. de Custine loudly affirms will terminate, with France, the day that Prince Kaunitz dies.

The Duke is very far from being relieved of all his fears concerning the projects of the Emperor, whose puissance and advisers he holds in infinite dread. True it is that his inconsistency should render his designs and the execution of them abortive; that the irrationality of his personal conduct should hasten his end; that the Archduke Francis appears to be a cipher; that among the persons who have influence there is not one formidable man, especially in the army; and that Alventzy and Kinsky, the one manufacturer for the infantry, and the other for the cavalry, possess only ambiguous abilities, etc. But men start up at the moment when they are least expected; accident only is necessary to rank them in their proper place. Condé, Spinola, and the Duke of Brunswick himself, prove that it is possible to be born a general. There is a Prince of Waldeck in the Austrian army, who, it is said, announces grand talents.

The numerous, trifling anecdotes, which the Duke and I have mutually related to each other, would be too tedious for insertion, and out of their place also here. An anecdote, merely as such, is equally devoid of propriety and information; such will have their turn hereafter; but there is one which relates too much to the Russian system for it to be passed over in silence.

The Czarina has, for some months past, appropriated to herself the possession and the revenues of the posts of Courland, leaving a small part only to the Duke, in order that this branch of administration might not appear to be wholly in the hands of foreigners. Thus does this same Russia, that maintains an envoy at Courland, although there is none at Courland from Petersburg, and that here, as in Poland, proclaims her will to the Duke and to the States, by her Ambassador, who is the real Sovereign of the country,—this Russia, that for some years past, has unequivocally and openly declared that a certain canton of Courland appertained to her, and without seeking any other pretext than that of giving a more

uniform line to her limits, makes no secret of not understanding any other code, any other claims, any other
manifestoes, than those which the Gauls alleged to the
Etruscans — "Our right exists in our arms. Whatever
the strong can seize upon that is the right of the strong."
She will one of these days declare Courland is hers, that
the Polish Ukraine is hers, and that Finland is hers.
And, for example, this latter revolution, which will be a
very salutary one to her because she will then truly become unattackable, and almost inaccessible, to all Europe
united, will be effected, whenever she shall make the
attempt, if we do not take good heed. Whenever the
time may come that I shall be informed of this having
taken place, and even of the new system of Sweden
being totally overthrown, I shall not feel any surprise.

The Duke also told me that the Emperor is greatly
improving his artillery; that his six-pounders are equivalent in force to our former eight-pounders; and to this
advantage they add that of lightness, in so great a degree,
that only four horses are necessary to draw them, while
even in Prussia six are still requisite. As well as I
remember he attributes this double improvement to the
CONICAL* construction of the chamber. I only relate this
that you may verify the truth of the fact by people who
are acquainted with such affairs; the diminution of two
horses in eight being a thing of infinite importance, and
the more so as there would be a servant the less.

The manner in which I have been received by the
Duke was infinitely friendly on his part, though somewhat participating, as far as relates to freedom of conversation, of my equivocal mode of existence at Berlin. I
believe I may, without presumption, affirm I am not
disagreeable to this Prince, and that, were I accredited
by any commission whatever, I should be one of most
proper persons to treat with him with efficacy. This
able man appears to me to have but one weakness,
which is the prodigious dread of having his reputation
injured, even by the most contemptible Zoilus. Yet has
he lately exposed himself to vexatious blame in deference
to his first Minister, M. von Feronce, which I cannot

* *Faite en poire* (made in the form of a pear).

comprehend. This M. von Feronce, and M. von Munchausen, Grand Master of the Court, a man who is reported to have little delicacy concerning money matters, have farmed the lottery,— an action shameful in itself, and which I cannot reconcile to Von Feronce, who is really a man of merit. Two merchants, named Oeltz and Nothnagel, have gained a *quaterne*, which is equivalent to the sum of eighteen thousand crowns. The payment of this has not only been refused, but as it was necessary to act with fraud to effect their purpose, the merchants have undergone numerous oppressions; they have even been imprisoned; all which acts they have lately published in a printed case, which contains nothing but the facts concerning the suit, and have laid an appeal against the Duke, or against his judges, before the tribunal of Wetzlar; I own I do not understand this absence of firmness, or of circumspection.

October 17th, 1786.

POSTSCRIPT.— I have just received authentic intelligence concerning the King of Prussia. It was one of his chasseurs to whom a very serious accident happened; the Monarch himself is in good health, and will arrive on the eighteenth or the nineteenth at Berlin.

I learn, at the same time, that Count Finckenstein is dying of an inflammation of the lungs, with which he was seized after a very warm altercation with Count Hertzberg, on the subject of Holland. His life is despaired of, and his loss to us will be very great; as well because he was absolutely ours, as because that, being a temporizer by nature, he would have acted as the moderator of Prince Henry. He would also have directed the conduct of Mademoiselle Voss, after the fall of virtue; and finally because Hertzberg will no longer have any counterpoise. With respect to the latter point, however, I am not averse to suppose that the time when this presumptuous man shall be in absolute discredit may but be the more quickly accelerated. Yet, not to mention the sterility of subjects by which this epoch may be retarded, who shall answer that a man so violent, and wholly imbued as he is with the hatred which the Germans in general bear the French, will not venture to make some very decisive false steps?

The Duke of York arrived here this evening, and had he been the Emperor he could not have been treated with more respect, especially by the Duchess and the courtiers. She, indeed, is wholly English, as well in her inclinations and her principles as in her manners; insomuch that her almost cynical independence, opposed to the etiquette of the Courts of German Princes, forms the most singular contrast I know. I do not, however, believe that there is any question concerning the marriage of the Princess Caroline, who is a most amiable, lively, playful, witty, and handsome lady; the Duke of York, a puissant hunter, a potent drinker, an indefatigable laugher, destitute of breeding and politeness, and who possesses, at least in appearance, much of the Duke de Lauzun, as well in mind as in person, is inspired with a kind of passion for a woman married to a jealous husband, who torments him, and will not suffer him to fix his quarters. I know not whether he will go to Berlin. The versions relative to him are various. Some affirm that, after having been an unbridled libertine, he feels a returning desire of doing his duty. For my own part, I find in him all the stiffness of a German Prince, with a double dose of English insolence, but wanting the free cordiality of that nation.

LETTER XXXVI.

BRUNSWICK, October 27th, 1786.

I HERE send you the continuation and conclusion of the preceding dispatch, to which I add the translation of a pamphlet, the singularity of which is increased by its having appeared at Vienna, with the permission of the Emperor; who, to the communication made by the censor, has added these very words, "Let this pass among others."

This is but a trifle compared to that caprice which three days afterwards induced him to release the unfortunate Szekely, whom the most powerful remonstrances could not save, and whose cause is here * ill enough defended. For what conclusions might he not have drawn from the confidence with which he imparted to the Emperor the situation of his accounts, from the disorder by which they had been brought into this state, from the ardent supplications he made him to purchase for the public a well-tried chemical secret at such a price as would have completed the deficiency in his accounts (I say completed, for Szekely and his family had paid the greatest part of the deficiencies), and from the answer of the Emperor himself,— "Do you address yourself to me as to a friend, or as to the Emperor? If to the former, I cannot be the friend of a man who has not been faithful to his trust. If as Emperor, I would advise you to go in person and make your declaration to the Courts of Justice."

This fact, which I have learned since my arrival at Berlin, attended with most aggravating circumstances, is one of the most odious I can recollect, yet might I relate fifty of the same species.

---

* By the word HERE, the author means in the pamphlet, to which the reader will immediately come.

*Free Observations on the Crime and Punishment of Lieu-
tenant-Colonel* SZEKELY, *of the Guards, by a Friend of
Truth*, 1786.

LET the voice of Truth be heard, let her at present be
seen without disguise, without veil, in all her awful
nakedness. Hear, ye incorrupt * judges. I am about to
speak of the crime and punishment of Szekely. My
heart melts, but my words shall be impartial. Hear and
pronounce sentence on me, on Szekely, and on those
who pronounced sentence on him.

Szekely announces a deficiency in the regimental chest
of the guards, and the disorder of his accounts; and
after some pretended examinations is brought before the
Council of War. Ninety-seven thousand florins of the
Empire have disappeared; but Szekely had placed his
whole confidence in the Sieur Lakner, who is deceased,
and who was the only keeper of the keys of the chest.
Szekely had more than once declared that he himself
was a very improper person to have pecuniary matters
committed to his charge, and that he never had revised
nor verified the accounts of the regimental chest confided to his care. He therefore cannot be suspected of
personal fraud, especially when his regiment renders justice to the goodness of his manners, and unanimously
points out the cashier Lakner as a person who was debased
by meanness, and rendered suspicious by incurring expenses infinitely above his fortune.

This, it is very true, was an exceedingly culpable negligence, but such was the only crime of Szekely; and it
was for this reason that the Council of War condemned
him to be imprisoned six years in a fortress. The punishment was doubtless in itself sufficient, since Szekely, in

---

* From the life of Baron Trenck, from the present fact, and from
numerous others, it appears that the appeal and the apostrophe are
absurd. Trenck informs us that his judges, after having held their
offices for a succession of years, were at last condemned to be common
scavengers of Vienna. The picture he gives of their intrigues, their
corruption, and their vices, is beyond conception horrible. How can
man dare to vaunt of the wisdom of the age, which has not yet discovered that justice, in its most extensive sense, is the most necessary, as well as the sublimest, attribute of man.

effect, and according to the language of the civilians, was *Nec confessus nec convictus* of any prevarication; yet was it aggravated by the Aulic* Council of War, which was commanded to make a revision of the process, and which increased his detention to a duration of eight years. Was this tribunal ignorant, then, that it is a custom with our MOST GRACIOUS Monarch himself to increase the severity of all sentences pronounced against criminals? Let us, therefore, believe that the judges, on this occasion, were only obedient to the rigor of the laws; but the after decision of the Emperor will most assuredly appear inconceivable. The following is the judgment which this Monarch uttered — Yes! uttered, yet did not blush:

" Szekely must, without hesitation, be broken, declared incapable of military service, and delivered over to the civil officer, who shall convey him to the place where the crime was committed in Vienna, where he shall stand in the pillory for three successive days, and remain two hours each day on a scaffold, in the high market place, that his example may be of public utility. As a favor and in consequence of his age, I limit the eight years' imprisonment to which he is condemned to four, during which he shall be confined at Segedin, a penal prison of the civil power of the Hungarian States, where he shall receive the same allowance for food as is granted to other criminals. »

The Court of Justice made remonstrances to the Emperor, in which it proved that the punishment was much too severe, and entirely contrary to law and to equity; but the Emperor continued inflexible, and thus confirmed his sentence:

"All superintendents of military chests might, like Szekely, plead that they knew not what was become of the money, even though it should have been stolen by themselves. Whenever there is a deficiency in any chest, and especially of a sum so considerable as ninety-seven thousand florins, there is no necessity for the judge to prove that the money has been taken by the accused person, but the accused person must show that

---

* We cannot find a better parallel to this AULIC Council than the formerly infamous Court of Star Chamber.

it has not been taken by him; and whenever he cannot demonstrate this he himself is the thief. As soon as Szekely shall have been broken, and shall be no longer an officer, the sentence against him shall be put in execution, and a paper shall be fixed round his neck on which shall be written — An unfaithful steward."

Let us take an attentive retrospect of these supreme decisions.

Szekely is punishable for having been exceedingly negligent; he is the same for having bestowed his whole confidence on a dishonest cashier, of whose pompous luxury he could not be ignorant, since it gave offense to the whole corps of the guards. It was easy to conclude that such a man could not live at an expense so great on his paternal income. It is even probable that Szekely himself, perceiving the disorder of his accounts, and the deficiency in his chest, and terrified by the infamy and punishment inflicted on such crimes, sacrificed much to alchemy and the occult sciences, in the hope of making gold, and of thus freeing himself from his embarrassments. This, no doubt, was a folly at which all men of sense would grieve; it is not, however, the less possible. It is certain that the love of chemistry was the ruling passion of Szekely, and that he indulged his inclinations the more because he expected sometime thus to recover his losses. To this excuse let us add the extreme ignorance of which he accused himself in all that related to pecuniary affairs.

True it is that, with such a conviction of his own incapacity, he never ought to have taken charge of a regimental chest; but were all those who are in possession of places, the duties of which are far beyond their abilities, obliged to abdicate them, what vast deserts would our public offices afford! Rabner encourages three different species of men,* by saying, "On whom God bestows an office he also bestows a sufficient degree of understanding for the exercise of that office." Szekely would not indubitably have adopted this opinion, could he have foreseen the evil consequences of his presumption.

* I know not why three different species, or what three; I can but follow my author.

Was not that flattering letter which was addressed to him by Maria Theresa, of glorious memory, in which, while she gave the highest praises to his probity and loyalty, this august Sovereign confided to his care, without any caution, the regimental chest of the guards, an authentic testimony in behalf of his honor? Has it been meant by the . forgetfulness of this distinction to add a new outrage to all the ingratitudes with which some have sullied themselves, relative to this immortal Empress? Was it intended to tax her with that levity, that silly credulity, which blind confidence produces? Alas! in despite of all the defects which envy so gratuitously imputes to her, Maria Theresa never was surrounded by such an army of knaves as those from whom all the rigor of the present Sovereign cannot preserve us. So true is it that gentleness and love, from a Prince toward his subjects, are more efficacious means, to preserve them within the bounds of duty, than all the violent acts tyranny can commit.

I return to Szekely and affirm it is impossible that this letter from the Empress Queen, though in some sort the pledge of the fidelity of Szekely, can serve as an excuse to the Prince of Esterhazy, whose personal negligence cannot be justified. Did not his right, as chief of the guards, impose it on him as a law to examine the regimental chest of Szekely? And is not such an infraction of the duties of his place most reprehensible?

Still less can be offered in defense of the fault committed by the Hungaro-Transylvanian Chancery; since according to its instructions, it was in like manner bound to inspect the administration of Szekely. But none of the acts of this superior Court ought to inspire astonishment, since it is no longer distinguished, except by disorder and ill faith; since its responsibility is no longer anything but a word; and since its ideas of exact calculation, and of receipt and expense, are exactly as just as those of Brambille * are on physic.

---

* This Brambille is first surgeon to the Emperor, by whom he has been ennobled, and who has made him inspector of the medical and chirurgical academies. He is said to be an ignorant quack, and a violent satire has lately been written against him, which, if report speaks

Judges, ye have condemned Szekely. Be it so. Act worthy of your office. Punish his superintendents also, who have by a non-performance of their duty placed him on the brink of that abyss into which you headlong plunged him, without humanity, and void of shame.

The Kings of Europe have all reserved to themselves the most benevolent of prerogatives; that of pardoning the guilty, or of softening the pains the sentence inflicts by which they are condemned. Joseph alone persists in other principles, more conformable to the feelings of his heart. He aggravates the punishment of the wretched. Alas! this no doubt is but to enjoy the ecstatic pleasure of terrifying his people, by the exercise of the most unlimited despotism. Unfortunate Szekely! Ill-starred man! I pity thee. Thou fallest a victim to the splenetic temper of the Monarch! Perhaps, at the very instant when he pronounced thy doom, a troublesome fly stung his brow, and thy dishonor was his vengeance. Deplorable sacrifice of a tyrannical and barbarous heart, yes, I pity thee! Men of worth, men of justice, what must the Monarch be who can ADD to the rigor of the Judge? — A tyrant! What can the Monarch be who tramples under foot the rights of humanity? — A tyrant!! What can the Monarch be who can make the laws and the justice of his kingdom his sport? — A tyrant!!! What can the Monarch be who in criminal decisions shall act only according to his caprice? — A Joseph!!!!

A Joseph! — Oh, God! Great God! What then is man? A poor and feeble creature, whom an imperious oppressor may at any moment reduce to dust; or may rend his heart, extort his last sigh, by the seven thousand raging torments which the Hydras with seven thousand heads in sport inflicts.

Dreadful image! Ignominious to humanity, yet woefully true, woefully exact, woefully confirmed by experience! Does not a Sovereign who increases the rigor of sentences openly proclaim: "Ye Judges, whom I have

truth, is very pleasant. This satire has been licensed and publicly sold at Vienna, which is another singular fact, and tends to prove that pasquinades will be much rather suffered in Austria than instructive and free works.

appointed to judge according to law and equity, ye are prevaricators; ye have betrayed your trust, falsified your consciences, and have endeavored to practice deceit upon me?" Such magistrates, therefore, ought not to be continued in office; for, to suffer them still to be Judges is to approve their conduct, and confirm their judgment. But, destructive as the thunderbolt, the Monarch, addressing them, exclaims: "Your sentence is too mild! It is my will arbitrarily to increase punishment, that I may prove myself the master of life and death!" What language, oh, God! from the mouth of a King whom thou hast, appointed to be our protector, and not our tyrant!

Szekely would never have been condemned, had he not been intimately connected with the Freemasons. When the Emperor pronounced sentence against this unfortunate man, he forgot himself so far as to say, "I will let those gentry (the Freemasons) understand there is no efficacy in their protection."

Where, then, is the equity of a Monarch who thus prostitutes the power he is in possession of, to the destruction of one of the members of a society which he detests? Who would not smile contemptuously at the poor malice of a peasant who should go in search of his neighbor, after twilight, that he might unseen give him a fillip on the nose, run away, and divert himself with having played him so cunning a trick. Oh, Justice! Justice! Shalt thou forever have eyes that thou mayst not see?

Yes, debased, corrupted was the mouth which increased the rigor of the sentence of Szekely, who previously had been destined to languish eight years in prison. Joseph has diminished the term of his detention. And are these, then, thy favors, sceptered executioner? Yes, this favor granted to a man of quality, who was for three successive days exposed in the pillory, resembles that which a criminal, condemned to the gallows, should receive from thee, whom thou shouldst permit to be racked upon the wheel, because he was too feeble to mount the ladder.

Couldst thou have survived the shame of such a crime, had not thy people themselves applauded thy fury? The

curiosity with which all Vienna enjoyed the spectacle the
wretched Szekely afforded, proves that the manners of
thy subjects already partake of thine own barbarity.
But let them tremble, slaves as they are, bowed beneath
the yoke. A new Nero promises new crimes, new horrors!

LETTER XXXVII.

Brunswick, October 18th, 1786.

I FEAR there are some waverings in the mind of the King, relative to Holland; for the Duke, after the arrival of his courier, and receiving information of the danger of Count Finckenstein, again spoke to me on the subject, with a degree of inquietude which was far from dissembled. The following were his precise words: "Holland will certainly occasion a war, especially should the death of the Elector of Bavaria intervene; do you act, therefore, as mediators to smother the rising flames. Come, come, the Stadtholder must have a council, without which he can perform nothing; and how shall this council be selected?"

I replied to the Duke that I was not sufficiently acquainted with those affairs to give any opinion on the subject, but that I was going to make him a proposition which he must regard as only ideal, and as coming from myself, although it might by no means be impracticable.

"Now that I know how far I can depend upon your prudence and your principles," I continued, "I am certain that you will see the affairs and the conduct of the Stadtholder in their true light; that you will not imagine friendship in politics can have any other basis than interests; or that we ought to renounce our alliance with Holland, in order that the Princess of Orange may nightly enjoy more agreeable dreams; that you cannot but comprehend how much it is impossible for us to place any confidence in Count Hertzberg, who, relative to us, is frantic, and how much our distrust may be increased should our sole counterpoise to this violent Minister disappear by the death of Count Finckenstein. I shall, therefore, thus far, willingly step forward to say that it appears to me very probable that France will be inclined to treat on this affair with you singly, should the King

of Prussia consent that you should be solely trusted with
the business on his behalf; and, as I may say, should
you be made arbitrator. I feel how important it is to
you, to us, and to all, that you should not endanger
yourself in the opinion of his Majesty. There are already but too many causes of distance existing between
you, and the country is entirely lost if the necessities of
the times do not oblige you to take the helm. But,
should you find the crisis so alarming as to dread decisive events should be the consequence, it appears to me
that then it will no longer be proper to keep beating against
the wind. For, if the King of Prussia be fated to commit
irreparable faults, it would be as well for all parties
that he should begin to-morrow, in order that we might
the sooner augur what his reign shall be, and choose
our sides in consequence. It is for you, therefore, to
know in what degree of favor you are with the King.
He cannot love you; for never yet did the weak man
love the strong. He cannot desire you should be his
Minister, for never yet did a vain and dark man desire
to possess one who was himself illustrious and luminous.
But it is neither his friendship nor his inclination that
are necessary to you; it is power. You ought to acquire
that ascendency over him which a grand character and
a vast genius may ever acquire over a confined understanding and an unstable mind. If you have enough of
this ascendency to inspire him with fears for his situation; to convince him that he is already betrayed to
danger; that the sending of Goertz, in your despite (or,
rather, without your knowledge, for you were not then
at Berlin), is a blunder of magnitude, which has been
committed without possessing the least pledge of docility
on the part of the Stadtholder; that the inconsiderate letters of Hertzberg form another equal blunder; that this
Minister pursues his PERSONAL INTERESTS, and those only, at
the hazard of depriving his master of PERSONAL RESPECT,
even from the commencement of his reign; since it is very
evident that, if he persist in his thoughtless interference (be
suppositions as favorable, nay, almost as romantic, as you
please), he will only have played the cards of the English, although they have spoiled their own game — if you

can make him sensible of all this, you will easily be able
to persuade him that he will but be too fortunate in accepting your mediation.   And, although mediation is
not exactly the phrase which may be employed, because
it does not exactly square with the rule of proportion,
such is the esteem in which you are held by the Cabinet
of Versailles that, should this negotiation once be committed to your care, all difficulties will vanish of themselves.   Such a measure, therefore, would have the
double advantage of accommodating the affair, which you
regard as the brand of discord, and of teaching the King
to feel that he presumes too much if he imagines that,
by the sole magic of the abrupt and *tudescan* * French of
Count Hertzberg, he will be able to preserve the same
respect for his Court which a succession of great acts,
heroical prosperity, vigilant activity, and perseverence,
even to a miracle, for forty-six years, have procured it;
that he has need of a man whose name abroad and whose
influence at home should attract confidence and serve as
the keystone to an arch which, according to its dimen-
sions, has but little solidity; or, to speak without a
metaphor, a kingdom, ill-situated, ill-constituted, ill-gov-
erned, and which possesses no real strength, except in
opinion, since its military position is wretched and its
resources precarious.   For, with respect to the treasury,
it will vanish if a hand of iron, yet not a hand of
avarice, should not guard it; and, as to an army, who
can be more convinced than you are, that years scarcely
are sufficient for its formation; but that six months of
relaxed discipline may degrade it so that it shall no
longer be cognizable? »

This discourse, which fixed the attention of the Duke,
and which was particularly intended to divine what he
himself imagined he might be able to accomplish, and
what he might become, appeared to produce a very
great effect.   Instead of beginning, as he always does,
by ambiguous and dilatory phrases, which may serve any
purpose he shall please, he immediately entered into the
spirit of my discourse, and, after having felt and owned,
with an effusion of heart and a penetrating tone, that I

* German.

presented him a prospect of the greatest honor his imagination could conceive, and which he should prefer to
the gaining of six victories, he joined with me in endeavoring to find some means of making the overture to
the King.

"I do not imagine," said he, "my situation will authorize the attempt without previous measures. I am more
afraid of injuring the cause than of injuring myself, but
it is certainly necessary the project should be conveyed
to him, and, should he afford the least opportunity, I will
explain everything. Cannot you speak to Count Finckenstein, should he recover?"

"No, for he strictly confines himself to his department. Neither is this anything more than an idea of
my own, and of small diplomatic value, since I have no
credentials."

"You have but few opportunities of speaking in private
to Welner?"

"Very few. Besides, how can that man ever be devoted to you? He determines to act the principal part
himself. He is industrious for his own interest, being
very sensible that, because of his obscurity, he has an
immense advantage over you, not to mention that he is
the intimate friend of your brother, who does not wish
your company at Berlin."

In fact, this brother hates the Duke, by whom he is
despised, and hopes for favor and influence under the
reign of mysticism.

We had proceeded thus far in our discourse when the
whole Court, leaving the opera for supper, and the Duke
of York, by entering without any precursor, obliged us
to break off. He has appointed to meet me this morning, the day of my departure, at nine o'clock, and to him
I am now going.

The Duke, as I expected, was shaken to-day in his
resolution of having himself named to the King. I say
as I expected, for his brilliant imagination and ambitious
energy easily catch fire at his first emotions, although he
should betray no exterior symptoms except those of tranquillity. But the rein he has so long put upon his
passions, which he has eternally had under command, and

in which habit he has been most persevering, reconducts
him to the hesitation of experience, and to that superabundant circumspection which his great diffidence of
mankind, and his foible, I mean his dread of losing his
reputation, incessantly inspire.   He made a circumstantial
display of the delicacy with which the petty glory, or,
to speak plainly, said he, the vainglory of the King must
be managed.

Taking up the conversation at the point where we had
left it, he assured me that, with respect to Welner, I
was deceived; that he was one of the persons in Berlin
on whom he depended, and who rather wished to see
him in power than any other; that I might easily speak
with him at the house of Moulines (his Resident, an
artful man, but too ostensibly artful, ready to serve that
he may better perform his office of spy, but proffering
his services with too much facility; appointed to take
part in the education of the Prince of Prussia, but,
hitherto, without any title; a deserter from Prince
Henry, since it has become pretty evident the Prince will
never be in power; inclined to serve France, in general,
and, indeed too visibly, for he is styled the Privy Counselor of Comte d'Esterno, but, in his heart, solely
attached to himself); that Welner goes there very often;
that he certainly would not speak openly, at first, but
that he would at length repeat to the King whatever I
should say.

The Duke often reiterated that he thought it useless
and dangerous for him to be named, and, in fine, although
with difficulty, and, as I may say, against his inclination,
he gave me the true reason. In a fortnight, he was to
be at Berlin, or, perhaps, sooner, for (take particular
notice of what follows) IT APPEARS THAT THE HOPE
AFFORDED BY SIR JAMES HARRIS (the English Ambassador
at The Hague) OF A POWERFUL AND EFFICACIOUS SUCCOR,
SHOULD THE KING OF PRUSSIA RESOLVE, WITH AN ARMED
FORCE, TO CREATE HIMSELF UMPIRE OF THE AFFAIRS OF
HOLLAND, HAS INSPIRED THE KING WITH A WISH TO CONFER
WITH HIS SERVANTS. I literally repeat the words the
Duke pronounced, who fixed his eyes upon me, but whom
I defy not only to have observed the least trait of emo-

tion in my countenance, but still more not to have been struck with a smile, almost imperceptible and very ironical, as if I had known and contemned the fact. My only reply at the end of his sentence was, shrugging up my shoulders:

"There is little need I should remark to you, monseigneur, that the conquest which Louis XIV., Turenne, De Condé, De Luxembourg, De Louvois, and two hundred thousand French, could not make of Holland, will never be effected by Prussia, watched by the Emperor, on that same country, now that it is supported by France." *

The Duke therefore is going, or wishes to make us believe he is going, to Berlin; where deliberations are to be held on the propositions of England.

So be it. So much the better. Do not be alarmed. The Duke is rather German than Prussian, and as good a statesman as he is a great warrior. He will prove such a proposition to be so absurd that it is probably no more than the personal conception of the audacious and artful Harris, who wishes, at any expense, to make his fortune, and in a fit of madness to poniard his nation, which is more able than sage.

Still, however, I think my journey to Brunswick is a lucky accident; for I confess, and with great pleasure, I found the principles of the Duke to be moderate, prudent, and, politically speaking, wholly French. I depicted the affair, or rather affairs, as a whole, under new points of view; and if, as I persist in believing, or rather as I have believed more strongly since I have known that he depends upon Welner for strengthening his party, his measures have long been taken (for Welner has been a canon at Halberstadt, where the regiment of the Duke remains), if, I say, the necessity of accident should oblige him to take the helm, I shall have acquired the greatest advantages to treat with and make him a party in our designs.

He has desired I would give Comte d'Esterno the very good advice, should Count Finckenstein die, or even

---

* Here, it must be confessed, the traveler was a false prophet, but whether it was precisely his fault still remains to be inquired.

should he not, to demand to treat on the affairs of Holland, and on all that relates to them, immediately with his Majesty. This is the most certain means of battering Hertzberg in breach, who certainly has been controverted with great firmness in these affairs by the King, and to obtain that which we shall seem only to expect from the judgment and personal will of the Monarch. It is a proceeding which is successful with all Kings, even with the greatest. Vanswieten obtained from Frederick II. himself the most important concessions by acting thus; and this is certainly a much more safe, as it is a more noble mode, than all the deceitful efforts which flattery can employ with Prince Henry, whose glaring protection is more injurious to the French Embassy than it ever can be productive of good, under the most favorable contingencies. For I am not very unapt to believe, as the Duke affirms without disguise, that this PARTITION PRINCE,* were he master of affairs, would be the most dangerous of the enemies of Germanic freedom. I must conclude, for I have not time to cipher; the remainder of this inestimable conversation will be sent you hereafter. Inform me, with all possible expedition, how I ought to act under the present circumstances, and be persuaded that, if you can find any means whatever of giving me secret official credit with the King, or even with the Duke, you will act very wisely.

Additional Note

If you do not imagine I am totally doting, mark me. I conjure you to read, and cause this to be read, with the utmost attention; and not to suffer me to wait a single moment for an answer, even though it should be absolutely necessary, for this purpose, to borrow some few hours from the levity of the country, or to be consistent for a whole day together.

*Ce Prince partageur: alluding, no doubt, to the dismemberment of Poland, in which he was as LAUDABLY active as the just, the philosophic, the GREAT King, his brother, and from motives EQUALLY PURE, as will be seen from the anecdote of the statue.

LETTER XXXVIII.

BERLIN, October 21st, 1786.

I ARRIVED at half-past five in the morning. The King was to exercise his cavalry at six. I immediately mounted my horse, that I might discover the state of his health, observe what aspect he wore, and if possible to find some person to whom I might address myself. His health is good, his brow cloudy; the troops were obliged to wait a considerable time, and after two charges he very abruptly and very ridiculously retired. Nothing sufficiently new or important has come to my knowledge to prevent my employing the few remaining moments before the departure of the courier, and which are greatly abridged by your eight pages of ciphers, in resuming the consequences which I have drawn from the very interesting conversation, an account of which I gave you in my last dispatch. It is impossible I should send you a complete and circumstantial narrative of all that passed, because that the Duke, an hour after I had left him, having sent me his Minister for Foreign Affairs (M. von Ardensberg von Reventlau), I have too much to add.

Four particulars appeared to me evident:

1. That, during the confidential conference with the Duke, a great complication of sensation, emotion, and design was mingled. He wishes we should aid him in becoming Prime Minister of Prussia, but that we should act with caution. He is not convinced that we desire to see him in that post (I did everything in my power to persuade him of it), yet perfectly satisfied that any interference in the affairs of Holland would be a stupid error, he is anxious that Prussia should act with propriety, and that, in this affair at least, we should acquire influence. He, therefore, while he informed me, endeavored to discover if I already had any information, and whether we were determined in the pursuit of our projects. To the same purport were the after commen-

(174)

taries of Ardensberg, his deceptive confidences, and Gazette secrets, the recall, not only of M. de Coetloury, but also of M. de Veyrac, our desertion of the patriotic party, etc., etc., to all which particulars I replied with a smile.

2. That the great inquietude of the Duke arises from not knowing whether we are or are not Austrians, or whether we are merely so undecided on the subject that the errors, or the cold distance, of the Cabinet of Berlin will be sufficient to induce us, at the hazard of all that can happen, to second the Emperor in his designs against Germany. In my opinion, were the Duke freed from his apprehensions on this very capital article, he would be French, for he is strongly German, and the English can only set Germany in flames; we alone have the power of maintaining it in peace. Should his connections with England appear to be strengthened, it is but, as I think, because he distrusts the destiny of Prussia, for he well knows that his English calculations are rather specious than solid, and that the Prussian, though perhaps somewhat more subaltern, are much less hazardous.

3. He and his Minister have so often demanded, and redemanded, on what basis I imagined the pacification of Holland might be established, that I have supposed the Duke probably thinks, should we exclude the Prince of Prussia from the Nassau alliance, there might be a necessity of choosing his daughter, the Princess Caroline of Brunswick, as a consort for the Prussian heir. The supposition is founded on circumstances so fugitive that it is impossible to give them written evidence, or perhaps probable, especially because, not having received any instructions on such a subject, I have not dared to make any advances. I therefore only give it for what it is worth. The being but little informed of the affairs of Holland has, in every respect, been highly injurious to me on this occasion. Might I have spoken more freely I might even have drawn the well dry. The only positive proposal which he made on the subject was a kind of coalition-council of regency, without which the Stadtholder could effect nothing, and in which should be included Gislaer, Vanberckel, etc., etc., but among whom

also must be seated M. Van Lynden, the governor of
the children of the Stadtholder, etc., etc. To my eternal
objection, " How will you support those measures which
shall be taken under the pledge of your aid ? " he continually replied : " Should the Stadtholder counteract these
arrangements, we will abandon him." " But how far ? " I replied. " And, if but amicably, how will he be injured,
should he be thus abandoned ? " In a word, I continued
with a kind of mysterious obstinacy, to maintain that the
Stadtholder would never be brought to reason, unless it
should be declared to him that the King of Prussia
would forsake his party, though his consort might be
secretly informed such was not the real intent.

4. It appeared to me that the Duke was ruminating
on some grand project for the reconstruction of the Germanic edifice, for this able Prince perceives the antique,
ruinous building must be propped in order to be preserved, and even in many parts repaired. The sole wish
which he clearly testified was the separation of the Electorate of Hanover from the English Monarchy, and the
secularization of certain provinces, which might one day
form an equivalent for Saxony. He supposes the first
point might be gained, and even without any great difficulty, should our politics become Anglicized, and that
the second might be accomplished, though contrary to
the confederation of the Princes, because, at the death
of the Elector of Mayence, there will be an opportunity
of retouching the league, as well as a natural and proper
occasion of coming to an explanation with the ecclesiastical Princes, who, more interested than any others in the
liberties of Germany, are always the first to tergiversate,
etc., etc. Hence, we at least may learn that, however
attached he may appear to be to the confederation, means
may be found of inducing him to listen to reason concerning modifications.

The instructions which are necessary for me, at present, are :

1. Whether we ought, on this occasion, to bring him
on the stage, which would be the real means of driving
him from it; and I certainly do not think the latter to
be our interest, for he is more prudent, more able, and

less susceptible of prejudice and passion, than any other who can be made Minister.

2. Whether his party ought to be encouraged and strengthened, which will be to act directly contrary to the party of Prince Henry; for the plan of the Duke is exclusive; and, to confess the truth, he appears tacitly so convinced that the Prince can effect nothing, that he has greatly fortified my own opinion on this subject.

3. What is the degree of confidence I ought to place in him? For it is impossible to obtain the confidence of, without placing confidence in, such a man; and in my apprehension he had better be told than suffered to divine.

Count Finckenstein is recovering.

The King arrived on the eighteenth, at eight in the morning, after having left Breslau, on the seventeenth, at seven in the morning. This was incredible diligence; no person could keep pace with him. He went on the same day to visit the Queen Dowager, and thus gave occasion to attribute the rapidity and danger of the journey to Mademoiselle Voss. She is said to be pregnant; but, in the first place, this cannot be known, and, in the second, I do not believe the haste would have been so great, had it been truth. According to report, she has demanded two hundred thousand crowns. Should this be so, the circle of her career will not be very ample.

The King made a multitude of nobles in Silesia, as elsewhere. But, without loading my letter, the Gazettes will tell you enough of their names. He is to remain a week at Potsdam, which is to be dedicated to his military labors. Great changes in the army are spoken of, such as will be favorable to the subalterns, and the reverse to the captains.

The Dantzickers, who, according to appearances, supposed Kings were hobgoblins, were so enraptured to meet with one who did not eat their children that, in the excess of their enthusiasm, they were willing to put themselves without restraint under the Prussian Government. The Magistrates eluded the folly of the populace as well as they could, under the pretence that Dantzic was dependent on Poland; but so great and so violent was the tumult, that Prussian and Polish couriers were sent off. This event will no doubt rouse the Emperor and Russia; a favorable circumstance to our affairs in Holland.

Count Hertzberg, who has indulged himself in very headlong acts in Silesia, and particularly in his discourse on the day of homage, in which he really braved the Emperor in a very indecent manner, as if it was not in his nature to accommodate himself to a peaceable order of affairs; Hertzberg, I say, has had the influence to retard the nomination of Alvensleben for the French Embassy, which had been announced by the King at supper. How might I have expected to be thus deceived, since, when I sent you the intelligence, I supposed it to be an affair so public that I did not even write it in a cipher?

LETTER XXXIX.

October 24th, 1786.

I SHALL begin my dispatch with an anecdote, the truth of which is undoubted, and which appears to me the most decisive of all I have learned concerning the new reign. Recollect that, in Number XVIII., August 29th, I wrote:

"The King apparently intends to renounce all his old habits. This is a proud undertaking. He retires before ten in the evening, and rises at four. Should he persevere, he will afford a singular example of habits of thirty years being vanquished. This will be an indubitable proof of a grand character, and show how we have all been mistaken."

When I spoke thus, I, like the rest of the world judged by appearances. The truth is that at half after nine the King disappeared, and was supposed to be gone to rest; whereas, in the most retired apartments of the palace, like another Sardanapalus, he held his orgies till night was far advanced. Hence it is easy to understand why hours of business were obliged to be inverted. Health would not allow him to be equally active upon the stage and behind the scenes.

Prince Henry regards himself as kept at a distance as well from system as from inclination. He is, or believes himself to be, persuaded that the innumerable follies which will result from his absence, for in his opinion the country without his aid is undone, will occasion recourse to be had to his experience and his abilities, and he then intends to refuse that tardy succor which his genius will be implored to yield. Even granting him the truth of all these vain dreams, he does not recollect that the expression of an undone country is only true relative to a certain lapse of time and that therefore in all probabil-

(179)

ity, he will be dead before the want of his assistance will be perceived. He comes to reside four months at Berlin, there, according to him, to suffer martyrdom, that it may not be supposed he has deserted the public cause. His places of asylum are afterward to be Rheinsberg, the Lake of Geneva, and France; but such he will easily find everywhere. Consolation will not be wanting to him, since consolation can be found at playing at blind man's buff, or hot cockles, with actresses more insipid than the very worst of our provincial companies can afford.

The distribution of influence continues the same. Hertzberg violently seizes on the King, who probably has more esteem for Count Finckenstein; but whom, not being so eternally hunted by him, he leaves in a subaltern degree of credit, which from apparent may become real, the easy temper of the master considered. The remaining Ministers are held to be so many ciphers.

Welner daily increases his jurisdiction, and Bishopswerder his influence, but he does not appear to exercise this influence either as a man of ostentation or a dupe. He neither asks for titles, ribbons, nor places. At most he will but make Ministers; he will never be one. Three hundred thousand livres for each of his daughters, an excellent fief for himself, with military rank (he is said to be a good officer), these are what he wishes, and these he most probably WILL obtain. In the meantime no person HAS anything; neither he nor Welner nor Goertz, who lives by borrowing.

Bowlet? — The influence of a mason engineer, and no other; for of no other is he capable.

Goltz the Tartar? — Artful, sly, dexterous; perhaps ambitious, but very selfish and covetous. Money is his ruling passion, and money he will have. He will probably have the greatest influence over military affairs, unless the Duke of Brunswick should take them to himself. The memorials relative to fortification are transmitted to him.

Colonel Wartensleben is evidently kept at a distance, and probably because of his family connections with Prince Henry; who, to all his other disadvantages, adds that of having every person who is about the King for his enemy.

Subalterns? — Their kingdom is not come. It should seem that having long, while Prince of Prussia, been deceived by them, the King knows and recollects this; although from compassion he wishes not to notice it, at least for a time.

The master? — What is he? I persist in believing it would be rash, at present, to pronounce, though one might be strongly tempted to reply KING LOG. No understanding, no fortitude, no consistency, no industry; in his pleasures the Hog of Epicurus and the hero only of pride; which, perhaps, we should rather denominate confined and vulgar vanity. Such hitherto have the symptoms been. And under what circumstances, in what an age, and at what a post? I am obliged to summon all my reason to divine, and to forget it all again to hope. The thing which is really to be feared is lest the universal contempt he must soon incur should irritate him, and deprive him of that species of benevolence of which he shows signs. That weakness is very formidable which unites an ardent thirst after pleasures, destitute of choice or delicacy, with the desire of keeping them secret in a situation where nothing can be kept secret.

Not that I here am writing a second part to Madame de Sévigné; I do not speak ill of Frederick William because he overlooks me, as she spoke well of Louis XIV., because he had lately danced a minuet with her.

Yesterday, at the Court of the Queen, he three times addressed himself to me, which he never before did in public. "You have been at Magdeburg and Brunswick." "Yes, Sire." "Were you pleased with the manœuvers?" "Sire, I was in admiration." "I ask to be informed of the truth, and not to be complimented." "In my opinion, Sire, there was nothing wanting to complete the splendor of this exhibition, except the presence of your Majesty." "Is the Duke in good health?" "Exceedingly good, Sire." "Will he be here soon?" "Your Majesty, I imagine, is the only person who knows." He smiled.

This is a specimen. You will well imagine it was, personally, very indifferent to me what he should say to me before the whole Court, but it was not so to the audience; and I note this as having appeared to make a part of the arranged reparation to France, which reparation was as follows. (From this, imagine the wit of the Court of Berlin; for I am convinced there was a real desire of giving satisfaction to Comte d'Esterno.)

First, it was determined the Queen should have a Lotto, and not a private party, in order that the company at her table might be the more numerous. After all the Princesses, Prince Henry, Prince Frederick of Brunswick, and the Prince of Holsteinbeck, had been invited, and taken their places, Mademoiselle Bishopswerder, the maid of honor, who regulated the party, named Comte d'Esterno. The Queen then, perceiving Lord Dalrymple, beckoned him, and at the same moment desired him to sit down. The Ambassadors of France and England were the only foreign ministers that were of the party, so that Princes Reuss and Romanzow were now excluded, as they before had appeared to have been favored. It would be difficult to imagine anything more awkward, or more inconsistent; and this increases my regret at remembering that Comte d'Esterno thought himself obliged to take offense on the first Court day of the Queen; for, after the absurdity of yesterday, I can see no possible hope of reparation which would not be slovenly daubing.

I am certain, however, that, far from wishing to wound, they were desirous to heal; and, to treat the subject less petitely, I am persuaded it is wrong to affirm the King hates the French. He hates nothing; he scarcely LOVES anything. He has been told that he must become wholly German, in order to pursue a new and glorious track, and he descends to the level of his nation, instead of desiring to elevate his nation superior to himself. His conduct is the result of the narrowness of his views. If he have a cordial dislike to anything, it is to men of wit; because he imagines that, in their company, it is absolutely requisite he should hear wit, and be himself a wit. He despairs of the one, and therefore hates the other. He has not yet learned that men of wit only are the people who can appear not to possess wit. He seems to have made a determination to treat all persons in an amicable manner, without haughtiness or threat. The Stadtholder always receives two very different accounts from Berlin, and does not fail to believe that which flatters his ruling passion.

A mile from this place some very secret experiments are making on the artillery, which are confided to Major Tempelhoff. A small number of superior officers are admitted; captains are excluded. The ground is covered by tents, and guarded by sentinels, night and day. I shall endeavor to learn the particulars.

I forgot to write you word, from Brunswick, that the Duchess informed me the Prince of Wales was consulting the most able civilians in Europe, to learn whether, by marrying a Catholic, the positive laws of England, the laws of any other nation, or the maxims of the civil laws of Europe, would disinherit an heir, and particularly an heir apparent. There appears to be much imprudence in this appeal of an heir apparent from the opinions of Great Britain to those of the civilians.

An anecdote less important, but perhaps more poignant, is that the Margrave of Baden-Baden has sent M. von Edelsheim here as his complimentary envoy, the brother of one of his ministers who is called the Choiseul of Carlsruhe. The following is the history of this complimentor, who has arrived long after all the others.

At a time when the prolific virtues of the father of the five royal children were held in doubt, there was a wish to bestow a lover on a lady (the afterward divorced Queen, banished to Stettin), who, had they not done so, would have made bold to have bestowed one on herself. The care of choosing was committed to the brothers of the Duke of Brunswick. They descended a little too low, and in consequence an eye was cast on Edelsheim, who was publicly enough charged with this great work. He was afterward sent to Paris to execute another commission, of which he acquitted himself ill. I have been assured he was thrown into the Bastille. On his return he was disgraced, but afterward employed, and sent to various courts of Germany in 1778. And this is the man whom, in his high wisdom, the Margrave selected for his envoy to the King of Prussia. The Monarch himself, when he saw him, could not forbear laughing.

POSTSCRIPT.— Yesterday, at eleven in the morning, the King, hidden in a gray coach, went alone to Mon-Bijou, where he remained an hour, whence he returned in a great glow. What does this mean? Is this the triumph of the Lady Voss? It is impossible at present to know. Neither has anything transpired concerning the letters which M. von Calenberg has brought from the Stadtholder.

Muller and Landsberg, private secretaries of the Cabinet, demanded their dismission with considerable chagrin, their services not being apparently necessary, said they, since they were not thought worthy of being instructed concerning the answers they had to return, and since the letters were sent ready composed to the King. They remain in their places, and the accommodation was effected by Bishopswerder. It appears that he is in league with Welner against Hertzberg, which he does not take any great precautions to conceal. The King will not go to Potsdam to make the military arrangements before Friday, in order, as it is supposed, to give the Duke time to arrive. The attempting to account for all the caprices of kings is a strange kind of frenzy.

LETTER XL.

October 28th, 1786.

I PASSED yesterday evening with Prince Henry. The King had dedicated almost the whole afternoon of the day before to this palace, for, after having been with the Prince, he visited the Princess, where he played, and drank tea with Mademoiselle Voss, among other ladies of honor. This kind of reconciliation with the Prince (which, however, is nothing more than a simple act of courtesy, as is evident from the succeeding visit to the Princess, whom the Prince regards as his most cruel enemy), this reconciliation (which is nearly an accurate phrase, for the coolness between them was very great) appears to be the political work of Welner, who wishes, in his struggle against Hertzberg, if not the support, at least the neutrality of the Prince; and the hatred of this feeble mortal is so blind in effect that, united with the hopes of his ambition, of which he is not easy to be cured, it was sufficient to induce him once more meanly to offer his services to the King, consequently to cast himself, if possible, to a greater distance. Not that he himself places any great dependence on this type of peace, which is the more suspicious because it happened on the eve of a succeeding fortnight's absence, after which it will not be difficult to find pretenses not to meet again for some time longer, should the King think proper. But the Prince imagines his enemy dead, and he enjoys himself, and chuckles like a child, without recollecting that this is the very way to promote his resurrection.

In reality, Count Hertzberg appears to have cast his own die. He had a tolerable run of ill luck in Silesia, —abrupt disputes, contradictions, the chagrin of seeing the name of the brother of his former mistress struck off from the list of Counts; he ought, even while in Prussia, to have perceived that his sounding speeches gave no pleasure. On the day of receiving homage, he read over the names of the Counts, and when he came to his own stopped, that the King, seated on his throne, might pronounce it himself, and the Monarch was malicious enough to remain silent, so that the inauguration of Count Hertzberg did not take place till the day after, and in the antechamber.

But what probably has occasioned his downfall, if fallen he has, was his haughty behavior to Welner, the least forgetful of men, and who, amid his ambitious projects, needed no such cause of rancor to occasion him to hate and injure the Minister. Hertzberg has made him wait for hours in his antechamber, has received and kept him standing, spoken to him but a very short time, and dismissed him with airs which are only proper to give offense. Welner vowed his destruction, and he is seconded by Bishopswerder.

Such at least are probabilities, according to every acceptation of the word influence; and I should have divined them to-day from the very politeness of Hertzberg. He gave a grand dinner to foreigners, among whom, for once, Comte d'Esterno and myself were invited. His attention seemed all directed to us. Such proceedings are awkward and mean. This mixture of stiffness and twining is a strange singularity by which half-formed characters ruin themselves. Machiavel rightly affirms that "all the evil in the world originates in not being sufficiently good, or sufficiently wicked." Whether my conjectures are or are not true, still it is certain Count Hertzberg has been very dryly and positively forbidden all interference, direct or indirect, in the affairs of Holland, from which country Callenberg does not appear to have brought any remarkable intelligence. He is really come to obtain admission into the Prussian service, and his letters were only recommendatory.

It is not the influence of Hertzberg that prevents the recall of Thulemeyer, but that of Count Finckenstein. The mother of the envoy has had a lasting and tender friendship for the Count; and indeed it was her husband who procured the Count a place in the Ministry. In fact it appears to me to be a matter of little moment, for the present, whether Thulemeyer should or should not be recalled. His embassy ended on the arrival of Goertz, nor do I believe he sends any dispatches.

The destiny of Launay was decided the day before yesterday by a very severe letter. He is no longer allowed to act, and they offer him a pension of only two thousand crowns to retire on, with the proviso that he shall remain in the Prussian States. It must be owned his estimate is a *chef-d'œuvre* of egotism and folly, and that he might be completely refuted; although the memorial of the commissioners who have undertaken his refutation is a pitable performance. He has proved two facts, the one of which is curious, and the other decisive against his own administration. First, that, in the space of nineteen years, he has brought into the King's coffers a surplus of 42,689,000 crowns of the empire, exclusive of the fixed revenue, which annually amounted to five millions of crowns. What dreadful oppression! The second, that the collecting of the customs is an annual expense of more than 1,400,000 crowns, which, on a first view of the business to be transacted, and of local circumstances, might at least be reduced two-thirds. But not one man is at this moment employed who appears to understand the elements of his profession. It is a fact that they have not yet been able to make any general statement of debtor and creditor, nor to class any single branch of the revenue; so that there is not one object, not even the King's dinner, which is yet regulated.

This is a chaos, but it is a chaos at rest. Finance, military and civil, are each alike in a state of stagnation; and such a state in general would indeed be better than the rage of governing too much, in a country with a fixed constitution, in which individual prudence might preponderate over public folly. But men are here so accustomed to see their King active, or rather exclusively active; they are so little in the habit of doing what he leaves undone, though, having once issued his orders, they very well understand the art of deceiving him; they even think so little of laying any proposals before him, that the stagnation is a real clog on the machine. But how injurious may this clog become in a

kingdom which rests on so brittle a basis, though inhabited, indeed, by a people so tardy, so heavy, so
unimpassioned, that it is scarcely possible a sudden shock
should happen? The vessel, however, must continue to
sink, more or less sensibly, if some pilot does not come
on board, although she will not suddenly founder.

Wait we must; it would be an act of temerity to
attempt to look into this darkness visible. I repeat, we
must wait before we can know whether the King will,
or will not, have the courage to take a Prime Minister.
Such an appointment would be equal to a revolution;
and, well or ill, would change the whole face of affairs.

The Duke of Brunswick is the person who ought to
be narrowly watched, if we wish to foretell the fate of
this Government; although he should not be the person
appointed, and should there be any appearance of a shipwreck. This Prince is only fifty, and is indisputably
ambitious. Should he ever resolve on hazardous and
daring designs, and should he no longer depend on
Prussia, he would shake all the German combinations as
the north wind shakes the reed. His manners and his
prudence are incompatible with the English party.
Neither can England act on the Continent, except accidentally. But I can imagine circumstances under which
I think him capable of going over to the Emperor, who
would receive him with open arms. And what might
not the Duke of Brunswick perform at the head of the
Austrian army? How great would be the danger of Germany! How vast a prospect for him whose passions might
be unbridled, should he be obliged to act a desperate part;
for he almost hates his sons, unless it be his youngest, who
promises not to be so stupid as the others.

The best manner of securing him has been missed,
which would have been to place him unconditionally at
the head of the Germanic Confederation. Should he desert it, I greatly fear he will be its destroyer.

Baron H —— is arrived, and has not been received
by the King in a manner equal to his expectations. A
certain musical demoniac, named Baron Bagge, is also
at Berlin. I imagine they are all in too much haste.
The King is in the high fervor of the German system,

and anxious to have it known that the ship is to be differently trimmed. Since his accession, the banker of La Valmour has received orders to send in his account, that it may be discharged, and to stop all future payments to that girl who had formerly so much power over him. It is said he is to return from Potsdam on the third, and I imagine it will be found that he goes there to the chase. The Prince of Dessau is to arrive there to-morrow evening, and I have no doubt there is to be a calling of the faithful.

LETTER XLI.

October 30th, 1786.

A T THE request of Struensee, I have sent him the following information: First, on the possibility of public loans to France, and, secondly, on the treaty of commerce, and on the manner of placing money in the French funds.

There are two species of public funds in France: those the interest of which is fixed and certain, and which does not vary with circumstances; and those which produce dividends, or a participation of gain, subject to vicissitudes and to rise or fall.

The public and favored companies principally appertain to this last class,—such as the Caisse d'Escompte, the Paris waterworks, and French East India Company; the prices of stock in which have successively, or all together, been agitated by every frenzy of stockjobbing. All true estimate of their real value and their effective gains has been, as it were, lost, that men might yield to the rage of gambling in funds which never could be reduced to any exact valuation. These jobbers have been less occupied by endeavors to reduce the price of shares to their true value than artfully to affect their price, by disputes and pretended reasonings on the impossibility of delivering all the shares that had been sold. Monopoly has succeeded to monopoly, association to association; some to raise, others to lower the price; to effect which every imaginary species of deceit, cabal, and cunning has been practiced; and, though this gambling mania has not continued more than two years, many people have already been ruined, and many others dishonored, by taking shelter under the laws to elude their engagements.

The other species of public funds, and the only one perhaps which merits the name, consists in contracts, and royal effects, properly so called. The contracts yield an interest of from five and a half to six per cent at the utmost. One only fund, the stock of which is paid at sight, is more productive. This is the loan of one hundred and twenty-five millions. Shares are sold, at present, at an advance of but two per cent, although there are nine months' interest due, and the real interest amounts to nearly seven per cent. The stock cannot remain long at this price, and, whether the purchasers wish to be permanent stockholders, or only to speculate for some months, this loan merits a preference to any other. Its advantages annually increase, since, while receiving a uniform interest of five per cent, a part of the capital is to be periodically repaid. In January, 1787 and 1788, these reimbursements are to be made at the rate of fifteen per cent on the capital advanced. They are afterward to proceed to pay off twenty per cent, and, at intervals of three years to twenty-five, thirty, thirty-five, forty, forty-five, fifty per cent, till, in the last year, the whole will be repaid, independent of the interest of five per cent to, and including, the years of reimbursement, the last year of payment only excepted. The stockholders may either have bills payable at sight, according to the original plan, or, if they please, may receive contracts in their stead, without any change taking place in the order of reimbursement.

Those who buy in with a design of remaining stockholders, must prefer contracts, because these are liable neither to be stolen, burned, nor destroyed. Those who purchase stock on speculation, intending to sell out, should rather receive bills, because the transfer would then be subject to none of the delays of office.

We ought to regard the public loans of France as at an end, all the debts of the war being paid, so that if any loans henceforth should take place, they can probably be only for small sums* to pay off the annual reimbursements with which the finances will, for five or six years to come, be burdened. But these loans can only offer trifling advantages to the moneyed men. The rate of interest must have a natural tendency to fall, because of the general prosperity of the kingdom, and, consequently,

---

* The world at that time was ignorant of, nor could it divine, the sublime invention of gradual and successive loans.

the loan of one hundred and twenty-five millions presents the probability of rising in price, which rise is each
day liable to take place, and which variation cannot be
profited by, unless stock is immediately purchased. This
probability might even be called a certainty, when, on
the one part, we recollect the nature of the loan, which
is the most wise, solid, and advantageous to the moneyed
men, and in every respect the best that has ever been
imagined; and, on the other, the concurrence of circumstances, which, all uniting, lead us to presume that the
credit of France, and the public confidence in its royal
effects, must daily increase.

On the Commercial Treaty.

It appears that the Treaty of Commerce is highly acceptable to both parties. The English perceive in it a
vast market for their woolen cloths, wrought cottons, and
hardware; we depend on the great exportation of our
wines, linens, and cambrics, and probably both nations
are right, but under certain modifications, the value of
which can only be taught by time.

The Treaty, in general, seems to have held a principle
as sacred which has too often been misunderstood, which
is, that moderate duties are the sole means of preserving
the revenue, and preventing illicit trade. Thus the English merchandise is rated at from ten to twelve per cent.
Should the advantage for some years appear to be wholly
on the side of the English, still it is evident the French
trade will gain ground, since nothing can prevent our
manufacturers gradually imitating the products of English industry, whereas, Nature having refused soil and
climate to England, our wines cannot be made there, and,
in this respect, the English must always depend on us.

True it is that the wines of Portugal will continue to
be drunk in England in great quantities, but the rising
generation will prefer the wines of France. Of this, Ireland affords a proof, in which ten times the quantities of
French wines are drunk in comparison with the wines of
Portugal. The French wines, henceforth, are only to pay

duties equivalent to those which the wines of Portugal at present pay in England, that is to say, forty pounds sterling per ton, or about one shilling per bottle. Our wines of Medoc may there be sold cheap, and will be preferred to the wines of Portugal. The English, it is true, are allowed to lower the present duties on the wines of Portugal, but they will fear to diminish them too sensibly, lest they should injure the revenue arising from their beer, which is the most essential of their excise duties, and annually produces more than 1,800,000 pounds sterling.

The Treaty, in fact, will incontestably be advantageous to both countries. It will procure an increase of enjoyment to the people, and of revenue to their respective monarchs. Its tendency is to render the English and French more friendly, and in general it is founded on those liberal principles which are worthy two such great nations, and of which France ought to be first to give an example since, of all countries on earth, it would, from its natural advantages, be the greatest gainer, should such principles be universally established in the commercial world.

13

LETTER XLII.

October 31st, 1786.

* * * * * * *

THEY have also affirmed (that is, Prince Ferdinand has)
that it was I who refuted the estimate * of Launay.
From that moment I have daily left my card at
the house of Launay, and have declared that to torment
people seemed to me to be a thing so unnecessary that,
exclusive of the cowardice of wantonly striking a man
under misfortunes, none but a fool could have invented
so silly and malicious a tale.

On the reply to the refutation of his estimate, Launay
received so severe a letter that he immediately demanded
permission to retire. The King answered this should be
granted him, when the commission should have no more
need of his assistance.

It is loudly rumored here, after having been long
whispered, that a treaty is concerting between Russia,
Austria, and Prussia; the pretext for which is the pacification of Holland. I own that at present I do not see
the least probability of truth in the report. Neither the
King, nor any one of his Ministers, appears to me to
have an understanding sufficiently enlarged for such a
project. Not but we most assuredly ought to pay very
serious attention to the rumor.

As I was finishing my phrase, I received information
that Dr. Roggerson, the favorite physician of the Czarina, the same whom she sent to Vienna, and of whom I
spoke to you in my former dispatches, is just arrived.
Now or never is the time for an EYE WAR; but this kind
of tilting can be performed only by ambassadors; they
alone possess the means, were we to exclude every other
except the all-puissance of supper parties, which are the
very sieves of secrets.

* *Compte rendu.*

(194)

Roggerson returns from England by way of Amsterdam, and Berlin is directly in his road. Still, I repeat, we ought, watchfully to observe Vienna and Petersburg, — convinced as I am at present that the Emperor is only spreading nets for this country. I must further add that I imagine I very clearly perceive the Gallomania of Prince Henry is on the decline. But this to him will be of no advantage, for it is to oppose the Prince that they are Anti-Gallican here. It is not to oppose the French that he is opposed. Prince Henry is turbulent, false, and perfidious. He formerly was successful at Petersburg. He may flatter himself that, should there be any need of that Court, he may be employed; and never will there be a better resemblance of the morality of the late Erostratus.*

The Duke of Brunswick arrived on Saturday at Potsdam. This is a kind of secret at Berlin. Nothing had been done on Sunday, except listening to music and looking at reviews; but two couriers were certainly sent off, from the Sunday to the Tuesday. I know nothing more. I am in want of pecuniary and other aid. The domestic disorder is a thing so inconvenient, some of the favorites are so interested to put an end to it, or to certain parts of it, since they have not a sixpence, and it is carried to such excess in the palace, that I cannot help supposing there is some grand object which employs the whole attention of the King, and the few moments he can prevail on himself to dedicate to business.

There has been a quarrel in the household, in which the master has committed some violence on himself. One of his favorite ushers, Rumpel, a man naturally very insolent, insomuch that at a review he once struck a gentleman without any serious notice being taken of the affair, has had a very passionate brawl with Lindenau, the new first usher, who is a Saxon, and the friend of Bishopswerder, who procured him the place. Lindenau put the insolent favorite under arrest, and gave an account of his

---

*Meaning the late King, who fired not only temples, but would have willingly extended the conflagration to the universe, could he have thrown on the oil without being scorched by the gust of the flames.

proceeding to the King. The Monarch started with astonishment; but, after a momentary silence, he not only
approved of the act of Lindenau, but confirmed the arrest
in a very cool manner, and for an indefinite term. By
this he has given some energy to the head servants, and
somewhat tempered the insolence of the subalterns.

Discord, on the other hand, reigns among the favorites.
Goltz and Bishopswerder had a very serious dispute in
Silesia. The King, having made some new appointments,
in favor of I know not whom, Goltz kept so cool a silence
that the King insisted on knowing the reason of this tacit
disapprobation. Goltz replied: "Your Majesty is overflowing the land with Saxons, as if you had not a subject
of your own." Bishopswerder came in, a few moments
afterward, and proposed another Saxon, on which the
King very abruptly exclaimed, "Zounds! you never propose anybody but Saxons." Probably, in the explanation
which succeeded this pettishness, the King told what
Goltz had said. Certain it is that Bishopswerder and
Goltz have been very warm. The wall is whitewashed
over, but we may with good reason conclude that Goltz,
the Tartar, and Bishopswerder, the debonair, neither do,
nor ever will, cordially esteem each other. It was the
latter who brought the insignificant Duke of Holsteinbeck
hither, and who is endeavoring to advance him to the
command of the guards, that he may deprive the former
favorite, Wartensleben, of the place.

To descend a step lower, it appears that Chauvier is
regaining credit. He imagined, at the beginning of the
reign, that the surliness of the secretary would promote
his interest. It did the reverse. Apparently he has altered
his route, and is in the pandar department, submits to
subaltern complaisance, and even to act the spy, in which
he finds his account.

The King returns on Wednesday, as it is said, to
depart again on Thursday. I cannot understand what
this means, unless it should be to keep Prince Henry at
a distance, without openly quarreling. The Prince will
remain ignorant of affairs by not knowing where to find
the King. The Minister, Blumenthal, has rather resolutely demanded his dismission, complaining that his

Majesty, having bedizened some of his servants, who were not of so long a standing as himself, with ribbons, had not bestowed on him that mark of honor. His retreat, which is not granted, is a matter of little moment; though it is affirmed the King could not be better pleased, for he would then have a place to bestow. I have heard, and from a good quarter, that this place, or rather a place of principal trust, will very soon be given to a remarkable man to the dissatisfaction of everybody. I can neither divine who this man is, nor believe the King has the fortitude to dissatisfy everybody. The credit of Hertzberg, if not ruined, is still on the decline. It is certain that he has not dined with the King since the return from Silesia.

Welner is at Potsdam.

Do not suffer your Ambassador to persuade you that there is nothing to apprehend from Austria; I am convinced the King is undetermined, that the Emperor is sounding him, and that there is something in agitation with which we are unacquainted. For my own part, nothing would appear less extraordinary to me. I own I am surprised at all the intelligence I obtain, however little that may be. But nothing can here be kept secret from a French Ambassador, who is in want of neither money nor industry.

I have just been told that General Rodig has sent a challenge to Count Goertz. I have not learned what was the cause of quarrel, and the truth of the news scarcely appears to be probable; yet it comes from a person who should know, though he is a young man.

LETTER XLIII.

November 4th, 1786.

A NEW letter, excessively rigorous, and tolerably incoherent, has suspended Launay in the exercise of all his functions. Yet I scarcely can believe it is intended to sully the beginning of a reign by useless cruelty. The victim is immolated to the nation the moment the man is no longer in place. The remainder would only be the explosion of gratuitous hatred, since the unfortunate Launay no longer can give umbrage to anyone. Verder is placed at the head of the customs. We shall see what the new established order will produce; or rather, whether they will know how to establish any new order. In the meantime the discharge of forty Frenchmen is determined on, *in petto*. But I cannot perceive that these kind of Sicilian vespers are likely even to gain the public favor. The theater here is not sufficiently vast to conceal from the pit what is passing behind the scenes. There is scarcely any illusion possible, except that of actually doing good. I shall endeavor to save Launay, by causing Prince Henry to say, who has at least preserved the privilege of uttering all he pleases, that hitherto the King has really acted in this business as the man of the nation; but that, should he go further, he will become the man of the persecutors of Launay; that there are public murmurs which affirm he has espoused their hatred, etc. Certain it is that the repetition of the self-important *I*, in Launay's estimate, has put the King out of humor, and even in a passion.

His Majesty arrived yesterday, and returned this morning. This seems to be an episode in the romance of Voss which approaches the *dénouement*, and which is suspended to obtain the three following articles: (1) two hundred thousand crowns for her portion. The King refuses (or will only count out a thousand crowns per month, so that the payment will not be completed in less than sixteen years and eight months, which will render the sum a little problematic); (2) a left-handed marriage (to this he consents, but the lady finds that a very equivocal kind of circumstance), or (3) to marry her to a man who shall depart on the bridal day as Ambassador to Sweden (there is no certainty of finding a man sufficiently base, in that class which should rank him among ambassadors). Mademoiselle avows that, without being amorous, she is rendered exceedingly sensible by a three years' siege. But what shall become of her, of her uncle, her family? What place shall she hold in the public opinion, in city, and Court? Such is the purport of the negotiation conducted by Bishopswerder. I do not suppose him young enough to be the King's substitute; so that the speculation does not appear to be very certain.

As to the King, there is, indeed, some little curiosity, a degree of obstinacy, and somewhat of vanity, but still greater want of a companion with whom he may be as much of a gossip, may loll, and dress as slovenly as he pleases. The circumstance that shackles the negotiation is that Rietz and her tribe must evacuate the country, and the King is exceedingly attached to her son. It is necessary, however, to add to all this that Mademoiselle Voss relates herself all the tales repeated in public, and even of the most secret courtiers, which concern herself; and this may render the probability of these conjectures suspicious.

The King, it is said, returns to Potsdam till the 8th. He is not there so entirely occupied by business or secret pleasure as to exclude all company. M. Arnim is one of his society; a kind of unfinished man of the world, who has acquired many friends by the affability and amenity of his manners and his great fortune, and whose understanding, sufficiently upright and little brilliant, being timid and wavering, neither gives umbrage to the King nor inspires him with fears. In all despotic countries, one grand means of good fortune is mediocrity of talents. If it be generally true that no positive assertions ought to be made in the presence of princes, and that hesitation and deliberation always please them, I think it peculiarly so applied to Frederick William II.

It is affirmed the assignments are made out, and that this has been the labor of Welner alone. For this reason all the ministers, Schulemburg excepted (perhaps because of his connections with Count Finckenstein, whom the inauguration of Mademoiselle Voss must render powerful), are restless and terrified. Some of them have not yet given in the least account to the King. Estimate by this the state of a country in which everything depends on the industry of the King. Be not astonished that so little mention is made of business, for no business is transacted; the affair of Launay is the only one which is pursued with activity and hatred; everything else slumbers.

A person who comes from Russia assures me that the Empress has long omitted going any more to the Senate, and that she habitually intoxicates herself with Champagne and Hungary wine (this is contradictory to every account I have hitherto received); that Potemkin elevates his ambition to the grandest projects, and that it is openly affirmed he will either be made Emperor or be beheaded, at the accession of the Grand Duke. This artful and decisive man, possessed of uncommon fortitude, has not a single friend; and yet the number of his creatures and creditors who with him would lose their all, is so great in every class of the people, that his party is extremely formidable. He amasses immense treasures, in a country where everything is venal. Accustomed never to pay his debts, and disposing of everything in Russia, he does not find any difficulty in accumulating enormous sums. He has an apartment, the key of which he keeps himself, partitioned out from top to bottom, and divided into a great number of boxes, filled with bank bills of Russia, Denmark, and particularly of Holland and England. A person in his employment proposed to him the purchase of a library, appertaining to a great lord that had lately died. Potemkin took him into his bank-bill apartment, where the only answer he made was asking whether he imagined this library was of equal value with the one proposed. Possessed of such pecuniary aid, he has no need of any other to perform whatever he shall dare to undertake at Petersburg.

I must here mention that Doctor Roggerson, who yesterday departed on his return to Petersburg, affirms that no person in Europe leads a more sober or regular life than Catherine II. He, however, has been eight months absent.

I have collected some particulars that are rather curious, relative to the usurpation made on the ducal rights of postage in Courland, of which I have spoken to you in my former dispatches. This is an object of some importance, in so small a State, independent of the inquisition that thence results, and of the infraction of the rights of nations. This branch of revenue does not annually amount to less than a hundred and sixty thousand livres. But the following is a singular circumstance, which characterizes Russian politics.

Not to commit an act of violence too openly, and to avoid marching troops, which always draws the attention of neighboring Powers, the Court of Russia proposed, or rather demanded, an amicable conference between the deputies of Courland and commissaries, named to that effect; and appointed their sittings to be at Riga, a Russian fortress on the frontiers of Courland, under the presidency of the Governor of that town. Four deputies from Courland repaired thither at the time appointed; and the Governor signified to them that he had received orders from his Sovereign to arrest them if they did not sign an act, which he produced ready drawn up, by which the ducal rights of the postage of Courland were transferred to Russia. The deputies, should they refuse, having no other prospect before their eyes but Siberia, purely and simply affixed their signatures: after this, several stipulations, which alienated lesser rights and even portions of the borders of Courland, were in like manner presented and sanctioned. One of the most artful, and the most important, of these stipulations is that which relates to reclaiming the subjects of Russia, who may be found in Courland, and in which the Cabinet of Petersburg have included the very descendants of those who may have been naturalized for ages. It is very evident that this concession leads to unlimited abuse, and innumerable disputes, which will be more injurious to

Courland than the most burdensome tax could be; for nothing can prevent the Russian superintendents from feigning, whenever they please, the existence of one or of several of such or such Russian subjects, in such or such a part of Courland, or from taking the refusal of restitution for granted, in order to lay the country under the contribution of an equal number of hundreds of ducats (the sum fixed by the stipulation for each Muscovite whom the Courlanders shall refuse to deliver up), whenever the Russian treasury, or the Russian delegate, shall stand in need of, or whenever the country shall be enabled to pay, such sums of money. I again repeat that similar practices, openly in Courland, in other parts more secretly, similar projects I say, are carried on in all the countries that border upon Russia. Let us return to Berlin.

Trumpel, the groom whom I mentioned to you in my last, is discharged. This exertion has excited much astonishment. The King certainly rouses himself as much as he can, that he may not be governed, and this is the most distinct act of self-will which has hitherto been discernible in the Monarch.

On Thursday evening he supped at the confidential table, at which there are no servants, but the guests are supplied by *tours*.* The supper was more than gay. Ten persons were present. When it was over, the ladies of honor were visited, one after the other.

Prince Henry, who has this week given grand dinners to the civil and military officers of the Court, a thing he never did before, supped on Monday with the reigning Queen and her whole Court. This proves nothing, except a desire to keep up the appearance of politeness. I forgot to say that he is to give a dinner to-morrow to all the subalterns of the regiment of Braun. This is gratuitous and ridiculous affectation, and will never make his peace with the army, by which he is truly despised.

---

* Dumb-waiters, or rather a kind of machinery, of French invention, made to ascend through the floor, or pass through apertures in the wall, that the unobserved guests may indulge in the most detestable licentiousness.

Baron Bagge, after refusing to pay any visits here, even those that common decorum required, saying that, according to the manner in which he had lived with the Heir Apparent, it was for the King to send him an invitation, yesterday received this invitation to Potsdam. The incident proves that music still is a passion.

That infamous C—— has written to Chauvier, affirming that he knew, past all dispute, it was to him he was indebted for the obligation of not being permitted to see the King; that he was going into a country in which he should find it easy to injure; and that he would use every exertion to effect his ruin; exclusive of the means with which he has been furnished by Chauvier himself. Chauvier has acted with propriety, and laid the letter before the King.

The nocturnal jaunts continue. I still remain ignorant of the object of the grand motions toward Austria, and reciprocally.

LETTER XLIV.

November 7th, 1786.

THE King himself has interfered to produce a reconciliation between Bishopswerder and Goltz, the Tartar.
Peace for the present, therefore, is concluded; and the more firmly, because that war, open and avowed, is hotly carried on between the first favorite and Count Goertz. There has been great difficulty in preventing them coming to blows. What may be argued of a King for whom they thus openly contend? Probably a regiment will be given to Goertz to send him out of the way; but the payment of his debts is the difficulty, for it appears that the last thing the King will part with is money. The treatment of the aids-de-camp is at length determined on. Bishopswerder has two thousand crowns; Goltz, the Tartar, and Bowlet each seventeen hundred. The head groom, Lindenau, also has two thousand crowns, with eight places of forage, which may be estimated at six hundred crowns, and fire and candle. Behold how the sandy plains of Brandenburg, with the aid of Silesia, be it understood, are capable of maintaining an army of two hundred thousand men.

The thermometer of business remains still at the same fixed point. There is no riddance of letters; one chamber is full of packets that remain unopened. The State Minister, Zedlis, has not been able to obtain an answer to his reports for more than three weeks. Everything is in arrear. Yet the mode of living at Potsdam appears to have been tolerably well regulated, though Madame Rietz has been there. The latest hour at which the King has risen has been six o'clock. The Prince of Dessau has never seen him before half-past twelve, and perhaps not half an hour each day, dinner time excepted. It is at supper that the women make their appearance, and that wrinkled cares are discarded.

Welner has not quitted Potsdam, and two men are continually writing in his apartment. Hitherto he may be regarded as the monarch of domestic affairs. That he is neither deficient in talents nor information is a point undisputed; and the eternal disorder of the accounts, added to suspicion of the financiers in power, must have impelled the King to have abandoned himself wholly to Welner, whose obscurity is his recommendation.

I say the ETERNAL DISORDER; because in effect Frederick William I., with whom all domestic regulations originated, in which no alterations were made by his son, kept no general and exact accounts,— and acted thus, systematically: being acquainted himself with the whole of his affairs, as he would not suffer any one of his Ministers to divine what the state of them was, he made out imperfect, over-charged, and false accounts. Frederick II., who never understood anything of finance, but who very well knew that money is the basis of all power, confined his views to the amassing of large sums; and he was so certain that his savings were enormous that he was satisfied with partial accounts. Such an interpretation is certainly more probable, in my opinion, than the imputation of having burned the general state of debtor and creditor, with the malicious intention of embarrassing his successor. The present King wishes for order, and he has reason so to do; but it is an Augean stable, and I see no Hercules,— at least among those by whom he intends to be served.

Count Finckenstein has written in very warm terms to the King, to inform him that the provocations of Count Hertzberg are so frequent that they are become insupportable; and that his great age and his last illness made him sincerely desirous of retreat. The King returned a very mild answer, very obliging, and what may be called apologetic; in which he earnestly requested him to remain in office, and promised that the cause of his complaints should cease. He promised, perhaps, more than he can perform. Men of the most opposite tempers served together under Frederick II., and this is one of the characteristic traits of his reign. But it is no small presumption to imitate his manner; it cannot be expected that such imitation should succeed; for, in spite of the servility of the country, liberties are taken that were not permitted under the late King, of whom the world spoke very freely, but with whom no person was familiar. The very Academicians now make encroachments. Three new members have been proposed — one Boden, an astronomer; one Meierotto, the rector of a college; and one Ancillon, a minister of the Holy Gospel. Admirable choice! The King testified his surprise with asperity at this unusual proposition, made without its being even known whether he did or did not intend to increase the number of Academicians. The indiscretion will probably occasion some regulation. He has, however, signed a large YES to the proposal for I know not what Druid of the name of Erman, author of a multitude of vile sermons, and a refugee history, of which four volumes are already written, that might be reduced to thirty pages; and who has been proposed by the curator only, Count Hertzberg, without the question having been put to the vote.

The Boden of Paris seems to be forgotten, or worse. The King was told that he had written three letters to his Majesty without having received any answer. "I have no answer to give; the fellow came here without orders." Such was the royal decision! The King returns to-morrow for a few days. He has been so accustomed to run from place to place, and to make only a momentary stay, that the habit seems to have become one of his wants. M. de H—— wrote to him, three days ago, to know when he might take his leave, but has received no answer.

The grand dinner of Prince Henry to the regiment of Braun was given yesterday, as I before wrote. All the officers and forty subalterns, who had served under him at the battle of Prague, sat at the Prince's table. He gave a medal worth fifteen ducats to each officer, a ducat to each subaltern, and a crown to each private. It would be difficult to be more awkwardly ostentatious. Had there been any need to have further injured himself in the King's opinion, he could not have found a better method; but this was completely done before, and it must be well known too, for Roggerson, who had often visited Prince Henry during his two journeys into Russia, has not been to pay him his respects. The King gave him an audience, it is said, but only for a few moments.

I do not at this instant recollect the name of the person who is arrived from Vienna, and who at the King's table was very pleasant at the Emperor's expense, which occasioned a coolness in the King and some gloominess, so as to denote marks of disapprobation — silent but strong.

The new ribbons are preparing. Moral coin seems to cost the King least. Never was the remark of Frederick II. to Pritwitz more true than at present. The latter complained that the ribbon had been bestowed on Braun before himself. "My ribbon," said the King, "is like saving grace; it may be given, cannot be merited."

Count Arnim has been appointed master of the hounds and a Minister of State, with a vote and a seat in the grand directory. In one of my former dispatches I have spoken of him circumstantially. This is a pure choice of favor (and is the more marked because that the place of master of the hounds, taken from Schulemburg, had continually been solicited by Colonel Stein, who was rather in the King's good graces), but of favor founded, as I imagine, merely on the pleasure taken in the company of Arnim who is irreproachable in mind and manners. It is only another person of incapacity added to the Ministry.

ROTTEN BEFORE RIPE. Such I greatly fear will be the motto of the Prussian power. But their millions are good. It will, therefore, be of use to remit new propositions for a loan, if it be really intended to erect a bank, as all packets, gazettes, and private letters affirm, so that, myself excepted, everybody is informed of the project; for in my opinion these would be of more importance than the loan of a hundred and twenty-five millions, which the bank apparently will be able to borrow on its own credit. Struensee, who doubtless will be glad of this occasion of rendering himself useful to the King, has in plain terms asked what he is to think of the disorder of the Caisse d'Escompte; of the letter of the Comptroller General to his administrators; of the project of a bank; of its approaching realization; of the principles on which it is to be established; and especially what kind of directors shall have the management. He thinks the plan good, but is convinced that everything depends on those who shall have the direction. To all these questions, as you must be sensible, I know not what to reply; yet it is requisite I should soon know, because not to mention that any negotiation of this kind cannot succeed here except by his aid,— for not one of the others understands anything of such affairs,— he has a right to interrogate me, since I made the first advances.

LETTER XLV.

November 20th, 1786.

UNFORTUNATELY, I cannot be blind to what is here daily confirmed by traits which are each more pitiable than the others, concerning the opinion that I have so long forborne to take of the man and of affairs.

The King has just bestowed the ribbon of the Black Eagle on Anhalt. This gentleman is the son of a cook-maid, and of a multitude of fathers. He was originally a groom; he next sold smuggled coffee to the officers. I know not by what means he became what he is, but I know that his principal function was that of a spy. He was afterward placed in the service of the present King while Prince of Prussia; and, as he mingled poisonous advice and odious tales, THEY destined him, as it is said (and the word THEY is in this case the most bitter of the enemies of the late King), to execute a crime which THEY neither had the address to color nor the courage to consummate. Anhalt possesses more military talents than his native folly could promise. His warlike vocation seems to be remarkable by this singular characteristic, that he never possesses coolness except when heading his men. He has arrived, whether by these or other means, at the rank of Lieutenant General. As he is without understanding (the little he had he was deprived of by a dreadful fall, for which he was obliged to be trepanned), he continued in favor.

He was detested at Königsberg, where he commanded, and this was a kind of recommendation to him at Potsdam, where the kingdom endured forty-six years of disgrace.*

Some days before the King's death, General Anhalt was sent for to Sans Souci. "You have lately married one of your daughters," said the King. "Yes, Sire, I

---

* By the kingdom, Prussia Royal is meant, for which province the late King had a fixed aversion.

feel I have." " How much did you give with her? " " Ten thousand crowns." " That is a large sum for you, who have nothing." On the morrow they were sent him by the King. Anhalt returned into Prussia. His benefactor died; he beheaded his portrait, and substituted the head of his successor. The new King repairs to Königsberg to receive homage, and bestows a superb box on Anhalt; but, indeed, gives him notice he must quit the government of Prussia in two months' time, that is to say, at present. Anhalt, being at an auction some days since and seeing a portrait of the late King sold at a low price, very coolly said, " Right, I'll give you the other * into the bargain." He retires with a pension of five thousand crowns, a ribbon, and a promise of being employed in war. This prostitution of reward, apparently extorted from weakness, is endeavored to be excused by alleging the fear that Anhalt should pass into the service of the Emperor, as he threatened in the following speech, which does not want dignity: " If you refuse me this favor, I must then go elsewhere, and prove that it is not because of my want of merit." I do not think this a sufficient reason, for the estates he had purchased near Magdeburg were a sufficient pledge for his person.

Be this as it may, and, however singular the choice may appear, which has made a strong impression upon the public, it must be allowed that Anhalt is a great commander, an officer worth preserving, and that some recompense was due to him for the loss of his government of Prussia, with which, mad as he was, and often furious, he could not be intrusted.

But none of these reasons can be alleged in behalf of Manstein, a simple captain, a common and even ignorant officer, but a devout mystic; who, without any pretext, has been sent for and is destined, as it is said, to be the governor of the young Princes, with the title of Lieutenant Colonel. To those who look into futurity, this is fearful. The whole army is offended. Indeed, it is probably not true; but the very suspicion speaks the public opinion.

A singularity which has not excited less murmuring is

* Meaning the present King.

that Heynitz, Minister of State for the department of the mines, is placed at the head of the commission against Wertenberg, a kind of disagreeable man who has long had the clothing of the troops; a subaltern knave, and perhaps nothing more; or perhaps less so than his predecessors. This species of inquisition, which appears to be the adopted method, and which will not easily be made familiar to the people, whom it will be difficult to persuade that the late King was negligent and a bad economist,— this species of inquisition, I say, seems to indicate suspicions of the commanding officers, since the direction of such trials is taken from these officers, to whom they entirely appertained. There are great complaints, and still greater contempt. This must be an ill symptom, especially after a reign of only two months.

Indolence and stagnation, its necessary result, continue to be felt. In consequence of not having the letters sent after him, as was the custom of Frederick II., the King is prodigiously in arrear. He found thousands on his return from Silesia, his journey through which is a striking contrast to the incredible activity of the late King; who, however, did not devote more time, or rather who devoted less, than another to his trade of King. He only set apart an hour and a half each day on ordinary occasions for this purpose; but he never put off the business of the present day to the morrow. He knew, so well was he acquainted with man, that a bad reply was better than none. A heap of memorials and projects are on the table of the present King, most of which relate to military changes, on which he has never cast his eyes, and which have been productive of nothing, except for his vehement aversion for memorials. He regards them as a tax on his sovereign authority; and supposes advice of any kind to be an avowal of an opinion of his incapacity. Among the useless writings which have been remitted to him, there is said to be a memorial from Baron Knyphausen, on foreign politics. There are indications which lead me to believe it is favorable to our system, and this has given him particular displeasure; its fate, therefore, was to be thrown aside, without hesitation, as the reveries of dotage. The

Baron, however, has disowned to me that he is the author of this memorial.

To the same sensation, apparently, which makes him so much detest advice, we must attribute the following singularity: Welner has only had a stipend of three thousand crowns, deducted from the pensions formerly paid to the head officers of the commercial departments; the smallest of which pensions only is granted him, so that he is but the equal of those who have least influence, and have not the same industry. As the few preparations which are made are all made by him his labor must be very great. A single statement of the money accounts is said to have given him much trouble. At present, the exceedings of the receipts over the expenditure, at least the civil, are known. The sum is greater than was supposed by near one-quarter, which is much. It is imagined that the chief part of this surplus will be applied to increase the pay of subalterns. Private soldiers undoubtedly deserve no greater honor than that of dying with hunger. But I scarcely can believe they will dare to offend the corps of the captains.

If the King give but little to those who seem to be his greatest favorites, there yet are indications that he bestows secret largesses; or that he has secret reasons for conferring such on some persons. The chamberlain Doernberg, an insignificant person in my opinion, who quitted the service of the Princess Amelia with ingratitude, she having paid his debts, to enter into that of the Queen, has twice within five days had his salary considerably augmented. At present he has two thousand crowns as chamberlain, a sum hitherto unheard of. What does this denote? Have they at length determined on the scheme of marrying Mademoiselle Voss? Have they cast their eyes on this fortunate mortal, who resembles a baboon? Do they intend insensibly to make his fortune? A captain in the Gendarmes said to me yesterday, "Since royal munificence is so amply showered on Doernberg, I for my part expect an annual gratification of fifty thousand crowns." This must be either an affair of mysticism, pimping, or marriage. But, if the last, why make so ridiculous a choice? What courtier is there who would refuse Mademoiselle Voss, with plenty of money? I did them too much honor in supposing such were to be found in this Vandalian Court. Not in places where men are accustomed to walk double will any be found who shall stand erect when such temptations are thrown in their way. Besides, what cannot money effect in a nation so poor! I not long since saw Brederic, late lackey to Prince Henry, become a kind of favorite, because of his art as a CHAMBER COUNSELOR, and ostentatiously display the cross and ribbon of a canonry of Magdeburg (Prince Henry is provost of this chapter). Seven thousand crowns, lent by the Prince, have purchased the stall; and the Prince's well-beloved groom bears the sacred insignia, in a country where there is so much delicacy pretended on the article of birth.

Apropos of his patron. For a week past I have not heard this musical Prince mentioned, the height and depth of whose thermometer are the greatest that ever fell under my observation. The Count of Brandenburg requested permission of him to be present at the banquet he gave to that part of the regiment of Braun who fought under him at Prague. The Prince granted the child permission; and, after highly caressing him, said, "It is difficult, my little friend, to converse with you here, but ask your father leave to come to my palace, and I shall be very glad to see you." Thus artful are his politics. He must employ a quantity of such stratagems to reimburse himself for his grand dinners. One of his table-confidants and admirers said to me the other day, "Is it not very singular that the Prince is so little esteemed, after all he has done for the army?" — and he meant by this to criminate the army! It appeared to me a notable speech.

The anecdote respecting the Academy is still more curious than according to the manner in which I related it in my last. The Academician Schutz has written a very violent letter to the King, against Count Hertzberg, and concerning the arbitrary manner in which he governs the Academy. The King sent the letter to Hertzberg, a marked token of disapprobation in this country. Busching,

the geographer, on the same day, refused a seat in the
Academy, unless a pension should be granted him of a
thousand crowns. The only answer given to the complaints of Schutz was the nomination of Erman, by
Hertzberg, without consulting any person; and the King
signed his YES, without objecting to this nomination.
Schutz wrote another letter, still more violent; what the
consequences were I do not know.

The disgrace of Launay is not so mild as it appears.
It is openly avowed that Government only waits till he
has furnished Silesia with coffee, and that then he is to
be displaced. He very rashly undertook this contract,
which he has bargained with traders to fulfill, who are
emboldened by his downfall to disown or break their engagements at the moment when, all the navigable canals
being frozen, there are such few means of repairing so
great a deficiency. But the truth is the commission is
suspended, because that they are secretly sending, through
different parts of the kingdom, in search of proofs; a
truly cruel and tyrannical inquisition, which shows that
they are rather desirous of the guilt of Launay than of
the public benefit.

A man named Dubosc, formerly an eminent merchant
at Leipsic, where, if I do not mistake, he failed, and
well known for his visionary adherence to mysticism,
has been sent for, and is at present employed, as is
supposed, to give in a plan of commercial regulations
as a substitute for exclusive privileges. It should seem
they meditate a sally against the Splittgerbers,* and that
means are seeking to deprive them of the monopoly of
sugar; a very just and salutary, but a very difficult and
delicate act.

An article of intelligence still more important is that
Baron Knyphausen has had a secret conversation with
the King; but, though it comes from a good quarter, I
will not warrant it to be true. Not that this would much
astonish me. I know past doubt that the King, enraged
at being obliged to send Count Goertz to Holland, at
the very moment when the House of Orange itself com-

* Splittgerber is a sugar baker at Berlin, who has for many years
enjoyed a monopoly of that commodity.

plains of this Ambassador, wished after venting a torrent of passion and abuse, to recall both Goertz and
Thulemeyer; but that he was stopped short, because of
the impossibility of finding a MAN in a country where
there are none; and particularly none fit for Ambassadors, a part of administration that was highly neglected
by the late King. His successor, perhaps, will be taught
that fools are not good for any one purpose.

POSTSCRIPT.— Nothing new since I wrote this long letter. Various particulars assure me that the Princess
Frederica, the daughter of the King, gains great influence, and never meets with any refusal. This doubtless
appertains to the history of Voss.

LETTER XLVI.

November 12th, 1786.

I FLATTERED myself that M. de H—— would bring me a packet from Your Grace. He informed me you had intended to intrust him with one, and I am exceedingly grateful for the intention, although I have not profited by it; this I attribute to unforeseen circumstances, which, while I pray for you, have my hearty maledictions.

I hope that the Abbé de P—— has sent you the news of the country, concerning which I have not neglected occasionally to remit anecdotes tolerably characteristic of the moment. I feel the poverty of my own harvest more forcibly than any person; but it ought not to be forgotten that I am neither provided with the pecuniary nor the ministerial means. It is impossible anything should escape the man of France* if he be adroit, active, liberal, and has the art to invite proper guests to his DAILY dinners and suppers; for these are the efficacious means, and not PUBLIC dinners. He is, besides, a kind of register office, to which all the discontented, the babblers, and the covetous resort. Besides that, his intercourse with subalterns is natural to him and permitted; I, on the contrary, have need of great art and circumspection, in order to speak without offense or intrusion on public affairs. I rarely can address my discourse to persons in power. My very aspect terrifies them too much. The King never deigns to look at me but their countenances lengthen and grow pale. I have acted however, to the best of my abilities, and, as I believe, done all I could with means that are very mutilated, very ungracious, and very sterile; nor can I tell whether the person on whom the King bestows a

* The author undoubtedly means the Ambassador.

salary of sixty thousand livres, and a post of honor here, sends much more information than I do. But I well know that I, under the same circumstances, would have penetrated many clouds through which, stationed as I am, I have very dark views; and that I would not discredit my nation, as he is accused of doing, by his haughty behavior, his bittersweet aspect and idleness that greatly resembles ignorance.

M. de H—— will more fully relate, as I suppose, the particulars I have sent. He will tell you our cause is a lost one here, unless a change should take place among the Judges; that the way to re-establish our affairs is not to be over hasty; since this would but prolong resistance among men naturally phlegmatic, and whose phlegm we may safely conclude will not suffer them to continue long impassioned; that he himself was too hasty to come to a country which at the beginning of the present reign, when each is looking for advancement, is too restless and jealous to suppose that a general officer and an inspector in the service of France could really wish to be in the service of Prussia; that the chaos (for so affairs at present may well be called) must be suffered to subside, and from the nature of things acquire consistency (if on the contrary it should not suffer destruction), though it be but the consistency of apathy, before attempts should be made to interfere; that no person is at present firmly placed; that the grand question — "Will the King, or will he not, have the courage to take a first Minister?" — is far from being resolved, even by the calculation of probabilities; that on this determination, however, the fate of the country depends, and even the ultimate capacity of the King, whose inability will be of little import if this remedy should be found to be a substitute for his indecision; that the symptoms are vexatious, and indeed disagreeable, but that we must not pronounce too hastily, because our information is the reverse of complete.

It appears to me indubitable that Prince Henry is ruined past resource; and I fear (in his behalf) that, on this occasion as on many others, chance has arranged affairs better than our precaution. But, whether or no,

his cunning, his boasting, his inconsistency, the intemperance of his tongue, and the vileness of his creatures,
seconded by the most universal discredit, have added to
personal antipathy, and the general and habitual fear of
appearing to be governed.

The destiny of the Duke of Brunswick is far otherwise
uncertain; nor do I believe it will be decided before
there is an open rupture. But it is peculiar to him, and
to him alone, that, should he once grasp power, it will
not afterward escape him; for a better courtier, a man
of deeper views, more subtle, and at the same time
more firm and more pertinacious, does not exist.

You may well imagine, Monseigneur, that, if I suppose
facts are too partial, and hitherto not sufficiently numerous to be reduced to system, on which conjectures may
be formed respecting the King and politics, I am still
much farther from thinking I can, with any appearance
of probability satisfactory for a wise man, divine what
will be the grand foreign connections, and political influence of Prussia, under the present reign. I have
sketched my ideas on the subject in a memorial, which is
a work of labor; but which (except the proofs the country
affords, and which here, as I imagine, will be found united
and compared more accurately than anywhere else) is
only a succession of conjectures. It contains many things
which may, and perhaps not one of which will, happen.
I am fortunate if, in this calculation of the arithmetic of
chances, I have so far succeeded as to describe things as
they are, and as they may be. From this memorial,
accompanied by three or four others, on parts of Germany which lucky chance has given me opportunities of
perfectly knowing, a plan may be formed according to
which the Germanic edifice may be reconstructed, a work
that ought to be begun, if its ruin is not desired. And
here, I confess, the indecision of man, the complication of
incidents, and the obscurity of future contingencies arrest
me at each step; and I have no other guide than what is
offered by your grand and noble project of coalition, between France and England, the end of which is to give
happiness to the world, and not afford amusement to
orators and newswriters.

M. de H—— has informed me that Your Grace intends coming hither in the spring. This certainly would be the only means of rendering my stay here supportable. But I hope you will not so long be left in inactivity so unworthy of your talents. As to myself, after having paid a tribute for six months, during which I have the satisfaction conviction gives of having employed uncommon assiduity and research, in compensation for the want of natural talents, I think I have a right to shake off an equivocal and doubtful existence, every way embarrassing, requiring dexterity and fortitude seldom found to preserve personal respect, and in which I consume my time and my strength in a species of labor that has no charms for me, or in the languor of etiquette and company still worse than this labor. Of this I have informed the Abbé de P—— in express terms.

LETTER XLVII.

November 24th, 1786.

THE most distressing incident possible has just happened to me. It is a very extraordinary story. Madame de F——the famous *Tribade*,* coming from the waters of Schwalback, has dropped here as if from the clouds, under a borrowed name, with an immense train, and not a single letter of recommendation except to bankers. Can you imagine what project this profoundly audacious and indeed capable woman has entertained? The conquest of the King! And as, in punishment for my sins, I have known her long and well, the damnable siren has addressed herself to me, to lay down a chart of the country for her; and, in return, receive, as a deposit, that high confidence which I should most willingly have bequeathed to Beelzebub. However, as she is a demon of seduction, as she does not ask for money, at least not at present, and as her qualities of body and mind in many respects correspond with those of the Monarch, if this be not an opportunity to be sought after neither is it one to reject. Besides, as the design is begun, and as it will be better to undertake the direction than be exposed to ridiculous broils, I am at present in search of means to afford her a decent pretense of remaining here a fortnight; taking care to draw my stake, or rather taking care not to put it down.

If the Comte d'Esterno were not in every respect one and the same, the affair might presently be managed. She might be going to Petersburg, through Warsaw, — waiting here till she could travel in a sledge, which from the setting in of the frost cannot be long delayed; might give a few select suppers; excite curiosity, etc., etc. But this mode is not to be depended on; it is too subtle for his understanding.

* A woman-lover.

Were not Prince Henry indiscretion itself, nothing could be more easy than by his aid to introduce her to the Court. She might have brought him letters. But in an hour's time the aide-de-camp, Tauensien, would be informed of everything; as would his aunt, Madame Knibbeck, in five minutes afterward; and her I suspect to be the go-between of Mademoiselle Voss. We must depend on our resources. I shall take care not to entangle myself; though, indeed, her very first step has entangled me. It is a kind of fatality; and how might I escape?

I have made many reflections on this odd adventure. Our plan must be not to abandon our purpose, and not to be too scrupulous concerning the means. The few we have are, in truth, impracticable.

If she remain in her present situation, there will be no means of seeing the King. The mystics, the Voss party, and the anti-French in general, will all be her enemies. If she conceal her intentions, she will be opposed by the party of the Rietz, and the subalterns. Either I must often visit her, which will render her suspected; or I must not, and she will conduct herself improperly.

If this partake of the adventurer, I voluntarily engross the blame.

Nothing can be done in haste, with a German prince. Should her stay be long, that stay will of itself divulge the secret.

It is not possible but that, in a week, her true name must be known. The reputation she has acquired will then spoil everything, in a country where seductive qualities will not excuse vice, and where a trip is not the less a trip because made by a woman.

The follies most inexcusable are those which expose to ridicule without compensation, of the number of which this is one. D'Esterno will relate his trifling tales; Boden his trifling scandal; Tauensien propagate his trifling intrigues; before appearance, it will be necessary to let the crowd go by, who will come and endeavor —— I will, therefore, send her to Warsaw, and procure her letters. She may return with other letters, if you do not inform me by what means she may be prevented, should such be your wish; for, though I can delay, how may I forbid her return? Such I have thought the least hazardous proceeding in this fantastic farce, which I, with good reason, think of greater importance than you may be tempted to do, because at Paris Madame de F—— is, like many others, little more than a courtesan; while here, the niece of an Ambassador and the widow of a P—— G——, etc, will never be supposed not to have been sent by Government, or, at least, not to have come hither under its protection. She, therefore, must not be suffered to commit any great folly.

The King has lately terminated a suit which had been in contest for three-and-twenty years. The Duke of Mecklenburg-Schwerin formerly borrowed a hundred thousand crowns of Frederick II., and gave some *bailliages* (or districts) as a security. Hither Frederick immediately sent a regiment of hussars into quarters. The regiment, as you may well suppose, raised recruits. The people of Mecklenburg were shocked by this act of despotism, and offered to repay the late King; who, during twenty-three years, always found pretenses to avoid receiving the money. His successor has withdrawn the troops. It is true he loses an opportunity of enlisting some of the country people, but he will annually save thirty thousand crowns; and there is likewise a new member gained for the Germanic confederation, and what that might be valued at, this is worth.

On Sunday (the 12th), at the principal inn in Berlin, the marriage of the Countess Matuska and a Prussian officer named Stutheren, was celebrated. The Countess is a sister of Mademoiselle Hencke (Madame Rietz). She thought to have married a Polish gentleman, who some months since withdrew. Once deceived, she next made choice of a young officer. The King has given money, and money enough. It is supposed that Mademoiselle Hencke, who now is said not to be married to Rietz, will retire and live with her sister, that she may not impede the projects formed to enjoy the maid of honor in peace.

There are whisperings of a very remarkable and very secret supper, at which the shade of Cæsar was taken.

The number of mystics increases. They affirm that the credit of Bishopswerder declines. I do not believe a word of it.

No new act of finance. Depositions against poor Launay are poured in, and in all probability his fortune must purchase his freedom.

Nothing new, or at least nothing certain, from Holland, except that Count Goertz has found the way to displease the States, the House of Orange, and the principal persons who are enumerated among the French faction. I well know what a philosopher would deduce from this: the politician will perceive there are commissions, the discharge of which he never ought to undertake.

LETTER XLVIII.

November 18th, 1786.

I T IS every day more apparent that the King does not forget those who were attached to him before his accession to the throne; and this propensity, which is successively developed, proves him, at least, an honest man. Count Alexander Wartensleben, an officer in the guards, whom I have several times mentioned, had been educated with him. Hence that intimacy which will not admit of secrets. The late King sent for Wartensleben, and said to him, "I am pleased to see you so very intimate with my nephew; continue your friendship. But it is also necessary you should serve the State. I ought to be informed of the proceedings of my successor. *Mein liebes Kind,* * you will come and let me know what passes at your parties of pleasure. I shall not forbid them. I shall only warn you when there is any danger; and of this you yourself will inform the Prince of Prussia. Depend upon me, *mein Schatz.*"† Wartensleben, who knew the old fox, replied "that he was the friend of the Prince, the friend of his heart, and that he would never become his spy." The King then assumed his furious countenance. " HERR LIEUTENANT, since you will not serve me, I will at least take care that you shall obey." On the morrow he was sent to Spandau, where he was imprisoned three months, and after that ordered to a garrison regiment in the very farther part of Prussia.‡ On the new King's accession he was recalled. After a momentary displeasure, which Wartensleben's refusal to go to Sweden occasioned, and which perhaps was the contriv-

---

* My good child.

† This corresponds very well with the Irish phrase, MY JEWEL or MY HONEY.

‡ This was a mode of punishment with the late King, and a very disagreeable one to the sufferers; for, besides confinement, little pay, and no hopes of preferment, it was a public mark of contempt.

(224)

ance of the other favorites, the King has bestowed a
prebendary on him, the income of which is valued at
twelve thousand crowns; and, according to all appearance, intends to give him the command of the
guards.

The following is a second example of a like kind.
When the suit was carried on against the Minister Goern,
who was superintendent of the College of Commerce,
among his papers was a bill on the Heir Apparent for
thirty thousand crowns. The money must be procured
within twenty-four hours. Arnim went in search of the
Prince, and offered him the sum, which was most joyfully accepted. This probably is the origin of the favor
which the new Minister enjoys; I cannot conjecture any
other, except what may be deduced from the King's easi-
ness of character, his indecision and mediocrity of mind;
which, however, is just and clear, as I have said in my
former dispatches.

The King has done a third humane and generous act.
His first wife, the Princess Elizabeth of Brunswick,* has
received an increase of allowance, consisting of the revenues of the *bailliage* of Ziganitz, which amount to twelve
thousand crowns, with liberty to retire whenever she
pleases. Certain of not being received by her family,
she will remain at Stettin. But the news has transported
her with joy. She has publicly declared that the lady
of General Schwerin, her *gouvernante*, has no more right
to give her any orders; and, for the first time these
eighteen years, she took an airing on horseback with
Mademoiselle Plates, that she might immediately enjoy
that liberty to which she was restored.

A trait which we ought to add, in proof of the King's
morals, is his having given up the letters to Prince
Henry, which passed in his correspondence with Frederick. Their number amounts to five hundred and
eighty-seven, on State affairs, from the year 1759 to the
year 1786. It had been unseasonably reported that the
Prince was privately of his brother's opinion concerning their nephew. These letters, however, have proved

* Divorced, banished the Court, and confined at Stettin, for her
incontinence.

15

that he did not wish it should be known. He even rendered him services; and, for example, when Count Wartensleben of whom I have just spoken, was imprisoned, he sent him a grant of a pension of a hundred a year, which he still enjoys.

The famous chamber hussar, Schoening, the confidential man of the deceased King, has lately been appointed assistant to the cashier of the military chest, with a salary of three thousand crowns. This certainly is not a rancorous act. Schoening, indeed, is not a man without intelligence; and he is the depositary of numerous secrets, which ought not at present to be made public, perhaps never.

In opposition to all these good actions, we must place the apathy of the King, on the subject of his personal debts. He is in no haste to pay those that are not of the household, and there is a very considerable sum appertaining to the latter which remains unsettled.

It is determined that the King is to discharge all the persons employed as taxgatherers on the French finance system, which in itself is a laudable act; for were there a necessity for some years to prolong the farming of the customs, yet, either the French collectors already have, or never will have, taught the Germans the mode of transacting the business. And is not the Prussian Monarch the King of Germans? But innovation is a very delicate thing; and I see no preparations made to lessen the shock that must be received. The farmers of tobacco and snuff have been informed that their administration must cease on the 1st of June, 1787. All persons thenceforward will be allowed to cultivate tobacco, and to make and sell snuff. This is a very important object; for the tobacco that grows on these barren sands is some of the best in Germany, and formerly was a very considerable branch of trade. On the 1st of July grants are to be delivered, gratis, to whoever shall make the requisition. (Nay, freedom is promised for coffee, too.) From 1783 to 1786, the duties on snuff and tobacco had yielded about sixteen hundred thousand livres more than the sum they had been estimated at by the King; so that these formed a revenue of something more than a million of crowns, and sometimes a million four hundred thousand. Yet the collectors had not the right of buying the leaf tobacco; they were obliged to purchase it from the warehouses of the Maritime Company, by whom it was sold at a profit of cent per cent. These collectors committed infinite vexations on the subject, to obtain a surplus, with which it was necessary to come before the King when they delivered in their accounts; otherwise, he could neither find wisdom in their proceedings nor talents in themselves. The King leaves the collectors their salaries till they can be provided for, and this is humane; for the change will affect not less than twelve hundred families. But how will they find a substitute for this revenue? A capitation tax is spoken of, and is certainly under deliberation. The subjects are to be comprised in twelve classes; the rich merchants are to pay twenty-four crowns; the rich inhabitants twelve crowns; two crowns for obscure citizens; and the peasants something less than two francs. What a manner of beginning a reign it is, to tax persons before property! In the collection of this odious tax, which sets a price on the right of existence, the tobacco excisemen are to be employed. The capitation, however, is somewhat softened by being paid by the family and not by the head. But the proselytes to, and even the apostles of, this project do not estimate the tax at more than two millions of crowns annually; which sum is the product of tobacco and coffee united, but which scarcely will supply the deficiency; and those who understand calculation in finance will be careful not to estimate a tax equally productive in figures and reality. I am surprised that he does not first gain a better knowledge of substitutes; and that he should begin by operations which I have pointed out as things to prepare, and should defer those with which I thought he ought to commence.*

Heinitz, Minister for the department of the mines, and president of the commission commanded to examine the administration of General Wartenberg, warned no doubt by universal clamor, has remonstrated to the King that it is requisite to add some military men to

---

* The author doubtless alludes to his memorial, which will be found at the end of this volume.

the commissioners.   His Majesty has in consequence appointed General Moellendorf.

To give a specimen of the malversations attributed to the Jew Wartenberg, which it is said were highly surpassed by his predecessors, the following trait is cited. He made up clothing for a regiment of foot, without having shrunk the cloth.   The coats were so tight that they scarcely would button on the men.   The first day they were worn by the regiment there happened a heavy shower.   The quartermaster said that, if the soldiers pulled off their regimentals, they never could put them on again; accordingly they were commanded to lie all night in their clothes, and dry them upon their backs.

The next is an example of another kind, and characteristic of Frederick II.   One of the cash keepers of Wartenberg stole eighty thousand crowns.   The General informed the King, and waited his commands.   Frederick replied he had nothing to say to the matter, for he was for his own part determined not to lose the money. Wartenberg understood this jargon, assembled all the army clothiers, and requested they would divide the loss, under pain of being no more employed.   The clothiers cried, cursed, lamented their wretched destiny, and subscribed.   Wartenberg wrote to the King that the money was again in the military chest.   Frederick sent a very severe answer, and concluded his letter by telling him "this was the last time he should be pardoned."

Private anecdotes continue much the same.   The general report is that the King is to espouse Mademoiselle Voss with the left hand,—a German mode of ennobling courtesans, invented by pliant courtiers and complaisant priests to save appearances, say they.   This lady still continues a mixture of prudery and *cynisme*,* affectation and ingenuousness.   She can find understanding only in the English, whose language she speaks tolerably well.

Manstein is suspected to be the author of some of the intended changes in the army, the purport of which is to better the condition of the soldier and the subaltern, at the expense of the captain.   I repeat, this last is a

*We know no such word.   Perhaps from κυω, or from κυων; the metaphorical and least offensive translation of which may be COQUETRY.

formidable cohort; and that innovations of such a kind require great foresight and inflexible fortitude. Prince Henry, who is profoundly silent, in public, concerning all operations, will very warmly take part with the army, should it find cause of complaint; and hopes thus to regain what, by his excessive haughtiness, he has lost. But the army aristocracy know him too well to confide in him; they know that the *Gitons** have been, and will always continue, with him, the sovereign arbiters; that, when circumstances have obliged him to seek the aid of men of merit, he has always found their presence a burden, which his crazy frame has shaken off as soon as possible,— that, in fine, his day is ended, with respect to war, and that he is odious to the Ministry.

It seems one Count Brühl is chosen governor of the Prince Royal; and nothing better proves the influence of Bishopswerder than this eternal preference of Saxons. Count Brühl, son of the ostentatious satrap of the same name,† brother of the Grand Master of the Saxon Artillery, amiable, well informed, really or pretentedly believing in the reveries of the mystics, with little of the soldier, yet willing to profit by circumstances and to enter the military career with gigantic strides — this Count, I say, demands to enter the service as a lieutenant general; a thing unheard of in the Prussian army, and which will cause infinite discontent.

An interdict has lately been issued, prohibiting the discount of bills at the bank; which is very wise in theory, but here accompanied by great inconveniences in practice; for either the bank or the King must pay the interest of two and a half per cent for about seventeen millions of crowns, which is the amount of the capital of, and the money brought into, the bank, in a country where moneyed men find no means of employing their

* This word has a meaning too offensive to be translated. If the reader has unfortunately ever heard of the most contemptible of wretches, and the most unnatural of crimes, he may then be his own interpreter.

† Who was page to Augustus II. of Saxony, Prime Minister to Augustus III., favorite to his Consort, hated by the late King of Prussia, and who had a greater number of coats, waistcoats, etc., than any other man in the world.

capitals. The bank cannot pay this two and a half per cent without becoming burdensome to the King, except by discounting bills of exchange; and it will hereafter be the less able, if the Maritime Company, founded as I have before said, on so frail a basis, and obliged to give at least ten per cent to the proprietors, should lose any one of its most beneficial exclusive privileges,—that of wood, for example,—and should not be able to afford the bank, to which the Maritime Society pays five per cent for all the money it there borrows, the same sources of profit which have hitherto been open.

First Postscript.—The Minister Schulemburg has resigned; his resignation is not yet accepted.

The King yesterday supped with his daughter, Mademoiselle Vierey—the intimate friend of Mademoiselle Voss, and placed by her in his daughter's service since his accession to the throne—and the well-beloved. Hence it should seem that the romance draws toward a conclusion.

It is more than ever certain that the King transacts no business, and that he is mad after pleasure. The secrets of the palace on this subject are very ill-kept indeed; and nothing, as I think, can better prove the feebleness of the master, the little awe in which he is held, and the worthlessness of his creatures.

Second Postscript.—The King is so terrified by the universal clamor which the capitation tax has excited, that it is renounced. Some of his intimates to-day spoke to me of substitutes; but what can be expected from an avaricious and weak Prince, whom two days' murmurings have caused to retreat, and to whom we can only say, " Tax the estates of the nobility, and lend out some of your millions; that you may procure the interest which nations in debt are obliged to pay."

LETTER XLIX.

November 21st, 1786.

THERE are suspicions — which are daily strengthened — of a secret negotiation between the Emperor and Prussia; or at least that propositions have been made, either by the first or reciprocally, on which deliberations are held. I neither have the money nor the requisite means to discover what they are. An Ambassador can effect anything of this kind, and with impunity. But, though I even possessed the great engine of corruption, what danger should I not be in, should I set it in motion? I have no credentials, direct or indirect. An act of authority might dispose of me and my papers in an instant; and I should be ruined, here and elsewhere, for my too inconsiderate zeal. Spur on your Ambassador, therefore, or hasten to oppose to this puissant coalition, which nothing could resist on this side of the Rhine, the system of union with England, the basis of which you have traced out, and which shall be the salvation of the world. Think on Poland, I conjure you. What they have done (if they did not extend their acquisitions it was in fact because they would not) they will again do, and that even without the intervention of Russia; of that sleeping giant, who, waking, may change the face of the globe.

In truth, it is the coolness between the two Imperial Courts which most confirms the suspicions of a new system. All that I can imagine, concerning its foundation, is that its pretext is the election of a King of the Romans, and its purport a strict alliance, which shall destroy the Germanic confederation. As this confederation was the work of the King while Prince of Prussia, or as he wishes to believe it his, and as he regards it as a masterpiece, it may be doubted whether the Emperor will succeed. But, if the news of yesterday be true, there is a great point gained. Advice is received that the Electress Palatine is beyond hope. Should she die, the Elector would marry again on the morrow, and affairs may and must assume a different face. If I am not mistaken, it is difficult to reflect too seriously on this subject. For my own part, unless my instructions and my means are amplified, I only can observe, according to the best of my power, the internal acts of government and the Court.

The reason that Count Schulemburg, one of the Ministers of State, has demanded to retire is, in part, that he was charged to carry the capitation tax into execution, which he neither conceived nor approved, and which he truly regarded as a very unpopular, if not a very odious, office. This Minister, a man of understanding, and who would have again been at the head of affairs if, at his first cause of disgust, he had determined to resign his place, is infinitely disagreeable to the domestic agents. The long favor he has enjoyed, his rapid fortune, and his watchful perspicacity, have angered or disturbed all his rivals. Neither is he one of those pliant instruments that will bend into any form. The incapacity of most of the other Ministers afforded him the pretense of being obstinate in opinion. The absurdities of the courtiers, not to say their extravagant follies, emboldened him to return that contempt which the reputation of his abilities incites with usury. For what will not such a reputation eradicate, especially in a country where men are so scarce? But if, as it is said (I have not yet had time to verify the fact), there be a coalition between Struensee and Welner, Schulemburg is undone, for they will no longer stand in need of him. As he made illness his pretense, the King, in a very friendly letter, only accepted his resignation *per interim* and on condition that his signature should sanction whatever related to his department.

Meantime the Aulic* systems, that of mysticism, and the favor of the mystics, are continued, or, rather, increased and adorned. The Duke of Weimar arrived here last night. He has the apartments of the Duke of

* AULIC, that is, Court.

Brunswick at the palace. This Prince, the great apostle of the fashionable sect, and of whom I spoke in my dispatches from Brunswick and Magdeburg, had long had the character of being only an *arbiter elegantiarum;* a zealous promoter of letters and arts; an economist by system; and a spendthrift by temperament. I some months since suspected him of military enthusiasm. It is now avowed. He comes to enter into the Prussian service. Such generals will never renew the War of Seven Years.

In other respects affairs continue the same. The King invited himself to sup with Prince Henry to-day. The Prince, who continues his awkward plans, stifling his pent-up rage, has informed the foreign ambassadors that the doors of his palace would be opened every Monday, and that, if they thought proper to form card parties there, he should receive them with pleasure. He wishes to change the custom which hitherto has prohibited all who appertain to the *corps diplomatique* from eating with princes of the blood, and insensibly to invite them to suppers. His credit is at the lowest ebb; yet I still believe, would he persevere in silence, abstain from all pretensions, impatience, and avidity of power, he would highly embarrass the opposite party, and would at length be triumphant.

Murmurs become general against the obscure agents of the Cabinet; and the nobility, now neglected to make room for the Saxons, would be better pleased to behold a prince at the head of administration than obscure clerks, who never can acquire great and acknowledged fortunes, except by great changes. Yet the aristocracy is little dependent on such subalterns, and holds them in little dread.

The Duke of Courland is soon to arrive. As he is to be reimbursed considerable sums, it is to be presumed that the whole of the debts of the Heir Apparent, which it is not decent to have left unpaid for several months after his accession, will then be discharged. This fact, combined with the suppers of the procuresses, the number of which suppers increases at the Princess Frederica's, and for which purpose her establishment has evidently

been granted, seriously attaint the moral character of
the King.

Madame de F——, who would not depart for Warsaw
without making some attempt, yesterday had a very gay
audience of the King; an audience of anecdote, at which
he complained of his tiresome trade, and was earnest in
his desires that she should remain at Berlin; reproached
her with having stolen the portrait of Suck from him;
and complained to her of the impoliteness and blunders
of the Prince de P——, who thought his very daughter,
the Princess Frederica, ugly and slatternly. This continued an hour, and probably if Madame de F—— had
come hither with greater precaution and for a longer
time, she might have had some success. But it is a being so perverse, so avaricious, and so dangerous, that it
is perhaps best she should travel with her talents elsewhere; to Paris, for example, where she is known, where
she would not increase licentiousness, and never could
obtain any important influence; whereas, if admitted to
the privy council of Kings, she might set Europe in
flames to obtain money, or even for her own private
diversion. I took advantage of the moment that she
thought proper to depart from the route I had traced
out, to reiterate my information that her proceedings
might have consequences much more serious than result
from wounded vanity, and to declare I no longer should
be a party concerned.

1. Because it did not become me to risk my character,
in an affair where my advice was not followed.

2. And because the ambition of ladies has not, cannot have, the same motives, principles, proceedings, and
conclusions, as that of a man who has a respect for
himself.

Should she succeed, which appears to me impossible,
she is too much in my power to escape my influence.

Postscript.—Lord Dalrymple, it is reported, is recalled,
and Ewart remains at the head of the embassy without
a superior. Dalrymple is a man of honor and sense;
sometimes wearisome, because he is continually wearied,
but endowed with more understanding than will be

believed by those who have not carefully observed him; and also with generous, liberal, and fixed principles. If pacific coalition be sincerely intended, it is necessary to bring Dalrymple Ambassador to Paris. With respect to Ewart, I believe the Cabinet at St. James's finds it convenient to maintain a spy here, who is the intimate friend of one Minister and the son-in-law of another. But what can be alleged in excuse of the Cabinet of Berlin, that shall tolerate such an encumbrance? This is but public report, which I suspect.

Commissions of inquiry begin to be fashionable; one has lately been appointed to examine the monopoly of sugars. The people of Hamburg offered to supply the same articles at less than half price.

Another to examine the cloth manufactory.

Another the wood monopoly, which is to be reduced to half its present price (independent of the suppression of the company, by which it is furnished). But how? By what means? The change is assuredly one of the most urgent, and the most profitable that could be made for the country; but the abolition of all these monopolies, sugar excepted, which is granted to an individual,* supposes the destruction of the Maritime Company, that strange firm, which has promised the proprietors a dividend of ten per cent, be circumstances what they may. This fantastic superstructure cannot be pulled down, unless by a very able hand, without risk of danger from its ruins. Therefore, in his letter to the Minister Schulemburg, the King renounces this project, and commands that it should be contradicted in all the public papers. What a fluctuation of plans, orders, and intentions! What poverty of power and of means!

* Splittgerber and Co., who had not only the monopoly of all the refining houses, but also a foundry for muskets, small arms, sword blades, etc., etc.; a manufactory for hardware, cutlery, etc., etc., and another for braziery; all monopolies that have existed for many years, and all granted by Frederick II., the King who is so emphatically and so falsely, held up as the mirror of wisdom, and the demigod to whom future ages are to erect statues, build temples, burn incense, and fall down in adoration.

LETTER L.

November 24th, 1786.

COUNT HERTZBERG has made a new attempt to interfere in the affairs of Holland, which had been
interdicted him by the King, and has presented a
memorial on the subject, in which he pretends to prove
that crowned heads have several times stood forth as
mediators between the States and the Stadtholder; and
that the insidious reply of France stated that as fact
which was in dispute. Prince Henry believes this memorial has produced some effect. I have my reasons for
being of a different opinion; however, I informed him
that, if he could procure me a copy, its futility should
soon be demonstrated. I doubt whether he has even
thus much power.

Here let me remark, we are reconciled. I refused
two invitations, and he has made every kind of advance
to me, which decorum requires I should receive with
politeness.

The journey of the Duke of Weimar certainly had no
other end but that of his admission into the Prussian
service, which is to strengthen the rising fame of the
Germanic confederation. This prince in reality warmly
protects the system of those who find, in the depth of
their mystical abilities, rules for governing a kingdom.
The favor in which these systems are held continually
increases in fervor; or rather, is become visible, for it
never was cool. The brother of the Margrave of Baden,
a fashionable enthusiast, has a natural son, for whom
he wishes to provide. This is the great affair of which
he is come hither personally to treat, and he has met a
miraculously kind welcome.

Business is not quite so well. There is so much confusion in domestic affairs that the King only issues

money on account to the various officers of the household. It is determined that all his debts, while Prince
of Prussia, are to be paid; that the Prince Royal shall
have an establishment, and a table of ten covers; that
the Princess Frederica shall have another, equal to the
establishment of the Queen; and that the period when
these arrangements are to take place is to be after the
statements of expense have been formed.

The army is discontented.

1. Because the King appears on the parade only once
a week.

2. Because commissions of major and lieutenant colonel
are multiplied to satiety (for example, all the captains
who have been in actual service have obtained them;
this is the second chapter of titles, and patents of nobility, by scores); a favor which never was formerly
granted, not even at the solicitation of the greatest
princes.*

3. Because much is talked of, little done; because
few are punished, and little is required; and, in a word,
because the army does not now, as formerly, absorb the
whole attention of the Sovereign.

It does not appear that Manstein diminishes the credit
of the aid-de-camp Goltz, who has become a count, and
who, in what relates to military affairs, has evidently
more influence than his rivals. He has great abilities,
without having such as are necessary to that place,
which, in fact, is equivalent to that of minister for the
war department.

It is subject of astonishment to the few men of
observation who are attentive to whatever may lead to
a knowledge of the moral character of the new King,
that he should behave so coldly to one of his aids-de-
camp named Boulet, whom I have before several times
mentioned. Boulet is a French refugee of no superior
understanding; an honest man, with little ambition; a
very ordinary engineer, though here a distinguished one,
because here there are none. He has been twenty years
attached to the Monarch, but never was admitted a party
in his secret pleasures, which were formerly almost neces-

* Rank in the Prussian service was formerly confined to seniority.

sary to support the solitude of Potsdam and the hatred
of the late King. He neither increases nor diminishes
in favor, and his influence is almost a nullity. Such a
repugnance for a man of some consequence in his profession, and who neither can offend nor disgust, is
enigmatical.

It is nearly certain that the capitation plan will be
rejected. This hasty expedient would not have been a
substitute equal to their wants. But you must feel how
much so many variations will diminish all confidence in
the subaltern and concealed administrators, who act instead of ministers; and how every circumstance concurs to
render a prime minister necessary. Nothing seems determined on except a desire to change. There is no system;
for I cannot call the vague desire of easing the people
by that term; nor any regular plans, formed from knowledge, examination, and reflection.

None of the difficulties, for example, had been foreseen that arise from the suppression of the monopoly
and administration of tobacco, which afforded an asylum
to twelve hundred invalids, army subalterns, and even
lieutenants. These invalids must live, and be maintained
by the King. Nor is this all. Shares in the tobacco
company originally cost a thousand crowns, and brought
in eleven per cent; the price afterward rose to fourteen
hundred crowns. The contract granted by the late King
was to be in force to the year 1793. Should the King
buy in these shares, at a thousand crowns each, this
would be unjust; since they have been purchased at
fourteen hundred, on the faith of a contract of which
seven years are unexpired. If he should pay interest for
them, at the rate of eight per cent till the year 1793,
he must then himself become a loser. Would it not
have been better not to have made any change till the
contract should expire of itself, or till he had found a
proper substitute? The effects which are the representatives of the capital, consist in utensils, warehouses,
houses, carriages, etc., etc. These cannot all be sold
without loss, which must likewise fall on the King. The
monopoly was burdened with pensions, bestowed on persons by whom they had been merited; or, if you please,

obtained for that very affair which paid those pensions.*
They must hereafter be discharged by some other fund,
etc.

Heaven forbid I should pretend such difficulties ought
not to be surmounted! Improvement would then be accomplished. But they ought to have been foreseen,
which they have not; so that the public only perceives,
in this suppression, a real evil in return for an unasked
good. This mania to undersell the smugglers, or to destroy illicit trade, if great care be not taken, will be
more injurious to the people than the trade itself was to
the State. Opposition to contraband trade ought to be
the consequence of one comprehensive system; and those
are short-sighted views which endeavor to correct partial
abuses, that appertain to the general vices of administration. The refining of sugar, the fabricating of arms,
silk, gauze, stuffs, cloths, in a word, whatever relates to
industry, all are directed by regulations destructive
to commerce. But may all this vanish by a single act of
volition? Impossible; without producing convulsions in
the State. And thus are truth and benevolence discred-
ited, and kings discouraged. Woe to him who pulls
down without precaution!

The principles of the two Kings, concerning their personal dignity, appear to be so different as to give room
for reflection, relative to this country. When Frederick II.
established the coffee monopoly, the citizens of Potsdam
were daring enough to load a cart with coffeepots and
coffeemills, to drive it through the town and overturn
it into the river. Frederick, who was a spectator of this
burlesque procession, opened his window and laughed
heartily. Here we have an anecdote of him whom they
call the Tiberius of Prussia. The following is another
of the Prussian Titus:

The day before yesterday, the clerk of a merchant,
named Olier, was imprisoned; and he was not informed,
till the morning after, that the cause of his imprisonment was some trifling speech relative to the King; and

---

* The author is here, as in many other places, obscure. The meaning most probably is that they were pensions granted in return for
the sums that were risked at the establishment of the monopoly.

that, should he commit a similar offense, the dungeon would give a good account of him! Such are the first fruits of a gloomy internal administration, of which the vanity and poverty of mind of the King have been productive. What a foreboding of tyranny,— whether it be royal, or, which is worse, subaltern! Under what circumstances, and in what a country! There, where the master, whose vanity is so irascible, wishes to appear good; and where there is no counterpoise to his power, in the public opinion; for the public has no opinion!

The commission of inquiry, sitting on Launay, remains silent, retards its proceedings, forces or seeks for facts, and decides on nothing. Du Bosc is very industrious. Two merchants are arrived from each province, who are to give their advice, relative to the best manner of rendering trade flourishing. It is not yet known here that, though merchants only should be trusted with the execution of a commercial plan, they never should be consulted concerning a general system; because their views and their interests are always partial. One of them, however, has given advice which is very sage, in the present state of affairs; and that is to forbid the silk manufactories, which are all on the royal establishment, to make any but plain silks. Should they determine so to do, the King of Prussia may supply Sweden, Poland, and a part of Russia.

The Princess Elizabeth, the divorced consort of the King, has requested to have a place five miles from Berlin, and that his Majesty would appoint the ladies and gentlemen who shall be her attendants. It is supposed that the attempts this Princess makes have been suggested to her by an adroit and intriguing officer; but it is not she who will become formidable to the Queen, though I really dare not say so much for Mademoiselle Voss. What must be the destiny of a country which soon is to be divided among priests, mystics, and prostitutes?

In despite of all my diligence to divine what is in treaty with the Court of Vienna, I can only form conjectures. However, when I reflect that the Prussian Ambassador to Austria is an incapable person, Count Podewils; and that the Emperor's Ambassador, Prince Reuss, has not altered his conduct; that Prince Henry, though generally ill-informed, would have some positive intelligence, if anything positive had been done, and that he has only vague suspicion,— I scarcely can believe any important or probable revolution is on the tapis. Did the Prince (Henry) possess but one of the twenty wills of which he is composed, and which do not all form the equivalent of a whole, so that he could expend his money properly, and act with consistency, his superior information must give him a great ascendency in the Cabinet.

But why do we not rid ourselves of this complication of political affairs, by at once changing our foreign system, and breaking down the only opposing barrier? I mean to say, by respectable arrangements and sincere advances. Why do we not stifle commercial jealousy, that mother of national animosity, which has silenced good sense, and pompously predicted, supported by the sophisms of mercantile cupidity, that total ruin, whether it be for France or England, must be the result of the unfavorable balance to which a freedom of trade could not fail to give birth? Is it, then, so difficult to demonstrate that the trade of France might be much more advantageous to Great Britain than that of any other country, and *vice versa?* Who that will but open his eyes will not see the reason? It is in the will of Nature, by which those monarchies are nearer each other than they are to other countries. The returns of the trade which might be carried on between the southern coast of England and northwest of France might take place five or six times a year, as in the more internal commerce. The capital employed in this trade might therefore, in both countries, be productive of five or six times its present quantity of industry, and might afford employment and subsistence to six times as many inhabitants as the same capital could effect in most other branches of foreign trade. Between those parts of France and Great Britain which are most distant from each other, the returns might at least be made once a year; and would consequently be thrice as profitable as the trade, formerly so much vaunted, with North America; in which the returns usually took place only once in three, and

16

very frequently only once in four or five years. The sage Smith asks, "If we consider its population, wants, and wealth, is not France at least a market eight times more extensive (for England), and, by reason of its quick returns, twenty-four times more advantageous than ever was that of the English colonies of North America?" * It is not less, or rather, it is more evident that the trade with Great Britain would be in an equal degree useful to France, in proportion to the wealth, population, and proximity of the two countries. It would eventually have the same superiority over that which France has made with her colonies. Oh, human folly! What labors do we undertake to deprive ourselves of the benefits of Nature! How prodigious a difference between that trade which the politics of the two nations have thought it right to discourage, and that which has been the most favored! It appears to me that a work which should develop these ideas, and which begin no longer to be thought monstrous by the English, would be very useful, and could not be intrusted to a man of too great abilities.

POSTSCRIPT.—I have circumstantial evidence that the King is more than ever indolent. Letters are answered in eight or ten days, and in a more long and careful manner than under the late King; which sufficiently proves that secretaries have great interference. Yet what must we say of a Cabinet in which the King never acts, although it is impossible to cite any minister whose influence has effected such or such a thing? Even into the assembly of the general directory, which sits twice a week, the King never comes. And this is the King who wishes to change the fiscal system! None but a Hercules can cleanse the Augean stables.

* Either we have not been fortunate enough to find the passage the author quotes, or he has taken the sense of various passages. Smith says, "A capital employed in the home trade will sometimes make twelve operations, or be sent out and returned twelve times, before a capital employed in the foreign trade of consumption has made one. If the capitals are equal, therefore, the one will give four-and-twenty times more encouragement and support to the industry of the country than the other."—Smith's "Wealth of Nations," vol. ii., p. 61, edit. 1786.

LETTER LI.

PEOPLE are not agreed concerning the kind of services which the committee of merchants, convoked from the different provinces, may render Government. These good folks are highly astonished to hear themselves consulted on affairs of State; for there is as great a distance between them and Mont-Audouin and Prémores, as there is between the Prussian Ministers and our Sully and Colbert. The question should be to reverse the general and fundamental system, and they seek only palliatives. The blood is infected, and instead of purifying it, they endeavor but to heal this or that ulcer. They will inflame the gangrene, and render the virus more envenomed.

There are great disputes concerning the manufactures. But, good God! ought they to begin with these? And, should they well and clearly have determined which were necessary to preserve, and which to neglect, ought they not, before they prescribe rules, to assume as a *datum* — that Berlin is not a place for manufacturers; because that the dearness of the labor, local, and national inconveniences, etc., etc., are there united; and because that the establishment of manufactures must there become a disastrous extravagance? for which reason the manufacturers themselves carry on a contraband trade, and sell French for Prussian stuffs. As they have no competitors, they affix what price they please on their merchandise; and, as nothing is easier than to smuggle, they take a part of their goods to the fairs of Frankfort, which they sell or do not sell, as it shall happen, and purchase Lyons silks, to which they affix Berlin stamps, and enter them without any other precaution, or the least risk: since the customhouse officers of the barriers, who are invalids either of the Court or army,

cannot distinguish whether what is shown them is taffeta
or satin; still less, whether it be woven at Lyons or
Berlin. This city neither possesses industry, emulation,
taste, genius, nor money, to effect such changes. Another
age, and I know not how many transitions among the
Germans, are necessary for them to imitate that luxury
of embellishment for which they have the folly to wish.
Incapable of choosing between that which is possible
and proper, and that which is chimerical and injurious,
without means, principles, or system, the present attempts of these men, to which they owe their ephemeral
existence, will have no other effect than that of leading,
the King first, and afterward the vulgar and the foolish,
to believe that the evil is irreparable.

The inheritance of the margraviate of Schwedt is an
affair at this moment, which, in other hands, might
have important consequences. The Margrave approaches
his end. After the partition of Poland, the late King
wrote to his brother, Prince Henry, that he was desirous
of bestowing on him a peculiar mark of his friendship
and gratitude, for the service he had rendered the State.
Frederick thought he should have rid himself of his
promise by a statue; but he was privately given to
understand that fame was left to the care of posterity,
and that the present question was an increase of possession. A few months afterward, the Margrave of
Schwedt, brother of the present Margrave, died; the King
seized the occasion to release himself from his word. In
a very authentic patent, and at a long term, he conferred
on Prince Henry the reversion of the margraviate, on
condition that he should discharge all the burdens with
which this great fief is loaded. Frederick dies, and his
successor declares that all survivances, and donations *in
futuro*, etc., are null, and that he will not confirm them.
Prince Henry finds himself among the number of those
on whom reversions were bestowed. There is little
probability these lands will be given him. The question
is, will he or will he not have any compensation?

Prince Henry certainly has pretenses to exclaim against
ingratitude, and exclaim he will. There it will end.
Melancholy mad at one moment, he will rave the next;

and thus, giving vent to his griefs, will save his life; for mute affliction only is dangerous.

Those, however, who are not among his partisans, will observe this proceeding with the greatest inquietude, because it begins to appear that even the personal promises of the King are susceptible of wavering. I spoke to you in one of my dispatches of the restitution of some *bailliages* to the Duke of Mecklenburg, which had been promised to the envoy of the Duke by the King himself. He has since withdrawn, or at least suspended, his promise. So much facility in departing from recent engagements, combined with the clamors of the people, and the exclusive contracts that are trodden under foot without pity, appear to be but ill omens. It has been inserted, for example, BY COMMAND, in the public papers, "that the King declares to all the army clothiers that, from paternal motives,"—all of which have been announced with emphasis, as you will see in every gazette, —"the King annuls their contracts; even those that have been recently confirmed." Which clause is the more gratuitously odious and absurd, as he had not confirmed anyone; he, therefore, need not have taken the trouble SOLEMNLY to inform his subjects that he knew very well how, when occasion should serve, SOLEMNLY to break his word.

The King spoke to me yesterday concerning the woolen manufactory. I endeavored to make him understand that, before we pulled down our house, we should know where to find a lodging, or how we might dispose of the ruins. He answered me, laughing, "Oh! Schmits is your banker." (He is the contractor for this manufactory.) "Very true, Sire," replied I; "but he has not hitherto made me a present of the money which has been remitted me through his hands." This may show you what engines are set at work to keep me at a distance. The following is a more circumstantial proof:

I was six days very ill, and did not make my appearance at Court, which I the less regretted because that nothing is learned in such grand company. The day before yesterday, the King said at his Lotto, "Where is the Comte de Mirabeau? It is an age since I saw him."

"That is not astonishing, Sire," said one of the household. "He passes his time at the house of Struensee, with Messrs. Biester and Nicolai." You must understand that Biester and Nicolai are two learned Germans, who have written much against Lavater and the mystics; that they never enter the house of, nor are they, as I believe, personally acquainted with, Struensee. The intention was to lead the King to suppose I was an anti-mystic.

The appointment of Count Charles Brühl to the place of Governor of the Prince Royal has made the party more than ever triumphant. To the merit of appertaining to that honorable sect, Count Leppel, the most incapable and ridiculous of men, is indebted for his Swedish Embassy; as are Baron Doernberg for favors of every kind, Prince Frederick for his intimacy, the Duke of Weimar, the brother of the Margrave of Baden, and the Prince of Dessau for their success, and the courtiers that surround the King for their influence and favor. It looks like a tacit confederacy, and that there is a determination to admit none but proved and fervent sectaries into administration. No one dares combat them; everybody bows before them. The slaves of the Court and the city, who were not the first to yield, mutter disapprobation, and, by degrees, will range themselves on the side of the prevailing party.

There is no parasite, however great, that attempts to excuse the prostitution of titles, patents of nobility, ribbons, academical places, and military promotions, which daily is aggravated. Seventeen majors, for example, have been made, merely in acquittal of vague and inconsiderate promises; and that there may be the semblance of recollecting, at LITTLE expense, hopes that had been given when every LITTLE aid was acceptable.

The King makes himself too public not to talk very idly. It would be better that, at the commencement of a reign, the Prussian Monarch should not find time daily to have a tiresome concert, or a more languid Lotto; especially when the world knows the nothings, or the worse, that employ his mornings. He more and more every day, constitutes himself the redressor of the wrongs committed by his uncle. Those colonels or generals that were dismissed return to the army with promotions or appointments that recompense their sufferings. The counselors that formerly were degraded, concerning the affair of the miller Arnold, have been reinstated in their functions. To say the truth, their punishment was one of the most iniquitous of the acts* of Frederick II. But his principal victim, the Chancellor Fürst, has hitherto been forgotten. His great age, indeed, will not permit him to occupy any post. But some solemn mark of good will some flattering recompense of strict justice, while so many other recompenses are granted, which are favors that are often more than suspicious — would this be impossible?

Under the late reign, the mines solely depended on the minister of that department. An arrangement has just been made, according to which four tribunals, erected in the provinces, greatly moderate his authority; and this was very necessary in a country where the public right of the mines was the most revolting tyranny. But the

*We ought to read PRIVATE acts. Arnold held a mill of Count Schmettau; and, being in arrear for several years' rent, the mill was seized and sold. Arnold laid a false complaint against one Gersdorf, for having robbed him of the water by which his mill had been supplied and his family maintained. The King ordered the sentence, that had condemned Arnold to lose his mill for the payment of arrears, to be revised. His orders were obeyed. The judgment was confirmed. Without proper examination the King sent for the judges, deprived them of their places, condemned them to pay the costs of Arnold, sentenced Gersdorf to restore the water or build a windmill, sent them to the prison for malefactors, ordered Baron Zedlitz to see punishment inflicted or to beware of punishment himself, ruined them all, and, without hearing him, commanded his Grand Chancellor Fürst, who came to prove that he could not be guilty because he had no concern in the trial, TO MARCH! and degraded him from all his dignities. The facts were, that the pond of Gersdorf, which Arnold affirmed had been dug to his detriment, had been a pond for ages; that Gersdorf was neither his landlord nor his prosecutor, but Schmettau; that Arnold actually paid no rent; and that the proofs of the legality of the sentence, by which he had been cast, were evident to all the judges, none of whom could have any interest in giving a false judgment. This act of tyranny was echoed with applause through all Europe, and, among others, by the English newspapers, magazines, annual registers, etc., most of which, with equal piety and patriotism, hoped in good time to see justice thus righteously administered in England.

arrangement does not announce the disgrace of Heinitz.
He has, on the contrary, had several new departments
committed to his charge within this fortnight; and particularly some that belonged to Schulemburg. It is a part
of the plan to restore all things to the state in which
they were left by Frederick William in 1740. This criticism on the last reign may be vengeance dearly purchased. At least it is necessary to be consistent; and,
since the grand directory has been restored according to
its first institution, it ought not to be left in indolence,
and in a state of humiliating insufficiency. The dismission of the Minister Gaudi is reported, who is the man
by whom Government might best profit, if he were employed. This conspiracy against capacity and knowledge,
with good reason, alarms those who know the persons
that inspire predilection.

If I am not mistaken, there is here, at this moment,
an acquisition to be made, worthy of the King of
France, and M. de Calonne is the very man who ought
to lay the proposal before his Majesty. The illustrious
La Grange, the greatest mathematician that has appeared since Newton, and who, by his understanding and
genius, is the man in all Europe who has most astonished
me; La Grange, the most sage, and perhaps the only
true practical philosopher that has ever existed; worthy
to be commended for the pertinacious calmness of his
mind, his manners, and his conduct; in a word, a man
affectionately respected by the small number of men
whom he would admit to be of his acquaintance; this La
Grange has lived twenty years at Berlin, whither
he was invited, in his youth by the late King, to succeed Euler, who had himself pointed him out as the
only man proper to be his successor. He is much disgusted, silently but irremediably disgusted, because that
his disgust originates in contempt. The passions, bru-
talities, and lunatic boastings of Hertzberg; the addition
of so many as Academicians with whom La Grange cannot, without blushing, associate; the very prudent dread
of seeing himself held in painful suspense, between the
philosophic repose which he regards as the first good,
and that respect which he owes himself, and which he

will not suffer to be insulted; all induce him to retire
from a country where the crime of being a foreigner is not
to be forgiven, and where he will not support an existence
which will only be tolerated. It cannot be doubted but
that he would willingly exchange the sun and the coin
of Prussia for the sun and the coin of France, the only
country on earth where men pay homage to the genius
of science, and confer lasting fame; the only country
where La Grange, the grandson of a Frenchman, and
who gratefully recollects that we have made him known
to Europe, would delight to live, if he must renounce
his old friends and the abode of his youth. Prince Car-
dito di Laffredo, Ambassador from Naples to Copenhagen, has made him the handsomest offers, in the name
of his Sovereign. He has received pressing invitations
from the Grand Duke and the King of Sardinia. But all
these proposals would easily be forgoten, if put in competition with ours. And will not the King of France
likewise, aided by a worthy comptroller general, at
the time when he would extend that empire of benevolence which appertains to him alone — would not the
King of France endeavor to acquire a man whose merit
is known to all Europe? La Grange here receives a pension of six thousand livres. And cannot the King of
France dedicate that sum to the first mathematician of
the age? Is it beneath Louis XVI. to invite a great
man, from a miserable academy, who is there misunderstood, misallied, and thus, by the most noble warfare, to
extirpate the only literary corps that has wrestled against
his proper academies? Would not this act of generosity
be superior to those that are usually performed? France,
with pernicious policy, has been the asylum of Princes,
with whose necessities she was burdened. Why will she
not welcome a great man who would but add to her
worth? Has she so long enriched others with her losses,
and will she not enrich herself by others' errors? In
fine, to speak of the Minister I love, one De Boynes has
given eighteen thousand livres a year, for a useless place,
to one Boscovich, — a man despised by all the learned
of Europe, as a literary quack of poor abilities; and why
will not M. de Calonne grant a pension of two thou-

sand crowns to the first man in Europe of his class, and probably to the last great genius the mathematical sciences shall possess; the passion for which diminishes, because of the excessive difficulties that are to be surmounted, and the infinitely few means of acquiring fame by discovery?

I have the hope exceedingly at heart, because I think it a noble one, and because I tenderly love the man. I entreat I may have an immediate answer; for I own I have induced M. de la Grange to suspend his declarations on the propositions that have been made him, till he has heard what ours may be. I need not repeat that — he whose hands are tied must call for help.

LETTER LII.

December 2d, 1786.

ON THE 29th, between one and two o'clock, a person from Courland came to me and asked for the Baron de Noldé. He said he was charged with some secret commission, and delivered him a letter from M. Rummel, his brother-in-law, a Syndic of the nobility, and fifty Prussian gold Fredericks. The letter desired Noldé would give faith to what the bearer should relate, and informed him that the regency of the Republic intended to confer on him the place of assessor, if he would repair to Courland that he might be put in nomination; and that the appointment was to be made at the beginning of the year. The bearer of the letter said he had known the Baron Noldé when a boy. The Baron supposed him to be an advocate, or a notary, of whom he had some confused idea. He neither told his name, where he lodged, how he traveled, when he came to Berlin, nor where he was going. Hamburg, Lübeck, Vienna, Munich, etc., are places through which he has passed, or means to pass. His journey has been very secret, very enigmatical, very mysterious. He only gave it to be understood that great changes would soon be seen in Courland, and that Woronzow was there to enact a grand part, of which he spoke so as to make it suspected he might become Duke. Such are the chief points of this odd interview.

We must combine this with the return of the Duke, who arrived three days ago, and with innumerable indications which demonstrate that a revolution is either in agitation or preparing in Courland. Consternation has seized on the Duke. It is only whispered, but it appears evident that the States have stopped the payment of his revenues, because he does not expend the money in the

(251)

country; and this is the least of the griefs, entertained at Petersburg, against this detested man. Certain it is that he has sent his wife, who is far advanced in her pregnancy, to Mittau, whither he dares not return him-self; hoping she shall be delivered of a male child, and that this presumptive heir will reconcile him to his country.

Add, further, that Baron Noldé is of one of the first houses of Courland; that his uncle, the Chamberlain Howen, a capable and enterprising man, is at present first Minister or Land Marshal; that all affairs pass through his hands, and that he is in the greatest credit; which, to say truth, may be reduced to this: that he has the power of selling, with more or less meanness, this fine but unfortunate province; which, however, should it be abandoned by all its neighbors, cannot act otherwise than to bestow, rather than suffer itself to be seized upon. It is very possible that the family of Noldé, which knows how much this studious young Baron has continually pre-ferred a civil to a military life, has only thought of placing him advantageously. (The post of assessor, which is worth from four to five thousand livres of Courland, per annum, is the post of preferment.) But it is equally possible, and, all circumstances considered, very probable, that his assistance is wished for in effect-ing a revolution.

This young Baron is possessed of honor, information, and understanding; has a great respect for the rights of mankind, an utter hatred for the Russians, and an ardent desire his country should rather appertain to any other Power. From his infancy the sport of chance, ruined by misfortunes of every kind, which all had a worthy origin; disgusted with the gloomy rank of subaltern officer, which impedes the progress of his studies, and moderate in his desires, he would accept a place which should be-stow on him the *otium cum dignitate;* but he would not be the slave of Russia. He loves France, and is attached to me, to whom he thinks himself obliged. He is desirous of serving his country, the Cabinet of Ver-sailles, and his friend. The indecision of his mind must have been afflicting, especially under circumstances when, laboring for these six months like a galley slave, and certainly in a manner more useful than had he been mounting guard, you have even neglected to prolong his furlough. This, at least, was perplexing. I have decided for him.

Making myself responsible for this prolongation, which it would be so iniquitous to refuse, and which surely will be granted if it be only out of respect to me, who find his coadjutorship necessary; imagining he still has the right of returning into Courland by throwing up his commission, or even without throwing it up, by suffering another nomination to take place; convinced that no one can inform us more exactly of the situation of the country in which he has so many relations; persuaded that this is an important step for several reasons, the principal of which I shall presently demonstrate, and not believing (independent of the expense of a journey of more than four hundred leagues) that I should be justified in absenting myself without having received express orders; confiding in the honor of this affectionate young gentleman, as well because of the recommendations of those to whom he is intimately known, as from having myself proved his principles and his conduct; and still farther convinced that confidence is the most powerful of motives with men of honor,—I have thought it the most prudent mode to suffer him immediately to depart on his promise of sending me information of whatever passes, and of returning to Berlin within two months. It has seemed to me that this will conciliate his interest and ours,—the latter because we shall be perfectly informed of whatever we wish to know concerning Courland, of which many things are to be learned, and by which step, at all events, we shall make a party in the country, where the simple title of consul, or the permission only of wearing our uniform, with a small pension, will secure to us a man of merit, should he determine to accept the offers of the regency; first, because Baron Noldé will inform himself, by this journey, what is the degree of stability and profit of the place they propose for him, and because, if he be not satisfied with this, he may again return to the service of France, with the recommendation of additional labors and strong zeal in her behalf; and, should he be satisfied with the offers of Courland, he may accept them, while we may better his situation and augment his respect and safety, by suffering him to wear our uniform, etc., etc.

Summarily, this young gentleman, who has served at the sieges of Port-Mahon and Gibraltar; who is esteemed and beloved by his commanders; who for six months has labored, under my direction, with uncommon zeal, and assiduity not less uncommon; I repeat, this gentleman would certainly merit such a mark of favor, though it had been on his own business solely that he had made a journey into Courland. But the truth is I send him thither because I am strongly invited by circumstances, and am convinced of two things. First, that were it only perfectly to understand this part of the politics of Russia, it is of importance to us at once to know at what to estimate the worth and destiny, as well as the changes of which this country is susceptible; which, independent of all interior circumstances, stands by situation the sentinel of Poland and of the Baltic, now that Sweden, our arm of the north, is so seriously menaced. My second conviction is that Baron Noldé is the most proper of men faithfully to send us this information. Wherefore not afford him aid? Wherefore not preserve such persons?

You must have seen, but perhaps you have not remarked, in the thirty-second abstract from the gazettes, that Springporten, formerly a colonel in the service of Sweden, has lately entered into the service of Russia, with the rank of major general; that he is the man who best knows Finland; that the Empress has granted him three thousand roubles for his equipment, an estate of six hundred peasants, in White Russia, and the key of chamberlain; that he is incessantly to make a journey into the Crimea, etc., etc. Though by acquiring such men, with the knowledge and connections which they bring with them, preparations are made for the execution of the greatest projects, still, by the same methods, such projects are rendered abortive.

There was not time, last post, to write the postscript

in cipher, which contains a curious fact, of which Panchand will probably make use and application.*

I informed you in No. VI. that "they have lately interdicted discounting bills of exchange at the bank, etc." This fact has not been verified. The merchants indeed required it might be done, but their request has not been granted, and it was opposed by Struensee. But to the news of the day.

There are two versions concerning Mademoiselle Voss. Both are derived from excellent sources, and probably the real one will be that which may be composed from the two.

1. There will be no marriage. Mademoiselle will depart in a month, for I know not where; and afterward will return to Potsdam. "I know," said she, "that I dishonor myself. All the compensation I ask is not to see any person; leave me in profound solitude; I neither wish for riches nor splendor." It is certain that, if she can keep him thus, she will lead him much the farther.

2. Wednesday, the 22d of last month, was the remarkable day on which Mademoiselle Voss accepted the King's hand, and promised him her own. It was determined the Queen should be brought to approve the plan of the left-handed marriage as a thing of necessity, should she obstinately display too much repugnance. It is singular that, for the consummation of this rare business, the arrival of the Duke of Saxe-Weimar was waited for, who is the brother-in-law of the Queen. The King thus will be father to four sorts of children.† The priests, who have been consulted on the manner of reconciling the claims of heaven with the pleasures of earth, have decided that it will be better to concentrate his enjoyments by an extraordinary marriage than incessantly to wander from error to error. Nothing has

* The last letter has no postscript. The author probably means the fact contained in the paragraphs to be found a few pages forward, which begin with the words— POSTSCRIPT MENTIONED IN THE BODY OF THE LETTER.

† Those of his first Queen, Elizabeth, from whom he was divorced, as before mentioned; those of his present Queen; his natural children, by Madame Rietz; and his half-bastard, half-legitimate, by Mademoiselle Voss, had this marriage taken place.

transpired concerning the manner in which this arrangement is to be made known to the uncles; of the name the
new Princess is to bear; or of her future establishment, etc.,
etc.   In all probability she soon will interfere in public
affairs; and, should she do so, the credit of Bishopswerder
will diminish.   She loves neither him nor his daughters.
Her party is, besides, very opposite to that of the
mystics, which gains ground in a very fearful manner.
I am going to relate a recent anecdote on that subject
which happened in the last months of Frederick II., and
which it is infinitely important, at least for my security
while I remain here, to keep secret; of the irrevocable
authenticity of which you yourself will judge; and which
will show you whither tends this imaginary theory of
the mystics connected with the Rosicrucian-Freemasons,
whom among us some look upon with pity, and others
treat as objects of amusement.

There is a rumor whispered about which terrifies
worthy people, and which, true or false, is a faithful indication of the public opinion.   It is affirmed that Prince
Henry, the Duke of Brunswick, and General Moellendorf, mean to quit the army.   The two first probably do
not yet think of such a step; but the latter is indubitably
the most discontented of the three.   Rich, loyal, simple,
firm, he possesses virtues which would do honor to a soil
on which virtue is more fruitful.   He certainly has not
been treated either as he himself expected, or as good
citizens have wished.   They were desirous, indeed, to create him a count; but among so many counts, what need
had he of such a title?   For which reason this respectable man replied, "WHAT HAVE I DONE?"   This artless,
noble question was too severe — on the herd of nobles
and the multitude of titles that have sprung up, warmed
by the breath of royal munificence — to be agreeable.
His modest and antique manners are become reproachful
to the Court; yet is the only reform truly beneficial and
universally approved, under the new reign, the work of
this general.   I mean the abolition of that iniquitous
contribution called GRASS FORAGE, which subjected the open
country to pillage, during three months of the year,

under the pretense of accustoming the cavalry to forage.
He has not since been consulted on any subject, or he
has had no influence. I should not be surprised should
he retire to his country seat; and it is impossible to exaggerate the unamiable light in which such a tacit profession of faith would place the King and his Government.

Three months more of similar proceedings, and he will
have no respect to lose,— at least, in his own country.
Every corrupt symptom is manifest. Rietz, a rascal,
avaricious, chief pimp, and an avowed *Giton*, insomuch
that *ipse confitetur, sibi cum Rege, dum princeps Borussiæ
esset, apud eius amicam stupri commercium fuisse.* In a
word, Rietz, the vilest and the most debased of men,
manages the royal household, and enjoys a great part of
the Court favor. Here it ought to be noted that he is
very susceptible of being bought; but he must be dearly
bribed, for he is covetous and prodigal, and his fortune
is to make, should ever France have occasion to direct
the Cabinet of Berlin. So long as the King shall have
any power, Rietz and Prince Frederick of Brunswick are
the two men most liable to temptation.

The following is an anecdote of a very low species,
but very characteristic for those who know the country.
The Italian and French dancers have received orders to
dance twice a week, at the German theater. The purport of such a capricious injunction was to give disgust
to this species of people, who are expensive enough, and
to find a pretense for dismissing them. They have been
well advised, and will dance; but such is the low spirit
of cunning which presides over the administration. Politics are treated as wisely as theatrical matters.

I this moment learned that Heinitz, one of the Ministers of State, a man of mediocrity, but laborious, has
written a letter to the King, of which the following is
nearly the sense: "Being a foreigner, not possessed of
any lands in your States, my zeal cannot be suspected
by your Majesty. It is consequently my duty to inform
you that the projected capitation tax will alienate the
hearts of Your Majesty's subjects; and proves that the
new regulators of the finances are, at present, little versed
in public business." The King said to him two days

17

after, "I thank you," and made no further inquiries.
Irresolution does not exclude obstinacy, although obstinacy is far from being resolution. I should not be astonished were the tobacco and snuff company to remain on
its former footing. As for the respect which government should preserve, that must take care of itself.

It was an attempt similar to that of Heinitz which
produced the last military promotion, to the disadvantage
of General Moellendorf. The General wrote, with respectful but firm dignity, against the nomination of
Count Brühl, and entreated the King would show less
indifference for the army. Thanks were returned,
accompanied with these words: "The place has been
promised a year and a half"; and two days after seventeen majors were created. Since this time, coldness
toward the General has increased, and civility has been
substituted for confidence. The letter is not thought
well of. It is said that he ought to have reserved this
vigorous blow for some occasion on which he should
not appear to be personally interested; and it is he himself who seemed most proper to fill the place of governor.

The Duke of Weimar is preparing to make a very
pompous wolf hunt, on the frontiers of Poland. The
orders and adjustments for this party of pleasure do not
very well agree with the projects and ceremonials of
economy. Twelve hundred peasants are commanded to
be in readiness; sixty horses have been sent, and eight
baggage wagons, with the masters of the forests, gentlemen, huntsmen, and cooks for this hunt, which is to
continue six days.

At present, I am nearly certain that my second version, relative to Mademoiselle Voss, is the true one; and
that the Queen is coaxed into the measure. The King
never lived on better terms with her. He has often
visited her within this week, pays her debts, and has
given her a concert. Probably she has made a virtue of
necessity. It appears evident that this connection of the
King highly deranges the plan of the mystic administrators. The family of Mademoiselle Voss wishes to profit
by her elevation; and their advice no way agrees with

that of the present favorites. Bishopswerder, far
from gaining upon the King, declines in his esteem. In
a word, revolution may come from that side. Will public affairs be the gainer? This question it is impossible
to answer. We can only turn the telescope toward the
spot; or rather the microscope; for, in truth, we are in
the reign and the country of the infinitely minute.

[*Postscript, mentioned in the body of the letter.*]

The current coins in Poland were formerly as follows:
The mark of fine silver of the Cologne weight was
coined at 13–3 r. or 80 fl. of Poland.

As to gold coins, there were none but Dutch ducats
that had any nominal value; that is to say—

At the royal treasuries, they were taken for $16\frac{1}{4}$ k.

By the public, for 18 k.; both of which rates were
fixed by decrees of the Diet.

In the Diet of 1786, the ducats were universally raised
to 18 k. each.

The assay of the silver consequently cannot any longer
be maintained; and it is affirmed there is a determination, hereafter, to coin the fine mark at 14 r. or 84 fl.

But neither can this coinage support itself; for, should
Berlin coin at 14 r., Poland will be obliged to keep up
an equal value at a greater expense, because of carriage.

Under the present circumstances, it might be advantageous to draw on Poland for ducats at 3 r. if the assay
of silver is at 14 r.

But, if the relative value of gold should fall, comparatively to that of silver, silver may be there bought with
profit.

Generally speaking, it appears to me that the recent
operations on gold should lead us to reflect on the state
of the silver, especially in Spain, should that power persist in the folly which, with the greatest part of Europe,
it has given into, of keeping two species of coin, and
hoarding the gold.

SECOND POSTSCRIPT.— The King, attended by a single
lackey and much disguised, has been to the corn and

straw warehouses, where he inquired of the soldiers who
worked there what their wages were. "Five groschen."
A moment after he put the same question to the superintendents. "Six groschen." Three soldiers being called
to confront the superintendents, and the fraud being
proved, a subaltern and three soldiers were ordered to
conduct the two superintendents to Spandau, a civil
prison; and there they are to be tried. The fact is very
praiseworthy. He makes evening peregrinations almost
unattended, and addicts himself to the minute inquiries
of a justice of the peace. At least this is the third time
he has acted thus. Some of his attendants imagine
he means to imitate the Emperor. After what has passed
between them, this perhaps would be the most severe
symptom of absolute incapacity.

LETTER LIII.

December 5th, 1786.

THE news of the cabals, which the Emperor again wishes to excite at Deux-Ponts, and which our Cabinet has published here, seem to have produced a very good effect upon the King, in despite of those who exclaim, *Ne crede Teucris* — an adage which is become the signal of rallying among the English, Dutch, anti-French, etc., etc. May we conduct ourselves so as never to admit of any other reproach. This discovery will probably, both at Berlin and Deux-Ponts, counteract the Emperor. It was very ill-judged of him not to suffer that torpor to increase, which is the infallible consequence of the langour of labor, or of the confusion which doing nothing produces.

But I resign these foreign politics to your ambassadors, to whom they are known, because I gained this intelligence by that means only by which I gain all other; because Comte d'Esterno did not say a word on the subject to me; because it would have been weak and little decent to have put many questions on a matter which I ought to have known; and because I, therefore, satisfied myself with vague annotations on our fidelity. I am not, and probably shall not be, circumstantially informed of the affair. You, perhaps, may feel on this occasion how important it is that better intelligence should be sent me from Versailles; but you will doubtless acknowledge I perform all I can, all I ought, when I trace the outlines of internal — since I have not the key to external — politics; though assuredly I shall not neglect the latter whenever lucky chance shall afford opportunities.

The libelist Crantz, who was expelled the country by Frederick II. for theft, and for having sold the same horse three times, is recalled, with a pension of eight hundred crowns. The King wrote to Count Hertzberg to give him some post. The Minister replied that the abilities of the gentleman were great, and that he was very estimable, but that he had too little discretion to be employed in foreign affairs. The King proposed him to the Minister Werder, who answered, the gentleman was exceedingly intelligent, exceedingly capable, but that there was money in his office, which, therefore, M. Crantz must not be suffered to enter. At last, the King has thrown the illustrious Crantz, praised by all and by all rejected, upon the States; and he receives a pension of eight hundred crowns for doing nothing.

The Minister Schulemburg, after having twice demanded his dismissal, has finally obtained it, without a pension. This is severe; but the ex-Minister is adroit. He has cast all the burden upon the first branch of his department, which has been retrenched. If there are any means of being restored, this was well done. You are acquainted with the qualities of this man. He had understanding, facility, and sagacity in the choice of his coadjutors; was indifferent concerning the means he employed; vain in prosperity; despairing in misfortune, of which his feelings are the sport; ready to serve others; susceptible of affection, and believing in friendship after having been fifteen years Minister of Frederick II. He thought himself immovable because he was necessary, and hopes that this necessity will surmount the cabals by which he has been driven from his post. Perhaps he deceives himself; for, while we are not difficult in our choice, and when the business is not of itself beyond vulgar capacities, agents may at any time be found. If monarchs wish for a Newton, they certainly must employ a Newton, or the place must remain vacant. But who is there who does not think himself capable of being a minister, and of whom may it be demonstrated he is not capable?

I am assured, from a good quarter, that Count Hertzberg regains confidence. He has bowed to the new agents, who have had the weakness to bring him again into favor because Mademoiselle Voss is the niece of Count Finckenstein, and because, her family being unable to obtain any advantage by her promotion except by the overthrow of those who surround the King, who are not ignorant that the lady detests them, it is requisite some one should be opposed to her. But, if she be a dame of mettle, change must be looked for on that side, which more or less address will hasten or retard. Whether or no, Hertzberg has advised Count Goertz to take part with Renneval, of whose prudence he has spoken in the highest terms to the King.

A new blunder has been committed in the military. All the first lieutenants have been made captains; and the captains, whether on whole or half pay, of the regiment of guards, are advanced to the rank of major. Except the war chancery, I do not see who will be the gainer by this arrangement. It is said the King intends to pay his personal debts, the payment of which, by the way of parenthesis, is more than ever eluded, with the produce of the commissions of officers, and the diplomas of counts, barons, chamberlains, etc.

The plan for the capitation tax was represented to the King as a kind of voluntary act, and which the people themselves would meet half way; but informed of the public disgust this project had occasioned, alarmed by the rumor, and heated by the letter of Heinitz, he told Werder, "People ought not to meddle with matters they do not understand." (Take good note that this be said to his Minister of Finance.) "Launay should have been consulted" (now under the fetters of the commission of inquiry). Werder excused himself in the best manner he could, by saying the plan did not originate with him (in fact, the project was Beyer's), as if he had not appropriated by approving it.

The general directory, that species of Council of State at which the King is never present, has projected remonstrances concerning the humiliating inactivity in which it is held; but Welner opposed them, giving the invincible repugnance of his Majesty for every species of advice to be understood. This arises from the strange supposition that those who give him advice have adopted the sentiments of his uncle, relative to his capacity. He is yet to learn that no one ventures to advise among the great, except such persons as they esteem.

In the meantime the mystics continue in the same degree of favor. Their conspiracy was denounced by the
great person whom I spoke of to you in my last, to General Moellendorf, the intimate friend of the brother of
Mademoiselle Voss (a man esteemed for his moral character; in other respects obscure, at least hitherto, yet
who probably will soon appear upon the stage), in order
that he might terrify his sister, and by her intervention
the Sovereign, concerning the crimes of a sect who
would sacrifice all whom they cannot rule. Biester — the
same, to say the least, to whom it has been insinuated
that he should spare the mystics — has a lawsuit in which
they are interested, which it is said he will lose. He
has accused M. Starck of being a Catholic. Starck is a
Professor of Jena, a man celebrated for the gift of persuasion, as well as for his understanding and knowledge,
a Lutheran born, and a Lutheran minister, but a known
professor of the Catholic religion. He has, notwithstanding, instituted a criminal action against Biester, for
having said this, and has summoned him to prove his
calumnious assertion. Never would such a suit have
been heard of under Frederick II. Starck has recently
published a book entitled " Nicaise," in which he attacks
Freemasonry. The Freemasons have replied by another,
entitled "Anti-Nicaise," in which are inserted authentic
letters from several princes, and, among others, from
Prince Charles of Hesse Cassel, and Prince Ferdinand of
Brunswick; which well prove, what all know who have
conversed with him, should they not likewise know his
creatures, Bauer and Wetsall, that a great general, or
rather a FAMOUS general, may be a very little man.

The statement of the expense is at length made out,
and the result is that the King may increase his treasury by two millions of crowns, and still reserve a considerable sum for his pleasures or his affections. But,
in this calculation, it is supposed that following receipts
will equal the preceding, which certainly is doubtful.
One paternal act has been performed; the country people have been freed from the obligation of lodging the
cavalry gratis, and supplying forage at a very low price.
This reform will cost the King two hundred and seventy

thousand crowns per annum. But it was extremely necessary. It is the result of the plan of Moellendorf for the abolition of the GREEN FORAGE.

One M. Moulines is the editor of the manuscripts of the late King. I have before given you his political character; and, as a literary man, he is destitute of taste and discernment, and without any profound knowledge of the language. But he is the friend of Welner; of that Welner to whom the King, at seven o'clock in the morning, sends the letters and requests of the day before, and who at four o'clock goes to give in his account, or rather to instruct the King. As for the Ministers, they receive orders, and do not give advice. Welner has had the wit to refuse the title of Minister, and to satisfy himself with that of superintendent of the buildings; but he is already fawned upon by the whole Court. These manuscripts are to be printed in eighteen volumes octavo. The two parts most curious are the " History of the Seven Years' War," and the " Memoirs of My Own Times." * In the former, Frederick has rather recounted what he ought to have done than what he did; and this is itself a trait of genius. He praises or excuses almost everybody; and blames only himself.†

The Marquis of Lucchesini, who had been, not the friend, not the favorite of Frederick, but his LISTENER, is, though he does not own it, highly piqued at the choice made of Moulines. He has demanded leave of absence for six months, to make a journey into his own country, from which, no doubt, he will no more return. How did it happen that he did not feel that the personal respect in which he would have been held would have been immense had he quitted Prussia a week after the death of the King, with this only reply to all the offers which would have been made him ? — " I was ambitious

---

* The publication has proved the author was mistaken. The letters are the most curious part of the work. There are few things in the history that were not known before, except that it exhibits the character of this extraordinary man, as drawn by himself, to those who are capable of discovering that character; and in this particular the letters are perhaps still superior.

† It is plain the author had never read the work, which was not then published.

only of a place which all the Kings on earth could not take from me, cannot restore; that of being the friend of Frederick II."

Two successors have been appointed to Count Schulemburg; for, as the King of France has four Ministers, twenty are necessary to the King of Prussia. One of these successors is M. Moschwitz, a magistrate; of whom neither good nor harm is spoken. The other is a Count Schulemburg von Blumbert, the son-in-law of Count Finckenstein. The latter possesses knowledge, an ardent and gloomy ambition, and a moral character that is suspected. He is studious, intelligent, assiduous, and is certainly a capable man. But he is supposed to want order; to possess rather a heated brain than an active mind; and to have more opinions of his own than dexterity to blend them with the opinions of others and render them successful. Neither is he at all accustomed to business; and is an absolute stranger to banking and commercial speculations, that is to say, to the principal branches of his department.

FIRST POSTSCRIPT.— The King, who is paying off the debts of his father, has granted twenty thousand crowns for the maintenance and privy purse of his two eldest sons. Their household is a separate expense.

SECOND POSTSCRIPT.— I did not believe I was so good a prophet. The brother of Mademoiselle Voss has the place of the President Moschwitz. This is the foot in the stirrup.

The course of exchange on Amsterdam is so exceedingly high that, there being no operation of finance or of commerce by which it may be accounted for, I have no doubt but remittances are made there to pay off the personal debts of the King. Struensee is of the same opinion; but he has no positive intelligence on the subject.

LETTER LIV.

December 8th, 1786.

Y ou may take it for granted that there are three principal shades in the character of the King — deceit, which he believes to be art; irascible vanity, whenever the least remonstrance is made to him; and the accumulation of money, which is not so much avarice in him as the passion of possessing. The first of these vices has rendered him suspicious; for he who deceives by system continually imagines he is deceived. The second induces him to prefer people of middling, or inferior abilities; and the latter contributes to make him lead an obscure and solitary life, by which the two former are strengthened. Violent in private, impenetrable in public, little animated by the love of fame in reality, and making this love to consist chiefly in leading the world to suppose he is not governed; rarely troubling himself with foreign politics; a soldier from necessity, and not from inclination; disposed to favor the mystics, not from conviction, but because he believes he shall, by their aid, examine the consciences and penetrate the hearts of men — such is the outline of the man.

His debts will be paid by the surplus money. Under the late King there was annually a considerable sum which was not brought to the Treasury, but was kept apart to raise new regiments, to increase the artillery, or to repair the fortresses. Now, as the artillery was not increased, as new regiments were not raised, and as the fortresses were not repaired, the money consequently accumulated. It is now employed in liquidation.

The revenues are upward of twenty-seven millions of crowns, including the customs; or about a hundred and eight millions of French livres. The expense of the army is twelve millions and a half of crowns; of the civil

administration, two millions three hundred thousand
crowns; of the King's, the Queen's, and the Princes'
household, one million two hundred thousand crowns;
and a hundred and thirty thousand for the payment of
pensions.   I am not acquainted with all the inferior
expenses; but when, for example, we know that the legation chest does not absorb more than seventy-five thousand crowns, and that the supplements amount on an
average to twenty-five thousand crowns (on which I have
to remark that the same object in Denmark costs three
millions of crowns; and in Russia, a country almost unknown to the greatest part of Europe, three hundred
thousand rubles), it is easy to understand that the sum
total of the annual surplus, the expense being deducted
from the receipt, is about three millions and a half
of crowns.

The manufacturers have presented a petition, in which
they supplicate to be informed whether any alterations
are intended to be made in the privileges granted them
by the late King, or his predecessors, that they may not
be exposed to the buying of materials, or contracting
agreements which they shall be unable to fulfill.   Frederick William has given his word of honor not to make
any change, at present, of this kind.

I have already said that the King intended to have
made Welner a Minister, which dignity it is affirmed he
refused.   This for many reasons was a master stroke, by
which he will be no loser; for he has lately been granted
an augmentation of three thousand crowns, that he may
enjoy the same pension as the Ministers of State.   The
King not only places no confidence in the latter, but he
affects never to mention them, unless it be to Count
Finckenstein, the uncle of the well-beloved; or to Count
Arnim, who interferes in the negotiations of the so much
desired marriage, and who is at present too much a
stranger to business to be suspected of any system.   The
supposition that he has one will, at least for some time,
be the rock on which the new Schulemburg is liable to
be wrecked.   He is supported by strength of character
and ardor of ambition.   As to the new President, to whom
already is attributed a depth of design which probably

he never possessed, I believe him little capable of enacting any great part.

The Sieur du Bosc, who is become a counselor of finance and of commerce, is also desirous of making his entrance. He has petitioned to be employed in the customs, and his request has been granted, but without an increase of respect. Speculators, joining this symptom to some others, have drawn a conclusion that this is some diminution in the credit of Bishopswerder, his protector. The party of the mystics, however, does but augment and flourish. To own the truth, the crowd of candidates may injure individuals. One of the most zealous members, Drenthal, is lately arrived. No office was found for him under the King; but he has in the interim been placed with the Princess Amelia, in quality of Marshal of the Court, with a promise of not being forgotten at the death of this Princess, whose end approaches.

Our knowledge of the new Sovereign may be increased by a sketch of the most distinguished people at his Court. Among these are an old count (Lendorf), gentle as Philinta, obliging as Bonneau, a shameless flatterer, an unfaithful talebearer, and, when need is, a calumniator. A prince in his pupilage (Holsteinbeck), smoking his pipe, drinking brandy, never knowing what he says, ever talking on what he does not understand, ready at any time to fly to the parade, to hunt, to go to church, to go to brothels, or to go to supper with a lieutenant, a lackey, or Madame Rietz. Another prince (Frederick of Brunswick), famous for the pains he took to dishonor his sister, and particularly his brother-in-law, the present King; a libertine under the Monarch who was called an atheist; at present a mystic, when the Monarch is supposed a devotee; a pensioner of the Freemason lodges, from which he annually receives six thousand crowns; talking nonsense from system; and, for the secrets which he wrests, returning a multitude of half secrets, which are partly invented, and partly useless. A kind of mad captain (Grothaus), who has seen all, had all, done all, known all; the intimate friend of the Prince of Wales; the favorite of the King of England, invited by Congress to be their president, on condition of conquering Canada;

master at pleasure of the Cape of Good Hope; the only
man capable of settling the affairs of Holland; an author,
a dancer, a runner, a jumper, a farmer, botanist, physician, chemist, and lieutenant colonel in the Prussian
service, with an income of seven hundred crowns per
annum. A minister (Count Arnim), who dreams instead
of thinking, smiles instead of replying, reasons instead
of determining, regrets at night the liberty he sacrificed
in the morning, and wishes at once to remain indolent
on his estate, and to acquire the reputation of a minister. A reigning prince (the Duke of Weimar), who
imagines he has wit because he can interpret a rebus; is
cunning, because he pretends to swallow his own sarcasms; a philosopher, because he has three poets at his
Court; and a species of hero, because he rides full speed
in search of wolves and boars. Such being his favorites,
judge of the man.

Do you wish to estimate his taste by his diversions?
Tuesday was the great day on which he went to enjoy
the pleasures of the imagination at the German theater.
Here, in grand pomp, he was accosted by a dramatic
compliment, which concluded with these words: "May
that kind Providence that rewards all, all great and good
actions, bless and preserve our most gracious King, that
august father of his people; bless and preserve all the
royal house; and bless and preserve us all! AMEN!"
The King was so highly enchanted with this dramatic
homily that he has added another thousand crowns to
the five thousand which he had granted the manager,
and has made him a present of four chandeliers, and
twelve glasses to decorate the boxes. Sarcasms innumerable, on the French theater, accompanied this act of
generosity.

Would you judge him by military favors? A pension
of three hundred crowns has been granted to Captain
Colas, who had been eight-and-twenty years imprisoned
in the citadel of Magdeburg; and the rank of lieutenant
general bestowed on Borck, his Majesty's Governor, who
is eighty-two years of age.

Or by his Court favors? The chamberlain's key sent
to that extravagant Baron Bagge; who indeed presented

a hundred louis to Rietz, and forty to the person who brought him this gift of royal munificence.

It has been insinuated to his Majesty that he had displeased the citizens, on his return from Prussia; the army, from the first day of his reign; the general directory, by rendering it null; his family, by being polite instead of friendly; the priests, by his project of a third marriage; the pensioners, by the suppression of the tobacco monopoly; the Court, by the confusion or the delay in the statement of the accounts; and that, therefore, it might perhaps be imprudent, for the present, in the moment of effervescence, to accept the statue that had been proposed by the city of Königsberg.

Are you desirous of an index to the respect in which he may be held by foreign nations? The Poles have refused a passage to the horses, for remounting the cavalry, coming from the Ukraine. I need not tell you such a refusal would never have been made to Frederick II.

Count Hertzberg pretends he has received letters written against himself, to persons in France, by Prince Henry. He showed them to the King, who made him no reply. I scarcely can believe there is not some fraud in this affair. I know the persons to whom the Prince writes in France; and, treachery out of the question, they certainly are not interested in favor of Count Hertzberg. But whether or no, there are rumors that Hertzberg and Blumenthal are soon to resign; that the latter will be replaced by M. Voss; and the first, who has imagined himself too necessary to be taken at his word, "by a man who will astonish the whole world." (This, it is affirmed, is the phrase of the King himself.) Hertzberg has the knowledge of a civilian, and is well read in archives, because his memory is prodigious. He also knows something of practical agriculture. But, on the reverse, he is violent, passionate, abundantly vain, and explains himself as he conceives, that is to say, with difficulty and confusion; is desirous but incapable of doing that good by which reputation is acquired; rather vindictive than malignant; subject to prejudices; disposed to injure those against whom he is prejudiced; and devoid of dignity, address, and resource.

Blumenthal is a faithful accountant, an ignorant Minister; ambitious, when he recollects ambition, and to please his family; and full of respect for the Treasury, which he places far above the State; and of indifference for the King, whom he more than neglected while he was Prince of Prussia.

The duty has been taken off beer, which yielded five hundred and fifty thousand crowns per annum, and a substitute, it is said, will be found by an additional tax on wines; but wines are already too much taxed, and cannot bear any such increase. The expenses of this part of the customs amount to twenty thousand crowns; sixty-nine persons employed have been dismissed; but their salaries are continued till they shall be replaced.

First Postscript. — Count Totleben (a Saxon), who has been appointed major in the regiment of Elben, was preceded by a letter the import of which was that he was sent to the regiment TO LEARN THE SERVICE. The equivoque of the expression is stronger in the German. The regiment wrote in a body to the King: "If Count Totleben be sent to instruct us, we have not merited, nor will we endure, such humiliation. If he come for instruction, he cannot serve as major." Some pretend that the dispute is already settled, and others that it will have consequences.

The King about a month since was reminded of Captain Forcade, who was formerly a favorite of the Prince of Prussia. His Majesty replied: "Let him write what his wishes are." Forcade requested the happiness of being one of his attendants. The King answered: "I have no need of useless officers; they only serve to make a dust."

Second Postscript. — By the last courier I sent you some calculations on the coins of Poland. Here follow others more absurd, relative to those of Denmark.

Denmark has adopted, according to law, the nominal value of its currency at $11\frac{1}{3}$ crowns for the fine mark of Cologne; yet it has for several years paid from thirteen to fourteen crowns the fine mark. Hence there are no silver coins in Denmark, and business is all transacted in bank bills, the value of which is never to be realized.

When the evil began to be evident, Schimmelmann wished it might be remedied. He coined crowns in specie $9\frac{1}{4}$ of which contained the fine mark, and calculated that the crown in specie was equal to one crown $9\frac{37}{100}$ sols currency *lubs*. The fact would have been true, if the silver currency had existed at $11\frac{1}{8}$ per mark; but as none such were to be found, each person willingly accepted the crowns in specie at one crown nine sols currency; but no one was willing to give a crown in specie for one crown nine sols currency. The result was that all these fine crowns in specie were melted down.

At present, now the evil is excessive, there is a wish to repeat a similar operation, after the following manner.

1. Crowns in specie are to be coined of $9\frac{1}{4}$ to a fine mark.

2. Bank bills are to be issued, which are to represent crowns in specie, and are to be realized or paid in specie.

3. It is wished to fix the value of these current crowns, in specie, by an edict; and, as they could not coin the crown at the assay of a crown nine sols without loss, it is intended to raise their value.

If, therefore, the present currency of Denmark, that is to say, the bank bills, have no real value, but their value consists in the balance of payment of this kingdom (or the rate of exchange) as it shall be for or against Denmark, this operation will be equally absurd with the former; for, if the bank shall pay crowns in specie, in lieu of the ideal value of the currency, it will rid itself of its crowns in specie, which will pass through the crucible, and the former confusion will continue to exist, or perhaps be increased to greater extravagance, by a new creation of bank bills representing the specie, which in like manner will, in a few months, be incapable of being realized.

THIRD POSTSCRIPT.— The new establishment of the bank of specie still appears to be obscure. It is intended to coin one million four hundred thousand crowns in specie, the silver for which should be at Altona.

18

There have been great debates, in the Council of State, between the Prince of Augustenborg, and the Minister of State, Rosencranz. The first requires the money should be coined at Altona, and the latter at Copenhagen. It is said that the Minister intends on this occasion to give in his resignation.

Bank bills equal to the value of one million four hundred thousand crowns are to be fabricated. This bank is to exchange the old bills of the Danish bank for the new bank bills, at a given rate.

Should this rate, as is very probable, be lower than the course of exchange, it would be an excellent manœuver to buy up bank bills, at present, and afterward convert them into specie.

LETTER LV.

THE true reason why the Duke of Weimar is so feasted is because he has undertaken to bring the Queen to consent to the marriage of Mademoiselle Voss. The Queen laughed at the proposal, and said: "Yes, they shall have my consent; but they shall not have it for nothing; on the contrary, it shall cost them dear." And they are now paying her debts, which amount to more than a hundred thousand crowns; nor do I believe this will satisfy her. While the King of Prussia is absorbed by meditations on this marriage, to me it appears evident that, if the Emperor be capable of a reasonable plan he is now wooing two wives, Bavaria and Silesia. Yes, Silesia; for I do not think that so many manœuvers on the Danube can be any other than the domino of the masquerade. But this is not the place in which he will make his first attempt. Everything demonstrates (and give me credit for beginning to know this part of Germany) that he will keep on the defensive, on the side of Prussia, which he will suffer to exhaust itself in efforts that he may freely advance on Bavaria; nor is it probable that he will trouble himself concerning the means of recovering Silesia, till he has first made that immense acquisition.

I say that he may freely advance; for, to speak openly, what impediment can we lay in his way? Omitting the million and one reasons of indolence or impotence which I could allege, let it be supposed that we should act — we should take the Low Countries, and he Bavaria; we the Milanese, and he the republic of Venice. What of all this would save Silesia? And what must soon after become of the Prussian power? It will be saved by the faults of its neighbors. It will fall! This grand fairy palace will come to the earth with a sudden crush, or its Government will undergo some revolution.

The King appears very tranquil concerning future contingencies. He is building near New Sans Souci, or rather repairing and furnishing a charming house, which formerly belonged to the Lord Marshal, and which is destined for Mademoiselle Voss. The Princess of Brunswick has requested to have a house at Potsdam; and the King has bestowed that on her which he inhabited as Prince Royal, which he is furnishing at his own expense. It is evident that this expiring Princess, crippled by David's disease, and consumed by inanity, is to be lady of honor to Mademoiselle Voss.

The debts of the Queen Dowager, the reigning Queen, the Prince Royal, now become King, and of some other complaisant people, male and female, are paid; and, if we add to these sums the pensions that have been bestowed, the houses that have been furnished, and the officers that have been created, we shall find the amount to be tolerably large. This is the true way to be prodigal without being generous. To this article it may be added that the King has given to Messieurs Blumenthal, Gaudi, and Heinitz, Ministers of State, each a *bailliage*. This is a new mode of making a present of a thousand louis. Apropos of the last of these Ministers, the King has replied to several persons employed in the Department of the Mines, who had complained of being superseded, that hereafter there shall be no claims of seniority.

He has terminated the affair of the Duke of Mecklenburg with some slight modifications.

He has given a miraculous kind reception to General Count Kalckreuth; who was aid-de-camp to and principal agent of Prince Henry; who quarreled with him outrageously for the Princess; and whom Frederick II. kept at a distance that he might not too openly embroil himself with his brother. Kalckreuth is a man of great merit, and an officer of the first class; but the affectation with which he has been distinguished by the King appears to me to be directed against his uncle; perhaps, too, there may be a mingled wish of reconciling himself to the army; but should Count Brühl persist in assuming, not only the rank which has been granted him, but that likewise of seniority, which will supersede all the generals, with Moellendorf at their head, I believe the dissatisfaction will be past remedy. All that is of little consequence while peace shall continue; and perhaps would be the same, were war immediately declared, for a year to come; but in process of time, that which has been sown shall be reaped. It is a strange kind of calculation which spreads discontent through an excellent army by favors and military distinctions, bestowed on a race of men who have always been such indifferent warriors.

Not that I pretend to affirm there are not brave and intelligent men in the service of Saxony. There are, for example two at present, very much distinguished — Captain Tielke of the artillery,* whom Frederick wished to gain but could not, though he offered him the rank of lieutenant colonel and an appointment of two thousand crowns; and Count Bellegarde, who is said to be one of the most able officers in the world. But these are not the persons whom they have gained for the Prussian service. Hitherto, in all the Saxon promotions, the thing consulted was the noble merit of being devoted to THE SECT, or that of being recommended by Bishopswerder.

POSTSCRIPT.— I forgot to mention to you that Comte d'Esterno had, at my intercession, addressed the Comte de Vergennes on the proposition of inviting M, de la Grange into France. It will be highly worthy of M. de Calonne to remove those money difficulties which M. de Brühl will not fail to raise.

*Well known to officers for his military history of the war of 1756, which has been translated from the German into several of the European languages.

LETTER LVI.

December 16th, 1786.

GENERAL COUNT KALCKREUTH continues to be in favor. It is a subject worthy of observation, that, should this favor be durable, should advantage be taken of the very great abilities of this gentleman, and should he be appointed to some place of importance, the King will then show he is not an enemy to understanding; he is not jealous of the merit of others; nor does he mean to keep all men of known talents at a distance. This will prove the mystics do not enjoy the exclusive privilege of royal favor. But all these deductions, I imagine, are premature; for, although Kalckreuth is the only officer of the army who has hitherto been thus distinguished; although he himself had conceived hopes he should be; although his merit is of the first order; Moellendorf having placed himself at the head of the malcontents, which the King will never pardon; Pritwitz being only a brave and inconsiderate soldier, the ridiculous echo of Moellendorf; Anhalt a madman; Gaudi almost impotent, because of his size, and lying likewise under the imputation of a defect in personal bravery, which occasioned Frederick II. to say of him, "He is a good professor, but when the boys are to repeat the lessons they have learned, he is never to be found." Although his other rivals are too young, and too inexperienced, to give him any uneasiness; in spite of all this, I say, I scarcely can imagine but that the principal cause of the distinction with which the King has treated him was the desire of humbling Prince Henry. At least I am very intimate with Kalckreuth, of whom I made a tolerably sure conquest at the reviews of Magdeburg, and I have reason to believe that I know everything which has passed between him and the King; in all which I do not perceive either anything conclusive, or anything of great promise.

The King supports his capitation tax. It is said it will be fixed according to the following rates: A lieutenant general, a Minister of State, or the widow of one of these, at about twelve crowns, or forty-eight French livres; a major general, or a privy councilor, at ten crowns; a chamberlain, or colonel, eight; a gentleman, six; a peasant, who holds lands in good provinces, three; a half-peasant (a peasant who holds lands has thirty acres, a half-peasant, ten), a crown twelve groschen. In the poor provinces, a peasant two crowns, a half-peasant, one.

Coffee hereafter is only to pay one groschen per pound, and tobacco the same. The general directory has received a memorial on the subject so strongly to the purpose that, although anonymous, it has been officially read, after which it was formally copied to be sent to the tobacco administration, in order to have certain facts verified. The step appeared to be so bold that the formal copy, or protocol, was only signed by four ministers — Messieurs Hertzberg, Arnim, Heinitz, and Schulemberg von Blumberg.

The merchants deputized by the city of Königsberg have written that, if salt is to continue to be monopolized by the Maritime Company, it will be useless for them to come to Berlin; for they can only be the bearers of grievances, without knowing what to propose. It is asserted, in consequence, that the Maritime Company will lose the monopoly of salt. This intelligence, to say the least, is very premature. Salt is an exceedingly important article; and Struensee, who has exerted his whole faculties to secure it to himself, has been so perfectly successful that he sells five thousand lasts of salt, twenty-eight muids constituting nine lasts. (The muid is one hundred and forty-four bushels.)

I ask once again, if the Maritime Company is to be deprived of its most lucrative monopolies, how can it afford to pay ten per cent for a capital of twelve hundred thousand crowns? When an edifice, the summit of which is so lofty and the basis so narrow, is once raised, before any part of it should be demolished, it were very necessary to consult concerning the props by which the remainder is to be supported. The King has declared that he will render trade perfectly free, if any means can be found of not lessening the revenue. Is not this declaration pleasantly benevolent? I think I hear Job on his dunghill, exclaiming, "I consent to be cured of all my ulcers, and to be restored to perfect health, provided you will not give me any physic, and will not subject me to any regimen."

The munificence is somewhat similar to that which shall restore freedom to all the merchandise of France, by obliging it to pay excessive heavy duties, the produce of which shall be applied to the encouragement of such manufactures as shall be supposed capable of rivaling the manufactures of foreign nations. I know not whether the King imagines he has conferred a great benefit on trade; but I know that throughout Europe all contraband commerce is become a mere article of insurance, the premium of which is more or less according to local circumstances; and that therefore a heavy duty (with respect to the revenue) is equivalent to a prohibition.

The King has ordered his subjects to be numbered, that he may not only know their number, but their age and sex. Probably, the changes which are projected to be made in the army are to be the result of this enumeration. But we know how difficult all such numberings are in every country upon earth. Another affair is in agitation, of a much more delicate nature, and which supposes a general plan and great fortitude; which is a land tax on the estates of the nobles. The project begins to transpire, and the provincial counselors have received orders to send certain informations, which seem to have this purpose in view. I will believe it is accomplished when I see it.

Single and distinct facts are of less importance to you than an intimate knowledge of him who governs. All the characters of weakness are united to those I have so often described. Spies already are employed; informers are made welcome; those who remonstrate meet anger, and the sincere are repulsed or driven to a distance. Women only preserve the right of saying what they please. There has lately been a private concert, at which Madame Hencke, or Rietz, for you know that this is one and the same person, was present, and stood behind a screen. Some noise was heard at the door. A *valet de chambre* half opened it, and there found the Princess Frederica of Prussia and Mademoiselle Voss. The first made a sign for him to be silent. The *valet de chambre* disobeyed. The King instantly rose, and introduced the two ladies. Some minutes afterward, a noise was again heard behind the screen. The King appeared to be embarrassed. Mademoiselle Voss asked what it was. Her royal lover replied, "Nothing but my people." The two ladies, however, had quitted the Queen's card table to indulge this pretty whim. The King was making a joke of the matter, on the morrow, when one of the ladies of the palace who was present said to him, "The thing is very true, Sire; but it were to be wished that it were not." Another lady asked him, the other day, at table, "But why, Sire, are all the letters opened at the post office? It is a very ridiculous and very odious proceeding."

He was told that the German plays, which he protects very much, are not good. "Granted," replied he; "but better these than a French playhouse, which would fill Berlin with hussies, and corrupt the manners of the people." From which, no doubt, you would conclude that the German actresses are Lucretias. You must also especially admire the morality of this protector of morals, who goes to sup in the house of his former mistress, with three women, and makes a procuress of his daughter.

He troubles himself as little with foreign politics as if he were entirely secure from all possible tempests. He speaks in panegyrics of the Emperor, of the French always with a sneer, of the English with respect. The fact is, the man appears to be nothing, less than nothing; and I fear lest those diversions which may be made in his favor are exaggerated. I shall, on this occasion, notice that the Duc de Deux Ponts escapes us; but he unites himself the closer to the Germanic league, which has so high an opinion of itself that it really believes it does not stand in need of our aid.   Under the standard of what chief it has acquired this presumption Heaven knows!

There is an anecdote which to me is prophetical, but the force of which you will not feel, for want of know-ing the country.   Prince Ferdinand has received the fifty thousand crowns which were due to him, according to the will of the King, on the simple order of Werder, conceived in these words: "His Majesty has given me his verbal command to lay down the fifty thousand crowns to Your Highness, which will be paid to you or your order, by the Treasury, at sight.— Welner." An order for fifty thousand crowns, to be paid down, signed by any other than the King, is a monstrosity in the political regulations of Prussia.

Erect a bank, and blessings be upon you; for it is the sole resource for finance which would not be horribly burdensome; the only money-machine which, instead of borrowing with dearness and difficulty, will cause you to receive; the only corner stone on which, under present circumstances, the basis of the power of the Minister of Finance can be supported.   Struensee, who is more stiff in the stirrups than ever, since he must necessarily be-come the professor of the new Ministry, has charged me to inform you that the King will probably purchase shares to the amount of several millions, if you will send him (Struensee) an abstract of the regulations of the bank, according to which he may make his report and proposals.

Apropos of Struensee, with whom I am daily more in-timate.   He has desired me to inform you that the change of the *commandite** for the dealing in *piastres* will very powerfully lower your exchange; and the following is his reasoning to prove his assertion:

"The remonstrances of the Bank of St. Charles to pre-serve the remittances of the Court, on commission, at the rate of ten per cent, have been entirely rejected; it has only been able to obtain them on speculation, and on the conditions proposed by the *Gremios;*† that is to say, at an interest of six per cent for the money advanced.

*Money agents.
†A company of Spanish merchants so called.

"The same bank has lately changed the *commandite* at Paris for the *piastre* business, and has substituted the house of Le Normand to that of Le Couteulx. As the former does not at present possess so extensive a credit as the latter, many people foresee that the Spanish bank will be under the necessity of keeping a greater supply of ready money with their *commandite*.

"In the interim, it has found itself extremely distressed. Desirous of settling its accounts with the House of Le Couteulx, and other houses in France, it was in want of the sum of three millions of French livres. To obtain this, it addressed itself to Government, and endeavoring to call in sixty millions of reals which were its due. Government having, under various pretenses, declined payment, the bank declared itself insolvent, and that it must render the state of its affairs public. This means produced its effect; Government came to its aid, and gave it assignments for twenty millions of reals, payable annually."

LETTER LVII.

THE comedy which Prince Henry had promised the world every Monday had its first representation on yesterday evening. The King came, contrary to the expectation of the Prince, and highly amused himself. I was a close observer of royalty, as you may suppose. It is incontrovertibly the cup of Circe which must be presented, in order to seduce him, but filled rather with beer than tokay. One remark sufficiently curious, which I made, was that Prince Henry amused himself for his own personal pleasure, and was not subject to the least absence of mind, neither of politics nor of attention to his guests. All the foreign ministers were present, but I was the only stranger who stayed to supper; and the King, who, when the comedy was over, behaved all the evening with great reserve, except when some burst of laughter was forced from him by the obscene jests of Prince Frederick of Brunswick, contemplated me with an eye more than cold. He is incessantly irritated against me by speeches which are made FOR ME; and the most harmless of my acquaintance are represented as personally offensive to his Majesty. For my own part, I am perfectly the reverse of disconsolate on the subject. I only notice this that I may describe my present situation, exactly as it is, without any hypocrisy.

It is true that Count Hertzberg has been on the point of losing his place, the occasion of which was what follows: He had announced the promised arrangement to the Duke of Mecklenburg, notwithstanding which, the affair was not expedited. Driven beyond his patience, and impatience in him is always brutal, he one day said to the members of the General Directory, "Gentlemen, you must proceed a little faster; business is not done thus; this is a State which can only proceed with activity " An account was given to the King of this vehement apostrophe. The Sovereign warmly reprimanded his Minister, who offered to resign. Blumenthal, it is said, accommodated the affair.

Apropos of the Duke of Mecklenburg, the King, when he received his thanks for the restitution of his *bailliages*, said to him, "I have done nothing more than my duty; read the device of my order" (*Suum cuique**). The Poles, when the Prussian arms were erected to denote the limits of the frontiers, after dismemberment by the late King, added *rapuit* to the motto.† I do not imagine Frederick William will ever give occasion to a similar epigram.

A very remarkable incident in the history of the human heart was the following: After various retrenchments had been made upon this Duke, especially in the promises that had been given him, one of the courtiers represented to the King that he would not be satisfied. "Well," said his Majesty, "then we must give him a yellow ribbon;" and, accordingly, yesterday the yellow ribbon was given. The vainglorious Duke at this moment found the arrangement of the *bailliages* perfectly satisfactory, and this was the occasion of his coming to return thanks.

Would you wish to obtain a tolerably just idea of the manner of living, in this noble TENNIS COURT, ‡ called the Court of Berlin? If so, pay some attention to the following traits, and recollect that I could collect a hundred of the same species.

The Princess Frederica of Prussia is now nineteen, and her apartment is open at eleven every morning.

The Dukes of Weimar, Holstein, and Mecklenburg, all ill-bred libertines, go in and out of it two or three times in the course of the forenoon.

The Duke of Mecklenburg was recounting I know not

---

* To every one his own.

† *Suum cuique rapuit.*—He took from every one his own.

‡ *Tripot.*—The just value of the author's word seems to be *show booth.* Tennis courts were formerly hired in France by ropedancers, tumblers, and showmen; in which we must not omit the allusion to the debauchery of manners of such people in France.

what tale to the King. The Prince of Brunswick, awkwardly enough, trod on the toe of a person present, to make him take notice of something which he thought ridiculous. The Duke stopped short in his discourse — "I believe, sir, you are diverting yourself at my expense." He went on with his conversation to the King, and presently stopped again — "I have long, sir, been acquainted with the venom of your tongue; if you have anything to say, speak it to my face, and I shall answer you." More conversation and other interruptions. "When I am gone, Sire, the Prince will paint me in charming colors; I beg Your Majesty will recollect what has just passed."

This same Prince Frederick is, as I have very often told you, the chief of the mystics, against whom he uttered the most horrid things to Baron Knyphausen.

"But how is this, my Lord?" replied the Baron; "I understood you were the Pope of that Church." "It is false." "I have too good an opinion of your honesty to imagine you can be of a sect which you disavow; I, therefore, give you my promise everywhere to declare you despise the mystics too much to be one of them; and thus you will recover your reputation." The Prince beat about the bush, and called off his dogs.

A courtier, a grand marshal of the Court, petitions for a place promised to five candidates. I remarked to him, "But how, monsieur, if the place be engaged?" "Oh, engagements are nothing at present," answered he, gravely; "for this month past we have left off keeping our word."

Welner, the real author of the disgrace of Schulemburg, went to see him, pitied him, and said, "You have too much merit not to have many enemies." "I, many enemies, monsieur!" said the ex-Minister; "I know of but three — Prince Frederick, because I would not give his huntsman a place; Bishopswerder, because I dismissed one of his dependents; and you, because — I know not why." Welner began to weep, and to swear that detraction was everywhere rending his character. "Tears are unworthy of men," said Schulemburg; "and I am unable to thank you for yours."

In a word, all is sunken to the diminutive, as all was exalted to the grand.

It is asserted that the Prussian merchants will be allowed a free trade in salt and wax. I cannot verify the fact to-day; Struensee will be too much occupied, it being post day; but if it be true, the Maritime Company, which at once will be deprived of salt, wax, coffee, tobacco, and probably of wood, cannot longer support the burden of eighteen per cent at the least; a profit which no solid trade can afford, and which, perhaps, Schulemburg himself, with all his lucrative exclusive privileges, could not have paid, but by perplexing the treasury accounts, so that the gains of one branch concealed the deficiencies of another.

As to the silk manufactures, which are proposed to be laid aside, I do not perceive that any inconvenience whatever will result from this. An annual bounty of forty thousand rix-dollars divided among the master weavers of Berlin, added to the prohibition of foreign silks, will never enable them to maintain a competition. Nay, as I have before explained to you, the very manufacturers themselves smuggle, and thus supply more than one-third of the silks that are used in the country; for it is easy to conceive that purchasers will prefer the best silks, which have more substance than, and are of superior workmanship to, those which monopoly would oblige them to buy. Not that the raw materials cost the manufacturer of Berlin more than they do the manufacturer of Lyons. They both procure them from the same countries, and the former does not pay the six per cent entrance duty to which the Lyons manufacturer is subject; besides that, the German workman will labor with more diligence than the French; nor is labor much dearer here than at Lyons. The one receives eighty centimes an ell for making, and the other ninety-five centimes for the same quantity, of equal fineness, which scarcely amounts to one and a half per cent. on the price of the silk, estimated at five livres the French ell. The Berlin manufacturer has likewise, by a multitude of local calculations of trade, to which I have paid severe attention, an advantage of thirty per cent over the Lyons trader, at the

fair of Frankfort on the Oder. And, whether it proceed
from a defect in the Government, the poverty of the
workmen, or the ignorance of the manufacturer, he still
cannot support the competition. Of what use, therefore,
are so many ruinous looms, of which there are not less
than sixteen hundred and fifty, at Berlin, Potsdam, Frankfort, and Koepnic?— the product of which, however, is
far from being equivalent to the same number of looms
at Lyons. The Berlin weaver will not, at the utmost,
do more than two-thirds of the work turned out of hand
by the weaver of Lyons. Of these sixteen hundred and
fifty looms, we may reckon about twelve hundred in
which are weaved taffetas, brocades, velvets, etc. The
remainder are employed in fabricating gauze, about nine
hundred and eighty thousand Berlin ells of which are
annually produced. (The French ell is equal to an ell
three-quarters of Berlin measure.) The twelve hundred
silk looms only produce about nine hundred and sixty
thousand ells; which in the whole amount to one million
nine hundred and forty thousand ells. The sum total
of the looms consume about one hundred and fourteen
thousand pounds weight of raw silk, at sixteen ounces
to the pound. (You know that seventy-six thousand
pounds weight of wrought silk will require about one
hundred and fourteen thousand pounds weight of undressed silk.) There are also twenty-eight thousand pair,
per annum, of silk stockings fabricated at Berlin; which
consume about five thousand pounds weight of raw silk.
It is principally in the stocking manufactory that the
silk of the country is employed; which, in reality, is superior in quality to that of the Levant; but they so ill
understand the art of spinning it, in the Prussian States,
that it is with difficulty worked in the silk loom. The
stocking manufacturers use it to a greater advantage,
because, being cheap, and of a strong quality, stockings
are made from it preferable to those of Nismes and
Lyons, in which cities the rejected silk alone is set apart
for stockings. From eight to twelve thousand pounds
weight of silk is annually obtained in the Prussian States,
in which there are mulberry trees enough to supply thirty
thousand pounds weight. This constitutes no very for-

midable rivalship with the silk produced in the States of the King of Sardinia.

The commission of inquiry has written to inform Launay that it has no further demand to make from him; and in consequence he has addressed the King for permission to depart. The King replied, "I have told you to wait here till the commission shall be closed." There is either cunning or tyranny on one side or the other.

19

LETTER LVIII.

December 23d, 1786.

MADEMOISELLE HENCKE, or Madame Rietz, as you think proper to call her, has petitioned the King to be pleased to let her know what she is to expect, and to give her an estate on which she may retire. The Sovereign offered her a country house, at the distance of some leagues from Potsdam. The lady sent a positive refusal, and the King, in return, will not hear any mention made of an estate. It is difficult to say what shall be the product of this conflict between cupidity and avarice. The pastoral, in the meantime, proceeds without relaxation. "*Inez de Castro*" has several times been performed at the German theater, imitated from the English, and not from the French. In the fourth act, the Prince repeats with ardor every oath of fidelity to a lady of honor. This has been the moment of each representation which the Queen has chosen to leave the house. Was it the effect of chance, or was it intendedly marked? This is a question that cannot be answered, from any consideration of the turbulent and versatile, but not very feeble, character of this Princess.

When her brother-in-law, the Duke of Weimar, arrived, the King gave him a very gracious reception; and, by degrees, his countenance changed to icy coldness. Conjectures are that he has been lukewarm, or has wanted address in his negotiation with the Queen, on the subject of the marriage, which is far from being determined on. Two private houses have been bought at Potsdam, and have been furnished with every degree of magnificence. And to what purpose, if marriage be intended? May not the wife be lodged in the palace? Speaking of arrangements, let me inform you that the King has sent a M. Paris, his *valet de chambre*, into France, to pay his personal debts there, and to purchase such things as are wanting to these newly bought houses which are consecrated to love.

The relations of Mademoiselle Voss, who four months since pressed her to depart for Silesia, there to marry a gentleman who asked her hand, are at present the first to declare that the projected royal marriage would be ridiculous, and even absurd. In fact, its consequences might be very dangerous; for, should disgust succeed enjoyment, a thing which has been seen to happen, Mademoiselle Voss must separate with a pension; instead of which, in her rank of favorite, she might rapidly make her own fortune, that of her family, and procure the advancement of her creatures.

Be this as it may, the time is passed at Potsdam in projecting bowers for love; and, though the Sovereign might not perhaps be exactly addressed in the words of La Hire to Charles VII.— "I assure you, Sire, it is impossible to lose a kingdom with greater gayety," it may at least be said, "It is impossible to risk a kingdom more tenderly." But whatever tranquillity may be affected, there are proceedings and projects which, without alarming, for he certainly has valor, occupy the Monarch. The journey of the Emperor to Cherson, the very abrupt and very formal declaration of Russia to the city of Dantzic, the intended camp of eighty thousand men in Bohemia, for the amusement of the King of Naples, are at least incidents that may compel attention, if not remark. There are doubts concerning the journey of the Empress into the Crimea, Potemkin being unwilling to make her a witness of the incredible poverty of the people and the army, in this newly acquired garden.

The discouragement of the Ministry of Berlin still continues to increase. The King, for these two months has not acted in concert with any single Minister. Hence their torpor and pusillanimity are augmented. Count Hertzberg is progressive in his descent, and Werder begins to decline. The King remains totally unconcerned; and never was the mania of reigning in person and of doing nothing carried to greater excess. Instead of the capitation, a tax on houses is talked of as a substitute. I begin to think that neither of these taxes will take place.

There is an inclination to retract without disgrace, if that be possible; and the pretext will be furnished by the advice of the provincial presidents. It is the more extraordinary that this capitation tax should be so much persisted in, since, under the reign of Frederick William I., a similar attempt was made, and which on the second year was obliged to be renounced.

The Prussian army has made a new acquisition, of the same kind with those by which it has been enriched for these four months past. I speak of Prince Eugene of Wurtemberg. He began his career by an excess of libertinage. He since has distinguished himself in the trade of *corporal-schlag*,* and by stretching the severity of discipline to ferocity. He, notwithstanding, has not acquired any great reputation by these means. He has lived at Paris, and plunged into mesmerism. He afterward professed to be a somnambulist, and next continued the farce, by the practice of midwifery. These different masquerades accompanied and concealed the real object of his ambition and his fervor, which is to give credit to the sect of the mystics, of whom he is one of the most enthusiastic chiefs. A regiment has lately been granted him, which brings him to Berlin. His fortune will not permit him to live wholly there; but his situation will allow him to make journeys to that city, where he will be useful to the fathers of the new church. Singular, ardent, and active, he delivers himself like an oracle and enslaves his hearers by his powerful and ecstatic elocution, with his eyes sometimes haggard, always inflamed, and his countenance in excessive emotion. In a word, he is one of those men whom hypocrites and jugglers make their successful precursors.

23d, at Noon.

I have just had a very deep and almost sentimental conversation with Prince Henry.

He is in a state of utter discouragement, as well on his own behalf as on behalf of his country. He has confirmed all I have related to you, and all I shall now

* The flogging-corporal; from *schlagen*, to strike or whip.

relate,— torpor in every operation, gloom at Court, stupefaction among Ministers, discontent everywhere. Little is projected, less still is executed. When it is noticed that business is suffered to languish, the King's being in love is very gravely given as the reason, and it is affirmed that the vigor of administration depends on the compliance of Mademoiselle Voss. Remarks at the same time are made how ridiculous it is thus to suspend the affairs of a whole kingdom, etc, etc.

The General Directory, which should be a Council of State, is nothing more than an office to expedite common occurrences. If Ministers make any proposition no answer is returned; if they remonstrate they meet with disgust. What they ought to do is so far from what they actually do that the debasement of their dignity occasions very disagreeable reflections. Never was a public opinion produced more suddenly than it has been by Frederick William II., in a country where the seeds of such opinion did not appear to exist.

Prince Henry can find no remedy for domestic vices, but he has no apprehensions concerning foreign affairs; because the King is at present wholly decided in favor of France, and still more destitute of confidence for the favorers of the English faction. Pray take notice that this is the version of the Prince; not that I am very incapable of believing it, if we do not throw up our own chances.

What the public papers have announced respecting the journey of Prince Henry, is without foundation. Some wish to go to Spa and France, but no plan is yet determined on; a vague hope, which he cannot suffer to expire, notwithstanding the blows he receives, will detain him at Rheinsberg. Year will succeed to year; the moment of rest will arrive, and habit will enchain him in his frosty castle, which he has lately enlarged and rendered more commodious. To these different motives, add a nullity of character, a will unstable as the clouds, frequent indisposition, and a heated imagination, by which he is exhausted. That which we desire without success, gives more torment than that which is executed with difficulty.

A second Minister is to be appointed for Silesia; one singly is a kind of viceroy. It is dangerous, say they, to see with the eyes of an individual only. *Divide et impera.* Thus far have they advanced in their politics.

Prince Frederick of Brunswick is ardently active in his intrigues against Prince Henry, and the Duke his brother. What he wishes is not known; but he wishes, and hence he has acquired a certain importance among the tumultuous crowd, who cannot perceive that a contemptible Prince is still more contemptible than an ordinary man. He neither can be of any durable utility, nor in the least degree agreeable or estimable; but, under certain given circumstances, he may be a very necessary spy.

LETTER LIX.

December 26th, 1786.

A GRAND list of promotions is spoken of, in which Prince Henry and the Duke of Brunswick are included, as field marshals. But the first says he will not be a field marshal. He continually opposed that title being bestowed on the Duke, under Frederick II., who refused to confer such a rank on the princes of the blood. This alternative of haughtiness and vanity, even aided by his ridiculous comedy, will not lead him far. He intends to depart in the month of September for Spa; he is afterward to visit our southern provinces, and from thence is to continue his journey to Paris, where he is to pass the winter. Such are his present projects, and the probability is sufficiently great that not anything of all this will happen.

The King has declared that he will not bestow any places on persons who are already in office under the Princes. This may perhaps be the cause that Count Nostitz has forsaken Prince Henry. The Count is a very strange kind of being.

First sent into Sweden, where he erected himself a chief of some envoys of the second order, finding himself dissatisfied with the severe laws of etiquette, he passed a slovenly life in an office, which he exercised without abilities. On his return he procured himself the appointment of one of the gentlemen who accompanied the Prince Royal into Russia, but the consent of the Prince he had forgotten to ask. He was consequently regarded as an inconvenient inspector, and was but sparingly produced on public occasions. Hence arose ill-humor, complaints, and murmurs. The late King sent him into Spain, where he dissipated the remainder of his fortune. The merchants of Embden, and of Königsberg, requested the Spaniards would lower the duties on I know not what species of merchandise. Count Nostitz solicited, negotiated, and presently wrote word "that the new regulations were wholly to the advantage of the Prussian subjects." The King ordered the Court of Spain to be thanked. Fortunately, Count Finckenstein, who had not received the regulations, delayed sending the thanks. The regulations came, and the Prussian merchants were found to be more burdened than formerly. His Majesty was in a rage. Nostitz was suddenly recalled, and arrived at Berlin without the fortune that he had spent, destitute of the respect that he had lost, and deprived of all future hopes. Prince Henry welcomed him to his palace, an asylum open to all malcontents. Here he remained eighteen months, and here displayed himself in the same manner that he had done everywhere else — inconsistent in his imaginations, immoral in mind, ungracious in manners, not capable of writing, not willing to read, as vain as a blockhead, as hot as a turkey cock, and unfit for any kind of office, because he neither possesses principles, seductive manners, nor knowledge. Such as here depicted, this insipid mortal, the true hero of the Dunciad, is in a few days to be appointed envoy to the Electorate of Hanover. In excuse for so capricious a choice, it is alleged that he will have nothing to do in the place. But wherefore send a man to a place where he has nothing to do?

Madame Rietz, who of all the mistresses of the Sovereign has most effectually resisted the inconstancy of men, and the intrigues of the wardrobe,* has modestly demanded the margraviate of Schwedt from the King, to serve as a place of retreat; and four gentlemen to travel with her son as with the son of a Monarch. This audacious request has not displeased the King, who had been offended by the demand made of an estate. He, no doubt, has discovered that he is highly respected, now that he receives propositions so honorable.

His former friends no longer can obtain a minute's audience; the gates to them are gates of brass. But a comedian, whose name is Marron, at present an innkeeper at Verviers, lately came to solicit his protection. He chose the moment when the King was stepping into his

---

* *La garde-robe.* "An ounce of civet, good apothecary."

carriage. The King said to him, "By and by; by and by." Marron waited; the King returned, sent for him into his apartments, spoke with him a quarter of an hour, received his request, and promised everything for which he petitioned. Never, no, never will subaltern influence decline; footmen will be all-puissant. Welner has publicly obtained the surname of VICEROY, or of PETTY KING.

The Monarch has written to the General of the gendarmes (Pritwitz), noticing that several of his officers played at games of chance; that these games were forbidden; that he should renew the prohibitions under pain of being sent to the fortress for the first offense, and of being broken for the second. The information and the threat were meant at the General himself, who has lost much money with the Duke of Mecklenburg.

It is affirmed that the Duke of Brunswick will be here from the eighth to the fifteenth of January. But Archimedes himself demanded a point of support, and I see none of any kind at Berlin. There are numerous wishes, but not one will; and the wishes themselves are incoherent, contradictory, and rash; he does not know, nor will he ever know, how to connect a single link in the chain: he will more especially never know how to lop off the parasitical and avaricious sucker. Agriculture is what is most necessary to be encouraged, particularly as soon as commercial oppression shall be renounced; though this oppression has hitherto been productive of gold, thanks to the situation of the Prussian States. But how may agriculture be encouraged in a country where the half of the peasants are attached to the glebe? For so they are in Pomerania, Prussia, and in other parts.

It would be a grand operation in the royal domains, were they divided into small farms, as has so long since been done by the great landholders in England. It is a subject of much greater importance than regulations of trade; but there are so many interested people to be controverted, and the habit of servitude is so rooted, that strength of understanding, energy, and consistency, not one grain of which I can find here, are necessary to make the attempt. More knowledge likewise is requisite than will here be found, for a long time to come, for it to be supposed that there is no town, no province, which would not most gladly consent to pay the King much more than the neat revenue he at present obtains, if he would suffer the inhabitants to assess themselves; taking care, however, continually to watch over the assessments, that the magistrates and nobles might not oppress the people; or for it to be imagined that the subject would not gain three-fourths of the expenses of collecting, and would be free of all those unworthy restraints which are at present imposed upon them by the fiscal treasury.

It is also necessary to recollect that it is not here as with us, where the body, the mass, of national wealth is so great, because of the excellence of the soil and the climate, the correspondence between the provinces, etc., etc., that we may cut as close as we will, provided we do not erect kilns to burn up the grass; and that in France the expenses of collecting only need be diminished; that no other relief is necessary; nay, that we may still prodigiously increase the load, provided that load be well poised. Here, two or three provinces at the utmost excepted, the basis is so narrow and the soil so little fruitful, so damp, so impoverished, that it is only for tutelary authority to perform the greatest part of all which can reconcile Nature to this her neglected offspring. The division of the domains itself, an operation so productive of every kind of resource, requires very powerful advances; for the farmer's stock and the implements of husbandry are, perhaps, those which, when wanting, the arm can least supply.

Independent of this grand point of view, we must not forget THE MILITARY POWER, which must here be respected, for here there are neither Alps nor Apennines, rivers nor seas, for ramparts; here, therefore, with six millions of inhabitants, Government is desirous, and, to a certain point, is obliged, to maintain two hundred thousand men in arms. In war there are no other means than those of courage or of obedience, and obedience is an innate idea in the SERF peasant; for which reason, perhaps, the grand force of the Prussian army consists in the union of the feudal and military systems. Exclusive of that vast consideration, which I shall elsewhere develop, let me add it will not be sufficient here to act like such or such a Russian or Polish lord, and say, "You are enfranchised," for the serfs here will reply, "We are very much obliged to you for your enfranchisement, but we do not choose to be free"; or even to bestow land gratuitously on them, for they will answer, "What would you have us do with lands?"* Proprietors and property can only be erected by making advances, and advances are expensive; and, as there are so few governments which have the wisdom to sow in order that they may reap, this will not be the first to begin. It is little probable that the morning of wholesome politics should first break upon this country.

At present it is almost publicly known that the Comte d'Esterno is to depart in the month of April for France. I shall submit it to your delicacy, and to your justice, to pronounce whether I can remain here the overseer of a *chargé d'affaires*. During his absence, functions might be bestowed on me; here I certainly would not remain under an envoy *per interim;* nor would this require more than the simple precaution of sending me secret credentials. But, as no such thing will be done, you will perceive that this is a new and very strong reason for my departure about that time. Those who would make me nothing more than a gazetteer are ill-acquainted with

---

* It is a melancholy truth that such is, and indeed such must necessarily be, the spirit of serf peasants; nay, in Russia this error is more rooted than in Prussia. The peasants have no examples of the possibility of existing in a state of independence; they think themselves certain of an asylum against hunger and old age in the domains of their tyrants, and, if enfranchised, would imagine themselves abandoned to an inhospitable world (which indeed, locally speaking, they would be), in which they must be exposed to perish with cold and hunger. Men in a body must be led to act from motives of interest, which, when well understood, are the best of motives. Nothing would be more easy than to convince the peasantry of the largest empire, in a few years, of what their true interest, and the true interest of all parties is, were not the majority of men, unfortunately, incapable of looking far beyond the trifling wants and the paltry passions of the moment. It is a melancholy consideration that so many ages must yet revolve before truths so simple shall be universally known, even now that the divine art of printing is discovered.

mankind; and still more so those who hope to oblige me to consent tacitly or perforce.

POSTSCRIPT.—The Count de Masanne, a fervent mystic, is the grand master of the Queen's household. Welner supped with her yesterday, and had the place of honor; that is to say, he sat opposite her. If he cede to wishes of such indecent vanity, he will presently be undone.

LETTER LX

December 30th, 1786.

YESTERDAY was a memorable moment for the man of
observation. Count Brühl, a Catholic, a foreigner,
assuming his rank in the Prussian army, was in-
stalled in his place as Governor, and the capitation tax
was intimated. This capitation, so openly contemned,
supported with so much obstinacy, demonstrated to be
vicious in its principle, impossible of execution, and
barren in product, at once announces the disgraceful
inanity of the General Directory, by which it was loudly
opposed, and the sovereign influence of the subaltern by
whom its chiefs have been resisted. How can we suppose the King has been deceived respecting the public
opinion of an operation so universally condemned? How
may he be excused, since his Ministers themselves have
informed him that he was in danger of, perhaps forever,
casting from him, at the very commencement of his
reign, the title of well-beloved, of which he was so ambitious? Here we at least behold the ambiguous morning
of a cloudy reign.

The Queen is not satisfied with the choice that has been
made of Count Brühl, neither is she with the regulations
of her household, and therefore she is again contracting
debts. She is allowed, for expenses of every kind, only
fifty-one thousand crowns per annum. It will be difficult
for her to make this sum supply her real wants, her
generous propensities, and her numerous caprices. Blind
to the amours of the King, she can see the disorder of his
domestic affairs. The day before yesterday there was no
wood for the fires of her apartments. Her house steward
entreated the steward of the royal palace to lend him
his assistance. The latter excused himself because of
the smallness of his remaining stock. How, you will ask,
can disorder so indecent happen? Because the quantity

(301)

consumed was regulated by the late King, on the supposition that the Queen and her children resided at
Potsdam. Since his death no person has thought of the
necessary addition. Such incidents, trifling as they are
in themselves, prove to what excess carelessness and the
defects of inconsistency are carried.

Count Brühl was waited for in order to furnish the
house of the Princes. As he is overwhelmed by debts,
and is a Saxon nobleman ruined, it was requisite the
King should cause the sum of twenty thousand crowns
to be paid at Dresden, to satisfy the most impatient
of his creditors. Opinions concerning him are divided.

The only points on which people are unanimous are,
that he is one of the flock of the elect (the mystics), and
that he plays exceedingly well on the violin. Those who
have been acquainted with him fifteen years ago speak
in raptures of his amenity. Those whose knowledge of
him is more recent are silent. Those who are totally
unacquainted with him say he is the most amiable of
men. His pupil smiles when he is praised. It is affirmed
that the Grand Duke has sent him here, and that it is
his intention to take him to himself whenever he shall
have the power.

The Prince Royal will soon be worthy the trouble of
observation; not merely because Frederick II. drew his
horoscope in the following terms — "I shall reign again
in him," for perhaps he only meant by that to testify
his contempt for the present King; but because all things
in him proclaim greatness, but ungraciousness of character; awkwardness, but a speaking countenance; unpol-
ished, but sincere. He asks the wherefore of everything,
nor will he ever be satisfied with a reply that is not
reasonable. He is severe and tenacious, even to ferocity,
and yet is not incapable of affection and sensibility. He
already knows how to esteem and contemn. His disdain
of his father approaches hatred, which he is not very
careful to conceal. His veneration of the late King partakes of idolatry, and this he proclaims. Perhaps the
youth is destined to great actions; and, should he become

the engine of some memorable revolution, men who can see to a distance will not be surprised.

Launay at length departs; and, as I believe, solely from the fear which the Ministry, or rather which Welner, has that the King should, in some weary or embarrassed moment, restore him to his place. His dismission has been granted to him only on condition that he would give up twenty-five thousand crowns of arrears, which are his due. This is a shameful piece of knavery. They have exacted an oath from him that he will not carry off any papers that relate to the State. This is pitiable weakness. For of what validity is such an oath? He may afford you some useful, or rather curious, annotations. In other respects, the man is nothing, less than nothing. He does not so much as suspect the elements of his own trade. His speech is perplexed, his ideas are confused; in a word, he could only act a great part in a country where he had neither judges nor rivals. But he is not, as he is accused of being, a malicious person. He is a very weak and a very vain man, and nothing more. He has acted the part of an executioner, no doubt; but where is the financier who has not? Where would be the justice of demanding the hangman to be racked because of the tortures he had inflicted in pursuance of the sentence which the judge had pronounced?

He will predict deficiencies in the revenue, and in this he will not be wrong; but he perhaps will not inform you, although it is exceedingly true, that economical principles, which are the guardians of this country, are already very sensibly on the decline. The service is more expensive, the houses of princes more numerous, the stables are better filled, pensions are multiplied, arrangements more costly, salaries of ambassadors almost doubled, the manners more elegant, etc. The greatest part of these expenses was necessary. The real misfortune is that there is no care taken for the proportionate increase of the revenue by slow, but certainly productive, means; and that they seem not to suppose there will be any deficiency, which will at length make an immense error in the sum total; so that, without war, a long reign may see the end of the Treasury, should the present measures be pursued. It is not the prodigality of pomp which excites murmurs. It is a prodigality in contrast to the personal avarice of the King which is to be dreaded. It is an insensible, but a continual wasting. Hitherto the evil is inconsiderable, and, no doubt, does not strike any person; but I begin to understand the country in the whole, and I perceive these things more distinctly than I can describe.

It was a custom with the late King, every year, on the twenty-fourth of December, to make presents to his brothers and sisters, the whole sum of which amounted to about twenty thousand crowns. This custom the nephew has suppressed. A habitude of forty years had led the uncles to consider these gratuities as a part of their income; nor did they expect that they should have SET the first examples, or rather have BEEN MADE the first examples, of economy. Faithful to his peculiar mode of making presents, the King has gratified the Duke of Courland with a yellow ribbon. It would be difficult more unworthily to prostitute his Order.

To this sordidness of metal, and this debauchery of moral, coin, examples of easy prodigality may be opposed. The house of the Jew Ephraim had paid two hundred thousand crowns, on account, for the late King, at Constantinople, during the Seven Years' War. The money was intended to corrupt some Turks, but the project failed. Frederick II. continually delayed the repayment of the sum. His successor yesterday reimbursed the heirs of Ephraim.*

A saddler who had thirty years been the creditor of the late King, who never would pay the debts he had contracted while Prince Royal, demanded the sum of

---

*It is curious to read, in the "History of the Seven Years' War" (Chap. ix.), the account which this conscientious King gives of the CORRUPTION he attempted and the profusion with which he scattered the money of the uncircumcised Jew, but whom he takes good care never to mention. It was the treasure of THE STATE, and the State, with all its goods and chattels, flocks and herds, biped and quadruped, serfs and Jews included, were his — for "was he not every inch a King?"

three thousand crowns from his present Majesty. The King wrote at the bottom of the petition: " Pay the bill at sight, with interest at six per cent."

The Duke of Holsteinbeck is at length to go to Königsberg, to take command of a battalion of grenadiers. I have elsewhere depicted this insignificant Prince, who will be a boy at sixty, and who will neither do harm to the enemies of the State nor good to his private friends.

20

LETTER LXI.

January 1st, 1787.

THE King has lately bestowed his Order on four of his subjects. The one is the keeper of his treasury (M. von Blumenthal), a faithful but a dull Minister. The second is the master of his horse, M. von Schwerin, a silly buffoon under the late King, a cipher during his whole life, a perplexed blockhead, and on whom the first experiment that was made, after the accession, was to deprive him of his place. The third is his Majesty's Governor, a man of eighty, who has been kept at a distance for these eighteen years past, and who is destitute of talents, service, dignity, and esteem for his pupil, which perhaps is the first mark of good sense he ever betrayed. The last who is not yet named, is Count Brühl, who is thus rewarded by titles, after receiving the most effective gratifications before he has exercised any office. What a prostitution of honors! I say what a prostitution; for the prodigality with which they are bestowed is itself prostitution.

Among others who have received favors, a mystic priest is distinguished,— a preacher of effrontery, who reposes on the couch of gratifications, at the expense of two thousand crowns. To him add Baron Boden, driven from Hesse Cassel, a spy of the police at Paris, known at Berlin to be a thief, a pickpocket, a forger, capable of everything except that which is honest, and of whom the King himself said he is a rascal, yet on whom he has bestowed a chamberlain's key. Pensions innumerable have been granted to obscure or infamous courtiers. The Academicians, Welner and Moulines, are appointed directors of the finances of the Academy.

All these favors announce a Prince without judgment, without delicacy, without esteem either for himself or his favors; reckless of his own fame, or of the opinion of the public; and as proper to discourage those who possess some capacity as to embolden such as are natively nothing, or worse than nothing.

The contempt of the people is the merited salary of so many good works; and this contempt is daily more pointed; the stupor by which it was preceded is now no more. The world was at first astonished to see the King faithful to his comedy, faithful to his concert, faithful to his old mistress, faithful to his new one, finding time to examine engravings, furniture, the shops of tradesmen, to play on the violoncello, to inquire into the tricks of the ladies of the palace, and seeking for moments to attend to ministers, who debate in his hearing on the interests of the State. But at present astonishment is incited if some new folly or some habitual sin has not consumed one of his days.

The new uniforms invented by his Majesty have this day made their appearance. This military bauble, prepared for the day on which men have the ridiculous custom of making a show of themselves, confirms the opinion that the sovereign who attaches so much importance to such a circumstance possesses that kind of understanding which induces him to believe that parading is a thing of consequence.

Is his heart better than his understanding? Of this men begin to doubt.

Count Alexander Wartensleben, a former favorite of the present King, who was imprisoned at Spandau for his fidelity to him, being sent for from the farther part of Prussia to Berlin, to command the guards, has lately been placed at the head of a Brandenburg regiment; and by this arrangement he loses a pension of a hundred guineas, which was granted him by the King while Prince Royal. This frank and honest officer is a stranger to the sect in favor; and, after having languished in a kind of forgetfulness, finally receives a treatment which neither can be called disgrace nor reward. This is generally considered as a deplorable proof that the King, to say the least, neither knows how to love nor hate.

Mademoiselle Voss has been persuaded that it would be more generous in her to prevent her lover committing a folly than to profit by such folly; for thus is the marriage publicly called, which would have become a subject of eternal reproach whenever the intoxication of passion should have slumbered.   The beauty, therefore, will be made a countess, become rich, and perhaps the sovereign of the will of the Sovereign, but not his spouse.   Her influence may be productive of great changes, and in other countries might render Count Schulemburg, the son-in-law of Count Finckenstein, first Minister.   He has acted very wisely in attaching Struensee to himself, who teaches him his trade with so much perspicuity that the Count imagines his trade is learned.   He has besides an exercised understanding, and an aptitude to industry, order, consistency, and energy.   Aided by his tutor, he will find no difficulties too great; and he is the man necessary for this King, whose will is feeble and cowardly.   The late King was equally averse to men of many difficulties, but it was from a conviction of his own superiority.   Great talents, however, are little necessary to reign over your men of Topinamboo.

The memorial against the capitation tax, which has been signed by Messieurs Hertzberg, Heinitz, Arnim, and Schulemburg, concludes with these words: "This operation, which alarms all classes of Your Majesty's subjects, effaces in their hearts the epithet of WELL-BELOVED, and freezes the fortitude of those whom you have appointed to your Council."   Struensee, on his part, has sent in two pages of figures, which demonstrate the miscalculations that will infallibly be discovered when the tax has been collected.   Messieurs Werder, Gaudi, and probably Welner, persist; and the King, who neither has the power to resist a plurality of voices, nor that of receding, dares not yet decide.

On the 15th of February, he is to depart for Potsdam, where he proposes to continue the remainder of the year; that period excepted when he journeys into Silesia and Prussia.

POSTSCRIPT — *Evening.* — The King has to-day advanced the Duke of Brunswick to the rank of field marshal. This is indubitably the first honorable choice he has made; and everybody approves his having singly promoted this Prince.

January 2d.

The Dutch envoy has thrown me into a state of great embarrassment, and into astonishment not less great. He has asked me, in explicit terms, whether I consented that endeavors should be made to procure me credentials to treat with the Princess of Orange, at Nimeguen. If deception might be productive of anything, I should have imagined he only wished to induce me to speak; but the question was accompanied with so many circumstances, all true and sincere, so many confidential communications of every kind, and a series of anecdotes so rational and so decisive, that, though I might find it difficult to account for the whim he had taken, I could not possibly doubt of the candor of the envoy. After this first consideration, I hesitated whether I should mention the affair to you, from a fear that the presumption should be imputed to me of endeavoring to rival M. de Renneval; but, besides that my cipher will pass under the inspection of my prudent friend, before it will fall into the hands of the King or his Ministers, and that I shall thus be certain he will erase whatever might injure me to no purpose, I have imagined it was not a part of my duty to pass over a proposition of so singular a kind in silence. I ought to add further, referring to the ample details which I shall give, after the long conference which I am to have with him to-morrow morning, that, if France has no latent intention, and means only to weaken the Stadtholder, in such a manner as that his influence cannot hereafter be of service to the English, the patriots are by no means so simple in their intentions. I have proofs that, from the year 1784 to the end of 1785, they were in secret correspondence with Baron Reede; and that they ceased precisely at the moment when the Baron wrote to them: "Make your proposals; I have a *carte blanche* from the Princess, and, on this condition, the King of Prussia will answer for the Prince." I have also proofs that M. de Renneval cannot succeed, and that the affair will never be brought to a conclusion, " so long as negotiation shall be continued instead of arbitration." These are his words, and they appear to me remarkable. It is equally evident that the implacable vengeance of the Duc de la Vauguyon arises from his having dared to make love to the Princess, and his love having been rejected. I shall leave those who are able to judge of the veracity of these allegations; but it is my duty to repeat verbally the following phrase of Baron Reede: "M. de Calonne is inimical to us, and his enemy opens his arms to receive us. What is it that M. de Calonne wishes? Is it to be Minister of Foreign Affairs? A successful pacification of the troubles of Holland would render him more service, in such case, than the continuation of those troubles, which may kindle a general conflagration. I demand a categorical answer to the following question: Should it be proved to M. de Calonne that the Stadtholder is in reality come over to the side of France, or, which is the same thing, if he shall be obliged to come over, will he then be against us? Has he any private interest which we counteract? Is it impossible he should explain himself? The chances certainly are all in his favor against M. de Breteuil, whom we have continually hated and despised. Wherefore will he spoil his own game."

I necessarily answered these questions in terms rather vague. I informed him that M. de Calonne, in what related to foreign affairs, continually pursued the line marked out by M. de Vergennes; that the former, far from coveting the place of the latter, would support him with all his power, if, which could not happen, he had need of his support; that a comptroller-general never could be desirous of anything but peace and political tranquillity; that whether M. de Calonne had or had not particular agents in Holland, was a fact of which I was ignorant (this Baron Reede positively assured me was the case, and probably was the reason of his afterward conceiving the idea of making me their substitute); but that he would suppose me a madman, should I speak to him of such a thing; and therefore if, as seemed very improbable, it were true that the Princess of Orange, on the recommendation of Baron Reede, should be capable of placing any confidence in me, it was necessary she should give this to be understood, through some medium with which I should be unacquainted, as, for example, by the way of Prussia; but it scarcely could be supposed that there would be any wish of substituting a person unknown in that walk to those who were already in the highest repute.

Baron Reede persisted, and further added, not to mention that M. de Renneval could not long remain in his station, the parties would undoubtedly come to a better understanding when the Princess could speak with confidence; that confidence was a sensation which she never could feel for this negotiator. In fine, he demanded, under the seal of profound secrecy, a conference with me, which I did not think it would be right to refuse; and his whole conversation perfectly demonstrated two things: the first, that his party supposes M. de Calonne is totally their enemy, and that he is the Minister of influence in this political conflict; and the second, that they believed him to be deceived. I am the more persuaded these suppositions are true, because he very strongly insisted even should I not receive any orders to repair to Holland, I should pass through Nimeguen, on my return to Paris; that, by the aid of the pledges of confidence which I should receive from him, I might sufficiently penetrate the thoughts of the Princess, so as to be able to render M. de Calonne a true report of the situation of affairs, and what might be the basis of a sincere and stable conciliation. It is not, therefore, so much another person, instead of M. de Renneval, that they desire, as another Couette Toury, or some particular confidant of M. de Calonne. I shall conclude with two remarks that are perhaps important.

1. My sentiments and principles concerning liberty are so known that I cannot be regarded as one of the Orange party. There is, therefore a real desire of accommodation at Nimeguen. And would not the success of this accommodation be of greater consequence to M. de Calonne than the machinations of M. de Breteuil? Wherefore will he not have the merit of the pacification, if it be necessary? And is it not in a certain

degree necessary, in the present political state of Europe?

2. The province of Friseland has ever been of the Anti-Stadtholder party, and it now begins to be on better terms with the Prince. Is it not because there has been the ill address of attacking the Stadtholder in some part hostile to the provinces, and in which neither the nobility nor the regencies do, or can, wish to see the Constitution absolutely overthrown? Has not the province of Holland drawn others too far into its particular measures?

These two considerations, which I can support by a number of corroborating circumstances, perhaps are worthy the trouble of being weighed. I shall send you, by the next courier, the result of our conference; but, if there are any orders, information or directions, to be given me on the subject, it is necessary not to leave me in suspense; for my situation relative to Reede is embarrassing, since I dare neither to repel nor invite advances, which most assuredly I never shall provoke, and which, by the well-avowed state of the Cabinet of Potsdam, it was even impossible I should provoke, had I been possessed of so much temerity.

Noldé has already written several letters to me from Courland, and mentions an important dispatch in cipher, which is to be sent by the next courier. But the evident result is that it is too late to save Courland; that everything which ought to have been prevented is done, or as good as done, and that the best physicians would but lose their time in prescribing for the incurable. The bearer of the letter, which occasioned the departure of Noldé is a merchant of Liebau, named Immermann. He has been charged with the negotiation of a loan in Holland and elsewhere, but, as it is said, has met with no success. It is supposed in the country that the Duke has thrown impediments in its way. The Diet of Courland is to sit in January. It is worthy of remark that, for two years past, no delegate has been sent from Courland to Warsaw.

Good information is said to be received that four corps of Russian troops have begun their march, purposely to

approach the Crimea at the time that the Empress shall
be there; and this not so much to inspire the Turks with
fear, as to remove the greatest and most formidable part
of the military from the vicinage of Petersburg and the
northern provinces of Russia; and especially from the
Grand Duke, that there may not be any possibility of
dangerous or vexatious events; for the unbounded love
of the Russians for their Grand Duke is apprehended.
Yet, if such terrors are felt, wherefore undertake so
useless a journey, which will cost from seven to eight
millions of rubles? So useless, I say, according to your
opinions, for, according to mine, the Empress believes
she is going to Constantinople, or she does not intend to
depart.

The troops are to be divided into four corps, of forty
thousand men each. The General of these armies will
be Field-Marshal Potemkin, who will have the immediate
command of a corps of forty thousand men, and the
superintendence of the others who are under him, to be
led by General Elvut, Michaelssohn, and Soltikow.
Prince Potemkin has under his particular and independent
orders sixty thousand irregular troops in the Crimea. It
is whispered he entertains the project of making himself
King of the country, and of a good part of the Ukraine.

LETTER LXII.

January 4th, 1787.

MY CONFERENCE with Baron Reede is over. It continued three hours and a half, and I have not the smallest remaining doubt concerning his intentions, after the confidence with which he spoke and the writings he showed me. He appears to be a good citizen, a constitutionalist by principle, a friend of liberty by instinct, loyal and true from character and habit, and rather the servant of the Princess of Orange from personal affection than from the place he holds under her husband; a person desirous of ending tumultuous and disquieting debates, because in pacification he contemplates the good of his country, and that of the Princess, whose confidence he possesses. He is, further, a Minister of passable talents, who has abstained from making advances so long as he presumed our political management of the Court of Prussia would greatly influence its intervention. and that he might prevail on that Court to speak firmly. At present, feeling that the respect in which the Cabinet of Berlin was held is on the decline, and especially perceiving the King is disinterested in the affairs of the Stadtholder, because he has no interest in anything, he knocks immediately at the door of reconciliation.

You may hold the following as probabilities:

1. That the Princess, who will finally decide what the catastrophe is to be, at least in a very great measure, is, to a certain point, desirous of accommodation, and to throw herself into the arms of France, because, in fine, she dreads risking a stake too great, to the injury of her family.

2. That she imagines M. de Calonne to be the Minister who influences the mind of the King, and the personal enemy of her house.

3. That successful attempts have been made to inspire her with very strong prejudices against his sincerity.

(314)

4. That still she seeks his friendship, and is desirous of a correspondence with him, either direct or indirect; and of an impartial trusty friend in Holland, who should possess her confidence.

5. That not only nothing is more possible than to retouch the regulations, without some modifications in which the influence of the Stadtholder cannot be repressed, but that this is what they expect, secretly convinced of its justice, and politically of its necessity; and that Baron Reede, as a citizen, and one of the first of the first rank, would be much vexed were they not retouched.

The reason of the sincere return of the Princess of Orange, who indeed was never entirely alienated, is that she seriously despairs of being efficaciously served at Berlin.

That of her opinion of the enmity of M. de Calonne is solely founded on his intimate connection with the Rhingrave of Salm, which the latter exaggerates; and the inconsiderate discourse of M. de C——, which really surpasses all imagination, and who is supposed to be the particular intimate of the Minister.

Her prejudices against M. de Calonne arise, in a great part, from the calumny spread by one Vandermey, who had formed I know not what enterprise on Bergue-Saint-Vinox (while this Minister was intendant of the province), in which he failed in such a manner as to cost the Stadtholder more than a hundred and sixty thousand florins; and, that he might excuse himself, he threw the whole blame on the opposition made by M. de Calonne. Add further, that all these causes of discontent, suspicion, and animosity are still kept in fermentation by a M. de Portail, the creature of M. de Breteuil, the which M. de Portail equally blames M. de Veyrac, M. de C——, the Rhingrave of Salm, M. de Renneval, the Comte de Vergennes, and all that has been done, all that is done, and all that shall be done; but especially M. de Calonne, whom he depicts as the incendiary of the Seven Provinces, which, with all Europe besides, cannot be saved but by the meekness of M. de Breteuil, the gentle, the polished, the pacificator.

With respect to the desire of the Princess to be on better terms with M. de Calonne, it is, I think, evident. Baron Reede is too circumspect and too artful to have taken such a step with me had he not been authorized. What follows will, perhaps, give you the genealogy of his ideas, which may sufficiently explain the whole episode. He could easily know that I wrote in cipher. He is the intimate friend of Hertzberg. And for whom do I cipher? Whoever is acquainted with the coast and the progress of our affairs must know it can only be for M. de Calonne. On what principle do I act? The Duke of Brunswick, who has had many conferences with him, cannot have left him in ignorance that my views on this subject were all for peace. Having been totally disappointed through the ignorance of Comte d'Esterno, which he affirms is complete in this respect, and which must, therefore, on this subject, redouble the native surliness of the Count; and by the stupidity of F——, who painfully comes to study his lesson with him, and returning does not always repeat it faithfully; well convinced that the influence of Count Hertzberg is null, the affection of the King cooled, and the credit of his Cabinet trifling, the Baron has proposed to the Princess to make this experiment.

With respect to her consent, whether express or tacit, and her serious determination to retouch the regulations, of this I have seen proofs in the letters of the Princess, and read them in the cipher of the Princess (for it will be well to know that she is very laborious, ciphers and deciphers herself, and with her own hand indites answers to all the writings of the contrary party), as I have done in those of Larrey and of Linden.

I did not think myself justified in disregarding such overtures. After having said everything possible in favor of M. de Calonne, his views, projects, and connections (nor, I confess, do I believe that the manner in which I am devoted to him left me at this moment without address), after having treated as I ought the perfidious duplicity of M. de Breteuil and his agents, and after having uttered what I thought on the prudence of M. de Vergennes, the delicate probity of the King, and the undoubted politics of our Cabinet, which certainly are to render the Stadtholder subservient to the public good, and the independence of the United Provinces, but which cannot be to procure his expulsion, it was agreed that I should write the day after to-morrow to demand a categorical answer from M. de Calonne, to know whether he wishes to begin a correspondence, direct or indirect, with the Princess; and whether he consents that any propositions for accommodation should be made him, for rendering which effectual his personal word should be accepted, when they shall be agreed on, and to an honorable pacification in behalf of the Stadtholder, suitable to the Sovereign.

Baron Reede, on his part, who is cautious, and wished to appear to act totally from himself, wrote to the Princess to inform her that this step was taken at his instigation, and to demand her prompt and formal authority to act. We are to meet to-morrow on horseback in the park that we may reciprocally show each other our minutes; it being certainly well understood that neither of us is to show the other more than the ostensible minutes we shall have prepared; and the whole is to depart on Saturday; because, said he, as not more than twelve or thirteen days were necessary for him to have an answer, this would be time enough, before yours should arrive, for us to form the proposed plan — at least, so far as to establish confidence.

This is the faithful abstract of our conversation. With respect to the propositions, I had only to listen; and as to the reflections, I have only to apologize. Should you be tempted to suppose I have been too forward in accepting the proposal to write, I beg the incident may be weighed, and that I may be informed how it may be possible, at the distance of six hundred leagues, ever to be successful, if I am never to exceed my literal instructions. And after all, what new information have I given the Baron? Who here, who is concerned in diplomatic affairs, has any doubt that I cipher? And on what subjects do men cipher? Is it philosophy, literature, or politics? Neither have I told of what kind my business is; and my constant formulæ have been — I SHALL

ENDEAVOR — I SHALL FIND SOME MODE — I SHALL TAKE AN OPPORTUNITY OF LETTING M. DE CALONNE KNOW, ETC.

At present, send me orders either to recede or to advance; and in the latter case give me instructions; for I have only hitherto been able to divine, and that the more vaguely because, as you must easily feel, it was necessary I should appear to the Baron to be better informed than I really am, and consequently to ask fewer questions than I should otherwise have done. Ask yourself what advantages might I not obtain, were I not obliged to have recourse entirely to my own poor stock.

In brief, what pledges do you desire of the sincerity of the Princess? What proofs of friendship will you afford her? What precaution do you require for the good conduct of the Stadtholder? What kind of restraints do you mean to lay him under? Will you in nothing depart from what was stipulated in the commission of the 27th of February, 1766? What are the modifications you propose? Must mediation be necessarily and formally accepted? Is it not previously requisite that the provinces of Guelderland and Utrecht should send their troops into their respective quarters? Will the province of Holland then narrow her military line? In this supposition, is there nothing to be feared from the Free Corps? and how may she answer for them? What will be the determinate constitutional functions of the Stadtholder? What the relations of subordination and influence toward the deputy counselors? What is the reformation intended to be made in the regulations?

These, and a thousand other particulars, are of consequence to me, if I am to be of any service in the business; otherwise I need none of them. But it is to me indispensable that you should immediately and precisely inform me how I ought to act and speak, how far I am to go, and where to stop.

Be kind enough to observe that it is requisite this step should be kept entirely secret from Comte d'Esterno, and that the intentions and proceedings of Baron Reede certainly do not merit that the Baron should be betrayed.

A curious and very remarkable fact is that the Duke of Brunswick was the first who spoke to Baron Reede of

the Prussian troops being put in motion, and asked him
what effect he imagined it would have on the affairs of
Holland if some regiments of cavalry were marched into,
and should it be needful, if a camp were formed in, the
principality of Cleves, which might be called a camp of
pleasure. Baron Reede replied this was a very delicate
step, and it was scarcely possible the Cabinet of Versailles
could remain an unconcerned spectator. Does the Duke
desire to be Prime Minister, be the event what it may?
And has he unworthily deceived me? Or was it only
his intention to acquire from Baron Reede such information as might aid him to combat the proposition
of Count Hertzberg? The Dutch Ambassador wished to
persuade me of the first. I imagine he is sincere; yet,
to own the truth, the public would echo his opinion, for
the Duke is in high renown for deceit. But here I ought
to oppose the testimony of Count Hertzberg himself, who
owned that the idea was his own, and who bitterly
repeated, more than once, "Ah! had not the Duke
deserted me!" It is necessary to have heard the expression and the accent to form any positive opinion on
the subject, which to a certain point may be warranted.

January 5th.

I found Baron Reede at the rendezvous, in the same
temper of mind; and, if possible, more fervent, more
zealous. The only delicacy in acting he required was
that I should not say he had written; in order, as he
observed, that, should these advances still fail in their
effect, a greater animosity might not be the result. He
related to me an example of this kind, concerning the
success of a confidential proceeding which happened,
some years ago, between himself and M. de Gaussin, at
that time *chargé d' affaires* from France to Berlin, and
who, having described the business in terms too ardent
to be accurate, receives a ministerial answer from M. de
Vergennes, of the most kind and amicable complexion,
which, passing directly to the Stadtholder, through the
medium of the Cabinet of Berlin, was by no means
found acceptable, as it might reasonably have been
supposed it would have been; and that this produced an

additional degree of coldness. True it is that the Prince of Orange had not, at that time, experienced the strength of his opponents; but this Prince is so passionate, and his mind is so perverse, that the Princess herself is obliged to take the utmost precautions when she has anything to communicate.

I promised Baron Reede to act entirely as he wished; yet have not thought it the less my duty to relate the whole affair, well convinced that people only of very narrow minds pique themselves on their policy; that M. de Calonne will think proper to know nothing of all this, except just as much as he ought to know; that in any case he will seem only to regard this overture as the simple attempt of two zealous men, who communicated a project which they supposed was most probable of success. In reality, though it may be the most pressing interest of the Stadtholder to obtain peace, how can our alliance with Holland be more effectually strengthened than by the concurrence of the Stadtholder? And with respect to the individual interests of M. de Calonne, should we happen to lose M. de Vergennes, through age or ill health, who is there capable of disputing the place with him, who shall have promoted the commercial treaty between France and England, and have accomplished the pacification of Holland? Enough at present concerning the business in which I am engaged. Let us return to Prussia.

January 6th.

Lieutenant-Colonel Goltz has long been on cold terms, and even has quarreled, with Bishopswerder. They had once been reconciled by the King, who felt that the first, being more firm of character, and more enterprising, had great advantages in the execution of affairs over the other, who was more the courtier, and more the humble servant of circumstances. To avoid domestic scandal, he has appointed M. von Hanstein, who possesses dignity, or rather haughtiness, and M. von Pritwitz, a man of mediocrity, and a victim to the caprices of the late King, to be general aids-de-camp. Thus Bishopswerder, after he has done everything in his power to remove all who had more understanding than himself from about the person of the King, having accomplished his purpose and secured the Monarch solely to himself, knows, not what he shall do with him.

Count Brühl has found neither arrangements ready prepared, apartments furnished, nor persons placed in the service of the Prince Royal. The consequences were — ill-humor, a visit to Welner, not admitted, visit returned late, and by a card, rising discontent, which is encouraged by Bishopswerder, who suspects Welner to have been softened concerning the nomination of the two general aids-de-camp.

A fact which appears very probable is that Welner, who is christened by the people The Little King, knows not how to perform three offices at once; and, as he foolishly believed he might yield to the eagerness of speculators, and has had the meanness to enjoy the despicable flatteries of those who six months ago treated him like a lackey, his days have glided away in these perilous pastimes of vanity. Business has been neglected, everything is in arrear, and it is presumed that, when he shall have been sufficiently bandied by the intrigues of the malcontents, the ingratitude of those whom he shall have served, the arts of courtiers, and the snares of his own subalterns, his brain will be entirely turned.

It is at length determined the capitation tax shall not be enforced. Thus it is withdrawn after having been announced! Without conviction! Without a substitute! What confusion! What forebodings! From the short prospect of the morning of the reign, how portentous are the steps of futurity!

The sending an envoy to London; which Court has not yet returned the compliment.

Another envoy sent to Holland, who, in every step he has taken, has risked the reputation of his Sovereign. It certainly was necessary either to act consistently, or totally to abstain from acting.

The commission of inquiry on the administration of the finances, which has been productive of nothing but injustice and rigor toward individuals, without the least advantage to the public.

21

Another commission to examine the conduct of General Wartenberg, appointed with ostentation, and suspended in silence.

The suppression of the administration of tobacco and snuff, which must be continued.

The project of the capitation tax, which is obliged to be withdrawn at the very moment it was to commence.

The convocation of the principal merchants of Prussia and Silesia, which has generated nothing but discussion, such as are proper to unveil the absurdity of the rulers, and the wretchedness of the people.

Do not so many false steps, so many recedings, suppose administrators who have reflected but little, who are groping in the dark, and who are ignorant of the elements of the science of governing?

Amid this series of follies, we must nevertheless remark a good operation, which is truly beneficial. I speak of the at present unlimited corn trade, and an annual exemption in behalf of that miserable Western Prussia, the amount of which I do not yet know. The domestic fermentation of the palace begins to be so great that it must soon become public. The agent of the wishes, or, more properly speaking, of the secret whims, is in opposition to Bishopswerder and Welner, who are on cold terms with Mademoiselle Voss, who is desirious that Madame Rietz should be discarded, who will agree that Mademoiselle Voss should be a rich mistress but not a wife. Among this multitude of opposing wills, where each, except the King, acts for himself, we may enumerate his Majesty's chamberlain, and the counselor of Mademoiselle Voss, Reuss; and the pacificator, the mediator, the counselor, the temporizer, the preacher, Count Arnim.

The Sovereign, amid these rising revolts, weathers the storm to the best of his abilities. The jeweler Botson has laid a complaint against Rietz, which occasioned a quarrel that might have had consequences, had not the King recollected that ten years might be necessary to replace a confidant whom he might have discharged in a moment of anger. The birthday of the Count of Brandenburg was likewise a circumstance which the Rietz party made subservient to their interest. His Majesty sent for the mother to dinner, and peace was the restorer of serenity.

The master of the horse, who was said to have lost his credit, appears to have risen from the dead. Exclusive of his yellow ribbon, which he hung over his shoulders on the last Court day, and which excited bursts of laughter from everybody, even from the Ministers, he requested his nephew might be created a count, and was answered with a «So be it.» The creating of a count is but a trifling evil, especially when so many have been created; but never to possess a will of one's own is a serious reflection.

Would you wish for a picture of the sinews of Government, and active facilities of the Governors? Take the following feature:

Various remonstrances had been made to the King finally to regulate the state of expenditure, and the salaries of his officers. He replied that he intended to keep a Court; and that, in order to regulate his expenses, he first desired to know the permanent state of his revenues, according as they should be collected and ascertained by his new financiers. After reflecting on various phrases, in all of which was repeated the word ASCERTAINED, the Ministers, under whose charge the excise and the daily expenditure were, began to have their apprehensions. Hence followed a multitude of trifling taxes, ridiculous, hateful, and unproductive, which sprang up in a single night. Oysters, cards, and an increase on the postage of letters, on stamps, on wines, eight groschen per ell on taffetas, thirty-three per cent on furs. They even went so far as to suppress the franchises of the Princes of the household. Not one of these new imposts but was most gratuitously odious; for they retard what they are meant to effect, and are productive of nothing but a demonstration of the heavy stupidity of those who neither can procure money nor satisfy the public.

POSTSCRIPT.—I have received a voluminous dispatch in cipher from Courland, the contents of which it is impossible I should at present send. I can only confirm former intelligence, that the chamberlain Howen, who is at present Burgrave, disposes of the province, and is wholly Russian; the circumstances by the next courier.

LETTER LXIII.

January 8th, 1787.

THE following is the substance of the news from Courland, as authentic as can possibly be procured.

The chamberlain Howen, an able man, the first and the only person of understanding in the country (for the chancellor Taubé, who might otherwise counterpoise his influence, is destitute of mind and character); Howen, I say, is become Ober Burgrave, by the sudden death of the Prime Minister, Klopman. After this event followed a torrent of re-placings and de-placings, in none of which you are interested, and concerning which it will be sufficient for you to know that every recommendation of the Duke has been absolutely rejected and contemned. The Baron of Mest-Machor, the Russian envoy by a formal and direct recommendation, occasioned the election to alight on Howen, who once was the violent enemy of the Russians, by whom he had been carried off from Warsaw, where he resided as envoy from Courland, and banished into Siberia. Here he remained several years. By a concurrence of circumstances he is become Russian. It appears that the Cabinet of Petersburg has preferred the gaining of its purpose by gentle measures, and intends amicably to accomplish all its designs on Courland. Howen is in reality Duke of Courland, for he executes all the functions of the dukedom, and converts or over-awes all opponents. Woronzow, Soltikow, Belsborotko, and Potemkin are absolute masters of Courland, as they are of Russia; with this only difference, that Potemkin, who possesses a library of mortgages and bank bills, who pays nobody, corrupts everybody, who subjects all by the energy of his will and the extent of his views, soars above Belsborotko, who is politically his friend; above Woronzow, who is capable but timid; and above Soltikow, who is wholly devoted to the Grand Duke.

The Duke of Courland will probably return no more to his country, because he has ruined his affairs in Russia, is unable to alter anything which has been done in his absence, is entangled in lawsuits, and by complaints laid against him without number, and because the regency, which preserves a good understanding with the chiefs of the equestrian order, under the guidance of Howen, reigns with moderation, conformable to the laws of the land, and brings down benedictions on its administration; insomuch that the people, who were ready to revolt because they were threatened by, and already were suffering, famine, wish affairs to continue in their present train. It is to them of little import whether the government be or be not Russian, if misery be not entailed on them. There is no possibility of reversing a system thus stable. Some sixty considerable estates have been granted as fiefs or farms. All the vacant places have been bestowed on persons of the greatest influence, abroad and at home; so that we may say the party of the administration of Howen or of the Russians in Courland, includes everybody. Several millions must be expended to counterpoise such a preponderance; and, if to counterpoise were to vanquish, victory itself would not be worth expenses so great.

One of the principal complaints against the Duke is the deterioration of Courland, which has been effected by the total impoverishment of the peasants and the lands, the ruin of the forests, and the exportation of the ducal revenues into foreign countries. But the grand crime, the crime not to be forgiven, is having displeased Russia. The Empress has been so enraged against him, by his anti-Russian proceedings in Courland, that she herself said: " The King of France would not have injured me as the Duke of Courland has dared to do." She probably meant, bestowing Courland on Prussia.

I cannot perceive how we can act better, in our present situation, than to wait with patience. Our young man will certainly have a place in his own country. Should it be thought proper to bestow on him the title of consul, with leave to wear our uniform, and a captain's commission, from which he might derive respect, he asks nothing more; and we should possess an intelligent, zealous, and incorruptible sentinel, who, from so well-situated a post, might inform us of whatever was passing in the North, and aid us in what relates to commerce.

I need not observe that great changes are not effected in a day. We may, however, depend upon a confirmation of the Maritime Company as a symptomatic anecdote of importance. Struensee has acted in a pleasant manner. "Gentlemen," said he, to the merchants of Königsberg and Prussia, "nothing can be more excellent than a free trade; but it is very just that you should buy all the salt in our warehouses." "True." "Very good. You must, therefore, give us security for one million, two hundred thousand crowns, as well as pay a hundred and twenty thousand crowns annually to the proprietors, in return for the ten per cent for which we are accountable; for public good will not admit an injury to be committed on private right." "True." "Very good. And, for the same reason, you must pay five per cent, which has been legally granted on the new shares." "True." "Very excellent, gentlemen. But who are to be your securities? Or, at least, where are your funds?" "Oh, we will form a company!" "A company, gentlemen! One company is as good as another. Why should not the King give the preference to the company that actually exists?"

All projects for the freedom of trade will, like this, go off *in fumo;* and, what is still more fatal, if possible, conclusions will be drawn, from the ignorance of the present administration, in favor of the impossibility of changing former regulations. Such are Kings without a will; such is the present, and such will he live and die! The other was all soul; this is all body. The symptoms of his incapacity increase with aggravation. I shall have continual occasion to repeat nearly the same words, the same opinions, the same remarks. But here, however, may be added, what I think a fact of weight, which is that one of the causes of the torpor of interior administration is the misunderstanding which reigns in the Ministry. Four Ministers are in opposition to two, and the seventh remains neuter. Messieurs Gaudi and Werder, who keep shifting the helm of finance, are counteracted by Messieurs Heinitz, Arnim, Schulemburg, and Blumenthal. The former of the last four is accused of attempting to add the department of the mines to that of the finances. In the meantime the expediting of business continues with Welner, and the impulse of influence with Bishopswerder.

The latter, either sincerely or insidiously, has become the associate of the plan to bring Prince Henry again into power, at least in military affairs. The Prince, for several years, has not been present at the manœuvers. It is affirmed that he not only will be this year, but that he will be made a kind of inspector general. The negotiation is carried on, with great secrecy, by General Moellendorf and the favorite.

The marriage of Mademoiselle Voss is again in report. Certain it is that every species of trinkets has been purchased, every kind of preparation has been made, and that a journey is rumored. Most of these circumstances are kept very secret; but I am well assured of their truth, because I have them from the Rietz family, who are very much interested in preventing the union being accomplished, under certain formalities, and who consequently are very actively on the watch. But I know not what form they will bestow on this half-conjugal, half-concubine state. Yesterday, however, when I supped with the King, I had ocular demonstration there was no longer any restraint laid on speaking together in public.

The King, at supper, asked me, "Who is one M. de Laseau?" "Du Saux, perhaps, Sire." "Yes, Du Saux." "A member of our academy of inscriptions." "He has sent me a large work on gaming." "Alas! Sire, you masters of the world only have the power of effecting the destruction of gaming. Our books will accomplish but little." "But he has embarrassed me by paying me a compliment which I by no means merit." "There are many, Sire, which you are too prudent to be in haste to merit." "He has congratulated me on having abolished the Lotto; I wish it were true, but it is not." "A wish from Your Majesty will effect much." "I am some thanks in your debt, on this subject, for this is one of the good counsels you gave me in a certain writing." * (I made a low bow.) "But you must excuse me for a time. There are funds assigned on that vile Lotto; the military school, for example." "Fortunately, Sire, a momentary deficiency of fifty thousand crowns is not a thing to inspire the richest King on earth, in ready money, with any great apprehensions." "True; but agreements —" "Will not be violated when the parties are reimbursed, or have any proportionate remuneration. Surely, since despotism has so often been employed to do ill, it might for once effect good." "Oh, oh! then you are somewhat reconciled to despotism." "Who can avoid being reconciled to it, Sire, where one head has four hundred thousand arms?" He laughed with a simple kind of grin, was informed the comedy was going to begin, and here ended our conversation. You perceive, there is still some desire of being praised in this lethargic soul.

POSTSCRIPT.—Launay this night departed incognito. I imagine you will give very serious offense to the Cabinet of Berlin if you do not prevent him going to press, as is his intention.

* Meaning the "Memorial."

LETTER LXIV.

January 13th, 1787.

I BELIEVE I have at length discovered what the Emperor was hatching here. He has, *sans* circumlocution, proposed to suffer Prussia to appropriate the remainder of Poland to itself, provided he might act in like manner by Bavaria. Fortunately, the bait was too gross. It was perceived he offered the gift of a country which he had not the power to bestow, and the invasion of which would be opposed by Russia, that he might, without impediment, seize on another which had been refused him, and of which, if once acquired, he never after could have been robbed. Your Ambassador, probably, has discovered this long before me, from whom you will have learned the circumstances. To him the discovery has been an affair of no difficulty; for confidence is easily placed, in politics, when it is determined that the proposal shall be rejected; besides that it is a prodigious step in advance to have the right of conferring with Ministers, from whom that may be divined which is not asked. For my own part, I can only inform you intrigues and machinations are carried on, and the very moment I discover more, I shall consider it as my duty to send you intelligence. But I do not suppose I can give you any new information of this kind. I have only promised to supply you with the current news of the Court and the country. The rest is out of my sphere. I want the necessary means effectually to arrive at the truth. God grant it never should enter the head of the Emperor to allure the King of Prussia more adroitly, and to say to him, "Suffer me to take Bavaria, and I will suffer you to seize on Saxony; by which you acquire the finest country in Germany, a formidable frontier, and near two millions of subjects; and by which, in a word, you will extend, round, and consolidate your dominions. Neither shall we have any great difficulties to combat. All of them may be obviated by making the

Elector King of Poland. The Saxon family possess the mania of royalty; and even should the kingdom become hereditary, wherein would be the inconvenience? It is good, or at least it very soon will be good, to possess a strong barrier against Russia."

Should they ever conceive such a project, it would be executed, with or without the consent of all Europe. But this they have not conceived. One is too inconsistent, the other too incapable; and after some disputes, more or less serious, the Emperor will filch a village, perhaps, from Bavaria, and the King of Prussia continue to crouch under his nullity.

The misfortune is that to treat him thus is to treat him with indulgence. The following is a fact entirely secret, but certain; and which, better than all those my preceding dispatches contain, will teach you to judge the man. Within this fortnight he has paid a debt of a million of crowns to the Emperor. And what was this debt? The Empress-Queen had lent the Prince Royal, now King of Prussia, a million of florins; which by accumulating interest, had become a million of crowns. And when? In the year 1778, during the Bavarian campaign, under the fatigues of which they imagined themselves certain that Frederick II. would sink. Thus was Frederick William base enough to accept the money of Austria, which he has had the imbecility to repay.* He had not the sense to say, "MY SUCCESSOR WILL REPAY YOU." No; he sanctions the act of the Imperial Court when lending money to the Princes Royal of Prussia. He imagines he has fulfilled his duties as a sovereign when he has had the honesty to pay his debts as an individual.

The sum total of these debts amounted to nine millions of crowns; and, though I do not indeed suppose that the agents are any losers, it is nevertheless true that

* If it be a crime for a prince to pay his debts, even though indebted to an enemy, it is a crime which no man but a politician can discover. It is not unpleasant to remark that Frederick II., when Prince Royal, eagerly negotiated a loan in Russia to promote which, his letters to Count Suhm inform us, he sent the Grand Duke — a dried salmon. Voltaire expected the largest diamond in the crown; he received a keg of wine.

the first months of his reign will cost Prussia thirty-six millions, exclusive of common expenses, gifts, gratifications, pensions, etc. The extraordinaries of the first campaign, in which it was necessary to remount all the cavalry, did not cost Frederick II. more than five millions, or five millions and a half, of crowns.

I have not yet depicted the Monarch as a warrior; the trade gives him the spleen, its *minutiæ* fatigue him, and he is weary of the company of generals. He goes to Potsdam, comes on the parade, gives the word, dines and departs. He went on Wednesday to the house of exercise at Berlin, uttered a phrase or two, bade the troops march, and vanished. And this is the house in which Frederick II., loaded with fame and years, regularly passed two hours daily, in the depth of winter, in disciplining, grumbling, cursing, praising, in a word, in keeping the tormented troops in perpetual action, who still were transported to see the Old One, for that was the epithet they gave him, at their head.

But a more important point is the new military regulations, which have been conceived, planned, approved, and, as it is said, are going to be printed, without either having been communicated to Prince Henry or the Duke of Brunswick. The tendency of this new plan is nothing less than the destruction of the army. The seven best regiments are converted into light troops, and among others that of Wunsch. I am yet unacquainted with the particulars of the changes made, but, according to the opinion of General Moellendorf, had Lascy himself been their promoter they would have been just as they are. The worthy Moellendorf is humbled, discouraged, afflicted. All is under the direction of Goltz, who is haughty, incapable of discussion, and who holds it as a principle that the army is too expensive, and too numerous, in times of peace. He is perpetually embroiled with Bishopswerder, often obliged to attend to business of this kind, and in some manner under the necessity of interfering in affairs in the conduct of which he is not supposed to be equally well versed.

The Duke of Brunswick does not come. He replied to some person who had complimented him on his promotion, and who, in a letter, had supposed he was soon expected to arrive at Berlin, that he had been exceedingly flattered by receiving a title, which, however, he did not think he had merited; that he never had, and never should, come to Berlin, unless sent for; and of this he saw no immediate prospect. I have very good information that he is exceedingly disgusted, and will doubtless be so more than ever, should the constitution of the army be reversed without his opinion being asked, who is the only field marshal of Prussia.

I do not scruple to affirm that, by the aid of a thousand guineas, in case of need, the whole secrets of the Cabinet of Berlin might be perfectly known. The papers which continually are spread upon the tables of the King might be read and copied by two clerks, four *valets de chambre*, six or eight footmen, and two pages, the women not included. For this reason the Emperor has an exact and daily journal of the proceedings of the King, and would be acquainted with all his projects, were he really to project anything.

Never did kingdom announce a more speedy decline. It is sapped on every side at once. The means of receipt are diminished, the expenses are multiplied, principles are despised, the public opinion sported with, the army enfeebled, the very few people who are capable of being employed are discouraged. Those even are disgusted, to please whom all others have been offended. Every foreigner of merit is kept at a distance, and the King is surrounded by the vulgar and the vile, that he may be thought to reign alone. This fatal frenzy is the most fruitful cause of all the evil which at present exists, and of that which is preparing for the future.

Were I to remain here ten years longer, I might furnish you with new particulars, but could not draw any new consequence. The man is judged; his creatures are judged; the system is judged. No change, no possible improvement, can take place, so long as there shall be no first Minister. When I say no change, I do not, by any means, wish you to understand no person shall be dismissed. Sand shall succeed to sand, but sand it still shall be, and nothing better, till piles shall be sunken on which a foundation may be laid. What, therefore, should I do here henceforth? I can be of no use; yet nothing but utility — great, direct, immediate utility — could reconcile me to the extreme indecency of the present amphibious existence which has been conferred upon me, should this existence be prolonged.

I am obliged to repeat that my abilities, what I merit and what I am worth, ought at present to be known to the King, and to the Ministry. If I am capable of nothing, and merit nothing, I am, while here, a bad bargain. If I am of some worth, and may effect some good purpose, if nine months (for nine months will have passed away before I shall return), if, I say, a subaltern test of nine months, most painful in itself, and during which I have encountered a thousand and a thousand impediments without once being aided, have enabled me to acquire some knowledge of men, some information, some sagacity, without enumerating the precious contents of my portfolio, I am, then, in duty bound to myself to ask, and either to obtain a place or to return to a private station, which will neither be so fatiguing to body nor mind, nor so barren of fame.

For these reasons I undisguisedly declare, or rather repeat, I cannot remain here, and I request my return may be formally authorized; whether it be intended to employ me hereafter or to restore me to myself. I certainly shall not revolt at any kind of useful occupation. My feelings are not superannuated, and though my enthusiasm may be benumbed, it is not extinct. I have in my sensations at this moment a strong proof to the contrary. The day which you inform me you have fixed for the convocation of the notables I shall regard as one of the most glorious days of my life. This convocation, no doubt, will soon be followed by a national assembly, and here I contemplate renovating order, which shall give new life to the monarchy. I should think myself loaded with honors were I but the meanest secretary of that assembly, the project of which I had the happiness to communicate, and to which there is so much need that you should appertain, or rather that you should become its soul. But to remain here, condemned to the rack, in company with fools, obliged to sound and to wade through the fœtid meanderings of an administration, each day of which is signalized by some new trait of cowardice and stupidity, this is beyond my strength; for I perceive no good purpose it can effect. Send me, therefore, my recall, and let me know whether I am to pass through Holland.

There, for example, I would accept a secret commission; because pacification there demands, as an indispensable preliminary, a secret agent, who can see and speak the truth, and who is capable of captivating confidence. I do not believe foreign politics afford any opportunity of rendering greater service to France. I fear, since it is necessary I should confess my fears, we rely too much on the ascendency which the aristocracy has gained, of late years, over the Stadtholdership. I think I perceive the system of the patriots has not acquired any decided superiority, except in the province of Holland, which does but disturb its coestates, or at least inasmuch as it excites their animosities. Nay, at Amsterdam itself, the very hotbed of anti-Stadtholder sentiments, was not the Grand Council though the first to rise against the concession of the Scotch brigade to England, the first to plead in favor of military convoys, and to demand the dismission of the Duke Louis of Brunswick? Was it not also the first to vote for a separate peace with England, and for the acceptance of the mediation of Russia? Was not its admiralty, several of the members of which depend on the regency, highly involved in the plot which occasioned the failure of the Brest expedition? How can it be otherwise? The Sovereign Council is only in possession of an imaginary authority. It is the burgomasters, who are annually changed; or even the president of the burgomasters, who is changed once in three months; or rather, in fine, such among the burgomasters as gain some influence of understanding or character over the others, who issue those orders that direct the important vote of the city of Amsterdam, in the Assembly of the States. When we recollect that the college of sheriffs, old and new, from which the burgomasters are elected, contains a great number of English partisans, and depends in some manner on the Stadtholder, who chooses those sheriffs, I know not how we can depend upon the future system of that city.

It is for such reasons that I cannot understand why it should not be for our interest to bring these disputes to a conclusion, if we do not wish to annul the Stadthold-ership, which cannot be annulled without giving birth to foreign and domestic convulsions. And is it possible we should wish for war? We ought not, doubtless, to suf-fer the family of the Stadtholder to remain possessed of legislative power, in the three provinces of Guelderland, Utrecht, and Over-Yssel, by what is called the rules of the regency; for this, added to the same prerogative in the provinces of Zealand and Groningen, inclines the balance excessively in his favor. Neither can it be doubted but that the power of the Stadtholder ought to be subservient to the legislative power of the States. It is of equal importance to our system, or rather to the regular system of foreign politics, that the legislative power of the States should be directed and maintained by the uniform influence of the people. But the preten-sions and passions of individuals, and the private inter-ests of the members of an aristocracy, have, in all countries, too often been supposed the public interest; which is peculiarly true here, where the union of the Seven Provinces was formed in troublesome times, and by the effect of chance, since the people did not think of erecting a republican government till the sovereignty had first been refused by France and England. Hence it resulted that the regents and the people never were agreed concerning the limitation of their rights and re-ciprocal duties. The regents have necessarily labored to render themselves independent of the people; and the people, supposing themselves absolute, since they never consigned over the sovereignty to the regents, nor have had any interest to support them, have on all critical occasions counteracted their attempts This was the ori-gin of the Stadtholder party, and that of fluctuation which has happened between the despotic will of an in-dividual, the perfidious tergiversations of the wavering, the feeble aristocratical colleges, and the impetuosity of an enraged populace. Should ever a link of union exist between the citizens and the regents, the despotism of the Stadtholder and the caprices of the oligarchy will have an end; but, while no such union does exist, while the mode in which the people influence the Government remains undetermined, so long must the system of France remain insecure.

Preserve the confederate constitution, between the provinces and the republican form, in its reciprocal state. Or, to reduce the proposition to the most simple terms, INSTEAD OF THE ODIOUS AND ILLEGAL RECOMMENDA-TIONS OF THE STADTHOLDER, OR OF A BURGOMASTER, SUBSTI-TUTE THE REGULAR AND SALUTARY RECOMMENDATIONS OF THE CITIZENS.* Such should be the palladium of the republic; such the pursuit of our politics.

This restriction rather demands a concurrence of cir-cumstances than the shock of contention. And shall we be able to effect it by those acts of violence which are attributed to us, even though they should not be ours, or by increasing fermentation on one part, and on the other suspicion? Have we not made our influence and our power sufficiently felt? Is it not time to show that we wish only for the abolition of the Stadtholder regu-lations, and not that of the Stadtholdership? And how shall we conclude without making the conclusion tragi-cal, since it is not in human wisdom to calculate all possible consequences, if we cannot effectually persuade the persons at Nimeguen† that such is our real and sole system.

Such is the rough draft of my profession of faith, relative to the affairs of Holland. From what I have said, and according to these principles, which I shall more circumstantially develop, if required, in a written memorial, it may be estimated whether I can or cannot be useful in the country; further supposing me pos-sessed of local information, which I shall with facility acquire.

* « Recommendations » implies elections or appointments.
† The Princess of Orange and her party.

22

LETTER LXV.

January 16th, 1787.

IN THE opinion of those who know that revolutions effected by arms are not often those that overturn States, it is truly a revolution in the Prussian monarchy to behold an example for the first time of a titled mistress, who is on the point of sequestrating the King, of forming a distinct Court, of exciting cabals which shall be communicated from the palace to the LEGIONS, and of arranging affairs, favorites, administration, and grants, after a manner absolutely unknown to these cold and phlegmatic countries. The moment of the disgrace, and the consequent elevation of Mademoiselle Voss approaches. Hence intrigues, sarcasms, opinions, and conjectures, or rather predictions. Amid this mass of suppositions, true or false, the following is what I can collect, which seems to have most probability. My translation is according to the text of one of the former friends of Mademoiselle Voss, to whom she has opened her heart.

This new Joan of Arc, on whose head devotion would invoke the nuptial benediction, has been persuaded that it is her duty to renounce marriage, and sacrifice herself, first to her country; in the second place, to her lover's glory; and, finally, to her family's advantage. The country, say her advisers, will gain a protectress, who will remove covetous and perverse counselors; the glory of the Monarch will not be tarnished by a double marriage; and her family will not be exposed to the danger of beholding her a momentary princess, and presently afterward exiled to an old castle, with some trifling pension. They affirm favor will be the more rapturous should rapture not be secured by the rites of Hymen, and that the instant this favor commences she will rain gold on her relations, with dignities and gratuities of every kind. Religious motives have been added to

(338)

motives of convenience. It has been demostrated that there was less evil in condescension than in contracting a pretended marriage while the former one remained in full force. At length it was concluded that this VICTIM TO HER COUNTRY'S GOOD should be taken to Potsdam and offered up at Sans Souci. A house has been prepared, sumptuously furnished, say some, and simply, according to others, and at which are all the paraphernalia of a favorite.

An anecdote, truly inconceivable, which requires confirmation, and which I am still averse to believe, is circulated: that the King prostitutes his daughter, the Princess Frederica, to be the companion of his mistress.

Mademoiselle Voss has a kind of natural wit, some information, is rather willful than firm, and is very obviously awkward, which she endeavors to disguise by assuming an air of simplicity. She is ugly, and that even to a degree; and her only excellence is the goodness of her complexion, which I think rather wan than white, and a fine neck, over which she threw a double handkerchief the other day, as she was leaving Prince Henry's comedy to cross the apartments, saying to the Princess Frederica, " I must take good care of them, for it is after these they run. " Judge what must be the manners of princesses who can laugh at such an expression. It is this mixture of eccentric licentiousness (which she accompanies with airs of ignorant innocence) and vestal severity, which, the world says, has seduced the King. Mademoiselle Voss, who holds it ridiculous to be German, and who is tolerably well acquainted with the English language, affects the Anglomaniac to excess, and thinks it a proof of politeness not to love the French. Her vanity, which has found itself under restraint when in company with some amiable people of that nation, hates those it cannot imitate, more especially because her sarcasms sometimes are returned with interest. Thus, for instance, the other day, I could not keep silence when I heard an exclamation, " Oh, Heavens! when shall I see, when shall we have an English play ? I really should expire with rapture!" " For my part, Mademoiselle," said I, dryly, " I rather wish you may not, sooner than you

imagine, stand in need of French play." All those who
began to be offended by her high airs smiled, and Prince
Henry, who pretended not to hear her, laughed aloud.
Her face was suffused with blushes, and she did not
answer a word; but it is easy to punish, difficult to correct.

She has hitherto declared open war against the mystics, and detests the daughters of the chief favorite, who
are maids of honor to the Queen.

But, as amid her weaknesses she is transported by
devotion even to superstition, nothing may be depended
on for futurity. Should ambition succeed primary sensations, it is to be presumed her family will govern the
State. At the head of this family stands Count Finckenstein, whose tranquillity would not be disturbed by the
fall of the empire, but who would with inexpressible joy
contemplate his children enacting great parts. Next in
rank is Count Schulemburg, who has newly been brought
into the Ministry; an active man, formerly even too
busy, but who seems to perceive that those who keep
most in the background become the principal figures.
This family preserves an inveterate hatred against Welner, who formerly carried off or seduced one of their
relations, who is at present his wife. To these we may
add the president Voss, the brother of the beauty; who
at least possesses that spirit of calculation, and that German avidity, by which such persons profit whenever fortune falls in their way. Should Mademoiselle Voss
render her situation in any degree subservient to such
purposes, she must, while at Potsdam, prepare the dismission of Bishopswerder and Welner, or render them
useless; for it is more the mode in Germany to dis-
pense with service than to dismiss. She herself may
possibly be ill-guided, and may confide in the first who
shall happen to be present, for she is indiscreet. She
depends on the constancy of her lover; for she is yet
inexperienced in the GRATITUDE of mankind. Having
never yet obliged anybody, she never yet has rendered
anyone ungrateful.

Should this happen, affairs will remain in their present state, or grow worse. The King will shut himself

up at Potsdam; whence, however, he will frequently make excursions to Berlin, because he has contracted a habit of restlessness, and because his favorite seraglio will always be at a brothel. He will then be totally idle, will tolerate rapaciousness, and, as much as he is able, hasten the kingdom's ruin, toward which it tends as rapidly as present circumstances and the *vis inertiæ* of the German character will allow; which does not permit madmen to commit anything more than follies, and preserves men from the destructive delirium of the passions.

Add to this, the Emperor dares attempt nothing, is consistent in nothing, concludes nothing, that he approaches his end, and that all his brothers are pacific. I should not be astonished were the hog of Epicurus, who, at least, is not addicted to pomp, and consequently will not of himself ruin the Treasury, to acquire, thanks to circumstances and interested men, a kind of glory during his reign.

Military regulations are again mentioned. The regiments of the line are not to be ruined, but it seems there is an intention to form a certain number of battalions of chasseurs, who, under good regulations, may become useful; and this, indeed, was the design of Frederick II. Nothing yet can be affirmed on the subject, except that it is exceedingly strange that Frederick William should imagine himself able to effect any reform, the economical part excepted, in the military system and in the army of Frederick II.

Prince Henry probably will have some influence in the army. His name stands the first on the list, although a field marshal has been appointed. The King sent him the list yesterday to assure him it was so, by M. von Goltz himself. They have given the child a bauble. What his military influence is to be must remain a secret till the appearance of the new regulations. He is often visited by the general aids-de-camp. Whether this is or is not known to the King is doubtful, and, if known, it is evident deceit only is meant, which, indeed, is a very fruitless trouble. He has no plan contrary to the politics of the kingdom. I do not say of the Cabinet, for

Cabinet there is none.   Indeed, he has no plan whatever.

Count Goertz is recalled, of which Count Hertzberg
was, this morning, ignorant.   There cannot be a better
proof that there is no desire to interfere in the affairs of
Holland, or not openly; nor simply to expose the nation
to a war, to promote the interests of the Stadtholder.   Of
this, unfortunately, the House of Orange is not persuaded,
but of the contrary, if I may judge from the letter of
the Princess, which came by the courier of this morning,
a part of which I read as soon as it was deciphered.   It
is in this point of view that my journey to Nimeguen,
under a borrowed name, and with secret authority, known
only to her and me, may become useful.   In this same
letter I have read that the patriots are endeavoring to
effect a loan of sixteen millions of florins, at three per
cent, although the province of Holland has never given
more than two and a half per cent, and that they find
difficulty in procuring the money.

There are three Bishops here: the Bishop of Warmia,
the Bishop of Culm (who is of the House of Hohenzol-
lern), and the Bishop of Paphos.   The first, whom I mentioned to you in my account of the King's journey into
Prussia, is the same whom Frederick II. robbed of near
eighty thousand crowns per annum, by reducing the
revenues of his bishopric to twenty-four thousand from a
hundred thousand crowns; for such was its value previous
to the partition of Poland.   The Monarch one day said
to him: "I have not, in my own right, any great claims
on Paradise; let me entreat you to take me in under your
cloak."   "That I would willingly," replied the prelate,
"if your Majesty had not cut it so short." *   He is a
man of pleasure and of the world, and who is only
acquainted with the fine arts, without other views or
projects, religious or political.

The second has been in the service of France.   He has
the rage of preaching upon him and of being eloquent;
and the desire of doing good; but as he has also the

---

* This is better told in the " *Anecdoten aus dem Leben Friedrichs des
Zweiten*," where the Bishop says he had cut his coat too short for it to
hide SMUGGLED GOODS.

rage of running in debt, and getting children, his sermons make no proselytes, and his charities relieve no distress. The latter is a suffragan of Breslau, formerly a great libertine, and a little of an atheist; at present impotent and superannuated.

These three prelates, who are to be reinforced by the Bishop of Lujavia, and the new coadjutor, the Prince of Hohenloe, Canon of Strasburg, will hold no council; nor will they justify the fears the orthodox Lutherans, and all Saxony, who suppose the corner stone of the Protestant religion to be laid here, have entertained concerning the inclination of the King to popery. The one came to obtain the order of the Black Eagle, and is gratified; the other for a benefice, vacant by the death of the Abbé Bathiani; the Prince Bishop of Warmia for a money loan, at two per cent, which may be sufficient to satisfy his creditors.

Prince Henry, after having given a comedy and a grand supper, concluded the banquet with a ball, which began gloomily enough, and so continued. While some were dancing in one room, others were gambling at the Lotto in another. The King neither danced nor gambled; his evening was divided between Mademoiselle Voss, and the Princess of Brunswick. He spoke a word to M. von Grotthaus, but not a syllable to anybody else. Most of the actors and spectators departed before him. The Bishop of Warmia and the Marquis of Lucchesini were not so much as remarked. I would have defied the most penetrating observer to have suspected there was a King in company. Langor and restraint were present, but neither eagerness nor flattery. He retired at half past twelve, after Mademoiselle Voss had departed. It is too visible that she is the soul of his soul, and that the soul which is thus wrapt up in a covering so coarse is very diminutive. You must expect this continual repetition; the place of the scene may change, the scene itself never.

POSTSCRIPT.—The news of the recall of Goertz is false; and, from the manner in which it was conveyed to me, either Comte d'Esterno wished to lay a snare for me, or has had a snare laid for himself. I am acquainted with circumstances which make me believe it possible the negotiation should again be resumed. I have not time to say more.

The Duke of Brunswick is sent for, and will be here in a few days.

Count Wartensleben, who had for five months been forgotten, yesterday morning was presented with between five and six hundred crowns per annum, and the command of the regiment of Roemer at Brandenburg.

LETTER LXVI.

January 19th, 1787. The day of my departure. This will not be sent off sooner than to-morrow, but it ought to arrive before me.

COUNT SCHMETTAU, the complaisant gentleman of the Princess Ferdinand, the indisputable father of two of her children, had eight years quitted the army, which he left in the midst of war, angered by a disdainful expression from Frederick II., and holding the rank of captain. He has lately been appointed a colonel, with the pay of fifteen hundred crowns per annum. The nomination has displeased the army, and particularly the General Aid-de-camp Goltz, who has been in harness five-and-twenty years, and still only enjoys the rank of lieutenant colonel. Count Schmettau has served with honor, has received many wounds, nor does he want intelligence, particularly in the art of fortification. He has drawn a great number of plans which are much esteemed. A military manual is also mentioned with praise, in which he teaches all that is necessary to be done from the raw recruit to the field marshal. In fine, this infringement on rank might have been supportable, but there has been another which has excited the height of discontent.

The commission of one Major Schenkendorff, the governor of the second son of the King, who gives up his pupil, has been antedated, by which he leaps over six-and-thirty heads. This dangerous expedient, which Frederick II. never employed but on solemn occasions, and in favor of distinguished persons, and which his successor had before practiced in behalf of Count Wartensleben, does but tend to spread incertitude over the reality of military rank, and to be destructive of all emulation. It is, besides, infinitely dangerous when employed by a feeble prince, absurd when resorted to at the commencement of his reign, and must finally deprive the Monarch himself of one of his greatest resources, the point of honor.

(345)

He has deposited five hundred thousand crowns in the provincial treasury, and has sent the transfer to Mademoiselle Voss. Thus happen what may, she will always have an income of a thousand a year, besides diamonds, plate, jewels, furniture, and a house that has been purchased for her at Berlin; which is a pleasure house, for she does not intend to inhabit it. Her royal lover has himself imagined all these delicate attentions, and the consequence is that the most disinterested of mistresses has managed her affairs better than the most artful of coquettes could have done. Time will show us whether her mind will aspire to the rank of favorite Sultana.

New taxes are intended to be laid on cards, wines, foreign silks, oysters, coffee, sugar, — contemptible resources! As the Ministry are proceeding blindfold on all these matters, they are kept in a kind of secrecy. It seems they will rather make attempts than carry them into execution.

To-day, the birthday of Prince Henry, the King has made him a present of a rich box, estimated to be worth twelve thousand crowns, has set out the gold plate, and has done everything which Frederick II. used to do, if we omit the rehearsal of a grand concert, the day before, in his chamber; for he has time for everything except for business.

" Let there be bawdyhouses on the wings, and I will easily beat him in the center." Beware that this saying of the Emperor does not become a prophecy. The prophet himself, fortunately, is not formidable; though I should not be astonished were he to be animated by so much torpor and baseness; but if he do not wait two years longer, the energy which the King wants may be found in the army.

POSTSCRIPT. — The Duke of Weimar is at Mayence, as it is said, for the nomination of a coadjutor; but, as he visits all the Courts of the Upper and Lower Rhine, it would be good to keep a watchful eye over him, in my opinion.

END OF THE SECRET HISTORY.

LETTER OR MEMORIAL

PRESENTED TO

FREDERICK WILLIAM II.

KING OF PRUSSIA

LETTER OR MEMORIAL

PRESENTED TO

FREDERICK WILLIAM II.

KING OF PRUSSIA

On the Day of His Accession to the Throne

BY

COMTE DE MIRABEAU

———

Arcus et statuas demolitur et obscurat oblivio, negligit carpitque posteritas. Contrà contemptor ambitionis et infinitæ potestatis domitor animus ipsâ vetustate florescit; nec ab ullis magis laudatur quàm quibus minimè necesse est.
PLIN., Panegy.

ADVERTISEMENT.

SOME imputations are at once so odious and absurd, that a person of sense is not tempted to make them any reply. If he be a worthy man, silence is his only answer when his calumniators are anonymous.

But, amid the abuse lately vented against me, and which I have enumerated rather among the rewards of my labors than estimated as a part of my misfortunes, there is one species of scandal to which I have not been insensible.

I have been accused of presenting the reigning King of Prussia with a libel against the immortal Frederick II.

Frederick II. himself sent for me, when I hesitated (much as I regretted, having lived his contemporary, to die unknown to him) lest I should disturb his last moments, during which it was so natural to desire to contemplate a great man. He deigned to welcome and distinguish me. No foreigner after me was admitted to his conversation. The last time he thus honored me he had refused the just and eager request which some of my countrymen, who had repaired to Berlin to see his military manœuvers, testified to be admitted to his presence. And could I, in return for so honorable a distinction, have written a libel?

Frederick is of himself too great for me ever to be tempted to write his panegyric. The very word is, in my apprehension, highly beneath a great King; it supposes exaggeration and insincerity, the wresting or dissimulation of truth; a view of the subject only on the favorable side. Panegyric, in fine, is to disguise, or to betray, the truth; for this is one of its inevitable inconveniences; never was panegyric true or honorable that was devoid of reproof. I therefore have not, nor shall

I ever have, written the eulogy of Frederick II., but I have for these two years past been endeavoring to raise a monument to his memory, that ought not to be wholly unworthy of the labors by which his reign has been illustrated, or of those grand lessons which his successes and his errors have equally taught. I have engaged in this considerable work, which will see the light in the course of the present year, and of which I make no secret.*

The Memorial which I presented to Frederick William II. on the day of his accession to the throne was entirely foreign to this plan. It was intended only to lay before him the hopes of worthy men, who knew how many events, rather great than splendid, might take birth in Prussia under a new reign and a Prince in the prime of manhood.

The following is the Memorial in question, which has been attributed to me as a crime. I lay my case before the world, that the world may judge. I have not altered a line, though my opinion has varied considerably in some circumstances, as will be seen in my work on Prussia. But I should have reproached myself had I made any change, however trifling, in a Memorial to which the venom of malignity has been imputed.

It has been often asked what right I had to present such a Memorial.

Besides the thanks which the present King of Prussia graciously was pleased to send me in a letter, he has not disdained personally to address me, in a numerous assembly, at the palace of his royal uncle, Prince Henry, a week before my departure from Berlin. This I have thought proper to make public, not in answer to idle tales, which never could deceive any person, but because the courage to love truth is even more honorable to a King than that of speaking truth is to a private person.

---

* This Memorial was published in 1787, and the work alluded to is « L' Histoire de la Monarchie Prussienne. »

LETTER OR MEMORIAL

PRESENTED TO

FREDERICK WILLIAM II.

SIRE, you are now King. The day is come when it has pleased the Creator to confide to you the destiny of some millions of men, and the power of bringing much evil, or much good, upon the earth. The scepter descends to you at a period of life when man is capable of sustaining its weight. You ought at present to be weary of vulgar enjoyments, to be dead to pleasures, one only excepted. But this one is the only great, the sole inexhaustible pleasure,—a pleasure hitherto interdicted, but now in your power. You are called to watch over the welfare of mankind.

The *epocha* at which you ascend the throne is fortunate; knowledge daily expands; it has labored, it continues to labor for you, and to collect wisdom; it extends its influence over your nation, which so many circumstances have contributed in part to deprive of its light. Reason has erected its rigorous empire. Men at present behold one of themselves only, though enveloped in royal robes, and from whom more than ever they require virtue. Their suffrages are not to be despised, and in their eyes but one species of glory is now attainable; all others are exhausted. Military success, political talents, the miraculous labors of art, the progress of the sciences, have each alternately appeared resplendent from one extremity of Europe to the other. But enlightened benevolence, which organizes, which vivifies empires, never yet has displayed itself pure and unmixed upon the throne. It is for you to seat it there. Yes, renown so sublime is reserved to you. Your predecessor has gained a sufficient number of battles, perhaps too many; has too much wearied fame and her hundred tongues; has dried up the fountain of military fame for several reigns, for several ages. Should accident oblige you to become his imitator, it is necessary you should appear worthy so to be, in which Your Majesty will not fail. But this is no reason why you should painfully seek honor in the beaten path, wherein you can but rank as second; while with greater ease, you may create a superior glory, and which shall be only yours. Frederick has enforced the admiration of men, but Frederick never obtained their love: Yes, SIRE, their love may be wholly yours.

SIRE, your mien, your stature, recall to mind the heroes of antiquity. These to the soldier are much; much to the people, whose simple good sense associates the noblest qualities of mind to beauty of person; and such was the first intention of Nature. In your person the heroic form is embellished by most remarkable tints of mildness and calm benevolence, which promise not a little, even to philosophers. You have a feeling heart, and the long necessity of behaving with circumspection must have tempered that native bounty which otherwise might have made you too compliant. Your understanding is just; by this I have often been struck. Your elocution is nervous and precise. You have several times demonstrated that you possess an empire over yourself. You have not been educated, but you have not been spoiled; and men possessed of energy can educate themselves. They are daily educated by experience, and thus are taught what they never forget. Your means are great. You are the only Monarch in Europe who, far from being in debt, is possessed of treasures. Your army is excellent, your nation docile, loyal, and possessed of much more public spirit than might be expected in so slavish a constitution. Some parts of the administration of Prussia, such as its responsibility and consistency, which are purely military, merit great praises. One of your uncles, crowned with glory and success, possesses the confidence of Europe, the genius of a hero, and the soul of a sage. He is a counselor, a coadjutor, a friend, whom Nature and destiny have sent you, at the moment when you have most need of him, at the time when the more voluntary your deference for him shall be, the more infallibly will it acquire your applause. You have rivals in power, but not a neighbor who is in reality to be feared. He who seemed to proclaim himself the most formidable has too long threatened to strike.* He has been taught to know you. He has hastily undertaken, and as hastily renounced. He will again renounce his new projects. He will require all, will obtain nothing, and will never be anything more than an irresolute adventurer, a burden to himself and others. To preserve yourself from his attempts, you need but to suffer his contradictory projects to counteract each other.

You, Sire, are the only Prince who is under the indispensable necessity of performing great things, and from whom great things are expected; and this necessity, this expectation, ought to be enumerated among your best resources. How admirable is your situation! How inestimable are the advantages you bring to that throne whereon being seated your power is boundless! A power formidable even to the possessor! But be it remembered that grand institutions, important changes, and the regeneration of empires, appertain only to absolute Monarchs. Deign, oh, deign, to accept the good that Providence has strewn beneath your feet! Merit the benefactions of the poor, the love of the people, the respect of Europe, and the approbation of the wise! Be just, be good; and you will be happy and great.

Great.— This, Sire, is the title you wish; but you wish it from history, from futurity; you would disdain it from the lips of courtiers, whom you HAVE heard, and whom you SHALL hereafter much oftener hear, prodigal of the grossest praise. Should you do that which the son of your slave could have hourly done better than yourself, they will affirm that YOU HAVE PERFORMED AN EXTRAORDINARY ACT. Should you obey your passions, they will affirm — YOU HAVE WELL DONE. Should you pour forth the blood of your subjects as a river does its waters, they will pronounce — YOU HAVE DONE WELL. Should you tax the free air, they will assert — YOU HAVE DONE WELL.

* The Emperor Joseph II.

Should you, puissant as you are, become revengeful, still would they proclaim you had DONE WELL. So they told the intoxicated Alexander when he plunged his dagger into the bosom of his friend. Thus they addressed Nero, having assassinated his mother.

But, SIRE, you need only to feel those sentiments of justice which are native to your bosom, and that enlightened consciousness of benevolence which you possess; your own heart will be your judge; and its decrees will be confirmed by your people, by the world, and by posterity. The esteem of these is indispensable; and how easily may their esteem be obtained! Should you indefatigably perform the duties of the day, and not remit its burdensome labors till the morrow; should you by grand and prolific principles know how to simplify these duties, so that they may be performed by a single man; should you accord your subjects all the liberty they are capable of enjoying; should you protect property, aid industry, and root out petty oppressors, who, abusing your name, will not permit men to do that for their own advantage which they might without injury to others; then will the unanimous voice of mankind bestow blessings on your authority, and thus render it more sacred and more potent. All things will then become easy to you, for every will and every power will unite with your will and your power, and your labors will daily acquire new enjoyments. Nature has rendered labor necessary to man; but she has also bestowed on him this precious advantage, that the change of labor is at once a recreation to him and a source of pleasure. And who more than a Monarch may live according to this order of Nature? A philosopher has said, "No man was so oppressed by langor as a King." He ought to have said A SLOTHFUL KING. How can languor overcome a Sovereign who shall perform his duties? How may he better maintain his body in health, or his mind in vigor than when by labor he preserves himself from that disgust which all men of understanding must feel, amid the babblers and the parasites who study but to corrupt, lull, benumb, and pilfer Princes? Their whole art is to inspire him with apathy and debility; or to render him impotent, rash, and indolent.   Your people will enjoy your virtues; for by these only can they prosper or improve.   Your courtiers will applaud your defects; for on these depend their influence and their hopes.

Habit, SIRE, no less than accident, influences men; and habit is determined by the beginning.   Therefore is the commencement of a reign of such value.   Everything is hoped, and the slightest effort seconds and confirms that hope, increasing it a hundredfold.   By the pleasure of having done, we are strengthened in the love of doing, good; and that which is wished is rendered more easy by that which has been effected.

The beginning, SIRE, depends absolutely on yourself. Acquire none but good habits; give no encouragement to those that are frivolous.   Display the man of order, the lover of the public welfare.   You will soon be joined by all your Ministers and all your courtiers.   Emulation will spring forth, and wisdom will inevitably be the result.   Emulation will aid you to judge the understandings of those by whom you shall be approached.   It may sometimes excite or produce a happy project, and you will even turn that propensity to flattery, which cannot totally be expelled from Courts, to the good of your people.

You may immediately ascertain to yourself that liberty of mind which grand affairs require, by interfering only with such as appertain to the sovereign authority, and by leaving to your Magistrates and Ministers all those which naturally should come under their consideration.

More than one estimable Monarch has rendered himself incapable of reigning with glory by overburdening his mind with private affairs.   As, SIRE, it will become you always to govern well, it will also be worthy of you not to govern too much.   Wherefore should a King concern himself with civil government which can be better exercised without his aid?   Authority once established, external safety ascertained, civil and criminal justice administered alike to all classes of citizens, landed property accurately estimated so as to be judiciously assessed, and public works, roads, and canals wisely attended to; what more has government to transact?   It has but to enjoy

the industry of the people, who, while active for their
own interest, are also acting for the interest of the State
and the Sovereign.

The King who shall examine whether it be not the
most wise not to lay any restraint on the general affairs
and business of men is yet to be born; yet this is the
King who would govern like a God; and, by the ministry of reason, leaving the interest of each individual to
himself, would ascertain to all the fruits of their industry and their knowledge. Where men are most free,
there will they be most numerous; and there, also, will
they pay the most submission, and have the greatest
attachment, to authority; for authority is essentially the
friend of that freedom which it protects. No man would
require more than to be left AT LIBERTY AND IN PEACE.

You surely, SIRE, are not to be told that the mania of
enacting and restraining laws is the characteristic of
inferior minds; of men incapable of generalizing, who
feed on timidity, and shake with ridiculous apprehensions.
This important truth will indicate to you the reformation you ought to make; and how much better you will
govern than your predecessors and rivals, by governing
less.

There are, doubtless, a multitude of good, useful,
necessary, and even urgent things, which it will be impossible you should immediately execute. You must first
learn them, must combine, and leave them to ripen.
And wherefore should you confide in the opinion of
another? This is one of the grand errors of which you
ought to be aware, as you ought also of being obliged
to retract what you have done. The inconsistency of
that Sovereign, among your rivals, who has attempted
the most, has been more injurious to the political respect
in which he might have been held than his worst errors.
Not only, therefore, must you learn what is to do, but,
which is more difficult, you must, perhaps, instruct your
Ministers, and certainly your people. Let persuasion
precede legislation, SIRE; and you will meet no contradiction, and scarcely any impediments in those operations
which require moments of greater calm, and less business, than are those of the beginning of a reign. But

there are things which you may instantly execute, and which, by propagating a high opinion of your worth, will acquire the fruits of confidence to your own profit, and facilitate the grand changes with which your reign ought to abound.

Suffer a man who loves you — pardon the freedom for the truth of the expression — suffer a man who loves you, for the good you may do, and for the grand example you shall afford of the evil that may be avoided, to point out a few of those things which a single voluntary act of yours may perform, and which can only be productive of good, without inconvenience, while they shall display the morning of the most paternal reign which has ever blessed mankind.

Among these, SIRE, and in the first rank, I shall enumerate the abolition of military slavery; that is to say, the obligation imposed in your States on all men from the age of eighteen to sixty and upward, if able, to serve for threepence a day.*

This fearful law, originating in the necessities of an iron age and a half-barbarous country; this law which depopulates and exhausts your kingdom, which dishonors the most numerous and the most useful class of your subjects, without whom you and your ancestors would only have been slaves more or less feathered and painted; this law, which is abused by your officers, who enroll more men than the military conscription permits, this law does not procure you a soldier more than you would acquire by an increase of pay, which might easily be made from the additional revenue which you would gain by the just suppression of those ruinous enlisters whom Frederick II. maintained in foreign countries; and by a sage mode of recruiting the Prussian army, in a manner that should elevate the mind, increase public spirit, and preserve the forms of freedom instead of those of brutalizing slavery.

Throughout Europe, SIRE, and in Prussia particularly, men have had the stupidity to deprive themselves of one of the most useful instinctive feelings on which the love

---

* *Huit gros tous les cinq jours.* — I suspect I have rated the groschen too high.

of our country can be founded. Men are required to go to war like sheep to the slaughterhouse; though nothing could be more easy than to unite the service of the public with emulation and fame.

Your subjects are obliged to serve from eighteen to sixty; and this they, with good reason, suppose to be the rigorous subjection of servility. The militia of France is the same, and though less cruel, is hateful to the people. Yet the Swiss have a similar obligation, which commences at the age of sixteen, and they believe themselves to be free men.

In fact, that natural confederacy which induces citizens of the same condition to repel the enemy, and to defend their own and their neighbor's inheritance, is so manifest, and the exercise of it is so pleasingly attractive to youth, that it is inconceivable how tyranny could be so weak as to render it a burden.

Impart, SIRE, to this obligation the forms of freedom and of fame, by making it voluntary, and necessary in order to merit esteem, by rendering it a point of honor; and your army will be better conditioned, while your subjects shall imagine they are, and shall really be, relieved from a yoke most odious.

Begin by remitting ten years of service; your army then will not be debilitated by age.

Let your peasants afterward form national companies, in all parishes, that shall exercise every Sunday.

Let such national companies choose their own grenadiers; and from these let the recruits for your regiments be selected,—not by your officers, not by the Magistrates, but by the plurality of votes among their comrades. Arbitrary proceedings would vanish, choice would become distinction, and the parishes responsible for the soldiers they have supplied. Being obliged to fill up their own vacancies when drafts are made, the regiments would be always complete, without effort, without tyranny, and without murmur.

Kings who have created power, impatient of enjoyment, have not confided in general principles. They have feared that the people they have invited into their countries should too soon be disgusted by the difficulties they must have to encounter at the beginning. Hence those tyrannical regulations, by the aid of which they have intended to fix the wretch to the soil on which he had been planted. In the present state of your kingdom there is no pretext for the continuance of this error. It is time to eradicate slavery at which the heart revolts, which drives away good subjects, or inspires them with the desire of escaping. Banish, therefore, all unnecessary constraint; and this, which of all others is the most unnecessary.

Yet, before deciding on any plan for the recruiting of the army, it is requisite to consider, with all the attention which it merits, that of the most worthy of your Ministers, Baron Hertzberg, who, to a comprehensive knowledge of the wounds of Prussia, and the means of prosperity and cure, joins the highest degree of public spirit and patriotic love. He supposes it possible to recruit the army by itself, so as to provide for everything that the most restless state of politics can require. Perhaps, and probably, his plan and mine may coalesce. It is incontestably one of those which ought to be executed at the very beginning of your reign; but let it be preceded by a law of enfranchisement, which shall procure your efforts the universal suffrages of mankind, and their combined aid.

It is not to a man so worthy as you, SIRE (and what greater praise can be bestowed upon a King?), it is not necessary to recommend, with respect to enrollments, the religious observation of all the stipulations so unworthily violated by your predecessors, or the pious rewarding of soldiers who have distinguished themselves by long and loyal service. Alas! SIRE, I have seen alms bestowed, under the windows of your palace, upon men who, while you were yet in your cradle, have shed their blood in defense of your family. Your generous equity doubtless will soften the rigor of their destiny. Remember also the duty, the necessity, of educating the children of soldiers, who at present are perishing in the most deplorable manner, in the orphan house of Potsdam, where more than four thousand are huddled together. Humanity implores your protection of these wretched victims, and provident policy, which but too loudly affirms how requisite a great army will long be to the Prussian States, will point out the real value of these children.

Men ought to be happy in your kingdom, SIRE; grant them liberty to leave their country, when not legally detained by individual obligations. Grant this freedom by a formal edict. This, SIRE, is another of the eternal laws of equity, which the situation of the times demands should be put in execution; which will do you infinite good, and which will not rob you of one enjoyment; for your people can nowhere seek a better condition than that which it depends on you to afford them; and could they be happy elsewhere they would not be detained by your prohibitions. Leave such laws to those Powers that have been desirous to render provinces prisons, forgetting that this was but to make them hateful. The most tyrannical laws respecting emigration have only impelled the people to emigrate, against the very wish of Nature, and perhaps the most powerful of all wishes, which attaches man to his native soil. How does the Laplander cherish the desolate climate under which he is born! And would the inhabitant of a kingdom enlightened by milder suns pronounce his own banishment, did not a tyrannical administration render the benefits of Nature useless or abhorred? Far from dispersing men, a law of enfranchisement would but detain them in what they would then call their GOOD COUNTRY; and which they would prefer to lands the most fertile; for man will submit to everything that Providence imposes; he only murmurs at injustice from man, to which, if he does submit, it is with a rebellious heart. Man is not a tree rooted to the earth in which he grows; therefore pertains not to the soil. He is neither field, meadow, nor brute; therefore cannot be bought and sold. He has an interior conviction of these simple truths; nor can he be persuaded that his chiefs have any right to attach him to the glebe. All powers in vain unite to inculcate a doctrine so infamous. The time when the sovereign of the earth might conjure him in the name of God, if such a time ever existed, is past; the language of justice and reason is the only one to which he will at present listen. Princes cannot too often recollect that English America enjoins all governments to be just and sage, if governors do not wish to rule over deserts.

Abolish, SIRE, the *traites foraines*,* and the *droits d' au-baine*.† Of what benefit to you can such remains of feudal barbarism be? Do not wait for a system of reciprocity, which never has any other effect than that of longer detaining nations in a state of folly and warfare. That which is good for the prosperity of any country needs no reciprocity. Objections of this kind are but the foolish objections of vanity. Should the tyranny which is exercised over man and property in one State be to the loss of another, this is an additional reason why the latter should put an end to such absurd customs. Similar absurdities, perhaps, have obliged its own subjects to seek their fortune elsewhere, and have even made them forbear to return and bring the fruits of their labors back to the country that gave them birth. As nothing is wanting but that some one should begin, how noble, how worthy is it of a great King to be first! Your commercial subjects who are somewhat wealthy could not acquire their wealth at home, they were obliged to seek it in foreign countries; who, therefore, SIRE, is more interested than you are to set the example of abolition, where to exact is so atrocious? Have England and Holland waited to renounce such rights till you should have renounced them in their behalf?

One of the most urgent changes which demands your attention, and which a word may accomplish, is a law to restore to the plebeians the liberty to purchase patrician lands, with all their annexed rights. The execution of the strange decree by which they were deprived of this liberty has been so iniquitously inflicted that, if a patrician estate was sold for debt, and a plebeian was desirous of paying all the creditors, with an additional sum to the debtor, he was not allowed so to do, without an express order from the King. This order was gener-

---

* The twentieth, levied on all merchandise entering or leaving the kingdom.

† The seizure of the effects of foreigners who happen to die in the kingdom.

ally refused by your predecessor; and the patrician by whom the creditors were defrauded, and the debtor kept without resource, had the preference. What was the consequence of this absurd law? The debasement of the price of land, that is to say, of the first riches of the State, and highly to the disadvantage of the noble landholders; the decay of agriculture, which was before discouraged by so many other causes, and of credit among the gentry; the aggravation of that fearful prejudice which wrongs the plebeian and renders the patrician stupid, by making him suppose his honorable rights are a sufficient source of respect, and that he need not acquire any other; in fine, the absolute necessity that those plebeians should quit the country who had acquired any capital; for they could not employ their money in trade, that being ruined by monopoly; nor in agriculture, because they were not allowed to hope they ever might be landholders. * Is not Mecklenburg full of the traders of Stettin and Königsberg, etc., who have employed the wealth they gained, during the last maritime war, in the purchase of the estates of the ruined nobility of that country? This, SIRE, would be a heavy loss to you, were Mecklenburg always to be separated from your kingdom; a loss beyond the powers of calculation, were the same regulations hereafter to subsist. It is a remark which could not escape sagacious travelers, that wealthy merchants have delighted, in retirement, to betake themselves to agriculture. The most barren land becomes fruitful in their possession. They labor for its improvement, and bear with them that spirit of order, that circumstantial precision, by which they grew rich in trade. Wherever merchants can purchase, and wherever trade is honorable, there the country flourishes, and wears the face of abundance and prosperity. Commercial industry awakens every other kind of industry, and the earth requires that ingenious tillage which animates vegetation in the most ungrateful soil. Ah! SIRE, deign to recollect this

* *Bourgeoisie* and *Roturiers* are terms which are here translated by the word PLEBEIAN, and this word is meant to include all classes, whether of tradesmen, husbandmen, or liberal professions, that do not appertain to the nobility.

tillage never was invented on patrician lands; for this we are indebted to those countries where illustrious birth vanishes when merit and talents appear.

Abolish, SIRE, those senseless prerogatives which bestow great offices on men who, to speak mildly, are not above mediocrity; and which are the cause that the greatest number of your subjects take no interest in a country where they have nothing to hope but fetters and humiliations. Beware, oh! beware, of that universal aristocracy which is the scourge of monarchical States, even more than of republics; an aristocracy by which, from one end of the earth to the other, the human species is oppressed. It is the interest of the most absolute Monarch to promulgate the most popular maxims. The people do not dread and revile Kings; but their Ministers, their courtiers, their nobles; in a word, the aristocracy. "OH, DID THE KING BUT KNOW!" Thus they exclaim. They daily invoke the royal authority, and are always ready to arm it against aristocracy. And whence is the power of the Prince derived, but from the people; his personal safety, but from the people; his wealth and splendor, but from the people; those benedictions which alone can make him more than mortal, but from the people? And who are the enemies of the Sovereign, but the grandees: the members of the aristocracy, who require the King should be only THE FIRST AMONG EQUALS, and who, wherever they could, have left him no other pre-eminence than that of rank, reserving power to themselves? By what strange error does it happen that Kings debase their friends, whom they deliver up to their enemies? It is the interest and the will of the people that the Prince should never be deceived. The interest and the will of the nobility are the very reverse. The people are easily satisfied: they give and ask not. Only prevent indolent pride from bearing too heavily upon them; leave but the career open which the Supreme Being has pointed out to them at their birth, and they will not murmur. Where is the Monarch who could ever satisfy the noble, the rich, the great? Do they ever cease to ask? Will they ever cease?

SIRE, equality of rights among those who support the

throne will form its firmest basis. Changes of this kind cannot be suddenly made; yet there is one of these which cannot be too suddenly: let no person who wishes to approach the throne, whatever may be his rank in life, be impeded by the prerogatives of the great. Let men feel the necessity of equal merit to obtain preference. It is for you to level distinctions, and seat merit in its proper place.

Declare open war on the prejudice which places so great a distance between military and civil functions. It is a prejudice which, under a feeble Prince, such as your august family, like every other, may some time produce, will expose the country, and the Crown itself, to all the convulsions of pretorian anarchy. The officer and the soldier, SIRE, should only be proud in the presence of the foe. To their countrymen they should be brothers; and, if they defend their fellow-citizens, be it remembered they are paid by their fellow-citizens. In a kingdom like yours, perhaps, the warrior ought to have the first degree of respect; but he ought not to have it exclusively. If you have an army only you will never have a kingdom. Render your civil officers more respectable than they were under your predecessor. Nothing is more just, or more easy to accomplish. The Prince who reigns over the affections engages them by the simplest attentions. Frederick II. had the frenzy of continually wearing a uniform, as if he were the King only of soldiers. This legionary habiliment did not a little contribute to discredit the civil officer. How happened it he never felt it was impossible a Sovereign should render men estimable, for whom he never would testify esteem? He who attempts to make those incorruptible to whom he will not assure pecuniary independence will be equally unsuccessful. Let the civil officer be better paid, and never forget, SIRE, that ill pay is ill economy. Among a thousand examples, I will but cite the enormous frauds that the Prussian Administrators have, for some years, committed on the public revenue. By an inconsistency, which is important in its effects, the financiers have been held in too much contempt, and those who have been convicted of acts the most dishonest have been too slightly punished. Such partiality could only raise the indignation of the poor, and encourage the fraudulent, who soon learned that to bribe an accomplice was to diminish the danger.

Prompt and gratuitous justice is evidently the first of Sovereign duties. If the Judge have no interest to elude the law, and can receive only his salary, gratuitous justice is soon rendered, and will be equitable, should your inspection be active and severe, and should you never forget that severity is the first duty of Kings. This grand regulation of rendering justice entirely gratuitous will, fortunately, not become burdensome in your States, for your people are well inclined, and not addicted to litigious disputes. But, burdensome or not, that which is strict equity is always necessary. Justice, SIRE, precedes utility itself; or, rather, where justice is not, there is there no utility. The Judge ought to be paid by the public, and not to receive fees. To deny this were absurd; for must not Judges subsist, though there should not, for a whole year, be a single lawsuit?

Be you, SIRE, the first to render the administration of justice gratuitous.

Be you also the first in whose States all men who wish to labor shall find work. All who breathe ought to feed by labor. It is the first law of Nature, and prior to all human conventions. It is the bond of society. The Government that should neglect to multiply the products of the earth, and that should not leave to each individual the use and profits of his industry, would be the accomplice or the author of all the crimes of men, and never could punish a culprit without committing a murder; for each man who offers labor in exchange for food, and meets refusal, is the natural and legitimate enemy of other men, and has a right to make war upon society.

Everywhere, in country as well as in town, let houses of industry be kept open at the expense of Government; that any man, of any country, may there gain his livelihood by his labor; and that your subjects there may be taught the value of time and industry.

Such institutions, SIRE, would be no burden; they would pay themselves. They would open a road to trade, facilitate the sale of natural products, enrich your lands, and improve your finances.

Such, SIRE, are the institutions which become a great King; and not manufactures protected by exclusive privileges, which only can be supported by injustice and mountains of gold, and which do but contribute to enrich a very small number of men; or to endow hospitals, which, if there were no poor, would create paupers.

There are, alas! too many poor in Prussia, especially at Berlin, and the poverty of whom demands your attention. In your capital it cannot be said without a painful emotion, a tenth of the inhabitants receive public alms; and this number annually augments. It is, no doubt, necessary to limit the extent of cities, where excessive population is productive of the worst consequences. In them not only poverty takes birth, but the worst of poverty, because it is not known how it may be remedied. The poor of cities are beings that have lost all good properties, moral and physical. But, speaking in general, the best opponent to this increasing poverty would be the houses of industry before mentioned, where all men who have arms may labor; and not those useless trades which are wretched in their pomp, and serve but to encourage the luxury of splendor, which already eats up your kingdom; nor those hospitals, fruitful sources of depredation, of benefit only to their directors, which engulf sums so considerable; while your schools, especially those of the open country, are so neglected and so miserable that the salaries of some of the headmasters scarcely amount to fifteen crowns a year. Let Your Majesty fit your subjects for labor by a proper mode of instruction, and they will have no need of hospitals.

You are not ignorant, SIRE, that to instruct is one of the most important duties of the Sovereign, as it is one of his greatest sources of wealth. The most able man could do nothing without forming those who surround him, and whom he is obliged to employ; nor without teaching them his language, and familiarizing them with his ideas and his principles. The entire freedom of the Press, therefore, ought to be enumerated among your first regulations, not only because the deprivation of this freedom is a deprivation of natural right, but because that all impediment to the progress of the human understanding is an evil, an excessive evil, and especially to yourself, who only can enjoy truth, and hear truth, from the Press, which should be the Prime Minister of good Kings.

They will tell you, SIRE, that with respect to the freedom of the Press you can add nothing at Berlin. But to abolish the censorship, of itself so useless, and always so arbitrary, would be much. If the printer's name be inserted in the title-page it is enough, perhaps more than enough. The only specious objection against an unlimited freedom of the Press is the licentiousness of libels; but it is not perceived that the freedom of the Press would take away the danger, because that, under such a regulation, truth only would remain. The most scandalous libels have no power except in countries that are deprived of the freedom of the Press. Its restrictions form an illicit trade, which cannot be extirpated; yet they lay restraints on none but honest people. Let not, therefore, that absurd contrast be seen in Prussia, which absolutely forbids foreign books to be inspected, and subjects national publications to so severe an inquisition. Give freedom to all. Read, SIRE, and suffer others to read. Knowledge will everywhere expand, and will center on the throne. Do you wish for darkness? Oh, no! Your mind is too great. Or, if you did, you would wish in vain; would act to your own injury, without obtaining the fatal success of extinguishing light. You will read, SIRE; you will begin a noble association with books; books that have destroyed shameful and cruel prejudices; that have smoothed your paths; that were beneficial to you previous even to your birth. You will not be ungrateful toward the accumulated labor of beneficent genius. You will read; you will protect those who write; for without them what were, what should be, the human species? They will instruct, they will aid you, will speak to you unseen, without approaching your throne; will introduce august Truth to your presence, who shall enter your palace unescorted, unattended; and, having entered, she will ask no dignities, no titles, but will remain invisible and

24

disinterested. You will read; but you would wish your
people should read also. You will not think you have
done enough by filling your academies with foreigners.
You will found schools, especially in the country, and
will multiply and endow them. You will not wish to
reign in darkness. Say but, "Let there be light," and
light shall appear at your bidding; while her divine beams
shall shine more resplendent round your head than all
the laurels of heroes and conquerors.

There is a devouring plague in your States, SIRE, which
you cannot too suddenly extirpate; and no doubt this
good deed will nobly signalize the first day of your
accession to the throne. I speak of the lottery, which
would but be the more odious and more formidable did
it procure you the wealth of worlds; but which, for the
wretched gain of fifty thousand crowns, hurries the industrious part of your subjects into all the calamities of
poverty and vice.

You will be told, SIRE, what some pretended statesmen
have not blushed to write, and publish, that the lottery
ought to be regarded as a voluntary tax. A tax? And
what a tax! One whose whole products are founded either
on delirium or despair. What a tax! To which the rich
landholder is not obliged to contribute. A tax which
neither wise nor good men ever pay. A voluntary tax?
Strange indeed is this kind of freedom! Each day, each
minute, the people are told it depends only on themselves
to become rich for a trifle: thousands may be gained by
a shilling. So the wretch believes who cannot calculate,
and who is in want of bread; and the sacrifice he makes
of that poor remaining shilling which was to purchase
bread, and appease the cries of his family, is a free gift!
—a tax, which he pays to his Sovereign!

You will be further told — yes, men will dare to tell
you — that this horrible invention, which empoisons even
hope itself, the last of the comforts of man, is indeed an
evil; but that it were better you should yourself collect
the harvest of the lottery than abandon your subjects to
foreign lotteries. Oh! SIRE, cast arithmetic so corrupt,
and sophisms so detestable, with horror from you. There
continually are means of opposing foreign lotteries. Secret

collectors are not to be feared. They will not penetrate far into your States when the pains and penalties are made severe; and in such instances only are informers encouraged without inconvenience, for they only inform against an ambulatory pestilence. The natural penalties against such as favor adventurers in foreign lotteries are: infamy, an exclusion from municipal offices, from trading companies, and the right of coming on 'Change. These penalties are very severe, and no doubt sufficient; yet if violent remedies are necessary to impede the progress of such a crime, the punishment of death, that punishment at which my mind revolts and my blood is frozen, that punishment so prodigally bestowed on so many crimes, and which perhaps no crime can merit, would be rendered more excusable from the fearful list of wretchedness and disorder, which originate in lotteries, than even from the most exaggerated consequences of domestic theft.

But, SIRE, the great, first, and immediate operation which I supplicate from YOUR MAJESTY, in the name of your dearest interest and glory, is a quick and formal declaration, accompanied with all the awful characteristics of sovereignty, that unlimited toleration shall prevail through your States, and that they shall ever remain open to all religions. You have a very natural, and not less estimable, opportunity of making such a declaration. Publish an edict which shall grant civil liberty to the Jews. This act of beneficence, at the very commencement of your reign, will make you surpass your illustrious predecessor in religious toleration, who was the most tolerant Prince that ever existed. Nor shall this excess of beneficence be without its reward. Exclusive of the numerous increase to population, and the large capitals which Prussia will infallibly acquire, at the expense of other countries, the Jews of the second generation will become good and useful citizens. To effect this they need but be encouraged in the mechanic arts and agriculture, which to them are interdicted. Free them from those additional taxes by which they are oppressed. Give them access to the courts of justice equal to your other subjects, by depriving their

Rabbis of all civil authority. Oh! SIRE, I conjure you, beware of delaying the declaration of the most universal tolerance. There are fears in your provinces of rather losing than gaining in this respect. Apprehensions are entertained concerning what are called your prejudices, your preconceived opinions, your doctrine. This, perhaps, is the only part in which you have been seriously attacked by calumny. Solemnly prove the falsehood of those who have affirmed you are intolerant. Show them that your respect for religious opinions equals your respect for the great Creator, and that you are far from desiring to prescribe laws concerning the manner in which He ought to be adored. Prove that, be your philosophic or religious opinions what they may, you make no pretensions to the absurd and tyrannical right of imposing opinions upon others.

After these preliminary acts, which, I cannot too often repeat, may as well be performed in an hour as in a year, and which consequently ought to be performed immediately, a glance on the economical and political system by which your kingdom is regulated will lead you to other considerations.

It is a most remarkable thing that a man like your predecessor, distinguished for the extreme justness of his understanding, should have embraced an economical and political system so radically vicious. Indirect taxes, extravagant prohibitions, regulations of every kind, exclusive privileges, monopolies without number! Such was the spirit of his domestic government, and to a degree that, besides being odious, was most ridiculous.

Is it not astonishing, for example, that a man like Frederick II. could waste his time in regulating, in such a city as Berlin, the rates that should be paid at inns; the pay of *laquais de louage*,* and the value of all the necessaries of life; or that ever he should conceive the project of prohibiting the entrance of French apples into the march of Brandenburg, which is only productive of wood and sands? As if the apples of his provinces were in dread of rivals! Thus, too, he asked, when he prohibited the eggs that were brought from Saxony, "Can-

* Footmen that are hired by the day, for the convenience of strangers.

not my hens lay eggs?"— Could he forget that the eggs
of the hens of Berlin must first be eaten before the inhabitants would send as far as Dresden for others? His
prohibition, too, of the mouse traps of Brunswick! As
if the man had ever before been born who founded his
hopes of fortune on a speculation in mouse traps! It
would be endless to collect all his singularities of this
kind. Who can reflect, without pain and pity, that four
hundred and twelve monopolies exist in your kingdom?
So interwoven was this equally absurd and iniquitous
system with the spirit of the government of Frederick
II. Or that a great number of these monopolies are still
active; at least that the prohibitive ordinances are effective, which bestowed such exclusive privileges on
persons many of whom have since been ruined, and have
become bankrupts or outlaws? Or that, in fine, the
number of prohibited commodities greatly exceeds that
of commodities that are permitted? These things would
appear incredible to men even most accustomed to indulge
the regulatory and fiscal delirium. Yet thus low could
even a great man sink, who was desirous of governing
too much.

Is it not equally astonishing that a Monarch so active,
so industrious in his royal functions, should leave the
system of direct taxation exactly in the state in which
it was under Frederick I., when the clergy were taxed
at a fiftieth of their income, the nobility at the thirty-
third, and the people at the seventeenth; a burden at
that time excessive, but which, by the different variations in value and the signs of property, is almost reduced to nothing? So that industry and trade have been
most unmercifully oppressed by your predecessor, at the
very time that he was establishing manufactures at an
excessive expense.

How might this same King, so consistent and pertinacious in what he had once ordained, at the time that
he settled new colonies by granting them franchises and
the right of property, the necessity of which to agriculture he consequently knew, suffer the absurd regulation
to subsist which excludes all right of property in the
greatest part of his kingdom? How was it that he did

not feel that, instead of expending sums so vast in forming colonies, he would much more rapidly have augmented his revenues and the population of his provinces,
by enfranchising those unfortunate beasts of burden who,
under the human form, cultivate the earth, by distribu-
ting among them the extensive tracts called domains
(which absorb almost the half of your estates) in pro-
prietaries, and on condition of paying certain hereditary
quitrents in kind?

All these particulars, and a thousand others of a like
kind, are strange, no doubt; yet it is not totally impossible to explain such eccentricities of mind in a great
man.   Without entering here into a particular inquiry
concerning that quality of mind whence it resulted that
Frederick II. was much rather a singular example of the
development of great character, in its proper place, than
of an elevated genius, bestowed by Nature, and superior
to other men, it is easy to perceive that, having applied
the whole power of his abilities to form a grand military
force, with provinces that were disunited, parceled out
and generally unfruitful; and, for that purpose, wishing
to outstrip the slow march of Nature, he principally
thought of money, because money was the only engine
of speed.   Hence originated with him his idolatry of
money; his love of amassing, realizing, and heaping.
Those fiscal systems which most effectually stripped the
people of their metal were those in which he most
delighted.   Every artifice, every fiscal extortion, that has
taken birth in kingdoms the most luxurious, which, unfortunately, in this as in other things, gave the fashion
to Europe, were by turns naturalized in his States.
Frederick II. was the more easily led to pursue this purpose, because such was the situation of some of his
provinces that they were almost necessarily a market for
the products of Saxony, Poland, etc., and thus the multiplicity and severity of his duties were less rapidly
destructive of the revenue arising from the tolls.   Besides that, his nation, but little active, and still, perhaps,
tainted by that Germanic improvidence which neglects
or disdains to save, did not afford him any other immediate resource than what might be found in the Royal

Treasury. He imagined the Prussians were in need of being goaded by additions, which, however, could only tend to slacken their pace. He supposed they might be taught wisdom by monopolies; as if monopolies were not injurious to the progress of knowledge. Having taken his first steps, his unconquerable spirit of consistency, which was his distinguishing characteristic; the multitude of his affairs, which obliged him to leave whatever did not appertain to the military system on the same basis, and with similar institutions, in which he found it; his habit of not suffering contradiction nor discussion; his extreme contempt for mankind, which, perhaps, will explain all his success, all his errors, all his conduct; his confidence in his own superiority, which confirmed him in the fatal resolution of seeing all, of all regulating, all ordaining, and personally interfering in all — these various causes combined have rendered fiscal robbery, and systematic monopoly, irrefragable and sacred in his kingdom; while they were daily aggravated by his despotic temper and the moroseness of age.

Evils so various and so great had indeed some compensations. To his numerous taxes Frederick II. joined a rigorous economy. He raised heavy contributions on his enemies. His first wars were paid by their money. He conquered a rich province, where great and wealthy industry, reduced no doubt by a government more sage than his, had previously been established. He drew subsidies from his allies; the folly of granting which is no longer in fashion. During four-and-twenty years of peace, he enjoyed a degree of respect which rather resembled worship than dread. He continually reserved, in his States, some part of the money he extorted. His new military discipline, a species of industry of which he was the creator, not a little contributed to his puissance; and his wealth, in the midst of indebted Europe, would have been almost sufficient for all his wishes; for, had the ardor of his ambition longer continued, what he could not have conquered he would have bought. Who, indeed, can say whether Frederick II. was not indebted, for a great part of his domestic success, to the deplorable state of the human species in Germany; through most of the States of which, if we except Saxony, the inhabitants were still more wretched than in Prussia ?

Yet, SIRE, with efforts so multiplied, what is the inheritance that has been left you by this great King ? Are your provinces rich, powerful, and happy ? Deprive them of their military renown and the resources of the Royal Treasury, which soon may vanish, and feeble will be the remainder. Had the provinces of which your kingdom is composed been under a paternal government, and peopled by freemen, the acquisition of Silesia might have been more distant; but how different would have been the present state and wealth of the whole remaining nation!

Your situation, SIRE, is entirely different from that of your predecessor. The destructive resources of fiscal regulation are exhausted. A change of system is, for this reason, indispensable. An army cannot always, cannot long, constitute the basis of the Prussian puissance. Your army must, therefore, be supported by all the internal aids which good administration can employ, built on permanent foundations. It is necessary that you should truly animate the national industry, in ably profiting by those extraordinary and perishable means which have been transmitted to you by your predecessor. These, it is to be presumed, you may long enjoy. It is not, therefore, absurd to advise you to sow in order that you may reap. Should momentary sacrifices, however great, be necessary to render the Prussian States (which hitherto have only constituted a vast and formidable camp) a stable and prosperous monarchy, founded on freedom and property, the immensity of your treasure will render such sacrifices infinitely less burdensome to you than they would be to any other Sovereign, and the barter will be prodigiously to your advantage, even should the rendering of men happy be estimated at nothing.

The basis of the system which it is your duty, SIRE, to form, must rest on the just ideas which you shall obtain of the true value of money, which is but a trifling part of national wealth, and of much less importance than the riches which annually spring from the bosom of the earth. The incorruptibility and the scarcity of gold have rendered it a pledge, and a mode of exchange between man and man; and this general use is the chief source of the deceitful opinions that are entertained of its value. The facility with which it may be removed, when men are obliged to fly, especially from places where tyranny is to be dreaded, has given every individual a desire of amassing gold; and the false opinions concerning that metal have been strengthened by this universal desire.

No less true is it that, gold being an engine or agent in trade, and that the multiplicity of agents is the increase of trade,* and still further that the increase of trade is the prosperity of nations, to imprison gold, or to act so as to oblige others to imprison it, is madness. What would you say of a Prince who, desiring to become a conqueror, should keep his army shut up in barracks? Yet Kings who amass gold act precisely thus. They render that lifeless which is of no value except when in motion.

But just ideas concerning the value of gold are necessarily connected with those of the government that shall respect property, and shall pursue principles of rigorous justice; such as shall inspire unshaken confidence, and render to each individual the most perfect security; for, without this, the true use of gold is traversed by innumerable accidents, that deprive it of the utility which would otherwise render national industry so fruitful.

Whatever you may do, SIRE, to inspire confidence, it still remains for you to observe that nations have commercial connections; and that gold forms one of those, because of its necessity to trade. It must flow here or there, according to the indefinite combinations of merchants. Hence no nation can unite sound opinions concerning trade with restraint on the exportation of gold. Each man must finally pay his debts, and no person gives or receives gold, from which little is to be gained, except when every means of paying in merchandise is exhausted; for from these, profits are derived to buyer and seller. What would you think, SIRE, of a Prince who should encourage the merchants of his kingdom to es-

* The whole reasoning here, and, indeed, through the greatest part of the Memorial, is taken from that almost inestimably valuable work, Smith's "Wealth of Nations."

tablish numerous manufactures, consequently to employ numerous agents, yet should forbid those agents to leave the kingdom that they might purchase the materials of which the manufacturers stand in need? This, however, is the picture of the Prince who should prevent, or lay restraint on, the exportation of gold; such would his frenzy be. But in what does this originate? In his fear that the gold will never come back. And wherefore? Because he secretly feels that his subjects are not perfectly secure of their property. Thus, SIRE, you perceive justice, security, respect for men, and a declaration of war against all tyranny, are indispensable conditions to every play of prosperity.

When your subjects shall be at ease in this respect, entertain no apprehensions should gold seem to vanish; it is but gone in search of gold, and to return with increase. Forget not, SIRE, that the value of gold is lost, irretrievably, when it is not absolutely subjected to the will of trade, which alone is its monarch. By trade I here understand the general action of all productive industry, from the husbandman to the artist.

What has been done in kingdoms where the security of the citizen is perfect, and where men have been convinced that gold never can be fixed, nor acquired in sufficient abundance for the supply of exchange? Why, in such kingdoms, banks have been imagined, and bills have been brought into circulation, which, from the conviction that they may at any time be turned into specie, have become a kind of coin, which not being universal has been an internal substitute for gold, and induced men not to disturb themselves concerning its external circulation.

Of such establishments you, SIRE, should be ambitious. Happy the State in which the Sovereign, having habituated his subjects to the opinion of perfect internal security, can cause sufficient sums to issue from his treasury for the establishment of such banks, to his own advantage.*

---

* Notwithstanding the general excellence of the counsel given in this Memorial, there seems to be a mixture of cunning in the present advice, of which perhaps the author was not conscious. But the preceding letters prove that he himself was addicted to speculations in

How many fiscal inventions, produced by the spirit of pilfering, under the protection of ignorance and the laws, how many absurd and tyrannical taxes might be annihilated, by gaining the interest of that money of which this confidential currency should be the representative? And what tax ever could be more mild, more natural, more productive, or more agreeble to the Monarch, than the interest of money which he may gain by a currency which costs him nothing? Such a tax is cheerfully paid, for industry is the borrower; and, wherever industry finds its reward, each individual wishes to be industrious.

The outline I have here traced, and which you, Sire, may strengthen by so many circumstances of which I am ignorant, and by so many others that would be too tedious to recapitulate at present, will naturally lead you—

1. To the distribution of your immense domains among husbandmen, whom you will supply with the sums they want, and who will become real landholders, that shall pay a perpetual quitrent in kind, in order that your revenues may augment in proportion to the augmentation of wealth.

2. To the due lowering (till such time as they may be wholly abolished) of indirect taxes, excise duties, customs, etc., the product of which will continually increase in an inverse ratio to the quantity of the duty and the vigor with which it is collected; for illicit trade, excited by too tempting lures, gains protectors among those by whom it ought to be repressed, and agents who had been appointed its opponents. Such disastrous taxes might likewise find substitutes in the natural and just increase of direct taxes; as on land, from which no estate ought to be free; for land finally bears the whole burden of taxation, which burden is the heavier the more the means of laying it on are indirect. How many disputes, shackles, inquisitions, and disorders would then vanish! Plagues which are more odious, more oppressive, than the burden of the tax itself; and even more intolerable

stockjobbing; and, still more, that he wished to procure loans from Prussia to supply the immediate necessities of France, and of his friend De Calonne. The advice, however, might be, and probably was, good.

from the mode of assessment than from the value! That artificial vice which, before the last reign, was unknown in your kingdom, the vice of illicit trade, which makes deceit the basis of commerce, depraves the manners, and inspires a general contempt for the laws, then would disappear. To the regions of hell itself would then be banished the infernal power which your predecessor conferred on the administrators of excise duties and tolls, of arbitrarily increasing the penalties and punishments inflicted on smugglers.

3. You will firmly and invariably determine on the system of favoring, by every possible means, the TRANSIT TRADE,* which must find new roads should foreigners longer be vexed; or rather, has already found new roads. The impositions and minute examinations, which are occasioned by the manner of levying duties on this trade, and the fatal vigilance that has been employed not to suffer contraband goods to find entrance at the fair of Frankfort on the Oder, has produced this fatal effect, that the Poles, who formerly carried on a very considerable trade at Frankfort and at Breslau, at present totally avoid both places, and condemn themselves to a circuit of near a hundred German miles† through a great part of Poland, Moravia, and Bohemia, that they may arrive at Leipsic; for which reason this last city, which is much less favorably situated than Frankfort on the Oder, where there is a great river, has within these fifteen years become flourishing; while the former, from the same cause, has fallen to decay; which decay continues increasing, and that at the very moment when the revolution in America threatens the North with so powerful a rivalship. Profit, SIRE, by the last stage in which perhaps, the transit trade can be an object of any importance. Favor it by taking off the chief of the duties which shackle it at present, and impart a confidence befitting of your candor and generous benevolence. How might you find a more fortunate moment in which to

---

*The passage of foreign goods through the Prussian States into other countries.

†The German mile is irregular. It contains from four to five, six, seven, and even more miles English.

manifest such intentions than that wherein your neighbors are signalizing themselves by so many prohibitive frenzies ?

4. To you, SIRE, is reserved the real and singular honor of abolishing monopolies, which are no less injurious to good sense than to equity; and which, in your kingdom, are so perpetual a source of hatred and malediction. The Prussian merchants, incited by the example of monopolizing companies (Nature, desirous of preserving the human race, ever causes evil itself to produce good), and, thanks to the excellent situation of your States, have made some progress, in despite of every effort to stifle their industry, on the first ray of hope that monopolies should disappear; and these merchants will, by voluntary contributions, afford a substitute for a part of the deficiency which the new system may at first occasion in your revenues.

5. You will, finally, arrive at the greatest of benefits, and at the most useful of speculations in politics and finance. You will set industry, arts, manufactures, and commerce free; commerce, which only can exist under the protection of freedom; commerce, which prefers no request to Kings except not to do it an injury. When you shall seriously have examined whether those manufactures which never can support a foreign rivalship deserve to be encouraged at an expense so heavy, prohibitions will then presently vanish from your States. The linens of Silesia never were otherwise favored than by exempting the weavers from military enrollment; and, of all the objects of Prussian trade, these linens are the most important. In none of your provinces are any manufactures to be found more flourishing than in that of Westphalia; namely, in the county of Marck; yet never has Government done anything to encourage the industry of this province, except in not inflicting internal vexations. I repeat, internal, for all the products of the industry of Prussian subjects, beyond the Weser, are accounted foreign and contraband, in all the other provinces; which odious and absurd iniquity you will not suffer to subsist. You will enfranchise all, SIRE, and will grant no more exclusive privileges. Those who

demand them are generally either knaves or fools; and to acquiesce in their requests is the surest method of strangling industry. If such are found in England, it is because the form in which they are granted renders them almost null. In Ireland they are no longer admitted. The Government and the Dublin Society afford support and give bounties, but on condition that no exclusive privilege is asked. The most magnificent, as well as the most certain, means of possessing everything Nature bestows is freedom, SIRE. It is the prodigality with which she bestows that attracts men, by moral feeling and physical good. All exclusive grants wound the first, and banish the second.

I entreat, SIRE, you would remark that I do not propose you should suddenly, and incautiously, lop away all the parasite suckers which disfigure and enfeeble the royal stock which you were born to embellish and strengthen; but I likewise conjure you not to be impeded by the fear of meeting your collectors with empty hands; for this fear, being solely occupied concerning self, they will not fail to increase. The only man among them who really possesses an extensive knowledge of the general connections of commerce, and from whom you may expect able services, whenever your system shall invariably be directed to obtain other purposes than those to which his talents have hitherto been prostituted, STRUENSEE, will confirm all my principles. He will indicate various means to Your Majesty, which may serve as substitutes to fiscal extortions. Thus, for instance, the commutation of duties, which is a new art, may, under the direction of a man so enlightened, greatly increase your revenues by lightening the public burden.

England, formed to afford lessons to the whole earth, and to astonish the human mind by demonstrating the infinite resources of credit, in support of which everything is made to concur — England has lately made a fine and fortunate experiment of this kind. She has commuted the duties on tea by a tax on windows, and the success is wonderful. Acquire a clear knowledge of this operation, SIRE. It is preserved, with all the effects it has produced, in a work which will open vast prospects to your view.   Your generalizing mind will take confidence in the industry of the honest man, and in the resources of his sensibility, aided by experience and talents; though the misfortune of heavy taxes and the vicious mode of assessment should necessarily be prolonged.

But, SIRE, were you obliged to accept that heavy interest which Powers in debt are obliged to pay, as a substitute for duties that, though destructive, are not commutable, where would be the misfortune?   What advantage might not result from treasures employed to obtain the payment of interest by which monarchies the most formidable are enfeebled?   Wherefore not seize the means which they themselves furnish at their own expense, no longer to stand in awe of them?   Do not you perceive, SIRE, that you would thus without danger make them pay you tribute?   For the governments which might be mad enough to wish to rob their creditors would be unable, thanks to the general intercourse of trade.

It remains to inquire to whom you would confide labors so difficult, yet so interesting.   It is not for a stranger to estimate the worth of your subjects.   Yet, SIRE, is there one whose talents are esteemed in France and England, and him, therefore, I may venture to name. Baron Knyphausen is well acquainted with men and things, in those countries in which he has served, and particularly with the system of the public funds.

But more especially, SIRE, summon the merchants. Among them are most commonly found probity and abilities.   From them is derived the theory of order; and without order what can be accomplished?   They are in general men of moderation, divested of pomp, and for that reason merit preference.   Be persuaded, SIRE, that the most enlightened, the most wise, and the most humane of mankind, would depart from you were their reward to consist in the vain decorations which titles bestow.   These cannot be accepted without trampling on principles to which men are indebted for the glory of having merited reward; nor without paying with contempt the class they honor.   The merchant who is worthy of your confidence will dread making himself guilty of such ingratitude toward his equals; and this is one of the characteristics by which he will be distinguished. In the title of Lord Chatham the great Pitt expired; nor did the lord ever console himself for having acted thus traitorously toward his own glory. The services of the merchants you may employ, far from multiplying, must destroy the monstrous inequalities which disorganize and deform your States. Thus will men like these find their reward, and not in silly titles, or the vain decorations of nobility.

But, SIRE, I have too long intruded upon the precious moments in which the scepter has so lately been confided to your hands. What can I add which your own reflections, increased by facts that daily must fall under your notice, will not convey a thousand times more forcibly than any words of mine can? I have imagined it might not be wholly fruitless to awaken these ideas at the moment of a change so new, under a variety of affairs so great, and a multitude of interests and intrigues which must traverse and combat each other round your throne, and which may deprive you of that calm of mind that is necessary to abstract and to select. Should you in any degree be affected by my frankness, I dare hope it will not be unpleasantly. Meditate, O FREDERICK! on this free, sincere, but respectful remonstrance, and deign to say:

"Here I find what no man has informed me of, and perhaps the reverse of what I shall be daily told. The most courageous present truth to Kings under a veil; I here behold her naked. This is more worthy of me than the venal incense of rhymers, with which I am suffocated; or academical panegyrics, which assaulted me in the cradle, and scarcely will quit me in the coffin. I was a man before I was a King. Wherefore then take offense at being treated like a man; or because a stranger, who asks nothing from me, and who soon will quit my Court, never to behold it more, speaks to me without disguise? He lays before me what inspection, experience, study, and understanding have collected. He gratis gives me that true and liberal advice of which no man stands so much in need as he who is devoted to the public good. Interest to deceive me he has none; his intentions cannot be evil.   Let me attentively examine what he has proposed; for the simple good sense, the native candor of the man, whose only employment is the cultivation of reason and reflection, may well be of equal value with the old routine of habit, artifice, forms, diplomatic chimeras, add the ridiculous dogmas of those who are statesmen by trade.»

May the eternal Disposer of human events watch over your welfare; may your days be beneficent and active; employed in those consolatory duties which elevate and fortify the soul; and may you, till the extremest old age, enjoy the pure felicity of having employed your whole faculties for the prosperity of the people for whose happiness you are responsible, for to you their happiness is intrusted!

THE END.

25

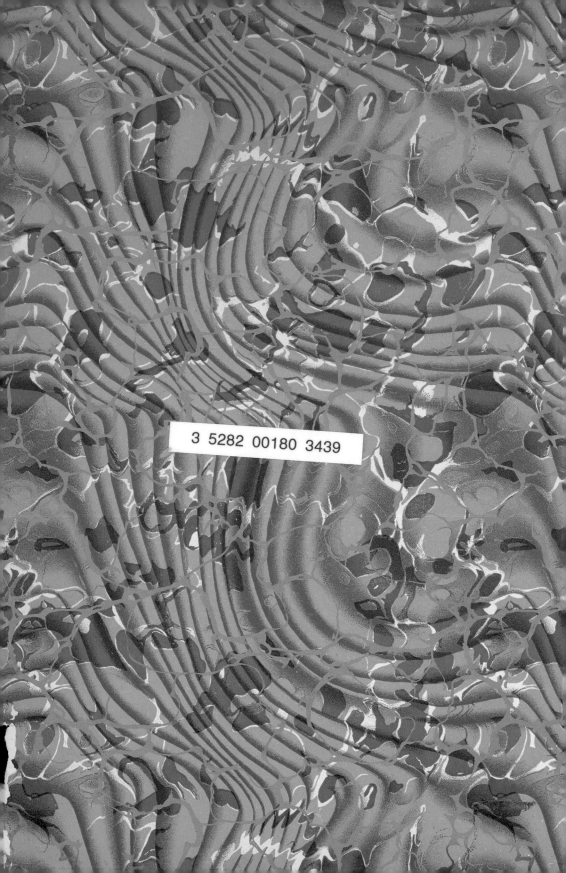

3 5282 00180 3439

P9-CMF-113

S. L. CLEMENS

808
W x4
y

LIBRARY

OF THE

WORLD'S BEST LITERATURE

Ancient and Modern

CHARLES DUDLEY WARNER

EDITOR

HAMILTON WRIGHT MABIE, LUCIA GILBERT RUNKLE,
GEORGE H. WARNER

ASSOCIATE EDITORS

THIRTY VOLUMES

VOL. VII

NEW YORK

R. S. PEALE AND J. A. HILL

PUBLISHERS

7657

Copyright 1897
By R. S. Peale and J. A. Hill

All rights reserved

THE ADVISORY COUNCIL

CRAWFORD H. TOY, A. M., LL. D.,
    Professor of Hebrew,   HARVARD UNIVERSITY, Cambridge, Mass.

THOMAS R. LOUNSBURY, LL. D., L. H. D.,
    Professor of English in the Sheffield Scientific School of
                YALE UNIVERSITY, New Haven, Conn.

WILLIAM M. SLOANE, PH. D., L. H. D.,
    Professor of History and Political Science,
            PRINCETON UNIVERSITY, Princeton, N. J.

BRANDER MATTHEWS, A. M., LL. B.,
    Professor of Literature, COLUMBIA UNIVERSITY, New York City.

JAMES B. ANGELL, LL. D.,
    President of the   UNIVERSITY OF MICHIGAN, Ann Arbor, Mich.

WILLARD FISKE, A. M., PH. D.,
    Late Professor of the Germanic and Scandinavian Languages
    and Literatures,   CORNELL UNIVERSITY, Ithaca, N. Y.

EDWARD S. HOLDEN, A. M., LL. D.,
    Director of the Lick Observatory, and Astronomer,
          UNIVERSITY OF CALIFORNIA, Berkeley, Cal.

ALCÉE FORTIER, LIT. D.,
    Professor of the Romance Languages,
           TULANE UNIVERSITY, New Orleans, La.

WILLIAM P. TRENT, M. A.,
    Dean of the Department of Arts and Sciences, and Professor of
    English and History,
          UNIVERSITY OF THE SOUTH, Sewanee, Tenn.

PAUL SHOREY, PH. D.,
    Professor of Greek and Latin Literature,
          UNIVERSITY OF CHICAGO, Chicago, Ill.

WILLIAM T. HARRIS, LL. D.,
    United States Commissioner of Education,
          BUREAU OF EDUCATION, Washington, D. C.

MAURICE FRANCIS EGAN, A. M., LL. D.,
    Professor of Literature in the ˡᵃ
        CATHOLIC UNIVERSITY OF AMERICA, Washington, D. C.

9377

TABLE OF CONTENTS

VOL. VII

———

LIST OF PORTRAITS

IN VOL. VII

CICERO.

MARCUS TULLIUS CICERO

(106–43 B. C.)

BY WILLIAM CRANSTON LAWTON

THE outward life, the political career, of Marcus Tullius Cicero, is to nearly all students of history a tragic and pathetic story. He seems peculiarly unfitted to the people and the time in which his lot was cast. His enlightened love for the traditions of the past, his passionate sentiment of patriotism, his forceful eloquence as a debater in the Senate or as an orator in the Forum,— these qualities of a Burke or a Webster stand out violently dissevered from the lurid history of his time. This humane scholarly life was flung into the midst of the wildest century in all Rome's grim annals; the hundred years of civic turmoil and bloodshed, from the elder Gracchus's murder to the death of Cleopatra.

And yet such was the marvelous activity, the all-sided productiveness, of the Ciceronian intellect, that perhaps no human mind has ever so fully exploited all its powers. Moreover, in each intellectual field which he entered, the chances of time have removed nearly every Roman rival, leaving us no choice save to accept Cicero's guidance. There was many another orator, and history of eloquence. There were other practical treatises on rhetoric. Many a notable correspondence was actually preserved and published, though now lost. Even his free transcriptions from Greek philosophical treatises — hastily conned and perhaps imperfectly understood — have acquired, through the disappearance of the Greek scrolls themselves, an ill-deserved authority as to the tenets of the Epicurean and other schools.

Before and above all else, Cicero was a pleader. Out of that activity grew his ill-starred political activity, while his other literary tastes were essentially but a solace in times of enforced retirement. With the discussion of his oratory, therefore, we may best combine a rapid outline of his life.

By their common birthplace, Arpinum, and by a slight tie of kinship, Cicero was associated with Marius; and he began life, like Disraeli, with radical sympathies. He was the elder son of a wealthy Roman citizen, but no ancestor had ennobled the family by attaining curule office. After a most thorough course of training in Latin and Greek, Cicero began to "practice law." The pleader in ancient Rome was supposed to receive no fee, and even more than with us, found his profession the natural stepping-stone to political honors.

At the age of twenty-six, Cicero (in 80 B. C.) defended his first important client in a criminal case. In the closing days of the Sullan proscriptions, young Roscius, of Ameria in Umbria, was charged with murdering his own father in Rome. A pair of Roscius's kinsmen were probably the real culprits, and had arranged with Chrysogonus, a wealthy freedman and favorite of the Dictator, to insert the dead man's name among the outlawed victims and to divide the confiscated estate. The son was persecuted because he resisted this second outrage. Cicero says he is himself protected by his obscurity, though no other advocate has dared to plead for the unlucky youth. In our present text there are some audacious words aimed at Sulla's own measures: they were probably sharpened in a later revision. The case was won, against general expectation. Cicero may have played the hero that day: certainly the brief remainder of Sulla's life was spent by the young democratic pleader traveling in the East,— "for his health," as Plutarch adds, truly enough. At this time his style was chastened and his manner moderated by the teachers of Athens, and especially by Molo in Rhodes.

Cicero's quæstorship was passed in Sicily, 75–4 B. C. Here he knit close friendships with many Greek provincials, and did a creditable piece of archæological work by rediscovering Archimedes's tomb. His impeachment of Verres for misgovernment in Sicily was in 70 B. C. This time the orator runs a less desperate risk. Since Sulla's death the old constitution has languidly revived. Speech was comparatively free and safe. The "knights" or wealthy middle class,— Cicero's own,— deprived by Sulla of the right to sit as the jurors in impeachment trials like Verres's, partially regain the privilege in this very year. The overwhelming mass of evidence made Verres flee into exile, and Hortensius, till then leader of the Roman bar, threw up the case in despair. Nevertheless Cicero published the stately series of orations he had prepared. They form the most vivid picture, and the deadliest indictments ever drawn, of Roman provincial government,— and of a ruthless art-collector. Cicero instantly became the foremost among lawyers. Moreover, this success made Cicero a leader in the time of reaction after Sulla, and hastened his elevation to posts where only men of sterner nature could be fully and permanently successful.

Pompey, born in the same year, was at this time leading the revolt against Sulla's measures. The attachment now formed, the warmer hearted Cicero never wholly threw off. The young general's later foreign victories are nowhere so generously set forth as in Cicero's too-rhetorical plea "for the Manilian Law," in 66 B. C.

Pompey was then wintering in the East, after sweeping piracy in a single summer from the Mediterranean. This plea gave him the larger command against Mithridates. Despite the most extravagant laudation, however, Pompey remains, here as elsewhere, one of those large but vague and misty figures that stalk across the stage of history without ever once turning upon us a fully human face. Far more distinct than he, there looms above him the splendid triumphal pageant of Roman imperialism itself.

Cicero's unrivaled eloquence won him not only a golden shower of gifts and legacies, but also the prætorship and consulship at the earliest legal age. Perhaps some of the old nobles foresaw and prudently avoided the Catilinarian storm of 63 B. C. The common dangers of that year, and the pride of assured position, may have hastened the full transfer of Cicero's allegiance to the old senatorial faction. Tiberius Gracchus, boldly praised in January, has become for Cicero a notorious demagogue; his slayers instead are the undoubted patriots, in the famous harangues of November. These latter, by the way, were certainly under the file three years afterward, —and it is not likely that we read any Ciceronian speech just as it was delivered. If there be any thread of consistency in Cicero's public career, it must be sought in his long but vain hope to unite the nobility and the *equites*, in order to resist the growing proletariat.

The eager vanity with which Cicero seized the proud title "Father of the fatherland" is truly pathetic. The summary execution of the traitors may have been prompted by that physical timidity so often associated with the scholarly temperament. Whether needless or not, the act returned to plague him.

The happiest effort of the orator in his consular year was the famous plea for Murena. This consul-elect for 62 was a successful soldier. Catiline must be met in the spring "in the jaws of Etruria." Cicero's dearest friend, Servius Sulpicius Rufus, a defeated candidate, accused Murena of bribery. The conditions of Roman politics, the character of Sulpicius, the tone of Cicero himself, bid us adjudge Murena probably guilty. Cicero had supported Sulpicius, but now feels it is no time to "go behind the returns," or to replace a bold soldier by a scholarly lawyer.

To win his case Cicero must heap ridicule upon his own profession in his friend's person, and upon Stoic philosophy, represented by Cato, Sulpicius's chief advocate. This he did so successfully that Cato himself exclaimed with a grim smile, "What a jester our consul is!" Cicero won his case—and kept his friends. This speech is cited *sixteen times* by Quintilian, and is a model of forensic ingenuity, wit, and grace. Its patriotism may be plausibly defended, but hardly its moral standards.

The next year produced the famous and successful defense of
Cluentius,—probably guilty of poisoning,—and also the most delightful of all Cicero's speeches, the oration for the poet Archias.
Whether the old Greek's claim to Roman citizenship was beyond
cavil we neither know nor greatly care. The legal argument is suspiciously brief. The praise of literature and the scholarly life, however, has re-echoed ever since, and still reaches all hearts. Brother
Quintus, sitting in judgment as prætor, is pleasantly greeted.

This is the culmination in Cicero's career of success. Some boast-
ful words uttered in these days make us doubt if he remembered
Solon's and Sophocles's maxim, "Count no life happy before its
close." The fast-growing power of Cæsar presently made the two
successful generals Pompey and Crassus his political tools. Cicero
refused to enter, on similar conditions, the cabal later known as the
"First Triumvirate." Cæsar, about to depart for his long absence in
Gaul, might well regard the patriotic and impulsive orator as the
most serious source of possible opposition in his absence. Marcus
refused, himself, to go along to Gaul a-soldiering, though Brother
Quintus accepted a commission and served creditably. At last,
reluctantly, Cæsar suffered Cicero's personal enemy Clodius to bring
forward a decree outlawing "those who had put Roman citizens to
death without trial" (March, 58 B. C.). Cicero meekly withdrew
from Rome, was condemned by name in absence, and his town
house and villas pillaged.

As to the cowardice of this hasty retreat, none need use severer
words than did the exile himself. It is the decisive event in his
career. His uninterrupted success was ended. His pride could
never recover fully from the hurt. Worst of all, he could never
again pose, even before his own eyes, as the fearless hero-patriot.
In short, Cæsar, the consummate master of action and of men, had
humanely but decisively crippled the erratic yet patriotic rheto-
rician.

In little more than a year the bad conduct of Clodius, the personal good-will of the "triumvirs," and the whirligig of politics,
brought round Cicero's return from Greece. His wings were however effectively clipped. After a brief and slight flutter of independence, he made full, even abject, submission to the dominant
Cæsarian faction. This was in 56 B. C. The next five years, inglo-
rious politically, were however full of activity in legal oratory and
other literary work. In his eloquent defense of Cælius Rufus,
charged with an attempt to poison Clodia, Cicero perforce white-
washes, or at least paints in far milder colors than of old, Catiline,
Cælius's lifelong friend! A still less pleasing feature is the abusive
attack on the famous and beautiful Clodia, probably the "Lesbia" of

Catullus. (The unhappy young poet seems to have preceded Cælius in the fickle matron's favor.)

The events of the year 52 well illustrate the unfitness of Cicero for politics in such an age. Rome was full of street brawls, which Pompey could not check. The orator's old enemy Clodius, at the head of his bravos, was slain by a fellow ruffian Milo in January. At Milo's trial in April Cicero defended him, or attempted to do so. A court-room encircled by a yelling mob and guarded by Pompey's legions caused him to break down altogether. As afterward written out at leisure, the speech is a masterpiece of special pleading. The exiled Milo's criticism on it is well known: "I'm glad you never delivered it: I should not now be enjoying the mullets of Marseilles."

The year 51–50 Cicero spent, most unwillingly, as proconsular governor in far-off Cilicia. Though really humane and relatively honest, he accumulated in these few months a handsome sum in "gifts" from provincials and other perquisites. Even Cicero was a Roman.

Meantime the civil war had all but broken out at home. Cicero hesitated long, and the correspondence with Atticus contains exhaustive analyses of his motives and temptations. His naïve selfishness and vanity at times in these letters seem even like self-caricature. Yet through it all glimmers a vein of real though bewildered patriotism. Still the craving for a triumph — he had fought some savage mountain clans in Asia Minor! — was hardly less dominant.

Repairing late and with many misgivings to Pompey's camp in Epirus, Cicero seems to have been there a "not unfeared, half-welcome" and critical guest. Illness is his excuse for absence from the decisive battle. He himself tells us little of these days. As Plutarch relates the tale, after Pompey's flight to Egypt Cicero refused the supreme command, and was thereupon threatened with death by young Gneius Pompey; but his life was saved by Cato.

One thing at least is undisputed. The last man to decide for Pompey's cause, he was the first to hurry back to Italy and crave Cæsar's grace! For many months he waited in ignoble retirement, fearing the success of his deserted comrades even more than Cæsar's victory. It is this action that gives the *coup de grace* to Cicero's character as a hero. With whatever misgivings, he had chosen his side. Whatever disturbing threats of violent revenge after victory he heard in Pompey's camp, he awaited the decisive battle. Then there remained, for any brave man, only constancy in defeat — or a fall upon his sword.

Throughout Cæsar's brief reign,— or long dictatorship,— from 48 to 44, Cicero is the most stately and the most obsequious of courtiers. For him who would plead for clemency, or return thanks for mercy accorded, at a despot's footstool, there are no more graceful models than the 'Pro Ligario' and the 'Pro Marcello.' Cæsar himself realized, and wittily remarked, how irksome and hateful such a part must be to the older, vainer, more self-conscious man of the twain.

Midway in this period Cicero divorced his wife after thirty years of wedlock, seemingly from some dissatisfaction over her financial management, and soon after married a wealthy young ward. This is the least pleasing chapter of his private life, but perhaps the mortification and suffering it entailed were a sufficient penalty. His only daughter Tullia's death in 45 B. C. nearly broke the father's heart.

Whatever the reason, Cicero was certainly not in the secret of Cæsar's assassination. Twice in letters to members of the conspiracy in later months he begins: "How I wish you had invited me to your glorious banquet on the Ides of March." "There would have been no remnants," he once adds. That is, Antony would not have been left alive.

We have now reached the last two years — perhaps the most creditable time — in Cicero's eventful life. This period runs from March 15th, 44 B. C., to December 7th, 43 B. C. It was one long struggle, first covert, then open, between Antony and the slayers of Cæsar. Cicero's energy and eloquence soon made him the foremost voice in the Senate once more. For the first time since his exile, he is now speaking out courageously his own real sentiments. His public action is in harmony with his own convictions. The cause was not hopeless by any means, so far as the destruction of Antony would have been a final triumph. Indeed, that wild career seemed near its end, when Octavian's duplicity again threw the game into his rival's reckless hands. However, few students of history imagine that any effective restoration of senatorial government was possible. The peculiar pathos of Cicero's end, patriot as he was, is this: it removed one of the last great obstacles to the only stable and peaceful rule Rome could receive — the imperial throne of Augustus.

This last period is however among the most creditable, perhaps the most heroic, in Cicero's career. Its chief memorials are the fourteen extant orations against Antony. The comparative sincerity of these 'Philippics,' and the lack of private letters for much of this time, make them important historical documents. The only one which ranks among his greatest productions — perhaps the classic masterpiece of invective — is the 'Second Philippic.' This was never delivered at all, but published as a pamphlet. This unquestioned fact throws a curious light on passages like — "He is agitated, he perspires, he turns pale!" describing Antony at the (imaginary) delivery of the oration. The details of the behavior of Catiline and others may be hardly more authentic. The 'Ninth Philippic' is a heartfelt funeral eulogy on that same Sulpicius whom he had ridiculed in the 'Pro Murena.'

> « The milestones into headstones turn,
> And under each a friend. »

A fragment from one of Livy's lost books says, " Cicero bore with becoming spirit none of the ills of life save death itself." He indeed perished not only bravely but generously, dissuading his devoted slaves from useless resistance, and extending his neck to Antony's assassins. Verres lived to exult at the news, and then shared his enemy's fate, rather than give up his Greek vases to Antony! Nearly every Roman, save Nero, dies well.

Upon Cicero's political career our judgment is already indicated. He was always a patriot at heart, though often a bewildered one. His vanity, and yet more his physical cowardice, caused some grievous blots upon the record. His last days, and death, may atone for all — save one. The precipitate desertion of the Pompeians is not to be condoned.

The best English life of Cicero is by Forsyth; but quaint, dogged, prejudiced old Middleton should not be forgotten. Plutarch's Cicero " needs no bush."

Cicero's oratory was splendidly effective upon his emotional Italian hearers. It would not be so patiently accepted by any Teutonic folk. His very copiousness, however, makes him as a rule wonderfully clear and easy reading. Quintilian well says: " From Demosthenes's periods not a word can be spared, to Cicero's not one could be added."

Despite the rout of Verres and of Catiline, the merciless dissection of Clodia, and the statelier thunders of the 'Philippics,' Cicero was most successful and happiest when " defending the interests of his friends." Perhaps the greatest success against justice was the 'Pro Cluentio,' which throws so lurid a light on ante-Borgian Italian criminology. This speech is especially recommended by Niebuhr to young philologues as a nut worthy of the strongest teeth. There is a helpful edition by Ramsay, but Hertland's 'Murena' will be a pleasanter variation for students wearying of the beaten track followed by the school editions. Both the failure of the 'Pro Milone' and the world-wide success of the 'Pro Archia' bid us repeat the vain wish, that this humane and essentially modern nature might have fallen on a gentler age. Regarding his whole political life as an uncongenial rôle forced on him by fate, we return devout thanks for *fifty-eight* orations, nearly all in revised and finished literary form! Fragments of seventeen, and titles of still thirty more, yet remain.

From all his rivals, predecessors, pupils, not one authentic speech survives.

The best complete edition of the orations with English notes is by George Long, in the Bibliotheca Classica. The 'Philippics' alone are better edited by J. R. King in the Clarendon Press series. School editions of select speeches are superabundant. They regularly include the four Catilinarians, the Manilian, and the pleas before the dictator, sometimes a selection from the 'Philippics' or Verrine orations.

There is no masterly translation comparable with the fine work done by Kennedy for Demosthenes. The Bohn version is respectable in quality.

Among Cicero's numerous works on rhetoric the chief is the 'De Oratore.' Actually composed in 55 B. C., it is a dialogue, the scene set in 91 B. C., the characters being the chief Roman orators of that day. L. Crassus, who plays the host gracefully at his Tusculan country-seat, is also the chief speaker. These men were all known to Cicero in his boyhood, but most of them perished soon after in the Marian proscriptions. Of real character-drawing there is little, and all alike speak in graceful Ciceronian periods. The exposition of the technical parts of rhetoric goes on in leisurely wise, with copious illustrations and digressions. There is much pleasant repetition of commonplaces. Wilkins's edition of the 'De Oratore' is a good but not an ideal one. The introductions are most helpful. Countless discussions on etymology, etc., in the notes, should be relegated to the dictionaries. Instead, we crave adequate cross-references to passages in this and other works. The notes seem to be written too largely piecemeal, each with the single passage in mind.

In Cicero's 'Brutus,' written in 46 B. C., Cicero, Brutus, and Atticus carry on the conversation, but it is mostly a monologue of Cicero and a historical sketch of Roman oratory. The affected modesty of the autobiographic parts is diverting. Brutus was the chief exponent of a terse, simple, direct oratory,—far nearer, we judge, to English taste than the Ciceronian; and the opposition between them already appears. A convenient American edition is that by Kellogg (Ginn).

The opposition just mentioned comes out more clearly in the 'Orator.' This portrays the ideal public speaker. His chief accomplishments are summed up in versatility,—the power to adapt himself to any case and audience. An interesting passage discusses the rhythms of prose. This book has been elaborately edited by J. E. Sandys. In these three dialogues Cicero says everything of importance, at least once; and the other rhetorical works in the Corpus may be neglected here, the more as the most practical working rhetoric among them all, the 'Auctor ad Herennium,' is certainly not

Cicero's. It is probably by Cornificius, and is especially important as the *first* complete prose work transmitted to us in authentic Latin form. (Cato's 'De Re Rustica' has been "modernized.")

The later history of the Ciceronian correspondence is a dark and much contested field. (The most recent discussion, with bibliography, is by Schanz, in Iwan Müller's Handbuch, Vol. viii., pp. 238–243.) Probably Cicero's devoted freedman Tiro laid the foundations of our collections. The part of Petrarch in recovering the letters during the "Revival of Learning" was much less than has been supposed.

The letters themselves are in wild confusion. There are four collections, entitled 'To Atticus,' 'To Friends,' 'To Brother Marcus,' 'To Brutus': altogether over eight hundred epistles, of which a relatively small number are written *to* Cicero by his correspondents. The order is not chronological, and the dates can in many cases only be conjectured. Yet these letters afford us our chief sources for the history of this great epoch,— and the best insight we can ever hope to have into the private life of Roman gentlemen.

The style of the cynical, witty Cælius, or of the learned lawyer Sulpicius, differs perceptibly in detail from Cicero's own; yet it is remarkable that all seem able to write clearly if not gracefully. Cicero's own style varies very widely. The letters to Atticus are usually colloquial, full of unexplained allusions, sometimes made intentionally obscure and pieced out with a Greek phrase, for fear of the carrier's treachery! Other letters again, notably a long 'Apologia' addressed to Lentulus after Cicero's return from exile, are as plainly addressed in reality to the public or to posterity as are any of the orations.

Prof. R. Y. Tyrrell has long been engaged upon an annotated edition of all the letters in chronological order. This will be of the utmost value. An excellent selection, illustrating the orator's public life chiefly, has been published by Professor Albert Watson. This volume contains also very full tables of dates, bibliography of all Cicero's works, and in general is indispensable for the advanced Latin student. The same letters annotated by Professor Watson have been delightfully translated by G. E. Jeans. To this volume, rather than to Forsyth's biography, the English reader should turn to form his impressions of Cicero at first hand. It is a model of scholarly— and also literary—translation.

The "New Academy," to which Cicero inclined in philosophy, was skeptical in its tendencies, and regarded absolute truth as unattainable. This made it easier for Cicero to cast his transcriptions in the form of dialogues, revealing the beliefs of the various schools through the lips of the several interlocutors. Thus the 'De Finibus Bonorum et Malorum' sets forth in three successive conversations

the ideas of Epicureans, of Stoics, and of the Academy, on the
Highest Good. It is perhaps the chief of these treatises,—though
we would still prefer to have even those later compendiums of the
Greek schools through which Cicero probably cited the chief philosophers at second hand! J. S. Reid, an eminent English scholar, has
spent many years upon this dialogue, and his work includes a
masterly translation.

With a somewhat similar plan, the three books of the 'De Natura
Deorum' contain the views of the three schools on the Divine
Beings. The speakers are Cicero's Roman contemporaries. This
rather sketchy work has been annotated by J. B. Mayor in his usual
exhaustive manner. The now fragmentary dialogue entitled 'The
Republic,' and its unfinished supplement 'The Laws,' were composed and named in avowed rivalry with Plato's two largest works,
but fail to approach the master. The Roman Constitution is
defended as the ideal mingling of monarchy, aristocracy, and
democracy. The student of pure literature can for the most part
neglect these, and others among the hastily written philosophic
works, with the explicit approval of so indefatigable a student as
Professor B. L. Gildersleeve.

The chief fragment preserved of the 'Republic' is the 'Dream of
Scipio.' Its dependence on the vision at the close of Plato's 'Republic' should be carefully observed. It may be fairly described as a
free translation and enlargement from Greek originals, of which
Plato's passage is the chief. Plagiarism was surely viewed quite
otherwise then than now. Still, the Roman additions and modifications are interesting also,—and even as a translator Cicero is no
ordinary cicerone! Moreover, in this as in so many other examples,
the Latin paraphrase had a wider and more direct influence than
the original. It has been accepted with justice ever since, as the
final and most hopeful pagan word in favor of the soul's immortality.
The lover of Chaucer will recall the genial paraphrase of 'Scipio's
Dream' in the 'Parlament of Foules' (stanzas 5-12). We give below,
entire, in our quotations from Cicero, the masterly version of the
'Dream,' prepared by Prof. T. R. Lounsbury for his edition of Chaucer's poems. The speaker is the younger Scipio Africanus, and his
visit to Africa as a subaltern here described was in 149 B. C., three
years previous to his own decisive campaign against Carthage which
ended in the destruction of the city.

Cicero shared in full the Roman tendency to give a practical, an
ethical turn to all metaphysical discussion. This is prominent in the
popular favorite among his larger volumes, the 'Tusculan Disputa-
tions.' In each of the five related books a thesis is stated nega-
tively, to be triumphantly reversed later on:—

(1) "Death seems to me an evil."

(2) "I think pain the greatest of all evils."

(3) "Misery seems to me to befall the wise man."

(4) "It does not appear to me that the wise man can be secure from distress of mind."

(5) "Character does not seem to me sufficient for happiness in life."

The original portion of this work is relatively large, and many Roman illustrations occur. Dr. Peabody has included the Tusculans, the two brief essays next mentioned, and the 'De Officiis,' in his excellent series of versions (Little, Brown and Company).

The little dialogue on 'Old Age' is perhaps most read of all Cicero's works. Its best thoughts, it must be confessed, are freely borrowed from the opening pages of Plato's 'Republic.' Still, on this theme of universal human interest, the Roman also offers much pleasant food for thought. The moderation of the Greek is forgotten by Cicero, the professional advocate and special pleader, who almost cries out to us at last:—

> "Grow old along with me:
> The best is yet to be,
> The last of life, for which the first was made!"

It was written in 45-4 B. C. The other little essay 'On Friendship' does not deserve to be bound up in such good company, though it usually is so edited. Bacon's very brief essay has more meat in it. Cicero had many good friends, but fully trusted hardly any one of them—not even Atticus. It was an age which put friendship to fearful trial, and the typical Roman seems to us rather selfish and cold. Certainly this essay is in a frigid tone. Professor Gildersleeve, I believe, has likened it to a treatise of Xenophon on hunting, so systematically is the *pursuit* of friends discussed.

Perhaps the most practical among Roman Manuals of Morals is the treatise on Duties ('De Officiis'), in three books. Here the personal experience of sixty years is drawn upon, avowedly for the edification of young Marcus, the author's unworthy son. This sole Ciceronian survivor of Antony's massacres lived to be famous for his capacity in wine-drinking, and to receive officially, as consul under Augustus, the news of Antony's final defeat and death—a dramatic revenge.

Most of these philosophic treatises were composed near the end of Cicero's life, largely in one marvelously productive year, 45-4 B. C., just previous to the slaying of Cæsar. Not all even of the extant works have been catalogued here. The 'Academica' and 'De Divinatione' should at least be mentioned.

Such were Cicero's distractions, when cut off from political life and oratory, and above all when bereft by Tullia's death. The especial 'Consolatio,' composed to regain his courage after this blow, must head the list of lost works. It took a most pessimistic view of human life, for which it was reproved by Lactantius. Another perished essay, the 'Hortensius,' introducing the whole philosophic series, upheld Milton's thesis, "How charming is divine philosophy," and first turned the thoughts of Augustine to serious study.

Cicero's poems, chiefly translations, are extant in copious fragments. They show metrical facility, a little taste, no creative imagination at all. A final proof of his unresting activity is his attempt to write history. Few even among professional advocates could have less of the temper for mere narration and truth. Indeed, reasonable disregard for the latter trammel is frankly urged upon a friend who was to write upon the illustrious moments of Cicero's own career!

We said at first that the caprice of fate had exaggerated some sides of Cicero's activity, by removing all competitors. In any case, however, his supremacy among Italian orators, and in the ornate discursive school of eloquence generally, could not have been questioned.

Yet more: as a stylist he lifted a language hitherto poor in vocabulary, and stiff in phrase, to a level it never afterward surpassed. Many words he successfully coined, chiefly either by translation or free imitation of Greek originals. His clear, copious, rhythmical phrase was even more fully his own creation. Indeed, at the present moment, four or five great forms of living speech testify to Cicero's amazing mastery over both word and phrase. The eloquence of Castelar, Crispi, and Gambetta, of Gladstone and of Everett, is shot through and through, in all its warp and woof, with golden Ciceronian threads. The 'Archias' speaks to any appreciative student of Western Europe, as it were, in a mother tongue which dominates his vernacular speech. Human language, then, has become a statelier memorial of Cicero than even his vanity can ever have imagined.

(After writing the substance of this paragraph, I was glad to find myself in close agreement with Mackail's words in his masterly little 'Latin Literature,' page 62.)

RESUMÉ OF GENERAL BIBLIOGRAPHY

The chief encyclopædia of facts and citations for this period is the cumbrous old 'Geschichte Roms, oder Pompeius Cæsar Cicero und ihre Zeitgenossen' of W. Drumann (Königsberg: 1834–44). The plan is ideally bad, being a series of *family chronicles*, while these three men are more completely isolated from their families and kin than any other great trio in all Roman history! The book is however an exhaustive, inexhaustible, little acknowledged, but still worked quarry of erudition. The best single book in English is Watson's edition of the (selected) letters (or Jeans's translation), until it shall be superseded by the complete annotated edition of the correspondence, by Tyrrell.

Mommsen's severe judgment on Cicero is well known. The other standard historians are less severe. Forsyth's life is not the final word on the subject by any means, but gives a good general view. The stately Ciceronian Lexicon by Merguet, already complete for the orations, will eventually provide a complete concordance and copious elucidation for all the works. The most accessible complete edition of Cicero's writings in Latin is by Baiter and Kayser, in eleven volumes. The Index Nominum alone fills four hundred closely printed pages of Vol. xi. The great critical edition is that of Orelli (Zurich: 1826–38).

On Cicero as an author, and indeed in the whole field of Latin literature, the 'Geschichte der Römischen Literatur' of Martin Schanz (in I. Müller's 'Handbuch') is most helpful, and even readable.

William Cranston Lawton,

OF THE OFFICES OF LITERATURE AND POETRY

From the 'Oration for the Poet Archias'

YOU ask us, O Gratius, why we are so exceedingly attached to this man. Because he supplies us with food whereby our mind is refreshed after this noise in the Forum, and with rest for our ears after they have been wearied with bad language. Do you think it possible that we could find a supply for our daily speeches, when discussing such a variety of matters, unless we were to cultivate our minds by the study of literature? or that our minds could bear being kept so constantly on the stretch if we did not relax them by that same study? But I confess that I am devoted to those studies; let others be ashamed of them if they have buried themselves in books without being able to produce anything out of them for the common advantage, or anything which may bear the eyes of men and the light. But why need I be ashamed, who for many years have lived in such a manner as never to allow my own love of tranquillity to deny me to the necessity or advantage of another, or my fondness for pleasure to distract, or even sleep to delay, my attention to such claims? Who then can reproach me, or who has any right to be angry with me, if I allow myself as much time for the cultivation of these studies as some take for the performance of their own business; or for celebrating days of festival and games; or for other pleasures; or even for the rest and refreshment of mind and body; or as others devote to early banquets, to playing at dice, or at ball? And this ought to be permitted to me, because by these studies my power of speaking and those faculties are improved, which as far as they do exist in me have never been denied to my friends when they have been in peril. And if that ability appears to any one to be but moderate, at all events I know whence I derive those principles which are of the greatest value. For if I had not persuaded myself from my youth upwards, both by the precepts of many masters and by much reading, that there is nothing in life greatly to be desired except praise and honor, and that while pursuing those things all tortures of the body, all dangers of death and banishment are to be considered but of small importance, I should never have exposed myself in defense of your safety to such numerous and arduous contests, and to these daily attacks of profligate men. But all books are full of such precepts, and all the sayings of philosophers, and all antiquity, are full of precedents teaching the same lesson; but all these things would lie buried in darkness if the light of literature and learning were not applied to them. How many images of the bravest men, carefully elaborated, have both the Greek and Latin writers bequeathed to us, not merely for us to look at and gaze upon, but also for our imitation! And I, always keeping them before my eyes as examples for my own public conduct, have endeavored to model my mind and views by continually thinking of those excellent men.

Some one will ask "What! were those identical great men, whose virtues have been recorded in books, accomplished in all that learning which you are extolling so highly?" It is difficult to assert this of all of them; but still I know what answer I can make to that question: I admit that many men have existed of admirable disposition and virtue, who without learning, by the almost divine instinct of their own mere nature, have been, of their own accord as it were, moderate and wise men. I even add this, that very often nature without learning has had more to do with leading men to credit and to virtue, than learning when not assisted by a good natural disposition. And I also contend that when to an excellent and admirable natural disposition there is added a certain system and training of education, then from that combination arises an extraordinary perfection of character: such as is seen in that godlike man whom our fathers saw in their time — Africanus; and in Caius Lælius and Lucius Furius, most virtuous and moderate men; and in that most excellent man, the most learned man of his time, Marcus Cato the elder: and all these men, if they had been to derive no assistance from literature in the cultivation and practice of virtue, would never have applied themselves to the study of it. Though even if there were no such great advantage to be reaped from it, and if it were only pleasure that is sought from these studies, still I imagine you would consider it a most reasonable and liberal employment of the mind: for other occupations are not suited to every time, nor to every age or place; but these studies are the food of youth, the delight of old age; the ornament of prosperity, the refuge and comfort of adversity; a delight at home, and no hindrance abroad; they are companions by night, and in travel, and in the country.

And if we ourselves were not able to arrive at these advantages, nor even taste them with our senses, still we ought to admire them even when we saw them in others. . . . And indeed, we have constantly heard from men of the greatest eminence and learning that the study of other sciences was made up of learning, and rules, and regular method; but that a poet was such by the unassisted work of nature, and was moved by the vigor of his own mind, and was inspired as it were by some divine wrath. Wherefore rightly does our own great Ennius call poets holy; because they seem to be recommended to us by some especial gift, as it were, and liberality of the gods. Let then, judges, this name of poet, this name which no barbarians even have ever disregarded, be holy in your eyes, men of cultivated minds as you all are. Rocks and deserts reply to the poet's voice; savage beasts are often moved and arrested by song; and shall we who have been trained in the pursuit of the most virtuous acts refuse to be swayed by the voice of poets? The Colophonians say that Homer was their citizen; the Chians claim him as theirs; the Salaminians assert their right to him;

but the men of Smyrna loudly assert him to be a citizen of
Smyrna, and they have even raised a temple to him in their
city.   Many other places also fight with one another for the
honor of being his birthplace.

They then claim a stranger, even after his death, because he
was a poet: shall we reject this man while he is alive, a man
who by his own inclination and by our laws does actually belong
to us? especially when Archias has employed all his genius with
the utmost zeal in celebrating the glory and renown of the
Roman people?   For when a young man, he touched on our
wars against the Cimbri and gained the favor even of Caius
Marius himself, a man who was tolerably proof against this sort
of study.   For there was no one so disinclined to the Muses as
not willingly to endure that the praise of his labors should be
made immortal by means of verse.   They say that the great
Themistocles, the greatest man that Athens produced, said when
some one asked him what sound or whose voice he took the
greatest delight in hearing, " The voice of that by whom his own
exploits were best celebrated. "   Therefore, the great Marius was
also exceedingly attached to Lucius Plotius, because he thought
that the achievement which he had performed could be celebrated
by his genius.   And the whole Mithridatic war, great and difficult as it was, and carried on with so much diversity of fortune
by land and sea, has been related at length by him; and the
books in which that is sung of, not only make illustrious Lucius
Lucullus, that most gallant and celebrated man, but they do
honor also to the Roman people.   For while Lucullus was general, the Roman people opened Pontus, though it was defended
both by the resources of the king and by the character of the
country itself.   Under the same general the army of the Roman
people, with no very great numbers, routed the countless hosts
of the Armenians.   It is the glory of the Roman people that by
the wisdom of that same general, the city of the Cyzicenes, most
friendly to us, was delivered and preserved from all the attacks
of the kind, and from the very jaws as it were of the whole war.
Ours is the glory which will be for ever celebrated, which is
derived from the fleet of the enemy which was sunk after its
admirals had been slain, and from the marvelous naval battle off
Tenedos: those trophies belong to us, those monuments are ours,
those triumphs are ours.   Therefore I say that the men by
whose genius these exploits are celebrated make illustrious at

the same time the glory of the Roman people. Our countryman Ennius was dear to the elder Africanus; and even on the tomb of the Scipios his effigy is believed to be visible, carved in the marble. But undoubtedly it is not only the men who are themselves praised who are done honor to by those praises, but the name of the Roman people also is adorned by them. Cato, the ancestor of this Cato, is extolled to the skies. Great honor is paid to the exploits of the Roman people. Lastly, all those great men, the Maximi, the Marcelli, and the Fulvii, are done honor to, not without all of us having also a share in the panegyric. . . .

Certainly, if the mind had no anticipations of posterity, and if it were to confine all its thoughts within the same limits as those by which the space of our lives is bounded, it would neither break itself with such severe labors, nor would it be tormented with such cares and sleepless anxiety, nor would it so often have to fight for its very life. At present there is a certain virtue in every good man, which night and day stirs up the mind with the stimulus of glory, and reminds it that all mention of our name will not cease at the same time with our lives, but that our fame will endure to all posterity.

Do we all who are occupied in the affairs of the State, and who are surrounded by such perils and dangers in life, appear to be so narrow-minded as, though to the last moment of our lives we have never passed one tranquil or easy moment, to think that everything will perish at the same time as ourselves? Ought we not, when many most illustrious men have with great care collected and left behind them statues and images, representations not of their minds but of their bodies, much more to desire to leave behind us a copy of our counsels and of our virtues, wrought and elaborated by the greatest genius? I thought, at the very moment of performing them, that I was scattering and disseminating all the deeds which I was performing, all over the world for the eternal recollection of nations. And whether that delight is to be denied to my soul after death, or whether, as the wisest men have thought, it will affect some portion of my spirit, at all events I am at present delighted with some such idea and hope.

HONORS PROPOSED FOR THE DEAD STATESMAN SULPICIUS

From the 'Ninth Philippic'

OUR ancestors indeed decreed statues to many men; public sepulchres to few. But statues perish by weather, by violence, by lapse of time; the sanctity of the sepulchres is in the soil itself, which can neither be moved nor destroyed by any violence; and while other things are extinguished, so sepulchres become holier by age.

Let then this man be distinguished by that honor also, a man to whom no honor can be given which is not deserved. Let us be grateful in paying respect in death to him to whom we can now show no other gratitude. And by that same step let the audacity of Marcus Antonius, waging a nefarious war, be branded with infamy. For when these honors have been paid to Servius Sulpicius, the evidence of his embassy having been insulted and rejected by Antonius will remain for everlasting.

On which account I give my vote for a decree in this form: "As Servius Sulpicius Rufus, the son of Quintus, of the Lemonian tribe, at a most critical period of the republic, and being ill with a very serious and dangerous disease, preferred the authority of the Senate and the safety of the republic to his own life; and struggled against the violence and severity of his illness, in order to arrive at the camp of Antonius, to which the Senate had sent him; and as he, when he had almost arrived at the camp, being overwhelmed by the violence of the disease, has lost his life in discharging a most important office of the republic; and as his death has been in strict correspondence to a life passed with the greatest integrity and honor, during which he, Servius Sulpicius, has often been of great service to the republic, both as a private individual and in the discharge of various magistracies: and as he, being such a man, has encountered death on behalf of the republic while employed on an embassy; the Senate decrees that a brazen pedestrian statue of Servius Sulpicius be erected in the rostra in compliance with the resolution of this order, and that his children and posterity shall have a place round this statue of five feet in every direction, from which to behold the games and gladiatorial combats, because he died in the cause of the republic; and that this reason be inscribed on the pedestal of the statue; and that Caius Pansa and

Aulus Hirtius the consuls, one or both of them, if it seem good to them, shall command the quæstors of the city to let out a contract for making that pedestal and that statue, and erecting them in the rostra; and that whatever price they contract for, they shall take care the amount is given and paid to the contractor; and as in old times the Senate has exerted its authority with respect to the obsequies of, and honors paid to, brave men, it now decrees that he shall be carried to the tomb on the day of his funeral with the greatest possible solemnity. And as Servius Sulpicius Rufus, the son of Quintus cf the Lemonian tribe, has deserved so well of the republic as to be entitled to be complimented with all those distinctions; the Senate is of opinion, and thinks it for the advantage of the republic, that the curule ædile should suspend the edict which usually prevails with respect to funerals, in the case of the funeral of Servius Sulpicius Rufus, the son of Quintus of the Lemonian tribe; and that Caius Pansa the consul shall assign him a place for a tomb in the Esquiline plain, or in whatever place shall seem good to him, extending thirty feet in every direction, where Servius Sulpicius may be buried; and that that shall be his tomb, and that of his children and posterity, as having been a tomb most deservedly given to them by the public authority.»

OLD FRIENDS BETTER THAN NEW

From the ‹Dialogue on Friendship›

B UT there arises on this subject a somewhat difficult question: Whether ever new friends, if deserving friendship, are to be preferred to old ones, just as we are wont to prefer young colts to old horses?—a perplexity unworthy of a man; for there ought to be no satiety of friendship as of other things: everything which is oldest (as those wines which bear age well) ought to be sweetest; and that is true which is sometimes said, "Many bushels of salt must be eaten together," before the duty of friendship can be fulfilled. But new friendships, if they afford a hope that, as in the case of plants which never disappoint, fruits shall appear, such are not to be rejected; yet the old one must be preserved in its proper place, for the power of age and custom is exceedingly great; besides, in the very case of the horse, which I just mentioned, if there is no impediment, there is no one who does not more pleasurably use that to which he is accustomed than one unbroken and strange to him; and habit asserts its power, and habit prevails, not only in the case of this, which is animate, but also in the cases of those things which are inanimate; since we take delight in the very mountainous or woody scenery among which we have long dwelt.

HONORED OLD AGE

From the 'Dialogue on Old Age'

BUT in my whole discourse remember that I am praising that old age which is established on the foundations of youth: from which this is effected which I once asserted with the great approbation of all present,—that wretched was the old age which had to defend itself by speaking. Neither gray hairs nor wrinkles can suddenly catch respect; but the former part of life honorably spent, reaps the fruits of authority at the close. For these very observances which seem light and common are marks of honor — to be saluted, to be sought after, to receive precedence, to have persons rising up to you, to be attended on the way, to be escorted home, to be consulted; points which, both among us and in other States, in proportion as they are the most excellent in their morals, are the most scrupulously observed. They say that Lysander the Lacedæmonian, whom I mentioned a little above, was accustomed to remark that Lacedæmon was the most honorable abode for old age; for nowhere is so much conceded to that time of life, nowhere is old age more respected. Nay, further: it is recorded that when at Athens during the games a certain elderly person had entered the theatre, a place was nowhere offered him in that large assembly by his own townsmen; but when he had approached the Lacedæmonians, who, as they were ambassadors, had taken their seats together in a particular place, they all rose up and invited the old man to a seat; and when reiterated applause had been bestowed upon them by the whole assembly, one of them remarked that the Athenians knew what was right, but were unwilling to do it. There are many excellent rules in our college, but this of which I am treating especially, that in proportion as each man has the advantage in age, so he takes precedence in giving his opinion; and older augurs are preferred not only to those who are higher in office, but even to such as are in actual command. What pleasures, then, of the body can be compared with the privileges of authority? which they who have nobly employed seem to me to have consummated the drama of life, and not like inexpert performers to have broken down in the last act. Still, old men are peevish, and fretful, and passionate, and unmanageable,— nay, if we seek for such, also covetous: but these are the faults of their characters, not of their old age. And yet that peevishness and those faults which I have mentioned have some excuse, not quite satisfactory indeed, but such as may be admitted. They fancy that they are neglected, despised, made a jest of; besides, in a weak state of body every offense is irritating. All which defects however are extenuated by good dispositions and qualities; and this may be discovered not only in real life, but on the stage, from the two brothers that are represented in 'The Brothers'; how much austerity in the one, and how much gentleness in the other! Such is the fact: for as it is not every wine, so it is not every man's life, that grows sour from old age. I approve of gravity in old age, but this in a moderate degree, like everything else; harshness by no means. What avarice in an old man can propose to itself I cannot conceive: for can anything be more absurd than, in proportion as less of our journey remains, to seek a greater supply of provisions?

DEATH IS WELCOME TO THE OLD

From the 'Dialogue on Old Age'

A N OLD man indeed has nothing to hope for; yet he is in so much the happier state than a young one, since he has already attained what the other is only hoping for. The one is wishing to live long, the other has lived long. And yet, good gods! what is there in man's life that can be called long? For allow the latest period: let us anticipate the age of the kings of the Tartessii. For there dwelt, as I find it recorded, a man named Arganthonius at Gades, who reigned for eighty years, and lived one hundred and twenty. But to my mind nothing whatever seems of long duration, in which there is any end. For when that arrives, then the time which has passed has flowed away; that only remains which you have secured by virtue and right conduct. Hours indeed depart from us, and days and months and years; nor does past time ever return, nor can it be discovered what is to follow. Whatever time is assigned to each to live, with that he ought to be content: for neither need the drama be performed entire by the actor, in order to give satisfaction, provided he be approved in whatever act he may be; nor need the wise man live till the *plaudite*. For the short period of life is long enough for living well and honorably; and if you should advance further, you need no more grieve than farmers do when the loveliness of springtime hath passed, that summer and autumn have come. For spring represents the time of youth and gives promise of the future fruits; the remaining seasons are intended for plucking and gathering in those fruits. Now the harvest of old age, as I have often said, is the recollection and abundance of blessings previously secured. In truth, everything that happens agreeably to nature is to be reckoned among blessings. What, however, is so agreeable to nature as for an old man to die? which even is the lot of the young, though nature opposes and resists. And thus it is that young men seem to me to die just as when the violence of flame is extinguished by a flood of water; whereas old men die as the exhausted fire goes out, spontaneously, without the exertion of any force: and as fruits when they are green are plucked by force from the trees, but when ripe and mellow drop off, so violence takes away their lives from youths, maturity from old men; a state which to me indeed is so delightful, that the nearer I approach to death, I seem as it were to be getting sight of land, and at length after a long voyage to be just coming into harbor.

GREAT ORATORS AND THEIR TRAINING

From the 'Dialogue on Oratory'

FOR who can suppose that amid the great multitude of students, the utmost abundance of masters, the most eminent geniuses among men, the infinite variety of causes, the most ample rewards offered to eloquence, there is any other reason to be found for the small number of orators than the incredible magnitude and difficulty of the art? A knowledge of a vast number of things is necessary, without which volubility of words is empty and ridiculous; speech itself is to be formed, not merely by choice, but by careful construction of words; and all the emotions of the mind which nature has given to man, must be intimately known; for all the force and art of speaking must be employed in allaying or exciting the feelings of those who listen.   To this must be added a certain portion of grace and wit, learning worthy of a well-bred man, and quickness and brevity in replying as well as attacking, accompanied with a refined decorum and urbanity.   Besides, the whole of antiquity and a multitude of examples is to be kept in the memory; nor is the knowledge of laws in general, or of the civil law in particular, to be neglected.   And why need I add any remarks on delivery itself, which is to be ordered by action of body, by gesture, by look, and by modulation and variation of the voice, the great power of which, alone and in itself, the comparatively trivial art of actors and the stage proves; on which though all bestow their utmost labor to form their look, voice, and gesture, who knows not how few there are, and have ever been, to whom we can attend with patience? What can I say of that repository for all things, the memory; which, unless it be made the keeper of the matter and words that are the fruits of thought and invention, all the talents of the orator, we see, though they be of the highest degree of excellence, will be of no avail? Let us then cease to wonder what is the cause of the scarcity of good speakers, since eloquence results from all those qualifications, in each of which singly it is a great merit to labor successfully; and let us rather exhort our children, and others whose glory and honor is dear to us, to contemplate in their minds the full magnitude of the object, and not to trust that they can reach the height at which they aim by the aid of the precepts, masters, and exercises that they are all now following, but to understand that they must adopt others of a different character.

In my opinion, indeed, no man can be an orator possessed of every praiseworthy accomplishment unless he has attained the knowledge of everything important, and of all liberal arts; for his language must be ornate and copious from knowledge, since unless there be beneath the surface matter understood and felt by the speaker, oratory becomes an empty and almost puerile flow of words. . . .

"I am then of opinion," said Crassus, "that nature and genius in the first place contribute most aid to speaking; and that to those writers on the art to whom Antonius just now

VI—232

alluded, it was not skill and method in speaking, but natural talent that was wanting; for there ought to be certain lively powers in the mind and understanding, which may be acute to invent, fertile to explain and adorn, and strong and retentive to remember; and if any one imagines that these powers may be acquired by art (which is false, for it is very well if they can be animated and excited by art; but they certainly cannot by art be ingrafted or instilled, since they are all the gifts of nature), what will he say of those qualities which are certainly born with the man himself — volubility of tongue, tone of voice, strength of lungs, and a peculiar conformation and aspect of the whole countenance and body? I do not say that art cannot improve in these particulars (for I am not ignorant that what is good may be made better by education, and what is not very good may be in some degree polished and amended); but there are some persons so hesitating in their speech, so inharmonious in their tone of voice, or so unwieldy and rude in the air and movements of their bodies, that whatever power they possess either from genius or art, they can never be reckoned in the number of accomplished speakers; while there are others so happily qualified in these respects, so eminently adorned with the gifts of nature, that they seem not to have been born like other men, but molded by some divinity. It is indeed a great task and enterprise for a person to undertake and profess that while every one else is silent, he alone must be heard on the most important subjects, and in a large assembly of men; for there is scarcely any one present who is not sharper and quicker to discover defects in the speaker than merits; and thus whatever offends the hearer effaces the recollection of what is worthy of praise. I do not make these observations for the purpose of altogether deterring young men from the study of oratory, even if they be deficient in some natural endowments. For who does not perceive that to C. Cælius, my contemporary, a new man, the mere mediocrity in speaking which he was enabled to attain was a great honor? Who does not know that Q. Varius, your equal in age, a clumsy uncouth man, has obtained his great popularity by the cultivation of such faculties as he has?

"But as our inquiry regards the complete orator, we must imagine in our discussion an orator from whom every kind of fault is abstracted, and who is adorned with every kind of merit. For if the multitude of suits, if the variety of causes, if the rabble and barbarism of the forum, afford room for even the most wretched speakers, we must not for that reason take our eyes from the object of our inquiry. In those arts in which it is not indispensable usefulness that is sought, but liberal amusement for the mind, how nicely, how almost fastidiously, do we judge! For there are no suits or controversies which can force men, though they may tolerate indifferent orators in the forum, to endure also bad actors upon the stage. The orator therefore must take the most studious precaution not merely to satisfy those whom he necessarily must satisfy, but to seem worthy of admiration to those who are at liberty to judge disinterestedly. If you would know what I myself think, I will express to you, my intimate friends, what I have hitherto never mentioned, and thought that I never should mention. To me, those who speak best and speak with the utmost ease and grace, appear, if they do not commence their speeches with some timidity, and show some confusion in the exordium, to have almost lost the sense of shame; though it is impossible that such should not be the case: for the better qualified a man is to speak, the more he fears the difficulties of speaking, the uncertain success of a speech, and the expectation of the audience. But he who can produce and deliver nothing worthy of his subject, nothing worthy of the name of an orator, nothing worthy the attention of his audience, seems to me, though he be ever so confused while he is speaking, to be downright shameless; for we ought to avoid a character for shamelessness, not by testifying shame, but by not doing that which does not become us. But the speaker who has no shame (as I see to be the case with many) I regard as deserving not only of rebuke but of personal castigation. Indeed, what I often observe in you I very frequently experience in myself; that I turn pale in the outset of my speech, and feel a tremor through my whole thoughts, as it were, and limbs. When I was a young man, I was on one occasion so timid in commencing an accusation, that I owed to Q. Maximus the greatest of obligations for immediately dismissing the assembly as soon as he saw me absolutely disheartened and incapacitated through fear." Here they all signified assent, looked significantly at one another, and began to talk together; for there was a wonderful modesty in Crassus, which however was not only no disadvantage to his oratory, but even an assistance to it, by giving it the recommendation of probity.

CICERO TO TIRO

[The following epistles are taken by permission from Jeans's 'Letters of Cicero.' This letter gives a vivid glimpse of Cicero's tenderness to his slaves and freedmen. Tiro was probably the first editor of his former master's letters.]

ÆGYPTA arrived here on the 12th of April. Although he reported that you were now quite rid of your fever and going on very well, he nevertheless caused me some anxiety by his report that you were not able to write to me, the more so because Hermia, who ought to have been here on the same day, has not yet come. I am more anxious than you can believe about your health. Only free me from this anxiety and I will free you from all duties. I would write you more if I thought you could now read more with pleasure. Use all the talents you possess, of which I have no small opinion, to keep yourself safe for my sake as well as your own. Again and again I repeat, take every precaution about your health. Good-by.

P. S.— Hermia is just come. I have your note with its poor weak handwriting—no wonder, too, after so severe an illness. I send out Ægypta to stay with you because he is not a bad companion, and appeared to me to be fond of you; and with him a cook, for you to make use of his services. Good-by.

CICERO TO ATTICUS

[The family affection of Cicero might be illustrated by many such letters as the following:]

IT BEING now eleven days since I left you, I am scrawling this little bit of a note just as I am leaving my country-house before it is light. I think of being at my place at Anagnia to-day, and Tusculum to-morrow; only one day there, so that I shall come up all right to time on the 28th; and oh, if I could but run on at once to embrace my Tullia and give Attica a kiss! Talking of this, by-the-by, do please write and let me know while I am stopping at Tusculum what her prattle is like, or if she is away in the country, what her letters to you are about. Meanwhile either send or give her my love, and Pilia too. And even though we shall meet immediately, yet will you write to me anything you can find to say?

P. S.— I was just fastening up this letter, but your courier has arrived here after a long night journey with your letter. I was very sorry, you may be sure, to find on reading it that Attica is feverish. Everything else that I was waiting for I now know from your note; but when you tell me that to have a little fire in the morning "*sent le vieillard,*" I retort *il le sent plus* for one's poor old memory to begin to totter: because it was the 29th I had promised to Axius; the 30th to you; and the day of my arrival, the 31st, to Quintus. So take that for your-self — you shall have no news. Then what on earth is the good of writing? And what good is it when we are together and chatter whatever comes to our tongues? Surely there is some-thing in *causerie* after all; even if there is nothing under it, there is always at least the delicious feeling that we are talking with one another.

SULPICIUS CONSOLES CICERO AFTER HIS DAUGHTER TULLIA'S DEATH

FOR some time after I had received the information of the death of your daughter Tullia, you may be sure that I bore it sadly and heavily, as much indeed as was right for me. I felt that I shared that terrible loss with you; and that had I but been where you are, you on your part would not have found me neglectful, and I on mine should not have failed to come to you and tell you myself how deeply grieved I am. And though it is true that consolations of this nature are painful and distressing, because those [dear friends and relations] upon whom the task naturally devolves are themselves afflicted with a similar burden, and incapable even of attempting it without many tears, so that one would rather suppose them in need of the consolations of others for themselves than capable of doing this kind office to others, yet nevertheless I have decided to write to you briefly such reflections as have occurred to me on the present occasion; not that I imagine them to be ignored by you, but because it is possible that you may be hindered by your sorrow from seeing them as clearly as usual.

What reason is there why you should allow the private grief which has befallen you to distress you so terribly? Recollect how fortune has hitherto dealt with us: how we have been

bereft of all that ought to be no less dear to men than their
own children — of country, position, rank, and every honorable
office. If one more burden has now been laid upon you, could
any addition be made to your pain? Or is there any heart that
having been trained in the school of such events, ought not now
to be steeled by use against emotion, and think everything after
them to be comparatively light?

Or it is for her sake, I suppose, that you are grieving? How
many times must you have arrived at the same conclusion as
that into which I too have frequently fallen, that in these days
theirs is not the hardest lot who are permitted painlessly to
exchange their life for the grave! Now what was there at the
present time that could attach her very strongly to life? what
hope? what fruition? what consolation for the soul? The prospect of a wedded life with a husband chosen from our young
men of rank? Truly, one would think it was always in your
power to choose a son-in-law of a position suitable to your rank
out of our young men, one to whose keeping you would feel you
could safely intrust the happiness of a child. Or that of being
a joyful mother of children, who would be happy in seeing
them succeeding in life; able by their own exertions to maintain
in its integrity all that was bequeathed them by their father;
intending gradually to rise to all the highest offices of the State;
and to use that liberty to which they were born for the good of
their country and the service of their friends. Is there any one
of these things that has not been taken away before it was
given? But surely it is hard to give up one's children? It is
hard; but this is harder still — that they should bear and suffer
what we are doing.

A circumstance which was such as to afford me no light consolation I cannot but mention to you, in the hope that it may
be allowed to contribute equally towards mitigating your grief.
As I was returning from Asia, when sailing from Ægina in the
direction of Megara, I began to look around me at the various
places by which I was surrounded. Behind me was Ægina, in
front Megara; on the right the Piræus, on the left Corinth;
all of them towns that in former days were most magnificent,
but are now lying prostrate and in ruins before one's eyes. "Ah
me," I began to reflect to myself, "we poor feeble mortals, who
can claim but a short life in comparison, complain as though a
wrong was done us if one of our number dies in the course of

nature, or has met his death by violence; and here in one spot are lying stretched out before me the corpses of so many cities! Servius, be master of yourself, and remember that it is the lot of man to which you have been born." Believe me, I found myself in no small degree strengthened by these reflections. Let me advise you too, if you think good, to keep this reflection before your eyes. How lately at one and the same time have many of our most illustrious men fallen! how grave an encroachment has been made on the rights of the sovereign people of Rome! every province in the world has been convulsed with the shock: if the frail life of a tender woman has gone too, who being born to the common lot of man must needs have died in a few short years, even if the time had not come for her now, are you thus utterly stricken down?

Do you then also recall your feelings and your thoughts from dwelling on this subject, and as beseems your character bethink yourself rather of this: that she has lived as long as life was of value to her; that she has passed away only together with her country's freedom; that she lived to see her father elected Prætor, Consul, Augur; that she had been the wife of young men of the first rank; that after enjoying well-nigh every blessing that life can offer, she left it only when the Republic itself was falling. The account is closed, and what have you, what has she, to charge of injustice against Fate? In a word, forget not that you are Cicero — that you are he who was always wont to guide others and give them good advice; and be not like those quack physicians who when others are sick boast that they hold the key of the knowledge of medicine, to heal themselves are never able; but rather minister to yourself with your own hand the remedies which you are in the habit of prescribing for others, and put them plainly before your own soul. There is no pain so great but the lapse of time will lessen and assuage it: it is not like yourself to wait until this time comes, instead of stepping forward by your philosophy to anticipate that result. And if even those who are low in the grave have any consciousness at all, such was her love for you and her tenderness for all around her that surely she does not wish to see this in you. Make this a tribute then to her who is dead; to all your friends and relations who are mourning in your grief; and make it to your country also, that if in anything the need should arise she may be able to trust to your energy and guidance. Finally, since such is the condition we have come to, that even this consideration must perforce be obeyed, do not let your conduct induce any one to believe that it is not so much your daughter as the circumstances of the Republic and the victory of others which you are deploring.

I shrink from writing to you at greater length upon this subject, lest I should seem to be doubtful of your own good sense; allow me therefore to put before you one more consideration, and then I will bring my letter to a close. We have seen you not once but many times bearing prosperity most gracefully, and gaining yourself great reputation thereby: let us see at last that you are capable also of bearing adversity equally well, and that it is not in your eyes a heavier burden than it ought to seem; lest we should think that of all the virtues this is the only one in which you are wanting.

As for myself, when I find you are more composed in mind I will send you information about all that is being done in these parts, and the state in which the province finds itself at present. Farewell.

CICERO'S REPLY TO SULPICIUS

YES, my dear Servius, I could indeed wish you had been with me, as you say, at the time of my terrible trial. How much it was in your power to help me if you had been here, by sympathizing with, and I may almost say, sharing equally in my grief, I readily perceive from the fact that after reading your letter I now feel myself considerably more composed; for not only was all that you wrote just what is best calculated to soothe affliction, but you yourself in comforting me showed that you too had no little pain at heart. Your son Servius however has made it clear, by every kindly attention which such an occasion would permit of, both how great his respect was for myself and also how much pleasure his kind feeling for me was likely to give you; and you may be sure that, while such attentions from him have often been more pleasant to me, they have never made me more grateful.

It is not however only your arguments and your equal share, — I may almost call it, — in this affliction which comforts me, but also your authority; because I hold it shame in me not to be bearing my trouble in a way that you, a man endowed with such wisdom, think it ought to be borne. But at times I do feel broken down, and I scarcely make any struggle against my grief, because those consolations fail me which under similar calamities were never wanting to any of those other people whom I put before myself as models for imitation. Both Fabius Maximus, for example, when he lost a son who had held the consulship, the hero of many a famous exploit; and Lucius Paulus, from whom two were taken in one week; and your own kinsman Gallus; and Marcus Cato, who was deprived of a son of the rarest talents and the rarest virtue,—all these lived in times when their individual affliction was capable of finding a solace in the distinctions they used to earn from their country. For me, however, after being stripped of all those distinctions which you yourself recall to me, and which I had won for myself by unparalleled exertions, only that one solace remained which has been torn away. My thoughts were not diverted by work for my friends, or by the administration of affairs of state; there was no pleasure in pleading in the courts; I could not bear the very sight of the Senate House; I felt, as was indeed too true, that I had lost all the harvest of both my industry and my success. But whenever I wanted to recollect that all this was shared with you and other friends I could name, and whenever I was breaking myself in and forcing my spirit to bear these things with patience, I always had a refuge to go to where I might find peace, and in whose words of comfort and sweet society I could rid me of all my pains and griefs. Whereas now, under this terrible blow, even those old wounds which seemed to have healed up are bleeding afresh; for it is impossible for me now to find such a refuge from my sorrows at home in the business of the State, as in those days I did in that consolation of home, which was always in store whenever I came away sad from thoughts of State to seek for peace in her happiness. And so I stay away both from home and from public life; because home now is no more able to make up for the sorrow I feel when I think of our country, than our country is for my sorrow at home. I am therefore looking forward all the more eagerly to your coming, and long to see you as early as that may possibly be; no greater alleviation can be offered me than a meeting between us for friendly intercourse and conversation. I hope however that your return is to take place, as I hear it is, very shortly. As for myself, while there are abundant reasons for wanting to see you as soon as possible, my principal one is in order that we may discuss together beforehand the best method of conduct for present circumstances, which must entirely be adapted to the wishes of one man only, a man nevertheless who is far-seeing and generous, and also, as I think I have thoroughly ascertained, to me not at all ill-disposed and to you extremely friendly. But admitting this, it is still a matter for much deliberation what is the line,—I do not say of action, but of keeping quiet,—that we ought by his good leave and favor to adopt. Farewell.

A HOMESICK EXILE

I SEND this with love, my dearest Terentia, hoping that you and my little Tullia and my Marcus are all well.

From the letters of several people and the talk of everybody I hear that your courage and endurance are simply wonderful, and that no troubles of body or mind can exhaust your energy. How unhappy I am to think that with all your courage and devotion, your virtues and gentleness, you should have fallen into such misfortunes for me! And my sweet Tullia too,—that she who was once so proud of her father should have to undergo such troubles owing to him! And what shall I say about my boy Marcus, who ever since his faculties of perception awoke has felt the sharpest pangs of sorrow and misery? Now could I but think, as you tell me, that all this comes in the natural course of things, I could bear it a little easier. But it has been brought about entirely by my own fault, for thinking myself loved by those who were jealous of me, and turning from those who wanted to win me. . . . I have thanked the people you wanted me to, and mentioned that my information came from you. As to the block of houses which you tell me you mean to sell—why, good heavens! my dear Terentia, what *is* to be done! Oh, what troubles I have to bear! And if misfortune continues to persecute us, what will become of our poor boy? I cannot continue to write—my tears are too much for me; nor would I wish to betray you into the same emotion. All I can say is that if our friends act up to their bounden duty we shall not want for money; if they do not, you will not be able to succeed only with your own. Let our unhappy fortunes, I entreat you, be a warning to us not to ruin our boy, who is ruined enough already. If he only has something to save him from absolute want, a fair share of talent and a fair share of luck will be all that is necessary to win anything else. Do not neglect your health; and send me messengers with letters to let me know what goes on, and how you yourselves are faring. My suspense in any case cannot now be long. Give my love to my little Tullia and my Marcus.

DYRRACHIUM, Nov. 26.

P. S.—I have moved to Dyrrachium because it is not only a free city, but very much in my interest, and quite near to Italy; but if the bustle of the place proves an annoyance I shall betake myself elsewhere and give you notice.

CICERO'S VACILLATION IN THE CIVIL WAR

BEING in extreme agitation about these great and terrible events, and having no means of discussing matters with you in person, I want at any rate to avail myself of your judgment. Now the question about which I am in doubt is simply this: If Pompeius should fly from Italy (which I suspect he will do), how do you think I ought to act? To make it easier for you to advise me, I will briefly set forth the arguments that occur to me on both sides of the question.

The obligations that Pompeius laid me under in the matter of my restoration, my own intimacy with him, and also my patriotism, incline me to think that I ought to make my decision as his decision, or in other words, my fortunes as his fortunes. There is this reason also: If I stay behind and desert my post among that band of true and illustrious patriots, I must perforce fall completely under the yoke of one man. Now although he frequently takes occasion to show himself friendly to me — indeed, as you well know, anticipating this storm that is now hanging over our heads, I took good care that he should be so long ago — still I have to consider two different questions: first, how far can I trust him; and secondly,—assuming it to be absolutely certain that he is friendly disposed to me,—would it show the brave man or the honest citizen to remain in a city where one has filled the highest offices of peace and war, achieved immortal deeds, and been crowned with the honors of her most dignified priesthood, only to become an empty name and undergo some risk, attended also very likely with considerable disgrace, should Pompeius ever again grasp the helm? So much for this side; see now what may be said on the other.

Pompeius has in our cause done nothing wisely, nothing strongly; nothing, I may add, that has not been contrary to my opinion and advice. I pass over those old complaints, that it was he who himself nourished this enemy of the republic, gave him his honors, put the sword into his hand — that it was he who advised him to force laws through by violence, trampling on the warnings of religion — that it was he who made the addition of Transalpine Gaul, he who is his son-in-law, he who as Augur allowed the adoption of Clodius; who showed more activity in recalling me than in preventing my exile; who took it on him to extend Cæsar's term of government; who supported all his proceedings while he was away; that he too even in his third consulship, after he had begun to pose as a defender of the constitution, actually exerted himself to get the ten tribunes to propose that absence should not invalidate the election; nay more, he expressly sanctioned this by one of his own acts, and opposed the consul Marcus Marcellus, who proposed that the tenure of the Gallic provinces should come to an end on the 1st of March — but anyhow, to pass over all this, what could be more discreditable, what more blundering, than this evacuation of the city, or I had better say, this ignominious flight? What terms ought not to have been accepted sooner than abandon our country? The terms were bad? That I allow; but is anything worse than this? But he will win back the constitution? When? What preparations have been made to warrant such a hope? Have we not lost all Picenum? have we not left open the road to the capital? have we not abandoned the whole of our treasure, public and private, to the foe? In a word, there is no common cause, no strength, no centre, to draw such people together as might yet care to show fight for the Republic. Apulia has been chosen — the most thinly populated part of Italy, and the most remote from the line of movement of this war: it would seem that in despair they were looking for flight, with some easy access to the coast. I took the charge of Capua much against my will — not that I would evade that duty, but in a cause which evoked no sympathy from any class as a whole, nor any openly even from individuals (there was some of course among the good

citizens, but as languid as usual), and where I saw for myself
that the mass of the people, and all the lowest stratum, were
more and more inclined to the other side, many even longing for
a revolution, I told him to his face I would undertake to do
nothing without forces and without money. Consequently I have
had no responsibility at all, because I saw from the very first
that nothing was really intended but flight. Say that I now
follow this; then whither? Not with him; I had already set out
to join him when I found that Cæsar was in those parts, so that
I could not safely reach Luceria. I must sail by the western
sea, in the depth of winter, not knowing where to steer for.
And again, what about being with my brother, or leaving him
and taking my son? How then must I act, since either alternative will involve the greatest difficulty, the greatest mental
anxiety? And then, too, what a raid he will make on me and
my fortunes when I am out of the way—fiercer than on other
people, because he will think perhaps that in outrages on me he
holds a means of popularity. Again, these fetters, remember,—
I mean these laurels on my attendants' staves,—how inconvenient
it is to take them out of Italy! What place indeed will be safe
for me, supposing I now find the sea calm enough, before I
have actually joined him? though where that will be and how
to get there, I have no notion.

On the other hand, say that I stop where I am and find
some place on this side of the water, then my conduct will precisely resemble that of Philippus, or Lucius Flaccus, or Quintus
Mucius under Cinna's reign of terror. And however this decision
ended for the last-named, yet still he at any rate used to say
that he saw what really did happen would occur, but that it was
his deliberate choice in preference to marching sword in hand
against the homes of the very city that gave him birth. With
Thrasybulus it was otherwise, and perhaps better; but still there
is a sound basis for the policy and sentiments of Mucius; as
there is also for this [which Philippus did]: to wait for your
opportunity when you must, just as much as not to lose your
opportunity when it is given. But even in this case, those staves
again of my attendants still involve some awkwardness; for say
that his feelings are friendly to me (I am not sure that this is
so, but let us assume it), then he will offer me a triumph. I
fear that to decline may be perilous—[to accept] an offense with
all good citizens. Ah, you exclaim, what a difficult, what an

insoluble problem! Yet the solution must be found; for what
can one do? And lest you should have formed the idea that I
am rather inclined towards staying because I have argued more
on that side of the question, it is quite possible, as is so frequently the case in debates, that one side has more words, the
other more worth. Therefore I should be glad if when you give
me your opinion you would look upon me as making up my
mind quite dispassionately on a most important question. I have
a ship both at Caieta and at Brundisium.

But lo and behold, while I am writing you these very lines
by night in my house at Cales, in come the couriers, and here is
a letter to say that Cæsar is before Corfinium, and that in Corfinium is Domitius, with an army resolute and even eager for
battle. I do not think our chief will go so far as to be guilty
of abandoning Domitius, though it is true he had already sent
Scipio on before with two cohorts to Brundisium, and written a
dispatch to the consuls ordering that the legion enrolled by
Faustus should go under the command of one consul to Sicily:
but it is a scandal that Domitius should be left to his fate when
he is imploring him for help. There is some hope, not in my
opinion a very good one, but strong in these parts, that there
has been a battle in the Pyrenees between Afranius and Trebonius; that Trebonius has been beaten off; that your friend
Fabius also has come over to us with all his troops; and to
crown it all, that Afranius is advancing with a strong force. If
this be so, we shall perhaps make a stand in Italy. As for me,
since Cæsar's route is uncertain — he is expected about equally by
way of Capua and of Luceria — I have sent Lepta to Pompeius
with a letter, while I myself, for fear of falling in with him anywhere, have started again for Formiæ. I thought it best to let
you know this, and am writing with more composure than I have
written of late; not inserting any opinion of my own, but trying
to elicit yours.

CICERO'S CORRESPONDENTS

It seems desirable to add a few letters by other hands than Cicero's, to indicate the manifold side-lights thrown on the inner history of this intensely interesting period. Sulpicius's famous attempt at consolation has already been given above. Two brief letters by Cæsar will illustrate the dictator's marvelous ability to comprehend and control other men. Pompey's gruff rudeness forms a contrast which is hardly accidental on the editor's part. Cælius's wit is biting as ever; and lastly, Matius's protest against being persecuted merely because he, who loved Cæsar, openly mourned for his dead friend, has an unconscious tone of simple heroism unequaled in the entire correspondence. W. C. L.

CÆSAR TO CICERO

You know me too well not to keep up your character as an Augur by divining that nothing is more entirely alien from my nature than cruelty: I will add that while my decision is in itself a great source of pleasure to me, to find my conduct approved by you is a triumph of gratification. Nor does the fact at all disturb me that those people whom I have set at liberty are reported to have gone their ways only to renew the attack upon me; because there is nothing I wish more than that I may ever be as true to my own character as they to theirs.

May I hope that you will be near town when I am there, so that I may as usual avail myself in everything of your advice and means of assistance? Let me assure you that I am charmed beyond everything with your relation Dolabella, to whom I shall acknowledge myself indeed indebted for this obligation; for his kindliness is so great, and his feeling and affection for me are such, that he cannot possibly do otherwise.

CÆSAR TO CICERO

Though I had fully made up my mind that you would do nothing rashly, nothing imprudently, still I was so far impressed by the rumors in some quarters as to think it my duty to write to you, and ask it as a favor due to our mutual regard that you will not take any step, now that the scale is so decisively turned, which you would not have thought it necessary to take even though the balance still stood firm. For it will really be both a heavier blow to our friendship, and a step on your part still less judicious for yourself, if you are to be thought not even to have bowed the knee to success—for things seem to have fallen out as entirely favorably for us as disastrously for them; nor yet to have been drawn by attachment to a particular cause—for that has undergone no change since you decided to remain aloof from their counsels;—but to have passed a stern judgment on some act of mine, than which, from you, no more painful thing could befall me; and I claim the right of our friendship to entreat that you will not take this course.

Finally, what more suitable part is there for a good peace-loving man, and a good citizen, than to keep aloof from civil dissensions? There were not a few who admired this course, but could not adopt it by reason of its danger: you, after having duly weighed both the conclusions of friendship and the unmistakable evidence of my whole life, will find that there is no safer nor more honorable course than to keep entirely aloof from the struggle.

POMPEY TO CICERO

TO-DAY, the 10th of February, Fabius Vergilianus has joined me. From him I learn that Domitius with his eleven cohorts, and fourteen cohorts that Vibullius has brought up, is on his way to me. His intention was to start from Corfinium on the 13th, Hirrus to follow soon after with five of the cohorts. I decide that you are to come to us at Luceria; here, I think, you will be most in safety.

CÆLIUS IN ROME TO CICERO IN CILICIA

THE capture of his Parthian Majesty and the storming of Seleuceia itself had not been enough to compensate for missing the sight of our doings here. Your eyes would never have ached again if you had only seen the face of Domitius when he was not elected! The election was important, and it was quite clear that party feeling determined the side which people took: only a few could be brought to acknowledge the claims of friendship. Consequently Domitius is so furious with me that he scarcely hates any of his most intimate friends as much as he does me; and all the more because he thinks that it was to do him wrong that his hopes of being in the College of Augurs are snatched away, and that I am responsible for it. He is savage now to see everybody so delighted at his mortification, and myself more active than anybody, with one exception, on behalf of Antonius.

As to political prospects, I have often mentioned to you that I do not see any chance of peace lasting a year; and the nearer that struggle which must infallibly take place, is drawing to us, the more manifest does its danger become. The point at issue about which our lords and masters are going to fight is this: Pompeius has absolutely determined not to allow Cæsar to be elected consul on any terms except a previous resignation of his army and his government, while Cæsar is convinced that he must inevitably fall if he separates himself from his army. He offers however this compromise, that they should both of them resign their armies. So you see their great affection for one another and their much-abused alliance has not even dwindled down into suppressed jealousy, but has broken out into open war. Nor can I discover what is the wisest course to take in my own interests: a question which I make no doubt will give much trouble to you also. For while I have both interest and connections among those who are on one side, on the other too it is the cause and not the men themselves I dislike. You are not, I feel sure, blind to the fact that where parties are divided within a country, we are bound, so long as the struggle is carried on with none but constitutional weapons, to support the more honorable cause, but when we come to blows and to open war, then the safer one; and to count that cause the better which is the less likely to be dangerous. In the present division of feeling I see that Pompeius will have the Senate and all judicially minded people on his side; those who have everything to dread and little to hope for will flock to Cæsar: the army is not to be compared. On the whole, we have plenty of time for balancing the strength of parties and making our decision.

I had all but forgotten my principal reason for writing. Have you heard of the wonderful doings of our censor Appius—how he is rigorously inquiring into our statues and pictures, our amount of land, and our debts? He has persuaded himself that his censorship is a moral soap or toilet powder. He is wrong, I take it; for while he only wants to wash off the dirt, he is really laying bare his veins and his flesh. Heaven and earth! you must run, and come to laugh at the things here — Appius questioning about pictures and statues. You must make haste, I assure you.

Our friend Curio is thought to have acted wisely in giving way about the pay of Pompeius's troops. If I must sum up my opinion, as you ask, about what will happen — unless one or other of them consents to go and fight the Parthians, I see a great split impending, which will be settled by the sword and by force; each is well inclined for this and well equipped. If it could only be without danger to yourself, you would find this a great and most attractive drama which Fortune is rehearsing.

MATIUS TO CICERO

I RECEIVED great pleasure from your letter, because I found that your opinion of me was what I had hoped and wished it to be; not that I was in any doubt about it, but for the very reason that I valued it so highly, I was most anxious that it should remain unimpaired. Conscious however that I had done nothing which could give offense to the feelings of any good citizen, I was naturally the less inclined to believe that you, adorned as you are with so many excellences of the most admirable kind, could have allowed yourself to be convinced of anything on mere idle report; particularly seeing that you were a friend for whom my spontaneous attachment had been and still was unbroken. And knowing now that it has been as I hoped, I will answer those attacks which you have often opposed on my behalf, as was fairly to be expected from your well-known generosity and the friendship existing between us.

For I am well aware of all they have been heaping on me since Cæsar's death. They make it a reproach against me that I go heavily for the loss of a friend, and think it cruel that one whom I loved should have fallen, because, say they, country must be put before friends — as though they have hitherto been successful in proving that his death really was the gain of the commonwealth. But I will not enter any subtle plea; I admit that I have not attained to your higher grades of philosophy: for I have neither been a partisan of Cæsar in our civil dissensions, — though I did not abandon my friend even when his action was a stumbling-block to me,— nor did I ever give my approval to the civil war, or even to the actual ground of quarrel, of which indeed I earnestly desired that the first sparks should be trampled out. And so in the triumph of a personal friend I was never ensnared by the charms either of place or of money; prizes which have been recklessly abused by the rest, though they had less influence with him than I had. I may even say that my own private property was impaired by that act of Cæsar, thanks to which many of those who are rejoicing at Cæsar's death continued to live in their own country. That our defeated fellow countrymen should be spared was as much an object to me as my own safety. Is it possible then for me, who wanted all to be left uninjured, not to feel indignation that he by whom this was secured is dead? above all when the very same men were the cause at once of his unpopularity and his untimely end. You shall smart then, say they, since you dare to disapprove of our deed. What unheard-of insolence! One man then may boast of a deed, which another is not even allowed to lament without punishment. Why, even slaves have always been free of this — to feel their fears, their joys, their sorrows as their own, and not at anybody else's dictation; and these are the very things which now, at least according to what your "liberators" have always in their mouths, they are trying to wrest from us by terrorism. But they try in vain. There is no danger which has terrors enough ever to make me desert the side of gratitude or humanity; for never have I thought that death in a good cause is to be shunned, often indeed that it deserves to be courted. But why are they inclined to be enraged with me, if my wishes are simply that they may come to regret their deed, desiring as I do that Cæsar's death may be felt to be untimely by us all? It is my duty as a citizen to desire the preservation of the constitution? Well, unless both my life in the past and all my hopes for the future prove without any words of mine that I do earnestly desire this, I make no demand to prove it by my professions.

To you therefore I make a specially earnest appeal to let facts come before assertions, and to take my word for it that, if you feel that honesty is the best policy, it is impossible I should have any association with lawless villains. Or can you believe that the principles I pursued in the days of my youth, when even error could pass with some excuse, I shall renounce now

that I am going down the hill, and with my own hands unravel
all the web of my life? That I will not do; nor yet will I commit any act that could give offense, beyond the fact that I do
lament the sad fall of one who was to me the dearest friend
and the most illustrious of men. But were I otherwise disposed,
I would never deny what I was doing, lest it should be thought
I was at once shameless in doing wrong and false and cowardly
in dissembling it.

But then I undertook the management of those games which
Cæsar's heir celebrated for Cæsar's victory? Well, this is a matter which belongs to one's private obligations, not to any political arrangement; it was however in the first place a tribute of
respect which I was called upon to pay to the memory and the
eminent position of a man whom I dearly loved, even though he
was dead, and also one that I could not refuse at the request of
a young man so thoroughly promising, and so worthy in every
way of Cæsar as he is.

Again, I have frequently paid visits of compliment to the consul Antonius. And you will find that the very men who think
me but a lukewarm patriot are constantly going to his house
in crowds, actually for the purpose of soliciting or carrying away
some favor. But what a monstrous claim it is, that while Cæsar
never laid any such embargo as this to prevent me from associating freely with anybody I pleased,— even if they were people
whom he personally did not like,— these men who have robbed
me of my friend should attempt by malicious insinuations to
prevent my showing a kindness to whomsoever I will!

I have however no fear that the moderation of my life will
hereafter prove an insufficient defense against false insinuations,
and that even those who do not love me, because of my loyalty
to Cæsar, would not rather have their own friend imitate me
than themselves. Such of life as remains to me, at least if I
succeed in what I desire, I shall spend in quiet at Rhodes; but
if I find that some chance has put a stop to this, I shall simply
live at Rome as one who is always desirous that right should be
done.

I am deeply grateful to our good friend Trebatius for having
thus disclosed to me your sincere and friendly feeling, and given
me even an additional reason for honoring and paying respect
to one whom it has always been a pleasure to me to regard as
a friend. Farewell heartily, and let me have your esteem.

THE DREAM OF SCIPIO

From the Dialogue 'The Republic': Translation of Prof. T. R. Lounsbury

WHEN I went into Africa with the consul Manius Manilius, holding the rank, as you are aware, of military tribune of the fourth legion, nothing lay nearer to my heart than to meet Masinissa, a king who, for good reasons, was on the most friendly terms with our family. When I had come to him, the old man embraced me with tears, and then looking up to heaven, said:—"I give thanks to thee, O supremest Sol, and to you, ye inhabitants of heaven! that before I depart this life I behold in my dominions, and under this roof, Publius Cornelius Scipio, by whose very name I am revived: so never passes away from my mind the memory of that best and most invincible hero." Thereupon I made inquiries of him as to the state of his own kingdom, and he of me as to our republic; and with many words uttered on both sides, we spent the whole of that day.

Moreover, after partaking of a repast prepared with royal magnificence, we prolonged the conversation late into the night. The old man would speak of nothing but Africanus, and remembered not only all his deeds, but likewise his sayings. After we parted to go to bed, a sounder sleep than usual fell upon me, partly on account of weariness occasioned by the journey, and partly because I had stayed up to a late hour. Then Africanus appeared to me, I think in consequence of what we had been talking about; for it often happens that our thoughts and speeches bring about in sleep something of that illusion of which Ennius writes in regard to himself and Homer, of which poet he was very often accustomed to think and speak while awake. Africanus showed himself to me in that form which was better known to me from his ancestral image than from my recollection of his person. As soon as I recognized him I was seized with a fit of terror; but he thereupon said:—

"Be of good courage, O Scipio! Lay aside fear, and commit to memory these things which I am about to say. Do you see that State which, compelled by me to submit to the Roman people, renews its former wars, and cannot endure to remain at peace?" At these words, from a certain lustrous and bright place, very high and full of stars, he pointed out to me Carthage. "To fight against that city thou now comest in a rank but little above that of a private soldier; but in two years from this time thou shalt as consul utterly overthrow it, and in consequence shalt gain by thy own exertions that very surname of Africanus which up to this time thou hast inherited from us. But when thou shalt have destroyed Carthage, shalt have had the honor of a triumph, and shalt have been censor, thou shalt during thy absence be chosen consul for a second time, shalt put an end to to a great war, and lay Numantia in ruins. But when thou shalt be carried in thy triumphal chariot to the capitol, thou wilt find the republic disturbed by the designs of my grandson. Then, O Scipio! it will be necessary that thou exhibit the purity and greatness of thy heart, thy soul, and thy judgment. But I see at that time a double way disclose itself, as if the Fates were undecided; for when thy life shall have completed eight times seven revolutions of the sun, and these two numbers (each one of which is looked upon as perfect; the one for one reason, the other for another) shall have accomplished for thee by their natural revolution the fatal product, to thee alone and to thy name the whole State shall turn; upon thee the Senate, upon thee all good men, upon thee the allies, upon thee the Latins, will fasten their eyes; thou wilt be the one upon whom the safety of the State shall rest; and in short, as dictator, it will be incumbent on thee to establish and regulate the republic, if thou art successful in escaping the impious hands of kinsmen.»

At this point, Lælius uttered an exclamation of sorrow, and the rest groaned more deeply; but Scipio, slightly smiling, said, Keep silence, I beg of you. Do not awake me from my dream, and hear the rest of his words:—

"But, O Africanus! that thou mayest be the more zealous in the defense of the republic, know this: For all who have preserved, who have succored, who have aggrandized their country, there is in heaven a certain fixed place, where they enjoy an eternal life of blessedness. For to that highest God who governs the whole world there is nothing which can be done on earth more dear than those combinations of men and unions, made under the sanction of law, which are called States. The rulers and preservers of them depart from this place, and to it they return.»

I had been filled with terror, not so much at the fear of death as at the prospect of treachery on the part of those akin to me; nevertheless at this point I had the courage to ask whether my father Paulus was living, and others whom we thought to be annihilated. "Certainly," said he: "they alone live who have been set free from the fetters of the body, as if from prison; for that which you call your life is nothing but death. Nay, thou mayest even behold thy father Paulus coming towards thee."

No sooner had I seen him than I burst into a violent fit of tears; but he thereupon, embracing and kissing me, forbade my weeping. I, as soon as I had checked my tears and was able again to speak, said to him, "Tell me, I beseech thee, O best and most sacred father! since this is life, as I hear Africanus say, why do I tarry upon earth? Why shall I not hasten to go to you?"—"Not so," said he; "not until that God, whose temple is all this which thou seest, shall have freed thee from the bonds of the body, can any entrance lie open to thee here. For men are brought into the world with this design, that they may protect and preserve that globe which thou seest in the middle of this temple, and which is called 'Earth.' To them a soul is given from these everlasting fires which you name constellations and stars, which, in the form of globes and spheres, run with incredible rapidity the rounds of their orbits under the impulse of divine intelligences. Wherefore by thee, O Publius! and by all pious men, the soul must be kept in the guardianship of the body; nor without the command of Him by whom it is given to you can there be any departure from this mortal life, lest you seem to have shunned the discharge of that duty as men which has been assigned to you by God. But, O Scipio! like as thy grandfather who stands here, like as I who gave thee life, cherish the sense of justice and loyal affection; which latter, in however great measure due to thy parents and kinsmen, is most of all due to thy country. Such a life is the way to heaven, and to that congregation of those who have ended their days on earth, and freed from the body, dwell in that place which you see,—that place which, as you have learned from the Greeks, you are in the habit of calling the Milky Way."

This was a circle, shining among the celestial fires with a most brilliant whiteness. As I looked from it, all other things seemed magnificent and wonderful. Moreover, they were such stars as we have never seen from this point of space, and all of such magnitude as we have never even suspected. Among them, that was the least which, the farthest from heaven, and the nearest to earth, shone with a borrowed light. But the starry globes far exceeded the size of the earth: indeed the earth

itself appeared to me so small that I had a feeling of mortification at the sight of our empire, which took up what seemed to
be but a point of it.

As I kept my eyes more intently fixed upon this spot, Africanus said to me:—"How long, I beg of thee, will thy spirit be
chained down to earth? Seest thou not into what a holy place
thou hast come? Everything is bound together in nine circles,
or rather spheres, of which the farthest is the firmament, which
embraces the rest, is indeed the supreme God himself, confining
and containing all the others. To that highest heaven are fixed
those orbits of the stars which eternally revolve. Below it are
seven spheres, which move backward with a motion contrary to
that of the firmament. One of these belongs to that star which
on earth they call Saturn; then follows that shining orb, the
source of happiness and health to the human race, which is
called Jupiter; then the red planet, bringing terror to the nations,
to which you give the name of Mars; then, almost directly under the middle region, stands the sun,—the leader, the chief,
the governor of the other luminaries, the soul of the universe,
and its regulating principle, of a size so vast that it penetrates
and fills everything with its own light. Upon it, as if they
were an escort, follow two spheres,—the one of Venus, the other
of Mercury; and in the lowest circle revolves the moon, illuminated by the rays of the sun. Below it there is nothing which is
not mortal and transitory, save the souls which are given to
mankind by the gift of the gods; above the moon, all things are
eternal. For that ninth sphere, which is in the middle, is the
earth: it has no motion; it is the lowest in space; and all heavy
bodies are borne toward it by their natural downward tendency."

I looked at these, lost in wonder. As soon as I had recovered
myself I said, "What is this sound, so great and so sweet,
which fills my ears?"—"This," he replied, "is that music
which, composed of intervals unequal, but divided proportionately
by rule, is caused by the swing and movement of the spheres
themselves, and by the proper combination of acute tones with
grave, creates with uniformity manifold and diverse harmonies.
For movements so mighty cannot be accomplished in silence;
and it is a law of nature that the farthest sphere on the one
side gives forth a base tone, the farthest on the other a treble;
for which reason the revolution of that uppermost arch of the
heaven, the starry firmament, whose motion is more rapid, is
attended with an acute and high sound; while that of the lowest,

or lunar arch, is attended with a very deep and grave sound. For the ninth sphere, the earth, embracing the middle region of the universe, stays immovably in one fixed place. But those eight globes between, two* of which have the same essential action, produce tones, distinguished by intervals, to the number of seven; which number indeed is the knot of almost all things. Men of skill, by imitating the result on the strings of the lyre, or by means of the human voice, have laid open for themselves a way of return to this place, just as other men of lofty souls have done the same by devoting themselves during their earthly life to the study of what is divine. But the ears of men, surfeited by this harmony have become deaf to it; nor is there in you any duller sense: just as, at that cataract which is called Catadupa,— where the Nile rushes down headlong from the lofty mountain-tops,— the people who dwell in that neighborhood have lost the sense of hearing in consequence of the magnitude of the sound. So likewise this harmony, produced by the excessively rapid revolution of the whole universe, is so great that the ears of men are not able to take it in, in the same manner as you are not able to look the sun in the eye, and your sight is overcome by the power of its rays." Though I was filled with wonder, nevertheless I kept turning my eyes from time to time to the earth.

"I perceive," then said Africanus, "that thou still continuest to contemplate the habitation of the home of man. If that seems to thee as small as it really is, keep then thy eyes fixed on these heavenly objects; look with contempt on those of mortal life. For what notoriety that lives in the mouths of men, or what glory that is worthy of being sought after, art thou able to secure? Thou seest that the earth is inhabited in a few small localities, and that between those inhabited places — spots as it were on the surface — vast desert regions lie spread out; and that those who inhabit the earth are not only so isolated that no communication can pass among them from one to another, but that some dwell in an oblique direction as regards you, some in a diagonal, and some stand even exactly opposite you. From these you are certainly not able to hope for any glory.

"Moreover, thou observest that this same earth is surrounded, and as it were, girdled, by certain zones, of which thou seest that two — the farthest apart, and resting at both sides on the very poles of the sky — are stiffened with frost; and that, again,

* Mercury and Venus.

the central and largest one is burnt up with the heat of the sun. Two are habitable: of these the southern one, in which dwell those who make their footprints opposite yours, is a foreign world to your race. But even this other one, which lies to the north, which you occupy,—see with how small a part of it you come into contact! For all the land which is cultivated by you, very narrow at the extremities but wider at the sides, is only a small island surrounded by that water which on earth you call the Atlantic, or the great sea, or the ocean. But though its name is so high-sounding, yet thou beholdest how small it is. From these cultivated and well-known regions can either thy name or the name of any of us surmount and pass this Caucasus which thou seest, or cross yonder flood of the Ganges? Who in the farthest remaining regions of the rising and the setting sun, or on the confines of the north and the south, will hear thy name? When these are taken away, thou assuredly perceivest how immense is the littleness of that space in which your reputation seeks to spread itself abroad. Moreover, even those who speak of us, for how long a time will they speak?

"Nay, even if the generations of men were desirous, one after the other, to hand down to posterity the praises of any one of us heard from their fathers, nevertheless, on account of the chanegs in the earth,—wrought by inundations and conflagration, which are sure to recur at certain fixed epochs,—we are not simply unable to secure for ourselves a glory which lasts forever, but are even unable to gain a glory which lasts for a long time. Moreover, of what value is it that the speech of those who are to be born hereafter shall be about thee, when nothing has been said of thee by all those who were born before, who were neither fewer in number and were unquestionably better men; especially when no one is able to live in the memory of those very persons by whom one's name can be heard, for the space of one year?

"For men commonly measure the year by the return to its place of the sun alone,—that is, of one star; but when all the stars shall have returned to that same point from which they once set out, and after a long period of time have brought back the same relative arrangement of the whole heaven, that, then, can justly be called the complete year. In it I hardly dare say how many ages of human life are contained. For once in the past the sun seemed to disappear from the eyes of men and to be annihilated, at the time when the soul of Romulus made its way into this very temple. When, from the same region of the sky and at the same moment of time, the sun shall have again vanished, then be sure that all constellations and stars have come back to the position they had in the beginning, and that the perfect year is completed. Of that year know that now not even the twentieth part has passed.

"Wherefore, if thou givest up the hope of a return to this place, in which all things exist for lofty and pre-eminent souls, yet of how much value is that human glory which can hardly endure for even the small part of a single year? But if, as I was saying, thou wishest to look on high, and to fix thy gaze upon this abode of the blest and this eternal home, never give thyself up to the applause of the vulgar, nor rest the recompense of thy achievements in the rewards which can be bestowed upon thee by men. It is incumbent on thee that Virtue herself shall draw thee by her own charm to true glory. As for the way in which others talk about thee, let them take care of that themselves; yet without doubt they will talk. But all such renown is limited to the petty provinces of the regions which thou seest: nor in the case of any one is it everlasting; for it both dies with the death of men and is buried in oblivion by the forgetfulness of posterity."

When he had said these things, "O Africanus!" I replied, "if the path that leads to the entrance of heaven lies open to those who have rendered great service to their country, although, in following from my boyhood in thy footsteps and in those of my father, I have not failed in sustaining the honor derived from you, yet henceforth I shall toil with far more zeal, now that so great a reward has been held out before me."—"Do thou indeed," said he, "continue to strive; and bear this in mind, that thou thyself art not mortal, but this body of thine. For thou art not the one which that form of thine proclaims thee to be: but the soul of any one, that alone is he; not that external shape which can be pointed out with the finger. Therefore know thyself to be a god, if that is essentially god which lives, which feels, which remembers, which foresees, which rules and regulates and moves that body over which it is put in authority, as the Supreme Being governs this universe. And as the eternal God moves the world, which in a certain point of view is perishable, so the incorruptible soul moves the corruptible body. For what always moves itself is eternal; but that which communicates to anything a motion which it has itself received from another source, must necessarily have an end of life when it has an end of motion: therefore that alone never ceases to move which moves itself, for the reason that it is never deserted by itself. This indeed is the well-head; this the beginning of motion to all other things that are moved. But to a beginning there is no birth; for all things are born from the beginning. But it itself cannot be born of anything; for that would not be a beginning which sprang from some other source. And just as it is never begotten, so it never dies; for a beginning anni-hilated could neither itself be brought back to life by anything else, nor could it create anything else out of itself, since it is necessary that all things should come from a beginning. So it results that the beginning of motion is in itself, because it is self-moved. And this can neither be born nor die, for if it did, the heavens would fall to ruin, and all nature would stand still; nor could it come into the possession of any power by the original impulse of which it might be put into motion.

"Since therefore it is clear that what is self-moved is eter-nal, who can deny that this essential characteristic has been imparted to the soul? For everything which is moved by a foreign impulse is without a soul; but that which lives is made to go by an inward motion of its own, for this is the special nature and power of the soul. But if it is the one thing among all which is self-moved, then certainly it has had no beginning, and is eternal. Do thou, then, employ it in the noblest duties. But those are the loftiest cares which are concerned with the well-being of our native land. The soul that is inspired by these, and occupied with them, will hasten the quicker into this its real home and habitation. So much the more speedily indeed will it do this, if while it is shut up in the body it shall pass beyond its limits, and by the contemplation of those things which are outside of it shall withdraw itself as far as possible from the body. For the souls of those who have given them-selves up to sensual pleasures, and have made themselves as it were ministers to these, and who under the pressure of desires which are subservient to these pleasures have violated the laws of God and man, when they shall have parted from the body, will fly about the earth itself, nor will return to this place until they shall have suffered torments for many ages." He departed. I awoke from my sleep.

THE CID

(1045 ? – 1099)

BY CHARLES SPRAGUE SMITH

N THE Cid we have two distinct personages, Rodrigo or Ruy Diaz (Dia son of Diego) who flourished during the last half of the eleventh century; and that legendary hero of Spanish epic poems, ballads, and dramas, whom Philip II. tried to have canonized. We are not left to our own conjectures as to the character and life of the historical Cid. Both Spanish and Arabic records place the main facts beyond all controversy.

He was born at Bivar, a hamlet three miles north of Burgos (circa 1040–1050), of an ancient Castilian family claiming descent from Lain Calvo,—one of the two judges who, tradition declares, was named by the Castilian people as their governor after the Leonese king had treacherously put their counts to death (circa 923).

The period of the Cid coincides with the political disruption of Arabic Spain. The Caliphate of Cordova, which in the preceding century had attained its high point in power and in all the arts of civilization, had fallen. A multitude of petty Moorish States disputed with each other the heritage of the Ommiad caliphs. The Christian States were not slow to profit by their opportunity. Ferdinand I. of Leon-Castile (surnamed the Great, 1037–65) not only extended his territory at the expense of the Moors, but also imposed tribute upon four of their more important States—Saragossa, Toledo, Badajoz, and Seville. Valencia only escaped a similar fate through his death.

The Peninsula was at this time divided among a large number of mutually independent and warring States, Christian and Moslem. The sentiments of loyalty to religion and to country were universally subordinated to those of personal interest; Christians fought under Moorish banners, Moors under Christian. Humanity toward the enemy, loyalty to oaths, were not virtues in the common estimation. Between the Christian States of Leon and Castile great jealousy ruled. Castile had come into being as a border province of the Asturian kingdom, governed by military counts. From the first there seems to have been a spirit of resistance to the overrule of the Asturian kings (later known as kings of Leon). Finally, under its Count Fernan Gonzalez (who died 970), Castile secured its independence. But whether leading a separate political existence, or united with Leon, Castile was ever jealously sensitive of any precedence claimed or exercised by its sister kingdom. Ferdinand I. of Leon-Castile, treating his territorial possessions as personal property,—a policy repeatedly fatal to all advance in Spanish history,—divided them at his death (1005), among his five children. Sancho, the eldest, received Castile, Nahera, and Pampeluna; Alfonso, Leon, and the Asturias; Garcia, Galicia, and that portion of Portugal which had been wrested from the Moors; Urraca received the city of Zamora; and Elvira, Toro.

The expected occurred. Sancho made war on his brothers, compelling both to flee to Moorish territories, and wrested Toro from Elvira. Rodrigo Diaz, the Cid, appears first at this period. He is the *alferez*, *i. e.*, the standard-bearer, or commander-in-chief under the King, in Sancho's army. The brother Kings, Sancho and Alfonso, had agreed to submit their dispute to a single combat, the victor to receive the territories of both. Alfonso's Leonese army conquered the Castilian, and relying upon the agreement withdrew to its tents. Rodrigo Diaz was already known as the Campeador,—a title won through his having vanquished in single combat the champion of Sancho of Navarre, and signifying probably one skilled in battle, or champion.

Rodrigo gave a wily counsel to the routed Castilians. "The Leonese are not expecting an attack," he said; "let us return and fall upon them at unawares." The counsel was followed; the victors, resting in their tents, were surprised at daybreak, and only a few, Alfonso among the number, escaped with their lives. Alfonso was imprisoned at Burgos, but soon released at the entreaty of the Princess Urraca, on condition of his becoming a monk. Availing himself of such liberty, he escaped from the monastery to the Moorish court of Mamoun, King of Toledo. Sancho ruled thus over the entire heritage of his father,—Zamora excepted, the portion of Urraca. While laying siege to that city, he was slain by a cavalier in Urraca's service, Bellido Dolfos, who, sallying from the city, made good his escape, though almost overtaken by the avenging Campeador, 1072.

Alfonso, the fugitive at Toledo, was now rightful heir to the throne; and however reluctant the Castilian nobles were to recognize the authority of a Leonese king, they yielded to necessity. It is asserted—but the historical evidence here is not complete—that before recognizing Alfonso's authority the Castilian nobles required of him an oath that he had no part in his brother's murder, and that it was the Campeador who administered this oath, 1073. Whatever the facts, Alfonso will have thought it wise to conciliate the good-will of the Castilian grandees, and especially that of their leader Rodrigo, until at least his own position became secure. To this we may attribute his giving to Rodrigo in marriage of Jimena, daughter of Diego, Count of Oviedo, and first cousin of the King. The marriage contract, bearing date 1074, is preserved at Burgos.

Some years later Rodrigo was sent to collect the tribute due Alfonso by his vassal Motamid, King of Seville. Finding the King of Granada at war with Motamid, Rodrigo requested him not to attack an ally of Alfonso. But prayers and threats were alike unavailing; it came to battle, and Rodrigo conquered. Among the prisoners were several Christians in the service of Granada, notably Garcia Ordonez, a scion of the royal Leonese house. Not long after, we find Rodrigo charged with having appropriated to his own use a portion of the tribute and gifts sent to Alfonso by Motamid, Garcia Ordonez being his chief accuser. Taking advantage of the pretext — it can have been but a pretext — of Rodrigo's attacking the Moors without first securing the royal consent, Alfonso banished him. Old wrongs still rankling in the King's memory furnished probably the real motive.

And now began that career as soldier of fortune which has furnished themes to Spanish poets of high and low degree, and which, transformed and idealized by tradition, has made of Rodrigo the perfect cavalier of crusading Christian Spain. He offered first, it would seem, his service and that of his followers to the Christian Count of Barcelona, and when refused by him, to the Moorish King of Saragossa. This State was one of the more important of those resulting from the distribution of the Caliphate of Cordova. The offer was accepted, and Rodrigo remained here until 1088, serving successively three generations of the Beni-Hud, father, son, and grandson, warring indifferently against Christians and Moors, and through his successes rising to extraordinary distinction and power.

At this time — 1088 — the attention of both Mostain, the King of Saragossa, and of his powerful captain Rodrigo, was drawn to Valencia. This city after the fall of the Caliphate of Cordova had been ruled for forty-four years by descendants of Almanzor, the great Prime Minister of the last period of the Ommiad dynasty. Mamoun, King of Toledo, who sheltered the fugitive Alfonso, deposed the last of these Valencian kings, his son-in-law, and annexed the State to his own dominion. At Mamoun's death in 1075 Valencia revolted; the governor declared himself independent and placed himself under Alfonso's protection.

Ten years later Mamoun's successor, the weak Cadir, finding his position a desperate one, offered to yield up to Alfonso his own capital Toledo, on condition that the latter should place Valencia in his hands. Alfonso consented. Valencia was too weak to offer resistance, but Cadir proved equally incompetent as king and as general. Depending entirely upon his Castilian soldiery, captained by Alvar

Fañez, a kinsman of Rodrigo, he grievously burdened the people in order to satisfy the demands of this auxiliary troop. But grinding taxes and extortions alike failed; and the soldiery, their wages in arrears, battened upon the country, the dregs of the Moorish population joining them. The territory was delivered at last from their robberies, rapes, and murders, by the appearance of the Almoravides. This new Moslem sect had grown strong in Africa, attaining there the political supremacy; and in their weakness the Moorish kings of Spain implored its assistance in repelling the attacks of the Christian North.

King Alfonso, alarmed at the appearance of these African hordes, recalled Alvar Fañez, was defeated by the Almoravides at Zallaca in 1086, and could think no more of garrisoning Valencia for Cadir. The position of Cadir became thus critical, and he appealed for help both to Alfonso and to Mostain of Saragossa. Mostain sent Rodrigo, ostensibly to his assistance; but a secret agreement had been made, Arabic historians assert, between the king and his general, whereby Cadir was to be despoiled, the city fall to Mostain, the booty to Rodrigo (1088).

The expedition was a successful one: Cadir's enemies were compelled to withdraw, and Rodrigo established himself in Valencian territory. As the recognized protector of the lawful king, in reality the suzerain of Valencia, Rodrigo received a generous tribute; but he had no intention of holding to his agreement with Mostain and assisting the latter to win the city. It is clear on the contrary that he had already resolved to secure, when opportunity offered, the prize for himself. Meanwhile he skillfully held off, now by force, now by ruse, all other competitors, Christian and Moslem alike; including among these King Alfonso, whose territories he wasted with fire and sword when that monarch attempted once, in Rodrigo's absence, to win Valencia for himself.

At another time we find him intriguing simultaneously with four different rivals for the control of the city,—Alfonso and Mostain among the number,—deceiving all with fair words.

As head of an independent army, Rodrigo made now successful forays in all directions; despoiling, levying tribute, garrisoning strongholds, strengthening thus in every way his position. At last the long awaited opportunity came. During his temporary absence, Cadir was dethroned and put to death; and the leader of the insurgents, the Cadi Ibn Djahhof, named president of a republic.

Rodrigo returned, and appealing in turn to ruse and force, at last sat down before the city to reduce it by famine. During the last period of the siege, those who fled from the city to escape the famine were thrown to dogs, or burned at slow fires. The city capitulated on favorable terms, June 15th, 1094. But all the conditions

of the capitulation were violated. The Cadi-President was buried in
a trench up to his arm-pits, surrounded with burning brands, and
slowly tortured to death, several of his kinsmen and friends sharing
his fate. Rodrigo was with difficulty restrained from throwing into
the flames the Cadi's children and the women of his harem. Yet
the lives and property of Ibn Djahhof and his family had been
expressly safeguarded in the capitulation. It is probable that Rodrigo's title of "the Cid" or "my Cid" (Arabic, Sid-y = my lord) was
given to him at this time by his Moorish subjects.

Master of Valencia, the Cid dreamed of conquering all that region
of Spain still held by the Moors. An Arab heard him say, "One
Rodrigo (the last king of the Goths) has lost this peninsula; another
Rodrigo will recover it." Success crowned his arms for several
years. But in 1099 the troops he had sent against the Almoravides
were utterly routed, few escaping. The Cid, already enfeebled in
health, died, it is said of grief and shame (July, 1099). His widow
held the city for two years longer. Besieged at that time by the
Almoravides, she sought help of Alfonso. He came and forced the
enemy to raise the siege; but judging that it was not possible for
him to defend a city so remote from his dominions, counseled its
abandonment. As the Christians, escorting the body of the Cid,
marched out, Valencia was fired; and only ruins awaited the Almoravides (1102).

The Cid's body was brought to San Pedro de Cardeña, a monastery not far from Burgos; enthroned, it is said, beside the high altar
for ten years, and thereafter buried. Jimena survived her husband
until 1104.

Ibn Bassam, an Arabic contemporary, writing at Seville only ten
years after the death of the Cid, after describing his cruelty and
duplicity, adds: — "Nevertheless, that man, the scourge of his time,
was one of the miracles of the Lord in his love of glory, the prudent
firmness of his character, and his heroic courage. Victory always
followed the banner of Rodrigo (may God curse him!); he triumphed
over the barbarians, . . . he put to flight their armies, and with
his little band of warriors slew their numerous soldiery."

The Cid, a man not of princely birth, through the exercise of virtues which his time esteemed,— courage and shrewdness,— had won
for himself from the Moors an independent principality. Legend will
have begun to color and transform his exploits already during his
lifetime. Some fifty years later he had become the favorite hero of
popular songs. It is probable that these songs (*cantares*) were at first
brief tales in rude metrical form; and that the epic poems, dating
from about 1200, used them as sources. The earliest poetic monument in Castilian literature which treats of the Cid is called 'The

Poem of My Cid.' While based upon history, its material is largely legendary. The date of its composition is doubtful,—probably about 1200. The poem—the beginning is lost—opens with the departure of "My Cid" from Bivar, and describes his Moorish campaigns, culminating with the conquest of Valencia. Two Leonese nobles, the Infantes (Princes) of Carrion, beseech Alfonso to ask for them in marriage the conqueror's daughters. The Cid assents—to his King he would refuse nothing—and the marriages are celebrated in Valencia with due pomp. But the princes are arrant cowards. To escape the gibes of the Cid's companions, after securing rich wedding portions they depart for Carrion. In the oak wood of Carpes they pretend a desire to be left alone with their wives. Despoiling them of their outer garments, with saddle-girth and spurred boot they seek to revenge upon the Cid's daughters the dishonor to which their own base conduct subjected them while at the Cid's court. But time brings a requital. The Infantes, called to account, forfeit property and honor, esteeming themselves fortunate to escape with their lives from the judicial duels. Princes of Navarre and Aragon present themselves as suitors, and in second marriages Doña Elvira and Doña Sola become queens of Spain. The marriages with the Infantes of Carrion are pure invention, intended perhaps to defame the Leonese nobility, these nobles being princes of the blood royal.

The second marriages, if we substitute Barcelona for Aragon, are historical. Of the Cid's two daughters, one married Prince Ramiro of Navarre and the other Count Raynard Berenger III. of Barcelona. In 1157 two of the Cid's great-grandchildren, Sancho VI. of Navarre and his sister Doña Blanca, queen of Sancho III. of Castile, sat on Spanish thrones. Through intermarriage the blood of the Cid has passed into the Bourbon and Habsburg lines, and with Eleanor of Castile into the English royal house.

The 'Poem of My Cid' is probably the earliest monument of Spanish literature. It is also in our opinion the noblest expression — so far as the characters are concerned; for the verse halts and the description sometimes lags — of the entire mediæval folk epic of Europe. Homeric in its simplicity, its characters are drawn with clearness, firmness, and concision, presenting a variety true to nature, far different from the uniformity we find in the 'Song of Roland.' The spirit which breathes in it is of a noble, well-rounded humanity, a fearless and gentle courage, a manly and modest self-reliance; an unswerving loyalty and simple trust toward country, king, kinsmen, and friends; a child-faith in God, slightly tinged with superstition, for "My Cid" believes in auguries; and a chaste tender family affection, where the wife is loved and honored as wife and as mother, and the children's welfare fills the father's thoughts.

The duplicity of the historical Cid has left indeed its traces. When abandoning Castile he sends to two Jewish money-lenders of Burgos, chests filled, as he pretends, with fine gold, but in reality with sand; borrows upon this security, and so far as we are informed, never repays the loan. The Princes of Carrion, his sons-in-law, are duped into thinking that they will escape from the accounting with the loss of Tizon and Colada, the swords which the Cid gave them. But a certain measure of prudent shrewdness is not out of place in dealing with men of the treacherous character of the Infantes. And as to the Jewish money-lenders, to despoil them would scarce have been regarded as an offense against the moral law in mediæval Spain.

The second poetic monument is variously named. Amadar de los Rios, a historian of Spanish literature, styles it 'The Legend or Chronicle of the Youth of Rodrigo.' Its date also is disputed, some authorities placing its composition earlier, others later than that of the Poem. The weight of evidence seems to us in favor of the later date. It is rude and of inferior merit, though not without vigorous passages. It treats the earliest period of the Cid's life, and is (so far as we know) purely legendary. The realm of Castile-Leon is at peace under the rule of Ferdinand (the First), when the Count Don Gomez of Gormaz makes an unprovoked descent upon the sheep-folds of Diego Lainez. A challenge of battle follows. Rodrigo, only son of Diego, a lad in his thirteenth year, insists upon being one of the hundred combatants on the side of his family, and slays Don Gomez in single combat. Jimena, the daughter of Gomez, implores justice of the King; but when Ferdinand declares that there is danger of an insurrection if Rodrigo be punished, she proposes reconciliation through marriage. Diego and his son are summoned to the court, where Rodrigo's appearance and conduct terrify all. He denies vassalship, and declares to King Ferdinand, "That my father kissed your hand has foully dishonored me."

Married to Jimena against his will (Jimena Diaz, not Jimena Gomez, was his historical wife), he vows never to recognize her as wife until he has won five battles with the Moors in open field. Ferdinand plays a very unkingly rôle in this poem. While his fierce vassal is absent the King is helpless; and Rodrigo draws near only to assert anew his contempt for the royal authority by blunt refusals of Ferdinand's requests. He is always ready, however, to take up the gauntlet and defend the realm against every enemy, Christian or Moor. But this rude courage is coupled with devout piety, and is not insensible to pity. At the ford of the Duero a wretched leper is encountered: all turn from him with loathing save Rodrigo, who gives to him a brother's care. It is Saint Lazarus, who departing blesses him.

At last a formidable coalition is formed against Spain. The Emperor of Germany and the King of France, supported by the Pope and Patriarch, require of Spain, in recognition of her feudal dependence upon the Roman empire, a yearly tribute of fifteen noble virgins, besides silver, horses, falcons, etc. Rodrigo appears when Ferdinand is in despair, and kisses at last the royal hand in sign of vassalship. Though the enemy gather "countless as the herbs of the fields," even Persia and Armenia furnishing contingents, their battle array is vain.

The five Kings of Spain cross the Pyrenees. Arrived before Paris, Rodrigo passes through the midst of the French army, strikes with his hand the gates of the city, and challenges the twelve French peers to combat. The allies in alarm implore a truce. At the council, Rodrigo, seated at the feet of his King and acting as Ferdinand's spokesman, curses the Pope when the latter offers the imperial crown of Spain. "We came for that which was to be won," he declares, "not for that already won." Against Rodrigo's advice the truce is accorded to all. Here the poem is interrupted.

Besides these two epic poems, we have in the earlier Spanish literature two chronicles in prose which describe the life of the Cid, —'The General Chronicle of Alfonso the Learned' and 'The Chronicle of the Cid,' the latter being drawn from the former. Both rest in part upon historical sources, in part upon legend and tradition. Two centuries and more after the Poem, we meet with the Romances or Ballads of the Cid. For the earliest of these do not in their present form date far back of 1500. These ballads derive from all sources, but chiefly from the Cid legend, which is here treated in a lyric, sentimental, popular, and at times even vulgar tone.

Guillem de Castro (1569–1631) chose two themes from the life of the Cid for dramatic treatment, composing a dual drama styled 'Las Mocedades del Cid' (The Youth of the Cid). The first part is the more important. De Castro, drawing from the ballads, told again the story of the insult to Don Diego (according to the ballads, a blow in the face given by Don Gomez in a moment of passion), its revenge, the pursuit of Rodrigo by Jimena, demanding justice of King Ferdinand, and finally the reconciliation through marriage. But De Castro added love, and the conflict in the mind of Rodrigo and in that of Jimena between affection and the claims of honor.

Corneille recast De Castro's first drama in his 'Le Cid,' condensing it and giving to the verse greater dignity and nobility. The French dramatist has worked with entire independence here, and both in what he has omitted and what he has added has usually shown an unerring dramatic instinct. In certain instances, however, through ignorance of the spirit and sources of the Spanish drama he has erred. But the invention is wholly De Castro's, and many of Corneille's most admired passages are either free translations from the Spanish or expressions of some thought or sentiment contained in De Castro's version.

In more recent times Herder has enriched German literature with free renderings of some of the Cid ballads. Victor Hugo has drawn from the Cid theme, in his 'La Legende des Siècles' (The Legend of the Centuries), fresh inspiration for his muse.

Charles Sprague Smith.

FROM 'THE POEM OF MY CID'

LEAVING BURGOS

WITH tearful eyes he turned to gaze upon the wreck behind,
 His rifled coffers, bursten gates, all open to the wind:
 Nor mantle left, nor robe of fur; stript bare his castle hall;
Nor hawk nor falcon in the mew, the perches empty all.
Then forth in sorrow went my Cid, and a deep sigh sighed he;
Yet with a measured voice and calm, my Cid spake loftily,—
"I thank thee, God our Father, thou that dwellest upon high,
I suffer cruel wrong to-day, but of mine enemy!"
As they came riding from Bivar the crow was on the right;
By Burgos's gate, upon the left, the crow was there in sight.
My Cid he shrugged his shoulders and he lifted up his head:
"Good tidings, Alvar Fañez! we are banished men!" he said.
With sixty lances in his train my Cid rode up the town,
The burghers and their dames from all the windows looking down;
And there were tears in every eye, and on each lip one word:
"A worthy vassal — would to God he served a worthy Lord!"

FAREWELL TO HIS WIFE AT SAN PEDRO DE CARDEÑA

THE prayer was said, the mass was sung, they mounted to depart;
My Cid a moment stayed to press Jimena to his heart;
Jimena kissed his hand,—as one distraught with grief was she;
He looked upon his daughters: "These to God I leave," said he. . . .
As when the finger-nail from out the flesh is torn away,
Even so sharp to him and them the parting pang that day.
Then to his saddle sprang my Cid, and forth his vassals led;
But ever as he rode, to those behind he turned his head.

BATTLE SCENE

THEN cried my Cid—"In charity, as to the rescue—ho!"
With bucklers braced before their breasts, with lances pointing low,
With stooping crests and heads bent down above the saddle-bow,
All firm of hand and high of heart they roll upon the foe.
And he that in a good hour was born, his clarion voice rings out,
And clear above the clang of arms is heard his battle shout:
"Among them, gentlemen! Strike home for the love of charity!
The champion of Bivar is here—Ruy Diaz—I am he!"
Then bearing where Bermuez still maintains unequal fight,
Three hundred lances down they come, their pennons flickering white;
Down go three hundred Moors to earth, a man to every blow;
And when they wheel, three hundred more, as charging back they go.
It was a sight to see the lances rise and fall that day;
The shivered shields and riven mail, to see how thick they lay;
The pennons that went in snow-white came out a gory red;
The horses running riderless, the riders lying dead;
While Moors call on Mohammed, and "St. James!" the Christians cry,
And sixty score of Moors and more in narrow compass lie.

THE CHALLENGES

[Scene from the challenges that preceded the judicial duels. Ferrando, one of the Infantes, has just declared that they did right in spurning the Cid's daughters. The Cid turns to his nephew.]

"Now is the time, 'Dumb Peter'; speak, O man that sittest mute!
My daughters' and thy cousins' name and fame are in dispute:
To me they speak, to thee they look to answer every word.
If I am left to answer now, thou canst not draw thy sword."
Tongue-tied Bermuez stood; a while he strove for words in vain,
But look you, when he once began he made his meaning plain.
"Cid, first I have a word for you: you always are the same,
In Cortes ever gibing me,—'Dumb Peter' is the name;
It never was a gift of mine, and that long since you knew;
But have you found me fail in aught that fell to me to do?—
You lie, Ferrando, lie in all you say upon that score.
The honor was to you, not him, the Cid Campeador;
For I know something of your worth, and somewhat I can tell.
That day beneath Valencia wall—you recollect it well—
You prayed the Cid to place you in the forefront of the fray;
You spied a Moor, and valiantly you went that Moor to slay;
And then you turned and fled—for his approach you would not stay.
Right soon he would have taught you 'twas a sorry game to play,
Had I not been in battle there to take your place that day.

I slew him at the first onfall; I gave his steed to you;
To no man have I told the tale from that hour hitherto.
Before my Cid and all his men you got yourself a name,
How you in single combat slew a Moor — a deed of fame;
And all believed in your exploit; they wist not of your shame.
You are a craven at the core, — tall, handsome, as you stand:
How dare you talk as now you talk, you tongue without a hand?. . .
Now take thou my defiance as a traitor, trothless knight:
Upon this plea before our King Alfonso will I fight;
The daughters of my lord are wronged, their wrong is mine to right.
That ye those ladies did desert, the baser are ye then;
For what are they? — weak women; and what are ye? — strong men.
On every count I deem their cause to be the holier,
And I will make thee own it when we meet in battle here.
Traitor thou shalt confess thyself, so help me God on high,
And all that I have said to-day my sword shall verify.»
　　Thus far these two.　Diego rose, and spoke as ye shall hear:
«Counts by our birth are we, of stain our lineage is clear.
In this alliance with my Cid there was no parity.
If we his daughters cast aside, no cause for shame we see.
And little need we care if they in mourning pass their lives,
Enduring the reproach that clings to scorned rejected wives.
In leaving them we but upheld our honor and our right,
And ready to the death am I, maintaining this, to fight.»
Here Martin Antolinez sprang upon his feet: «False hound!
Will you not silent keep that mouth where truth was never found?
For you to boast! the lion scare have you forgotten too?
How through the open door you rushed, across the court-yard flew;
How sprawling in your terror on the wine-press beam you lay?
Ay! never more, I trow, you wore the mantle of that day.
There is no choice; the issue now the sword alone can try:
The daughters of my Cid ye spurned; that must ye justify.
On every count I here declare their cause the cause of right,
And thou shalt own thy treachery the day we join in fight.»
He ceased, and striding up the hall Assur Gonzalez passed;
His cheek was flushed with wine, for he had stayed to break his fast;
Ungirt his robe, and trailing low his ermine mantle hung;
Rude was his bearing to the court, and reckless was his tongue.
«What a to-do is here, my lords! was the like ever seen?
What talk is this about my Cid — him of Bivar I mean?
To Riodouirna let him go to take his millers' rent,
And keep his mills a-going there, as once he was content.
He, forsooth, mate his daughters with the Counts of Carrion!»
Upstarted Muño Gustioz: «False, foul-mouthed knave, have done!

Thou glutton, wont to break thy fast without a thought or prayer;
Whose heart is plotting mischief when thy lips are speaking fair;
Whose plighted word to friend or lord hath ever proved a lie;
False always to thy fellow-man, falser to God on high,—
No share in thy good-will I seek; one only boon I pray,
The chance to make thee own thyself the villain that I say."
Then spoke the king: "Enough of words: ye have my leave to fight,
The challenged and the challengers; and God defend the right."

Conclusion

AND from the field of honor went Don Roderick's champions three.
Thanks be to God, the Lord of all, that gave the victory!   . . .
But in the lands of Carrion it was a day of woe,
And on the lords of Carrion it fell a heavy blow.
He who a noble lady wrongs and casts aside — may he
Meet like requital for his deeds, or worse, if worse there be!
But let us leave them where they lie — their meed is all men's scorn.
Turn we to speak of him that in a happy hour was born.
Valencia the Great was glad, rejoiced at heart to see
The honored champions of her lord return in victory:
And Ruy Diaz grasped his beard: "Thanks be to God," said he,
"Of part or lot in Carrion now are my daughters free;
Now may I give them without shame, whoe'er their suitors be."
And favored by the king himself, Alfonso of Leon,
Prosperous was the wooing of Navarre and Aragon.
The bridals of Elvira and of Sol in splendor passed;
Stately the former nuptials were, but statelier far the last.
And he that in a good hour was born, behold how he hath sped!
His daughters now to higher rank and greater honor wed:
Sought by Navarre and Aragon, for queens his daughters twain;
And monarchs of his blood to-day upon the thrones of Spain.
And so his honor in the land grows greater day by day.
Upon the feast of Pentecost from life he passed away.
For him and all of us the grace of Christ let us implore.
And here ye have the story of my Cid Campeador.

                                        Translation of John Ormsby.

EARL OF CLARENDON

(EDWARD HYDE)

(1609 – 1674)

THE statesman first known as Mr. Hyde of the Inner Temple, then as Sir Edward Hyde, and finally as the Earl of Clarendon, belongs to the small but most valuable and eminent band who have both made and written history; a group which includes among others Cæsar, Procopius, Sully, and Baber, and on a smaller scale of active importance, Ammianus and Finlay. Born in Dinton, Wiltshire, 1609, he was graduated at Oxford in 1626, and had attained a high standing in his profession when the civil troubles began, and he determined to devote all his energies to his public duties in Parliament. During the momentous period of the Long Parliament he was strongly on the side of the people until the old abuses had been swept away; but he would not go with them in paralyzing the royal authority from distrust of Charles, and when the civil war broke out he took the royal side, accompanying the King to Oxford, and remaining his ablest adviser and loyal friend.

EARL OF CLARENDON

He was the guardian of Charles II. in exile; and in 1661, after the Restoration, was made Lord Chancellor and chief minister. Lord Macaulay says of him:—"He was well fitted for his great place. No man wrote abler state papers. No man spoke with more weight and dignity in council and Parliament. No man was better acquainted with general maxims of statecraft. No man observed the varieties of character with a more discriminating eye. It must be added that he had a strong sense of moral and religious obligation, a sincere reverence for the laws of his country, and a conscientious regard for the honor and interest of the Crown." But his faults were conspicuous. One of his critics insists that "his temper was arbitrary and vehement. His arrogance was immeasurable. His gravity assumed the character of censoriousness."

He took part in important and dangerous negotiations, and eventually alienated four parties at once: the royalists by his Bill of

Indemnity; the low-churchmen and dissenters by his Uniformity act; the many who suffered the legal fine for private assemblages for religious worship; and the whole nation by selling Dunkirk to France. By the court he was hated because he censured the extravagance and looseness of the life led there; and finally Charles, who had long resented his sermons, deprived him of the great seal, accused him of high treason, and doomed him to perpetual banishment. Thus, after being the confidential friend of two kings (and the future grandfather of two sovereigns, Mary and Anne), he was driven out of England, to die in poverty and neglect at Rouen in 1674. But these last days were perhaps the happiest and most useful of his life. He now indulged his master passion for literature, and revised his 'History of the Rebellion,' which he had begun while a fugitive from the rebels in the Isle of Jersey. In this masterpiece, "one of the greatest ornaments of the historical literature of England," he has described not only the events in which he participated, but noted people of the time whom he had personally known. The book is written in a style of sober and stately dignity, with great acuteness of insight and weightiness of comment; it incorporates part of an autobiography afterwards published separately, and is rather out of proportion. His other works are 'The Essay on an Active and Contemplative Life'; 'The Life of Edward, Earl of Clarendon'; 'Dialogues on Education and the Want of Respect Paid to Age'; 'Miscellaneous Essays,' and 'Contemplation of the Psalms of David.'

THE CHARACTER OF LORD FALKLAND

IF CELEBRATING the memory of eminent and extraordinary persons, and transmitting their great virtues for the imitation of posterity, be one of the principal ends and duties of history, it will not be thought impertinent in this place to remember a loss which no time will suffer to be forgotten, and no success or good fortune could repair. In this unhappy battle was slain the Lord Viscount Falkland; a person of such prodigious parts of learning and knowledge, of that inimitable sweetness and delight in conversation, of so flowing and obliging a humanity and goodness to mankind, and of that primitive simplicity and integrity of life, that if there were no other brand upon this odious and accursed civil war than that single loss, it must be most infamous and execrable to all posterity.

Before this Parliament, his condition of life was so happy that it was hardly capable of improvement. Before he came to

twenty years of age he was master of a noble fortune, which
descended to him by the gift of a grandfather without passing
through his father or mother, who were then both alive, and not
well enough contented to find themselves passed by in the
descent. His education for some years had been in Ireland,
where his father was Lord Deputy; so that when he returned
into England to the possession of his fortune, he was unentan-
gled with any acquaintance or friends, which usually grow up
by the custom of conversation; and therefore was to make a
pure election of his company, which he chose by other rules
than were prescribed to the young nobility of that time. And
it cannot be denied, though he admitted some few to his friendship for the agreeableness of their natures and their undoubted
affection to him, that his familiarity and friendship, for the
most part, was with men of the most eminent and sublime parts,
and of untouched reputation in the point of integrity; and such
men had a title to his bosom.

He was a great cherisher of wit and fancy and good parts in
any man; and if he found them clouded with poverty or want, a
most liberal and bountiful patron towards them, even above his
fortune; of which, in those administrations, he was such a dis-
penser as if he had been trusted with it to such uses; and if
there had been the least of vice in his expense he might have been
thought too prodigal. He was constant and pertinacious in
whatsoever he resolved to do, and not to be wearied by any
pains that were necessary to that end. And therefore having
once resolved not to see London, which he loved above all
places, till he had perfectly learned the Greek tongue, he went
to his own house in the country and pursued it with that indefatigable industry that it will not be believed in how short a
time he was master of it, and accurately read all the Greek
historians.

In this time, his house being within ten miles of Oxford, he
contracted familiarity and friendship with the most polite and
accurate men of that university; who found such an immenseness
of wit and such a solidity of judgment in him, so infinite a
fancy bound in by a most logical ratiocination, such a vast
knowledge that he was not ignorant in anything, yet such an
excessive humility as if he had known nothing, that they frequently resorted and dwelt with him, as in a college situated in
a purer air; so that his house was a university bound in a less

volume, whither they came not so much for repose as study, and to examine and refine those grosser propositions which laziness and consent made current in vulgar conversation. . . .

The great opinion he had of the uprightness and integrity of those persons who appeared most active, especially of Mr. Hampden, kept him longer from suspecting any design against the peace of the kingdom; and though he differed commonly from them in conclusions, he believed long their purposes were honest. When he grew better informed what was law, and discerned (in them) a desire to control that law by a vote of one or both Houses, no man more opposed those attempts, and gave the adverse party more trouble by reason and argumentation; insomuch as he was, by degrees, looked upon as an advocate for the court, to which he contributed so little that he declined those addresses and even those invitations which he was obliged almost by civility to entertain. And he was so jealous of the least imagination that he should incline to preferment, that he affected even a morosity to the court and to the courtiers, and left nothing undone which might prevent and divert the King's or Queen's favor towards him, but the deserving it. For when the King sent for him once or twice to speak with him, and to give him thanks for his excellent comportment in those councils which his Majesty graciously termed doing him service, his answers were more negligent and less satisfactory than might have been expected; as if he cared only that his actions should be just, not that they should be acceptable, and that his Majesty should think that they proceeded only from the impulsion of conscience, without any sympathy in his affections; which from a stoical and sullen nature might not have been misinterpreted; yet from a person of so perfect a habit of generous and obsequious compliance with all good men, might very well have been interpreted by the King as more than an ordinary averseness to his service: so that he took more pains and more forced his nature to actions unagreeable and unpleasant to it, that he might not be thought to incline to the court, than any man hath done to procure an office there. . . .

Two reasons prevailed with him to receive the seals, and but for those he had resolutely avoided them. The first, consideration that it [his refusal] might bring some blemish upon the King's affairs, and that men would have believed that he had refused so great an honor and trust because he must have been with it obliged to do somewhat else not justifiable. And this he made matter of conscience, since he knew the King made choice of him before other men especially because he thought him more honest than other men. The other was, lest he might be thought to avoid it out of fear to do an ungracious thing to the House of Commons, who were sorely troubled at the displacing of Harry Vane, whom they looked upon as removed for having done them those offices they stood in need of; and the disdain of so popular an incumbrance wrought upon him next to the other. For as he had a full appetite of fame by just and generous actions, so he had an equal contempt of it by any servile expedients; and he had so much the more consented to and approved the justice upon Sir Harry Vane in his own private judgment, by how much he surpassed most men in the religious observation of a trust, the violation whereof he would not admit of any excuse for.

For these reasons he submitted to the King's command and became his secretary, with as humble and devout an acknowledgment of the greatness of the obligation as could be expressed, and as true a sense of it in his own heart. Yet two things he could never bring himself to whilst he continued in that office, that was to his death; for which he was contented to be reproached, as for omissions in a most necessary part of his office. The one, employing of spies, or giving any countenance or entertainment to them. I do not mean such emissaries as with danger would venture to view the enemy's camp and bring intelligence of their number and quartering, or such generals as such an observation can comprehend; but those who by communication of guilt or dissimulation of manners wound themselves into such trusts and secrets as enabled them to make discoveries for the benefit of the State. The other, the liberty of opening letters upon a suspicion that they might contain matter of dangerous consequence. For the first he would say, such instruments must be void of all ingenuity and common honesty, before they could be of use; and afterwards they could never be fit to be credited: and that no single preservation could be worth so general a wound and corruption of human society as the cherishing such persons would carry with it. The last, he thought such a violation of the law of nature that no qualification by office could justify a single person in the trespass; and though he was convinced by the necessity and iniquity of the time that those

advantages of information were not to be declined and were
necessarily to be practiced, he found means to shift it from himself; when he confessed he needed excuse and pardon for the
omission: so unwilling he was to resign anything in his nature
to an obligation in his office.

In all other particulars he filled his place plentifully, being
sufficiently versed in languages to understand any that [are] used
in business, and to make himself again understood. To speak
of his integrity, and his high disdain of any bait that might
seem to look towards corruption, *in tanto viro, injuria virtutum
fuerit* [in the case of so great a man, would be an insult to his
merits].   .   .   .

He had a courage of the most clear and keen temper, and so
far from fear that he was not without appetite of danger; and
therefore, upon any occasion of action, he always engaged his
person in those troops which he thought by the forwardness of
the commanders to be most like to be farthest engaged; and in
all such encounters he had about him a strange cheerfulness and
companionableness, without at all affecting the execution that
was then principally to be attended, in which he took no
delight, but took pains to prevent it, where it was not by
resistance necessary; insomuch that at Edgehill, when the
enemy was routed, he was like to have incurred great peril by
interposing to save those who had thrown away their arms, and
against whom, it may be, others were more fierce for their having thrown them away: insomuch as a man might think he
came into the field only out of curiosity to see the face of
danger, and charity to prevent the shedding of blood. Yet in
his natural inclination he acknowledged that he was addicted to
the profession of a soldier; and shortly after he came to his
fortune, and before he came to age, he went into the Low
Countries with a resolution of procuring command, and to give
himself up to it, from which he was converted by the complete
inactivity of that summer: and so he returned into England and
shortly after entered upon that vehement course of study we
mentioned before, till the first alarm from the North; and then
again he made ready for the field, and though he received some
repulse in the command of a troop of horse of which he had a
promise, he went volunteer with the Earl of Essex.

From the entrance into this unnatural war his natural cheerfulness and vivacity grew clouded, and a kind of sadness and

dejection of spirit stole upon him which he had never been
used to; yet being one of those who believed that one battle
would end all differences, and that there would be so great a
victory on the one side that the other would be compelled to
submit to any conditions from the victor (which supposition and
conclusion generally sunk into the minds of most men, and prevented the looking after many advantages which might then
have been laid hold of), he resisted those indispositions, *et in
luctu, bellum inter remedia erat* [and in his grief, strife was one
of his curatives].   But after the King's return from Brentford,
and the furious resolution of the two Houses not to admit any
treaty for peace, those indispositions which had before touched
him grew into a perfect habit of uncheerfulness; and he who
had been so exactly unreserved and affable to all men that his
face and countenance was always present and vacant to his company, and held any cloudiness and less pleasantness of the visage
a kind of rudeness or incivility, became, on a sudden, less com-
municable; and thence, very sad, pale, and exceedingly affected
with the spleen.   In his clothes and habit, which he had
intended before always with more neatness and industry and
expense than is usual in so great a mind, he was now not only
incurious, but too negligent; and in his reception of suitors, and
the necessary or casual addresses to his place, so quick and
sharp and severe that there wanted not some men (who were
strangers to his nature and disposition) who believed him proud
and imperious,—from which no mortal man was ever more free.

The truth is, that as he was of a most incomparable gentleness, application, and even a demissness and submission to good
and worthy and entire men, so he was naturally (which could not
but be more evident in his place, which objected him to another
conversation and intermixture than his own election had done)
adversus malos injucundus [toward evil-doers ungracious] and was
so ill a dissembler of his dislike and disinclination to ill men
that it was not possible for such not to discern it.   There was
once in the House of Commons such a declared acceptation of
the good service an eminent member had done to them, and as
they said, to the whole kingdom, that it was moved, he being
present, that the Speaker might in the name of the whole House
give him thanks; and then, that every member might as a testimony of his particular acknowledgment stir or move his hat
towards him; the which (though not ordered) when very many

did, the Lord Falkland (who believed the service itself not to be
of that moment, and that an honorable and generous person
could not have stooped to it for any recompense), instead of
moving his hat, stretched both his arms out and clasped his
hands together upon the crown of his hat, and held it close
down to his head; that all men might see how odious that flattery was to him, and the very approbation of the person, though
at that time most popular.

When there was any overture or hope of peace, he would be
more erect and vigorous, and exceedingly solicitous to press
anything which he thought might promote it; and sitting amongst
his friends, often, after a deep silence and frequent sighs, would
with a shrill and sad accent ingeminate the word *Peace*, *Peace;*
and would passionately profess that the very agony of the war
and the view of the calamities and desolation the kingdom
did and must endure, took his sleep from him, and would
shortly break his heart. This made some think or pretend to
think that he was so much enamored on peace, that he would
have been glad the King should have bought it at any price;
which was a most unreasonable calumny. As if a man that
was himself the most punctual and precise in every circumstance
that might reflect upon conscience or honor, could have wished
the King to have committed a trespass against either. . . .

In the morning before the battle, as always upon action, he
was very cheerful, and put himself into the first rank of the
Lord Byron's regiment, who was then advancing upon the
enemy, who had lined the hedges on both sides with musketeers,
from whence he was shot with a musket in the lower part of the
belly, and in the instant falling from his horse, his body was
not found till the next morning; till when, there was some hope
he might have been a prisoner; though his nearest friends, who
knew his temper, received small comfort from that imagination.
Thus fell that incomparable young man, in the four-and-thirtieth
year of his age, having so much dispatched the business of life
that the oldest rarely attain to that immense knowledge, and the
youngest enter not into the world with more innocence: and
whosoever leads such a life needs not care upon how short
warning it be taken from him.

MARCUS A. H. CLARKE

(1846–1881)

LTHOUGH a native of England, Marcus Clarke is always classed as an Australian novelist. The son of a barrister, he was born in Kensington April 24th, 1846. In 1864 he went to seek his fortune in Australia. His taste for adventure soon led him to "the bush," where he acquired many experiences afterwards used by him for literary material. Drifting into journalism, he joined the staff of the Melbourne Argus. After publishing a series of essays called 'The Peripatetic Philosopher,' he purchased the Australian Magazine, the name of which he changed to the Colonial Monthly, and in 1868 published in it his first novel, entitled 'Long Odds.' Owing to a long illness, this tale of sporting life was completed by other hands. When he resumed his literary work he contributed to the Melbourne Punch, and edited the Humbug, a humorous journal. He dramatized Charles Reade's and Dion Boucicault's novel of 'Foul Play'; adapted Molière's 'Bourgeois Gentilhomme'; wrote a drama entitled 'Plot,' successfully performed at the Princess Theatre in 1873; and another play called 'A Daughter of Eve.' He was connected with the Melbourne press until his death, August 2d, 1881.

Clarke's literary fame rests upon the novel 'His Natural Life,' a strong story, describing the life of an innocent man under a life sentence for felony. The story is repulsive, but gives a faithful picture of the penal conditions of the time, and is built upon official records. It appeared in the Australian Magazine, and before it was issued in book form, Clarke, with the assistance of Sir Charles Gavin Duffy, revised it almost beyond recognition. It was republished in London in 1875 and in New York in 1878. He was also the author of 'Old Tales of a New Country'; 'Holiday Peak,' another collection of short stories; 'Four Stories High'; and an unfinished novel called 'Felix and Felicitas.'

Clarke was a devoted student of Balzac and Poe, and some of his sketches of rough life in Australia have been compared to Bret Harte's pictures of primitive California days. His power in depicting landscape is shown by this glimpse of a midnight ride in the bush, taken from 'Holiday Peak':—

"There is an indescribable ghastliness about the mountain bush at midnight, which has affected most imaginative people. The grotesque and distorted trees, huddled here and there together in the gloom like whispering

conspirators; the little open flats encircled by bowlders, which seem the forgotten altars of some unholy worship; the white, bare, and ghostly gum-trees,
gleaming momentarily amid the deeper shades of the forest; the lonely pools
begirt with shivering reeds and haunted by the melancholy bittern only; the
rifted and draggled creek-bed, which seems violently gouged out of the lacer-
ated earth by some savage convulsion of nature; the silent and solitary places
where a few blasted trees crouch together like withered witches, who, brood-
ing on some deed of blood, have suddenly been stricken horror-stiff. Riding
through this nightmare landscape, a whirr of wings and a harsh cry disturb
you from time to time, hideous and mocking laughter peals above and about
you, and huge gray ghosts with little red eyes hop away in gigantic but
noiseless bounds. You shake your bridle, the mare lengthens her stride, the
tree-trunks run into one another, the leaves make overhead a continuous curtain, the earth reels out beneath you like a strip of gray cloth spun by a
furiously flying loom, the air strikes your face sharply, the bush — always gray
and colorless — parts before you and closes behind you like a fog. You lose
yourself in this prevailing indecision of sound and color. You become drunk
with the wine of the night, and losing your individuality, sweep onward, a
flying phantom in a land of shadows.»

HOW A PENAL SYSTEM CAN WORK

From ‹His Natural Life›

THE next two days were devoted to sight-seeing. Sylvia Frere
was taken through the hospital and the workshops, shown
the semaphores, and shut up by Maurice in a "dark cell."
Her husband and Burgess seemed to treat the prison like a tame
animal, whom they could handle at their leisure, and whose
natural ferocity was kept in check by their superior intelligence.
This bringing of a young and pretty woman into immediate
contact with bolts and bars had about it an incongruity which
pleased them. Maurice Frere penetrated everywhere, questioned
the prisoners, jested with the jailers; even, in the munificence of
his heart, bestowed tobacco on the sick.

With such graceful rattlings of dry bones, they got by-and-by
to Point Puer, where a luncheon had been provided.

An unlucky accident had occurred at Point Puer that morning, however; and the place was in a suppressed ferment. A
refractory little thief named Peter Brown, aged twelve years,
had jumped off the high rock and drowned himself in full view
of the constables. These "jumpings-off" had become rather
frequent lately, and Burgess was enraged at one happening on

this particular day. If he could by any possibility have brought the corpse of poor little Peter Brown to life again, he would have soundly whipped it for its impertinence.

"It is most unfortunate," he said to Frere, as they stood in the cell where the little body was laid, "that it should have happened to-day."

"Oh," says Frere, frowning down upon the young face that seemed to smile up at him, "it can't be helped. I know those young devils. They'd do it out of spite. What sort of a character had he?"

"Very bad. Johnson, the book."

Johnson bringing it, the two saw Peter Brown's iniquities set down in the neatest of running-hand, and the record of his punishments ornamented in quite an artistic way with flourishes of red ink.

"20th November, disorderly conduct, 12 lashes. 24th November, insolence to hospital attendant, dict reduced. 4th December, stealing cap from another prisoner, 12 lashes. 15th December, absenting himself at roll-call, two days' cells. 23d December, insolence and insubordination, two days' cells. 8th January, insolence and insubordination, 12 lashes. 20th January, insolence and insubordination, 12 lashes. 22d February, insolence and insubordination, 12 lashes and one week's solitary. 6th March, insolence and insubordination, 20 lashes."

"That was the last?" asked Frere.

"Yes, sir," says Johnson.

"And then he — hum — did it?"

"Just so, sir. That was the way of it."

Just so! The magnificent system starved and tortured a child of twelve until he killed himself. That was the way of it. . . .

After the farce had been played again, and the children had stood up and sat down, and sung a hymn, and told how many twice five were, and repeated their belief in "One God the Father Almighty, maker of Heaven and earth," the party reviewed the workshops, and saw the church, and went everywhere but into the room where the body of Peter Brown, aged twelve, lay starkly on its wooden bench, staring at the jail roof which was between it and heaven.

Just outside this room Sylvia met with a little adventure. Meekin had stopped behind, and Burgess being suddenly summoned for some official duty, Frere had gone with him, leaving his wife to rest on a bench that, placed at the summit of the cliff, overlooked the sea. While resting thus she became aware of another presence, and turning her head, beheld a small boy with his cap in one hand and a hammer in the other. The appearance of the little creature, clad in a uniform of gray cloth that was too large for him, and holding in his withered little hand a hammer that was too heavy for him, had something pathetic about it.

"What is it, you mite?" asked Sylvia.

"We thought you might have seen him, mum," said the little figure, opening its blue eyes with wonder at the kindness of the tone.

"Him? Whom?"

"Cranky Brown, mum," returned the child; "him as did it this morning. Me and Billy knowed him, mum; he was a mate of ours, and we wanted to know if he looked happy."

"What do you mean, child?" said she, with a strange terror at her heart; and then, filled with pity at the aspect of the little being, she drew him to her, with sudden womanly instinct, and kissed him.

He looked up at her with joyful surprise. "Oh!" he said. Sylvia kissed him again.

"Does nobody ever kiss you, poor little man?" said she.

"Mother used to," was the reply; "but she's at home. Oh, mem," with a sudden crimsoning of the little face, "may I fetch Billy?"

And taking courage from the bright young face, he gravely marched to an angle of the rock, and brought out another little creature, with another gray uniform, and another hammer.

"This is Billy, mum," he said. "Billy never had no mother. Kiss Billy."

The young wife felt the tears rush to her eyes.

"You two poor babies!" she cried. And then, forgetting that she was a lady, dressed in silk and lace, she fell on her knees in the dust, and folding the friendless pair in her arms, wept over them.

"What is the matter, Sylvia?" said Frere, when he came up. "You've been crying."

"Nothing, Maurice; at least, I will tell you by-and-by."

When they were alone that evening she told him of the two little boys, and he laughed.

"Artful little humbugs," he said, and supported his argument by so many illustrations of the precocious wickedness of juvenile felons that his wife was half convinced against her will.

Unfortunately, when Sylvia went away, Tommy and Billy put into execution a plan which they had carried in their poor little heads for some weeks.

"I can do it now," said Tommy. "I feel strong."

"Will it hurt much, Tommy?" said Billy, who was not so courageous.

"Not so much as a whipping."

"I'm afraid! Oh, Tom, it's so deep! Don't leave me, Tom!"

The bigger boy took his little handkerchief from his neck, and with it bound his own left hand to his companion's right.

"Now I *can't* leave you."

"What was it the lady that kissed us said, Tommy?"

"Lord, have pity of them two fatherless children!" repeated Tommy.

"Let's say it, Tom."

And so the two babies knelt on the brink of the cliff, and raising the bound hands together, looked up at the sky, and ungrammatically said, "Lord, have pity on we two fatherless children." And then they kissed each other, and "did it."

THE VALLEY OF THE SHADOW OF DEATH

From 'His Natural Life'

IT was not until they had scrambled up the beach to safety that the absconders became fully aware of the loss of another of their companions. As they stood on the break of the beach, wringing the water from their clothes, Gabbett's small eye, counting their number, missed the stroke oar.

"Where's Cox?"

"The fool fell overboard," said Jemmy Vetch, shortly. "He never had as much sense in that skull of his as would keep it sound on his shoulders."

Gabbett scowled. "That's three of us gone," he said, in the tones of a man suffering some personal injury.

They summed up their means of defense against attack. Sanders and Greenhill had knives. Gabbett still retained the axe in his belt. Vetch had dropped his musket at the Neck; and Bodenham and Cornelius were unarmed.

"Let's have a look at the tucker," said Vetch.

There was but one bag of provisions. It contained a piece of salt pork, two loaves, and some uncooked potatoes. Signal Hill station was not rich in edibles.

"That ain't much," said the Crow, with rueful face. "Is it, Gabbett?"

"It must do, anyway," returned the giant, carelessly.

The inspection over, the six proceeded up the shore, and encamped under the lee of a rock. Bodenham was for lighting a fire; but Vetch, who by tacit consent had been chosen leader of the expedition, forbade it, saying that the light might betray them. "They'll think we're drowned, and won't pursue us," he said. So all that night the miserable wretches crouched fireless together.

Morning breaks clear and bright, and — free for the first time in ten years — they comprehend that their terrible journey has begun. "Where are we to go? How are we to live?" asks Bodenham, scanning the barren bush that stretches to the barren sea. "Gabbett, you've been out before — how's it done?"

"We'll make the shepherds' huts, and live on their tucker till we get a change o' clothes," said Gabbett, evading the main question. "We can follow the coast-line."

"Steady, lads," said prudent Vetch; "we must sneak round yon sandhills, and so creep into the scrub. If they've a good glass at the Neck, they can see us."

"It does seem close," said Bodenham, "I could pitch a stone on to the guard-house. Good-by, you bloody spot!" he adds, with sudden rage, shaking his fist vindictively at the penitentiary, "I don't want to see you no more till the Day o' Judgment."

Vetch divides the provisions, and they travel all that day until dark night. The scrub is prickly and dense. Their clothes are torn, their hands and feet bleeding. Already they feel out-wearied. No one pursuing, they light a fire, and sleep. The second day they come to a sandy spit that runs out into the sea, and find that they have got too far to the eastward, and must follow the shore-line to East Bay Neck. Back through the scrub they drag their heavy feet. That night they eat the last crumb of the loaf. The third day at high noon, after some toilsome walking, they reach a big hill, now called Collins's Mount, and see the upper link of the ear-ring, the isthmus of East Bay

Neck, at their feet. A few rocks are on their right hand, and blue in the lovely distance lies hated Maria Island. "We must keep well to the eastward," said Greenhill, "or we shall fall in with the settlers and get taken." So, passing the isthmus, they strike into the bush along the shore, and tightening their belts over their gnawing bellies, camp under some low-lying hills.

The fourth day is notable for the indisposition of Bodenham, who is a bad walker, and falling behind, delays the party by frequent cooeys. Gabbett threatens him with a worse fate than sore feet if he lingers. Luckily, that evening Greenhill espies a hut; but not trusting to the friendship of the occupant, they wait until he quits it in the morning, and then send Vetch to forage. Vetch, secretly congratulating himself on having by his counsel prevented violence, returns bending under half a bag of flour. "You'd better carry the flour," said he to Gabbett, "and give me the axe." Gabbett eyes him for a while, as if struck by his puny form, but finally gives the axe to his mate Sanders. That day they creep along cautiously between the sea and the hills, camping at a creek. Vetch, after much search, finds a handful of berries, and adds them to the main stock. Half of this handful is eaten at once, the other half reserved for "to-morrow." The next day they come to an arm of the sea, and as they struggle northward Maria Island disappears, and with it all danger from telescopes. That evening they reach the camping-ground by twos and threes; and each wonders — between the paroxysms of hunger — if his face is as haggard and his eyes as blood-shot as those of his neighbor.

On the seventh day Bodenham says his feet are so bad he can't walk, and Greenhill, with a greedy look at the berries, bids him stay behind. Being in a very weak condition, he takes his companion at his word, and drops off about noon the next day. Gabbett, discovering this defection, however, goes back, and in an hour or so appears, driving the wretched creature before him with blows, as a sheep is driven to the shambles. Greenhill remonstrates at another mouth being thus forced upon the party, but the giant silences him with a hideous glance. Jemmy Vetch remembers that Greenhill accompanied Gabbett once before, and feels uncomfortable. He gives hint of his suspicions to Sanders, but Sanders only laughs. It is horribly evident that there is an understanding among the three.

The ninth sun of their freedom, rising upon sandy and barren hillocks, bristling thick with cruel scrub, sees the six famine-stricken wretches cursing their God, and yet afraid to die. All round is the fruitless, shadeless, shelterless bush. Above, the pitiless heaven. In the distance the remorseless sea. Something terrible must happen. That gray wilderness, arched by gray heaven stooping to gray sea, is a fitting keeper of hideous secrets. Vetch suggests that Oyster Bay cannot be far to the eastward,— the line of ocean is deceitfully close,— and though such a proceeding will take them out of their course, they resolve to make for it. After hobbling five miles they seem no nearer than before, and nigh dead with fatigue and starvation, sink despairingly upon the ground. Vetch thinks Gabbett's eyes have a wolfish glare in them, and instinctively draws off from him. Said Greenhill, in the course of a dismal conversation, "I am so weak that I could eat a piece of a man."

On the tenth day Bodenham refuses to stir, and the others, being scarcely able to drag along their limbs, sit on the ground about him. Greenhill, eyeing the prostrate man, said slowly, "I have seen the same done before, boys, and it tasted like pork."

Vetch, hearing his savage comrade give utterance to a thought all had secretly cherished, speaks out, crying, "It would be murder to do it; and then perhaps we couldn't eat it."

"Oh," said Gabbett, with a grin, "I'll warrant you that; but you must all have a hand in it."

Gabbett, Sanders, and Greenhill then go aside, and presently Sanders, coming to the Crow, said, "He consented to act as flogger. He deserves it."

"So did Gabbett, for that matter," shudders Vetch.

"Ay, but Bodenham's feet are sore," said Sanders, "and 'tis a pity to leave him."

Having no fire, they made a little break-wind; and Vetch, half dozing behind this, at about three in the morning hears some one cry out "Christ!" and awakes, sweating ice.

No one but Gabbett and Greenhill would eat that night. That savage pair, however, make a fire, fling ghastly fragments on the embers, and eat the broil before it is right warm. In the morning the frightful carcass is divided.

That day's march takes place in silence, and at the midday halt Cornelius volunteers to carry the billy, affecting great restoration from the food. Vetch gives it him, and in half an hour afterward Cornelius is missing. Gabbett and Greenhill pursue him in vain, and return with curses. "He'll die like a dog," said Greenhill, "alone in the bush." Jemmy Vetch, with his intellect acute as ever, thinks that Cornelius prefers such a death to the one in store for him, but says nothing.

The twelfth morning dawns wet and misty, but Vetch, seeing the provision running short, strives to be cheerful, telling stories of men who have escaped greater peril. Vetch feels with dismay that he is the weakest of the party, but has some sort of ludicro-horrible consolation in remembering that he is also the leanest. They come to a creek that afternoon, and look until nightfall in vain for a crossing-place. The next day Gabbett and Vetch swim across, and Vetch directs Gabbett to cut a long sapling, which being stretched across the water, is seized by Greenhill and the Moocher, who are dragged over.

"What would you do without me?" said the Crow, with a ghastly grin.

They cannot kindle a fire, for Greenhill, who carries the tinder, has allowed it to get wet. The giant swings his axe in savage anger at enforced cold, and Vetch takes an opportunity to remark privately to him what a *big* man Greenhill is.

On the fourteenth day they can scarcely crawl, and their limbs pain them. Greenhill, who is the weakest, sees Gabbett and the Moocher go aside to consult, and crawling to the Crow, whimpers, "For God's sake, Jemmy, don't let 'em murder me!"

"I can't help you," says Vetch, looking about in terror. "Think of poor Tom Bodenham."

"But he was no murderer. If they kill me, I shall go to hell with Tom's blood on my soul."

He writhes on the ground in sickening terror, and Gabbett, arriving, bids Vetch bring wood for the fire. Vetch going, sees Greenhill clinging to wolfish Gabbett's knees, and Sanders calls after him, "You will hear it presently, Jem."

The nervous Crow puts his hands to his ears, but is conscious, nevertheless, of a dull crash and a groan. When he comes back, Gabbett is putting on the dead man's shoes, which are better than his own.

"We'll stop here a day or so and rest," said he, "now we've got provisions."

Two more days pass, and the three, eying each other suspiciously, resume their march. The third day — the sixteenth of their awful journey — such portions of the carcass as they have with them prove unfit to eat. They look into each other's famine-sharpened faces, and wonder "Who next?"

"We must all die together," said Sanders, quickly, "before anything else must happen."

Vetch marks the terror concealed in the words, and when the dreaded giant is out of ear-shot, says, "For God's sake, let's go on alone, Alick. You see what sort of a cove that Gabbett is, — he'd kill his father before he'd fast one day."

They made for the bush, but the giant turned and strode toward them. Vetch skipped nimbly on one side, but Gabbett struck the Moocher on the forehead with the axe. "Help! Jem, help!" cried the victim, cut but not fatally, and in the strength of his desperation tore the axe from the monster who bore it, and flung it to Vetch. "Keep it, Jemmy," he cried; "let's have no more murder done!"

They fare again through the horrible bush until nightfall, when Vetch, in a strange voice, called the giant to him.

"He must die."

"Either you or he," laughs Gabbett. "Give me the axe."

"No, no," said the Crow, his thin malignant face distorted by a horrible resolution. "I'll keep the axe. Stand back! You shall hold him, and I'll do the job."

Sanders, seeing them approach, knew his end had come, and submitted, crying, "Give me half an hour to pray for myself." They consent, and the bewildered wretch knelt down and folded his hands like a child. His big stupid face worked with emotion. His great cracked lips moved in desperate agony. He wagged his head from side to side, in pitiful confusion of his brutalized senses. "I can't think o' the words, Jem!"

"Pah," snarled the cripple, swinging the axe, "we can't starve here all night."

Four days had passed, and the two survivors of this awful journey sat watching each other. The gaunt giant, his eyes gleaming with hate and hunger, sat sentinel over the dwarf. The dwarf, chuckling at his superior sagacity, clutched the fatal axe. For two days they had not spoken to each other. For two days each had promised himself that on the next his companion must *sleep* — and die. Vetch comprehended the devilish scheme of the monster who had entrapped five of his fellow-beings to aid him by their deaths to his own safety, and held aloof.

Gabbett watched to snatch the weapon from his companion, and make the odds even for once and forever. In the daytime they traveled on, seeking each a pretext to creep behind the other. In the night-time when they feigned slumber, each stealthily raising a head caught the wakeful glance of his companion. Vetch felt his strength deserting him, and his brain overpowered by fatigue. Surely the giant, muttering, gesticulating, and slavering at the mouth, was on the road to madness. Would the monster find opportunity to rush at him, and braving the blood-stained axe, kill him by main force? or would he sleep, and be himself a victim? Unhappy Vetch! It is the terrible privilege of insanity to be sleepless.

On the fifth day, Vetch, creeping behind a tree, takes off his belt, and makes a noose. He will hang himself. He gets one end of the belt over a bough, and then his cowardice bids him pause. Gabbett approaches; he tries to evade him, and steal away into the bush. In vain. The insatiable giant, ravenous with famine and sustained by madness, is not to be shaken off. Vetch tries to run, but his legs bend under him. The axe that has tried to drink so much blood feels heavy as lead. He will fling it away. No — he dares not. Night falls again. He must rest, or go mad. His limbs are powerless. His eyelids are glued together. He sleeps as he stands. This horrible thing must be a dream. He is at Port Arthur, or will wake on his pallet in the penny lodging-house he slept at when a boy. Is that the deputy come to wake him to the torment of living? It is not time — surely not time yet. He sleeps — and the giant, grinning with ferocious joy, approaches on clumsy tiptoe and seizes the coveted axe.

On the northeast coast of Van Diemen's Land is a place called St. Helen's Point, and a certain skipper, being in want of fresh water, landing there with a boat's crew, found on the banks of the creek a gaunt and blood-stained man, clad in tattered yellow, who carried on his back an axe and a bundle. When the sailors came within sight of him he made signs to them to approach, and opening his bundle with much ceremony, offered them some of its contents. Filled with horror at what the maniac displayed, they seized and bound him. At Hobart Town he was recognized as the only survivor of the nine desperadoes who had escaped from Colonel Arthur's "natural penitentiary."

MATTHIAS CLAUDIUS

(1740–1815)

ATTHIAS CLAUDIUS, best known as "the Wandsbecker Bote" (the Messenger from Wandsbeck), was born at Reinfeld in Holstein, August 15th, 1740. He was of excellent stock, coming from a long line of clergymen. It was said that scarcely another family in Schleswig-Holstein had given to the church so many sons.

There is but little to record of the quiet boyhood passed in the picturesque stillness of the North German village. At the outset the

MATTHIAS CLAUDIUS

education of Claudius was conducted by his father, the village pastor. From beginning to end his life was simple, moderate, and well ordered. After finishing his school days at Ploen, he entered the University of Jena (1759), with the intention of studying theology, in order to follow the traditions of the family and enter the ministry. This idea he was soon obliged to relinquish on account of a pulmonary weakness, and he turned instead to the study of jurisprudence. His strongest attraction was towards literature. He became a member of the literary guild in Jena; and later, when he had attained fame as the "Wands-

becker Bote," he was intimately associated with Voss, F. L. Stolberg, Herder, and others of the Göttingen fraternity. His first verses, published in Jena in 1763, under the title 'Tändeleien und Erzählungen' (Trifles and Tales), gave no indication of his talents, and were no more than the usual student efforts of unconscious imitation; they have absolutely no poetic value, and are interesting only as they indicate a stage of development. In editing his works in later years, Claudius preserved of this early poetry only one song, 'An eine Quelle' (To a Spring).

After leaving the university in 1764, he took a position as private secretary to Count Holstein in Copenhagen; and here, under the powerful influence of Klopstock, whose friendship was at this time the most potent element of his life, and in the brilliant circle which that poet had drawn around him, Claudius entered fully into the life of sentiment and ideas which conduced so largely to his intellectual development. Some years later, after a fallow period spent in the quiet of his father's house at Reinfeld, he settled at Wandsbeck, near Altona (1771), where in connection with Bode he published the Wandsbecker Bote, the popular weekly periodical so indissolubly associated with his name. His contributions under the name of «Asmus» found everywhere the warmest acceptance. In 1775, through Herder's recommendation, Claudius was appointed Chief Land Commissioner at Darmstadt; but circumstances rendering the position uncongenial, he returned to his beloved Wandsbeck, where he supported his family by his pen until 1788, when Crown Prince Frederick of Denmark appointed him revisor of the Holstein Bank at Altona. He died in Hamburg, January 1st, 1815, in the house of his son-in-law, the bookseller Perthes.

A collection of his works, with the title 'Asmus omnia sua secum portans, oder Sämmtliche Werke des Wandsbecker Boten' (The Collected Works of the Wandsbeck Messenger), appeared at Hamburg, 1775–1812. These collected works comprise songs, romances, fables, poems, letters, etc., originally published in various places. The translation of Saint Martin and Fénelon marked the pietistic spirit of his later years, and is in strong contrast to the exuberance which produced the 'Rheinweinlied' (Rhine Wine Song) and 'Urian's Reise um die Welt' (Urian's Journey around the World).

Claudius as a poet won the hearts of his countrymen. His verses express his idyllic love of nature and his sympathy with rustic life. The poet and the man are one. His pure and simple style appealed to the popular taste, and some of his lyrics have become genuine folk-songs.

SPECULATIONS ON NEW YEAR'S DAY

From the Wandsbecker Bote

A HAPPY new year! A happy new year to my dear country, the land of old integrity and truth! A happy new year to friends and enemies, Christians and Turks, Hottentots and Cannibals! To all on whom God permits his sun to rise and his rain to fall! Also to the poor negro slaves who have to work all day in the hot sun. It's wholly a glorious day, the New Year's Day! At other times I can bear that a man should be a little bit patriotic, and not make court to other nations. True, one must not speak evil of any nation. The wiser part are everywhere silent; and who would revile a whole nation for the sake of the loud ones? As I said, I can bear at other times that a man should be a little patriotic: but on New Year's Day my patriotism is dead as a mouse, and it seems to me on that day as if we were all brothers, and had one Father who is in heaven; as if all the goods of the world were water which God has created for all men, as I once heard it said.

And so I am accustomed, every New Year's morning, to sit down on a stone by the wayside, to scratch with my staff in the sand before me, and to think of this and of that. Not of my readers. I hold them in all honor: but on New Year's morning, on the stone by the wayside, I think not of them; but I sit there and think that during the past year I saw the sun rise so often, and the moon,—that I saw so many rainbows and flowers, and breathed the air so often, and drank from the brook,—and then I do not like to look up, and I take with both hands my cap from my head and look into that.

Then I think also of my acquaintances who have died during the year; and how they can talk now with Socrates and Numa, and other men of whom I have heard so much good, and with John Huss. And then it seems as if graves opened round me, and shadows with bald crowns and long gray beards came out of them and shook the dust out of their beards. That must be the work of the "Everlasting Huntsman," who has his doings about the twelfth. The old pious long-beards would fain sleep. But a glad new year to your memory and to the ashes in your graves!

RHINE WINE

WITH laurel wreathe the glass's vintage mellow,
    And drink it gayly dry!
Through farthest Europe, know, my worthy fellow,
    For such in vain ye'll try.

Nor Hungary nor Poland e'er could boast it;
    And as for Gallia's vine,
Saint Veit the Ritter, if he choose, may toast it,—
    We Germans love the Rhine.

Our fatherland we thank for such a blessing,
    And many more beside;
And many more, though little show possessing,
    Well worth our love and pride.

Not everywhere the vine bedecks our border,
    As well the mountains show,
That harbor in their bosoms foul disorder;
    Not worth their room below.

Thuringia's hills, for instance, are aspiring
    To rear a juice like wine;
But that is all; nor mirth nor song inspiring,
    It breathes not of the vine.

And other hills, with buried treasures glowing,
    For wine are far too cold;
Though iron ores and cobalt there are growing,
    And 'chance some paltry gold.

The Rhine,— the Rhine,— there grow the gay plantations!
    Oh, hallowed be the Rhine!
Upon his banks are brewed the rich potations
    Of this consoling wine.

Drink to the Rhine! and every coming morrow
    Be mirth and music thine!
And when we meet a child of care and sorrow,
    We'll send him to the Rhine.

WINTER

A Song to Be Sung Behind the Stove

OLD Winter is the man for me —
    Stout-hearted, sound, and steady;
    Steel nerves and bones of brass hath he:
    Come snow, come blow, he's ready!

If ever man was well, 'tis he;
    He keeps no fire in his chamber,
And yet from cold and cough is free
    In bitterest December.

He dresses him out-doors at morn,
    Nor needs he first to warm him;
Toothache and rheumatis' he'll scorn,
    And colic don't alarm him.

In summer, when the woodland rings,
    He asks "What mean these noises?"

Warm sounds he hates, and all warm things
    Most heartily despises.

But when the fox's bark is loud;
    When the bright hearth is snapping;
When children round the chimney crowd,
    All shivering and clapping; —

When stone and bone with frost do break,
    And pond and lake are cracking, —
Then you may see his old sides shake,
    Such glee his frame is racking.

Near the North Pole, upon the strand,
    He has an icy tower;
Likewise in lovely Switzerland
    He keeps a summer bower.

So up and down — now here — now there —
    His regiments manœuvre;
When he goes by, we stand and stare,
    And cannot choose but shiver.

NIGHT SONG

THE moon is up in splendor,
    And golden stars attend her;
        The heavens are calm and bright;
Trees cast a deepening shadow;
And slowly off the meadow
    A mist is rising silver-white.

Night's curtains now are closing
Round half a world, reposing
    In calm and holy trust;
All seems one vast, still chamber,
Where weary hearts remember
    No more the sorrows of the dust.

                    Translations of Charles T. Brooks.

HENRY CLAY.

HENRY CLAY

(1777–1852)

BY JOHN R. PROCTER

ENRY CLAY must not be judged as an orator by his reported speeches, which are but skeletons of the masterly originals, but by the lasting effect of these speeches on those who heard them, and by his ability as an originator of important measures and his success in carrying these measures to a conclusion by convincing and powerful oratory. Judged by his achievements and by his wide-spread influence, he must take rank as a statesman and orator of pre-eminent ability. The son of a poor Baptist clergyman, with but scant advantages for acquiring an education; leaving home at an early age and going among strangers to a community where family ties and social connections were a controlling element;—this poor boy, with no family influence, assumed at once, by sheer force of character and ability, a leadership which he held undisputed until his death. And years after he had passed away, it was the "followers of Henry Clay" who kept Kentucky from joining the States of the South in their unsuccessful efforts to withdraw from the Union.

Of his oratory Robert C. Winthrop wrote after a lapse of years: "I can only bear witness to an impressiveness of speech never exceeded, if ever equaled, within an experience of half a century, during which I have listened to many of the greatest orators on both sides of the Atlantic." As a parliamentary leader, Rhodes calls him the greatest in our history. "His leadership," says Mr. Schurz, "was not of that mean order which merely contrives to organize a personal following; it was the leadership of a statesman zealously striving to promote great public interests."

As a presiding officer he was the most commanding Speaker the National House of Representatives has ever had. Winthrop, who served long with him in Congress, said of him:—"No abler or more commanding presiding officer ever sat in the Speaker's chair on either side of the Atlantic. Prompt, dignified, resolute, fearless, he had a combination of intellectual and physical qualities which made him a natural ruler over men." He was six times elected Speaker, sometimes almost by acclamation; and during the many years which he presided over the House not one of his decisions was ever reversed.

VII—236

As a Secretary of State, during his term of four years the treaties with foreign countries negotiated by him exceeded in numbers all that had been negotiated by other secretaries, during the previous thirty-five years of our constitutional history. As a diplomat, he showed himself at Ghent more than a match for the trained diplomatists of the old world.

And with all these he was—at his ideal country home, Ashland, surrounded by wooded lawns and fertile acres of beautiful blue-grass land—a most successful farmer and breeder of thoroughbred stock, from the Scotch collie to the thoroughbred race-horse. I have been told by one who knew him as a farmer that no one could guess nearer to the weight of a Shorthorn bullock than he. He was as much at home with horses and horsemen as with senators and diplomats. I have known many men who were friends and followers of Mr. Clay, and from the love and veneration these men had for his memory, I can well understand why the historian Rhodes says, "No man has been loved as the people of the United States loved Henry Clay."

Clay seemed to have had honors and leadership thrust upon him. Arriving in Kentucky in 1797, he at once advocated the gradual emancipation of slaves, regardless of the strong prejudices to the contrary of the rich slaveholding community in which he had cast his lot; yet, unsolicited on his part, this community elected him to the State Legislature by a large majority in 1803, and before three years of service he was chosen by his fellow members to fill a vacancy in the United States Senate. And until his death in 1852, his constituents in Kentucky vied with each other in their desires to keep him as their representative in either the national Senate or House of Representatives. He entered the latter in 1811, and was selected as Speaker of that body almost by acclamation on the first day of his taking his seat. After a long life spent in his country's service he was elected *unanimously* to the Senate in 1848, despite party strife and the fact that the two parties were almost evenly divided in Kentucky.

No attempt can here be made to even recapitulate the events of importance connected with his long public services. I will call attention only to some of the most important measures which he carried by his magnificent leadership.

WAR OF 1812

Clay assumed the leadership of those who urged resistance to the unjust and overbearing encroachments of Great Britain, and he more than any one else was instrumental in overcoming opposition and

forcing a declaration of war. This war — a second war for independence, which changed this country from a disjointed confederacy
liable to fall asunder, to a compact, powerful, and self-respecting
Union — will ever be regarded as one of the crowning glories of his
long and brilliant career. He proved more than a match in debate
for Randolph, Quincy, and other able advocates for peace. When
asked what we were to gain by war, he answered, "What are we not
to lose by peace? Commerce, character,— a nation's best treasure,
honor!"

In answer to the arguments that certificates of protection authorized by Congress were fraudulently used, his magnificent answer,
"The colors that float from the mast-head should be the credentials
of our seamen," electrified the patriots of the country. There is
but a meagre report of this great speech, but the effect produced was
overwhelming and bore down all opposition. It is said that men of
both parties, forgetting all antipathies under the spell of his eloquence, wept together. Mr. Clay's first speech on entering Congress
was in favor of the encouragement of domestic manufactures, mainly
as a defensive measure in anticipation of a war with Great Britain;
arguing that whatever doubts might be entertained as to the general
policy of encouraging domestic manufactures by import duties, none
could exist regarding the propriety of adopting measures for producing such articles as are requisite in times of war. If his measure for
the increase of the standing army had been adopted in time, the
humiliating reverses on land during the early part of the war would
have been averted. He carried through a bill for the increase of the
navy, and the brilliant naval victories of the war of 1812 followed.
In the debate on the bill to provide for a standing army, it was
argued that twenty-five thousand could not be had in the United
States. Clay aroused the people of Kentucky to such enthusiasm that
fifteen thousand men volunteered in that State alone, and members of
Congress shouldered their muskets and joined the ranks.

TREATY OF GHENT

Henry Clay's faith in the destiny of his country, and his heroic
determination that a continuation of the war was preferable to the
terms proposed, prevented humiliating concessions. The American
Commissioners were Henry Clay, John Quincy Adams, Albert Gallatin, James A. Bayard, and Jonathan Russell, and the British Commissioners Lord Gambier, Henry Goulbourn, and William Adams.
The news received by Clay on his arrival in Europe was not calculated to inspire him with hope. From Mr. Bayard he received a

letter (dated April 20th, 1814) with news of the triumph of the allies over Napoleon, and stating:—

« There is reason to think that it has materially changed the views of the British Ministry. . . . The great augmentation of their disposable force presents an additional temptation to prosecute the war. »

By the same mail Mr. Gallatin writes from London (April 22d, 1814):—

« You are sufficiently aware of the total change in our affairs produced by the late revolution, and by the restoration of universal peace in the European world, from which we are alone excluded. A well-organized and large army is at once liberated from any European employment, and ready, together with a superabundant naval force, to act independently against us. How ill prepared we are to meet it in a proper manner, no one knows better than yourself; but above all, our own divisions and the hostile attitude of the Eastern States give room to apprehend that a continuation of the war might prove vitally fatal to the United States. »

Mr. Russell writes from Stockholm (July 2d, 1814):—

« My distress at the delay which our joint errand has encountered has almost been intolerable, and the kind of comfort I have received from Mr. Adams has afforded very little relief. His apprehensions are rather of a gloomy cast with regard to the result of our labors. »

Mr. Crawford, our Minister to France, who with Clay favored a vigorous prosecution of the war, writes to him (July 4th, 1814):—

« I am thoroughly convinced that the United States can never be called upon to treat under circumstances less auspicious than those which exist at the present moment, unless our internal bickerings shall continue to weaken the effects of the government. »

With discouraging news from home, the seat of government taken, and the Capitol burned, the Eastern States opposing the war and threatening to withdraw from the Union, and his fellow commissioners in the despondent mood evidenced by the above-quoted letters,— it is amazing that Clay, whom some historians have called a compromiser by nature, opposed any and all concessions and wished that the war should go on.

By the third article of the treaty of 1783 it was agreed that citizens of the United States should not fish in the waters or cure fish on the land of any of the maritime provinces north of the United States after they were settled, without a previous agreement with the inhabitants or possessors of the ground.

By the eighth article of the same treaty, it was agreed that the navigation of the Mississippi River should *ever* remain free and open to the subjects of Great Britain and the United States. It was then supposed that the British Canadian possessions included the head-waters of this river. By the Jay treaty of 1794 this was confirmed, and "that all ports and places on its eastern side, to whichsoever of the parties belonging, might be freely resorted to and used by both parties." At this time Spain possessed the sovereignty of the west side of the river, and both sides from its mouth to 31° north latitude. The United States acquired by the Louisiana purchase of 1803 all the sovereignty of Spain which had previously been acquired by France.

Gallatin proposed to insert a provision for the renewal to the United States of the rights in the fisheries, and as an equivalent to give to Great Britain the right to the navigation of the Mississippi River. This was favored by Gallatin, Adams, and Bayard, and opposed by Clay and Russell. Mr. Clay, seeing that he was in a minority, stated that he would affix his name to no treaty which contained such a provision. After his firm stand Mr. Bayard left the majority. Clay's "obstinacy" in opposing concessions is well shown in Mr. Adams's Journal:—

"To this last article [the right of the British to navigate the Mississippi River] Mr. Clay makes strong objections. He is willing to leave the matter of the fisheries as a nest-egg for another war. . . . He considers it a privilege much too important to be conceded for the mere liberty of drying fish upon a desert, but the Mississippi was destined to form a most important part of the interests of the American Union. . . . Mr. Clay, of all the members, had alone been urgent to present an article stipulating the abolition of impressment. Mr. Clay lost his temper, as he generally does whenever the right of the British to navigate the Mississippi is discussed. . . .

"December 11th. He [Clay] was for war three years longer. He had no doubt but three years more of war would make us a warlike people, and that then we should come out of the war with honor. . . . December 22d. At last he turned to me, and asked me whether I would not join him now and break off negotiations."

After five months of weary negotiations under most adverse conditions so far as the American commissioners were concerned, the treaty was signed on December 24th, 1814. During all these months Clay had resisted any and all concessions, and none were made. The Marquis of Wellesley declared in the House of Lords that the American commissioners had shown a most astonishing superiority over the British during the whole of the correspondence.

During Mr. Clay's absence at Ghent, his admiring constituents returned him to Congress by an almost unanimous vote. A year later in Congress, Clay referred to his part in the bringing on the war as follows:—

"I gave a vote for a declaration of war. I exerted all the little influence and talent I could command to make the war. The war was made. It is terminated. And I declare with perfect sincerity, if it had been permitted to me to lift the veil of futurity and to foresee the precise series of events which had occurred, my vote would have been unchanged. We had been insulted and outraged and spoliated upon by almost all Europe,— by Great Britain, by France, Spain, Denmark, Naples, and to cap the climax, by the little contemptible power of Algiers. We had submitted too long and too much. We had become the scorn of foreign powers and the derision of our own citizens. What have we gained by the war? Let any man look at the degraded condition of this country before the war, the scorn of the universe, the contempt of ourselves; and tell me if we have gained nothing by the war? What is our situation now? Respectability and character abroad, security and confidence at home."

Clay more than any other man forced the war. It was the successful military hero of this war—the victor of New Orleans—who defeated him in after years for the Presidency.

MISSOURI COMPROMISE

The heated struggle in Congress over the admission of Missouri into the Union first brought prominently forward the agitation of the slavery question. This struggle, which lasted from 1818 to 1821, threatened the very existence of the Union. Jefferson wrote from Monticello:—

"The Missouri question is the most portentous one that has ever threatened the Union. In the gloomiest moments of the Revolutionary War I never had any apprehension equal to that I feel from this source."

Mr. Schurz, writing of the feeling at the time, says:—

"While thus the thought of dissolving the Union occurred readily to the Southern mind, the thought of maintaining the government and preserving the Union by means of force hardly occurred to anybody. It seemed to be taken for granted on all sides that if the Southern States insisted on cutting loose from the Union, nothing could be done but to let them go."

The two sections were at this time so evenly balanced that the maintenance of the Union by force could not have been successfully attempted. The compromise which admitted Missouri to the Union as a slave State, and recognized the right of settlers to carry slaves into the territory south of 36° 30', was carried through by the splendid leadership of Clay, who thus earned the title of "the great pacificator.» Future historians will accord to him the title of the savior of the Union.

Upon the adoption of the compromise measures Mr. Clay resigned his seat in Congress to give his attention to his private affairs, being financially embarrassed by indorsing for a friend. During his stay at home there was a fierce controversy over the issue of paper money and relief measures to favor debtors who had become involved through the recklessness following such inflation. Against what seemed to be an overwhelming popular feeling, Clay arrayed himself on the side of sound money and sound finance. In 1823 he was again returned to the House of Representatives without opposition, and was chosen Speaker by a vote of 139 to 42.

INTERNAL IMPROVEMENTS

Soon after his entrance into Congress Clay took advanced ground in favor of building roads, improving water-ways, and constructing canals by the general government, in order to connect the seaboard States with the «boundless empire» of the growing West. He became the leader, the foremost champion, of a system which was bitterly opposed by some of the ablest statesmen of the time as unauthorized by the Constitution. Clay triumphed, and during his long public service was the recognized leader of a system which though opposed at first, has been accepted as a national policy by both of the great political parties. That he was actuated by a grand conception of the future destiny of the country, and the needs of such improvements to insure a more perfect union, his able speeches on these questions will show. In one he said:—

«Every man who looks at the Constitution in the spirit to entitle him to the character of statesman, must elevate his views to the height to which this nation is destined to reach in the rank of nations. We are not legislating for this moment only, or for the present generation, or for the present populated limits of the United States; but our acts must embrace a wider scope,— reaching northward to the Pacific and southwardly to the river Del Norte. Imagine this extent of territory with sixty or seventy or a hundred millions of people. The powers which exist now will exist then; and those which will exist then exist now. . . . What was the object of the Convention in framing the Constitution? The leading object was UNION,— Union, then peace. Peace external and internal, and commerce, but more particularly union and peace, the great objects of the framers of the Constitution, should be kept steadily in view in the interpretation of any clause of it; and when it is susceptible of various interpretation, that construction should be preferred which tends to promote the objects of the framers of the Constitution, to the consolidation of the Union. . . . No man deprecates more than I do the idea of consolidation; yet between separation and consolidation, painful as would be the alternative, I should greatly prefer the latter.»

Congress now appropriates yearly for internal improvements a sum far greater than the entire revenue of the government at the time Clay made this speech.

SPANISH-AMERICAN INDEPENDENCE

It was but natural that Clay's ardent nature and his love of liberty would incline him to aid the people of Central and South America in their efforts to free themselves from Spanish oppression and misrule. Effective here as in all things undertaken by him, his name must always be linked with the cause of Southern American independence. Richard Rush, writing from London to Clay in 1825, says: "The South-Americans owe to you, more than to any other man of either hemisphere, their independence." His speeches, translated into Spanish, were read to the revolutionary armies, and "his name was a household name among the patriots." Bolivar, writing to him from Bogotá in 1827, says:—"All America, Colombia, and myself, owe your Excellency our purest gratitude for the incomparable services which you have rendered to us, by sustaining our cause with sublime enthusiasm."

In ne of his speeches on this subject Clay foreshadows a great America Zollverein. The failure of the Spanish-American republics to attain the high ideals hoped for by Clay caused him deep regret in after years.

THE AMERICAN SYSTEM

The tariff law of 1824 was another triumph of Clay's successful leadership, since which time he has been called the father of what has been termed the "American System." It must be remembered that Clay was first led to propose protective duties in order to prepare this country for a war which he felt could not be avoided without loss of national honor. When in 1824 he advocated increased tariff duties in order to foster home industries, protection was universal; even our agricultural products were excluded from British markets by the Corn Laws. The man who would now advocate in Congress duties as low as those levied by the tariff law of 1824, would be called by protectionists of the present day a free-trader. When in 1833 nullification of the tariff laws was threatened, Clay, while demanding that the laws should be enforced and that if necessary nullification should be put down by the strong arm of the government, feared that the growing discontent of the South and the obstinacy of a military President threatened the Union, introduced and carried to a conclusion a compromise tariff measure that brought peace to the country.

SECRETARY OF STATE

It was unfortunate that Clay temporarily relinquished his leadership in Congress to accept the premiership in the Cabinet of President Adams. Although the exacting official duties were not congenial, and proved injurious to his health, his administration of this high office was brilliant and able, as is well attested by the number of important treaties concluded, and by his brilliant state papers. His instructions to the United States delegates to the Panama Congress of American Republics will grow in importance in the years to come, because of the broad principles there enunciated,— that private property should be exempt from seizure on the high seas in times of war.

His chivalrous loyalty to President Adams was fully appreciated, and his friendship reciprocated. After the close of his administration Mr. Adams in a speech said:—

«As to my motives for tendering him the Department of State when I did, let the man who questions them come forward. Let him look around among the statesmen and legislators of the nation and of that day. Let him select and name the man whom, by his pre-eminent talents, by his splendid services, by his ardent patriotism, by his all-embracing public spirit, by his fervid eloquence in behalf of the rights and liberties of mankind, by his long experience in the affairs of the Union, foreign and domestic, a President of the United States intent only upon the honor and welfare of his country ought to have preferred to Henry Clay.»

Just before the close of his administration President Adams offered him a position on the bench of the Supreme Court, which he declined.

HIS POSITION ON AFRICAN SLAVERY

Clay was a slaveholder,— a kind master,— but through his entire public life an open advocate of emancipation. He probably received his early predilections against slavery from his association with Chancellor Wythe, before removing from Virginia, as indeed the best part of his education probably came from personal contact with that able man. The intellectual forces of the border slave States were arrayed in favor of emancipation, until, as Clay writes with some feeling in 1849, they were driven to an opposite course "by the violent and indiscreet course of ultra abolitionists in the North"; but Clay remained to his death hopeful that by peaceable means his country might be rid of this great evil. In the letter above quoted, writing of his failure to establish a system of gradual emancipation in Kentucky, he says:—

« It is a consoling reflection that although a system of gradual emancipation cannot be established, slavery is destined inevitably to extinction by the operation of peaceful and natural causes. And it is also gratifying to believe that there will not be probably much difference in the period of its existence, whether it terminates legally or naturally. The chief difference in the two modes is that according to the first, we should take hold of the institution intelligently and dispose of it cautiously and safely; while according to the other it will some day or other take hold of us, and constrain us in some manner or other to get rid of it. »

As early as 1798, he made his first political speeches in Kentucky advocating an amendment to the State Constitution, providing for the gradual emancipation of the slaves. Referring to the failure to adopt this amendment, he said in a speech delivered in the capital of Kentucky in 1829: —

« I shall never cease to regret a decision, the effects of which have been to place us in the rear of our neighbors who are exempt from slavery, in the state of agriculture, the progress of manufactures, the advance of improvements, and the general progress of society. »

In these days, when public men who should be leaders bend to what they believe to be the popular wishes, the example of Clay, in his bold disregard of the prejudices and property interests of his constituents, is inspiring.

George W. Prentice was sent from New England to Kentucky to write a life of Clay, and writing in 1830 he says: —

« Whenever a slave brought an action at law for his liberty, Mr. Clay volunteered as his advocate, and it is said that in the whole course of his practice he never failed to obtain a verdict in the slave's favor. . . . He has been the slaves' friend through life. In all stations he has pleaded the cause of African freedom without fear from high or low. To him more than to any other individual is to be ascribed the great revolution which has taken place upon this subject — a revolution whose wheels must continue to move onward till they reach the goal of universal freedom. »

Three years before this was written, Clay in a speech before the Colonization Society said: —

« If I could be instrumental in eradicating this deepest stain upon the character of my country, and removing all cause of reproach on account of it by foreign nations; if I could only be instrumental in ridding of this foul blot that revered State which gave me birth, or that not less beloved State which kindly adopted me as her son, I would not exchange the proud satisfaction which I should enjoy for the honor of all the triumphs ever decreed to the most successful conqueror. »

He longed to add the imperial domain of Texas to this country, but feared that it would so strengthen the slave power as to endanger the Union; and when finally he yielded to the inevitable, the Free-Soilers threw their votes to Birney and thus defeated Clay for the Presidency. He deprecated the war with Mexico, yet gave his favorite son as a soldier, who fell at Buena Vista. He stood for the reception of anti-slavery petitions by Congress, against the violent opposition of the leading men of his own section. He continued steadfast to the end, writing in 1849 that if slavery were, as claimed, a blessing, "the principle on which it is maintained would require that one portion of the white race should be reduced to bondage to serve another portion of the same race, when black subjects of slavery could not be obtained." He proposed reasonable schemes for gradual emancipation and deportation, which would, if adopted, have averted the war and settled peaceably the serious problem. He warned the Southerners in 1849 that their demands were unreasonable, and would "lead to the formation of a sectional Northern party, which will sooner or later take permanent and exclusive possession of the Government."

Seeming inconsistencies in Mr. Clay's record on this subject will disappear with a full understanding of the difficulties of his position. Living in a State midway between the North and South, where slavery existed in its mildest and least objectionable form, yet fully alive to its evils, recognizing that the grave problem requiring solution was not alone slavery, but the presence among a free people of a numerous, fecund, servile, alien race; realizing that one section of the country, then relatively too powerful to be ignored, was ready to withdraw from the Union rather than to submit to laws that would endanger slavery; loving the Union with an ardor not excelled by that of any public man in our history; wishing and striving for the emancipation of the slaves, yet too loyal to the Union to follow the more zealous advocates of freedom in their "higher law than the Constitution" crusade,— Mr. Clay in his whole course on this question was consistent and patriotic in the highest degree.

THE COMPROMISE OF 1850

The crowning triumph of a long life of great achievements was his great compromise measures of 1850. These, with their predecessors of 1821 and 1833, have caused some writers to speak of Clay as a man of compromising nature. The reverse is true. Bold, aggressive, uncompromising, and often dictatorial by nature, he favored compromise when convinced that only by such means could civil war or a disruption of the Union be averted. And he was right. He averted a conflict or separation from the Union when the relative strength of the South was such as to have rendered impossible the preservation of the Union by force. The Constitution was a compromise, without which there would have been no union of States. That the compromise did not long survive him was no fault of Clay's, but chargeable to the agitators of both sections, who cared less for the Union than for their pet theories or selfish interests.

Two years after his death the compromise measures were repealed, and the most destructive civil war of modern times and a long list of resultant evils are the result. Those who knew Henry Clay and had felt his wonderful power as a leader, are firm in the belief that had he been alive and in the possession of his faculties in 1861, the Civil War would have been averted. His name and the memory of his love for the Union restrained his adopted State from joining the South.

The struggle over the passage of the compromise measures, lasting for seven months, was one of the most memorable parliamentary struggles on record. The old hero, Henry Clay, broken in health, with the stamp of death upon him, for six weary months led the fight with much of his old-time fire and ability. Sustained by indomitable will and supreme love of country, "I am here," he said, "expecting soon to go hence, and owing no responsibility but to my own conscience and to God."

In his opening speech, which lasted for two days, he said:—

"I owe it to myself to say that no earthly power could induce me to vote for a specific measure for the introduction of slavery where it had not before existed, either south or north of that line. Sir, while you reproach, and justly too, our British ancestors for the introduction of this institution upon the continent of America, I am for one unwilling that the posterity of the present inhabitants of California and New Mexico shall reproach us for doing just what we reproach Great Britain for doing to us."

He upbraided on the one hand the ultra abolitionists as reckless agitators, and hurled defiance at disunionists of the South, while at the same time appealing to the loftier nature and patriotic impulses of his hearers:—

"I believe from the bottom of my soul that this measure is the reunion of the Union. And now let us discard all resentments, all passions, all petty jealousies, all personal desires, all love of peace, all hungering after gilded crumbs which fall from the table of power. Let us forget popular fears, from whatever quarter they may spring. Let us go to the fountain of unadulterated patriotism, and performing a solemn lustration, return divested of all selfish, sinister, and sordid impurities, and think alone of our God, our country, our conscience, and our glorious Union."

As described by Bancroft, Clay was "in stature over six feet, spare and long-limbed; he stood erect as if full of vigor and vitality, and ever ready to command. His countenance expressed perpetual wakefulness and activity. His voice was music itself, and yet penetrating and far-reaching, enchanting the listeners; his words flowed rapidly without sing-song or mannerism, in a clear and steady stream. Neither in public nor in private did he know how to be dull."

Bold, fearless, commanding, the lordliest leader of his day, he was yet gentle, and as an old friend wrote, "was the most emotional man I ever knew. I have seen his eyes fill instantly on shaking the hand of an old friend, however obscure, who had stood by him in his early struggles." The manliest of men, yet his voice would tremble with emotion on reading aloud from a letter the love messages from a little grandchild.

The following, told me by a gentleman who knew Mr. Clay, illustrates the true gentleman he was:—

"When I was a small boy my father took me with him to visit Mr. Clay at his home Ashland. We found some gentlemen there who had been invited to dinner. Just before they went in to dinner my father told me privately to run out and play on the lawn while they were dining. As the gentlemen came out, Mr. Clay saw me, and calling me to him said, 'My young friend, I owe you an apology.' Turning to the gentlemen he said, 'Go into the library, gentlemen, and light your cigars—I will join you presently.' Taking me by the hand he returned with me to the table, ordered the servants to attend to my wants, and conversed most delightfully with me until I had finished my dinner."

He had the faculty of making friends and holding them through life by ties which no circumstances or conditions could sever.

When Clay passed away there was no one whose Unionism embraced all sections, who could stand between the over-zealous advocates of abolition of slavery on the one side and the fiery defenders of the "divine institution" on the other. Sectionalism ran riot, and civil war was the result. During the many years when the North and South were divided on the question of slavery, and sectional feeling ran high, Henry Clay was the only man in public life whose broad nationalism and intense love for the Union embraced all sections, with no trace of sectional bias. He can well be called "The Great American."

John K. Porter

PUBLIC SPIRIT IN POLITICS

From a Speech at Buffalo, July 17th, 1839

ARE we not then called upon by the highest duties to our country, to its free institutions, to posterity, and to the world, to rise above all local prejudices and personal partialities, to discard all collateral questions, to disregard every subordinate point, and in a genuine spirit of compromise and concession, uniting heart and hand to preserve for ourselves the blessings of a free government, wisely, honestly, and faithfully administered, and as we received them from our fathers, to transmit them to our children? Should we not justly subject ourselves to eternal reproach, if we permitted our differences about mere men to bring defeat and disaster upon our cause? Our principles are imperishable, but men have but a fleeting existence, and are themselves liable to change and corruption during its brief continuance.

ON THE GREEK STRUGGLE FOR INDEPENDENCE

From a Speech in 1824

ARE we so mean, so base, so despicable, that we may not attempt to express our horror, utter our indignation, at the most brutal and atrocious war that ever stained earth or shocked high Heaven? at the ferocious deeds of a savage and infuriated soldiery, stimulated and urged on by the clergy of a fanatical and inimical religion, and rioting in all the excesses of blood and butchery, at the mere details of which the heart sickens and recoils?

If the great body of Christendom can look on calmly and coolly while all this is perpetrated on a Christian people, in its own immediate vicinity, in its very presence, let us at least evince that one of its remote extremities is susceptible of sensibility to Christian wrongs, and capable of sympathy for Christian sufferings; that in this remote quarter of the world there are hearts not yet closed against compassion for human woes, that can pour out their indignant feelings at the oppression of a people endeared to us by every ancient recollection and every modern tie. Sir, attempts have been made to alarm the

committee by the dangers to our commerce in the Mediterranean; and a wretched invoice of figs and opium has been
spread before us to repress our sensibilities and to eradicate our
humanity. Ah, sir! "What shall it profit a man if he gain the
whole world and lose his own soul?" or what shall it avail a
nation to save the whole of a miserable trade and lose its liberties?

SOUTH-AMERICAN INDEPENDENCE AS RELATED TO THE UNITED STATES

From a Speech before the House of Representatives in 1818

IT is the doctrine of thrones that man is too ignorant to govern himself. Their partisans assert his incapacity, in reference to all nations; if they cannot command universal assent
to the proposition, it is then demanded as to particular nations;
and our pride and our presumption too often make converts of
us. I contend that it is to arraign the dispositions of Providence
himself, to suppose that he has created beings incapable of
governing themselves, and to be trampled on by kings. Self-
government is the natural government of man, and for proof I
refer to the aborigines of our own land. Were I to speculate in
hypotheses unfavorable to human liberty, my speculations should
be founded rather upon the vices, refinements, or density of
population. Crowded together in compact masses, even if they
were philosophers, the contagion of the passions is communicated and caught, and the effect too often, I admit, is the overthrow of liberty. Dispersed over such an immense space as that
on which the people of Spanish America are spread, their physical and I believe also their moral condition both favor their
liberty.

With regard to their superstition, they worship the same God
with us. Their prayers are offered up in their temples to the
same Redeemer whose intercession we expect to save us. Nor
is there anything in the Catholic religion unfavorable to freedom. All religions united with government are more or less
inimical to liberty. All separated from government are compatible with liberty. If the people of Spanish America have not
already gone as far in religious toleration as we have, the difference in their condition from ours should not be forgotten.

Everything is progressive; and in time I hope to see them imitating in this respect our example. But grant that the people of Spanish America are ignorant, and incompetent for free government; to whom is that ignorance to be ascribed? Is it not to the execrable system of Spain, which she seeks again to establish and to perpetuate? So far from chilling our hearts, it ought to increase our solicitude for our unfortunate brethren. It ought to animate us to desire the redemption of the minds and bodies of unborn millions from the brutifying effects of a system whose tendency is to stifle the faculties of the soul, and to degrade them to the level of beasts. I would invoke the spirits of our departed fathers. Was it for yourselves only that you nobly fought? No, no! It was the chains that were forging for your posterity that made you fly to arms; and scattering the elements of these chains to the winds, you transmitted to us the rich inheritance of liberty.

FROM THE VALEDICTORY TO THE SENATE, DELIVERED IN 1842

FROM 1806, the period of my entrance upon this noble theatre, with short intervals, to the present time, I have been engaged in the public councils at home or abroad. Of the services rendered during that long and arduous period of my life it does not become me to speak; history, if she deign to notice me, and posterity, if the recollection of my humble actions shall be transmitted to posterity, are the best, the truest, and the most impartial judges. When death has closed the scene, their sentence will be pronounced, and to that I commit myself. My public conduct is a fair subject for the criticism and judgment of my fellow men; but the motives by which I have been prompted are known only to the great Searcher of the human heart and to myself; and I trust I may be pardoned for repeating a declaration made some thirteen years ago, that whatever errors — and doubtless there have been many — may be discovered in a review of my public service, I can with unshaken confidence appeal to that divine Arbiter for the truth of the declaration that I have been influenced by no impure purpose, no personal motive; have sought no personal aggrandizement; but that in all my public acts I have had a single eye directed and a warm and devoted heart dedicated to what, in my best judgment, I believed the true interests, the honor, the union, and the happiness of my country required.

During that long period, however, I have not escaped the fate of other public men, nor failed to incur censure and detraction of the bitterest, most unrelenting, and most malignant character; and though not always insensible to the pain it was meant to inflict, I have borne it in general with composure and without disturbance, waiting as I have done, in perfect and undoubting confidence, for the ultimate triumph of justice and of truth, and in the entire persuasion that time would settle all things as they should be; and that whatever wrong or injustice I might experience at the hands of man, He to whom all hearts are open and fully known, would by the inscrutable dispensations of His providence rectify all error, redress all wrong, and cause ample justice to be done.

But I have not meanwhile been unsustained. Everywhere throughout the extent of this great continent I have had cordial, warm-hearted, faithful, and devoted friends, who have known me, loved me, and appreciated my motives. To them, if language were capable of fully expressing my acknowledgments, I would now offer all the return I have the power to make for their genuine, disinterested, and persevering fidelity and devoted attachment, the feelings and sentiments of a heart overflowing with never-ceasing gratitude. If, however, I fail in suitable language to express my gratitude to them for all the kindness they have shown me, what shall I say, what can I say, at all commensurate with those feelings of gratitude with which I have been inspired by the State whose humble representative and servant I have been in this chamber?

I emigrated from Virginia to the State of Kentucky now nearly forty-five years ago; I went as an orphan boy who had not yet attained the age of majority; who had never recognized a father's smile, nor felt his warm caresses; poor, penniless, without the favor of the great, with an imperfect and neglected education, hardly sufficient for the ordinary business and common pursuits of life; but scarce had I set my foot upon her generous soil when I was embraced with parental fondness, caressed as though I had been a favorite child, and patronized with liberal and unbounded munificence. From that period the highest honors of the State have been freely bestowed upon me; and when in the darkest hour of calumny and detraction

I seemed to be assailed by all the rest of the world, she inter-posed her broad and impenetrable shield, repelled the poisoned shafts that were aimed for my destruction, and vindicated my good name from every malignant and unfounded aspersion. I return with indescribable pleasure to linger a while longer, and mingle with the warm-hearted and whole-souled people of that State; and when the last scene shall forever close upon me, I hope that my earthly remains will be laid under her green sod with those of her gallant and patriotic sons. . . .

That my nature is warm, my temper ardent, my disposition — especially in relation to the public service — enthusiastic, I am ready to own; and those who suppose that I have been assuming the dictatorship, have only mistaken for arrogance or assumption that ardor and devotion which are natural to my constitution, and which I may have displayed with too little regard to cold, calculating, and cautious prudence, in sustaining and zealously supporting important national measures of policy which I have presented and espoused. . . .

I go from this place under the hope that we shall mutually consign to perpetual oblivion whatever personal collisions may at any time unfortunately have occurred between us; and that our recollections shall dwell in future only on those conflicts of mind with mind, those intellectual struggles, those noble exhibitions of the powers of logic, argument, and eloquence, honorable to the Senate and to the nation, in which each has sought and con-tended for what he deemed the best mode of accomplishing one common object, the interest and the most happiness of our beloved country. To these thrilling and delightful scenes it will be my pleasure and my pride to look back in my retirement with unmeasured satisfaction. . . .

May the most precious blessings of Heaven rest upon the whole Senate and each member of it, and may the labors of every one redound to the benefit of the nation and to the advancement of his own fame and renown. And when you shall retire to the bosom of your constituents, may you receive the most cheering and gratifying of all human rewards,— their cor-dial greeting of "Well done, good and faithful servant."

FROM THE LEXINGTON 'SPEECH ON RETIREMENT TO PRIVATE LIFE'

IT WOULD neither be fitting, nor is it my purpose, to pass judgment on all the acts of my public life; but I hope I shall be excused for one or two observations which the occasion appears to me to authorize.

I never but once changed my opinion on any great measure of national policy, or on any great principle of construction of the national Constitution. In early life, on deliberate consideration, I adopted the principles of interpreting the federal Constitution which have been so ably developed and enforced by Mr. Madison in his memorable report to the Virginia Legislature; and to them, as I understood them, I have constantly adhered. Upon the question coming up in the Senate of the United States to re-charter the first Bank of the United States, thirty years ago, I opposed the re-charter upon convictions which I honestly entertained. The experience of the war which shortly followed, the condition into which the currency of the country was thrown without a bank, and I may now add, later and more disastrous experience, convinced me I was wrong. I publicly stated to my constituents, in a speech in Lexington (that which I made in the House of Representatives of the United States not having been reported), my reasons for that change, and they are preserved in the archives of the country. I appeal to that record, and I am willing to be judged now and hereafter by their validity.

I do not advert to the fact of this solitary instance of change of opinion as implying any personal merit, but because it is a fact. I will however say that I think it very perilous to the utility of any public man to make frequent changes of opinion, or any change, but upon grounds so sufficient and palpable that the public can clearly see and approve them. If we could look through a window into the human breast and there discover the causes which led to changes of opinion, they might be made without hazard. But as it is impossible to penetrate the human heart and distinguish between the sinister and honest motives which prompt it, any public man that changes his opinion, once deliberately formed and promulgated, under other circumstances than those which I have stated, draws around him distrust, impairs the public confidence, and lessens his capacity to serve his country.

I will take this occasion now to say, that I am and have been long satisfied that it would have been wiser and more politic in me to have declined accepting the office of Secretary of State in 1825. Not that my motives were not as pure and as patriotic as ever carried any man into public office. Not that the calumny which was applied to the fact was not as gross and as unfounded as any that was ever propagated. Not that valued friends and highly esteemed opponents did not unite in urging my acceptance of the office. Not that the administration of Mr. Adams will not, I sincerely believe, advantageously compare with any of his predecessors, in economy, purity, prudence, and wisdom. Not that Mr. Adams was himself wanting in any of those high qualifications and upright and patriotic intentions which were suited to the office. . . .

But my error in accepting the office arose out of my underrating the power of detraction and the force of ignorance, and abiding with too sure a confidence in the conscious integrity and uprightness of my own motives. Of that ignorance I had a remarkable and laughable example on an occasion which I will relate. I was traveling in 1828 through — I believe it was Spottsylvania County in Virginia, on my return to Washington, in company with some young friends. We halted at night at a tavern, kept by an aged gentleman who, I quickly perceived from the disorder and confusion which reigned, had not the happiness to have a wife. After a hurried and bad supper the old gentleman sat down by me, and without hearing my name, but understanding that I was from Kentucky, remarked that he had four sons in that State, and that he was very sorry they were divided in politics, two being for Adams and two for Jackson; he wished they were all for Jackson. "Why?" I asked him.— "Because," he said, "that fellow Clay, and Adams, had cheated Jackson out of the Presidency." — "Have you ever seen any evidence, my old friend," said I, "of that?" — "No," he replied, "none," and he wanted to see none. "But," I observed, looking him directly and steadily in the face, "suppose Mr. Clay were to come here and assure you upon his honor that it was all a vile calumny, and not a word of truth in it, would you believe him?" — "No," replied the old gentleman, promptly and emphatically. I said to him in conclusion, "Will you be good enough to show me to bed?" and bade him good-night. The next morning, having in the interval learned my name, he came to me full of apologies; but I at once put him at his ease by assuring him that I did not feel in the slightest degree hurt or offended with him. . . .

If to have served my country during a long series of years with fervent zeal and unshaken fidelity, in seasons of peace and war, at home and abroad, in the legislative halls and in an executive department; if to have labored most sedulously to avert the embarrassment and distress which now overspread this Union, and when they came, to have exerted myself anxiously at the extra session, and at this, to devise healing remedies; if to have desired to introduce economy and reform in the general administration, curtail enormous executive power, and amply provide at the same time for the wants of the government and the wants of the people, by a tariff which would give it revenue and then protection; if to have earnestly sought to establish the bright but too rare example of a party in power faithful to its promises and pledges made when out of power: if these services, exertions, and endeavors justify the accusation of ambition, I must plead guilty to the charge.

I have wished the good opinion of the world; but I defy the most malignant of my enemies to show that I have attempted to gain it by any low or groveling arts, by any mean or unworthy sacrifices, by the violation of any of the obligations of honor, or by a breach of any of the duties which I owed to my country. . . .

How is this right of the people to abolish an existing government, and to set up a new one, to be practically exercised? Our revolutionary ancestors did not tell us by words, but they proclaimed it by gallant and noble deeds. Who are the people that are to tear up the whole fabric of human society, whenever and as often as caprice or passion may prompt them? When all the arrangements and ordinances of existing organized society are prostrated and subverted, as must be supposed in such a lawless and irregular movement as that in Rhode Island, the established privileges and distinctions between the sexes, between the colors, between the ages, between natives and foreigners, between the sane and the insane, and between the innocent and the guilty convict, all the offspring of positive institutions, are cast down and abolished, and society is thrown into one heterogeneous and unregulated mass. And is it contended that the

major part of this Babel congregation is invested with the right
to build up at its pleasure a new government? that as often,
and whenever, society can be drummed up and thrown into
such a shapeless mass, the major part of it may establish another
and another new government in endless succession? Why, this
would overturn all social organization, make revolutions — the
extreme and last resort of an oppressed people — the commonest
occurrences of human life, and the standing order of the day.
How such a principle would operate in a certain section of this
Union, with a peculiar population, you will readily conceive.
No community could endure such an intolerable state of things
anywhere, and all would sooner or later take refuge from such
ceaseless agitation in the calm repose of absolute despotism. . . .

Fellow-citizens of all parties! The present situation of our
country is one of unexampled distress and difficulty; but
there is no occasion for any despondency. A kind and bountiful
Providence has never deserted us; punished us he perhaps has,
for our neglect of his blessings and our misdeeds. We have a
varied and fertile soil, a genial climate, and free institutions.
Our whole land is covered in profusion with the means of subsistence and the comforts of life. Our gallant ship, it is unfortunately true, lies helpless, tossed on a tempestuous sea amid
the conflicting billows of contending parties, without a rudder
and without a faithful pilot. But that ship is our country,
embodying all our past glory, all our future hopes. Its crew is
our whole people, by whatever political denomination they are
known. If she goes down, we all go down together. Let us
remember the dying words of the gallant and lamented Law-
rence, "Don't give up the ship." The glorious banner of our
country, with its unstained stars and stripes, still proudly floats
at its mast-head. With stout hearts and strong arms we can
surmount all our difficulties. Let us all, all, rally round that
banner, and finally resolve to perpetuate our liberties and regain
our lost prosperity.

Whigs! Arouse from the ignoble supineness which encom-
passes you; awake from the lethargy in which you lie bound;
cast from you that unworthy apathy which seems to make you
indifferent to the fate of your country. Arouse! awake! shake
off the dewdrops that glitter on your garments, and once more
march to battle and to victory. You have been disappointed,
deceived, betrayed; shamefully deceived and betrayed. But will

you therefore also prove false and faithless to your country, or obey the impulses of a just and patriotic indignation? As for Captain Tyler, he is a mere snap, a flash in the pan; pick your Whig flints and try your rifles again.

From 'The Speeches of Henry Clay; Edited by Calvin Colton.' Copyright, 1857, by A. S. Barnes and Company.

CLEANTHES

(331–232 B. C.)

CLEANTHES, the immediate successor of Zeno, the founder of Stoicism, was born at Assos, in the Troad, in B. C. 331. Of his early life we know nothing, except that he was for a time a prize-fighter. About the age of thirty he came to Athens with less than a dollar in his pocket, and entered the school of Zeno, where he remained for some nineteen years. At one time the Court of Areopagus, not seeing how he could make an honest livelihood, summoned him to appear before it and give an account of himself. He did so, bringing with him his employers, who proved that he spent much of the night in carrying water for gardens, or in kneading dough. The court, filled with admiration, offered him a pension, which he refused by the advice of his master, who thought the practice of self-dependence and strong endurance an essential part of education. Cleanthes's mind was slow of comprehension but extremely retentive; like a hard tablet, Zeno said, which retains clearest and longest what is written on it. He was not an original thinker, but the strength and loftiness of his character and his strong religious sense gave him an authority which no other member of the school could claim. For many years head of the Stoa, he reached the ripe age of ninety-nine, when, falling sick, he refused to take food, and died of voluntary starvation in B. C. 232. Long afterwards, the Roman Senate caused a statue to be erected to his memory in his native town. Almost the only writing of his that has come down to us is his noble Hymn to the Supreme Being.

HYMN TO ZEUS

MOST glorious of all the Undying, many-named, girt round with
    awe!
    Jove, author of Nature, applying to all things the rudder of
    law —
Hail! Hail! for it justly rejoices the races whose life is a span
To lift unto thee their voices — the Author and Framer of man.
For we are thy sons; thou didst give us the symbols of speech at
        our birth,
Alone of the things that live, and mortal move upon earth.

Wherefore thou shalt find me extolling and ever singing thy
      praise;
Since thee the great Universe, rolling on its path round the world,
      obeys:—
Obeys thee, wherever thou guidest, and gladly is bound in thy
      bands,
So great is the power thou confidest, with strong, invincible hands,
To thy mighty ministering servant, the bolt of the thunder, that
      flies,
Two-edged, like a sword, and fervent, that is living and never dies.
All nature, in fear and dismay, doth quake in the path of its stroke,
What time thou preparest the way for the one Word thy lips have
      spoke,
Which blends with lights smaller and greater, which pervadeth and
      thrilleth all things,
So great is thy power and thy nature — in the Universe Highest of
      Kings!
On earth, of all deeds that are done, O God! there is none without
      thee;
In the holy ether not one, nor one on the face of the sea,
Save the deeds that evil men, driven by their own blind folly, have
      planned;
But things that have grown uneven are made even again by thy
      hand;
And things unseemly grow seemly, the unfriendly are friendly to
      thee;
For so good and evil supremely thou hast blended in one by decree.
For all thy decree is one ever — a Word that endureth for aye,
Which mortals, rebellious, endeavor to flee from and shun to obey —
Ill-fated, that, worn with proneness for the lordship of goodly things,
Neither hear nor behold, in its oneness, the law that divinity brings;
Which men with reason obeying, might attain unto glorious life,
No longer aimlessly straying in the paths of ignoble strife.
There are men with a zeal unblest, that are wearied with following
      of fame,
And men with a baser quest, that are turned to lucre and shame.
There are men too that pamper and pleasure the flesh with delicate
      stings:
All these desire beyond measure to be other than all these things.
Great Jove, all-giver, dark-clouded, great Lord of the thunderbolt's
      breath!
Deliver the men that are shrouded in ignorance dismal as death.
O Father! dispel from their souls the darkness, and grant them the
      light

Of reason, thy stay, when the whole wide world thou rulest with
        might,
That we, being honored, may honor thy name with the music of
        hymns,
Extolling the deeds of the Donor, unceasing, as rightly beseems
Mankind; for no worthier trust is awarded to God or to man
Than forever to glory with justice in the law that endures and is
        One.

SAMUEL LANGHORNE CLEMENS (MARK TWAIN)

(1835–)

AMUEL L. CLEMENS has made the name he assumed in his earliest "sketches" for newspapers so completely to usurp his own in public and private, that until recently the world knew him by no other; his world of admirers rarely use any other in referring to the great author, and even to his intimate friends the borrowed name seems the more real. The pseudonym so lightly picked up has nearly universal recognition, and it is safe to say that the name "Mark Twain" is known to more people of all conditions, the world over, than any other in this century, except that of some reigning sovereign or great war captain. The term is one used by the Mississippi River pilots to indicate the depth of water (two fathoms) when throwing the lead. It was first employed by a river correspondent in reporting the state of the river to a New Orleans newspaper. This reporter died just about the time Mr. Clemens began to write, and he "jumped" the name.

Mr. Clemens was born in Hannibal, Missouri, a small town on the west bank of the Mississippi, in 1835. He got the rudiments of an education at a village school, learned boy-life and human nature in a frontier community, entered a printing office and became an expert compositor, traveled and worked as a journeyman printer, and at length reached the summit of a river boy's ambition in a Mississippi steamboat in learning the business of a pilot. It is to this experience that the world is indebted for some of the most amusing, the most real and valuable, and the most imaginative writing of this century, which gives the character and interest and individuality to this great Western river that history has given to the Nile. If he had no other title to fame, he could rest securely on his reputation as the prose poet of the Mississippi. Upon the breaking out of the war the river business was suspended. Mr. Clemens tried the occupation of war for a few weeks, on the Confederate side, in a volunteer squad which does not seem to have come into collision with anything but scant rations and imaginary alarms; and then he went to Nevada with his brother, who had been appointed secretary of that Territory. Here he became connected with the Territorial Enterprise, a Virginia City newspaper, as a reporter and sketch-writer, and immediately opened a battery of good-natured and exaggerated and complimentary description that was vastly amusing to those who were not its targets.

Afterwards he drifted to the Coast, tried mining, and then joined that group of young writers who illustrated the early history of California. A short voyage in the Sandwich Islands gave him new material for his pen, and he made a successful début in San Francisco as a humorous lecturer.

The first writing to attract general attention was 'The Jumping Frog of Calaveras,' which was republished with several other sketches in book form in New York. Shortly after this he joined the excursion of the Quaker City steamship to the Orient, wrote letters about it to American newspapers, and advertised it quite beyond the expectations of its projectors. These letters, collected and revised, became 'The Innocents Abroad,' which instantly gave him a world-wide reputation. This was followed by 'Roughing It,' most amusing episodes of frontier life. His pen became immediately in great demand, and innumerable sketches flowed from it, many of them recklessly exaggerated for the effect he wished to produce; always laughter-provoking, and nearly always having a wholesome element of satire of some sham or pretense or folly. For some time he had charge of a humorous department in the Galaxy Magazine. These sketches and others that followed were from time to time collected into volumes which had a great sale. About this time he married, and permanently settled in Hartford, where he began the collection of a library, set himself to biographical and historical study, made incursions into German and French, and prepared himself for the more serious work that was before him.

A second sojourn in Europe produced 'A Tramp Abroad,' full of stories and adventures, much in the spirit of his original effort. But with more reading, reflection, and search into his own experiences, came 'Old Times on the Mississippi,' 'Tom Sawyer,' and 'Huckleberry Finn,' in which the author wrote out of his own heart. To interest in social problems must be attributed the beautiful idyl of 'The Prince and the Pauper,' and 'The Yankee at the Court of King Arthur,' which latter the English thought lacked reverence for the traditions of chivalry.

During all this period Mr. Clemens was in great demand as a lecturer and an after-dinner speaker. His remarks about New England weather, at a New England dinner in New York, are a favorite example of his humor and his power of poetic description. As a lecturer, a teller of stories, and delineator of character, he had scarcely a rival in his ability to draw and entertain vast audiences. He made a large income from his lectures in America and in England, and from his books, which always had a phenomenally large sale. Very remunerative also was the play of 'Colonel Sellers,' constructed out of a novel called 'The Gilded Age.'

Since 1890 Mr. Clemens and his family have lived most of the time in Europe. For some time before he had written little, but since that his pen has again become active. He has produced many magazine papers, a story called 'Pudd'nhead Wilson,' and the most serious and imaginative work of his life in 'The Personal Recollections of Joan of Arc,' feigned to be translated from a contemporary memoir left by her private secretary. In it the writer strikes the universal chords of sympathy and pathos and heroic elevation. In 1895-6 he made a lecturing tour of the globe, speaking in Australia, New Zealand, South Africa, and India, and everywhere received an ovation due to his commanding reputation. He is understood to be making this journey the subject of another book.

Mr. Clemens is universally recognized as the first of living humorists; but if the fashion of humor changes, as change it may, he will remain for other qualities — certain primordial qualities such as are exhibited in his work on the Mississippi — a force to be reckoned with in the literature of this century. Mr. Clemens's humor has the stamp of universality, which is the one indispensable thing in all enduring literary productions, and his books have been translated and very widely diffused and read in German, French, and other languages. This is a prophecy of his lasting place in the world of letters.

THE CHILD OF CALAMITY

From 'Life on the Mississippi': copyright 1883, by James R. Osgood and Company

BY WAY of illustrating keelboat talk and manners, and that now departed and hardly remembered raft life, I will throw in, in this place, a chapter from a book which I have been working at by fits and starts during the past five or six years, and may possibly finish in the course of five or six more. The book is a story which details some passages in the life of an ignorant village boy, Huck Finn, son of the town drunkard of my time out West there. He has run away from his persecuting father, and from a persecuting good widow who wishes to make a nice truth-telling respectable boy of him; and with him a slave of the widow's has also escaped. They have found a fragment of a lumber raft (it is high water and dead summertime), and are floating down the river by night and hiding in the willows by day,—bound for Cairo,—whence the negro will seek freedom in the heart of the free States. But in a fog, they

pass Cairo without knowing it.   By-and-by they begin to suspect the truth, and Huck Finn is persuaded to end the dismal
suspense by swimming down to a huge raft which they have
seen in the distance ahead of them, creeping aboard under cover
of the darkness, and gathering the needed information by eaves-
dropping : —

But you know a young person can't wait very well when he
is impatient to find a thing out. We talked it over, and by-and-
by Jim said it was such a black night now that it wouldn't be
no risk to swim down to the big raft and crawl aboard and
listen, — they would talk about Cairo, because they would be calculating to go ashore there for a spree, maybe, or anyway they
would send boats ashore to buy whisky or fresh meat or something.   Jim had a wonderful level head, for a nigger: he could
'most always start a good plan when you wanted one.

I stood up and shook my rags off and jumped into the river,
and struck out for the raft's light.   By-and-by, when I got down
nearly to her, I eased up and went slow and cautious.   But
everything was all right — nobody at the sweeps.   So I swum
down along the raft till I was 'most abreast the camp fire in the
middle, then I crawled aboard and inched along and got in
amongst some bundles of shingles on the weather side of the
fire.   There was thirteen men there — they was the watch on
deck, of course.   And a mighty rough-looking lot too.   They
had a jug, and tin cups, and they kept the jug moving.   One
man was singing — roaring, you may say; and it wasn't a nice
song — for a parlor anyway.   He roared through his nose, and
strung out the last word of every line very long.   When he was
done they all fetched a kind of Injun war-whoop, and then
another was sung.   It begun : —

> " There was a woman in our towdn,
>   In our towdn did dwed'l (dwell),
>   She loved her husband dear-i-lee,
>   But another man twyste as wed'l.
>
> "Singing too, riloo, riloo, riloo,
>   Ri-loo, riloo, rilay - - - e,
>   She loved her husband dear-i-lee,
>   But another man twyste as wed'l.»

And so on — fourteen verses.   It was kind of poor, and when he
was going to start on the next verse one of them said it was

the tune the old cow died on; and another one said, "Oh, give us a rest." And another one told him to take a walk. They made fun of him till he got mad and jumped up and begun to cuss the crowd, and said he could lam any thief in the lot.

They was all about to make a break for him, but the biggest man there jumped up and says: —

"Set whar you are, gentlemen. Leave him to me; he's my meat."

Then he jumped up in the air three times and cracked his heels together every time. He flung off a buckskin coat that was all hung with fringes, and says, "You lay thar tell the chawin-up's done;" and flung his hat down, which was all over ribbons, and says, "You lay thar tell his sufferins is over."

Then he jumped up in the air and cracked his heels together again and shouted out: —

"Whoo-oop! I'm the old original iron-jawed, brass-mounted, copper-bellied corpse-maker from the wilds of Arkansaw! — Look at me! I'm the man they call Sudden Death and General Deso-lation! Sired by a hurricane, dam'd by an earthquake, half-brother to the cholera, nearly related to the small-pox on the mother's side! Look at me! I take nineteen alligators and a bar'l of whisky for breakfast when I'm in robust health, and a bushel of rattlesnakes and a dead body when I'm ailing! I split the everlasting rocks with my glance, and I squench the thunder when I speak! Whoo-oop! Stand back and give me room according to my strength! Blood's my natural drink, and the wails of the dying is music to my ear! Cast your eye on me, gentlemen! — and lay low and hold your breath, for I'm 'bout to turn myself loose!"

All the time he was getting this off, he was shaking his head and looking fierce and kind of swelling around in a little circle, tucking up his wrist-bands and now and then straightening up and beating his breast with his fist, saying "Look at me, gen-tlemen!" When he got through he jumped up and cracked his heels together three times, and let off a roaring "Whoo-oop! I'm the bloodiest son of a wildcat that lives!"

Then the man that had started the row tilted his old slouch hat down over his right eye; then he bent stooping forward, with his back sagged and his south end sticking out far, and his fists a-shoving out and drawing in in front of him, and so went around in a little circle about three times, swelling himself up

and breathing hard. Then he straightened, and jumped up and
cracked his heels together three times before he lit again (that
made them cheer), and he begun to shout like this:—

"Whoo-oop! bow your neck and spread, for the kingdom of
sorrow's a-coming! Hold me down to the earth, for I feel my
powers a-working! whoo-oop! I'm a child of sin; *don't* let me
get a start! Smoked glass, here, for all! Don't attempt to look
at me with the naked eye, gentlemen! When I'm playful I use
the meridians of longitude and parallels of latitude for a seine,
and drag the Atlantic Ocean for whales! I scratch my head
with the lightning and purr myself to sleep with the thunder!
When I'm cold I bile the Gulf of Mexico and bathe in it; when
I'm hot I fan myself with an equinoctial storm; when I'm thirsty
I reach up and suck a cloud dry like a sponge; when I range
the earth hungry, famine follows in my tracks! Whoo-oop! Bow
your neck and spread! I put my hand on the sun's face and
make it night in the earth; I bite a piece out of the moon and
hurry the seasons; I shake myself and crumble the mountains!
Contemplate me through leather — *don't* use the naked eye! I'm
the man with a petrified heart and biler-iron bowels! The massa-
cre of isolated communities is the pastime of my idle moments,
the destruction of nationalities the serious business of my life!
The boundless vastness of the great American desert is my
inclosed property, and I bury my dead on my own premises!"
He jumped up and cracked his heels together three times before
he lit (they cheered him again), and as he came down he shouted
out: "Whoo-oop! bow your neck and spread, for the pet child of
calamity's a-coming!"

Then the other one went to swelling around and blowing
again — the first one — the one they called Bob; next, the Child
of Calamity chipped in again, bigger than ever; then they both
got at it at the same time, swelling round and round each other
and punching their fists 'most into each other's faces, and whoop-
ing and jawing like Injuns; then Bob called the Child names,
and the Child called him names back again: next, Bob called
him a heap rougher names, and the Child come back at him with
the very worst kind of language; next, Bob knocked the Child's
hat off, and the Child picked it up and kicked Bob's ribbony hat
about six foot; Bob went and got it and said never mind, this
warn't going to be the last of this thing, because he was a man
that never forgot and never forgive, and so the Child better look

out; for there was a time a-coming, just as sure as he was a living man, that he would have to answer to him with the best blood in his body. The Child said no man was willinger than he was for that time to come, and he would give Bob fair warning, *now*, never to cross his path again, for he could never rest till he had waded in his blood; for such was his nature, though he was sparing him now on account of his family, if he had one.

Both of them was edging away in different directions, growling and shaking their heads and going on about what they was going to do; but a little black-whiskered chap skipped up and says: —

"Come back here, you couple of chicken-livered cowards, and I'll thrash the two of ye!"

And he done it, too. He snatched them, he jerked them this way and that, he booted them around, he knocked them sprawling faster than they could get up. Why, it warn't two minutes till they begged like dogs — and how the other lot did yell and laugh and clap their hands all the way through, and shout "Sail in, Corpse-Maker!" "Hi! at him again, Child of Calamity!" "Bully for you, little Davy!" Well, it was a perfect pow-wow for a while. Bob and the Child had red noses and black eyes when they got through. Little Davy made them own up that they was sneaks and cowards, and not fit to eat with a dog or drink with a nigger; then Bob and the Child shook hands with each other very solemn, and said they had always respected each other and was willing to let bygones be bygones. So then they washed their faces in the river; and just then there was a loud order to stand by for a crossing, and some of them went forward to man the sweeps there, and the rest went aft to handle the after-sweeps.

A STEAMBOAT LANDING AT A SMALL TOWN

From 'Life on the Mississippi': copyright 1883, by James R. Osgood and
Company

ONCE a day a cheap gaudy packet arrived upward from St.
Louis, and another downward from Keokuk. Before these
events, the day was glorious with expectancy; after them,
the day was a dead and empty thing. Not only the boys but
the whole village felt this. After all these years I can picture
that old time to myself now, just as it was then: the white town
drowsing in the sunshine of a summer's morning; the streets
empty, or pretty nearly so; one or two clerks sitting in front of
the Water Street stores, with their splint-bottomed chairs tilted
back against the wall, chins on breasts, hats slouched over their
faces, asleep — with shingle-shavings enough around to show
what broke them down; a sow and a litter of pigs loafing along
the sidewalk, doing a good business in watermelon rinds and
seeds; two or three lonely little freight piles scattered about the
" levee"; a pile of " skids" on the slope of the stone-paved
wharf, and the fragrant town drunkard asleep in the shadow of
them; two or three wood flats at the head of the wharf, but nobody to listen to the peaceful lapping of the wavelets against
them; the great Mississippi, the majestic, the magnificent Mississippi, rolling its mile-wide tide along, shining in the sun; the
dense forest away on the other side; the " point" above the
town and the " point" below, bounding the river-glimpse and
turning it into a sort of sea, and withal a very still and brilliant
and lonely one. Presently a film of dark smoke appears above
one of those remote " points"; instantly a negro drayman, famous for his quick eye and prodigious voice, lifts up the cry,
" S-t-e-a-m-boat a-comin'!" and the scene changes! The town
drunkard stirs, the clerks wake up, a furious clatter of drays
follows, every house and store pours out a human contribution,
and all in a twinkling the dead town is alive and moving.
Drays, carts, men, boys, all go hurrying from many quarters to
a common centre, the wharf. Assembled there, the people fasten
their eyes upon the coming boat, as upon a wonder they are seeing for the first time. And the boat *is* rather a handsome sight
too. She is long and sharp and trim and pretty; she has two
tall fancy-topped chimneys, with a gilded device of some kind

swung between them; a fanciful pilot-house, all glass and "gingerbread," perched on top of the "texas" deck behind them; the paddle-boxes are gorgeous with a picture or with gilded rays above the boat's name; the boiler deck, the hurricane deck, and the texas deck are fenced and ornamented with clean white railings; there is a flag gallantly flying from the jack-staff; the furnace doors are open and the fires glaring bravely; the upper decks are black with passengers; the captain stands by the big bell, calm, imposing, the envy of all; great volumes of the blackest smoke are rolling and tumbling out of the chimneys—a husbanded grandeur created with a bit of pitch-pine just before arriving at a town; the crew are grouped on the forecastle; the broad stage is run far out over the port bow, and an envied deck hand stands picturesquely on the end of it with a coil of rope in his hand; the pent steam is screaming through the gauge-cocks; the captain lifts his hand, a bell rings, the wheels stop; then they turn back, churning the water to a foam, and the steamer is at rest. Then such a scramble as there is to get aboard, and to get ashore, and to take in freight and to discharge freight, all at one and the same time; and such a yelling and cursing as the mates facilitate it all with! Ten minutes later the steamer is under way again, with no flag on the jack-staff and no black smoke issuing from the chimneys. After ten more minutes the town is dead again, and the town drunkard asleep by the skids once more.

THE HIGH RIVER: AND A PHANTOM PILOT

From 'Life on the Mississippi': copyright 1883, by James R. Osgood and Company

DURING this big rise these small-fry craft were an intolerable nuisance. We were running chute after chute,—a new world to me,—and if there was a particularly cramped place in a chute, we would be pretty sure to meet a broad-horn there; and if he failed to be there, we would find him in a still worse locality, namely, the head of the chute, on the shoal water. And then there would be no end of profane cordialities exchanged.

Sometimes, in the big river, when we would be feeling our way cautiously along through a fog, the deep hush would suddenly be broken by yells and a clamor of tin pans, and all in an instant a log raft would appear vaguely through the webby veil, close upon us; and then we did not wait to swap knives, but snatched our engine bells out by the roots and piled on all the steam we had, to scramble out of the way! One doesn't hit a rock or a solid log raft with a steamboat when he can get excused.

You will hardly believe it, but many steamboat clerks always carried a large assortment of religious tracts with them in those old departed steamboating days. Indeed they did. Twenty times a day we would be cramping up around a bar, while a string of these small-fry rascals were drifting down into the head of the bend away above and beyond us a couple of miles. Now a skiff would dart away from one of them, and come fighting its laborious way across the desert of water. It would "ease all," in the shadow of our forecastle, and the panting oarsmen would shout, "Gimme a pa-a-per!" as the skiff drifted swiftly astern. The clerk would throw over a file of New Orleans journals. If these were picked up *without comment*, you might notice that now a dozen other skiffs had been drifting down upon us without saying anything. You understand, they had been waiting to see how No. 1 was going to fare. No. 1 making no comment, all the rest would bend to their oars and come on now; and as fast as they came the clerk would heave over neat bundles of religious tracts, tied to shingles. The amount of hard swearing which twelve packages of religious literature will command when impartially divided up among twelve raftsmen's crews, who have pulled a heavy skiff two miles on a hot day to get them, is simply incredible.

As I have said, the big rise brought a new world under my vision. By the time the river was over its banks we had forsaken our old paths and were hourly climbing over bars that had stood ten feet out of water before; we were shaving stumpy shores, like that at the foot of Madrid Bend, which I had always seen avoided before; we were clattering through chutes like that of 82, where the opening at the foot was an unbroken wall of timber till our nose was almost at the very spot. Some of these chutes were utter solitudes. The dense untouched forest overhung both banks of the crooked little crack, and one could believe that human creatures had never intruded there before. The swinging grapevines, the grassy nooks and vistas, glimpsed as we swept by, the flowering creepers waving their red blossoms from the tops of dead trunks, and all the spendthrift richness of the forest foliage, were wasted and thrown away there. The chutes were lovely places to steer in; they were deep, except at the head; the current was gentle; under the "points" the water was absolutely dead, and the invisible banks so bluff that where the tender willow thickets projected you could bury your boat's broadside in them as you tore along, and then you seemed fairly to fly.

Behind other islands we found wretched little farms and wretcheder little log cabins; there were crazy rail fences sticking a foot or two above the water, with one or two jeans-clad, chills-racked, yellow-faced male miserables roosting on the top rail, elbows on knees, jaws in hands, grinding tobacco and discharging the result at floating chips through crevices left by lost teeth; while the rest of the family and the few farm animals were huddled together in an empty wood flat riding at her moorings close at hand. In this flatboat the family would have to cook and eat and sleep for a lesser or greater number of days (or possibly weeks), until the river should fall two or three feet and let them get back to their log cabin and their chills again — chills being a merciful provision of an all-wise Providence to enable them to take exercise without exertion. And this sort of watery camping out was a thing which these people were rather liable to be treated to a couple of times a year: by the December rise out of the Ohio, and the June rise out of the Mississippi. And yet these were kindly dispensations, for they at least enabled the poor things to rise from the dead now and then, and look upon life when a steamboat went by. They appreciated the blessing too, for they spread their mouths and eyes wide open and made the most of these occasions. Now what *could* these banished creatures find to do to keep from dying of the blues during the low-water season!

Once in one of these lovely island chutes we found our course completely bridged by a great fallen tree. This will serve to show how narrow some of the chutes were. The passengers had an hour's recreation in a virgin wilderness while the boat hands chopped the bridge away; for there was no such thing as turning back, you comprehend.

From Cairo to Baton Rouge, when the river is over its banks, you have no particular trouble in the night, for the thousand-mile wall of dense forest that guards the two banks all the way is only gapped with a farm or wood-yard opening at intervals, and so you can't "get out of the river" much easier than you could get out of a fenced lane; but from Baton Rouge to New Orleans it is a different matter. The river is more than a mile wide, and very deep — as much as two hundred feet, in places. Both banks, for a good deal over a hundred miles, are shorn of their timber and bordered by continuous sugar plantations, with only here and there a scattering sapling or row of ornamental China-trees. The timber is shorn off clear to the rear of the plantations, from two to four miles. When the first frost threatens to come, the planters snatch off their crops in a hurry. When they have finished grinding the cane, they form the refuse of the stalks (which they call *bagasse*) into great piles and set fire to them, though in other sugar countries the bagasse is used for fuel in the furnaces of the sugar-mills. Now the piles of damp bagasse burn slowly, and smoke like Satan's own kitchen.

An embankment ten or fifteen feet high guards both banks of the Mississippi all the way down that lower end of the river, and this embankment is set back from the edge of the shore from ten to perhaps a hundred feet, according to circumstances; say thirty or forty feet as a general thing. Fill that whole region with an impenetrable gloom of smoke from a hundred miles of burning bagasse piles, when the river is over the banks, and turn a steamboat loose along there at midnight and see how she will feel. And see how you will feel too! You find yourself away out in the midst of a vague dim sea that is shoreless, that fades out and loses itself in the murky distances; for you cannot discern the thin rib of embankment, and you are always imagining you see a straggling tree when you don't. The plantations themselves are transformed by the smoke and look like a part of the sea. All through your watch you are tortured with the exquisite misery of uncertainty. You hope you are keeping in the river, but you do not know. All that you are sure about is that you are likely to be within six feet of the bank *and* destruction, when you think you are a good half-mile from shore. And you are sure also that if you chance suddenly to fetch up against the embankment and topple your chimneys overboard, you will have the small comfort of knowing that it is about what you were expecting to do. One of the great Vicksburg packets darted out into a sugar plantation one night, at such a time, and had to stay there a week. But there was no novelty about it: it had often been done before.

I thought I had finished this chapter, but I wish to add a curious thing while it is in my mind. It is only relevant in that it is connected with piloting. There used to be an excellent pilot on the river, a Mr. X., who was a somnambulist. It was said that if his mind was troubled about a bad piece of river, he was pretty sure to get up and walk in his sleep and do strange things. He was once fellow pilot for a trip or two with George Ealer, on a great New Orleans passenger packet. During a considerable part of the first trip George was uneasy, but got over it by-and-by, as X. seemed content to stay in his bed when asleep. Late one night the boat was approaching Helena, Arkansas; the water was low, and the crossing above the town in a very blind and tangled condition. X. had seen the crossing since Ealer had, and as the night was particularly drizzly, sullen, and dark, Ealer was considering whether he had not better have X. called to assist in running the place, when the door opened and X. walked in. Now on very dark nights, light is a deadly enemy to piloting; you are aware that if you stand in a lighted room on such a night, you cannot see things in the street to any purpose; but if you put out the lights and stand in the gloom you can make out objects in the street pretty well. So on very dark nights pilots do not smoke; they allow no fire in the pilot-house stove if there is a crack which can allow the least ray to escape; they order the furnaces to be curtained with huge tarpaulins and the skylights to be closely blinded. Then no light whatever issues from the boat. The undefinable shape that now entered the pilot-house had Mr. X.'s voice. This said: —

" Let me take her, George; I've seen this place since you have, and it is so crooked that I reckon I can run it myself easier than I could tell you how to do it. "

" It is kind of you, and I swear *I* am willing. I haven't got another drop of perspiration left in me. I have been spinning around and around the wheel like a squirrel. It is so dark I can't tell which way she is swinging till she is coming around like a whirligig. "

So Ealer took a seat on the bench, panting and breathless. The black phantom assumed the wheel without saying anything, steadied the waltzing steamer with a turn or two, and then stood at ease, coaxing her a little to this side and then to that, as gently and as sweetly as if the time had been noonday. When Ealer observed this marvel of steering, he wished he had not confessed! He stared and wondered, and finally said:—

"Well, I thought I knew how to steer a steamboat, but that was another mistake of mine."

X. said nothing, but went serenely on with his work. He rang for the leads; he rang to slow down the steam; he worked the boat carefully and neatly into invisible marks, then stood at the centre of the wheel and peered blandly out into the blackness, fore and aft, to verify his position; as the leads shoaled more and more, he stopped the engines entirely, and the dead silence and suspense of "drifting" followed; when the shoalest water was struck, he cracked on the steam, carried her handsomely over, and then began to work her warily into the next system of shoal marks; the same patient, heedful use of leads and engines followed, the boat slipped through without touching bottom, and entered upon the third and last intricacy of the crossing; imperceptibly she moved through the gloom, crept by inches into her marks, drifted tediously till the shoalest water was cried, and then, under a tremendous head of steam, went swinging over the reef and away into deep water and safety!

Ealer let his long-pent breath pour out in a great relieving sigh, and said:—

"That's the sweetest piece of piloting that was ever done on the Mississippi River! I wouldn't believed it could be done, if I hadn't seen it."

There was no reply, and he added:—

"Just hold her five minutes longer, partner, and let me run down and get a cup of coffee."

A minute later Ealer was biting into a pie, down in the "texas," and comforting himself with coffee. Just then the night watchman happened in, and was about to happen out again, when he noticed Ealer and exclaimed:—

"Who is at the wheel, sir?"

"X."

"Dart for the pilot-house, quicker than lightning!"

The next moment both men were flying up the pilot-house companion-way, three steps at a jump! Nobody there! The great steamer was whistling down the middle of the river at her own sweet will! The watchman shot out of the place again; Ealer seized the wheel, set the engine back with power, and held his breath while the boat reluctantly swung away from a "tow-head" which she was about to knock into the middle of the Gulf of Mexico!

By-and-by the watchman came back and said:—

"Didn't that lunatic tell you he was asleep when he first came up here?"

"No."

"Well, he was. I found him walking along on top of the railings, just as unconcerned as another man would walk a pavement; and I put him to bed; now just this minute there he was again, away astern, going through that sort of tight-rope deviltry the same as before."

"Well, I think I'll stay by, next time he has one of those fits. But I hope he'll have them often. You just ought to have seen him take this boat through Helena crossing. *I* never saw anything so gaudy before. And if he can do such gold-leaf, kid-glove, diamond-breastpin piloting when he is sound asleep, what *couldn't* he do if he was dead!"

AN ENCHANTING RIVER SCENE

From 'Life on the Mississippi': copyright 1883, by James R. Osgood and Company

THE face of the water in time became a wonderful book— a book that was a dead language to the uneducated passenger, but which told its mind to me without reserve, delivering its most cherished secrets as clearly as if it uttered them with a voice. And it was not a book to be read once and thrown aside, for it had a new story to tell every day. Throughout the long twelve hundred miles there was never a page that was void of interest, never one that you could leave unread without loss, never one that you would want to skip, thinking you could find higher enjoyment in some other thing. There never was so wonderful a book written by man; never one whose interest was so absorbing, so unflagging, so sparklingly renewed with every re-perusal. The passenger who could not read it was charmed with a peculiar sort of faint dimple on its surface (on the rare occasions when he did not overlook it altogether); but to the pilot that was an *italicized* passage; indeed it was more than that,— it was a legend of the largest capitals, with a string of shouting exclamation-points at the end of it; for it meant that a wreck or a rock was buried there, that could tear the life out of the strongest vessel that ever floated. It is the faintest and simplest expression the water ever makes, and the most hideous to a pilot's eye.   In truth, the passenger who could not read this book saw nothing but all manner of pretty pictures in it, painted by the sun and shaded by the clouds; whereas to the trained eye these were not pictures at all, but the grimmest and most dead-earnest of reading matter.

Now when I had mastered the language of this water and had come to know every trifling feature that bordered the great river as familiarly as I knew the letters of the alphabet, I had made a valuable acquisition.   But I had lost something too.   I had lost something which could never be restored to me while I lived.   All the grace, the beauty, the poetry had gone out of the majestic river!   I still kept in mind a certain wonderful sunset which I witnessed when steamboating was new to me.   A broad expanse of the river was turned to blood; in the middle distance the red hue brightened into gold, through which a solitary log came floating, black and conspicuous; in one place a long slant-ing mark lay sparkling upon the water; in another the surface was broken by boiling tumbling rings that were as many-tinted as an opal; where the ruddy flush was faintest, was a smooth spot that was covered with graceful circles and radiating lines, ever so delicately traced; the shore on our left was densely wooded, and the sombre shadow that fell from this forest was broken in one place by a long ruffled trail that shone like sil-ver; and high above the forest wall a clean-stemmed dead tree waved a single leafy bough, that glowed like a flame in the un-obstructed splendor that was flowing from the sun.   There were graceful curves, reflected images, woody heights, soft distances; and over the whole scene, far and near, the dissolving lights drifted steadily, enriching it every passing moment with new marvels of coloring.

I stood like one bewitched.   I drank it in, in a speechless rapture.   The world was new to me, and I had never seen any-thing like this at home.   But as I have said, a day came when I began to cease from noting the glories and the charms which the moon and the sun and the twilight wrought upon the river's face; another day came when I ceased altogether to note them. Then, if that sunset scene had been repeated, I should have looked upon it without rapture and should have commented upon it inwardly after this fashion: This sun means that we are going to have wind to-morrow; that floating log means that the river is rising, small thanks to it; that slanting mark on the water refers to a bluff reef which is going to kill somebody's steamboat one of these nights, if it keeps on stretching out like that; those tumbling "boils" show a dissolving bar and a changing channel there; the lines and circles in the slick water over yonder are a warning that that troublesome place is shoaling up dangerously; that silver streak in the shadow of the forest is the "break" from a new snag, and he has located himself in the very best place he could have found to fish for steamboats; that tall dead tree, with a single living branch, is not going to last long, and then how is a body ever going to get through this blind place at night without the friendly old landmark?

No, the romance and the beauty were all gone from the river. All the value any feature of it had for me now was the amount of usefulness it could furnish toward compassing the safe piloting of a steamboat. Since those days I have pitied doctors from my heart. What does the lovely flush in a beauty's cheek mean to a doctor but a "break" that ripples above some deadly disease? Are not all her visible charms sown thick with what are to him the signs and symbols of hidden decay? Does he ever see her beauty at all, or doesn't he simply view her professionally and comment upon her unwholesome condition all to himself? And doesn't he sometimes wonder whether he has gained most or lost most by learning his trade?

THE LIGHTNING PILOT

From 'Life on the Mississippi': copyright 1883, by James R. Osgood and Company

NEXT morning I felt pretty rusty and low-spirited. We went booming along, taking a good many chances, for we were anxious to "get out of the river" (as getting out to Cairo was called) before night should overtake us. But Mr. Bixby's partner, the other pilot, presently grounded the boat, and we lost so much time getting her off that it was plain the darkness would overtake us a good long way above the mouth. This was a great misfortune; especially to certain of our visiting pilots, whose boats would have to wait for their return, no matter how long that might be. It sobered the pilot-house talk a good deal. Coming up-stream, pilots did not mind low water or any kind of darkness; nothing stopped them but fog. But down-stream work was different; a boat was too nearly helpless, with a stiff current pushing behind her; so it was not customary to run down-stream at night in low water.

There seemed to be one small hope, however: if we could get through the intricate and dangerous Hat Island crossing before night, we could venture the rest, for we would have plainer sailing and better water. But it would be insanity to attempt Hat Island at night. So there was a deal of looking at watches all the rest of the day, and a constant ciphering upon the speed we were making; Hat Island was the eternal subject; sometimes hope was high, and sometimes we were delayed in a bad crossing, and down it went again. For hours all hands lay under the burden of this suppressed excitement; it was even communicated to me, and I got to feeling so solicitous about Hat Island, and under such an awful pressure of responsibility, that I wished I might have five minutes on shore to draw a good full relieving breath, and start over again. We were standing no regular watches. Each of our pilots ran such portions of the river as he had run when coming up-stream, because of his greater familiarity with it; but both remained in the pilot-house constantly.

An hour before sunset, Mr. Bixby took the wheel and Mr. W—— stepped aside. For the next thirty minutes every man held his watch in his hand and was restless, silent, and uneasy. At last somebody said with a doomful sigh:—

"Well, yonder's Hat Island—and we can't make it."

All the watches closed with a snap, everybody sighed and muttered something about its being "too bad, too bad—ah, if we could *only* have got here half an hour sooner!" and the place was thick with the atmosphere of disappointment. Some started to go out, but loitered, hearing no bell-tap to land. The sun dipped behind the horizon, the boat went on. Inquiring looks passed from one guest to another; and one who had his hand on the door-knob and had turned it, waited, then presently took away his hand and let the knob turn back again. We bore steadily down the bend. More looks were exchanged, and nods of surprised admiration — but no words. Insensibly the men drew together behind Mr. Bixby, as the sky darkened and one or two dim stars came out. The dead silence and sense of waiting became oppressive. Mr. Bixby pulled the cord, and two deep mellow notes from the big bell floated off on the night. Then a pause, and one more note was struck. The watchman's voice followed, from the hurricane deck: —

"Labboard lead, there! Stabboard lead!"

The cries of the leadsmen began to rise out of the distance, and were gruffly repeated by the word-passers on the hurricane deck.

"M-a-r-k three! . . . M-a-r-k three! . . . Quarter-less-three! . . . Half twain! . . . Quarter twain! . . . M-a-r-k twain! . . . Quarter-less —"

Mr. Bixby pulled two bell-ropes, and was answered by faint jinglings far below in the engine-room, and our speed slackened. The steam began to whistle through the gauge-cocks. The cries of the leadsmen went on — and it is a weird sound always in the night. Every pilot in the lot was watching now, with fixed eyes, and talking under his breath. Nobody was calm and easy but Mr. Bixby. He would put his wheel down and stand on a spoke, and as the steamer swung into her (to me) utterly invisible marks — for we seemed to be in the midst of a wide and gloomy sea — he would meet and fasten her there. Out of the murmur of half-audible talk one caught a coherent sentence now and then, such as: —

"There; she's over the first reef all right!"

After a pause, another subdued voice: —

"Her stern's coming down just *exactly* right, by *George!*"

"Now she's in the marks; over she goes!"

Somebody else muttered: —

"Oh, it was done beautiful — *beautiful!*"

Now the engines were stopped altogether, and we drifted with the current. Not that I could see the boat drift, for I could not, the stars being all gone by this time. This drifting was the dismalest work; it held one's heart still. Presently I discovered a blacker gloom than that which surrounded us. It was the head of the island. We were closing right down upon it. We entered its deeper shadow, and so imminent seemed the peril that I was likely to suffocate; and I had the strongest impulse to do *something*, anything, to save the vessel. But still

Mr. Bixby stood by his wheel, silent, intent as a cat, and all the pilots stood shoulder to shoulder at his back.

"She'll not make it!" somebody whispered.

The water grew shoaler and shoaler, by the leadsman's cries, till it was down to —

"Eight-and-a-half! . . . E-i-g-h-t feet! . . . E-i-g-h-t feet! . . . Seven-and —"

Mr. Bixby said warningly through his speaking-tube to the engineer: —

"Stand by, now!"

"Ay-ay, sir!"

"Seven-and-a-half! Seven feet! *Six*-and —"

We touched bottom! Instantly Mr. Bixby set a lot of bells ringing, shouted through the tube, "*Now* let her have it — every ounce you've got!" then to his partner, "Put her hard down! snatch her! snatch her!" The boat rasped and ground her way through the sand, hung upon the apex of disaster a single tremendous instant, and then over she went! And such a shout as went up at Mr. Bixby's back never loosened the roof of a pilot-house before!

There was no more trouble after that. Mr. Bixby was a hero that night; and it was some little time, too, before his exploit ceased to be talked about by river men.

AN EXPEDITION AGAINST OGRES

From 'A Connecticut Yankee in King Arthur's Court': copyright 1889, by Charles L. Webster and Company

MY EXPEDITION was all the talk that day and that night, and the boys were very good to me, and made much of me, and seemed to have forgotten their vexation and disappointment, and come to be as anxious for me to hive those ogres and set those ripe old virgins loose as if it were themselves that had the contract. Well, they *were* good children — but just children, that is all. And they gave me no end of points about how to scout for giants, and how to scoop them in; and they told me all sorts of charms against enchantments, and gave me salves and other rubbish to put on my wounds. But it never occurred to one of them to reflect that if I was such a wonderful necromancer as I was pretending to be, I ought not to need salves, or instructions, or charms against enchantments, and least of all arms and armor, on a foray of any kind — even against fire-spouting dragons and devils hot from perdition, let alone such poor adversaries as these I was after, these commonplace ogres of the back settlements.

I was to have an early breakfast, and start at dawn, for that was the usual way; but I had the demon's own time with my armor, and this delayed me a little. It is troublesome to get into, and there is so much detail. First you wrap a layer or two of blanket around your body for a sort of cushion, and to keep off the cold iron; then you put on your sleeves and shirt of chain-mail — these are made of small steel links woven together, and they form a fabric so flexible that if you toss your shirt on to the floor it slumps into a pile like a peck of wet fish-net; it is very heavy and is nearly the uncomfortablest material in the world for a night-shirt, yet plenty used it for that — tax collectors and reformers, and one-horse kings with a defective title, and those sorts of people; then you put on your shoes — flatboats roofed over with interleaving bands of steel — and screw your clumsy spurs into the heels. Next you buckle your greaves on your legs and your cuisses on your thighs; then come your backplate and your breastplate, and you begin to feel crowded; then you hitch on to the breastplate the half-petticoat of broad overlapping bands of steel which hangs down in front but is scolloped out behind so you can sit down, and isn't any real improvement on an inverted coal-scuttle, either for looks, or for wear, or to wipe your hands on; next you belt on your sword; then you put your stove-pipe joints on to your arms, your iron gauntlets on to your hands, your iron rat-trap on to your head, with a rag of steel web hitched on to it to hang over the back of your neck — and there you are, snug as a candle in a candle-mold. This is no time to dance. Well, a man that is packed away like that is a nut that isn't worth the cracking, there is so little of the meat, when you get down to it, by comparison with the shell.

The boys helped me, or I never could have got in. Just as we finished, Sir Bedivere happened in, and I saw that as like as not I hadn't chosen the most convenient outfit for a long trip. How stately he looked; and tall and broad and grand. He had on his head a conical steel casque that only came down to his ears, and for visor had only a narrow steel bar that extended

down to his upper lip and protected his nose; and all the rest of
him, from neck to heel, was flexible chain-mail, trousers and all.
But pretty much all of him was hidden under his outside garment, which of course was of chain-mail, as I said, and hung
straight from his shoulders to his ankles; and from his middle to
the bottom, both before and behind, was divided, so that he
could ride and let the skirts hang down on each side. He was
going grailing, and it was just the outfit for it, too. I would
have given a good deal for that ulster, but it was too late now
to be fooling around. The sun was just up; the king and the
court were all on hand to see me off and wish me luck; so it
wouldn't be etiquette for me to tarry. You don't get on your
horse yourself; no, if you tried it you would get disappointed.
They carry you out, just as they carry a sun-struck man to the
drug-store, and put you on, and help get you to rights, and fix
your feet in the stirrups; and all the while you do feel so
strange and stuffy and like somebody else — like somebody that
has been married on a sudden, or struck by lightning, or something like that, and hasn't quite fetched around yet, and is sort
of numb, and can't just get his bearings. Then they stood up
the mast they called a spear in its socket by my left foot, and I
gripped it with my hand; lastly they hung my shield around my
neck, and I was all complete and ready to up anchor and get to
sea. Everybody was as good to me as they could be, and a
maid of honor gave me the stirrup-cup her own self. There was
nothing more to do now but for that damsel to get up behind
me on a pillion, which she did, and put an arm or so around
me to hold on.

And so we started; and everybody gave us a good-by and
waved their handkerchiefs or helmets. And everybody we met,
going down the hill and through the village, was respectful to us
except some shabby little boys on the outskirts. They said:—

"Oh, what a guy!" and hove clods at us.

In my experience boys are the same in all ages. They
don't respect anything, they don't care for anything or anybody.
They say "Go up, bald-head!" to the prophet going his unoffend-
ing way in the gray of antiquity; they sass me in the holy
gloom of the Middle Ages; and I had seen them act the same
way in Buchanan's administration; I remember, because I was
there and helped. The prophet had his bears and settled with
his boys; and I wanted to get down and settle with mine, but it

wouldn't answer, because I couldn't have got up again. I hate a country without a derrick.

Straight off, we were in the country. It was most lovely and pleasant in those sylvan solitudes in the early cool morning in the first freshness of autumn. From hilltops we saw fair green valleys lying spread out below, with streams winding through them, and island groves of trees here and there, and huge lonely oaks scattered about and casting black blots of shade; and beyond the valleys we saw the ranges of hills, blue with haze, stretching away in billowy perspective to the horizon, with at wide intervals a dim fleck of white or gray on a wave-summit, which we knew was a castle. We crossed broad natural lawns sparkling with dew, and we moved like spirits, the cushioned turf giving out no sound of footfall; we dreamed along through glades in a mist of green light that got its tint from the sun-drenched roof of leaves overhead, and by our feet the clearest and coldest of runlets went frisking and gossiping over its reefs and making a sort of whispering music comfortable to hear; and at times we left the world behind and entered into the solemn great deeps and rich gloom of the forest, where furtive wild things whisked and scurried by and were gone before you could even get your eye on the place where the noise was; and where only the earliest birds were turning out and getting to business, with a song here and a quarrel yonder and a mysterious far-off hammering and drumming for worms on a tree-trunk away somewhere in the impenetrable remoteness of the woods. And by-and-by out we would swing again into the glare.

About the third or fourth or fifth time that we swung out into the glare—it was along there somewhere, a couple of hours or so after sun-up—it wasn't as pleasant as it had been. It was beginning to get hot. This was quite noticeable. We had a very long pull, after that, without any shade. Now it is curious how progressively little frets grow and multiply after they once get a start. Things which I didn't mind at all at first, I began to mind now—and more and more, too, all the time. The first ten or fifteen times I wanted my handkerchief I didn't seem to care; I got along, and said never mind, it isn't any matter, and dropped it out of my mind. But now it was different: I wanted it all the time; it was nag, nag, nag, right along, and no rest; I couldn't get it out of my mind; and so at last I lost my temper, and said hang a man that would make a suit of armor without any pockets in it. You see I had my handkerchief in my helmet, and some other things; but it was that kind of a helmet that you can't take off by yourself. That hadn't occurred to me when I put it there; and in fact I didn't know it. I supposed it would be particularly convenient there. And so now the thought of its being there, so handy and close by, and yet not get-at-able, made it all the worse and the harder to bear. Yes, the thing that you can't get is the thing that you want, mainly; every one has noticed that. Well, it took my mind off from everything else; took it clear off and centred it in my helmet; and mile after mile there it stayed, imagining the handkerchief, picturing the handkerchief; and it was bitter and aggravating to have the salt sweat keep trickling down into my eyes, and I couldn't get at it. It seems like a little thing on paper, but it was not a little thing at all; it was the most real kind of misery. I would not say it if it was not so. I made up my mind that I would carry along a reticule next time, let it look how it might and people say what they would. Of course these iron dudes of the Round Table would think it was scandalous, and maybe raise sheol about it, but as for me, give me comfort first and style afterwards. So we jogged along, and now and then we struck a stretch of dust, and it would tumble up in clouds and get into my nose and make me sneeze and cry; and of course I said things I oughtn't to have said,— I don't deny that. I am not better than others. We couldn't seem to meet anybody in this lonesome Britain, not even an ogre; and in the mood I was in then, it was well for the ogre; that is, an ogre with a handkerchief. Most knights would have thought of nothing but getting his armor; but so I got his bandana, he could keep his hardware for all me.

Meantime it was getting hotter and hotter in there. You see the sun was beating down and warming up the iron more and more all the time. Well, when you are hot, that way, every little thing irritates you. When I trotted I rattled like a crate of dishes, and that annoyed me; and moreover I couldn't seem to stand that shield slatting and banging, now about my breast, now around my back; and if I dropped into a walk my joints creaked and screeched in that wearisome way that a wheelbarrow does, and as we didn't create any breeze at that gait, I was like to get fried in that stove; and besides, the quieter you went the heavier the iron settled down on you, and the more and more tons you seemed to weigh every minute. And you had to be always changing hands and passing your spear over to the other foot, it got so irksome for one hand to hold it long at a time.

Well, you know when you perspire that way, in rivers, there comes a time when you—when you—well, when you itch. You are inside, your hands are outside: so there you are; nothing but iron between. It is not a light thing, let it sound as it may. First it is one place; then another; then some more; and it goes on spreading and spreading, and at last the territory is all occupied, and nobody can imagine what you feel like, nor how unpleasant it is. And when it had got to the worst, and it seemed to me that I could not stand anything more, a fly got in through the bars and settled on my nose, and the bars were stuck and wouldn't work, and I couldn't get the visor up; and I could only shake my head, which was baking hot by this time, and the fly—well, you know how a fly acts when he has got a certainty: he only minded the shaking enough to change from nose to lip, and lip to ear, and buzz and buzz all around in there, and keep on lighting and biting in a way that a person already so distressed as I was simply could not stand. So I gave in, and got Alisande to unship the helmet and relieve me of it. Then she emptied the conveniences out of it and fetched it full of water, and I drank and then stood up and she poured the rest down inside the armor. One cannot think how refreshing it was. She continued to fetch and pour until I was well soaked and thoroughly comfortable.

It was good to have a rest—and peace. But nothing is quite perfect in this life at any time. I had made a pipe a while back, and also some pretty fair tobacco; not the real thing, but what some of the Indians use: the inside bark of the willow, dried. These comforts had been in the helmet, and now I had them again, but no matches.

Gradually, as the time wore along, one annoying fact was borne in upon my understanding—that we were weather-bound. An armed novice cannot mount his horse without help and plenty of it. Sandy was not enough; not enough for me, anyway. We had to wait until somebody should come along. Waiting in silence would have been agreeable enough, for I was full of matter for reflection, and wanted to give it a chance to

work. I wanted to try and think out how it was that rational or
even half-rational men could ever have learned to wear armor,
considering its inconveniences; and how they had managed to
keep up such a fashion for generations when it was plain that
what I had suffered to-day they had had to suffer all the days
of their lives. I wanted to think that out; and moreover I
wanted to think out some way to reform this evil and persuade
the people to let the foolish fashion die out: but thinking was
out of the question in the circumstances. You couldn't think
where Sandy was. She was a quite biddable creature and good-
hearted, but she had a flow of talk that was as steady as a
mill and made your head sore like the drays and wagons in a
city. If she had had a cork she would have been a comfort.
But you can't cork that kind; they would die. Her clack was
going all day, and you would think something would surely
happen to her works by-and-by; but no, they never got out of
order; and she never had to slack up for words. She could
grind and pump and churn and buzz by the week, and never
stop to oil up or blow out. And yet the result was just nothing
but wind. She never had any ideas, any more than a fog has.
She was a perfect blatherskite; I mean for jaw, jaw, jaw, talk,
talk, talk, jabber, jabber, jabber; — but just as good as she could
be. I hadn't minded her mill that morning, on account of having that hornet's nest of other troubles; but more than once in
the afternoon I had to say: —

"Take a rest, child; the way you are using up all the
domestic air, the kingdom will have to go to importing it by
to-morrow, and it's a low enough treasury without that."

By permission of S. L. Clemens and his publishers.

THE TRUE PRINCE AND THE FEIGNED ONE

From 'The Prince and the Pauper': copyright 1889, by Charles L. Webster
and Company

A T LAST the final act was at hand. The Archbishop of Canter-
bury lifted up the crown of England from its cushion and
held it out over the trembling mock king's head. In the
same instant a rainbow radiance flashed along the spacious tran-
sept; for with one impulse every individual in the great concourse of nobles lifted a coronet and poised it over his or her
head — and paused in that attitude.

A deep hush pervaded the Abbey. At this impressive
moment a startling apparition intruded upon the scene — an apparition observed by none in the absorbed multitude, until it
suddenly appeared, moving up the great central isle. It was a
boy, bare-headed, ill shod, and clothed in coarse plebeian garments that were falling to rags. He raised his hand with a
solemnity which ill comported with his soiled and sorry aspect,
and delivered this note of warning: —

"I forbid you to set the crown of England upon that forfeited head. *I* am the king!"

In an instant several indignant hands were laid upon the boy,
but in the same instant Tom Canty, in his regal vestments, made
a swift step forward and cried out in a ringing voice: —

"Loose him and forbear! He *is* the king!"

A sort of panic of astonishment swept the assemblage, and
they partly rose in their places and stared in a bewildered way
at one another and at the chief figures in this scene, like persons
who wondered whether they were awake and in their senses or
asleep and dreaming. The Lord Protector was as amazed as the
rest, but quickly recovered himself and exclaimed in a voice of
authority: —

"Mind not his Majesty, his malady is upon him again — seize
the vagabond!"

He would have been obeyed, but the mock king stamped his
foot and cried out: —

"On your peril! Touch him not, he is the king!"

The hands were withheld; a paralysis fell upon the house; no
one moved, no one spoke; indeed no one knew how to act or
what to say, in so strange and surprising an emergency. While
all minds were struggling to right themselves, the boy still

moved steadily forward, with high port and confident mien; he
had never halted from the beginning; and while the tangled
minds still floundered helplessly, he stepped upon the platform,
and the mock king ran with a glad face to meet him, and fell on
his knees before him and said:—

"O my lord the king, let poor Tom Canty be first to swear
fealty to thee, and say, 'Put on thy crown and enter into thine
own again!'"

The Lord Protector's eye fell sternly upon the new-comer's
face; but straightway the sternness vanished away, and gave
place to an expression of wondering surprise. This thing happened also to the other great officers. They glanced at each
other, and retreated a step by a common and unconscious impulse. The thought in each mind was the same: "What a
strange resemblance!"

The Lord Protector reflected a moment or two in perplexity;
then he said, with grave respectfulness:—

"By your favor, sir, I desire to ask certain questions
which—"

"I will answer them, my lord."

The duke asked him many questions about the court, the late
king, the prince, the princesses,— the boy answered them correctly and without hesitating. He described the rooms of state
in the palace, the late king's apartments, and those of the
Prince of Wales.

It was strange; it was wonderful; yes, it was unaccountable—
so all said that heard it. The tide was beginning to turn, and
Tom Canty's hopes to run high, when the Lord Protector shook
his head and said:—

"It is true it is most wonderful—but it is no more than our
lord the king likewise can do." This remark, and this reference
to himself as still the king, saddened Tom Canty, and he felt his
hopes crumbling under him. "These are not *proofs*," added the
Protector.

The tide was turning very fast now, very fast indeed—but
in the wrong direction; it was leaving poor Tom Canty stranded
on the throne, and sweeping the other out to sea. The Lord
Protector communed with himself—shook his head; the thought
forced itself upon him, "It is perilous to the State and to us all,
to entertain so fateful a riddle as this; it could divide the nation
and undermine the throne." He turned and said:—

"Sir Thomas, arrest this— No, hold!" His face lighted, and he confronted the ragged candidate with this question:—

"Where lieth the Great Seal? Answer me this truly, and the riddle is unriddled; for only he that was Prince of Wales *can* so answer! On so trivial a thing hang a throne and a dynasty!"

It was a lucky thought, a happy thought. That it was so considered by the great officials was manifested by the silent applause that shot from eye to eye around their circle in the form of bright approving glances. Yes, none but the true prince could dissolve the stubborn mystery of the vanished Great Seal —this forlorn little impostor had been taught his lesson well, but here his teachings must fail, for his teacher himself could not answer *that* question—ah, very good, very good indeed; now we shall be rid of this troublesome and perilous business in short order! And so they nodded invisibly and smiled inwardly with satisfaction, and looked to see this foolish lad stricken with a palsy of guilty confusion. How surprised they were, then, to see nothing of the sort happen—how they marveled to hear him answer up promptly in a confident and untroubled voice and say:—

"There is naught in this riddle that is difficult." Then, without so much as a by-your-leave to anybody, he turned and gave this command with the easy manner of one accustomed to doing such things: "My lord St. John, go you to my private cabinet in the palace,—for none knoweth the place better than you,—and close down to the floor, in the left corner, remotest from the door that opens from the ante-chamber, you shall find in the wall a brazen nail-head; press upon it and a little jewel-closet will fly open, which not even you do know of—no, nor any soul else in all the world but me and the trusty artisan that did contrive it for me. The first thing that falleth under your eye will be the Great Seal—fetch it hither."

All the company wondered at this speech, and wondered still more to see the little mendicant pick out this peer without hesitancy or apparent fear of mistake, and call him by name with such a placidly convincing air of having known him all his life. The peer was almost surprised into obeying. He even made a movement as if to go, but quickly recovered his tranquil attitude and confessed his blunder with a blush. Tom Canty turned upon him and said sharply:—

"Why dost thou hesitate? Hast not heard the king's command? Go!"

The lord St. John made a deep obeisance — and it was observed that it was a significantly cautious and non-committal one, it not being delivered at either of the kings, but at the neutral ground about half-way between the two — and took his leave.

Now began a movement of the gorgeous particles of that official group which was slow, scarcely perceptible, and yet steady and persistent,— a movement such as is observed in a kaleidoscope that is turned slowly, whereby the components of one splendid cluster fall away and join themselves to another — a movement which little by little, in the present case, dissolved the glittering crowd that stood about Tom Canty and clustered it together again in the neighborhood of the new-comer. Tom Canty stood almost alone. Now ensued a brief season of deep suspense and waiting — during which even the few faint-hearts still remaining near Tom Canty gradually scraped together courage enough to glide, one by one, over to the majority. So at last Tom Canty, in his royal robes and jewels, stood wholly alone and isolated from the world, a conspicuous figure, occupying an elegant vacancy.

Now the lord St. John was seen returning. As he advanced up the mid-aisle, the interest was so intense that the low murmur of conversation in the great assemblage died out and was succeeded by a profound hush, a breathless stillness, through which his footfalls pulsed with a dull and distant sound. Every eye was fastened upon him as he moved along. He reached the platform, paused a moment, then moved toward Tom Canty with a deep obeisance, and said: —

"Sire, the Seal is not there!"

A mob does not melt away from the presence of a plague-patient with more haste than the band of pallid and terrified courtiers melted away from the presence of the shabby little claimant of the crown. In a moment he stood all alone, without friend or supporter, a target upon which was concentrated a bitter fire of scornful and angry looks. The Lord Protector called out fiercely: —

"Cast the beggar into the street, and scourge him through the town — the paltry knave is worth no more consideration!"

Officers of the guard sprang forward to obey, but Tom Canty waved them off and said; —

"Back! Whoso touches him perils his life!"

The Lord Protector was perplexed in the last degree. He said to the lord St. John:—

"Searched you well?—but it boots not to ask that. It doth seem passing strange. Little things, trifles, slip out of one's ken, and one does not think it matter for surprise; but how so bulky a thing as the Seal of England can vanish away and no man be able to get track of it again—a massy golden disk—"

Tom Canty, with beaming eyes, sprang forward and shouted:

"Hold, that is enough! Was it round?—and thick?—and had it letters and devices graved upon it?—Yes? Oh, *now* I know what this Great Seal is, that there's been such worry and pother about! An ye had described it to me, ye could have had it three weeks ago. Right well I know where it lies; but it was not I that put it there—first."

"Who then, my liege?" asked the Lord Protector.

"He that stands there—the rightful king of England. And he shall tell you himself where it lies—then you will believe he knew it of his own knowledge. Bethink thee, my king—spur thy memory—it was the last, the very *last* thing thou didst that day before thou didst rush forth from the palace, clothed in my rags, to punish the soldier that insulted me."

A silence ensued, undisturbed by a movement or a whisper, and all eyes were fixed upon the new-comer, who stood with bent head and corrugated brow, groping in his memory among a thronging multitude of valueless recollections for one single little elusive fact, which, found, would seat him upon a throne—unfound, would leave him as he was for good and all—a pauper and an outcast. Moment after moment passed—the moments built themselves into minutes—still the boy struggled silently on, and gave no sign. But at last he heaved a sigh, shook his head slowly, and said, with a trembling lip and in a despondent voice:—

"I call the scene back—all of it—but the Seal hath no place in it." He paused, then looked up, and said with gentle dignity, "My lords and gentlemen, if ye will rob your rightful sovereign of his own for lack of this evidence which he is not able to furnish, I may not stay ye, being powerless. But—"

"Oh folly, oh madness, my king!" cried Tom Canty in a panic; "wait!—think! Do not give up!—the cause is not lost! nor *shall* be, neither! List to what I say—follow every word—

I am going to bring that morning back again, every hap just as it happened. We talked — I told you of my sisters, Nan and Bet — ah yes, you remember that; and about my old grandam — and the rough games of the lads of Offal Court — yes, you remember these things also; very well, follow me still, you shall recall everything. You gave me food and drink, and did with princely courtesy send away the servants, so that my low breeding might not shame me before them — ah yes, this also you remember."

As Tom checked off his details, and the other boy nodded his head in recognition of them, the great audience and the officials stared in puzzled wonderment; the tale sounded like true history, yet how could this impossible conjunction between a prince and a beggar boy have come about? Never was a company of people so perplexed, so interested, and so stupefied before.

"For a jest, my prince, we did exchange garments. Then we stood before a mirror; and so alike were we that both said it seemed as if there had been no change made — yes, you remember that. Then you noticed that the soldier had hurt my hand — look! here it is, I cannot yet even write with it, the fingers are so stiff. At this your Highness sprang up, vowing vengeance upon that soldier, and ran toward the door — you passed a table — that thing you call the Seal lay on that table — you snatched it up and looked eagerly about, as if for a place to hide it — your eye caught sight of — "

"There, 'tis sufficient! — and the dear God be thanked!" exclaimed the ragged claimant, in a mighty excitement. "Go, my good St. John, — in an arm-piece of the Milanese armor that hangs on the wall, thou'lt find the Seal!"

"Right, my king! right!" cried Tom Canty; "*now* the sceptre of England is thine own; and it were better for him that would dispute it that he had been born dumb! Go, my lord St. John, give thy feet wings!"

The whole assemblage was on its feet now, and well-nigh out of its mind with uneasiness, apprehension, and consuming excitement. On the floor and on the platform a deafening buzz of frantic conversation burst forth, and for some time nobody knew anything or heard anything or was interested in anything but what his neighbor was shouting into his ear, or he was shouting into his neighbor's ear. Time — nobody knew how much of it — swept by unheeded and unnoted. — At last a sudden hush fell upon the house, and in the same moment St. John appeared upon the platform and held the Great Seal aloft in his hand. Then such a shout went up!

"Long live the true king!"

For five minutes the air quaked with shouts and the crash of musical instruments, and was white with a storm of waving handkerchiefs; and through it all a ragged lad, the most conspicuous figure in England, stood, flushed and happy and proud, in the centre of the spacious platform, with the great vassals of the kingdom kneeling around him.

Then all rose, and Tom Canty cried out:—

"Now, O my king, take these regal garments back, and give poor Tom thy servant his shreds and remnants again."

The Lord Protector spoke up:—

"Let the small varlet be stripped and flung into the Tower."

But the new king, the true king, said:—

"I will not have it so. But for him I had not got my crown again — none shall lay a hand upon him to harm him. And as for thee, my good uncle, my Lord Protector, this conduct of thine is not grateful toward this poor lad, for I hear he hath made thee a duke" — the Protector blushed — "yet he was not a king; wherefore, what is thy fine title worth now? To-morrow you shall sue to me, *through him*, for its confirmation, else no duke, but a simple earl, shalt thou remain."

Under this rebuke his Grace the Duke of Somerset retired a little from the front for the moment. The king turned to Tom, and said kindly:—

"My poor boy, how was it that you could remember where I hid the Seal, when I could not remember it myself?"

"Ah, my king, that was easy, since I used it divers days."

"Used it,— yet could not explain where it was?"

"I did not know it was *that* they wanted. They did not describe it, your Majesty."

"Then how used you it?"

The red blood began to steal up into Tom's cheeks, and he dropped his eyes and was silent.

"Speak up, good lad, and fear nothing," said the king. "How used you the Great Seal of England?"

Tom stammered a moment in a pathetic confusion, then got it out:—

"To crack nuts with!"

Poor child, the avalanche of laughter that greeted this nearly swept him off his feet. But if a doubt remained in any mind that Tom Canty was not the king of England and familiar with the august appurtenances of royalty, this reply disposed of it utterly.

Meantime the sumptuous robe of state had been removed from Tom's shoulders to the king's, whose rags were effectually hidden from sight under it. Then the coronation ceremonies were resumed; the true king was anointed and the crown set upon his head, whilst cannon thundered the news to the city, and all London seemed to rock with applause.

By permission of S. L. Clemens and his publishers.

ARTHUR HUGH CLOUGH

(1819–1861)

BY CHARLES ELIOT NORTON

THE intellectual mood of many of the finest spirits in England and New England during the second quarter of the nineteenth century had something of the nature of a surprise to themselves, no less than to those who came within their influence. It was indeed a natural though unforeseen result of forces, various in kind, that had long been silently at work. The conflicting currents of thought and moral sentiment, which in all ages perplex and divide the hearts of men, took a new direction and seemed to have gathered volume and swiftness. Hardly since the Reformation had there been so deep and general a stirring of the questions, the answers to which, whether they be final or merely provisional, involve conclusions relating to the deepest interests of men. Old convictions were confronted by new doubts; ancient authority was met by a modern spirit of independence. This new intellectual mood was perhaps first distinctly manifest in England in Carlyle's essays, and correspondingly in New England in the essays and poems of Emerson; it was expressed in 'In Memoriam' and 'Maud'; it gave the undertone of Arnold's most characteristic verse, and it found clear and strikingly distinctive utterance in the poems of Clough. His nature was of rare superiority alike of character and intellect. His moral integrity and sincerity imparted clearness to his imagination and strength to his intelligence, so that while the most marked distinction of his poems is that which they possess as a mirror of spiritual conditions shared by many of his contemporaries, they have hardly less interest as the expression and image of his own individuality.

Arthur Hugh Clough was born at Liverpool on New Year's Day, 1819.* His father, who came of an old Welsh family (his mother, Anne Perfect, was from Yorkshire), had established himself in Liverpool as a cotton merchant. Toward the end of 1822 he emigrated with his wife and four children to Charleston, South Carolina, and here for four years was their home. For Arthur they were important years. He was a shy, sensitive boy, "already considered as the genius of the family." He was his mother's darling. She was a woman "rigidly simple in her tastes and habits, of stern integrity"; of cultivated intelligence, fond of poetry, a lover of nature, and

* Ruskin and Lowell were his close contemporaries; they were born in February of the same year.

quickly sympathetic with high character, whether in real life or in the pages of romance. While his father taught him his Latin grammar and his arithmetic, his mother read with him from Pope's Iliad and Odyssey, from Scott's novels and other books fitted to quicken the imagination. Her influence was strong in the shaping of his taste and disposition.

In 1828 the family returned for a visit to England, and Arthur was put to school at Chester, whence in the next year he was transferred to Rugby. Dr. Arnold had then very lately become the headmaster at Rugby, and was already giving to the school a tone and quality unknown previously to the public schools of England. He strove to impress upon the boys the sense of personal responsibility, and to rouse their conscience to the doing of duty, not so much as a matter essential to the discipline of the school as to the formation of manly and religious character. The influence of his high, vigorous, and ardent nature was of immense force. But its virtue was impaired by the artificiality of the ecclesiastical system of the Church of England, and the irrationality of the dogmatic creed which, even to a nature as liberal as Dr. Arnold's, seemed to belong to the essentials of religion, and to be indissoluble from the foundation of morality.

Clough became Arnold's devoted disciple, but he had intellectual independence and sincerity enough to save him from yielding his own individuality to any stream of external influence, however powerful. What he called "the busy argufying spirit of the prize schoolboy" stood him in good stead. But the moral stress was great, and it left him early with a sense of strain and of perplexity, as his mind opened to the wider and deeper problems of life, for the solution of which the traditional creed seemed insufficient. His career at school was of the highest distinction; and when he was leaving Rugby for Oxford in 1836, Dr. Arnold broke the rule of silence to which he almost invariably adhered in the delivery of prizes, and congratulated Clough on having gained every honor which Rugby could bestow, and on having done the highest credit to the school at the University,— for he had won the Balliol Scholarship, "then and now the highest honor which a schoolboy could obtain."

Clough went into residence at Oxford in October, 1837. It was a time of stirring of heart and trouble of mind at the University. The great theological controversy which was to produce such far-reaching effects upon the lives of individuals, and upon the Church of England as a whole, was then rising to its height. Newman was at the acme of his popularity and influence. His followers were zealous and active. Ward, his most earnest disciple, was one of Clough's nearest friends. Clough, not yet nineteen years old, but morally and intellectually developed beyond his years and accustomed already to independent speculation in regard to creed and conduct, was inevitably drawn into the deep waters of theological discussion. He heard, too, those other voices which Matthew Arnold in his admirable lecture on Emerson has spoken of as deeply affecting the more sensitive youthful spirits of the Oxford of this time,— the voices of Goethe, of Carlyle, and of Emerson. He studied hard, but his studies seemed, for the moment at least, to be of secondary importance. Although unusually reserved in demeanor and silent in general company, his reputation grew, not merely as a scholar, but as a man distinguished above his fellows for loftiness of spirit, for sweetness of disposition, and for superiority of moral no less than of intellectual qualities. With much interior storm and stress, his convictions were gradually maturing. He resisted the prevailing tendencies of Oxford thought, but did not easily find a secure basis for his own beliefs. In 1841 he tried for and missed his first class in the examinations. It was more a surprise and disappointment to others than to himself. He knew that he had not shown himself in the examinations for what he really was, and his failure did not affect his confidence in his own powers, nor did others lose faith in him, as was shown by his election in the next year to a fellowship at Oriel, and the year later to his appointment as tutor.

His livelihood being thus assured, he led from 1843 to 1848 a «quiet, hard-working, uneventful tutor's life, diversified with reading parties» in the vacations. He was writing poems from time to time, but his vocation as poet was not fully recognized by himself or by others. He had been obliged, in assuming the duties of tutor, to sign the Thirty-nine Articles,— though as he wrote to a friend, «reluctantly enough, and I am not quite sure whether or not in a justifiable sense. However, I have for the present laid by that perplexity, though it may perhaps recur at some time or other; and in general, I do not feel perfectly satisfied about staying in my tutor capacity at Oxford.»

The perplexity would not down, but as the years went on, the troubled waters of his soul gradually cleared themselves. He succeeded in attaining independence of mind such as few men attain, and in finding, if not a solution of the moral perplexities of life, at least a position from which they might be frankly confronted without blinking and without self-deception. It became impossible for him to accept, however they might be interpreted, the doctrines of any church. He would not play tricks with words nor palter with the integrity of his soul. This perfect mental honesty of Clough, and his entire sincerity of expression, were a stumbling-block to many of his more conventional contemporaries, and have remained as a rock of offense to many of the readers of his poetry, who find it disturbing to be obliged to recognize in his work a test of their own sincerity in dealing with themselves. With how few are conviction and profession perfectly at one! The difficulty of the struggle in Clough's case, the difficulty of freeing himself from the chains of association, of tradition, of affection, of interest, which bound him to conformity with and acceptance of the popular creed in one or the other of its forms, has led superficial critics of his life and poetry to find in them evidence that the struggle was too hard for him and the result unsatisfactory. There could not be a greater error. Clough's honest acceptance of the insolubility of the vain questions which men are perpetually asking, and his recognition of the insufficiency of the answers which they are ready to accept or to pretend to accept, left him as regards his most inward soul one of the serenest of men. The questions of practical life, of action, of duty, indeed presented themselves to his sensitive and contemplative nature with their full perplexity; but his spiritual life was based on a foundation that could not be shaken. He had learned the lesson of skepticism, and accepted without trouble the fact of the limitation of human faculties and the insolubility of the mystery of life. He was indeed tired with the hard work of years, and worried by the uncertainty of his future; when at length, in order to deliver himself from a constrained if not a false position, and to obtain perfect freedom of expression as well as of thought, he resigned in 1848 both his fellowship and tutorship.

It was a momentous decision, for it left him without any definite means of support, it alienated the authorities of the University, it isolated him from many old friends. Immediately after resigning his tutorship Clough went to Paris with Emerson, then on a visit to Europe, as his companion. They were drawn thither by interest in the strange Revolution which was then in progress, and by desire to watch its aspects. The social conditions of England had long been matter of concern to Clough. He had been deeply touched by the misery of the Irish famine in 1847, and had printed a very striking pamphlet in the autumn of that year, urging upon the students at Oxford retrenchment of needless expenditure and restrictions of waste and luxury. His sympathies were with the poor, and he was convinced of the need of radical social reform. He therefore observed the course of revolution on the Continent not merely with curiosity, but with sympathetic hope.

In the autumn of this year, after his return home, and while at Liverpool with his mother and sister, he wrote his first long poem, 'The Bothie of Tober-na-Vuolich; a Long-Vacation Pastoral.' It had no great immediate success, but it made him known to a somewhat wider public than that of Oxford. It was in its form the fruit of the reading parties in the Highlands in previous summers. It was in hexameters, and he asked Emerson to "convey to Mr. Longfellow the fact that it was a reading of his 'Evangeline' aloud to my mother and sister, which, coming after a re-perusal of the Iliad, occasioned this outbreak of hexameters." It is a delightful poem, full of vitality and variety, original in design, simple in incident. It has the freshness and wholesomeness of the open air, the charm of nature and of life, with constant interplay of serious thought and light humor, of gravity and gayety of sentiment.

Its publication was followed speedily by a little volume entitled 'Ambarvalia,' made up of two parts; one, of poems by Clough, and one, of those by an old school and college friend, Mr. Burbidge. Clough's part consisted, as he wrote to Emerson, of "old things, the casualties of at least ten years." But many of these "casualties" are characteristic expressions of personal experience, to which Clough's absolute sincerity gives deep human interest. They are the records of "his search amid the maze of life for a clue whereby to move." They deal with the problems of his own life, and these problems perplex other men as well. "I have seen higher, holier things than these," he writes in 1841:—

> "I have seen higher, holier things than these,
>   And therefore must to these refuse my heart,
>   Yet I am panting for a little ease;
>   I'll take, and so depart."

But he checks himself:—

> "Ah, hold! the heart is prone to fall away,
>   Her high and cherished visions to forget;
>   And if thou takest, how wilt thou repay
>   So vast, so dread a debt?"

The little volume appealed to but a small band of readers. The poems it contained did not allure by fluency of fancy or richness of diction; they were not of a kind to win sudden popularity: but they gave evidence of a poet who, though not complete master of his art, and not arrived at a complete understanding of himself, had yet a rare power of reflection and expression and a still rarer sincerity of imaginative vision. They were poems that gave large promise, and that promise was already in part fulfilled by the 'Bothie.'

Early in 1849 the headship of University Hall in London was offered to Clough and accepted by him. This was an institution professedly non-sectarian, established for the purpose of receiving students in attendance upon the lectures at University College. He was not to enter upon the duties of the place until October, and he spent the greater part of the intervening period in a fruitful visit to

Italy. He reached Rome in April. All Italy was in revolution. The Pope had fled from Rome. The Republic had been declared, and Mazzini was in control of the government. The French army was approaching to besiege the city, and Clough resolved to await the event. No more vivid and picturesque account of aspects of the siege exists than is to be found in his poem of 'Amours de Voyage,' written in great part at Rome, under the pressure and excitement of the moment; then laid aside in the poet's desk, and not published till long afterward. It consists of a series of letters supposed to be written by various persons, in which a narrative of passing events is interwoven with a love story. The hero of the story is a creation of extraordinary subtlety and interest. He has much of the temperament of Hamlet: not wanting in personal courage, nor in resolution when forced to action, but hesitating through sensitiveness of conscience, through dread of mistaking momentary impulse for fixed conviction, through the clearness with which diverging paths of conduct present themselves to his imagination, with the inevitable doubt as to which be the right one to follow. The character, though by no means an exact or complete image of the poet's own, is yet drawn in part from himself, and affords glimpses of his inner nature, of the delicacy of his sensitive poetic spirit, of his tendency to subtle introspective reflection, of his honesty in dealing with facts and with himself. To see things as they are, to keep his eyes clear, to be true to

« The living central inmost I
Within the scales of mere exterior — »

was the principle of his life. The charm of 'Amours de Voyage,' however, consists not merely in animated description, in delicate sentiment, and in the poetic representation of sensitive, impressionable, and high-minded youth, but in its delicate humor in the delineation of character, and in its powerful, imaginative, picturesque reproduction of the atmosphere and influence of Rome, and of the spirit of the moment to which the poem relates. It is as unique and as original in its kind as the 'Bothie.' It is a poem that appeals strongly to the lovers of the poetry of high culture, and is not likely to lack such readers in future generations.

From Rome in July Clough went to Naples, and there wrote another of his most striking poems, 'Easter Day.' In the autumn of 1850 he again went during a short vacation to Italy, but now to Venice; and while there began his third long poem, 'Dipsychus,' of which the scene is in that city. In this poem, which represents the conflict of the soul in its struggles to maintain itself against the temptations of the world and the Devil, Clough again wrote out much of his inner life. It is not so much a piece of strict autobiography of the spirit of an individual, as an imaginative drama of the spiritual experience common in all times to men of fine nature, seeking a solution of the puzzle of their own hearts. In none of his other poems is there such variety of tone, or such an exhibition of mature poetic power. It is indeed loosely constructed; but its separate parts, each contributing to the development of its main theme, with their diversity of imagination, reflection, wit, and sentiment, combine in an impressive unity of effect.

The position at University Hall proved not altogether satisfactory; and no other opening for him offering itself in England, Clough determined after much hesitation and deliberation to try his fortune as a teacher and writer in America. He sailed in October, 1852, on a steamer on which he had Lowell and Thackeray for fellow passengers. He spent the next eight months at Cambridge, employed in tutoring and in literary work, winning the warm regard of the remarkable group of men of letters who then gave distinction to the society of Cambridge and of Boston, and especially keeping up his friendship with Emerson by frequent visits to Concord. There seemed a fair prospect of success for him in his new career. But his friends at home, deeply attached to him, and ill content that he should leave them, obtained for him an appointment as examiner in the Education Department of the Council Office. The salary would give to him a secure though moderate income. He was the more drawn to accept the place, because shortly before leaving England he had become engaged to be married; and accordingly in July, 1853, he returned home and at once entered on the duties of his office. In June 1854 he married. For the next seven years his life was tranquil, laborious, and happy. The account of these years contained in the beautiful sketch of his life by his wife, which is prefixed to the collection of his 'Letters, Poems and Prose Remains,' * gives a picture of Clough's domestic felicity, and of the various interests which engaged him outside of the regular drudgery of official work. His own letters bear witness to the content of his days. He had little leisure for poetry. He was overworked, and in 1860 his health gave way. Leave of absence from the office was given to him. He went to the seashore; he visited the Continent: but though at times he seemed to gain strength, there was no steady recovery. In the autumn of 1861 he went to Italy, accompanied by his wife; he enjoyed the journey, but they had only reached the Lakes when he experienced a touch of fever. They went on to Florence; he became more seriously ill. He began however apparently to recover, but a

* It is on this sketch of his life that the present account of him is mainly based.

sudden blow of paralysis struck him down, and on the 13th day of November he died.

Among the most original and beautiful of Matthew Arnold's poems is his 'Thyrsis, a Monody,' to commemorate his friend Arthur Hugh Clough. Thyrsis his mate has gone:—

«No purer or more subtle soul»

than he ever sought the light that

«leaves its seeker still untired,—
Still onward faring by his own heart inspired.»

The lament is as true as it is tender. The singer continues:—

«What though the music of thy rustic flute
Kept not for long its happy country tone;
Lost it too soon, and learnt a stormy note
Of men contention-tost, of men who groan,
Which tasked thy pipe too sore, and tired thy throat,—
It failed, and thou wast mute!
Yet hadst thou always visions of our light.»

Yes, always visions of the light! But Arnold's usual felicity of discrimination is lacking in this last stanza. The stormy note is not the characteristic note of Clough's mature song, nor does his art betray the overtasked pipe. His pipe indeed is not attuned, as was Arnold's own, to the soft melancholy of regret at leaving behind the happy fields of the past in the quest for the light that shines beyond and across the untraveled and dim waste before them; its tone was less pathetic, but not less clear. The music of each is the song of travelers whose road is difficult, whose goal is uncertain. Their only guide is the fugitive light, now faint, now distinct, which allures them with irresistible compulsion. Their pathways at times diverge; but when most divergent, the notes of their accordant pipes are heard in the same direction.

The memory of Clough remains, with those who had the happiness of knowing him in life, distinct and precious. It is that of one of the highest and purest souls. Sensitive, simple, tender, manly, his figure stands as one of the ideal figures of the past, the image of the true poet, the true friend, the true man. He died too young for his full fame, but not too young for the love which is better than fame.

C. E. Norton.

THERE IS NO GOD

"THERE is no God," the wicked saith,
    "And truly it's a blessing,
For what he might have done with us
    It's better only guessing."

"There is no God," a youngster thinks,
    "Or really, if there may be,
He surely didn't mean a man
    Always to be a baby."

"There is no God, or if there is,"
    The tradesman thinks, "'twere funny
If he should take it ill in me
    To make a little money."

"Whether there be," the rich man says,
    "It matters very little,
For I and mine, thank somebody,
    Are not in want of victual."

Some others, also, to themselves,
    Who scarce so much as doubt it,
Think there is none, when they are well,
    And do not think about it.

But country folks who live beneath
    The shadow of the steeple;
The parson and the parson's wife,
    And mostly married people;

Youths green and happy in first love,
    So thankful for illusion;
And men caught out in what the world
    Calls guilt, in first confusion;

And almost every one when age,
    Disease, or sorrows strike him,—
Inclines to think there is a God,
    Or something very like him.

THE LATEST DECALOGUE

Thou shalt have one God only: who
    Would be at the expense of two?
No graven images may be
Worshiped, save in the currency.
Swear not at all; since for thy curse
Thine enemy is none the worse.
At church on Sunday to attend
Will serve to keep the world thy friend:
Honor thy parents; that is, all
From whom advancement may befall.
Thou shalt not kill; but need'st not strive
Officiously to keep alive.
Adultery it is not fit
Or safe (for woman) to commit.
Thou shalt not steal: an empty feat,
When 'tis as lucrative to cheat.
Bear not false witness: let the lie
Have time on its own wings to fly.
Thou shalt not covet; but tradition
Approves all forms of competition.

TO THE UNKNOWN GOD

O Thou whose image in the shrine
    Of human spirits dwells divine;
        Which from that precinct once conveyed,
To be to outer day displayed,
Doth vanish, part, and leave behind
Mere blank and void of empty mind,
Which willful fancy seeks in vain
With casual shapes to fill again!

O Thou that in our bosom's shrine
Dost dwell, unknown because divine!
I thought to speak, I thought to say,
"The light is here," — "Behold the way," —
"The voice was thus," — and "Thus the word," —
And "Thus I saw," — and "That I heard," —
But from the lips that half assayed
The imperfect utterance fell unmade.

O Thou, in that mysterious shrine
Enthroned, as I must say, divine!
I will not frame one thought of what
Thou mayest either be or not.
I will not prate of "thus" and "so,"
And be profane with "yes" and "no";
Enough that in our soul and heart
Thou, whatsoe'er Thou may'st be, art.

Unseen, secure in that high shrine
Acknowledged present and divine,
I will not ask some upper air,
Some future day to place Thee there;
Nor say, nor yet deny, such men
And women say Thee thus and then:
Thy name was such, and there or here
To him or her Thou didst appear.

Do only Thou in that dim shrine,
Unknown or known, remain, divine;
There, or if not, at least in eyes
That scan the fact that round them lies,
The hand to sway, the judgment guide,
In sight and sense Thyself divide:
Be Thou but there, in soul and heart,—
I will not ask to feel Thou art.

EASTER DAY

NAPLES, 1849

THROUGH the great sinful streets of Naples as I past,
    With fiercer heat than flamed above my head,
My heart was hot within me; till at last
    My brain was lightened when my tongue had said—
        Christ is not risen!

        Christ is not risen, no—
        He lies and molders low;
        Christ is not risen!

What though the stone were rolled away, and though
        The grave found empty there?—
        If not there, then elsewhere;
If not where Joseph laid him first, why then
        Where other men

Translaid him after, in some humbler clay.
Long ere to-day
Corruption that sad perfect work hath done,
Which here she scarcely, lightly, had begun:
The foul engendered worm
Feeds on the flesh of the life-giving form
Of our most Holy and Anointed One.
He is not risen, no —
He lies and molders low;
Christ is not risen!

What if the women, ere the dawn was gray,
Saw one or more great angels, as they say
(Angels, or Him himself)? Yet neither there, nor then,
Nor afterwards, nor elsewhere, nor at all,
Hath he appeared to Peter or the Ten;
Nor, save in thunderous terror, to blind Saul;
Save in an after-Gospel and late Creed,
He is not risen, indeed, —
Christ is not risen!

Or what if e'en, as runs a tale, the Ten
Saw, heard, and touched, again and yet again?
What if at Emmaüs's inn, and by Capernaum's Lake,
Came One, the bread that brake —
Came One that spake as never mortal spake,
And with them ate, and drank, and stood, and walked about?
Ah! "some" did well to "doubt"!
Ah! the true Christ, while these things came to pass,
Nor heard, nor spake, nor walked, nor lived, alas!
He was not risen, no —
He lay and moldered low;
Christ was not risen!

As circulates in some great city crowd
A rumor changeful, vague, importunate, and loud,
From no determined centre, or of fact
Or authorship exact,
Which no man can deny
Nor verify;
So spread the wondrous fame;
He all the same
Lay senseless, moldering low;
He was not risen, no —
Christ was not risen!

Ashes to ashes, dust to dust;
As of the unjust, also of the just—
    Yea, of that Just One, too!
This is the one sad Gospel that is true—
    Christ is not risen!

Is he not risen, and shall we not rise?
    Oh, we unwise!
What did we dream, what wake we to discover?
Ye hills, fall on us, and ye mountains, cover!
    In darkness and great gloom
Come ere we thought it is *our* day of doom;
From the cursed world, which is one tomb,
    Christ is not risen!

Eat, drink, and play, and think that this is bliss:
    There is no heaven but this;
    There is no hell,
Save earth, which serves the purpose doubly well,
    Seeing it visits still
    With equalest apportionment of ill
Both good and bad alike, and brings to one same dust
    The unjust and the just
    With Christ, who is not risen.

Eat, drink, and die, for we are souls bereaved:
    Of all the creatures under heaven's wide cope
    We are most hopeless, who had once most hope,
And most beliefless, that had most believed.

    Ashes to ashes, dust to dust;
    As of the unjust, also of the just—
    Yea, of that Just One, too!
    It is the one sad Gospel that is true—
    Christ is not risen!

    Weep not beside the tomb,
    Ye women, unto whom
He was great solace while ye tended him;
    Ye who with napkin o'er the head
And folds of linen round each wounded limb
    Laid out the Sacred Dead;
And thou that bar'st him in thy wondering womb;
    Yea, Daughters of Jerusalem, depart,
Bind up as best you may your own sad bleeding heart:

Go to your homes, your living children tend,
Your earthly spouses love;
Set your affections *not* on things above,
Which moth and rust corrupt, which quickliest come to end:
Or pray, if pray ye must, and pray, if pray ye can,
For death; since dead is he whom ye deemed more than man,
Who is not risen: no —
But lies and molders low —
Who is not risen!

Ye men of Galilee!
Why stand ye looking up to heaven, where him ye ne'er may see,
Neither ascending hence, nor returning hither again?
Ye ignorant and idle fishermen!
Hence to your huts, and boats, and inland native shore,
And catch not men, but fish;
Whate'er things ye might wish,
Him neither here nor there ye e'er shall meet with more.
Ye poor deluded youths, go home,
Mend the old nets ye left to roam,
Tie the split oar, patch the torn sail:
It was indeed an "idle tale" —
He was not risen!

And oh, good men of ages yet to be,
Who shall believe *because* ye did not see —
Oh, be ye warned, be wise!
No more with pleading eyes,
And sobs of strong desire,
Unto the empty vacant void aspire,
Seeking another and impossible birth
That is not of your own, and only mother earth.
But if there is no other life for you,
Sit down and be content, since this must even do;
He is not risen!

One look and then depart,
Ye humble and ye holy men of heart;
And ye! ye ministers and stewards of a Word
Which ye would preach, because another heard —
Ye worshipers of that ye do not know,
Take these things hence and go: —
He is not risen!

Here, on our Easter Day
We rise, we come, and lo! we find Him not,
Gardener nor other, on the sacred spot:
Where they have laid Him there is none to say;
No sound, nor in, nor out—no word
Of where to seek the dead or meet the living Lord.
There is no glistering of an angel's wings,
There is no voice of heavenly clear behest:
Let us go hence, and think upon these things
    In silence, which is best.
    Is He not risen? No—
    But lies and molders low?
    Christ is not risen?

IT FORTIFIES MY SOUL TO KNOW

IT FORTIFIES my soul to know
    That though I perish, Truth is so;
    That howsoe'er I stray and range,
Whate'er I do, Thou dost not change;
I steadier step when I recall
That if I slip, Thou dost not fall!

SAY NOT, THE STRUGGLE NAUGHT AVAILETH

SAY not, the struggle naught availeth,
    The labor and the wounds are vain,
The enemy faints not, nor faileth,
    And as things have been, they remain.

If hopes were dupes, fears may be liars;
    It may be, in yon smoke concealed,
Your comrades chase e'en now the fliers,
    And but for you, possess the field.

For while the tired waves, vainly breaking,
    Seem here no painful inch to gain,
Far back, through creeks and inlets making,
    Comes silent, flooding in, the main.

And not by eastern windows only,
    When daylight comes, comes in the light;
In front, the sun climbs slow, how slowly!
    But westward, look, the land is bright.

COME BACK

COME back, come back! behold with straining mast
　And swelling sail, behold her steaming fast:
　With one new sun to see her voyage o'er,
With morning light to touch her native shore.
　　　Come back, come back!

Come back, come back! while westward laboring by,
With sailless yards, a bare black hulk we fly.
See how the gale we fight with sweeps her back
To our lost home, on our forsaken track.
　　　Come back, come back!

Come back, come back! across the flying foam
We hear faint far-off voices call us home:
Come back! ye seem to say; ye seek in vain;
We went, we sought, and homeward turned again.
　　　Come back, come back!

Come back, come back! and whither back, or why?
To fan quenched hopes, forsaken schemes to try;
Walk the old fields; pace the familiar street;
Dream with the idlers, with the bards compete.
　　　Come back, come back!

Come back, come back! and whither and for what?
To finger idly some old Gordian knot,
Unskilled to sunder, and too weak to cleave,
And with much toil attain to half-believe.
　　　Come back, come back!

Come back, come back! yea, back indeed do go
Sighs panting thick, and tears that want to flow;
Fond fluttering hopes upraise their useless wings,
And wishes idly struggle in the strings.
　　　Come back, come back!

Come back, come back! more eager than the breeze
The flying fancies sweep across the seas,
And lighter far than ocean's flying foam
The heart's fond message hurries to its home.
　　　Come back, come back!

Come back, come back!
Back flies the foam; the hoisted flag streams back;
The long smoke wavers on the homeward track;
Back fly with winds things which the wind obey:
The strong ship follows its appointed way.

AS SHIPS BECALMED

A s ships becalmed at eve, that lay
    With canvas drooping, side by side,
Two towers of sail, at dawn of day,
    Are scarce long leagues apart descried.

When fell the night, up sprang the breeze,
    And all the darkling hours they plied;
Nor dreamt but each the self-same seas
    By each was clearing, side by side:

E'en so — but why the tale reveal
    Of those whom, year by year unchanged,
Brief absence joined anew, to feel,
    Astounded, soul from soul estranged?

At dead of night their sails were filled,
    And onward each rejoicing steered;
Ah! neither blame, for neither willed
    Or wist what first with dawn appeared.

To veer, how vain! On, onward strain,
    Brave barks! — in light, in darkness too!
Through winds and tides one compass guides
    To that and your own selves be true.

But O blithe breeze! and O great seas!
    Though ne'er that earliest parting past,
On your wide plain they join again,
    Together lead them home at last.

One port, methought, alike they sought,—
    One purpose hold, where'er they fare;
O bounding breeze, O rushing seas,
    At last, at last, unite them there.

THE UNKNOWN COURSE

WHERE lies the land to which the ship would go?
   Far, far ahead, is all her seamen know;
    And where the land she travels from? Away,
Far, far behind, is all that they can say.

On sunny noons upon the deck's smooth face,
Linked arm in arm, how pleasant here to pace!
Or, o'er the stern reclining, watch below
The foaming wake far widening as we go.

On stormy nights, when wild Northwesters rave,
How proud a thing to fight with wind and wave!
The dripping sailor on the reeling mast
Exults to bear, and scorns to wish it past.

Where lies the land to which the ship would go?
Far, far ahead, is all her seamen know.
And where the land she travels from? Away,
Far, far behind, is all that they can say.

THE GONDOLA

AFLOAT; we move—delicious! Ah,
   What else is like the gondola?
    This level flow of liquid glass
Begins beneath us swift to pass.
It goes as though it went alone
By some impulsion of its own.
(How light it moves, how softly! Ah,
Were all things like the gondola!)

How light it moves, how softly! Ah,
Could life, as does our gondola,
Unvexed with quarrels, aims, and cares,
And moral duties and affairs,
Unswaying, noiseless, swift, and strong,
For ever thus—thus glide along!
(How light we move, how softly! Ah,
Were life but as the gondola!)

With no more motion than should bear
A freshness to the languid air;

With no more effort than expressed
The need and naturalness of rest,
Which we beneath a grateful shade
Should take on peaceful pillows laid!
(How light we move, how softly! Ah,
Were life but as the gondola!)

In one unbroken passage borne
To closing night from opening morn,
Uplift at whiles slow eyes to mark
Some palace-front, some passing bark;
Through windows catch the varying shore,
And hear the soft turns of the oar!
(How light we move, how softly! Ah,
Were life but as the gondola!)

THE POET'S PLACE IN LIFE

COME, Poet, come!
A thousand laborers ply their task
And what it tends to, scarcely ask,
And trembling thinkers on the brink
Shiver, and know not what to think.
To tell the purport of their pain,
And what our silly joys contain;
In lasting lineaments portray
The substance of the shadowy day;
Our real and inner deeds rehearse,
And make our meaning clear in verse —
Come, Poet, come! for but in vain
We do the work or feel the pain,
And gather up the evening gain,
Unless before the end thou come
To take, ere they are lost, their sum.

Come, Poet, come!
To give an utterance to the dumb,
And make vain babblers silent, come;
A thousand dupes point here and there,
Bewildered by the show and glare;
And wise men half have learnt to doubt
Whether we are not best without.
Come, Poet; both but wait to see
Their error proved to them in thee.

Come, Poet, come!
In vain I seem to call. And yet
Think not the living times forget.
Ages of heroes fought and fell
That Homer in the end might tell;
O'er groveling generations past
Upstood the Doric fane at last;
And countless hearts on countless years
Had wasted thoughts, and hopes, and fears,
Rude laughter and unmeaning tears,—
Ere England Shakespeare saw, or Rome
The pure perfection of her dome.
Others, I doubt not, if not we,
The issue of our toils shall see;
Young children gather as their own
The harvest that the dead had sown —
The dead forgotten and unknown.

ON KEEPING WITHIN ONE'S PROPER SPHERE

From 'The Bothie of Tober-na-Vuolich'

[A party of ⸻ ford men spend their long vacation in Scotland. In due
course they return to their colleges. Adam, one of the party,—
«The grave man nicknamed Adam,
White-tied, clerical, silent, with antique square-cut waistcoat,»
receives a letter at Christmas from Philip (Heuston),
«The Chartist, the poet, the eloquent speaker.»]

WHAT I said at Balloch has truth in it; only distorted.
    Plants are some for fruit, and some for flowering only;
    Let there be deer in parks as well as kine in paddocks,
Grecian buildings upon the earth, as well as Gothic.
There may be men perhaps whose vocation it is to be idle,
Idle, sumptuous even, luxurious, if it must be:
Only let each man seek to be that for which Nature meant him,
Independent surely of pleasure, if not regardless,
Independent also of station, if not regardless;
Irrespective also of station, as of enjoyment;
Do his duty in that state of life to which God, not man, shall
    call him.

If you were meant to plow, Lord Marquis, out with you and do it;
If you were meant to be idle, O beggar, behold I will feed thee:

Take my purse; you have far better right to it, friend, than the
    Marquis.
If you were born for a groom,—and you seem by your dress to
    believe so,—
Do it like a man, Sir George, for pay, in a livery-stable;
Yes, you may so release that slip of a boy at the corner,
Fingering books at the window, misdoubting the Eighth Command-
    ment.
What, a mere Dean with those wits, that debtor-and-creditor head-
    piece!
Go, my detective D. D., take the place of Burns the gauger.
Ah, fair Lady Maria, God meant you to live and be lovely:
Be so then, and I bless you. But ye, ye spurious ware, who
Might be plain women, and can be by no possibility better!
Ye unhappy statuettes, ye miserable trinkets,
Poor alabaster chimney-piece ornaments under glass cases,
Come, in God's name, come down! the very French clock by you
Puts you to shame with ticking; the fire-irons deride you.
Break your glasses; ye can! come down; ye are not really plaster,
Come, in God's name, come down! do anything, be but some-
    thing!

You, young girl, who have had such advantages, learnt so quickly,
Can you not teach? Oh, yes, and she likes Sunday-school extremely,
Only it's soon in the morning. Away! if to teach be your calling,
It is no play, but a business: off! go teach and be paid for it.
Surely that fussy old dowager yonder was meant for the counter;
Oh, she is notable very, and keeps her servants in order
Past admiration. Indeed, and keeps to employ her talent
How many, pray? to what use? Away! the hotel's her vocation.

Lady Sophie's so good to the sick, so firm and so gentle:
Is there a nobler sphere than of hospital nurse and matron?
Hast thou for cooking a turn, little Lady Clarissa? in with them,
In with your fingers! Their beauty it spoils, but your own it
    enhances;
For it is beautiful only to do the thing we are meant for.

But they will marry, have husbands, and children, and guests, and
    households—
Are there so many trades for a man,—for women one only,
First to look out for a husband and then to preside at his table?

Have you ever, Philip, my boy, looked at it in this way?
When the armies are set in array, and the battle beginning,
Is it well that the soldier whose post is far to the leftward
Say, I will go to the right, it is there I shall do best service?
There is a great Field-Marshal, my friend, who arrays our battalions;
Let us to Providence trust, and abide and work in our stations.

CONSIDER IT AGAIN

"OLD things need not be therefore true."
    O brother men, nor yet the new;
        Ah! still awhile the old thought retain,
And yet consider it again!

The souls of now two thousand years
Have laid up here their toils and fears,
And all the earnings of their pain,—
Ah, yet consider it again!

We! what do you see? each a space
Of some few yards before his face;
Does that the whole wide plan explain?
Ah, yet consider it again!

Alas! the great world goes its way,
And takes its truth from each new day;
They do not quit, nor yet retain,
Far less consider it again.

SAMUEL TAYLOR COLERIDGE.

SAMUEL TAYLOR COLERIDGE

(1772–1834)

BY GEORGE E. WOODBERRY

AMUEL TAYLOR COLERIDGE, the English poet and philosopher, was born at Ottery St. Mary, in Devonshire, October 21st, 1772. He was the ninth and youngest son of the vicar of the parish,—a man characterized by learning and also by some of its foibles,—under whose care he passed his childhood; but on the death of his father he was sent up to London to be educated at Christ's Hospital, and there spent, in companionship with Lamb, his school days from 1782 to 1791. He went in the latter year to Jesus College Cambridge. His career as an undergraduate was marked by an escapade,—his enlistment in the King's Regiment of Light Dragoons in the winter of 1793–94, from which he was released by the influence of his relatives; and in more important ways by his friendship with Southey, whom he found on a visit to Oxford, and his engagement to Sarah Fricker in the summer of 1794. He had already been attached to another young lady, Mary Evans, with whose family he had been intimate. In December 1794 he left Cambridge without taking a degree, and on October 21st, 1795, he was married. His biography from this point is one of confused and intricate detail, which only a long story could set forth plainly and exactly. Its leading external events were a residence in Germany in 1798–99 and a voyage to Malta, with travel in Sicily and Italy in 1804–6; in its inward development, the turning-points of his life were his first intimacy with the Wordsworths in 1797, during which his best poems were composed; his subjection to the opium habit, with increasing domestic unhappiness, in 1801–2; and his retreat under medical control to Highgate in 1816. He was practically separated from his family from the time of his voyage to Malta. Troubles of many kinds filled all these years, but he had always a power to attract friends who were deeply interested in his welfare, and he was never without admirers and helpers. Before he withdrew to Highgate he had resided first at Stowey in the neighborhood of Tom Poole, and later at Greta Hall near the Wordsworths; but he was often away from home, and after he ceased to be an inmate there, from 1806 to 1816, he led a wandering life, either in lodgings frequently changed, or in visits to his friends. His resources were always small, and from the start his friends were his patrons, making up subscriptions, loans, and gifts for him; in 1798 the Wedgwoods gave him a pension of £150 for life, which was soon secured for the support of his family, and in 1812 one-half of this was withdrawn; in 1825 he was granted a royal pension of one hundred guineas, and when this lapsed in 1830 Frere made it up to him. De Quincey had distinguished himself by an act of singular and impulsive generosity to him, upon first acquaintance. He was always cared for, though his indulgence in opium made it difficult for those who knew the fact to assist him directly in a wise way. His pecuniary embarrassment, however, was constant and trying during a great part of his life; his own wretchedness of spirit, under the painful conditions of his bodily state and his moral as well as material position, was very great; but through all these sufferings and trials he maintained sufficient energy to leave behind him a considerable body of literary work. He died July 25th, 1834.

The poetic genius of Coleridge, the highest of his many gifts, found brilliant and fascinating expression. His poems — those in which his fame lives — are as unique as they are memorable; and though their small number, their confined range, and the brief period during which his faculty was exercised with full freedom and power, seem to indicate a narrow vein, yet the remainder of his work in prose and verse leaves an impression of extraordinary and abundant intellectual force. In proportion as his imaginative creations stand apart, the spirit out of which they came must have possessed some singularity: and if the reader is not content with simple æsthetic appreciation of what the gods provide, but has some touch of curiosity leading him to look into the source of such remarkable achievement and its human history, he is at once interested in the personality of the "subtle-souled psychologist," as Shelley with his accurate critical insight first named him; in experiencing the fascination of the poetry one remembers the charm which Coleridge had in life, that quality which arrested attention in all companies and drew men's minds and hearts with a sense of something marvelous in him — "the most wonderful man," said Wordsworth, "that I ever met." The mind and heart of Coleridge, his whole life, have been laid open by himself and his friends and acquaintances without reserve in many volumes of letters and memoirs; it is easy to figure him as he lived and to recover his moods and aspect: but in order to conceive his nature and define its traits, it is necessary to take account especially of his incomplete and less perfect work, of his miscellaneous interests, and those activities which filled and confused his life without having any important share in establishing his fame.

The intellectual precocity which is the leading trait of Coleridge's boyhood, in the familiar portrait of "the inspired charity-boy" drawn by Lamb from schoolboy memories, is not unusual in a youth of genius; but the omnivorousness of knowledge which he then displayed continued into his manhood. He consumed vast quantities of book-learning. It is a more remarkable characteristic that from the earliest period in which he comes into clear view, he was accustomed to give out his ideas with freedom in an inexhaustible stream of talk. The activity of his mind was as phenomenal as its receptivity. In his college days, too, he was fanatical in all his energies. The remark of Southey after Shelley's visit to him, that here was a young man who was just what he himself had been in his college days, is illustrative; for if Southey was then inflamed with radicalism, Coleridge was yet more deeply infected and mastered by that wild fever of the revolutionary dawn. The tumult of Coleridge's mind, its incessant action, the lack of discipline in his thought, of restraint in his expression, of judgment in his affairs, are all important elements in his character at a time which in most men would be called the formative period of manhood, but which in him seems to have been intensely chaotic; what is most noticeable, however, is the volume of his mental energy. He expressed himself, too, in ways natural to such self-abundance. He was always a discourser, if the name may be used, from the London days at the "Salutation and the Cat" of which Lamb tells, saying that the landlord was ready to retain him because of the attraction of his conversation for customers; and as he went on to the more set forms of such monologue, he became a preacher without pay in Unitarian chapels, a journalist with unusual capacity for ready and sonorous writing in the press, a composer of whole periodicals such as his ventures The Watchman and The Friend, and a lecturer using only slight notes as the material of his remarks upon literature, education, philosophy, theology, or whatever the subject might be. In all these methods of expression which he took up one after the other, he merely talked in an ample way upon multifarious topics; in the conversation, sermon, leading article, written discourse, or flowing address, he was master of a swelling and often brilliant volubility, but he had neither the certainty of the orator nor the unfailing distinction of the author; there was an occasional and impromptu quality, a colloquial and episodical manner, the style of the irresponsible speaker. In his earlier days especially, the dominant note in Coleridge's whole nature was excitement. He was always animated, he was often violent, he was always without the principle of control. Indeed, a weakness of moral power seems to have been congenital, in the sense that he was not permanently bound by a practical sense of duty nor apparently observant of what place duty has in real life. There was misdirection of his affairs from the time when they came into his own hands; there was impulsiveness, thoughtlessness, a lack of judgment which augured ill for him; and in its total effect this amounted to folly. His intoxication with the scheme known as Pantisocracy, by which he with Southey and a few like-minded projectors were to found a socialistic community on the banks of the Susquehanna, is the most obvious comment on his practical sense. But his marriage, with the anecdotes of its preliminaries (one of which was that in those colloquies with Lamb at the London tavern, so charmingly described by his boon companion, he had forgotten his engagement or was indifferent to it), more strikingly exemplifies the irresponsible course of his life, more particularly as it proved to be ill-sorted, full of petty difficulties and makeshift expedients, and in the end a disastrous failure. A radical social scheme and an imprudent marriage might have fallen to his share of human folly, however, without exciting remark, if in other ways or at a later time he had exhibited the qualities which would allow one to dismiss these matters as mere instances of immaturity; but wherever Coleridge's reasonable control over himself or his affairs is looked to, it appears to have been feeble. On the other hand, the constancy of his excitement is plain. It was not only mental, but physical.. He was, as a young man, full of energy and capable of a good deal of hard exercise; he had animal spirits, and Wordsworth describes him as "noisy" and "gamesome," as one who

> "His limbs would toss about him with delight,
> Like branches when strong winds the trees annoy;"

and from several passages of his own writing, which are usually disregarded, the evidence of a spirit of rough humor and fun is easily obtained. The truth is that Coleridge changed a great deal in his life; he felt himself to be very different in later years from what he was in the time when to his memory even he was a sort of glorified spirit: and this earlier Coleridge had many traits which are ignored sometimes, as Carlyle ignored them, and are sometimes remembered rather as idealizations of his friends in their affectionate thoughts of him, but in any event are irreconcilable with the figure of the last period of his life.

It has been suggested that there was something of disease or at least of ill health in Coleridge always, and that it should be regarded as influencing his temperament. Whether it were so or not, the plea itself shows the fact. If excitement was the dominant note, as has been said, in his whole nature, it could not exist without a physical basis and accompaniment; and his bodily state appears to have been often less one of animation than of agitation, and his correspondence frequently discloses moods that seem almost frantic. In the issue, under stress of pain and trouble, he became an opium-eater; but his physical nature may fairly be described as predisposed to such states as lead to the use of opium and also result from its use, with the attendant mental moods. His susceptibility to sensuous impressions, to a voluptuousness of the entire being, together with a certain lassitude and languor, lead to the same conclusion, which thus seems to be supported on all sides,—that Coleridge was, in his youth and early manhood, fevered through all his intellectual and sensuous nature, and deficient on the moral and practical sides in those matters that related to his personal affairs. It is desirable to bring this out in plain terms, because in Coleridge it is best to acknowledge at once that his character was, so far as our part—the world's part—in him is concerned, of less consequence than his temperament; a subtler and more profound thing than character, though without moral meaning. It is not unfair to say, since literature is to be regarded most profitably as the expression of human personality, that with Coleridge the modern literature of temperament, as it has been lately recognized in extreme phases, begins; not that temperament is a new thing in the century now closing, nor that it has been without influence hitherto, but that now it is more often considered, and has in fact more often been, an exclusive ground of artistic expression. The temperament of Coleridge was one of diffused sensuousness physically, and of abnormal mental moods,—moods of weakness, languor, collapse, of visionary imaginative life with a night atmosphere of the spectral, moonlit, swimming, scarcely substantial world; and the poems he wrote, which are the contributions he made to the world's literature, are based on this temperament, like some Fata Morgana upon the sea. The apparent exclusion of reality from the poems in which his genius was most manifest finds its analogue in the detachment of his own mind from the moral, the practical, the usual in life as he led it in his spirit; and his work of the highest creative sort, which is all there is to his enduring fame, stands amid his prose and verse composition of a lower sort like an island in the waste of waters. This may be best shown, perhaps, by a gradual approach through his cruder to his more perfect compositions.

The cardinal fact in Coleridge's genius is that notwithstanding his immense sensuous susceptibilities and mental receptivity, and the continual excitement of his spirit, he never rose into the highest sphere of creative activity except for the brief period called his *annus mirabilis*, when his great poems were written; and with this is the further related fact that in him we witness the spectacle of the imaginative instinct overborne and supplanted by the intellectual faculty exercising its speculative and critical functions; and in addition, one observes in his entire work an extraordinary inequality not only of treatment, but also of subject-matter. In general, he was an egoistic writer. His sensitiveness to nature was twofold: in the first place he noticed in the objects and movements of nature evanescent and minute details, and as his sense of beauty was keen, he saw and recorded truly the less obvious and less common loveliness in the phenomena of the elements and the seasons, and this gave distinction to his mere description and record of fact; in the second place he often felt in himself moods induced by nature, but yet subjective, — states of his own spirit, which sometimes deepened the charm of night, for example, by his enjoyment of its placid aspects, and sometimes imparted to the external world a despair reflected from his personal melancholy. In his direct treatment of nature, however, as Mr. Stopford Brooke points out, he seldom achieves more than a catalogue of his sensations, which though touched with imaginative detail are never lifted and harmonized into lyrical unity; though he can moralize nature in Wordsworth's fashion, when he does so the result remains Wordsworth's and is stamped with that poet's originality; and in his own original work Coleridge never equaled either the genius of Shelley, who can identify nature with himself, or the charm of Tennyson, who can at least parallel nature's phenomena with his own human moods. Coleridge would not be thought of as a poet of nature, except in so far as he describes what he observes in the way of record, or gives a metaphysical interpretation to phenomena. This is the more remarkable because he had to an eminent degree that intellectual power, that overmastering desire of the mind, to rationalize the facts of life. It was this quality that made him a philosopher, an analyst, a critic on the great lines of Aristotle, seeking to impose an order of ethics and metaphysics on all artistic productions. But in those poems in which he describes nature directly and without metaphysical thought, there is no trace of anything more than a sensuous order of his own perceptions. Beautiful and often unique as his nature poems are, they are not creative. They are rather in the main autobiographic; and it is surprising to notice how large a proportion of his verse is thus autobiographic, not in those phases of his own life which may be, or at least are thought of as representative of human life in the mass, but which are personal, such as the lines written after hearing Wordsworth read the 'Prelude,' or those entitled 'Dejection.' When his verse is not confined to autobiographic expression, it is often a product of his interest in his friends or in his family. What is not personal in it, of this sort, is apt to be domestic or social.

If we turn from the poems of nature to those concerned with man, a similar shallowness, either of interest or of power, appears. He was in early years a radical; he was stirred by the Revolution in France, and he was emotionally charged with the ideas of the time, —ideas of equality, fraternity, and liberty. But this interest died out, as is shown by his political verse. He had none but a social and a philosophical interest in any case. Man, the individual, did not at any time attract him. There was nothing dramatic in his genius, in the narrow and exact sense; he did not engage his curiosity or his philosophy in individual fortunes. It results from this limitation that his verse lacks human interest of the dramatic kind. The truth was that he was interested in thought rather than in deeds, in human nature rather than in its concrete pity and terror. Thus he did not seize on life itself as the material of his imagination and reflection. In the case of man as in the case of nature he gives us only an egoistic account, telling us of his own private fortune, his fears, pains, and despairs, but only as a diary gives them; as he did not transfer his nature impressions into the world of creative art, so he did not transfer his personal experiences into that world.

What has been said would perhaps be accepted, were it not for the existence of those poems, 'The Ancient Mariner,' 'Christabel,' 'Kubla Khan,' which are the marvelous creations of his genius. In these it will be said there is both a world of nature new created, and a dramatic method and interest. It is enough for the purpose of the analysis if it be granted that nowhere else in Coleridge's work, except in these and less noticeably in a few other instances, do these high characteristics occur. The very point which is here to be brought out is that Coleridge applied that intellectual power, that overmastering desire of the mind to rationalize the phenomena of life, which has been mentioned as his great mental trait,—that he applied this faculty with different degrees of power at different times, so that his poetry falls naturally into higher and inferior categories; in the autobiographic verse, in the political and dramatic verse which forms so large a part of his work, it appears that he did not have sufficient feeling or exercise sufficient power to raise it out of the lower levels of composition; in his great works of con-structive and impersonal art, of moral intensity or romantic beauty and fascination, he did so exercise the creative imagination as to make these of the highest rank, or at least one of them.

'The Ancient Mariner,' apart from its many minor merits, has this distinction in Coleridge's work,—it is a poem of perfect unity. 'Christabel' is a fragment, 'Kubla Khan' is a glimpse; and though the 'Ode to France,' 'Love, Youth, and Age,' and possibly a few other short pieces, have this highest artistic virtue of unity, yet in them it is of a simpler kind. 'The Ancient Mariner,' on the other hand, is a marvel of construction in that its unity is less complex than manifold; it exists, however the form be examined. In the merely external sense, the telling of the tale to the Wedding Guest, with the fact that the wedding is going on, gives it unity; in the merely internal sense, the moral lesson of the salvation of the slayer of the albatross by the medium of love felt toward living things, subtly yet lucidly worked out as the notion is, gives it unity: but in still other ways, as a story of connected and consequential incidents with a plot, a change of fortune, a climax, and the other essentials of this species of tale-telling, it has unity; and if its conception either of the physical or the ethical world be analyzed, these too — and these are the fundamental things — are found consistent wholes. It nevertheless remains true that this system of nature as a vitalized but not humanized mode of life, with its bird, its spirit, its magical powers, is not the nature that we know or believe to be, — it is a modern presentation of an essentially primitive and animistic belief; and similarly this system of human life, — if the word human can be applied to it, with its dead men, its skeleton ship, its spirit sailors, its whole miracle of spectral being, — is not the life we know or believe to be; it is an incantation, a simulacrum. It may still be true therefore that the imaginative faculty of Coleridge was not applied either to nature or human life, in the ordinary sense. And this it is that constitutes the uniqueness of the poem, and its wonderful fascination. Coleridge fell heir, by the accidents of time and the revolutions of taste, to the ballad style, its simplicity, directness, and narrative power; he also was most attracted to the machinery of the supernatural, the weird, the terrible, almost to the grotesque and horrid, as these literary motives came into fashion in the crude beginnings of romanticism in our time; his subtle mind, his fine senses, his peculiar susceptibility to the mystic and shadowy in nature, — as shown by his preference of the moonlight, dreamy, or night aspects of real nature, to its brilliant beauties in the waking world, — gave him ease and finesse in the handling of such subject-matter; and he lived late enough to know that all this eerie side of human experience and imaginative capacity, inherited from primeval ages but by no means yet deprived of plausibility, could be effectively used only as an allegoric or scenic setting of what should be truth to the ethical sense; he combined one of the highest lessons of advanced civilization, one of the last results of spiritual perception, — the idea of love toward life in any form, — with the animistic beliefs and supernatural fancies of the crude ages of the senses. This seems to be the substantial matter; and in this he was, to repeat Shelley's phrase, the "subtle-souled psychologist." The material of his imagination, on the sensuous side, was of the slightest: it was the supernaturalism of the romantic movement, somewhat modified by being placed in connection with the animal world; and he put this to use as a means of illustrating spiritual truth. He thus became the first of those who have employed the supernatural in our recent literature without losing credence for it, as an allegory of psychological states, moral facts, or illusions real to the eye that sees them and having some logical relation to the past of the individual; of such writers Hawthorne and Poe are eminent examples, and both of them, it may be remarked, are writers in whom temperament rather than character is the ground of their creative work. The intimate kinship between imagination so directed and the speculative philosophical temper is plain to see. In 'Christabel' on the other hand, the moral substance is not apparent: the place filled by the moral ideas which are the centres of the narrative in 'The Ancient Mariner,' is taken here by emotional situations; but the supernaturalism is practically the same in both poems, and in both is associated with that mystery of the animal world to man, most concentrated and vivid in the fascination ascribed traditionally to the snake, which is the animal motive in 'Christabel' as the goodness of the albatross in the 'The Ancient Mariner.' In these poems the good and the bad omens that ancient augurs minded are made again dominant over men's imagination. Such are the signal and unique elements in these poems, which have besides that wealth of beauty in detail, of fine diction, of liquid melody, of sentiment, thought, and image, which belong only to poetry of the highest order, and which are too obvious to require any comment. 'Kubla Khan' is a poem of the same kind, in which the mystical effect is given almost wholly by landscape; it is to 'The Ancient Mariner' and 'Christabel' what protoplasm is to highly organized cells.

If it be recognized then that the imagery of Coleridge in the characteristic parts of these cardinal poems is as pure allegory, is as remote from nature or man, as is the machinery of fairy-land and chivalry in Spenser, for example, and he obtains credibility by the psychological and ethical truth presented in this imagery, it is not surprising that his work is small in amount; for the method is not only a difficult one, but the poetic machinery itself is limited and meagre. The poverty of the subject-matter is manifest, and the restrictions to its successful use are soon felt. It may well be doubted whether 'Christabel' would have gained by being finished. In 'The Ancient Mariner' the isolation of the man is a great advantage; if there had been any companion for him, the illusion could not have been entire: as it is, what he experiences has the wholeness and truth within itself of a dream, or of a madman's world,—there is no

standard of appeal outside of his own senses and mind, no real
world; but in 'Christabel' the serpentine fable goes on in a world of
fact and action, and as soon as the course of the story involved this
fable in the probabilities and actual occurences of life, it might well
be that the tale would have turned into one of simple enchantment
and magic, as seems likely from what has been told of its continuation; certainly it could not have equaled the earlier poem, or have
been in the same kind with it, unless the unearthly magic, the spell,
were finally completely dissolved into the world of moral truth as is
the case with 'The Ancient Mariner.' Coleridge found it still more
impossible to continue 'Kubla Khan.' It seems a fair inference to
conclude that Coleridge's genius, however it suffered from the misfortunes and ills of his life, was in these works involved in a field,
however congenial, yet of narrow range and infertile in itself. In
poetic style it is to be observed that he kept what he had gained;
the turbid diction of the earlier period never came back to trouble
him, and the cadences he had formed still gave their music to his
verse. The change, the decline, was not in his power of style; it
was in his power of imagination, if at all, but the fault may have
laid in the capacities of the subject-matter. A similar thing certainly
happened in his briefer ballad poetry, in that of which 'Love,' 'The
Three Graces,' 'Alice Du Clos,' and 'The Dark Ladie,' are examples;
the matter there, the machinery of the romantic ballad, was no
longer capable of use; that sort of literature was dead from the
exhaustion of its motives. The great 'Ode to France,' in which he
reached his highest point of eloquent and passionate expression,
seems to mark the extinction in himself of the revolutionary impulse.
On the whole, while the excellence of much of the remainder of his
verse, even in later years, is acknowledged, and its originality in
several instances, may it not be that in his greatest work Coleridge
came to an end because of an impossibility in the kind itself? The
supernatural is an accessory rather than a main element in the interpretation of life which literary genius undertakes; Coleridge so
subordinates it here by making it contributory to a moral truth; but
such a practice would seem to be necessarily incidental to a poet
who was also so intellectual as Coleridge, and not to be adopted as
a permanent method of self-expression.

From whatever cause, the fact was that Coleridge ceased to create
in poetry, and fell back on that fluent, manifold, voluminous faculty
he possessed of absorbing and giving out ideas in vast quantities, as
it were by bulk. He attended especially to the theory of art as he
found it illustrated in the greatest poets, and he popularized among
literary men a certain body of doctrine regarding criticism, its
growth and methods; and in later years he worked out metaphysical

theological views which he inculcated in ways which won for him recognition as a practical influence in contemporary church opinion. In these last years of his lecturing and discoursing in private, the figure he makes is pathetic, though Carlyle describes it with a grim humor, as any one may read in the 'Life of Sterling': over against that figure should be set the descriptions of the young Coleridge by Dorothy Wordsworth and Lamb; and after these perhaps the contrast which Coleridge himself draws between his spirit and his body may enable a reader to fuse the two—youth and age—into one. Whatever were the weaknesses of his nature and the trials of his life, of which one keeps silent, he was deeply loved by friends of many different minds, who if they grew cold, had paid at least once this tribute to the charm, the gentleness, and the delight of his human companionship.

G. E. Woodberry

KUBLA KHAN

IN XANADU did Kubla Khan
   A stately pleasure-dome decree,
  Where Alph the sacred river ran
Through caverns measureless to man
   Down to a sunless sea.
So twice five miles of fertile ground
With wall and towers were girdled round;
And there were gardens bright with sinuous rills,
   Where blossomed many an incense-bearing tree;
And here were forests ancient as the hills,
   Enfolding sunny spots of greenery.

But oh! that deep romantic chasm which slanted
   Down the green hill athwart a cedarn cover:
A savage place! as holy and enchanted
As e'er beneath a waning moon was haunted
   By woman wailing for her demon lover!
And from this chasm, with ceaseless turmoil seething,
As if this earth in fast thick pants were breathing,

A mighty fountain momently was forced;
  Amid whose swift half-intermitted burst
Huge fragments vaulted like rebounding hail,
Or chaffy grain beneath the thresher's flail;
And 'mid these dancing rocks at once and ever
It flung up momently the sacred river.
Five miles meandering with a mazy motion
   Through wood and dale the sacred river ran,
   Then reached the caverns measureless to man,
And sank in tumult to a lifeless ocean:
And 'mid this tumult Kubla heard from far
Ancestral voices prophesying war!

  The shadow of the dome of pleasure
    Floated midway on the waves;
  Where was heard the mingled measure
    From the fountain and the caves.
It was a miracle of rare device,
A sunny pleasure-dome with caves of ice!
    A damsel with a dulcimer
    In a vision once I saw;
    It was an Abyssinian maid,
    And on her dulcimer she played,
    Singing of Mount Abora.
   Could I revive within me
    Her symphony and song,
To such a deep delight 'twould win me
  That with music loud and long,
  I would build that dome in air —

That sunny dome! those caves of ice!
  And all who heard should see them there,
And all should cry, Beware! beware
  His flashing eyes, his floating hair!
Weave a circle round him thrice,
   And close your eyes with holy dread,
   For he on honey-dew hath fed,
And drunk the milk of Paradise.

THE ALBATROSS

From 'The Rime of the Ancient Mariner'

WITH sloping masts and dripping prow,
    As who, pursued with yell and blow,
    Still treads the shadow of his foe,
        And forward bends his head,
The ship drove fast, loud roared the blast,
    And southward aye we fled.

And now there came both mist and snow,
    And it grew wondrous cold;
And ice, mast-high, came floating by,
    As green as emerald.

And through the drifts the snowy clifts
    Did send a dismal sheen;
Nor shapes of men nor beasts we ken —
    The ice was all between.

The ice was here, the ice was there,
    The ice was all around;
It cracked and growled, and roared and howled,
    Like noises in a swound!

At length did cross an Albatross:
    Thorough the fog it came;
As if it had been a Christian soul,
    We hailed it in God's name.

It ate the food it ne'er had eat,
    And round and round it flew.
The ice did split with a thunder-fit;
    The helmsman steered us through!

And a good south-wind sprung up behind;
    The Albatross did follow,
And every day, for food or play,
    Came to the mariner's hollo!

In mist or cloud, on mast or shroud,
    It perched for vespers nine;
Whilst all the night, through fog-smoke white,
    Glimmered the white moonshine.—

God save thee, ancient Mariner!
 From the fiends that plague thee thus!
Why look'st thou so?—With my cross-bow
 I shot the Albatross!

THE Sun now rose upon the right;
 Out of the sea came he,
Still hid in mist, and on the left
 Went down into the sea.

And the good south-wind still blew behind,
 But no sweet bird did follow,
Nor any day for food or play
 Came to the mariner's hollo!

And I had done a hellish thing,
 And it would work 'em woe:
For all averred, I had killed the bird
 That made the breeze to blow.
Ah wretch! said they, the bird to slay,
 That made the breeze to blow!

Nor dim nor red, like God's own head
 The glorious Sun uprist:
Then all averred, I had killed the bird
 That brought the fog and mist.
'Twas right, said they, such birds to slay,
 That bring the fog and mist.

The fair breeze blew, the white foam flew,
 The furrow followed free;
We were the first that ever burst
 Into that silent sea.

Down dropt the breeze, the sails dropt down,
 'Twas sad as sad could be;
And we did speak only to break
 The silence of the sea!

All in a hot and copper sky,
 The bloody Sun, at noon,
Right up above the mast did stand,
 No bigger than the Moon.

Day after day, day after day,
 We stuck, nor breath nor motion;

As idle as a painted ship
    Upon a painted ocean.

Water, water, everywhere,
    And all the boards did shrink:
Water, water, everywhere,
    Nor any drop to drink.

The very deep did rot: O Christ!
    That ever this should be!
Yea, slimy things did crawl with legs
    Upon the slimy sea.

About, about, in reel and rout
    The death-fires danced at night;
The water, like a witch's oils,
    Burnt green, and blue, and white.

And some in dreams assurèd were
    Of the spirit that plagued us so;
Nine fathoms deep he had followed us
    From the land of mist and snow.

And every tongue, through utter drought,
    Was withered at the root;
We could not speak, no more than if
    We had been choked with soot.

Ah! well-a-day! what evil looks
    Had I from old and young!
Instead of the cross, the Albatross
    About my neck was hung.

TIME, REAL AND IMAGINARY

ON THE wide level of a mountain's head
    (I knew not where, but 't was some faery place),
Their pinions, ostrich-like, for sails outspread,
    Two lovely children run an endless race,
        A sister and a brother!
        This far outstript the other;
Yet ever runs she with reverted face,
And looks and listens for the boy behind:
        For he, alas! is blind!
O'er rough and smooth with even step he passed,
And knows not whether he be first or last.

DEJECTION: AN ODE

> Late, late yestreen I saw the new Moon,
>   With the old Moon in her arms;
> And I fear, I fear, my Master dear!
>   We shall have a deadly storm.
>
>   BALLAD OF SIR PATRICK SPENCE.

WELL! if the bard was weather-wise, who made
        The grand old ballad of Sir Patrick Spence,
        This night, so tranquil now, will not go hence
    Unroused by winds that ply a busier trade
Than those which mold yon cloud in lazy flakes,
Or the dull sobbing draft that moans and rakes
    Upon the strings of this Æolian lute,
        Which better far were mute.

    For lo! the New Moon, winter-bright
    And overspread with phantom light,
With swimming phantom light o'erspread,
    But rimmed and circled by a silver thread;
I see the old Moon in her lap, foretelling
    The coming on of rain and squally blast.
And oh! that even now the gust were swelling,
    And the slant night-shower driving hard and fast!
Those sounds, which oft have raised me, whilst they awed,
        And sent my soul abroad,
    Might now perhaps their wonted impulse give —
Might startle this dull pain and make it move and live.

    A grief without a pang, void, dark, and drear —
    A stifled, drowsy, unimpassioned grief,
    Which finds no natural outlet, no relief,
        In word, or sigh, or tear —
O Lady! in this wan and heartless mood,
To other thoughts by yonder throstle wooed,
All this long eve, so balmy and serene,
    Have I been gazing on the western sky,
    And its peculiar tint of yellow-green;
And still I gaze — and with how blank an eye!
And those thin clouds above, in flakes and bars,
That give away their motion to the stars, —
Those stars that glide behind them or between,
Now sparkling, now bedimmed, but always seen;

Yon crescent Moon, as fixed as if it grew
In its own cloudless, starless lake of blue:
I see them all so excellently fair —
I see, nor feel, how beautiful they are!

My genial spirits fail;
And what can these avail,
To lift the smothering weight from off my breast?
It were a vain endeavor,
Though I should gaze forever
On that green light that lingers in the west:
I may not hope from outward forms to win
The passion and the life whose fountains are within.

O lady! we receive but what we give,
And in our life alone does Nature live;
Ours is her wedding garment, ours her shroud!
And would we aught behold of higher worth
Than that inanimate cold world allowed
To the poor loveless, ever-anxious crowd —
Ah! from the soul itself must issue forth
A light, a glory, a fair luminous cloud
Enveloping the earth;
And from the soul itself must there be sent
A sweet and potent voice of its own birth,
Of all sweet sounds the life and element!

O pure of heart! thou need'st not ask of me
What this strong music in the soul may be,
What and wherein it doth exist,
This light, this glory, this fair luminous mist,
This beautiful and beauty-making power:
Joy, virtuous lady! Joy that ne'er was given
Save to the pure, and in their purest hour,
Life, and life's effluence, cloud at once and shower —
Joy, lady, is the spirit and the power
Which wedding nature to us, gives in dower
A new Earth and Heaven,
Undreamt-of by the sensual and the proud;
Joy is the sweet voice, Joy the luminous cloud —
We in ourselves rejoice!
And thence flows all that charms or ear or sight,
All melodies the echoes of that voice,
All colors a suffusion from that light.

There was a time when, though my path was rough,
  This joy within me dallied with distress;
And all misfortunes were but as the stuff
  Whence fancy made me dreams of happiness.
For hope grew round me like the twining vine;
And fruits and foliage, not my own, seemed mine.

But now afflictions bow me down to earth,
Nor care I that they rob me of my mirth;
     But oh! each visitation
Suspends what nature gave me at my birth,
  My shaping spirit of imagination.
For not to think of what I needs must feel,
  But to be still and patient, all I can;
And haply by abstruse research to steal
    From my own nature all the natural man —
    This was my sole resource, my only plan:
Till that which suits a part infects the whole,
And now is almost grown the habit of my soul.

Hence, viper thoughts that coil around my mind —
     Reality's dark dream!
I turn from you, and listen to the wind,
  Which long has raved unnoticed. What a scream
Of agony, by torture lengthened out,
That lute sent forth! Thou wind, that ravest without!
  Bare crag, or mountain-tairn, or blasted tree,
Or pine-grove whither woodman never clomb,
Or lonely house, long held the witches' home,
  Methinks were fitter instruments for thee,
Mad lutanist! who in this month of showers,
Of dark-brown gardens, and of peeping flowers,
Makest devils' Yule, with worse than wintry song,
The blossoms, buds, and timorous leaves among!
  Thou actor, perfect in all tragic sounds!
Thou mighty poet, e'en to frenzy bold!
    What tell'st thou now about?
   'Tis of the rushing of a host in rout,
With groans of trampled men, with smarting wounds —
At once they groan with pain, and shudder with the cold.

But hush! there is a pause of deepest silence!
  And all that noise, as of a rushing crowd,
With groans and tremulous shudderings — all is over —
  It tells another tale, with sounds less deep and loud!

A tale of less affright,
And tempered with delight,
As Otway's self had framed the tender lay:
'Tis of a little child
Upon a lonesome wild —
Not far from home, but she hath lost her way;
And now moans low in bitter grief and fear —
And now screams loud, and hopes to make her mother hear.

'Tis midnight, but small thoughts have I of sleep;
Full seldom may my friend such vigils keep!
Visit her, gentle Sleep, with wings of healing!
And may this storm be but a mountain-birth;
May all the stars hang bright above her dwelling,
Silent as though they watched the sleeping earth!
With light heart may she rise,—
Gay fancy, cheerful eyes —
Joy lift her spirit, joy attune her voice;
To her may all things live, from pole to pole —
Their life the eddying of her living soul!
O simple spirit, guided from above!
Dear Lady! friend devoutest of my choice!
Thus mayest thou ever, evermore rejoice.

THE THREE TREASURES

COMPLAINT

How seldom, Friend! a good great man inherits
Honor or wealth, with all his worth and pains!
It sounds like stories from the land of spirits,
If any man obtain that which he merits,
Or any merit that which he obtains.

REPROOF

For shame, dear Friend; renounce this canting strain!
What wouldst thou have a good great man obtain?
Place — titles — salary — a gilded chain —
Or throne of corses which his sword has slain?
Greatness and goodness are not means, but ends!
Hath he not always treasures, always friends,
The good great man? three treasures,— love and light,
And calm thoughts, regular as infant's breath;
And three firm friends, more sure than day and night —
Himself, his Maker, and the angel Death.

TO A GENTLEMAN

COMPOSED ON THE NIGHT AFTER HIS RECITATION OF A POEM ON
THE GROWTH OF AN INDIVIDUAL MIND

FRIEND of the Wise! and Teacher of the Good!
　　Into my heart have I received that lay
　　More than historic, that prophetic lay,
Wherein (high theme by thee first sung aright)
Of the foundations and the building up
Of a Human Spirit thou hast dared to tell
What may be told, to the understanding mind
Revealable; and what within the mind,
By vital breathings secret as the soul
Of vernal growth, oft quickens in the heart
Thoughts all too deep for words!

　　　　　　　　　　　　Theme hard as high!
Of smiles spontaneous, and mysterious fears,
The first-born they of Reason, and twin-birth;
Of tides obedient to external force,
And currents self-determined, as might seem,
Or by some inner Power; of moments awful,
Now in thy inner life, and now abroad,
When Power stream'd from thee, and thy soul received
The light reflected, as a light bestowed —
Of fancies fair, and milder hours of youth,
Hyblean murmurs of poetic thought,
Industrious in its joy, in Vales and Glens
Native or outland, Lakes and famous Hills!
Or on the lonely High-road, when the Stars
Were rising; or by secret mountain Streams,
The Guides and the Companions of thy way!

　　Of more than Fancy, of the Social Sense
Distending wide, and Man beloved as Man,
Where France in all her town lay vibrating
Like some becalmèd bark beneath the burst
Of Heaven's immediate thunder, when no cloud
Is visible, or shadow on the Main.
For thou wert there, thine own brows garlanded,
Amid the tremor of a realm aglow,
Amid a mighty nation jubilant,
When from the general heart of humankind

Hope sprang forth like a full-born Deity!
.   .   .   Of that dear Hope afflicted and struck down
So summoned homeward, thenceforth calm and sure,
From the dread watch-tower of man's absolute Self
With light unwaning on her eyes, to look
Far on — herself a glory to behold,
The Angel of the vision! Then (last strain)
Of Duty, chosen laws controlling choice,
Action and Joy! — An Orphic song indeed,
A song divine of high and passionate thoughts,
To their own music chanted!

                              O great Bard!
Ere yet that last strain, dying, awed the air,
With stedfast eye I viewed thee in the choir
Of ever-enduring men. The truly Great
Have all one age, and from one visible space
Shed influence! They, both in power and act,
Are permanent, and Time is not with *them*,
Save as it worketh *for* them, they *in* it.
Nor less a sacred roll than those of old,
And to be placed, as they, with gradual fame
Among the archives of mankind, thy work
Makes audible a linkèd lay of Truth,
Of Truth profound a sweet continuous lay,
Not learnt, but native, her own natural notes!
Ah! as I listened with a heart forlorn,
The pulses of my being beat anew:
And even as life returns upon the drowned,
Life's joy rekindling roused a throng of pains —
Keen Pangs of Love, awakening as a babe
Turbulent, with an outcry in the heart;
And Fears self-willed that shunned the eye of Hope,
And Hope that scarce would know itself from Fear,
Sense of past Youth; and Manhood come in vain,
And all which I had culled in wood-walks wild,
And all which patient toil had reared, and all,
Commune with *thee* had opened out — but flowers
Strewed on my corse, and borne upon my bier,
In the same coffin, for the self-same grave!

That way no more! and ill beseems it me
Who came a welcomer in herald's guise
Singing of Glory and Futurity,
To wander back on such unhealthful road,

Plucking the poisons of self-harm! And ill
Such intertwine beseems triumphal wreaths
Strewed before *thy* advancing!

                Nor do thou,
Sage Bard! impair the memory of that hour
Of my communion with thy nobler mind
By Pity or Grief, already felt too long!
Nor let my words import more blame than needs.
The tumult rose and ceased: for Peace is nigh
Where Wisdom's voice has found a listening heart.
Amid the howl of more than wintry storms,
The Halcyon hears the voice of vernal hours
Already on the wing.

              Eve following eve,
Dear tranquil time, when the sweet sense of Home
Is sweetest! moments for their own sake hailed
And more desired, more precious for thy song,
In silence listening, like a devout child,
My soul lay passive, by the various strain
Driven as in surges now beneath the stars,
With momentary Stars of my own birth,
Fair constellated Foam, still darting off
Into the darkness; now a tranquil sea,
Outspread and bright, yet swelling to the Moon.

And when — O Friend! my comforter and guide!
Strong in thyself, and powerful to give strength! —
Thy long-sustained song finally closed,
And thy deep voice had ceased — yet thou thyself
Wert still before my eyes, and round us both
That happy vision of beloved faces —
Scarce conscious, and yet conscious of its close,
I sate, my being blended in one thought
(Thought was it? or Aspiration? or Resolve?)
Absorbed, yet hanging still upon the sound —
And when I rose, I found myself in prayer.

ODE TO GEORGIANA, DUCHESS OF DEVONSHIRE

On the Twenty-fourth Stanza in Her 'Passage over Mount Gothard'

And hail the Chapel! hail the Platform wild!
　　Where Tell directed the avenging Dart,
　With well-strung arm, that first preserved his Child,
Then aim'd the arrow at the Tyrant's heart.

　　Splendor's fondly fostered child!
　　And did you hail the platform wild
　　　　Where once the Austrian fell
　　　　Beneath the shaft of Tell?
　　O Lady, nursed in pomp and pleasure!
　　Whence learnt you that heroic measure?

Light as a dream your days their circlets ran;
From all that teaches Brotherhood to Man,
Far, far removed! from want, from hope, from fear.
Enchanting music lulled your infant ear,
Obeisance, praises, soothed your infant heart:
　Emblazonments and old ancestral crests,
With many a bright obtrusive form of art,
　Detained your eye from nature's stately vests
That veiling strove to deck your charms divine;
Rich viands and the pleasurable wine,
Were yours unearned by toil; nor could you see
The unenjoying toiler's misery.
And yet, free Nature's uncorrupted child,
You hailed the Chapel and the Platform wild,
　　　Where once the Austrian fell
　　　Beneath the shaft of Tell!
　　O Lady, nursed in pomp and pleasure!
　　Where learnt you that heroic measure?

　　There crowd your finely fibred frame,
　　　All living faculties of bliss;
　　And Genius to your cradle came,
　　His forehead wreathed with lambent flame,
　　　And bending low, with godlike kiss
　　　Breathed in a more celestial life;
　　But boasts not many a fair compeer
　　A heart as sensitive to joy and fear?

And some, perchance, might wage an equal strife,
　　Some few, to nobler being wrought,
　　Co-rivals in the nobler gift of thought.
　　　　Yet *these* delight to celebrate
　　　　Laureled War and plumy State;
　　　　Or in verse and music dress,
　　　　Tales of rustic happiness—
　　Pernicious Tales! insidious Strains!
　　　　That steel the rich man's breast,
　　　　And mock the lot unblest,
　　The sordid vices and the abject pains,
　　　　Which evermore must be
　　　　The doom of Ignorance and Penury!
　　But you, free Nature's uncorrupted child,
　　You hailed the Chapel and the Platform wild,
　　　　Where once the Austrian fell
　　　　Beneath the shaft of Tell!
　　O Lady, nursed in pomp and pleasure!
　　Where learnt you that heroic measure?

　　You were a Mother! That most holy name,
　　　　Which Heaven and Nature bless,
　　I may not vilely prostitute to those
　　　　Whose Infants owe them less
　　Than the poor Caterpillar owes
　　　　　Its gaudy Parent Fly.
　　You were a Mother! at your bosom fed
　　　　The Babes that loved you. You, with laughing eye,
　　Each twilight-thought, each nascent feeling read,
　　　　Which you yourself created. Oh, delight!
　　A second time to be a Mother,
　　　　Without the Mother's bitter groans:
　　Another thought, and yet another,
　　　　By touch, or taste, by looks or tones,
　　　　O'er the growing Sense to roll,
　　　　The Mother of your infant's Soul!
　　The Angel of the Earth, who while he guides
　　　　His chariot-planet round the goal of day,
　　All trembling gazes on the Eye of God,
　　　　A moment turned his face away;
　　And as he viewed you, from his aspect sweet
　　　　New influences in your being rose,
　　Blest Intuitions and Communions fleet
　　　　With living Nature, in her joys and woes!

Thenceforth your soul rejoiced to see
The shrine of social Liberty!
O beautiful! O Nature's child!
'Twas thence you hailed the Platform wild,
Where once the Austrian fell
Beneath the shaft of Tell!
O Lady, nursed in pomp and pleasure!
Thence learnt you that heroic measure.

THE PAINS OF SLEEP

ERE on my bed my limbs I lay,
It hath not been my use to pray
    With moving lips or bended knees;
But silently, by slow degrees,
My spirit I to Love compose,
In humble Trust mine eyelids close,
With reverential resignation;
No wish conceived, no thought expressed!
Only a *sense* of supplication,
A sense o'er all my soul imprest
That I am weak, yet not unblest;
Since in me, round me, everywhere,
Eternal Strength and Wisdom are.

But yesternight I prayed aloud
    In anguish and in agony,
Upstarting from the fiendish crowd
    Of shapes and thoughts that tortured me:
A lurid light, a trampling throng,
Sense of intolerable wrong,
And whom I scorned, those only strong!
Thirst of revenge, the powerless will
Still baffled, and yet burning still!
Desire with loathing strangely mixed
On wild or hateful objects fixed.
Fantastic passions! maddening brawl!
And shame and terror over all!
    Deeds to be hid which were not hid,
Which, all confused, I could not know
    Whether I suffered, or I did:
For all seemed guilt, remorse, or woe,—
My own or others', still the same
Life-stifling fear, soul-stifling shame.

So two nights passed: the night's dismay
Saddened and stunned the coming day.
Sleep, the wide blessing, seemed to me
Distemper's worst calamity.
The third night, when my own loud scream
Had waked me from the fiendish dream,
O'ercome with sufferings strange and wild,
I wept as I had been a child;
And having thus by tears subdued
My anguish to a milder mood,
Such punishments, I said, were due
To natures deepliest stained with sin;
For aye entempesting anew
The unfathomable hell within,
The horror of their deeds to view,
To know and loathe, yet wish to do!

Such griefs with such men well agree,
But wherefore, wherefore fall on me?
To be beloved is all I need,
And whom I love, I love indeed.

SONG, BY GLYCINE

A sunny shaft did I behold,
　From sky to earth it slanted;
　　And poised therein a bird so bold —
Sweet bird, thou wert enchanted!

He sunk, he rose, he twinkled, he trolled
　Within that shaft of sunny mist;
His eyes of fire, his beak of gold,
　　All else of amethyst!

And thus he sang: "Adieu! adieu!
　Love's dreams prove seldom true.
The blossoms, they make no delay:
The sparkling dewdrops will not stay.
　Sweet month of May,
　　We must away;
　　　Far, far away!
　　　　To-day! to-day!"

YOUTH AND AGE

VERSE, a breeze 'mid blossoms straying,
　　Where Hope clung feeding, like a bee —
Both were mine! Life went a-Maying
　With Nature, Hope, and Poesy,
　　　When I was young!
When I was young? — Ah, woful *when!*
Ah, for the change 'twixt now and then!
This breathing house not built with hands,
　This body that does me grievous wrong,
O'er airy cliffs and glittering sands,
　　How lightly *then* it flashed along: —
Like those trim skiffs, unknown of yore,
　On winding lakes and rivers wide,
That ask no aid of sail or oar,
　　That fear no spite of wind or tide!
Naught cared this body for wind or weather
When Youth and I lived in't together.

Flowers are lovely; Love is flower-like,
　Friendship is a sheltering tree;
O the joys that came down shower-like,
　Of Friendship, Love, and Liberty!
　　　Ere I was old!
Ere I was old? Ah, woful *Ere*,
Which tells me Youth's no longer here!
O Youth! for years so many and sweet,
　'Tis known that thou and I were one;
I'll think it but a fond conceit —
　　It cannot be that thou art gone!
Thy vesper bell hath not yet tolled: —
And thou wert aye a masker bold!
What strange disguise hast now put on
To *make believe* that thou art gone?
I see these locks in silvery slips,
　This drooping gait, this alter'd size:
But spring-tide blossoms on thy lips,
　　And tears take sunshine from thine eyes!
Life is but thought: so think I will
That Youth and I are housemates still.

PHANTOM OR FACT?

AUTHOR

A LOVELY form there sate beside my bed,
      And such a feeding calm its presence shed,
      A tender love, so pure from earthly leaven
That I unnethe the fancy might control,
'Twas my own spirit newly come from heaven,
Wooing its gentle way into my soul!
But ah! the change — it had not stirred, and yet —
Alas! that change how fain would I forget!
That shrinking back like one that had mistook!
That weary, wandering, disavowing Look!
'Twas all another, — feature, look, and frame, —
And still, methought, I knew it was the same!

FRIEND

This riddling tale, to what does it belong?
Is't history? vision? or an idle song?
Or rather say at once, within what space
Of time this wild disastrous change took place?

AUTHOR

Call it a *moment's* work (and such it seems);
This tale's a fragment from the life of dreams;
But say that years matured the silent strife,
And 'tis a record from the dream of Life.

WILLIAM COLLINS

(1721–1759)

THERE is much to inspire regretful sympathy in the short life of William Collins. He was born at Chichester, and received his education at Winchester College and at Magdalen College, Oxford. A delicate, bookish boy, he had every stimulus toward a literary career. With a fine appreciation of beauty in all forms of art, and a natural talent for versification, he wrote poems of much promise when very young. His 'Persian Eclogues' appeared when he was only seventeen. Then Collins showed his impatient spirit and fickleness of purpose by deserting his work at Oxford and going to London with the intention of authorship. His head was full of brilliant schemes,—too full; for with him as with most people, conception was always easier than execution. But finding it far more difficult to win fame than he anticipated, he had not courage to persevere, and fell into dissipated, extravagant ways which soon exhausted his small means.

WILLIAM COLLINS

In 1846 he published the 'Odes, Descriptive and Allegorical,' his most characteristic work. They were never widely read, and it took the public some time to appreciate their lyric fervor, their exquisite imagery, and their musical verse. In spite of occasional obscurities induced by careless treatment, they are among the finest of English odes. His love for nature and sympathy with its calmer aspects is very marked. Speaking of the 'Ode to Evening,' Hazlitt says that "the sounds steal slowly over the ear like the gradual coming on of evening itself." According to Swinburne, the 'Odes' do not contain "a single false note." "Its grace and vigor, its vivid and pliant dexterity of touch," he says of the 'Ode to the Passions,' "are worthy of their long inheritance of praise."

But the inheritance did not come at once, although Collins has always received generous praise from fellow poets. His mortified self-love resented lack of success. With a legacy bequeathed him by an uncle he bought his book back from the publisher Millar, and the unsold impressions he burned in "angry despair."

Meantime he went on planning works quite beyond his power of execution. He advertised 'Proposals for a History of the Revival of Learning,' which he never wrote. He began several tragedies, but his indolent genius would not advance beyond devising the plots. As he was always wasteful and dissipated, he was continually in debt. In spite of his unusual gifts, he had not the energy and self-control necessary for adequate literary expression. Dr. Johnson, who admired and tried to befriend him, found a bailiff prowling around the premises when he went to call. At his instigation a bookseller advanced money to get Collins out of London, for which in return he was to translate Aristotle's 'Poetics' and to write a commentary. Probably he never fulfilled the agreement. Indeed, he had some excuse. "A man doubtful of his dinners, or trembling at a creditor, is not disposed to abstract meditation or remote inquiries," comments Dr. Johnson.

Collins was always weak of body, and when still a young man was seized by mental disease. Weary months of despondency were succeeded by madness, until he was, as Dr. Wharton describes it, with "every spark of imagination extinguished, and with only the faint traces of memory and reason left." Then the unhappy poet was taken to Chichester and cared for by a sister. There he who had loved music so passionately hated the cathedral organ in his madness, and when he heard it, howled in distress.

Among the best examples of his verse, besides the poems already mentioned, are the 'Dirge to Cymbeline,' 'Ode to Fear,' and the 'Ode on the Poetical Character,' which Hazlitt calls "the best of all."

HOW SLEEP THE BRAVE

How sleep the brave, who sink to rest
　　By all their country's wishes blest!
　　When Spring, with dewy fingers cold,
　　Returns to deck their hallowed mold,
She there shall dress a sweeter sod
Than Fancy's feet have ever trod.

By fairy hands their knell is rung,
By forms unseen their dirge is sung;
There Honor comes, a pilgrim gray,
To bless the turf that wraps their clay,
And Freedom shall a while repair,
To dwell a weeping hermit there!

THE PASSIONS

WHEN Music, heavenly maid! was young,
　　While yet in early Greece she sung,
　　The Passions oft, to hear her shell,
　　Thronged around her magic cell.
Exulting, trembling, raging, fainting,
Possest beyond the Muse's painting;
By turns they felt the glowing mind
Disturbed, delighted, raised, refined:
Till once, 'tis said, when all were fired,
Filled with fury, rapt, inspired,
From the supporting myrtles round
They snatched her instruments of sound,
And as they oft had heard apart
Sweet lessons of her forceful art,
Each — for Madness ruled the hour —
Would prove his own expressive power.

First Fear his hand, its skill to try,
　　Amid the chords bewildered laid;
And back recoiled, he knew not why,
　　E'en at the sound himself had made.

Next Anger rushed; his eyes on fire,
　　In lightnings owned his secret stings:
In one rude clash he struck the lyre,
　　And swept with hurried hand the strings.

With woful measures wan Despair —
　　Low solemn sounds — his grief beguiled,
A sullen, strange, and mingled air;
　　'Twas sad by fits, by starts 'twas wild.

But thou, O Hope! with eyes so fair,
　　What was thy delighted measure?
　　Still it whispered promised pleasure,
And bade the lovely scenes at distance hail!
　　Still would her touch the strain prolong,
And from the rocks, the woods, the vale,
　　She called on Echo still through all the song;
And where her sweetest theme she chose,
A soft responsive voice was heard at every close,
And Hope enchanted smiled, and waved her golden hair.

And longer had she sung,— but with a frown,
Revenge impatient rose;
He threw his blood-stained sword in thunder down,
And with a withering look
The war-denouncing trumpet took,
And blew a blast so loud and dread,
Were ne'er prophetic sounds so full of woe!
And ever and anon he beat
The doubling drum with furious heat;
And though sometimes, each dreary pause between,
Dejected Pity, at his side,
Her soul-subduing voice applied,
Yet still he kept his wild unaltered mien,
While each strained ball of sight seemed bursting from his head.

Thy numbers, Jealousy, to naught were fixed,
Sad proof of thy distressful state!
Of differing themes the veering song was mixed,
And now it courted Love, now raving called on Hate.

With eyes upraised, as one inspired,
Pale Melancholy sat retired;
And from her wild sequestered seat,
In notes by distance made more sweet,
Poured through the mellow horn her pensive soul:
And dashing soft from rocks around,
Bubbling runnels joined the sound.
Through glades and glooms the mingled measure stole,
Or o'er some haunted streams with fond delay,
Round an holy calm diffusing,
Love of peace and lonely musing,
In hollow murmurs died away.

But oh, how altered was its sprightlier tone
When Cheerfulness, a nymph of healthiest hue,
Her bow across her shoulders flung,
Her buskins gemmed with morning dew,
Blew an inspiring air that dale and thicket rung!
The hunter's call, to Faun and Dryad known.
The oak-crowned Sisters, and their chaste-eyed Queen,
Satyrs and sylvan boys were seen,
Peeping from forth their alleys green;
Brown Exercise rejoiced to hear,
And Sport leapt up, and seized his beechen spear.

Last came Joy's ecstatic trial;
  He with viny crown advancing,
First to the lively pipe his hand addrest;
  But soon he saw the brisk awakening viol,
Whose sweet entrancing voice he loved the best.
  They would have thought who heard the strain,
They saw in Tempe's vale her native maids,

  Amidst the festal sounding shades,
  To some unwearied minstrel dancing;
While, as his flying fingers kissed the strings,
Love framed with Mirth a gay fantastic round;
Loose were her tresses seen, her zone unbound;
  And he, amidst his frolic play,
As if he would the charming air repay,
Shook thousand odors from his dewy wings.

O Music! sphere-descended maid,
Friend of pleasure, Wisdom's aid!
Why, goddess, why, to us denied,
Lay'st thou thy ancient lyre aside?
As in that loved Athenian bower,
You learned an all-commanding power,
Thy mimic soul, O nymph endeared!
Can well recall what then it heard.
Where is that native simple heart,
Devote to Virtue, Fancy, Art?
Arise, as in that elder time,
Warm, energetic, chaste, sublime!
Thy wonders, in that godlike age,
Fill thy recording Sister's page.
'Tis said — and I believe the tale —
Thy humblest reed could more prevail,
Had more of strength, diviner rage,
Than all which charms this laggard age;
E'en all at once together found
Cecilia's mingled world of sound.
Oh bid our vain endeavors cease,
Revive the just designs of Greece;
Return in all thy simple state!
Confirm the tales her sons relate!

TO EVENING

IF AUGHT of oaten stop, or pastoral song,
  May hope, chaste Eve, to soothe thy modest ear
      Like thy own solemn springs,
      Thy springs and dying gales;

O nymph reserved! while now the bright-haired sun
Sits in yon western tent, whose cloudy skirts,
      With brede ethereal wove,
      O'erhang his wavy bed:—

Now air is hushed, save where the weak-eyed bat
With short shrill shriek flits by on leathern wing;
      Or where the beetle winds
      His small but sullen horn,

As oft he rises 'midst the twilight path,
Against the pilgrim borne in heedless hum:
      Now teach me, maid composed,
      To breathe some softened strain,

Whose numbers, stealing through thy dark'ning vale,
May not unseemly with its stillness suit,
      As, musing slow, I hail
      Thy genial loved return!

For when thy folding-star arising shows
His paly circlet, at his warning lamp
      The fragrant hours, and elves
      Who slept in buds the day,

And many a nymph who wreathes her brows with sedge,
And sheds the freshening dew, and lovelier still,
      The pensive Pleasures sweet,
      Prepare thy shadowy car,—

Then let me rove some wild and heathy scene,
Or find some ruin 'midst its dreary dells,
      Whose walls more awful nod
      By thy religious gleams.

Or if chill blustering winds, or driving rain,
Prevent my willing feet, be mine the hut
      That from the mountain's side
      Views wilds and swelling floods,

And hamlets brown, and dim-discovered spires,
And hears their simple bell, and marks o'er all
      Thy dewy fingers draw
      The gradual dusky veil.

While Spring shall pour his showers, as oft he wont,
And bathe thy breathing tresses, meekest Eve!
      While Summer loves to sport
      Beneath thy lingering light:

While sallow Autumn fills thy lap with leaves;
Or Winter, yelling through the troublous air,
      Affrights thy shrinking train,
      And rudely rends thy robes:

So long, regardful of thy quiet rule,
Shall Fancy, Friendship, Science, smiling Peace,
      Thy gentlest influence own,
      And love thy favorite name!

ODE ON THE DEATH OF THOMSON

IN YONDER grave a Druid lies,
    Where slowly winds the stealing wave!
  The year's best sweets shall duteous rise,
    To deck its poet's sylvan grave!

In yon deep bed of whisp'ring reeds
    His airy harp shall now be laid;
That he whose heart in sorrow bleeds
    May love through life the soothing shade.

Then maids and youths shall linger here,
    And while its sounds at distance swell,
Shall sadly seem in Pity's ear
    To hear the woodland pilgrim's knell.

Remembrance oft shall haunt the shore
    When Thames in summer wreaths is drest;
And oft suspend the dashing oar
    To bid his gentle spirit rest.

And oft as Ease and Health retire
    To breezy lawn, or forest deep,
The friend shall view yon whitening spire,
    And 'mid the varied landscape weep.

But thou, who own'st that earthly bed,
    Ah! what will every dirge avail!
Or tears which Love and Pity shed,
    That mourn beneath the gliding sail!

Yet lives there one, whose heedless eye
    Shall scorn thy pale shrine glimm'ring near —
With him, sweet bard, may Fancy die,
    And Joy desert the blooming year.

But thou, lorn stream, whose sullen tide
    No sedge-crowned sisters now attend,
Now waft me from the green hill's side,
    Whose cold turf hides the buried friend!

And see, the fairy valleys fade,
    Dun Night has veiled the solemn view!
Yet once again, dear parted shade,
    Meek Nature's child, again adieu!

The genial meads, assigned to bless
    Thy life, shall mourn thy early doom!
There hinds and shepherd girls shall dress
    With simple hands thy rural tomb.

Long, long, thy stone and pointed clay
    Shall melt the musing Briton's eyes:
« O vales and wild woods! » shall he say,
    « In yonder grave your Druid lies! »

WILLIAM WILKIE COLLINS

(1824–1889)

ILKIE COLLINS has proved that the charm of a story does not necessarily depend upon the depiction of character or an appeal to the sympathies. As he said:—"I have always held the old-fashioned opinion that the primary object of a work of fiction should be to tell a story." He also aspired to draw living men and women, in which he was less successful. Count Fosco, Miss Gwilt, Armadale, Laura Fairlie, and others, are indeed distinct; but the interest centres not on them but on the circumstances in

which they are involved. This is the main reason why the critics, even in admiring his talent, speak of Collins with faint depreciation, as certainly not one of the greatest novelists of the century, although holding a place of his own which forces recognition. For novel-readers have delighted in his many volumes in spite of the critics, and there is a steady demand for the old favorites. Translated into French, Italian, Danish, and Russian, many of them continue to inspire the same interest in foreign lands.

WILKIE COLLINS

Wilkie Collins, born January 8th, 1824, did not show any special precocity in boyhood and youth. He probably learned much more from his self-guided reading than from his schooling at Highbury, especially after his acquisition of French and Italian during two years in Italy in his early teens. The influences about him were strongly artistic. His father, William Collins, was distinguished as a landscape painter. The well-known portrait painter Mrs. Carpenter was his aunt, and the distinguished Scotch artist David Wilkie his godfather. But human action and emotion interested him more than art. He was very young when he expressed a desire to write, and perpetrated blank verse which justified his father in vigorous opposition to his adoption of authorship as a profession. So, his school days ended, he presented the not unusual figure of a bright young Englishman who must earn his bread, yet had no particular aptitude for doing it. He tried business first, and became articled clerk with a City house in the tea trade. But the work was uncongenial; and after a few unsatisfactory years he fell in with his father's views, and was entered at Lincoln's Inn and in due time admitted to the bar, although he never practiced law.

He continued writing for amusement, however, producing sketches and stories valuable as training. On his father's death he prepared a biography of that artist in two volumes (1848), which was considered a just as well as a loving appreciation. His first novel, however, was rejected by every publisher to whom he submitted it. His second, 'Antonina,' a story of the fall of Rome, was mediocre. He was about twenty-six when he met Charles Dickens, then a man of forty, at the height of his fame, and with the kindliest feeling for younger writers still struggling for recognition. Dickens, whose own work was always prompted by sympathetic intuition, and to whom character development came more easily than ingenious plots, cordially admired Collins's skill in devising and explaining the latter. He invited the younger man to become collaborator upon Household Words, and thus initiated a warm friendship which lasted until his own death. Encouraged by him, Collins essayed drama and wrote 'The Light-House,' played at Gadshill by distinguished amateurs, Dickens himself among them. At first thought, his would seem an essentially dramatic talent, and several of his novels have been successfully dramatized. But the very cleverness and intricacy of his situations make them unsuited to the stage. They are too difficult of comprehension to be taken in at a glance by an average audience, in the swift passage of stage action.

It was also the influence of Dickens which inspired Collins to attempt social reform. In 'Man and Wife' he tries to show the injustice of Scotch marriage laws; in 'The New Magdalen,' the possible regeneration of fallen women; in 'Heart and Science,' the abuses of vivisection; and other stories are incumbered with didactic purpose. Mr. Swinburne comments upon this aspect of his career in a jocular couplet—

«What brought good Wilkie's genius nigh perdition?
  Some demon whispered, 'Wilkie! have a mission!'»

But in all «tendency» novels it is not the discussion of problems that makes them live; and Wilkie Collins, like others, survives by purely literary qualities. Soon after his death the critic of the Spectator gave the following capable summary of his peculiar method:—

«He was a literary chess player of the first force, with power of carrying his plan right through the game and making every move tell. His method was to introduce a certain number of characters, set before them a well-defined object, such as the discovery of a secret, the re-vindication of a fortune, the tracking of a crime, or the establishment of a doubted marriage, and then bring in other characters to resist or counterplot their efforts. Each side makes moves, almost invariably well-considered and promising moves; the counter-moves are equally good; the interest goes on accumulating till the looker-on — the reader is always placed in that attitude — is rapt out of himself by strained attention; and then there is a sudden and totally unexpected mate. It is chess which is being played; and in the best of all his stories, the one which will live for years,— 'The Moonstone,' — the pretense that it is anything else is openly disregarded.»

This analysis however must not be too narrowly construed, as petty critics often do, to mean that the only interest in Mr. Collins's novels is that of disentangling the plot. If this were so, no one would read them more than once; while in fact the best of them are eminently readable again and again. This shallow judgment evidently galled the novelist himself, and 'The New Magdalen' in one aspect was a throwing-down of the gauntlet to the critics; for in it he tells the plot page by page, almost paragraph by paragraph, as he goes along, and even far in advance of the story, yet it is one of the most fascinating of his novels. He proved that he could do admirably what they said he could not do at all — make people read his story with breathless absorption when they knew its end long before they came to it; and it was as interesting backward as forward. 'No Name' is in some sort a combination of the two methods, — a revelation of the end, with perpetual interest in the discovery of means.

'The Moonstone' and 'The Woman in White' are unquestionably his masterpieces. In both he throws light upon a complex plot by means of his favorite expedient of letters and diaries written by different characters, who thus take the reader into their confidence and bewilder him with conflicting considerations, until the author comes forward with an ingenious and lucid solution. 'The Moonstone,' however, is immensely superior in matter even to its fellow; its plot is better (in one place 'The Woman in White' comes to a dead wall which the author calmly ignores and goes on), and some passages are worth reading over and over for pure pathos or description. Mr. Collins was in fact, aside from his special gift, a literary artist of no mean power, even if not the highest: with an eye for salient effects, a skill in touching the more obvious chords of emotion, a knowledge of life and books, that enrich his stories with enough extraneous wealth to prolong their life for many years, and some of them perhaps for generations.

THE SLEEP-WALKING

From 'The Moonstone'

[This episode is related by the physician in charge of Mr. Franklin Blake, whose good name he wishes to clear from a charge of fraud.]

TWO O'CLOCK A. M.—The experiment has been tried. With what result I am now to describe.

At eleven o'clock I rang the bell for Betteredge and told Mr. Blake that he might at last prepare himself for bed. . . . I followed Betteredge out of the room, and told him to remove the medicine chest into Miss Verinder's sitting-room.

The order seemed to take him completely by surprise. He looked as if he suspected me of some occult design on Miss Verinder! "Might I presume to ask," he said, "what my young lady and the medicine chest have got to do with each other?"

"Stay in the sitting-room and you will see."

Betteredge appeared to doubt his own unaided capacity to superintend me effectually, on an occasion when a medicine chest was included in the proceedings.

"Is there any objection, sir," he asked, "to taking Mr. Bruff into this part of the business?"

"Quite the contrary! I am now going to ask Mr. Bruff to accompany me down-stairs."

Betteredge withdrew to fetch the medicine chest without another word. I went back into Mr. Blake's room, and knocked at the door of communication. Mr. Bruff opened it, with his papers in his hand—immersed in Law, impenetrable to Medicine.

"I am sorry to disturb you," I said. "But I am going to prepare the laudanum for Mr. Blake; and I must request you to be present and to see what I do."

"Yes," said Mr. Bruff, with nine-tenths of his attention riveted on his papers, and with one-tenth unwillingly accorded to me. "Anything else?"

"I must trouble you to return here with me, and to see me administer the dose."

"Anything else?"

"One thing more. I must put you to the inconvenience of remaining in Mr. Blake's room to see what happens."

"Oh, very good!" said Mr. Bruff. "My room or Mr. Blake's room,—it doesn't matter which; I can go on with my papers anywhere. Unless you object, Mr. Jennings, to my importing *that* amount of common-sense into the proceedings?"

Before I could answer, Mr. Blake addressed himself to the lawyer, speaking from his bed.

"Do you really mean to say that you don't feel any interest in what you are going to do?" he asked. "Mr. Bruff, you have no more imagination than a cow!"

"A cow is a very useful animal, Mr. Blake," said the lawyer. With that reply he followed me out of the room, still keeping his papers in his hand.

We found Miss Verinder pale and agitated, restlessly pacing her sitting-room from end to end. At a table in a corner stood Betteredge, on guard over the medicine chest. Mr. Bruff sat down on the first chair that he could find, and (emulating the usefulness of the cow) plunged back again into his papers on the spot.

Miss Verinder drew me aside, and reverted instantly to her one all-absorbing interest—the interest in Mr. Blake.

"How is he now?" she asked. "Is he nervous? is he out of temper? Do you think it will succeed? Are you sure it will do no harm?"

"Quite sure. Come and see me measure it out."

"One moment. It is past eleven now. How long will it be before anything happens?"

"It is not easy to say. An hour, perhaps."

"I suppose the room must be dark, as it was last year?"

"Certainly."

"I shall wait in my bedroom—just as I did before. I shall keep the door a little way open. It was a little way open last year. I will watch the sitting-room door; and the moment it moves I will blow out my light. It all happened in that way on my birthday night. And it must all happen again in the same way, mustn't it?"

"Are you sure you can control yourself, Miss Verinder?"

"In *his* interests I can do anything!" she answered fervently.

One look at her face told me I could trust her. I addressed myself again to Mr. Bruff.

"I must trouble you to put your papers aside for a moment," I said.

"Oh, certainly!" He got up with a start—as if I had disturbed him at a particularly interesting place—and followed me to the medicine chest. There, deprived of the breathless excitement incidental to the practice of his profession, he looked at Betteredge and yawned wearily.

Miss Verinder joined me with a glass jug of cold water which she had taken from a side table. "Let me pour out the water," she whispered; "I *must* have a hand in it!"

I measured out the forty minims from the bottle, and poured the laudanum into a glass. "Fill it till it is three parts full," I said, and handed the glass to Miss Verinder. I then directed Betteredge to lock up the medicine chest, informing him that I had done with it now. A look of unutterable relief overspread the old servant's countenance. He had evidently suspected me of a medical design on his young lady!

After adding the water as I had directed, Miss Verinder seized a moment—while Betteredge was locking the chest and while Mr. Bruff was looking back at his papers—and slyly kissed the rim of the medicine glass. "When you give it to him," whispered the charming girl, "give it to him on that side."

I took the piece of crystal which was to represent the Diamond from my pocket and gave it to her.

"You must have a hand in this too," I said. "You must put it where you put the Moonstone last year."

She led the way to the Indian cabinet, and put the mock Diamond into the drawer which the real Diamond had occupied on the birthday night. Mr. Bruff witnessed this proceeding, under protest, as he had witnessed everything else. But the strong dramatic interest which the experiment was now assuming proved (to my great amusement) to be too much for Betteredge's capacity of self-restraint. His hand trembled as he held the candle, and he whispered anxiously, "Are you sure, miss, it's the right drawer?"

I led the way out again, with the laudanum and water in my hand. At the door I stood to address a last word to Miss Verinder.

"Don't be long in putting out the lights," I said.

"I will put them out at once," she answered. "And I will wait in my bedroom with only one candle alight."

She closed the sitting-room door behind us. Followed by Bruff and Betteredge, I went back to Mr. Blake's room.

We found him moving restlessly from side to side of the bed, and wondering irritably whether he was to have the laudanum that night. In the presence of the two witnesses I gave him the dose, and shook up his pillows, and told him to lie down again quietly and wait.

His bed, provided with light chintz curtains, was placed with the head against the wall of the room, so as to leave a good open space on either side of it. On one side I drew the curtains completely, and in the part of the room thus screened from his view I placed Mr. Bruff and Betteredge to wait for the result. At the bottom of the bed I half drew the curtains, and placed my own chair at a little distance, so that I might let him see me or not see me, just as the circumstances might direct. Having already been informed that he always slept with a light in the room, I placed one of the two lighted candles on a little table at the head of the bed, where the glare of the light would not strike on his eyes. The other candle I gave to Mr. Bruff; the light in this instance being subdued by the screen of the chintz curtains. The window was open at the top so as to ventilate the room. The rain fell softly; the house was quiet. It was twenty minutes past eleven by my watch when the preparations were completed, and I took my place on the chair set apart at the bottom of the bed.

Mr. Bruff resumed his papers, with every appearance of being as deeply interested in them as ever. But looking toward him now, I saw certain signs and tokens which told me that the Law was beginning to lose its hold on him at last. The suspended interest of the situation in which we were now placed was slowly asserting its influence even on *his* unimaginative mind. As for Betteredge, consistency of principle and dignity of conduct had become in his case mere empty words. He forgot that I was performing a conjuring trick on Mr. Franklin Blake; he forgot that I had upset the house from top to bottom; he forgot that I had not read 'Robinson Crusoe' since I was a child. "For the Lord's sake, sir," he whispered to me, "tell us when it will begin to work."

"Not before midnight," I whispered back. "Say nothing and sit still."

Betteredge dropped to the lowest depth of familiarity with me, without a struggle to save himself. He answered by a wink!

Looking next toward Mr. Blake, I found him as restless as ever in his bed; fretfully wondering why the influence of the laudanum had not begun to assert itself yet. To tell him in his present humor that the more he fidgeted and wondered the longer he would delay the result for which we were now waiting, would have been simply useless. The wiser course to take was to dismiss the idea of the opium from his mind by leading him insensibly to think of something else.

With this view I encouraged him to talk to me, contriving so to direct the conversation, on my side, as to lead him back again to the subject which had engaged us earlier in the evening,— the subject of the Diamond. I took care to revert to those portions of the story of the Moonstone which related to the transport of it from London to Yorkshire; to the risk which Mr. Blake had run in removing it from the bank at Frizinghall; and to the expected appearance of the Indians at the house on the evening of the birthday. And I purposely assumed, in referring to these events, to have misunderstood much of what Mr. Blake himself had told me a few hours since. In this way I set him talking on the subject with which it was now vitally important to fill his mind — without allowing him to suspect that I was making him talk for a purpose. Little by little he became so interested in putting me right that he forgot to fidget in the bed. His mind was far away from the question of the opium at the all-important time when his eyes first told me that the opium was beginning to lay its hold upon his brain.

I looked at my watch. It wanted five minutes to twelve when the premonitory symptoms of the working of the laudanum first showed themselves to me.

At this time no unpracticed eye would have detected any change in him. But as the minutes of the new morning wore away, the swiftly subtle progress of the influence began to show itself more plainly. The sublime intoxication of opium gleamed in his eyes; the dew of a steady perspiration began to glisten on his face. In five minutes more the talk which he still kept up with me failed in coherence. He held steadily to the subject of the Diamond; but he ceased to complete his sentences. A little later the sentences dropped to single words. Then there was an interval of silence. Then he sat up in bed. Then, still busy with the subject of the Diamond, he began to talk again — not to me but to himself. That change told me the first stage in the experiment was reached. The stimulant influence of the opium had got him.

The time now was twenty-three minutes past twelve. The next half-hour, at most, would decide the question of whether he would or would not get up from his bed and leave the room.

In the breathless interest of watching him — in the unutterable triumph of seeing the first result of the experiment declare itself in the manner, and nearly at the time, which I had anticipated — I had utterly forgotten the two companions of my night vigil. Looking toward them now, I saw the Law (as represented by Mr. Bruff's papers) lying unheeded on the floor. Mr. Bruff himself was looking eagerly through a crevice left in the imperfectly drawn curtains of the bed. And Betteredge, oblivious of all respect for social distinctions, was peeping over Mr. Bruff's shoulder.

They both started back on finding that I was looking at them, like two boys caught out by their schoolmaster in a fault. I signed to them to take off their boots quietly, as I was taking off mine. If Mr. Blake gave us the chance of following him, it was vitally necessary to follow him without noise.

Ten minutes passed — and nothing happened.

Then he suddenly threw the bedclothes off him. He put one leg out of bed. He waited.

"I wish I had never taken it out of the bank," he said to himself. "It was safe in the bank."

My heart throbbed fast; the pulses at my temples beat furiously. The doubt about the safety of the Diamond was once more the dominant impression in his brain! On that one pivot the whole success of the experiment turned. The prospect thus suddenly opened before me was too much for my shattered nerves. I was obliged to look away from him, or I should have lost my self-control.

There was another interval of silence.

When I could trust myself to look back at him he was out of his bed, standing erect at the side of it. The pupils of his eyes were now contracted; his eyeballs gleamed in the light of the candle as he moved his head slowly to and fro. He was thinking; he was doubting; he spoke again.

"How do I know?" he said. "The Indians may be hidden in the house."

He stopped, and walked slowly to the other end of the room. He turned, — waited, — came back to the bed.

"It's not even locked up," he went on. "It's in the drawer of her cabinet. And the drawer doesn't lock."

He sat down on the side of the bed. "Anybody might take it," he said.

He rose again restlessly, and reiterated his first words. "How do I know? The Indians may be hidden in the house."

He waited again. I drew back behind the half-curtain of the bed. He looked about the room, with the vacant glitter in his eyes. It was a breathless moment. There was a pause of some sort. A pause in the action of the opium? a pause in the action of the brain? Who could tell? Everything depended now on what he did next.

He laid himself down again on the bed!

A horrible doubt crossed my mind. Was it possible that the sedative action of the opium was making itself felt already? It was not in my experience that it should do this. But what is experience where opium is concerned? There are probably no two men in existence on whom the drug acts in exactly the same manner. Was some constitutional peculiarity in him feeling the influence in some new way? Were we to fail, on the very brink of success?

No! He got up again very abruptly. "How the devil am I to sleep," he said, "with *this* on my mind?"

He looked at the light burning on the table at the head of his bed. After a moment he took the candle in his hand.

I blew out the second candle burning behind the closed curtains. I drew back, with Mr. Bruff and Betteredge, into the farthest corner by the bed. I signed to them to be silent, as if their lives depended on it.

We waited — seeing and hearing nothing. We waited, hidden from him by the curtains.

The light which he was holding on the other side of us moved suddenly. The next moment he passed us, swift and noiseless, with the candle in his hand.

He opened the bedroom door and went out.

We followed him along the corridor. We followed him down the stairs. We followed him along the second corridor. He never looked back; he never hesitated.

He opened the sitting-room door and went in, leaving it open behind him.

The door was hung (like all the other doors in the house) on large old-fashioned hinges. When it was opened, a crevice was opened between the door and the post. I signed to my two companions to look through this, so as to keep them from showing themselves. I placed myself — outside the door also — on the opposite side. A recess in the wall was at my left hand, in which I could instantly hide myself if he showed any signs of looking back into the corridor.

He advanced to the middle of the room, with the candle still in his hand; he looked about him, — but he never looked back.

I saw the door of Miss Verinder's bedroom standing ajar. She had put out her light. She controlled herself nobly. The dim white outline of her summer dress was all that I could see. Nobody who had not known it beforehand would have suspected that there was a living creature in the room. She kept back in the dark; not a word, not a movement escaped her.

It was now ten minutes past one. I heard through the silence the soft drip of the rain, and the tremulous passage of the night air through the trees.

After waiting irresolute for a minute or more in the middle of the room, he moved to the corner near the window where the Indian cabinet stood.

He put his candle on the top of the cabinet. He opened and shut one drawer after another, until he came to the drawer in which the mock Diamond was put. He looked into the drawer for a moment. Then he took the mock Diamond out with his right hand. With the other hand he took the candle from the top of the cabinet.

He walked back a few steps toward the middle of the room and stood still again.

Thus far he had exactly repeated what he had done on the birthday night. Would his next proceeding be the same as the proceeding of last year? Would he leave the room? Would he go back now, as I believed he had gone back then, to his bedchamber? Would he show us what he had done with the Diamond when he had returned to his own room?

His first action, when he moved once more, proved to be an action which he had *not* performed when he was under the influence of the opium for the first time. He put the candle down on a table and wandered on a little toward the farther end of the room. There was a sofa here. He leaned heavily on the back of it with his left hand — then roused himself and returned to the middle of the room. I could now see his eyes.

They were getting dull and heavy; the glitter in them was fast dying out.

The suspense of the moment proved too much for Miss Verinder's self-control. She advanced a few steps,— then stopped again. Mr. Bruff and Betteredge looked across the open doorway at me for the first time. The prevision of a coming disappointment was impressing itself on their minds as well as on mine. Still, so long as he stood where he was, there was hope. We waited in unutterable expectation to see what would happen next.

The next event was decisive. He let the mock Diamond drop out of his hand.

It fell on the floor, before the doorway — plainly visible to him and to every one. He made no effort to pick it up; he looked down at it vacantly, and as he looked, his head sank on his breast. He staggered — roused himself for an instant — walked back unsteadily to the sofa — and sat down on it. He made a last effort; he tried to rise, and sank back. His head fell on the sofa cushions. It was then twenty-five minutes past one o'clock. Before I had put my watch back in my pocket he was asleep.

It was over now. The sedative influence had got him; the experiment was at an end.

I entered the room, telling Mr. Bruff and Betteredge that they might follow me. There was no fear of disturbing him. We were free to move and speak.

"The first thing to settle," I said, "is the question of what we are to do with him. He will probably sleep for the next six or seven hours at least. It is some distance to carry him back to his own room. When I was younger I could have done it alone. But my health and strength are not what they were — I am afraid I will have to ask you to help me."

Before they could answer, Miss Verinder called to me softly. She met me at the door of her room with a light shawl and with the counterpane from her own bed.

"Do you mean to watch him while he sleeps?" she asked.

"Yes. I am not sure enough of the action of the opium in this case, to be willing to leave him alone."

She handed me the shawl and the counterpane.

"Why should you disturb him?" she whispered. "Make his bed on the sofa. I can shut my door and keep in my room."

It was infinitely the simplest and the safest way of disposing of him for the night. I mentioned the suggestion to Mr. Bruff and Betteredge, who both approved of my adopting it. In five minutes I had laid him comfortably on the sofa, and had covered him lightly with the counterpane and the shawl. Miss Verinder wished us good-night and closed the door. At my request we three then drew round the table in the middle of the room, on which the candle was still burning, and on which writing materials were placed.

"Before we separate," I began, "I have a word to say about the experiment which has been tried to-night. Two distinct objects were to be gained by it. The first of these objects was to prove that Mr. Blake entered this room and took the Diamond last year, acting unconsciously and irresponsibly, under the influence of opium. After what you have both seen, are you both satisfied so far?"

They answered me in the affirmative, without a moment's hesitation.

"The second object," I went on, "was to discover what he did with the Diamond after he was seen by Miss Verinder to leave her sitting-room with the jewel in his hand on the birthday night. The gaining of this object depended, of course, on his still continuing exactly to repeat his proceedings of last year. He has failed to do that; and the purpose of the experiment is defeated accordingly. I can't assert that I am not disappointed at the result — but I can honestly say that I am not surprised by it. I told Mr. Blake from the first that our complete success in this matter depended on our completely reproducing in him the physical and moral conditions of last year; and I warned him that this was the next thing to a downright impossibility. We have only partially reproduced the conditions, and the experiment has been only partially successful in consequence. It is also possible that I may have administered too large a dose of laudanum. But I myself look upon the first reason that I have given as the true reason why we have to lament a failure, as well as to rejoice over a success."

After saying those words I put the writing materials before Mr. Bruff, and asked him if he had any objection, before we separated for the night, to draw out and sign a plain statement of what he had seen. He at once took the pen, and produced the statement with the fluent readiness of a practiced hand.

"I owe you this," he said, signing the paper, "as some atonement for what passed between us earlier in the evening. I beg your pardon, Mr. Jennings, for having doubted you. You have done Franklin Blake an inestimable service. In our legal phrase, you have proved your case."

Betteredge's apology was characteristic of the man.

"Mr. Jennings," he said, "when you read 'Robinson Crusoe' again (which I strongly recommend you to do), you will find that he never scruples to acknowledge it when he turns out to have been in the wrong. Please to consider me, sir, as doing what Robinson Crusoe did on the present occasion." With those words he signed the paper in his turn.

Mr. Bruff took me aside as we rose from the table.

"One word about the Diamond," he said. "Your theory is that Franklin Blake hid the Moonstone in his room. My theory is that the Moonstone is in the possession of Mr. Luker's bankers in London. We won't dispute which of us is right. We will only ask, which of us is in a position to put his theory to the test first?"

"The test in my case," I answered, "has been tried to-night, and has failed."

"The test in my case," rejoined Mr. Bruff, "is still in process of trial. For the last two days I have had a watch set for Mr. Luker at the bank; and I shall cause that watch to be continued until the last day of the month. I know that he must take the Diamond himself out of his bankers' hands, and I am acting on the chance that the person who has pledged the Diamond may force him to do this by redeeming the pledge. In that case I may be able to lay my hand on the person. And there is a prospect of our clearing up the mystery exactly at the point where the mystery baffles us now! Do you admit that, so far?"

I admitted it readily.

"I am going back to town by the ten o'clock train," pursued the lawyer. "I may hear, when I get back, that a discovery has been made — and it may be of the greatest importance that I should have Franklin Blake at hand to appeal to if necessary. I intend to tell him, as soon as he wakes, that he must return with me to London. After all that has happened, may I trust to your influence to back me?"

"Certainly!" I said.

Mr. Bruff shook hands with me and left the room. Better-edge followed him out.

I went to the sofa to look at Mr. Blake. He had not moved since I had laid him down and made his bed,— he lay locked in a deep and quiet sleep.

While I was still looking at him I heard the bedroom door softly opened. Once more Miss Verinder appeared on the threshold in her pretty summer dress.

"Do me a last favor," she whispered. "Let me watch him with you."

I hesitated — not in the interest of propriety; only in the interest of her night's rest. She came close to me and took my hand.

"I can't sleep; I can't even sit still in my own room," she said. "Oh, Mr. Jennings, if you were me, only think how you would long to sit and look at him! Say yes! Do!"

Is it necessary to mention that I gave way? Surely not!

She drew a chair to the foot of the sofa. She looked at him in a silent ecstasy of happiness till the tears rose in her eyes. She dried her eyes and said she would fetch her work. She fetched her work, and never did a single stitch of it. It lay in her lap — she was not even able to look away from him long enough to thread her needle. I thought of my own youth; I thought of the gentle eyes which had once looked love at *me*. In the heaviness of my heart I turned to my Journal for relief, and wrote in it what is written here.

So we kept our watch together in silence,— one of us absorbed in his writing; the other absorbed in her love.

Hour after hour he lay in deep sleep. The light of the new day grew and grew in the room, and still he never moved.

Toward six o'clock I felt the warning which told me that my pains were coming back. I was obliged to leave her alone with him for a little while. I said I would go up-stairs and fetch another pillow for him out of his room. It was not a long attack this time. In a little while I was able to venture back and let her see me again.

I found her at the head of the sofa when I returned. She was just touching his forehead with her lips. I shook my head as soberly as I could, and pointed to her chair. She looked back at me with a bright smile and a charming color in her face. "You would have done it," she whispered, "in my place!" . . .

It is just eight o'clock. He is beginning to move for the first time.

Miss Verinder is kneeling by the side of the sofa. She has so placed herself that when his eyes first open they must open upon her face.

Shall I leave them together?

Yes!

COUNT FOSCO

From 'The Woman in White'

HE LOOKS like a man who could tame anything. If he married a tigress instead of a woman, he would have tamed the tigress. If he had married *me*, I should have made his cigarettes as his wife does; I should have held my tongue when he looked at me as she holds hers.

I am almost afraid to confess it even to these secret pages. The man has interested me, has attracted me, has forced me to like him. In two short days he has made his way straight into my favorable estimation; and how he has worked the miracle is more than I can tell.

It absolutely startles me, now he is in my mind, to find how plainly I see him! how much more plainly than I see Sir Percival, or Mr. Fairlie, or Walter Hartright, or any other absent person of whom I think, with the one exception of Laura herself. I can hear his voice as if he was speaking at this moment. I know what his conversation was yesterday, as well as if I was hearing it now. How am I to describe him? There are peculiarities in his personal appearance, his habits, and his amusements, which I should blame in the boldest terms or ridicule in the most merciless manner, if I had seen them in another man. What is it that makes me unable to blame them or to ridicule them in *him?*

For example, he is immensely fat. Before this time, I have always especially disliked corpulent humanity. I have always maintained that the popular notion of connecting excessive grossness of size and excessive good-humor as inseparable allies was equivalent to declaring either that no people but amiable people ever get fat, or that the accidental addition of so many pounds of flesh has a directly favorable influence over the disposition of the person on whose body they accumulate. I have invariably combated both these absurd assertions by quoting examples of fat people who were as mean, vicious, and cruel as the leanest and worst of their neighbors. I have asked whether Henry the Eighth was an amiable character? whether Pope Alexander the Sixth was a good man? whether Mr. Murderer and Mrs. Murderess Manning were not both unusually stout people? whether hired nurses, proverbially as cruel a set of women as are to be found in all England, were not, for the most part, also as fat a set of women as are to be found in all England?—and so on through dozens of other examples, modern and ancient, native and foreign, high and low. Holding these strong opinions on the subject with might and main, as I do at this moment, here nevertheless is Count Fosco, as fat as Henry the Eighth himself, established in my favor at one day's notice, without let or hindrance from his own odious corpulence. Marvelous indeed!

Is it his face that has recommended him?

It may be his face. He is a most remarkable likeness, on a large scale, of the great Napoleon. His features have Napoleon's magnificent regularity; his expression recalls the grandly calm immovable power of the Great Soldier's face. This striking resemblance certainly impressed me, to begin with; but there is something in him besides the resemblance, which has impressed me more. I think the influence I am now trying to find is in his eyes. They are the most unfathomable gray eyes I ever saw; and they have at times a cold, clear, beautiful, irresistible glitter in them, which forces me to look at him, and yet causes me sensations, when I do look, which I would rather not feel. Other parts of his face and head have their strange peculiarities. His complexion, for instance, has a singular sallow-fairness, so much at variance with the dark-brown color of his hair that I suspect the hair of being a wig; and his face, closely shaven all over, is smoother and freer from all marks and wrinkles than mine, though (according to Sir Percival's account of him) he is close on sixty years of age. But these are not the prominent personal characteristics which distinguish him, to my mind, from all the other men I have ever seen. The marked peculiarity which singles him out from the rank and file of humanity lies entirely, so far as I can tell at present, in the extraordinary expression and extraordinary power of his eyes.

His manner, and his command of our language, may also have assisted him in some degree to establish himself in my good opinion. He has that quiet deference, that look of pleased attentive interest, in listening to a woman, and that secret gentleness in his voice in speaking to a woman, which say what we may, we can none of us resist. Here too his unusual command of the English language necessarily helps him. I had often heard of the extraordinary aptitude which many Italians show in mastering our strong hard Northern speech, but until I saw Count Fosco I had never supposed it possible that any foreigner could have spoken English as he speaks it. There are times when it is almost impossible to detect by his accent that he is not a countryman of our own; and as for fluency, there are very few born Englishmen who can talk with as few stoppages and repetitions as the Count. He may construct his sentences more or less in the foreign way; but I have never yet heard him use a wrong expression, or hesitate for a moment in his choice of words.

All the smallest characteristics of this strange man have something strikingly original and perplexingly contradictory in them. Fat as he is, and old as he is, his movements are astonishingly light and easy. He is as noiseless in a room as any of us women; and more than that, with all his look of unmistakable mental firm___ and power, he is as nervously sensitive as the weakest of us. He starts at chance noises as inveterately as Laura herself. He winced and shuddered yesterday when Sir Percival beat one of the spaniels, so that I felt ashamed of my own want of tenderness and sensibility by comparison with the Count.

The relation of this last incident reminds me of one of his most curious peculiarities, which I have not yet mentioned — his extraordinary fondness for pet animals.

Some of these he has left on the Continent; but he has brought with him to this house a cockatoo, two canary-birds, and a whole family of white mice. He attends to all the necessities of these strange favorites himself, and he has taught the creatures to be surprisingly fond of him and familiar with him. The cockatoo, a most vicious and treacherous bird toward every one else, absolutely seems to love him. When he lets it out of its cage it hops on to his knee, and claws its way up his great big body, and rubs its topknot against his sallow double chin in

the most caressing manner imaginable. He has only to set the
doors of the canaries' cage open, and to call them; and the
pretty little cleverly trained creatures perch fearlessly on his
hand, mount his fat outstretched fingers one by one when he
tells them to "go up-stairs," and sing together as if they would
burst their throats with delight when they get to the top finger.
His white mice live in a little pagoda of gayly painted wire-
work, designed and made by himself. They are almost as tame
as the canaries, and they are perpetually let out, like the canaries. They crawl all over him, popping in and out of his waistcoat, and sitting in couples, white as snow, on his capacious
shoulders. He seems to be even fonder of his mice than of his
other pets; smiles at them, and kisses them, and calls them all
sorts of endearing names. If it be possible to suppose an
Englishman with any taste for such childish interests and amusements as these, that Englishman would certainly feel rather
ashamed of them, and would be anxious to apologize for them
in the company of grown-up people. But the Count apparently
sees nothing ridiculous in the amazing contrast between his
colossal self and his frail little pets. He would blandly kiss his
white mice and twitter to his canary-birds amidst an assembly
of English fox-hunters, and would only pity them as barbarians
when they were all laughing their loudest at him.

It seems hardly credible while I am writing it down, but it
is certainly true that this same man, who has all the fondness
of an old maid for his cockatoo, and all the small dexterities
of an organ-boy in managing his white mice, can talk, when
anything happens to rouse him, with a daring independence of
thought, a knowledge of books in every language, and an
experience of society in half the capitals of Europe, which
would make him the prominent personage of any assembly
in the civilized world. This trainer of canary-birds, this archi-
tect of a pagoda for white mice, is (as Sir Percival himself has
told me) one of the first experimental chemists living, and has
discovered among other wonderful inventions a means of petri-
fying the body after death, so as to preserve it, as hard as
marble, to the end of time. This fat, indolent, elderly man,
whose nerves are so finely strung that he starts at chance
noises, and winces when he sees a house spaniel get a whipping,
went into the stable-yard the morning after his arrival, and put
his hand on the head of a chained bloodhound—a beast so

savage that the very groom who feeds him keeps out of his
reach. His wife and I were present, and I shall not forget the
scene that followed, short as it was.

"Mind that dog, sir," said the groom; "he flies at everybody!" "He does that, my friend," replied the Count quietly,
"because everybody is afraid of him. Let us see if he flies at
me." And he laid his plump yellow-white fingers, on which the
canary-birds had been perching ten minutes before, upon the
formidable brute's head, and looked him straight in the eyes.
"You big dogs are all cowards," he said, addressing the animal
contemptuously, with his face and the dog's within an inch of
each other. "You would kill a poor cat, you infernal coward.
You would fly at a starving beggar, you infernal coward. Anything that you can surprise unawares — anything that is afraid
of your big body, and your wicked white teeth, and your slob-
bering, bloodthirsty mouth, is the thing you like to fly at. You
could throttle me at this moment, you mean miserable bully;
and you daren't so much as look me in the face, because I'm
not afraid of you. Will you think better of it, and try your
teeth in my fat neck? Bah! not you!" He turned away, laughing at the astonishment of the men in the yard; and the dog
crept back meekly to his kennel. "   my nice waistcoat!" he
said pathetically. "I am sorry I came here. Some of that
brute's slobber has got on my pretty clean waistcoat." Those
words express another of his incomprehensible oddities. He is
as fond of fine clothes as the veriest fool in existence, and has
appeared in four magnificent waistcoats already — all of light
garish colors and all immensely large, even for him — in the
two days of his residence at Blackwater Park.

His tact and cleverness in small things are quite as noticeable
as the singular inconsistencies in his character, and the childish
triviality of his ordinary tastes and pursuits.

I can see already that he means to live on excellent terms
with all of us during the period of his sojourn in this place.
He has evidently discovered that Laura secretly dislikes him (she
confessed as much to me when I pressed her on the subject),
but he has also found out that she is extravagantly fond of
flowers. Whenever she wants a nosegay he has got one to give
her, gathered and arranged by himself; and greatly to my amusement, he is always cunningly provided with a duplicate, composed of exactly the same flowers, grouped in exactly the same

way, to appease his icily jealous wife, before she can so much as think herself aggrieved. His management of the Countess (in public) is a sight to see. He bows to her; he habitually addresses her as "my angel"; he carries his canaries to pay her little visits on his fingers, and to sing to her; he kisses her hand when she gives him his cigarettes; he presents her with sugar-plums in return, which he puts into her mouth playfully, from a box in his pocket. The rod of iron with which he rules her never appears in company — it is a private rod and is always kept up-stairs.

His method of recommending himself to *me* is entirely different. He flatters my vanity by talking to me as seriously and sensibly as if I was a man. Yes! I can find him out when I am away from him; I know he flatters my vanity, when I think of him up here in my own room — and yet when I go downstairs and get into his company again he will blind me again, and I shall be flattered again, just as if I had never found him out at all! He can manage me as he manages his wife and Laura, as he manages the bloodhound in the stable yard, as he manages Sir Percival himself every hour in the day. "My good Percival! how I like your rough English humor!" — "My good Percival! how I enjoy your solid English sense!" He puts the rudest remarks Sir Percival can make on his effeminate tastes and amusements quietly away from him in that manner — always calling the baronet by his Christian name; smiling at him with the calmest superiority; patting him on the shoulder; and bearing with him benignantly, as a good-humored father bears with a wayward son.

The interest which I really cannot help feeling in this strangely original man has led me to question Sir Percival about his past life.

Sir Percival either knows little, or will tell me little about it. He and the Count first met many years ago, at Rome, under the dangerous circumstances to which I have alluded elsewhere. Since that time they have been perpetually together, in London, in Paris, and in Vienna — but never in Italy again; the Count having, oddly enough, not crossed the frontiers of his native country for years past. Perhaps he has been made the victim of some political persecution? At all events, he seems to be patriotically anxious not to lose sight of any of his own countrymen who may happen to be in England. On the evening of his arrival, he asked how far we were from the nearest town, and whether we knew of any Italian gentlemen who might happen to be settled there. He is certainly in correspondence with people on the Continent, for his letters have all sorts of odd stamps on them; and I saw one for him this morning, waiting in his place at the breakfast-table, with a huge official-looking seal on it. Perhaps he is in correspondence with his government? And yet that is hardly to be reconciled, either, with my other idea that he may be a political exile.

How much I seem to have written about Count Fosco! And what does it all amount to?—as poor dear Mr. Gilmore would ask in his impenetrable business-like way. I can only repeat that I do assuredly feel, even on this short acquaintance, a strange, half-willing, half-unwilling liking for the Count. He seems to have established over me the same sort of ascendency which he has evidently gained over Sir Percival. Free and even rude as he may occasionally be in his manner toward his fat friend, Sir Percival is nevertheless afraid, as I can plainly see, of giving any serious offense to the Count. I wonder whether I am afraid too? I certainly never saw a man, in all my experience, whom I should be so sorry to have for an enemy. Is this because I like him, or because I am afraid of him? *Chi sa?*—as Count Fosco might say in his own language. Who knows?

GEORGE COLMAN THE ELDER

(1733-1794)

F THE two George Colmans, father and son, familiar to the student of English drama and humor, the son was for two or three generations much the better known to the public, through the inclusion of some humorous poems — of the coarse practical-joking sort dear to the British public, and not unaptly characterized by Macaulay as "blackguard doggerel" — in popular anthologies. But the improvement in taste has retired these, and the father's work as a dramatist has solider merits.

George Colman was the son of an English diplomatist, and born at Florence, but educated in England; entering Christ Church College, Oxford, in 1751, and becoming M. A. in 1758. He studied law in London; but his tastes and an intimacy with Garrick soon led him to abandon this for poetry and play-writing. His first piece, 'Polly Honeycomb,' was acted at Drury Lane with great success in 1760; and the following year 'The Jealous Wife' — "rich in borrowed excellences" — had an equal welcome.

GEORGE COLMAN

Neither of them has much originality, but they show an excellent sense of stage effect and humorous situation, and are well put together and harmonized. Later it occurred to Garrick and Colman that an entertaining play might be made on the lines of Hogarth's 'Marriage à la Mode,' and the result of their joint labors was 'The Clandestine Marriage' (1766). Garrick made a great hit in this as Lord Ogleby, a faded but witty old man.

Colman also wrote some excellent detached pieces for the Connoisseur, and about 1761 became owner of the St. James's Chronicle and contributed humorous matter to it. In 1764 he published a translation of the comedies of Terence into English blank verse, which was much praised. In 1768 he became an owner of Covent Garden Theatre, and later managed the Haymarket. For many years he wrote and translated pieces for the stage, and was much respected as a manager and liked as a man. In 1783 he published a translation of Horace's 'Art of Poetry.' He died in 1794, after five years of insanity.

THE EAVESDROPPING

From 'The Jealous Wife'

Scene, Mr. Oakly's *House:*   *Enter* Harriot *following a Servant*

HARRIOT — Not at home! are you sure that Mrs. Oakly is not at home, sir?

Servant — She is just gone out, madam.

Harriot — I have something of consequence: if you will give me leave, sir, I will wait till she returns.

Servant — You would not see her if you did, madam. She has given positive orders not to be interrupted with any company to-day.

Harriot — Sure, sir, if you were to let her know that I had particular business —

Servant — I should not dare to trouble her, indeed, madam.

Harriot — How unfortunate this is! What can I do? Pray, sir, can I see *Mr.* Oakly then?

Servant — Yes, madam: I'll acquaint my master, if you please.

Harriot — Pray do, sir.

Servant — Will you favor me with your name, madam?

Harriot — Be pleased, sir, to let him know that a lady desires to speak with him.

Servant — I shall, madam.   [*Exit Servant.*

Harriot [*alone*] — I wish I could have seen Mrs. Oakly! What an unhappy situation am I reduced to! What will the world say of me? And yet what could I do? To remain at Lady Freelove's was impossible. Charles, I must own, has this very day revived much of my tenderness for him; and yet I dread the wildness of his disposition. I must now however solicit Mr. Oakly's protection; a circumstance (all things considered) rather disagreeable to a delicate mind, and which nothing but the absolute necessity of it could excuse. Good Heavens, what a multitude of difficulties and distresses am I thrown into, by my father's obstinate perseverance to force me into a marriage which my soul abhors!

Enter Oakly

Oakly — Where is this lady? [*Seeing her.*] Bless me, Miss Russet, is it you? [*Aside*] — Was ever anything so unlucky? — Is it possible, madam, that I see you here?

Harriot—It is true, sir! and the occasion on which I am now to trouble you is so much in need of an apology, but—the favor, sir, which I would now request of you is that you will suffer me to remain for a few days in your house.

Oakly [*aside*]—If my wife should return before I get her out of the house again!—I know of your leaving your father, by a letter we had from him. Upon my soul, madam, I would do anything to serve you; but your being in my house creates a difficulty that—

Harriot—I hope, sir, you do not doubt the truth of what I have told you?

Oakly—I religiously believe every tittle of it, madam; but I have particular family considerations that—

Harriot—Sure, sir, you cannot suspect me to be base enough to form any connections in your family contrary to your inclinations, while I am living in your house.

Oakly—Such connections, madam, would do me and all my family great honor. I never dreamed of any scruples on that account. What can I do? Let me see—let me see—suppose—

[*Pausing.*

Enter Mrs. Oakly *behind, in a capuchin, tippet, etc.*

Mrs. Oakly—I am sure I heard the voice of a woman conversing with my husband. Ha! [*Seeing* Harriot.] It is so, indeed! Let me contain myself! I'll listen.

Harriot—I see, sir, you are not inclined to serve me. Good Heaven, what am I reserved to? Why, why did I leave my father's house, to expose myself to greater distresses?

[*Ready to weep.*

Oakly—I would do anything for your sake, indeed I would. So pray be comforted; and I'll think of some proper place to bestow you in.

Mrs. Oakly—So, so!

Harriot—What place can be so proper as your own house?

Oakly—My dear madam, I—I— ·

Mrs. Oakly—My dear madam! mighty well!

Oakly—Hush! hark! what noise? No, nothing. But I'll be plain with you, madam; we may be interrupted. The family consideration I hinted at is nothing else than my wife. She is a little unhappy in her temper, madam; and if you were to be admitted into the house, I don't know what might be the consequence.

Mrs. Oakly — Very fine!

Harriot — My behavior, sir —

Oakly — My dear life, it would be impossible for you to behave in such a manner as not to give her suspicion.

Harriot — But if your nephew, sir, took everything upon himself —

Oakly — Still that would not do, madam. Why, this very morning, when the letter came from your father, though I positively denied any knowledge of it, and Charles owned it, yet it was almost impossible to pacify her.

Mrs. Oakly — The letter! How have I been bubbled!

Harriot — What shall I do? what will become of me?

Oakly — Why, look ye, my dear madam, since my wife is so strong an objection, it is absolutely impossible for me to take you into the house. Nay, if I had not known she was gone out just before you came, I should be uneasy at your being here even now. So we must manage as well as we can: I'll take a private lodging for you a little way off, unknown to Charles or my wife or anybody; and if Mrs. Oakly should discover it at last, why the whole matter will light upon Charles, you know.

Mrs. Oakly — Upon Charles!

Harriot — How unhappy is my situation! [*Weeping.*] I am ruined forever.

Oakly — Ruined! not at all. Such a thing as this has happened to many a young lady before you, and all has been well again. Keep up your spirits! I'll contrive, if I possibly can, to visit you every day.

Mrs. Oakly [*advancing*] — Will you so? O Mr. Oakly! I have discovered you at last? I'll visit you, indeed. And you, my *dear* madam, I'll —

Harriot — Madam, I don't understand —

Mrs. Oakly — I understand the whole affair, and have understood it for some time past. You shall have a private lodging, miss! It is the fittest place for you, I believe. How dare you look me in the face?

Oakly — For Heaven's sake, my love, don't be so violent! You are quite wrong in this affair; you don't know who you are talking to. That lady is a person of fashion.

Mrs. Oakly — Fine fashion, indeed! to beguile other women's husbands!

Harriot — Dear madam, how can you imagine —

Oakly — I tell you, my dear, this is the young lady that Charles —

Mrs. Oakly — Mighty well! But that won't do, sir! Did not I hear you lay the whole intrigue together? did not I hear your fine plot of throwing all the blame upon Charles?

Oakly — Nay, be cool a moment! You must know, my dear, that the letter which came this morning related to this lady.

Mrs. Oakly — I know it.

Oakly — And since that, it seems, Charles has been so fortunate as to —

Mrs. Oakly — O, you deceitful man! that trick is too stale to pass again with me. It is plain now what you meant by your proposing to take her into the house this morning. But the gentlewoman could introduce herself, I see.

Oakly — Fie, fie, my dear! she came on purpose to inquire for you.

Mrs. Oakly — For me! Better and better! Did not she watch her opportunity, and come to you just as I went out? But I am obliged to you for your visit, madam. It is sufficiently paid. Pray don't let me detain you.

Oakly — For shame, for shame, Mrs. Oakly! How can you be so absurd? Is this proper behavior to a lady of her character?

Mrs. Oakly — I have heard her character. Go, my fine runaway madam! Now you've eloped from your father, and run away from your aunt, go! You shan't stay here, I promise you.

Oakly — Prithee, be quiet. You don't know what you are doing. She shall stay.

Mrs. Oakly — She shan't stay a minute.

Oakly — She shall stay a minute, an hour, a day, a week, a month, a year! 'Sdeath, madam, she shall stay forever, if I choose it.

Mrs. Oakly — How!

Harriot — For Heaven's sake, sir, let me go. I am frighted to death.

Oakly — Don't be afraid, madam! She shall stay, I insist upon it.

Russet [*within*] — I tell you, sir, I will go up. I am sure that the lady is here, and nothing shall hinder me.

Harriot — Oh, my father, my father!   [*Faints away.*

Oakly—See! she faints. [*Catching her.*] Ring the bell! who's there?

Mrs. Oakly—What, take her in your arms too! I have no patience.

Enter Russet *and servants*

Russet—Where is this—Ha! fainting! [*Running to her.*] Oh, my dear Harriot! my child! my child!

Oakly—Your coming so abruptly shocked her spirits. But she revives. How do you, madam?

Harriot [*to Russet*]—Oh, sir!

Russet—Oh, my dear girl! how could you run away from your father, that loves you with such fondness! But I was sure I should find you here.

Mrs. Oakly—There, there! Sure he should find her here! Did not I tell you so? Are not you a wicked man, to carry on such base underhand doings with a gentleman's daughter?

Russet—Let me tell you, sir, whatever you may think of the matter, I shall not easily put up with this behavior. How durst you encourage my daughter to an elopement, and receive her in your house?

Mrs. Oakly—There, mind that! the thing is as plain as the light.

Oakly—I tell you, you misunderstand—

Russet—Look you, Mr. Oakly, I shall expect satisfaction from your family for so gross an affront. Zounds, sir, I am not to be used ill by any man in England!

Harriot—My dear sir, I can assure you—

Russet—Hold your tongue, girl! you'll put me in a passion.

Oakly—Sir, this is all a mistake.

Russet—A mistake! Did not I find her in your house?

Oakly—Upon my soul, she has not been in the house above—

Mrs. Oakly—Did not I hear you say you would take her to a lodging? a private lodging?

Oakly—Yes; but that—

Russet—Has not this affair been carried on a long time, in spite of my teeth?

Oakly—Sir, I never troubled myself—

Mrs. Oakly—Never troubled yourself! Did not you insist on her staying in the house, whether I would or no?

Oakly — No.

Russet — Did not you send to meet her when she came to town ?

Oakly — No.

Mrs. Oakly — Did not you deceive me about the letter this morning ?

Oakly — No, no, no. I tell you, no!

Mrs. Oakly — Yes, yes, yes. I tell you, yes!

Russet — Shan't I believe my own eyes ?

Mrs. Oakly — Shan't I believe my own ears ?

Oakly — I tell you, you are both deceived.

Russet — Zounds, sir, I'll have satisfaction.

Mrs. Oakly — I'll stop these fine doings, I warrant you.

Oakly — 'Sdeath, you will not let me speak! And you are both alike, I think. I wish you were married to one another, with all my heart.

Mrs. Oakly — Mighty well! mighty well!

Russet — I shall soon find a time to talk with you.

Oakly — Find a time to talk! you have talked enough now for all your lives.

Mrs. Oakly — Very fine! Come along, sir! leave that lady with her father. Now she is in the properest hands.

Oakly — I wish I could leave you in his hands. [*Going, returns.*] I shall follow you, madam! One word with you, sir! The height of your passion, and Mrs. Oakly's strange misapprehension of this whole affair, makes it impossible to explain matters to you at present. I will do it when you please, and how you please.   [*Exit.*

Russet — Yes, yes; I'll have satisfaction. So, madam! I have found you at last. You have made a fine confusion here.

Harriot — I have indeed been the innocent cause of a great deal of confusion.

Russet — Innocent! what business had you to be running hither after —

Harriot — My dear sir, you misunderstand the whole affair. I have not been in this house half an hour.

Russet — Zounds, girl, don't put me in a passion! You know I love you; but a lie puts me in a passion! But come along; we'll leave this house directly. [*Charles singing without.*] Heyday! what now?

After a noise without, enter Charles, *drunk and singing :—*

But my wine neither nurses nor babies can bring,
And a big-bellied bottle's a mighty good thing.

What's here—a woman? a woman? Harriot!—Impossible!—
My dearest, sweetest Harriot! I have been looking all over the
town for you, and at last, when I was tired and weary and
disappointed,— why then the honest Major and I sat down
together to drink your health in pint bumpers.

[*Running up to her.*

Russet—Stand off! How dare you take any liberties with
my daughter before me? Zounds, sir, I'll be the death of you!

Charles—Ha, 'Squire Russet, too! You jolly old cock, how
do you? But Harriot! my dear girl! [*Taking hold of her.*] My
life, my soul, my —

Russet—Let her go, sir! Come away, Harriot! Leave him
this instant, or I'll tear you asunder.   [*Pulling her.*

Harriot—There needs no violence to tear me from a man
who could disguise himself in such a gross manner, at a time
when he knew I was in the utmost distress.

[*Disengages herself, and exit with Russet.*

Charles [*alone*]—Only hear me, sir! Madam! My dear
Harriot! Mr. Russet! Gone! She's gone; and egad, in a very
ill humor and in very bad company! I'll go after her. But
hold! I shall only make it worse, as I did, now I recollect,
once before. How the devil came they here? Who would have
thought of finding her in my own house? My head turns round
with conjectures. I believe I am drunk, very drunk; so egad,
I'll e'en go and sleep myself sober, and then inquire the meaning of all this—

"For I love Sue, and Sue loves me," etc.

[*Exit singing.*

JOHANN AMOS COMENIUS

(1592–1671)

BY BURKE A. HINSDALE

JOHANN AMOS COMENIUS, the Slavic educational reformer, was born March 28th, 1592, at Nivnitz, a village of Moravia. His family belonged to the small but well-known body that takes its name from the country,—"the Moravian Brethren," or simply "the Moravians," whose origin goes back to Huss, the Bohemian reformer. The Brethren are known for their simple evangelical faith, their humble fraternal lives, their interest in education, and particularly their devotion to the cause of missions. Comenius was a Moravian, a minister, and a bishop, and he illustrated the best ideas and inspirations of the Brotherhood in his teachings and life.

COMENIUS

The parents of Comenius died when he was still a child, and he fell into the hands of guardians, who allowed his education to be neglected. He received his elementary education in one of the people's schools that sprang out of the Hussite movement. When sixteen years of age he attended a Latin school, and at twenty he was studying theology at Hebron College, in the duchy of Nassau. Next he spent some time in travel and in study at Heidelberg. and returned to Moravia in 1614, being twenty-two years of age. Too young to be ordained to the ministry, he was made rector of a Moravian school at Prerau, near Olmütz, where his career as a teacher and educator began. His attention had already been turned to the teaching art as practiced in the schools, both by observation and by reading the schemes of educational reform that had been propounded. In 1616 he was ordained to the pastorate, and two years later he was set over the flourishing church of Fulneck, where he also had the supervision of a school. Here he married, and "for two or three years," says Professor Laurie, "spent a happy and active life, enjoying the only period of tranquillity in his native country which it was ever his fortune to experience. For the restoration of a time so happy he never ceased to pine during all his future wanderings.»

Soon the Thirty Years' War broke out, and in 1621 Fulneck fell into the hands of the Spaniards, who dealt with it according to their usual habit in such cases. Comenius lost all his property, including his library and manuscripts, and became for the rest of his life an exile. His wife and child he lost soon after. He had been so unfortunate as to incur the enmity of the Jesuits. We cannot follow him closely in his wanderings. For some time he lived in secrecy in Moravia and Bohemia. Then he found a resting-place at Lissa, in Poland, where in 1621 he published a little work that at once made him famous. This was the 'Janua Linguarum Reserata,' (the Gate of Tongues Unlocked), which was translated into the principal languages of Europe and several languages of Asia. The next year he was elected chief bishop of the Brethren, and henceforth there came upon him daily, as upon the great Apostle, the care of all the churches. Still he never ceased reading, thinking, and writing on educational matters, and was often engaged in the practical work of teaching. He visited England, called there to confer with the Long Parliament in reference to the reform of education. He visited Sweden, where he discussed education and learning with the great Oxenstierna. Then he lived for a time at Elbing in East Russia. Next he was called to Transylvania and Hungary on an educational errand, and then returned to Lissa.

In the course of the war this town was destroyed, and Comenius again lost all of his possessions. The great Pansophic dictionary that had engaged him for many years went with the rest,— a loss, he said, that he should cease to lament only when he should cease to breathe. His next home was Amsterdam, where he set himself to collect, revise, and supplement his writings on didactics, and where they were published in four folio volumes in 1657. At some time, according to Cotton Mather, he was offered the presidency of Harvard College. After the publication of his works he lived thirteen years, employed in teaching, in writing, and in pastoral labors. He died November 15th, 1671, in his eightieth year, having fully merited Von Raumer's characterization:—"Comenius is a grand and venerable figure of sorrow. Wandering, persecuted, and homeless during the terrible and desolating Thirty Years' War, he yet never despaired; but with enduring truth, and strong in faith, he labored unweariedly to prepare youth by a better education for a better future." In 1892, on the three-hundredth anniversary of his birth, the educators of the world united to honor his memory, and at that time a monument was erected at Naärden, Holland, the little village where he died and was buried. At Leipzig there is a pedagogical library founded in his honor on the two-hundredth anniversary of his birth, which numbers more than 66,000 volumes.

Comenius wrote one hundred and thirty-five books and treatises, most of which were translated during his lifetime into all the languages of Europe and several languages of Asia. Not all of them related to education; he wrote voluminously on religious subjects also. To name and characterize his didactic works would far transcend the limits of this notice; we can do no more than draw an outline of his pedagogical system.

Early in the Renaissance the ancient literatures took complete possession of the minds of scholars and teachers. As these literatures were nowhere the vernacular, the schools were made machines for teaching the Latin and Greek languages. Sometimes the results were better, sometimes worse. We may hope that Comenius spoke of the schools at their worst estate when he said that they were "the terror of boys and the slaughter-houses of minds," — "places where hatred of literature and books was contracted,"—"where what ought to be poured in gently was forced in violently," and "where what ought to be put clearly was presented in a confused and intricate manner, as if it were a collection of puzzles." "Ten years," he said, "are given to the study of the Latin tongue, and after all the result is disappointing. Boyhood is distracted for years with precepts of grammar, infinitely prolix, perplexed, and obscure, and for the most part useless. Boys are stuffed with vocabularies without associating the words with things, or indeed with one another." For the time it was impossible, even if desirable, to overturn the established system; and Comenius, while still at Prerau, addressed himself to the problem of simplifying the teaching of Latin. His first book, 'Grammaticæ Facilioris Præcepta,' written for his own pupils, was published at Prague in 1616. The great impression that the 'Janua' produced, shows how ready men were to welcome anything that promised to mitigate the evils of the prevailing methods of teaching.

But deeply interested as he was in teaching languages, Comenius still saw that this was by no means the great educational question of the time. Early in life he had become a disciple of the new inductive philosophy; and of all the titles that have been conferred upon him, that of "the Bacon of education" is the most significant. The impression that he received from Bacon was most profound. Several of his titles, as 'Didactica Magna,' 'Pansophiæ Prodromus,' and 'Silva,' suggest titles before used by his master. Looking at education from the Baconian point of view, Comenius proposed to make it an inductive science. He found in nature the great storehouse of education material. "Do we not dwell in the Garden of Eden," he demanded, "as well as our predecessors? Why should not we use our eyes and ears and noses as well as they? and why need we other teachers than these in learning to know the works of nature? Why should we not, instead of these dead books, open to the children the living book of nature? Why not open their understandings to the things themselves, so that from them, as from living springs, many streamlets may flow?" Holding these views and putting them effectively before the world, he became the founder of the pedagogical school known as the Sense-Realists. But much more than this, he had the rare merit of seeing that modern education must be built on the basis of the modern languages; and so he proposed to call the elementary school the "vernacular school,"—things before words, and vernacular words before foreign words.

Comenius's best known books are the 'Didactica Magna' and the 'Orbis Sensualium Pictus.' The first was written in Czech, the author's vernacular, one of the best of the Slavonic dialects, during his first residence in Lissa; but was not published until a later day, and then in Latin. It is a general treatise on method. "After many workings and tossings of my thoughts," he says, "by setting everything to the immovable laws of nature," he lighted upon this treatise, "which shows the art of readily and solidly teaching all things." The 'Orbis Pictus,' which was only a modification of the 'Janua,' first appeared in 1657. Hoole, the English translator, renders the Latin title thus: 'Visible World; or a Nomenclature and Pictures of all the Chief Things that are in the World, and of Men's Employments Therein.' The 'Orbis Pictus' has been called 'Children's First Picture-Book,' and it obtained much the widest circulation and use of all the reformer's works. It was written to illustrate his ideas of teaching things and words together. Its keynote is struck by the legend, "There is nothing in the intellect that is not first in the sense." The lessons, of which there are one hundred and ninety-four words, are given in Latin and German, and are each illustrated with a copper cut. While the book is wholly unsuited to our use, it is still an interesting pedagogical memorial, archaic and quaint.

But Bacon's influence on Comenius was far greater than has yet appeared. The philosopher had large conceptions of the kingdom of knowledge, and the disciple accepted these conceptions in their most exaggerated form. He became the founder of 'Pansophia': men could attain to universal knowledge if they were rightly taught and guided. When his eye had once caught this vision, it never wandered from it to the day of his death. He projected a Pansophic school, and spent half a lifetime in seeking a patron who would help him to realize his dream. Save some of the first ones, his didactic treatises were written as means to a Pansophic end. The books that have made him immortal he counted but as dust in the balance, compared with the piles of manuscripts that he produced devoted to all knowledge. In fact, he almost despised himself because, partly persuaded by his patrons and advisers and partly compelled by the necessities of livelihood, he gave so much time to things didactic. Thus Comenius was like Bacon, in that his real service to the world was something quite different from what he proposed for its benefit. He was like Bacon also in this, that he put forth the same work — practically so — in more than one form.

The mistakes of Comenius lie upon the surface. He entertained exaggerated views of the results to flow to mankind from the enlargement of knowledge, he greatly overestimated the value of method, and so, very naturally, greatly magnified what the human mind is able to accomplish in the field of learning. He carried much too far his sensational principles, and seriously underestimated the ancient learning and letters. But these mistakes, and even Pansophism itself, may be not only excused but welcomed; since they undoubtedly contributed at the time, and since, to educational progress.

It must not be supposed that Comenius had no precursors. Bacon had disclosed to men his vision of the kingdom of knowledge. Rabelais had published his realistic views of education and his vast scheme of studies. Montaigne had delivered his criticisms on current teaching and submitted his suggestions for reform. Mulcaster had given to the world his far-reaching anticipations of the future. Ratich, the John the Baptist of the new movement, to whom Comenius was probably most indebted next to Bacon, had gone far in revolt from the existing régime. But it was left to Comenius to give the new pedagogy a shaping and an impulse that well entitle him to be called its founder.

Comenius has still other credentials to permanent fame. He advocated popular education, contended for the union of knowledge with morals and piety, proposed the higher education of women, propounded the existing tripartite division of education, and devised a system of graded instruction for schools of a decidedly modern character. His place in the educational pantheon is secure; but not so much by reason of his didactics, which are now largely antiquated, as by reason of his spirit. As Mr. Quick has said: — "He saw that every human creature should be trained up to become a reasonable being, and that the training should be such as to draw out the God-given faculties. Thus he struck the keynote of the science of education."

B. A. Hinsdale

AUTHOR'S PREFACE TO THE 'ORBIS PICTUS'

INSTRUCTION is the means to expel rudeness, with which young wits ought to be well furnished in Schools: but so as that the teaching be — 1, True; 2, Full; 3, Clear; and 4, Solid.

1.   It will be true, if nothing be taught but such as is beneficial to one's life; lest there be a cause of complaining afterwards.   We know not necessary things, because we have not learned things necessary.

2.   It will be full, if the mind be polished for wisdom, the tongue for eloquence, and the hands for a neat way of living. This will be that grace of one's life: to be wise, to act, to speak.

3, 4.   It will be clear, and by that, firm and solid, if whatever is taught and learned be not obscure or confused, but apparent, distinct, and articulate as the fingers on the hands.

The ground of this business is, that sensual objects may be rightly presented to the senses, for fear they may not be received.   I say, and say it again aloud, that this last is the foundation of all the rest: because we can neither act nor speak wisely, unless we first rightly understand all the things which are to be done, and whereof we are to speak.   Now there is nothing in the understanding which was not before in the sense. And therefore to exercise the senses well about the right perceiving the differences of things, will be to lay the grounds for all wisdom, and all wise discourse, and all discreet actions in one's course of life.   Which, because it is commonly neglected in our schools, and the things which are to be learned are offered to scholars without being understood or being rightly presented to the senses, it cometh to pass that the work of teaching and learning goeth heavily onward, and affordeth little benefit.

See here then a new help for schools, a Picture and Nomenclature of all the chief things in the world, and of men's actions in their way of living: which that you, good masters, may not be loath to run over with your scholars, I tell you, in short, what good you may expect from it.

It is a little book, as you see, of no great bulk, yet a brief of the whole world, and a whole language; full of Pictures, Nomenclatures, and Descriptions of things.

I.   The Pictures are the representations of all visible things (to which also things invisible are reduced after their fashion) of the whole world.   And that in that very order of things in which they are described in the 'Janua Latinæ Linguæ'; and with that fullness, that nothing very necessary or of great concernment is omitted.

II.   The Nomenclatures are the Inscriptions, or Titles, set every one over their own Pictures, expressing the whole thing by its own general term.

III.   The Descriptions are the explications of the parts of the Picture, so expressed by their own proper terms; as the same figure which is added to every piece of the Picture, and the term of it, always showeth what things belongeth one to another.

Which such book, and in such a dress, may (I hope) serve.

I.   To entice witty children to it, that they may not conceit it a torment to be in school, but dainty fare.   For it is apparent that children (even from their infancy almost) are delighted with pictures, and willingly please their eyes with these lights; and it will be very well worth the pains to have once brought it to pass, that scarecrows may be taken away out of wisdom's gardens.

II.   This same little book will serve to stir up the attention, which is to be fastened upon things, and even to be sharpened more and more; which is also a great matter.   For the senses (being the main guides of childhood, because therein the mind doth not as yet raise up itself to an abstracted contemplation of things) evermore seek their own objects, and if they may be away, they grow dull, and wry themselves hither and thither out of a weariness of themselves; but when their objects are present, they grow merry, wax lively, and willingly suffer themselves to be fastened upon them, till the thing be sufficiently discerned. This book then will do a good piece of service in taking especially flickering wits, and preparing them for deeper studies.

III.   Whence a third good will follow: that children being won thereunto, and drawn over with this way of heeding, may be furnished with the knowledge of the prime things that are in the world, by sport and merry pastime.   In a word, this Book will serve for the more pleasing using of the 'Vestibulum' and 'Janua Linguarum,' for which end it was even at the first chiefly intended.   Yet if it like any that it be bound up in their native tongues also, it promiseth three good things of itself.

I. First, it will afford a device for learning to read more
easily than hitherto, especially having a symbolical alphabet set
before it; to wit, the characters of the several letters, with the
image of that creature whose voice that letter goeth about to
imitate, pictured by it. For the young A B C scholar will easily
remember the force of every character by the very looking upon
the creature, till the imagination, being strengthened by use, can
readily afford all things; and then having looked over a table of
the chief syllables also (which yet was not thought necessary to
be added to this book), he may proceed to the viewing of the
pictures and the inscriptions set over them. Where again, the
very looking upon the thing pictured suggesting the name of the
thing, will tell him how the title of the picture is to be read.
And thus the whole book being gone over by the bare titles of
the pictures, reading cannot but be learned; and indeed too,
which thing is to be noted, without using any ordinary tedious
spelling, that most troublesome torture of wits, which may wholly
be avoided by this method. For the often reading over the book,
by those larger descriptions of things, and which are set after the
pictures, will be able perfectly to beget a habit of reading.

II. The same book being used in English, in English schools,
will serve for the perfect learning of the whole English tongue,
and that from the bottom; because by the aforesaid descriptions
of things, the words and phrases of the whole language are
found set orderly in their proper places. And a short English
Grammar might be added at the end, clearly resolving the speech
already understood into its parts; showing the declining of the
several words, and reducing those that are joined together under
certain rules.

III. Thence a new benefit cometh, that that very English
Translation may serve for the more ready and pleasant learning
of the Latin tongue: as one may see in this edition, the whole
book being so translated that everywhere one word answereth to
the word over against it, and the book is in all things the same,
only in two idioms, as a man clad in a double garment. And
there might be also some observations and advertisements added
at the end, touching those things only wherein the use of the
Latin tongue differeth from the English. For where there is no
difference, there needeth no advertisements to be given. But
because the first tasks of the learner ought to be little and
single, we have filled this first book of training one up to see a

thing of himself, with nothing but rudiments; that is, with the chief of things and words, or with the grounds of the whole world, and the whole language, and of all our understanding about things. If a more perfect description of things, and a fuller knowledge of a language, and a clearer light of the understanding, be sought after (as they ought to be), they are to be found somewhere whither there will now be an easy passage by this our little Encyclopædia of things subject to the senses. Something remaineth to be said touching the more cheerful use of this book.

I. Let it be given to children into their hands to delight themselves withal as they please with the sight of the pictures, and making them as familiar to themselves as may be, and that even at home before they are put to school.

II. Then let them be examined ever and anon (especially now in the school) what this thing or that thing is, and is called, so that they may see nothing which they know not how to name, and that they can name nothing which they cannot show.

III. And let the things named them be showed, not only in the picture, but also in themselves; for example, the parts of the body, clothes, books, the house, utensils, etc.

IV. Let them be suffered also to imitate the pictures by hand, if they will; nay, rather let them be encouraged that they may be willing: first, thus to quicken the attention also towards the things, and to observe the proportion of the parts one towards the other; and lastly, to practice the nimbleness of the hand, which is good for many things.

V. If anything here mentioned cannot be presented to the eye, it will be to no purpose at all to offer them by themselves to the scholars; as colors, relishes, etc., which cannot here be pictured out with ink. For which reason it were to be wished that things rare and not easy to be met withal at home might be kept ready in every great school, that they may be showed also, as often as any words are to be made by them, to the scholars.

SCHOOL OF INFANCY

CLAIMS OF CHILDHOOD

THAT children are an inestimable treasure, the Spirit of God
by the lips of David testifies, saying:—"Lo, the children
are the heritages of the Lord; the fruit of the womb his
reward; as arrows in the hand, so are children. Blessed is the
man who has filled his quiver with them; he shall not be confounded." David declares those to be happy on whom God
confers children.

The same is also evident from this: that God, purposing to
testify his love towards us, calls us children, as if there were no
more excellent name by which to commend us.

Moreover, he is very greatly incensed against those who
deliver their children to Moloch. It is also worthy our most
serious consideration that God, in respect of the children of even
idolatrous parents, calls them children born to him; thus indicating that they are born not for ourselves but for God, and
as God's offspring they claim our most profound respect.

Hence in Malachi children are called the seed of God, whence
arises the offspring of God.

For this reason the eternal Son of God, when manifested in
the flesh, not only willed to become the participator of the flesh
of children, but likewise deemed children a pleasure and a
delight. Taking them in his arms, as little brothers and sisters,
he carried them about, and kissed them and blessed them.

Not only this: he likewise uttered a severe threat against any
one who should offend them even in the least degree, commanding them to be respected as himself, and condemning even
with severe penalties any who offend even the smallest of them.

Should any one wish to inquire why he so delighted in little
children, and so strictly enjoined upon us such respectful attention to them, many reasons may be ascertained. And first, if
the little ones seem unimportant to you, regard them not as
they now are, but as in accordance with the intention of God
they may and ought to be. You will see them not only as the
future inhabitants of the world and possessors of the earth, and
God's vicars amongst his creatures when we depart from this
life, but also equally participators with us in the heritage of

Christ, a royal priesthood, a chosen people, associates of angels, judges of devils, the delight of heaven, the terror of hell — heirs of the most excellent dignities throughout all the ages of eternity. What can be imagined more excellent than this?

Philip Melanchthon of pious memory, having upon one occasion entered a common school, looked upon the pupils therein assembled, and began his address to them in these words:— "Hail, reverend pastors, doctors, licentiates, superintendents! Hail! most noble, most prudent, most learned lords, consuls, prætors, judges, prefects, chancellors, secretaries, magistrates, professors, etc." When some of the bystanders received these words with a smile, he replied:— "I am not jesting; my speech is serious; for I look on these little boys, not as they are now, but with a view to the purpose of the Divine mind, on account of which they are delivered to us for instruction. For assuredly some such will come forth from among the number, although there may be an intermixture of chaff among them as there is among wheat." Such was the animated address of this most prudent man. But why should not we with equal confidence declare, in respect of all children of Christian parents, those glorious things which have been mentioned above? since Christ, the promulgator of the eternal secrets of God, has pronounced that "of such is the kingdom of Heaven."

But if we consider only their present state, it will at once be obvious why children are of inestimable value in the sight of God, and ought to be so to their parents.

In the first place, they are valuable to God because, being innocent with the sole exception of original sin, they are not yet the defaced image of God by having polluted themselves with actual guilt, and are "unable to discern between good and evil, between the right hand and the left." That God has respect to this is abundantly manifest from the above words addressed to John, and from other passages of the Sacred Writ.

Secondly, they are the pure and dearly purchased possession of Christ; since Christ, who came to seek the lost, is said to be the Savior of all, except those who by incredulity and impenitence shut themselves out from being participators in his merits. These are the purchased from among men, that they may be the first-fruits unto God and the Lamb; having not yet defiled themselves with the allurements of sin; but they follow the Lamb whithersoever he goeth. And that they may continue so to follow, they ought to be led as it were with the hand by a pious education.

Finally, God so embraces children with abounding love that they are a peculiar instrument of divine glory; as the Scriptures testify, "From the lips of infants and sucklings thou hast perfected praise, because of mine enemies; that thou mayest destroy the enemy and avenger." How it comes to pass that God's glory should receive increase from children, is certainly not at once obvious to our understanding; but God, the discerner of all things, knows and understands, and declares it to be so.

That children ought to be dearer and more precious to parents than gold and silver, than pearls and gems, may be discovered from a comparison between both of these gifts from God: for first, gold, silver, and such other things, are inanimate, being only somewhat harder and purer than the clay which we tread beneath our feet; whereas children are the lively image of the living God.

Secondly, gold and silver are rudimentary objects produced by the command of God; whereas children are creatures in the production of which the all-sacred Trinity instituted special council, and formed them with his own fingers.

Thirdly, gold and silver are fleeting and transitory things; children are an immortal inheritance. For although they yield to death, yet they neither return to nothing, nor become extinct; they only pass out of a mortal tabernacle into immortal regions. Hence, when God restored to Job all his riches and possessions, even to the double of what he had previously taken away, he gave him no more children than he had before; namely, seven sons and three daughters. This, however, was the precise double; inasmuch as the former sons and daughters had not perished, but had gone before to God.

Fourthly, gold and silver come forth from the earth, children come from our own substance; being a part of ourselves, they consequently deserve to be loved by us, certainly not less than we love ourselves: therefore God has implanted in the nature of all living things so strong an affection towards their young that they occasionally prefer the safety of their offspring to their own. If any one transfer such affections to gold or silver, he is, in the judgment of God, condemned as guilty of idolatry.

Fifthly, gold and silver pass away from one to another as though they were the property of none, but common to all:

whereas children are a peculiar possession, divinely assigned to their parents; so that there is not a man in the world who can deprive them of this right or dispossess them of this inheritance, because it is a portion descended from heaven and not a transferable possession.

Sixthly, although gold and silver are gifts of God, yet they are not such gifts as those to which he has promised an angelic guardianship from heaven; nay, Satan mostly intermingles himself with gold and silver so as to use them as nets and snares to entangle the unwary, drawing them as it were with thongs, to avarice, haughtiness, and prodigality: whereas the care of little children is always committed to angelic guardianship, as the Lord himself testifies. Hence he who has children within his house may be certain that he has therein the presence of angels; he who takes little children in his arms may be assured that he takes angels; whosoever, surrounded with midnight darkness, rests beside an infant, may enjoy the certain consolation that with it he is so protected that the spirit of darkness cannot have access. How great the importance of these things!

Seventhly, gold, silver, and other external things do not procure for us the love of God, nor as children do, defend us from his anger; for God so loved children that for their sake he occasionally pardons parents; Nineveh affords an example: inasmuch as there were many children therein, God spared the parents from being swallowed up by the threatened judgment.

Eighthly, human life does not consist in abundance of wealth, as our Lord says, since without God's blessings neither food nourishes, nor plaster heals, nor clothing warms; but his blessing is always present with us for the sake of children, in order that they may be sustained. For if God liberally bestows food on the young ravens calling on him, how much more should he not care for children, his own image? Therefore Luther has wisely said:— "We do not nourish our children, but they nourish us; for because of these innocents God supplies necessaries, and we aged sinners partake of them."

Finally, silver, gold, and gems afford us no further instruction than other created things do, namely, in the wisdom, power, and beneficence of God; whereas children are given to us as a mirror, in which we may behold modesty, courteousness, benignity, harmony, and other Christian virtues, the Lord himself declaring, "Unless ye be converted and become as little children, ye shall not enter into the kingdom of Heaven." Since then God has willed that children should be unto us in the place of preceptors, we judge that we owe to them the most diligent attention.

Thus at last this school would become a school of things obvious to the senses, and an entrance to the school intellectual. But enough. Let us come to the thing itself.

PHILIPPE DE COMINES

(1445–1510)

THE last in date among the great French chroniclers of the Middle Ages was Philippe de Comines (also written Commines or Comynes). He was the scion of an old and wealthy family that attained to nobility by marrying into the house of the barons of Comines, the privilege being a reward for faithful allegiance in the times of trouble and warfare. The approximate date of his birth is the year 1445; his birthplace is not known with certainty, though it may be assumed to have been either on the estate of Comines, near Lille in northern France, or at the Château de Renescure, near Saint-Omer. He lost his mother in 1447, and his father died in 1453, leaving an entangled inheritance that netted a sum of about two thousand five hundred livres, which in those days sufficed to defray the child's current expenses and provide for his education. Under the guardianship of one of his relatives, Jean de Comines, the young orphan was brought up in the true spirit of the feudal times to which he belonged, and was taught the profession of arms. Reading and writing he also acquired, but whatever intellectual training he received beyond this point was owing altogether to his own efforts and exertions.

It was a matter of sincere regret to him that his education never included the study of Latin. He became skilled with the pen, but used it for his own amusement, not with a thought of leaving anything more than notes that might serve others as a basis for fuller historical descriptions. His style is terse, and not devoid of charm; for he was not lacking in imagination, and by quaint simile or other rhetorical effect enlivened many a page of his Chronicles. His vocabulary, without being very rich, is carefully selected, but his syntactical constructions are often abstruse and obscure. On the whole, however, this justice must be done to Philippe de Comines: that what he may lose for want of natural ease of expression is compensated for by his virility of speech and true eloquence. His chief merit lies in his pithy remarks, replete with suggestion. But literary pursuits were not his proper field. In his days such occupations were left almost exclusively to the clergy, in whom alone was supposed to be vested the need and uses of book learning.

He sought, as he grew up, to remedy the shortcomings of his training, and acquired through contact with the numerous foreigners he was in a position to meet, a fair knowledge of Italian, Spanish, and German.

"On coming forth from childhood," he writes, "and being old enough to ride horseback, I was led to Lille before Duke Charles of Burgundy, then Count of Charolais, who took me in his service; and this was in the year 1464." Philippe de Comines was then in his twentieth year, a youth polished in manners, refined in tastes, and above all, a most acute observer,—and these qualities stamped him as a coming diplomat of rare natural ability, in touch with his time, and understanding himself and others sufficiently well to moralize and philosophize about men and things, to reach many a sound conclusion, and to utter many a true and wise saying. He is among the first thinking men of France who committed to paper the results of his labors as a moral philosopher, as a statesman, and as a trusted adviser to royalty.

For eight full years Philippe de Comines remained in the confidential service of the Duke of Burgundy, by whom he was sent, young as he was, on various diplomatic missions of the greatest importance,—first to London, then to Brittany, finally to Orange and Castile. In the course of these expeditions he came in contact with Louis XI., King of France, and knew how to ingratiate himself into his favor. Whatever the reasons for his rupture with the Duke of Burgundy, whatever the special inducements offered by Louis XI., the fact remains that he suddenly left his former master; and possessed of knowledge of the utmost political importance to the King of France, he entered the royal service and remained there until the King's death in August, 1483. His work was generously recognized by Louis XI., and even after his noble patron's death Comines retained his court position for a time. He gradually fell away, however, from his allegiance to the royal cause, and threw himself heart and soul into a movement, set on foot by a number of the feudal lords and directed by the Duke of Orleans himself, against the person of the young King Charles VIII. Arrested on a charge of conspiracy, he spent over two years in various prisons (1486–1489), with ample time to think over the vicissitudes of human happiness. A light sentence was finally passed upon him, and having regained his liberty he was so far restored to favor as to be sent on diplomatic missions, first to Venice and then to Milan.

Though he lived in honor under Louis XII., he retired shortly to private life on his estate of Argenton, where he died in 1510.

It was in the solitude of his prison that Philippe de Comines began to write his reminiscences. The 'Chronique et Hystoire Faicte et Composée par Messire Philippe de Comines' (Paris, 1524) was written between the years 1488 and 1493. It deals with the history of France from 1464 (when Comines went to the court of Charles the Bold) to the death of Louis XI. in 1483. The sequel, 'Chroniques du Roy Charles Huytiesme' (Paris, 1528), written subsequently to 1497, relates the story of the famous expedition to Italy undertaken by Charles VIII. In the pages of 'Quentin Durward,' where Walter Scott has given a graphic portrayal of the great men of that turbulent time, Philippe de Comines stands out beside the crafty and superstitious Louis XI. and the martial Charles of Burgundy as one of the most striking figures of a picturesque age.

THE VIRTUES AND VICES OF KING LOUIS XI.

From the 'Memoirs of Philippe de Comines'

THE chief reason that has induced me to enter upon this subject is because I have seen many deceptions in this world, especially in servants toward their masters; and I have always found that proud and stately princes who will hear but few, are more liable to be imposed upon than those who are open and accessible: but of all the princes that I ever knew, the wisest and most dexterous to extricate himself out of any danger or difficulty in time of adversity was our master King Louis XI. He was the humblest in his conversation and habit, and the most painful and indefatigable to win over any man to his side that he thought capable of doing him either mischief or service: though he was often refused, he would never give over a man that he wished to gain, but still pressed and continued his insinuations, promising him largely, and presenting him with such sums and honors as he knew would gratify his ambition; and for such as he had discarded in time of peace and prosperity, he paid dear (when he had occasion for them) to recover them again; but when he had once reconciled them, he retained no enmity towards them for what had passed, but employed them freely for the future. He was naturally kind and indulgent to persons of mean estate, and hostile to all great men who had no need of him. Never prince was so conversable nor so inquisitive as he, for his desire was to know everybody he could; and indeed he knew all persons of any authority or worth in England, Spain, Portugal, and Italy, in the territories of the Dukes of Burgundy and Bretagne, and among his own subjects: and by those qualities he preserved the crown upon his head, which was in much danger by the enemies he had created to himself upon his accession to the throne.

But above all, his great bounty and liberality did him the greatest service: and yet, as he behaved himself wisely in time of distress, so when he thought himself a little out of danger, though it were but by a truce, he would disoblige the servants and officers of his court by mean and petty ways which were little to his advantage; and as for peace, he could hardly endure the thoughts of it. He spoke slightingly of most people, and rather before their faces than behind their backs; unless he was afraid of them, and of that sort there were a great many, for he was naturally somewhat timorous. When he had done himself any prejudice by his talk, or was apprehensive he should do so, and wished to make amends, he would say to the person whom he had disobliged, "I am sensible my tongue has done me a good deal of mischief; but on the other hand, it has sometimes done me much good: however, it is but reason I should make some reparation for the injury." And he never used this kind of apologies to any person but he granted some favor to the person to whom he made it, and it was always of considerable amount.

It is certainly a great blessing from God upon any prince to have experienced adversity as well as prosperity, good as well as evil, and especially if the good outweighs the evil, as it did in the King our master. I am of opinion that the troubles he was involved in in his youth, when he fled from his father and resided six years together with Philip, Duke of Burgundy, were of great service to him; for there he learned to be complaisant to such as he had occasion to use, which was no slight advantage of adversity. As soon as he found himself a powerful and crowned king, his mind was wholly bent upon revenge; but he quickly found the inconvenience of this, repented by degrees of his indiscretion, and made sufficient reparation for his folly and error by regaining those he had injured. Besides, I am very confident that if his education had not been different from the usual education of such nobles as I have seen in France, he could not so easily have worked himself out of his troubles: for they are brought up to nothing but to make themselves ridiculous, both in their clothes and discourse; they have no knowledge of letters; no wise man is suffered to come near them, to improve their understandings; they have governors who manage their business, but they do nothing themselves: nay, there are some nobles who though they have an income of thirteen livres, will take pride to bid you "Go to my servants and let them answer you," thinking by such speeches to imitate the state and grandeur of a prince; and I have seen their servants take great advantage of them, giving them to understand they were fools; and if afterwards they came to apply their minds to business and attempted to manage their own affairs, they began so late they could make nothing of it. And it is certain that all those who have performed any great or memorable action worthy to be recorded in history, began always in their youth; and this is to be attributed to the method of their education, or some particular blessing of God.

THE VIRTUES OF THE DUKE OF BURGUNDY AND THE TIME OF HIS HOUSE'S PROSPERITY

I SAW a seal-ring of his after his death at Milan, with his arms cut curiously upon a sardonyx, that I have often seen him wear in a riband at his breast; which was sold at Milan for two ducats, and had been stolen from him by a varlet that waited on him in his chamber. I have often seen the duke dressed and undressed in great state and formality, and by very great persons; but at his last hour all this pomp and magnificence ceased, and both he and his family perished on the very spot where he had delivered up the Constable not long before, out of a base and avaricious motive. But may God forgive him! I have known him a powerful and honorable prince, in as great esteem and as much courted by his neighbors (when his affairs were in a prosperous condition) as any prince in Europe, and perhaps more so; and I cannot conceive what should have provoked God Almighty's displeasure so highly against him unless it was his self-love and arrogance, in attributing all the success of his enterprises and all the renown he ever acquired to his own wisdom and conduct, without ascribing anything to God: yet, to speak truth, he was endowed with many good qualities. No prince ever had a greater desire to entertain young noblemen than he, or was more careful of their education. His presents and bounty were never profuse and extravagant, because he gave to many, and wished everybody should taste of his generosity.

No prince was ever more easy of access to his servants and subjects. Whilst I was in his service he was never cruel, but a little before his death he became so, which was an infallible sign of the shortness of his life. He was very splendid and pompous in his dress and in everything else, and indeed a little too much. He paid great honors to all ambassadors and foreigners, and entertained them nobly. His ambitious desire of glory was insatiable, and it was that which more than any other motive induced him to engage eternally in wars. He earnestly desired to imitate the old kings and heroes of antiquity, who are still so much talked of in the world, and his courage was equal to that of any prince of his time. . . .

I am partly of the opinion of those who maintain that God gives princes, as he in his wisdom thinks fit, to punish or chastise their subjects; and he disposes the affections of subjects to their princes as he has determined to exalt or depress them. Just so it has pleased him to deal with the house of Burgundy; for after a long series of riches and prosperity, and sixscore years' peace under three illustrious princes, predecessors to Duke Charles (all of them of great prudence and discretion), it pleased God to send this Duke Charles, who continually involved them in bloody wars, winter as well as summer, to their great affliction and expense, in which most of their richest and stoutest men were either killed or taken prisoners. Their misfortunes began at the siege of Nuz, and continued for three or four battles successively, to the very hour of his death; so much so that at the last the whole strength of the country was destroyed, and all were killed or taken prisoners who had any zeal or affection for the house of Burgundy, or power to defend the state and dignity of that family; so that in a manner their losses equaled if they did not overbalance their former prosperity: for as I have seen these princes puissant, rich, and honorable, so it fared with their subjects; for I think I have seen and known the greatest part of Europe, yet I never knew any province or country, though of a larger extent, so abounding in money, so extravagantly fine in their furniture, so sumptuous in their buildings, so profuse in their expenses, so luxurious in their feasts and entertainments, and so prodigal in all respects, as the subjects of these princes in my time; and if any think I have exaggerated, others who lived in my time will be of opinion that I have rather said too little.

But it pleased God at one blow to subvert this great and sumptuous edifice and ruin this powerful and illustrious family, which had maintained and bred up so many brave men, and had acquired such mighty honor and renown far and near, by so many victories and successful enterprises as none of all its neighboring States could pretend to boast of. A hundred and twenty years it continued in this flourishing condition, by the grace of God; all its neighbors having in the mean time been involved in troubles and commotions, and all of them applying to it for succor or protection,— to wit, France, England, and Spain,— as you have seen by experience of our master the King of France, who in his minority, and during the reign of Charles VII. his father, retired to this court, where he lived six years and was nobly entertained all that time by Duke Philip the Good. Out of England I saw there also two of King Edward's brothers, the Dukes of Clarence and Gloucester (the last of whom was afterwards called King Richard III.); and of the house of Lancaster, the whole family or very near, with all their party. In short, I have seen this family in all respects the most flourishing and celebrated of any in Christendom; and then in a short space of time it was quite ruined and turned upside down, and left the most desolate and miserable of any house in Europe, as regards both princes and subjects. Such changes and revolutions of States and kingdoms, God in his providence has wrought before we were born and will do again when we are dead; for this is a certain maxim, that the prosperity or adversity of princes depends wholly on his divine disposal.

THE LAST DAYS OF LOUIS XI.

THE King towards the latter end of his days caused his castle of Plessis-les-Tours to be encompassed with great bars of iron in the form of thick grating, and at the four corners of the house four sparrow-nests of iron, strong, massy, and thick, were built. The grates were without the wall on the other side of the ditch, and sank to the bottom. Several spikes of iron were fastened into the wall, set as thick by one another as was possible, and each furnished with three or four points. He likewise placed ten bowmen in the ditches, to shoot at any man that durst approach the castle before the opening of the gates; and he ordered they should lie in the ditches, but retire to the sparrow-nests upon occasion. He was sensible enough that this fortification was too weak to keep out an army or any great body of men, but he had no fear of such an attack: his great apprehension was that some of the nobility of his kingdom, having intelligence within, might attempt to make themselves masters of the castle by night, and having possessed themselves of it partly by favor and partly by force, might deprive him of the regal authority and take upon themselves the administration of public affairs; upon pretense that he was incapable of business and no longer fit to govern.

The gate of the Plessis was never opened nor the draw-bridge let down before eight o'clock in the morning, at which time the officers were let in; and the captains ordered their guards to their several posts, with pickets of archers in the middle of the court, as in a town upon the frontiers that is closely guarded; nor was any person admitted to enter except by the wicket and with the King's knowledge, unless it were the steward of his household, and such persons as were not admitted into the royal presence.

Is it possible then to keep a prince (with any regard to his quality) in a closer prison than he kept himself? The cages which were made for other people were about eight feet square; and he (though so great a monarch) had but a small court of the castle to walk in, and seldom made use of that, but generally kept himself in the gallery, out of which he went into the chambers on his way to mass, but never passed through the court. Who can deny that he was a sufferer as well as his neighbors? considering how he was locked up and guarded, afraid of his own children and relations, and changing every day those very servants whom he had brought up and advanced; and though they owed all their preferment to him, yet he durst not trust any of them, but shut himself up in those strange chains and inclosures. If the place where he confined himself was larger than a common prison, he also was much greater than common prisoners.

It may be urged that other princes have been more given to suspicion than he, but it was not in our time; and perhaps their wisdom was not so eminent, nor were their subjects so good. They might too, probably, have been tyrants and bloody-minded; but our King never did any person a mischief who had not offended him first, though I do not say all who offended him deserved death. I have not recorded these things merely to represent our master as a suspicious and mistrustful prince, but to show that by the patience which he expressed in his sufferings (like those which he inflicted on other people) they may be looked upon, in my judgment, as a punishment which Our Lord inflicted upon him in this world in order to deal more mercifully with him in the next; . . . and likewise, that those princes who may be his successors may learn by his example to be more tender and indulgent to their subjects, and less severe in their punishments than our master had been: although I will not censure him, or say I ever saw a better prince; for though he oppressed his subjects himself, he would never see them injured by anybody else.

After so many fears, sorrows, and suspicions, God by a kind of miracle restored him both in body and mind, as is his divine method in such kind of wonders: for he took him out of this miserable world in perfect health of mind and understanding and memory; after having received the sacraments himself, discoursing without the least twinge or expression of pain, and repeating his paternosters to the very last moment of his life. He gave directions for his own burial, appointed who should attend his corpse to the grave, and declared that he desired to die on a Saturday of all days in the week; and that he hoped Our Lady would procure him that favor, for in her he had always placed great trust, and served her very devoutly. And so it happened; for he died on Saturday, the 30th of August, 1433, at about eight in the evening, in the castle of Plessis, where his illness seized him on the Monday before. May Our Lord receive his soul, and admit it into his kingdom of Paradise!

CHARACTER OF LOUIS XI.

SMALL hopes and comfort ought poor and inferior people to
     have in this world, considering what so great a king suf-
     fered and underwent, and how he was at last forced to
leave all, and could not, with all his care and diligence, protract
his life one single hour. I knew him and was entertained in
his service in the flower of his age and at the height of his
prosperity, yet I never saw him free from labor and care. Of
all diversions he loved hunting and hawking in their seasons;
but his chief delight was in dogs. . . . In hunting, his
eagerness and pain were equal to his pleasure, for his chase was
the stag, which he always ran down. He rose very early in the
morning, rode sometimes a great distance, and would not leave
his sport, let the weather be never so bad; and when he came
home at night he was often very weary, and generally in a violent passion with some of his courtiers or huntsmen; for hunting
is a sport not always to be managed according to the master's
direction; yet in the opinion of most people, he understood it
as well as any prince of his time. He was continually at these
sports, lodging in the country villages to which his recreations
led him, till he was interrupted by business; for during the
most part of the summer there was constantly war between him
and Charles, Duke of Burgundy, and in the winter they made
truces; . . . so that he had but a little time during the
whole year to spend in pleasure, and even then the fatigues he
underwent were excessive. When his body was at rest his mind
was at work, for he had affairs in several places at once, and
would concern himself as much in those of his neighbors as in
his own; putting officers of his own over all the great families,
and endeavoring to divide their authority as much as possible.
When he was at war he labored for a peace or a truce, and
when he had obtained it he was impatient for war again. He
troubled himself with many trifles in his government which he
had better have left alone: but it was his temper, and he could
not help it; besides, he had a prodigious memory, and he forgot
nothing, but knew everybody, as well in other countries as in
his own.

And in truth he seemed better fitted to rule a world than
to govern a single kingdom. I speak not of his minority, for

then I was not with him; but when he was eleven years he was, by the advice of some of the nobility and others of his kingdom, embroiled in a war with his father, Charles VII., which lasted not long, and was called the Praguerie. When he was arrived at man's estate he was married, much against his inclination, to the King of Scotland's daughter; and he regretted her existence during the whole course of her life. Afterwards, by reason of the broils and factions in his father's court, he retired into Dauphiny (which was his own), whither many persons of quality followed him, and indeed more than he could entertain. During his residence in Dauphiny he married the Duke of Savoy's daughter, and not long after he had great disputes with his father-in-law, and a terrible war was begun between them. His father, King Charles VII., seeing his son attended by so many good officers and raising men at his pleasure, resolved to go in person against him with a considerable body of forces, in order to disperse them. While he was upon his march he put out proclamations, requiring them all as his subjects, under great penalties, to repair to him; and many obeyed, to the great displeasure of the Dauphin, who finding his father incensed, though he was strong enough to resist, resolved to retire and leave that country to him; and accordingly he removed with but a slender retinue into Burgundy to Duke Philip's court, who received him honorably, furnished him nobly, and maintained him and his principal servants by way of pensions; and to the rest he gave presents as he saw occasion during the whole time of their residence there. However, the Dauphin entertained so many at his own expense that his money often failed, to his great disgust and mortification; for he was forced to borrow, or his people would have forsaken him; which is certainly a great affliction to a prince who was utterly unaccustomed to those straits. So that during his residence at the court of Burgundy he had his anxieties, for he was constrained to cajole the duke and his ministers, lest they should think he was too burdensome and had laid too long upon their hands; for he had been with them six years, and his father, King Charles, was constantly pressing and soliciting the Duke of Burgundy, by his ambassadors, either to deliver him up to him or to banish him out of his dominions. And this, you may believe, gave the Dauphin some uneasy thoughts and would not suffer him to be idle. In which season of his life, then, was it that he may be said to have enjoyed himself? I believe from his infancy and innocence to his death, his whole life was nothing but one continued scene of troubles and fatigues; and I am of opinion that if all the days of his life were computed in which his joys and pleasures outweighed his pain and trouble, they would be found so few that there would be twenty mournful ones to one pleasant.

AUGUSTE COMTE

(1798–1857)

THE name of Auguste Comte is associated with two such utterly conflicting systems, the "Positive Philosophy" and the "Positive Polity," that the impression conveyed by his name is apt to be a rather confused one. Littré, Comte's most distinguished disciple, takes no notice of his later speculations, attributing them to a nervous malady complicated by a violent passion for Madame de Vaux; while Carid, on the other hand, considers Comte's return to metaphysical ideas the saving grace in his career. His conception of human knowledge, as defined in the Positive Philosophy, is in a measure the general property of the age. He developed the germs latent in the works of Turgot, Condorcet, and Kant, his immediate predecessors in the world of thought. Universality was the essential characteristic of his intellect, enabling him to penetrate profoundly into the domain of abstract science from mathematics to sociology.

AUGUSTE COMTE

Auguste Comte was born at Montpellier on the 19th of January, 1798, and entered college at the age of nine years. Before attaining his fourteenth year he had already felt the need of fundamental reconstruction in politics and philosophy. This maturity is all the more remarkable that philosophical minds mature slowly. In 1814 he entered the Polytechnic School. When Louis XVIII. suppressed it, Comte, not having graduated, found himself without a career. At the age of twenty he came in contact with Saint-Simon, whose devoted disciple he became. The attraction mutually felt by them was due to their common conviction of the need of a complete social reform, based on a widespread mental renovation.

There was now no place in the national system of education for free-thinkers, and Comte, cut off from all hope of employment in that direction, turned to private instruction for support. At the age of twenty-two, in a pamphlet entitled 'System of Positive Polity,' he announced his discovery of the laws of sociology. The work had no success, and Comte bent his energies during a meditation of twenty-four hours to the conception of a system which would force conviction on his readers. This he so far elaborated that in 1826 he published a plan of the work,—a plan requiring twelve years for its execution.

As his ideas were being appropriated by other people, he now began a dogmatic exposition of Positivism in a course of lectures delivered in his own home. These lectures opened under encouraging auspices, but after the third, Comte's mind gave way. The determining cause of this collapse lay in the excessive strain of his method of work, aided by a bad digestion and mental irritability growing out of the violent attacks made upon him by Saint-Simon's followers. In 1827 he was sufficiently recovered to take up intellectual work again, and the following year he resumed his lectures at the point of their interruption. After the accession of Louis Philippe, Comte was appointed assistant teacher of mathematics at the Polytechnic, and later, examiner of candidates, while he taught in a private school.

Unshakable firmness in philosophical matters and great disinterestedness were characteristic of this social critic, who cared nothing for the money his books might bring. His early sympathies were with the Revolution; he defended the socialist Marrast, though his position in a government school might have been compromised thereby. When in 1830 the Committee of the Polytechnic undertook to give free lectures to the people, he assumed the department of astronomy and lectured on that subject weekly for sixteen years.

The second and great period of Comte's life extends from his recovery in 1828 to the completion of his 'Positive Philosophy' in 1848; though what he calls his "second life" began after that. The intense satisfaction which he felt on the completion of that work became infatuation. He was no longer capable of judging his position sanely, and by his attacks antagonized the scientists.

In 1842 John Stuart Mill gave his adherence to Positivism. When Comte lost his tutorship in the Polytechnic, and shortly after, his position as examiner, Mill raised a small sum for him in England. Afterward Littré organized a subscription, and this formed henceforth Comte's sole resource. He now threw himself more completely than before into the problems of social life, elucidating them in his 'Positive Polity,' whose really scientific elements are almost crowded out of sight by a mass of extravagant theories.

The Positive Calendar, in which the names of great men replace the saints of the Catholic Church, was adopted by Comte in his correspondence. He consecrated an altar to his friend Madame de Vaux, entitled himself High Priest of Humanity, married people, called his letters his briefs, administered the sacraments of his cult in commemoration of birth, the choice of a profession, marriage, etc. He subordinated the intellect to the feelings, wished to suppress independent thought, to center a dictatorship in a triumvirate of bankers, and to concentrate the entire spiritual power of the world in the hands of a single pontiff. He acquired a hatred of scientific and purely literary pursuits, and considered that men reasoned more than was good for them. Comte's absolute faith in himself passes belief. He lauds the moral superiority of fetishism, pronounces the æsthetic civilization of the Greeks inferior to the military civilization of the Romans; is indifferent to proof, provided he attains theoretic coherency; and pushes his spiritual dictatorship to the length of selecting one hundred books to constitute the library of every Positivist, recommending the destruction of all other books, as also that of all plants and animals useless to man. He associates science with sentiment, endows the planets with feeling and will, calls the Earth "le grand fétiche," includes all concrete existence in our adoration along with "le grand fétiche," and names space "le grand milieu," endowing the latter with feeling as the representative of fatality in general. Many of these conceits can be attributed to his ardor for regulating things in accordance with his peculiar conception of unity. He died in Paris at the age of fifty-nine years, on September 5th, 1857.

Throughout life, Comte's method of work was unprecedented. He thought out his subject in its entirety before writing down a word, proceeding from general facts to secondary matters, and thence to details. The general and detailed sketch outlined, he considered the work done. When he began to write, he took up his ideas in their respective order. His memory was wonderful; he did all his reading in his early youth, and the provision then amassed sufficed to elaborate a work for which he had to bear in mind an unusual number of scientific and historical facts. In consequence of his abstention from contemporary literature he became less and less in touch with the age, and missed the corrective force of friction with other minds.

The word "religion," when applied to Comte's later speculations, must not be taken in its ordinary sense. His attitude towards theology was and continued to be purely negative. The obligation of duty was towards the human race as a continuous whole, to whose providence we owe all the benefits conferred by previous generations. If he has not succeeded in suppressing the Absolute, he has co-ordinated all the abstract sciences into one consistent system. Some of them he found ready to hand, and merely revised and rearranged in their philosophical relation, eliminating all non-positive elements. The first three volumes of the 'Positive Philosophy' are devoted to this task. The other three volumes, as well as the last two of the 'Positive Polity,' are dedicated to the solution of the problems of sociology unattempted until then. While they may not have solved these, they have a scientific value independent of any absolute results.

The distinctive characteristic of Positivism is that it subjects all phenomena to invariable laws. It does not pretend to know anything about a future life, but believes that our ideas and intelligence will go to swell the sum total of spirituality, just as our bodies go to fertilize matter.

The complaint has been made that there has been very little serious criticism of the 'Positive Polity,' which Comte regarded as the most original and important of his works. If the form in which he reproduces metaphysics and theology has any value, it is because he has come to see that they are based on perennial wants in man's nature. In the 'Positive Philosophy' he excludes the Absolute; in the 'Positive Polity' he substitutes Humanity in lieu thereof; but his moral intention, however misguided at times, is passionately sincere, and his conviction that his mission was to exalt humanity through all time, sustained him during the course of a long life devoted to a generous ideal, fraught with disappointment, saddened by want of recognition and by persecution and neglect.

THE EVOLUTION OF BELIEF

From the 'Positive Philosophy'

EACH of our leading conceptions passes through three different theoretical conditions: the Theological, or fictitious; the Metaphysical, or abstract; and the Scientific, or positive. Hence arise three philosophies, or general systems of conceptions on the aggregate of phenomena, each of which excludes the others. The first is the necessary point of departure of the human understanding, and the third is its fixed and definite state. The second is merely a state of transition.

In the theological state, the human mind, seeking the essential nature of beings, the first and final causes of all effects,— in short, absolute knowledge,— supposes all phenomena to be produced by the immediate action of supernatural beings.

In the metaphysical state, which is only a modification of the first, the mind supposes, instead of supernatural beings, abstract forces, veritable entities (that is, personified abstractions) inherent in all beings, and capable of producing all phenomena. What is called the explanation of phenomena is, in this stage, a mere reference of each to its proper entity.

In the final, the positive state, the mind has given over the vain search after absolute notions, the origin and destination of the universe, and the causes of phenomena, and applies itself to the study of their laws,—that is, their invariable relations of succession and resemblance. Reasoning and observation, duly combined, are the means of this knowledge. What is now understood when we speak of an explanation of facts, is simply the establishment of a connection between single phenomena and some general facts, the number of which continually diminishes with the progress of science.

The Theological system arrived at the highest perfection of which it is capable, when it substituted the providential action of a single Being for the varied operations of numerous divinities which had been before imagined. In the same way, in the last stage of the Metaphysical system, men substitute one great entity (Nature) as the cause of all phenomena, instead of the multitude of entities at first supposed. In the same way, again, the ultimate perfection of the Positive system would be (if such perfection could be hoped for) to represent all phenomena as particular aspects of a single general fact,—such as gravitation, for instance.

There is no science which, having attained the positive stage, does not bear marks of having passed through the others.

The progress of the individual mind is not only an illustration but an indirect evidence of that of the general mind. The point of departure of the individual and of the race being the same, the phases of the mind of a man correspond to the epochs of the mind of the race. Now each of us is aware, if he looks back upon his own history, that he was a theologian in his childhood, a metaphysician in his youth, and a natural philosopher in his manhood.

THE STUDY OF LAW SUBSTITUTED FOR THAT OF CAUSES

From the 'Positive Philosophy'

THE first characteristic of the Positive Philosophy is, that it regards all phenomena as subjected to invariable natural Laws. Our business is — seeing how vain is any research into what are called Causes, whether first or final — to pursue an accurate discovery of these Laws with a view to reducing them to the smallest possible number. By speculating upon causes we could solve no difficulty about origin and purpose. Our real business is to analyze accurately the circumstances of phenomena, and to connect them by their natural relations of succession and resemblance. The best illustration of this is in the case of the doctrine of Gravitation. We say that the general phenomena of the universe are explained by it, because it connects under one head the whole immense variety of astronomical facts; exhibiting the constant tendency of atoms towards each other in direct proportion to their masses, and in inverse proportion to the square of their distances; whilst the general fact itself is but a mere extension of one which is familiar to us, and which we therefore say that we know — the weight of bodies on the surface of the earth. As to what weight and attraction are, we have nothing to do with that, for it is not a matter of knowledge at all. Theologians and metaphysicians may imagine and refine about such questions; but Positive Philosophy rejects them. When any attempt has been made to explain them, it has ended only in saying that attraction is universal weight and that weight is terrestrial attraction: that is, that the two orders of phenomena are identical; which is the point from which the question set out.

Before ascertaining the stage which the Positive Philosophy has reached, we must bear in mind that the different kinds of our knowledge have passed through the three stages of progress at different rates, and have not therefore reached their goal at the same time. Any kind of knowledge reaches the positive stage early in proportion to its generality, simplicity, and independence of other departments. Astronomical science, which is above all made up of facts that are general, simple, and independent of other sciences, arrived first; then terrestrial physics; then chemistry; and at length physiology.

It is difficult to assign any precise date to this revolution in science. It may be said, like everything else, to have been always going on, and especially since the labors of Aristotle and the school of Alexandria; and then from the introduction of natural science into the west of Europe by the Arabs. But if we must fix upon some marked period to serve as a rallying-point, it must be that about two centuries ago,—when the human mind was astir under the precepts of Bacon, the conceptions of Descartes, and the discoveries of Galileo. Then it was that the spirit of the Positive Philosophy rose up, in opposition to that of the superstitious and scholastic systems which had hitherto obscured the true character of all science. Since that date, the progress of the Positive Philosophy and the decline of the other two have been so marked that no rational mind now doubts that the revolution is destined to go on to its completion,— every branch of knowledge being, sooner or later, within the operation of Positive Philosophy.

SUBJECTION OF SELF–LOVE TO SOCIAL LOVE

From the ‹Positive Polity›

IT is one of the first principles of Biology that organic life always preponderates over animal life. By this principle the sociologist explains the superior strength of the self-regarding instincts, since these are all connected more or less closely with the instinct of self-preservation. But although there is no evading the fact, Sociology shows that it is compatible with the existence of benevolent affections which Catholicism asserted were altogether alien to our nature, and entirely dependent on superhuman grace. The great problem, then, is to raise social feeling by artificial effort to the position which in the natural condition is held by selfish feeling. The solution is to be found in another biological principle; viz., that functions and organs are developed by constant exercise and atrophied by long inaction. Now the effect of the social state is, that while our sympathetic instincts are constantly stimulated, the selfish propensities are restricted; since if free play were given to them, human intercourse would very soon become impossible. Both of the tendencies naturally increase with the progress of humanity, and their increase is the best measure of the degree of perfection that we have attained. Their growth, however spontaneous, may be materially hastened by organized intervention both of individuals and of society; the object being to increase all favorable influences and to diminish unfavorable ones. This is the aim of the science of Morals. Like every other science, it is restricted within certain limits.

The first principle of Positive morality is the preponderance of social sympathy. Full and free expansion of the benevolent emotions is made the first condition of individual and social well-being, since these emotions are at once the sweetest to experience, and the only feelings which can find expression simultaneously in all. This doctrine is as deep and pure as it is simple and true. It is essentially characteristic of a philosophy which by virtue of its attribute of reality subordinates all scientific conceptions to the social point of view, as the sole point from which they can be co-ordinated into a whole.

THE CULTUS OF HUMANITY

From the 'Positive Polity'

THE cultus of Positivism is not addressed to an absolute, isolated, incomprehensible Being whose existence cannot be demonstrated or compared with reality. No mystery surrounds this Supreme Being. It is composed of the continuous succession of human generations.

Whereas the old God could not receive our homage without degrading himself by a puerile vanity, the new God will only accept praise which is deserved and which will improve him as much as ourselves. This reciprocity of affection and influence can belong only to the final cultus, modifiable and perfectible, addressed to a relative being composed of its own adorers, and better subjected than another to law which permits of foreseeing its wishes and tendencies.

The superiority of demonstrated over revealed religion is shown by the substitution of the love of Humanity for the love of God. To love Humanity constitutes all healthy morality, when we understand the character of such a love and the conditions exacted by its habitual ascendency.

The universal reign of Humanity is to replace the provisory reign of God. Demonstrated religion has its dogmas, its regimen, and its cultus corresponding respectively to three fundamental attributes; viz., thoughts, acts, and sentiments.

The Religion of Humanity transforms the coarse idea of objective immortality into the real objective immortality common to the whole race. The first hypothesis is anti-social; the latter constitutes real sociability.

THE DOMINATION OF THE DEAD

From the 'Positive Polity'

ALWAYS and everywhere, the living are more and more dominated by the dead. This irresistible domination represents the unmodifiable element in all social existence, and regulates the total human movement.

When the "Grand Être" shall occupy the whole planet, each city will live more and more under the weight of preceding generations, not only of its defunct citizens but of the total sum of terrestrial ancestors.

This ascendency was long ignored, and a dominating principle was sought elsewhere, by transporting the human type to external beings, first real, then fictitious. So long as the search for Causes predominated over the study of Law, it was impossible to recognize the true Providence of the race, owing to thus diverting the attention to chimerical influences. At the same time continuous conflicts and discordance made the conception of a collective being impossible. When these fictitious struggles exhausted themselves, Humanity, prepared during their domination, became aroused, and founded on peace and truth the advent of the new religion.

THE WORSHIP OF WOMAN

From the 'Positive Polity'

WOMAN's function in society is determined by the constitution of her nature. As the spontaneous organ of feeling, on which the unity of human nature entirely depends, she constitutes the purest and most natural element of the moderating power; which while avowing its own subordination to the material forces of society, purposes to direct them to higher uses.

First as mother, afterwards as wife, it is her office to conduct the moral education of Humanity.

Woman's mission is a striking illustration of the truth that happiness consists in doing the work for which we are naturally fitted. Their mission is always the same; it is summed up in one word,— Love. It is the only work in which there can never be too many workers; it grows by co-operation; it has nothing to fear from competition. Women are charged with the education of sympathy, the source of real human unity; and their highest happiness is reached when they have the full consciousness of their vocation and are free to follow it. It is the admirable feature of their social mission, that it invites them to cultivate qualities which are natural to them, to call into exercise emotions which all allow to be the most pleasurable. All that is required of them in a better organization of society is a better adaptation of their circumstances to their vocation, and improvements in their internal condition. They must be relieved from outdoor labor, and other means must be taken to secure due weight to their moral influence. Both objects are contemplated in the material, intellectual, and moral ameliorations which Positivism is destined to effect in the life of women. But besides the pleasure inherent in their vocation, Positivism offers a recompense for their services which Catholic Feudalism foreshadowed but could not realize. As men become more and more grateful for the blessing of the moral influence of women, they will give expression to this feeling in a systematic form. In a word, the new doctrine will institute the Worship of Woman, publicly and privately, in a far more perfect way than has ever been possible. It is the first permanent step towards the worship of Humanity; which is the central principle of Positivism viewed either as a philosophy or as a polity.

WILLIAM CONGREVE

(1670–1729)

ONGREVE was the most brilliant of all the English dramatists of the later Stuart period. Born at Bardsley, near Leeds, in 1670, he passed his childhood and youth in Ireland, and was sent to the University of Dublin, where he was highly educated; and on finishing his classical studies he went to London to study law and was entered at the Middle Temple. He had two ambitions, not altogether reconcilable — to shine in literature and to shine in society. His good birth, polished manners, and witty conversation procured him entrance to the best company; but the desire for literary renown had the mastery at the start. His first work was 'Incognita,' a novel of no particular value, published under the name of "Cleophil." In 1693 he wrote 'The Old Bachelor,' a comedy; it was brought out with a phenomenal cast. Under the supervision of Dryden, who generously admired the author, it achieved triumph; and Montagu, then Lord of the Treasury, gave him a desirable place (commissioner for licensing hackney-coaches) and the reversion of another. The plot is not interesting, but the play is celebrated for its witty and eloquent dialogue,

WILLIAM CONGREVE

which even Sheridan did not surpass; it has a lightness which nothing that preceded it had equaled. The characters are not very original, yet it has variety and diverting action.

Returning now to his rival ambition, that of achieving social success, Congreve pretended that he had merely "scribbled a few scenes for his own amusement," and had yielded unwillingly to his friends' desire to try his fortune on the stage. But in 1694 he brought out his second play, 'The Double Dealer.' It was not a favorite, though in it all the powers which made a success of 'The Old Bachelor' were present, mellowed and improved by time. The dialogue is light and natural; but the grim and offensive characters of Maskwell and Lady Touchwood disgusted even an audience of the seventeenth century. Dryden, however, wrote a most ingenious piece of commendatory verse for the play; gradually the public came to his way of thinking; and when, the next year, 'Love for Love' appeared, it was said that "scarcely any comedy within the memory of the oldest man had been equally successful." This play was the triumph of his art; and it won Congreve a share in the theatre in which it was played, —the new theatre which Betterton and others had opened near Lincoln's Inn. Jeremy, the gentleman's gentleman, is delightfully witty, —he has "the seeds of rhetoric and logic in his head,"—and Valentine's mock madness is amusing; but as Sir Sampson remarks of him, "Body o' me, he talks sensibly in his madness! has he no intervals?" Jeremy replies, "Very short, sir."

In about two years Congreve produced 'The Mourning Bride,' a tragedy which was over-lauded, but stands high among the dramas of the century. It ranks with Otway's 'Venice Preserved' and 'The Fair Penitent.' A noble passage describing the temple, in Act ii., Scene 3, was extolled by Johnson. The play was successful, and is more celebrated than some far better plays. But Congreve was unequal to a really great flight of passion; tragedy was out of his range; though he was now hailed, at the age of twenty-seven, as the first tragic as well as the first comic dramatist of his time.

Now, however, a reformer arose who was destined to make his mark on the English drama. The depravation of the national taste which had made the success of Congreve, Wycherley, Farquhar, and others, was the result of a reaction against the Puritan strictness under the Commonwealth. Profligacy was the badge of a Cavalier, and Congreve's heroes exactly reproduced the superficial fine gentleman of a time when to be a man of good breeding it was necessary to make love to one's neighbor's wife, even without preference or passion. In the plays of this period nearly all the husbands are prim, precise, and uncomfortable, while the lovers are without exception delightful fellows. The Puritan writers regarded an affair of gallantry as a criminal offense; the poet of this period made it an elegant distinction.

Jeremy Collier came to change all this. He was a clergyman and a high-churchman, fanatical in the cause of decency. In 1698 he published his 'Short View of the Profaneness and Immorality of the English Stage,' and threw the whole literary world into convulsions. He attacked Congreve, among others, somewhat injudiciously, not only for his sins against decency but for some unreal transgressions; and he had at his command all the weapons of ridicule and indignation. The country sided with the eloquent preacher, but waited for some champion— Dryden presumably— to pick up the gauntlet. Dryden however declined, acknowledging later that Collier was in the right. Congreve stepped in "where angels feared to tread," and succeeded in putting himself entirely in the wrong. His reply was dull, and he was unwise enough to show anger. Collier's cause remained in the ascendant, and with the younger race of poets who now came forward a reform began.

In 1700 Congreve wrote one more play, 'The Way of the World,' the most brilliant and thoughtful of his works. Lady Wishfort's character is perhaps too repulsive for comedy, though the reader, carried on by the ease and wit of the dialogue, will accept her. Mirabell's brilliant chase and winning of Millamant; the diverting character of Witwould, an incarnation of feeble repartee; and the love scene in Act v., Scene 5, in which both lady and gentleman are anxious and willing to be free and tolerant, are original and amusing studies. But whether it was the influence of his defeat by Collier or not, this play, the best comedy written after the civil war, failed on the stage.

Congreve produced nothing more of consequence, though he lived for twenty-eight years in the most brilliant society that London afforded; he suffered from gout and from failing eyesight, and by way of consolation contracted a curious friendship with the Duchess of Marlborough, widow of the great Marlborough, with whom he passed a part of every day. In the summer of 1728 he met with an accident while driving, and died from the effects of it in January, 1729. The Duchess buried him with pomp; he lay in state in the Jerusalem Chamber, and was interred in Westminster Abbey.

Congreve was held in the highest esteem by his fellow writers, and Pope dedicated to him his translation of the Iliad. Yet he would not hear his literary works praised, and always declared that they were trifles. When Voltaire during his visit to England desired to see him, Congreve asked that he would "consider him merely as a gentleman." "If you were merely a gentleman," said Voltaire, "I should not care to see you."

Congreve was not a great poet, but he had more wit than any English writer of the last two centuries except Sheridan; he had at the same time great skill in character-drawing and in constructing plots. The profligacy of his plays was the natural consequence of a period of Puritanical austerity. While not free from the blame of intentional indecency, he at least lacks the brutality and coarseness of Wycherley, Vanbrugh, and Farquhar.

MRS. FORESIGHT AND MRS. FRAIL COME TO AN UNDER-STANDING

From 'Love for Love'

Scene:—A Room in the Foresight House. Enter Mrs. Foresight *and* Mrs. Frail

MRS. FRAIL — What have you to do to watch me? 'Slife, I'll do what I please.

Mrs. Foresight — You will?

Mrs. Frail — Yes, marry, will I. A great piece of business, to go to Covent Garden Square in a hackney-coach and take a turn with one's friend!

Mrs. Foresight — Nay, two or three turns, I'll take my oath.

Mrs. Frail — Well, what if I took twenty? I warrant if you had been there, it had been only innocent recreation. Lord, where's the comfort of this life, if we can't have the happiness of conversing where we like?

Mrs. Foresight — But can't you converse at home? I own it, I think there's no harmless like conversing with an agreeable man; I don't quarrel at that, nor I don't think but your conversation was very innocent; but the place is public, and to be seen with a man in a hackney-coach is scandalous; what if anybody else should have seen you alight, as I did? How can anybody be happy, while they're in perpetual fear of being seen and censured? Besides, it would not only reflect upon you, sister, but me.

Mrs. Frail — Pooh, here's a clutter! Why should it reflect upon you? I don't doubt but you have thought yourself happy in a hackney-coach before now. If I had gone to Knightsbridge, or to Chelsea, or to Spring Garden, or Barn Elms, with a man alone, something might have been said.

Mrs. Foresight — Why, was I ever in any of those places? what do you mean, sister?

Mrs. Frail — "Was I?" What do you mean?

Mrs. Foresight — You have been at a worse place.

Mrs. Frail — I at a worse place, and with a man!

Mrs. Foresight — I suppose you would not go alone to the World's-End.

Mrs. Frail — The world's end! what, do you mean to banter me?

Mrs. Foresight — Poor innocent! you don't know that there's a place called the World's-End? I'll swear you can keep your countenance purely; you'd make an admirable player.

Mrs. Frail — I'll swear you have a great deal of confidence, and in my mind too much for the stage.

Mrs. Foresight — Very well; that will appear who has most. You never were at the World's-End?

Mrs. Frail — No.

Mrs. Foresight — You deny it positively to my face?

Mrs. Frail — Your face! what's your face?

Mrs. Foresight — No matter for that; it's as good a face as yours.

Mrs. Frail — Not by a dozen years' wearing. But I do deny it positively to your face, then.

Mrs. Foresight — I'll allow you now to find fault with my face, for I'll swear your impudence has put me out of countenance; but look you here now, — where did you lose this gold bodkin? O sister, sister!

Mrs. Frail — My bodkin?

Mrs. Foresight — Nay, 'tis yours; look at it.

Mrs. Frail — Well, if you go to that, where did you find this bodkin? O sister, sister! — sister every way.

Mrs. Foresight [*aside*] — Oh, devil on't, that I could not discover her without betraying myself!

Mrs. Frail — I have heard gentlemen say, sister, that one should take great care, when one makes a thrust in fencing, not to lay open one's self.

Mrs. Foresight — It's very true, sister; well, since all's out, and as you say, since we are both wounded, let us do what is often done in duels, — take care of one another, and grow better friends than before.

Mrs. Frail — With all my heart: ours are but slight flesh wounds, and if we keep 'em from air, not at all dangerous: well, give me your hand in token of sisterly secrecy and affection.

Mrs. Foresight — Here 'tis, with all my heart.

Mrs. Frail — Well, as an earnest of friendship and confidence, I'll acquaint you with a design that I have. To tell truth, and speak openly one to another, I'm afraid the world have observed us more than we have observed one another. You have a rich husband and are provided for; I am at a loss, and have no great stock either of fortune or reputation; and therefore must look sharply about me. Sir Sampson has a son that is expected to-night, and by the account I have heard of his education, can be no conjuror; the estate, you know, is to be made over to him: —now if I could wheedle him, sister, ha? you understand me?

Mrs. Foresight—I do, and will help you to the utmost of my power. And I can tell you one thing that falls out luckily enough; my awkward daughter-in-law, who you know is designed to be his wife, is grown fond of Mr. Tattle; now if we can improve that, and make her have an aversion for the booby, it may go a great way towards his liking you. Here they come together; and let us contrive some way or other to leave 'em together.

ANGELICA'S PROPOSAL

From 'Love for Love'

Scene:—A Room in the Foresight House. Enter Angelica *and* Jenny

Angelica—Where is Sir Sampson? did you not tell me he would be here before me?

Jenny—He's at the great glass in the dining-room, madam, setting his cravat and wig.

Angelica—How! I'm glad on't. If he has a mind I should like him, it's a sign he likes me; and that's more than half my design.

Jenny—I hear him, madam.

Angelica—Leave me; and d'ye hear, if Valentine should come or send, I am not to be spoken with.

Enter Sir Sampson

Sir Sampson—I have not been honored with the commands of a fair lady a great while:—odd, madam, you have revived me!—not since I was five-and-thirty.

Angelica—Why, you have no great reason to complain, Sir Sampson; that is not long ago.

Sir Sampson—Zooks, but it is, madam; a very great while, to a man that admires a fine woman as much as I do.

Angelica—You're an absolute courtier, Sir Sampson.

Sir Sampson—Not at all, madam; odsbud, you wrong me; I am not so old, neither, to be a bare courtier; only a man of words: odd, I have warm blood about me yet, and can serve a lady any way. Come, come, let me tell you, you women think a man old too soon, faith and troth, you do! Come, don't despise fifty; odd, fifty, in a hale constitution, is no such contemptible age.

Angelica — Fifty a contemptible age! not at all; a very fashionable age, I think. I assure you, I know very considerable beaux that set a good face upon fifty. Fifty! I have seen fifty in a side-box, by candle-light, outblossom five-and-twenty.

Sir Sampson — Outsides, outsides; a pize take 'em, mere outsides! hang your side-box beaux! No, I'm none of those, none of your forced trees, that pretend to blossom in the fall, and bud when they should bring forth fruit; I am of a long-lived race; . . . none of my ancestors married till fifty; . . . I am of your patriarchs, I, a branch of one of your antediluvian families, fellows that the flood could not wash away. Well, madam, what are your commands? has any young rogue affronted you, and shall I cut his throat? or —

Angelica — No, Sir Sampson, I have no quarrel upon my hands. I have more occasion for your conduct than your courage at this time. To tell you the truth, I'm weary of living single, and want a husband.

Sir Sampson — Odsbud, and 'tis pity you sho' a! — [*Aside.*] Odd, would she would like me, then I should hamper my young rogues: odd, would she would; faith and troth, she's devilish handsome! [*Aloud.*] Madam, you deserve a good husband, and 'twere pity you should be thrown away upon any of these young idle rogues about the town. Odd, there's ne'er a young fellow worth hanging! that is, a very young fellow. Pize on 'em! they never think beforehand of anything; and if they commit matrimony, 'tis as they commit murder — out of a frolic, and are ready to hang themselves, or to be hanged by the law, the next morning: odso, have a care, madam.

Angelica — Therefore I ask your advice, Sir Sampson. I have fortune enough to make any man easy that I can like, if there were such a thing as a young agreeable man with a reasonable stock of good-nature and sense; . . . for I would neither have an absolute wit nor a fool.

Sir Sampson — Odd, you are hard to please, madam; to find a young fellow that is neither a wit in his own eye nor a fool in the eye of the world, is a very hard task. But faith and troth, you speak very discreetly; for I hate both a wit and a fool.

Angelica — She that marries a fool, Sir Sampson, forfeits the reputation of her honesty or understanding: and she that marries a very witty man is a slave to the severity and insolent conduct of her husband. I should like a man of wit for a lover, because I would have such a one in my power; but I would no more be his wife than his enemy. For his malice is not a more terrible consequence of his aversion than his jealousy is of his love.

Sir Sampson — None of old Foresight's Sibyls ever uttered such a truth. Odsbud, you have won my heart! I hate a wit; I had a son that was spoiled among 'em; a good hopeful lad, till he learned to be a wit; and might have risen in the State. But a pox on't! his wit run him out of his money, and now his poverty has run him out of his wits.

Angelica — Sir Sampson, as your friend, I must tell you, you are very much abused in that matter; he's no more mad than you are.

Sir Samson — How, madam? would I could prove it!

Angelica — I can tell you how that may be done. But it is a thing that would make me appear to be too much concerned in your affairs.

Sir Sampson [*aside*] — Odsbud, I believes she likes me! [*Aloud.*] Ah, madam, all my affairs are scarce worthy to be laid at your feet: and I wish, madam, they were in a better posture, that I might make a more becoming offer to a lady of your incomparable beauty and merit. — If I had Peru in one hand, and Mexico in t'other, and the Eastern Empire under my feet, it would make me only a more glorious victim to be offered at the shrine of your beauty.

Angelica — Bless me, Sir Sampson, what's the matter?

Sir Sampson — Odd, madam, I love you! and if you would take my advice in a husband —

Angelica — Hold, hold, Sir Sampson! I asked your advice for a husband, and you are giving me your consent. I was indeed thinking to propose something like it in jest, to satisfy you about Valentine: for if a match were seemingly carried on between you and me, it would oblige him to throw off his disguise of madness, in apprehension of losing me; for you know he has long pretended a passion for me.

Sir Sampson — Gadzooks, a most ingenious contrivance! if we were to go through with it. But why must the match only be seemingly carried on? Odd, let it be a real contract.

Angelica — Oh fy, Sir Sampson! what would the world say?

Sir Sampson — Say! they would say you were a wise woman and I a happy man. Odd, madam, I'll love you as long as I live, and leave you a good jointure when I die.

Angelica — Ay; but that is not in your power, Sir Sampson; for when Valentine confesses himself in his senses, he must make over his inheritance to his younger brother.

Sir Sampson — Odd, you're cunning, a wary baggage! faith and troth, I like you the better. But I warrant you, I have a proviso in the obligation in favor of myself. Body o' me, I have a trick to turn the settlement! . . .

Angelica — Will you? Well, do you find the estate, and leave the other to me.

Sir Sampson — O rogue! but I'll trust you. And will you consent? is it a match, then?

Angelica — Let me consult my lawyer concerning this obligation; and if I find what you propose practicable, I'll give you my answer.

Sir Sampson — With all my heart: co   with me and I'll lend you the bond. You shall consult your lawyer, and I'll consult a parson. Odzooks, I'm a young man: odzooks, I'm a young man, and I'll make it appear. Odd, you're devilish handsome: faith and troth, you're very handsome; and I am very young, and very lusty! Odsbud, hussy, you know how to choose, and so do I; odd, I think we are very well met. Give me your hand, — odd, let me kiss it; 'tis as warm and as soft — as what? — Odd, as t'other hand; give me t'other hand, and I'll mumble 'em and kiss 'em till they melt in my mouth.

Angelica — Hold, Sir Sampson: you're profuse of your vigor before your time: you'll spend your estate before you come to it.

Sir Sampson — No, no, only give you a rent-roll of my possessions, — ha! baggage! . . . Odd, Sampson's a very good name for an able fellow: your Sampsons were strong dogs from the beginning.

Angelica — Have a care, and don't overact your part. If you remember, Sampson, the strongest of the name, pulled an old house over his head at last!

VII—248

ALMERIA IN THE MAUSOLEUM

From 'The Mourning Bride'

Enter Almeria *and* Leonora

A LMERIA —   It was a fancied noise, for all is hushed.
   Leonora — It bore the accent of a human voice.
   Almeria — It was thy fear, or else some transient wind
     Whistling through hollows of this vaulted aisle.
     We'll listen.
Leonora — Hark!
Almeria — No, all is hushed and still as death. — 'Tis dreadful!
     How reverend is the face of this tall pile,
     Whose ancient pillars rear their marble heads,
     To bear aloft its arched and ponderous roof,
     By its own weight made steadfast and immovable,
     Looking tranquillity! It strikes an awe
     And terror on my aching sight; the tombs
     And monumental caves of death look cold,
     And shoot a chillness to my trembling heart.
     Give me thy hand, and let me hear thy voice;
     Nay, quickly speak to me, and let me hear
     Thy voice — my own affrights me with its echoes.
Leonora — Let us return; the horror of this place,
     And silence, will increase your melancholy.
Almeria — It may my fears, but cannot add to that.
     No, I will on: show me Anselmo's tomb;
     Lead me o'er bones and skulls and moldering earth
     Of human bodies; for I'll mix with them:
     Or wind me in the shroud of some pale corse
     Yet green in earth, rather than be the bride
     Of Garcia's more detested bed: that thought
     Exerts my spirits; and my present fears
     Are lost in dread of greater ill. Then show me,
     Lead me, for I am bolder grown; lead on
     Where I may kneel, and pay my vows again
     To him, to Heaven, and my Alphonso's soul.
Leonora — I go; but Heaven can tell with what regret.

*The Scene opening discovers a place of tombs; one monument fronting the
view greater than the rest*

Enter Heli

Heli —   I wander through this maze of monuments,
     Yet cannot find him. — Hark! sure 'tis the voice

Of one complaining.—There it sounds: I'll follow it.

[*Exit.*

Leonora—Behold the sacred vault, within whose womb
The poor remains of good Anselmo rest,
Yet fresh and unconsumed by time or worms!
What do I see? O Heaven! either my eyes
Are false, or still the marble door remains
Unclosed: the iron gates that lead to death
Beneath, are still wide-stretched upon their hinge,
And staring on us with unfolded leaves.

Almeria—Sure, 'tis the friendly yawn of death for me;
And that dumb mouth, significant in show,
Invites me to the bed where I alone
Shall rest; shows me the grave, where nature, weary
And long oppressed with woes and bending cares,
May lay the burden down, and sink in slumbers
Of peace eternal. Death, grim death, will fold
Me in his leaden arms, and press me close
To his cold clayey breast: my father then
Will cease his tyranny; and Garcia too
Will fly my pale deformity with loathing.
My soul, enlarged from its vile bonds, will mount,
Aud range the starry orbs, and milky ways,
Of that refulgent world, where I shall swim
In liquid light, and float on seas of bliss
To my Alphonso's soul. O joy too great!
O ecstasy of thought! Help me, Anselmo:
Help me, Alphonso; take me, reach thy hand;
To thee, to thee I call, to thee, Alphonso:
O Alphonso!

Osmyn *ascends from the tomb*

Osmyn— Who calls that wretched thing that was Alphonso?
Almeria—Angels, and all the host of heaven, support me!
Osmyn— Whence is that voice, whose shrillness, from the grave,
And growing to his father's shroud, roots up Alphonso?
Almeria—Mercy! Providence! O speak!
Speak to it quickly, quickly! speak to me,
Comfort me, help me, hold me, hide me, hide me,
Leonora, in thy bosom, from the light,
And from my eyes!
Osmyn—   Amazement and illusion!
Rivet and nail me where I stand, ye powers;

[*Coming forward.*

That motionless I may be still deceived.
Let me not stir, nor breathe, lest I dissolve
That tender lovely form of painted air,
So like Almeria. Ha! it sinks, it falls;
I'll catch it ere it goes, and grasp her shade.
'Tis life! 'tis warm! 'tis she! 'tis she herself!
Nor dead nor shade, but breathing and alive!
It is Almeria, 'tis, it is my wife!

HENRI CONSCIENCE

(1812–1883)

BY WILLIAM SHARP

ENRI CONSCIENCE (not Hendrik Conscience, as commonly written, for though the great romancist was a Fleming by maternal descent and by native sympathy, he was the son of a naturalized Frenchman and was christened Henri), who is popularly known as the Walter Scott of Flanders, is with the exception of Georges Eckhoud the one Belgian author who has succeeded in gaining the ear of Europe. There is not one of the leading languages, and few of the less important, into which one or more of his books have not been translated: indeed, his works are to be found complete or all but complete in French, German, Norwegian, and English. One story for example, 'Rikke-Tikke-Tak,' has not only been rendered into every European tongue, but has been paraphrased to such an extent that variants of it occur, in each instance as an indigenous folk-tale, in every land, from Great Britain in the west to India and even to China in the east.

HENRI CONSCIENCE

To-day to our changed tastes the tales of Conscience may seem somewhat insipid, — that is, in translation; for the style of the original is characterized by singular verve and charm,—but there must be a radical appeal in writings which have reached the home-circle readers of Belgium and Holland, of Germany and of Scandinavia, of France and England and America. Born in Antwerp in 1812, of a French father and a Flemish mother, the childhood of the novelist-to-be was passed during the French domination in the Netherlands. While a youth, he watched with eager intelligence the growing pressure of the Dutch yoke upon Flanders, the restless vicissitudes and memorable events which culminated in the revolution of 1830 and the separation of Belgium from the neighboring country. This uprising of the Flemish people was followed by a re-birth of Flemish literature, of which the informing spirit was Henri Conscience. Thitherto, the young writers of his day modeled themselves upon the then all-potent romantic school of literature in France; moreover, without exception they wrote in French, in accordance with the all-but universal prejudice that Flemish was merely a patois used only by the vulgar people. Although Conscience's first literary efforts — martial songs and poems — were written in French, he exclaimed in 1830, when he was only a youth of eighteen, and with prophetic insight: — "I confess I find in the real Flemish something indescribably romantic, mysterious, profound, energetic, even savage. If ever I gain the power to write, I shall throw myself head over ears into Flemish literature."

The little Henri was a cripple till his seventh year, and the child's mother was wont to amuse him by the narration of wonderful tales of fairies and angels. Later he passed his time in reading forgotten books that were stowed away in the garret, or in exercising his creative faculties in inventing local stories for his admiring companions. At his mother's death his father removed to a lonely spot a mile from the old Antwerp wall, and here was first aroused in the boy the warm love of nature that is so strongly marked in all his writings. After acting as assistant master for two years at Delin College, he in 1830 joined the Belgian patriots as a volunteer. During the six years of his service in the country he gained an insight not only into the beauties of nature, but into the lives and feelings of the Flemish peasantry, into their manners and customs; he grew intimate with the gentle nobility of their character, which underlies the stern melancholy of their outward disposition. Conscience's first important work was written in 1836 — after the cessation of the war — to gain him admission to the Olijftak (Olive Branch), a literary club of young enthusiasts. 'Het Wonder Jaar' (1566) was written in Flemish, and was published in Ghent in 1837. This historical romance, full of color and rich in dramatic incident, gave the death-blow to the existing didactic prose and poetry, and was the foundation-stone on which arose the new Flemish school of literature. Pierre Conscience, however, saw his son's partisanship in the Flemish literary movement with such displeasure that eventually the young man had to leave home altogether. His friend Wappers, the eminent painter, procured him a small appointment in the department of political archives, which however he lost, owing to a violent political speech. A funeral oration at the tomb of a director of the Antwerp Academy was the indirect means of his gaining a post in the offices of the Academy, where he remained till 1855. In 1857 he was appointed to the local administration of Courtrai; and in 1868 the Belgian government conferred on him the title of Conservateur des Musées Royaux de Peinture et de Sculpture, a guardianship held by him until his death in 1883.

Conscience's literary career divides itself into two periods, and shows him as historical romancist and as a writer of novels and short tales. The success of 'Het Wonder Jaar' inspired him to a second venture, and in 1858 he published his 'De Leeuw van Vlaenderen' (The Lion of Flanders), an undertaking which despite its subsequent fame brought the author six francs for net profit! He writes of himself that "the enthusiasm of my youth and the labors of my manhood were rooted in my love for my country." To raise Flanders was to him a holy aim. France threatened Flemish freedom: therefore he wrote his two finest historical novels, those which depict the uprising of the Flemings against French despotism, 'The Lion of Flanders' and 'The Peasants' War.'

From the literary point of view the second book is superior to its predecessor; the plot is not so closely linked to history, and though there is less regard to historical accuracy, the story gains more in dramatic unity. As a historical novelist Conscience does not belong to the school of realism and archæology: in a word, he pertains to the school of Walter Scott, not to that of Gustave Flaubert. He writes of himself, "In Holland my works have met with the same favor from Catholics and Lutherans alike;" yet his Catholic predilections have in many instances impaired his historical accuracy, and even deprived his brilliant, vivid 'History of Belgium' of scientific value.

To his second period belong his stories, in which he directs his powers to the task of social regeneration, and of painting the life of his own day as he saw it around him. In such novels as 'De Gierigaerd' (The Miser), 'De Arme Edelman' (The Poor Nobleman), he resolved "to apply the glowing steel to the cankered wounds of which society is dying." He describes the qualities which equipped him for his task when he says, "I am one whom God endowed at least with moral energy and with a vast instinct of affection." It is however in the tales of Flemish peasant life,—'Rikke-Tikke-Tak,' 'How Men Become Painters,' 'What a Mother Can Suffer,' 'The Happiness of Being Rich,' etc.,—that the author's exquisite style shows itself at its finest. There is nothing in the conception of the stories to show great inventive talent; but the execution, the way in which these simple things are recounted, is of the highest artistic excellence. In the matter of style his dual nationality proved an advantage; for to the homely vigor of the Teuton he added the gracefulness, the sobriety, the sense of measure and proportion, which are peculiar to the best French prose. Georges Eckhoud, his celebrated fellow-countryman, says of him:—"In simplicity of form, coupled with the intensity of the idea expressed, lies the eloquence of this Flemish author's tales. Thus is explained the popularity of that delicate casket to the furthest ends of the earth, to the simplest as well as to the most cultivated circles. . . . The work of Conscience is like a sociable country-house, a place where men can regain the simplicity which they had lost through cheating and deception.»

No better summing-up of the writings of Henri Conscience can be given than that penned by himself in his biographical notes:—

«I write my books to be read by the people. I have always made the intellectual development and education of the ignorant my aim. . . . I have sketched the Flemish peasant as he appeared to me. I drew him calm, peaceable, religious, patriotic, attached to his traditions and opposed somewhat vehemently to all innovations; in short, as he appeared to me at that period of my life in 1830, when, hungry and sick, I enjoyed hospitality and the tenderest care amongst them. I have never inspired my heroes with the poetic glamour for which I have been reproached; it is they who inspired me. And then a man may dwell by preference on the defective side and the coarseness of the laborer, may sketch him as the slave of drunkenness and animal passion. I shall not deny the picturesqueness of this work. But between that and the admission of my delusion there is a wide margin. My neighbor's heroes are not necessarily mine, nor do I see them in the same light. People are constantly discussing whether he who paints things in their darkest colors, or he who sees all in a materialistic light, or he who presents everything in its happiest form,— whether he who takes a subjective or an objective point of view,— is right. All I know is,— and it is my settled conviction,— that a conscientious writer is never wrong; and I believe myself to be conscientious.»

This is a frank, manly, and honest pronouncement, and will surely be admitted as such even by those who may not care either for the matter or manner, the method or the literary principles, of Henri Conscience. Perhaps the best commentary is, that after a European success ranking only after that of Scott, Balzac, Dumas, Hugo, and Hans Andersen, Henri Conscience is still (thirteen years after his death at an advanced age) a name of European repute; is still, in his own country, held in highest honor and affection.

William Sharp

THE HORSE-SHOE

From 'Rikke-Tikke-Tak'

IN THE village of Westmal, some two or three miles from Antwerp, on the road toward Turnhout, stood a little smithy, in which four men — the master and his three journeymen — were busy at various work in the way of their trade; and at the same time were conversing — as much, that is, as the noise of hammers and files would let them — of Napoleon and his mighty deeds of war. One of the journeymen, who had lost two fingers of his left hand, was just beginning a story of the Italian wars, when two horsemen pulled up before the door, and one of them called out, "Hola, my men! my horse wants shoeing."

The journeymen looked curiously at the strangers, who by this time had dismounted. They were evidently both military men. One of them had a great scar right across his face and wore a red riband in his button-hole: the other, though dressed like a gentleman, seemed in some sort his subordinate; he held the horse by the bridle and asked, "Which shoe, colonel?"

"The near forefoot, lieutenant," was the reply.

One of the journeymen took the horse and led it into the shed; and meanwhile the colonel entered the smithy, looked about him, and took up first one, then another, of the tools, as if looking out for an old acquaintance. At last he seemed to have found what he wanted; in one hand he held a heavy pair of tongs, in the other a hammer, both of which he surveyed with so peculiar a smile that the journeymen stood round, gaping and staring in no little amaze.

Meanwhile the iron was in the fire, the bellows panted away, and a garland of sparks spurted from the glowing coals. The journeymen stood by the anvil, hammers in hand, till the master took the iron from the fire; then began the work of forging.

The colonel evidently took a lively interest in what was going on; his features lighted up, as they might have done at the finest music. But when the shoe was taken from the anvil, as ready for putting on, he eyed it a moment not a little disdainfully, took the tongs which held it from the master-smith's hand, and put it back into the fire.

"That will never do," said he; "the shoe's too clumsy by half, master. Now, my lads! look alive! blow away!"

And while one of the journeymen, with an air of great respect, obeyed his directions, he threw off his coat and bared his sinewy arms. Soon the iron was at a white heat: he turned it twice or thrice in the fire with all the air of an experienced hand, laid it on the anvil, and then called to the journeymen in a cheerful tone:—

"Now, my men! look out! I'll give the time, and we'll turn out a shoe fit for the Emperor's nags. So now, attention:—

> 'Rikketikketak,
> Rikketikketoo;
> The iron's warm;
> Up with your arm,
> Now strike,—one, two,
> Rikketikketoo.
>
> 'Rikketikketak,
> Rikketikketoo,
> Strike while it is hot,
> And tarry not.
> Again,—one two,
> Rikketikketoo.'

There, look at the shoe now!"

The journeymen eyed the light neat piece of work agape, and as it were, struck dumb. The master meanwhile seemed to be turning some thought in his head, which he every now and then shook, as though quite unable to come to a satisfactory conclusion. He drew near the stranger, who by this time had resumed his coat; but however closely he scanned him, he seemed unable to recognize him.

The horse was soon shod, and now stood before the smithy ready for its master to mount, who took leave of the party with a friendly shake of the hand to each, laying also a couple of gold pieces on the anvil.

"One for the master, one for the men. Drink my health together and good-by to you."

With these words he threw himself into the saddle and rode off with his companion.

"Well," said the master, "I never in my life knew but one man who could knock off a shoe like that,—so light and neat, and so handily; and I must be greatly mistaken if the colonel isn't just Karl van Milgem himself; he, you know,—but to be sure you don't know,—he that the folks used always to call Rikke-Tikke-Tak."

THE PATIENT WAITER

From 'Rikke-Tikke-Tak'

S HE took her way with the cow toward the brook, which was edged about with a scanty growth of grass. Slowly she went, step by step, leading the creature after her by a cord. At last she reached the line where the heath passed into a range of low-lying boggy pastures, and the alder and juniper bushes formed a closer thicket; there she left the foot-path. A solitary beech stood there — sown probably by a bird, for as far as the eye could see it descried no similar foliage. Magdalen sank down at the foot of the tree. Deeply she bowed her head; motionless she gazed on space; the cord fell from her hand and her accustomed reverie came over her.

Now in the free open air, under the beautiful deep-blue heaven, the sore load of trouble which weighed upon her heart fell from it. Her lips did not move, no sigh escaped from them; but a quiet stream of tears trickled into her lap. Long, very long she sat there without changing her position; but by degrees her tears fell more slowly, till at last she lifted her head, and with a calmer air murmured her old favorite tune:

> "Rikketikketak,
> Rikketikketoo;
> The iron's warm;
> Up with your arm,
> Now strike,— one, two,
> Rikketikketoo."

What could this strange jingle mean? It would have been useless to ask Magdalen, for she herself knew not how it was that of themselves, almost without will or consciousness of hers, the meaningless words came tripping over her lips. A faint recollection she had of some one having often sung them to her; but that was long, long ago. They spoke but indistinctly, still they had ever more and more fixed themselves in her train of associations, had become ever more and more the accompaniment both of her joys and of her sorrows.

After she had repeated the rhyme a few times, and each time less sadly, she seemed quite to forget her melancholy and the causes of it. She stood up, her face radiant with contentment, briskly led the cow to a place where there was better pasture,

and ran towards a sandy hillock which rose a little above the
general surface of the heath. She had often visited this spot.
Steadying herself with her hands upon her knees, she fixed her
eyes on a bluish point far away upon the extremest verge of the
horizon, — a town it was probably, or a large village.   .   .   .
With unwearied eyes she gazed upon the road, doubtless in the
unconscious hope that by it he who should release her from her
bondage would one day approach that way.

THE LOST GLOVE

"THIS is the celebrated bear-pit of Berne," said the guide.
"Pass here when you choose, you will always find people
of all ages who are amusing themselves throwing bread
and fruit to these ferocious beasts. Here is a good place. See
the tricks of these bears, and how they lift up their arms like
real beggars."

While Max Rapelings was entirely absorbed in contemplating
the amusing antics of the bears, Herman, glancing round, noticed
a lady wrapped in a red shawl, who had dropped a yellow glove,
and who would probably have lost it, as she continued walking
on. He picked up the glove, ran after the lady, and said to her
in French, "You have lost something, madam."

The lady turned. Herman seemed transfixed. This lady was
no other than the pale maiden of the Aarberggasse, whom he
had not recognized at first, owing to her wearing a colored shawl.

She made a step toward him, took her glove with a smile of
thanks, and said in a voice whose sweetness was great, "I thank
you infinitely, sir."

But at once appeared beside her the old gentleman with the
crabbed face, who fixed upon the young man a look both piercing and interrogative.

Just at this moment Max turned toward his friend and cried
out: —

"Here, Herman; come quick; there are some bears fighting
furiously."

This cry produced upon the young girl and old gentleman an
extraordinary effect — it seemed to strike them with terror and
affright. They turned away and walked off rapidly, as if in the
young doctor they had recognized a dreaded enemy.

Max had observed this inopportune meeting; he left the Swiss, who was still amusing himself by looking into the bear-pit, ran towards his friend, looked at his face attentively, and cried with astonishment:—

"You are pale! What did she say to you? Did her tyrant insult you? You do not answer. Alas! there is an end of all our pleasure for to-day! I would give the poor five francs were you nevermore to meet the pale maiden and her dragon!"

"Hush, hush, Max! I have heard her voice; it is marvelously sweet and fascinating—it still resounds in my ear like a cry of distress."

"A cry of distress! Did she complain to you? What did she say?"

"Only 'I thank you infinitely, sir.'"

"And you call that a cry of distress? You are surely losing your wits!"

"Yes, but her voice was so plaintive, her smile—"

"Oh! she smiled upon you, did she? The Devil! Things begin to look serious."

"Her smile is so sweet, sad, and plaintive."

"There now; you are beginning to talk in verse! This does not seem to me the fitting spot, beside a bear-pit. Come, behave yourself, Herman; here is our host coming. For the love of Heaven, do not mention the pale maiden before him, for he might think you have lost your wits."

THE IRON TOMB

IT WOULD be difficult to describe to you the strange life I led at Bodeghem. I wandered daily along the walks of the uninhabited country-houses, in the woods and shady groves, my mind enveloped as it were in a dream, which like a thick cloud held me aloof from the outer world. It was useless to call to my assistance all my energy and will to dissipate the fog that thus covered my intellect; it was trouble lost. I could only see Rose and her pitiful look; I could only feel the worm of sorrow that gnawed at my heart and only heard the terrible words—"Do you know the news? Rose is going to be married"— that followed me everywhere, without giving me one moment's peace. The violence of passion, the bitterness of despair, had left me entirely. I hated no one, accused no one, not even my cruel fate; not even the future husband, my rival. An intense sorrow, a dreamy resignation, a species of quiet sympathy with my anguish, took the place of all violent emotion in my heart.

Convinced that I was never destined to experience real happiness in this world, I recalled one by one all the recollections of my past life, and with these reminiscences I created for myself an imaginary world, wherein my soul could find a source of peace and consolation.

In walking through the garden I would stop on the bridge and gaze into the water, then returning to less sad thoughts I would contemplate for hours together the lawn that stretched itself before me. I saw in imagination a delicate little girl, pretty as an angel; by her side was a little boy who could not talk, but his eyes at the least word or smile from the little girl would lighten with admiration, gratitude, and pride. I followed these happy children; I trembled with heartfelt emotion when I perceived upon the little girl's face a smile of friendship for the poor boy. I shared in their games as they traced out a bed of flowers in the grass; I ran behind them as they chased the butterflies — I listened to their childish chatterings and each beating of their little hearts, and I recognized with cruel satisfaction that even then a fatal power dominated over these innocent creatures and had already sown in their hearts a seed of a future love. I spoke to the trees, the flowers, the birds, to revive again the memory of my lost happiness, until nightfall and the weary throbbings of my heart warned me that it was time to return home. On other days I would wander in the woods and try to find out those trees to whom I had confided my sorrows and hopes. I recognized the old places where I had once sat, and I thought I could see glittering among the grass the tears I had shed some eight long years ago.

Then I used to weep from pure happiness; the sun of hope inundated my heart with its light. Now I had none; my life was closed by the dark wall of the impossible — it was on that account I had no more tears. Tears are both a prayer and an intercession for help and pity. Why should I complain or implore? — I, to whom no earthly power could give back to my heart what it desired; whose sorrows by their very nature were to be life-lasting.

Again at other times I would sit down on the hedge-side, where the dumb child had worked for weeks carving wooden figures — loved treasures with which he hoped to win a smile. I saw again the spot where the child rolled on the ground, a prey to convulsions of despair, because his tongue refused to utter any intelligible sounds. I saw the white poplar-trees whose bark still bore the mysterious signs with which he tried to make himself understood. The cows that were grazing in the fields, the cracking of the shepherd's whip, the silvery dew arising from the running brook, the splendor of the rising sun, all recalled the memory of my childhood and helped me to forget my mournful sadness, recalling to my mind a picture of happiness that had been, but could never return.

SISKA VAN ROOSEMAEL

Not many years ago, you might have seen in one of the streets behind the green churchyard of Antwerp, a famous old grocer's shop, which through many generations had descended from father to son, and had always been conspicuous for good wares and low prices. The last proprietor of the shop was James van Roosemael, son of Frank, son of Charles, son of Gaspard van Roosemael, and had married Siska Pot, a descendant of the famous Peter Pot, whose name is still to be met in the two Peter-Pot Streets.

This wedded pair, trained from early youth to a life of industry, and now unremittingly busied with their small trade, had never found time to take part in the progress of modern civilization, — or in other words, to *Frenchify* themselves. Their dress, made of stout cloth, was plain, and hardly ever changed its cut; they merely distinguished working dress, Sunday dress, and Easter dress. The latter was never taken from the cupboard but on great holidays, and when the Van Roosemaels took the Holy Communion, or were invited by friends as godparents or marriage guests. It was easily to be seen that the simple people of the old Flemish world, in their quaint though valuable dress, looked rather strangely if compared with many a fine beau, who for a few francs had decked himself out in a fine showy dress, and would, in passing, regard the Van Roosemaels with disdain. But they did not mind it, and thought, "Every man has his own

point to gain — you the shadow, we the substance.» They were
sufficiently uneducated not to know that gentlefolks do not dine
at noon, and they therefore were vulgar enough to sit down to
dinner when the clock struck twelve; yea, more, they never
forgot to say grace both before and after dinner. But there
were other imperfections with which they ought to be charged:
for instance, they did not understand a word of French, and
had never felt the want of this accomplishment; they were religious, humble, industrious, and above all peaceable. But the
height of their stupidity was, that they in their Flemish simplicity considered it better every day to lay by an honest stiver,
than by lies and fraud to amass such riches in a few years, that
all the world should exclaim in astonishment, "In what hole
did the rat find it?" In a word, they were Flemish burghers of
the old school.

A PAINTER'S PROGRESS

A T THE funeral of Baron de Erct, a humble vehicle followed
the procession afar off. Arrived at the burial-ground,
three persons alighted from the poor conveyance. They
turned into a by-lane near the cemetery, and did not show themselves during the ceremony. But when all was over, and the
splendid carriages were returning in speed with all the mourners
to the town, three persons were seen entering the churchyard
with slow steps. It was Frank, his aged grandmother leaning
on his arm and supported by his mother on the other side.
Nobody saw them; all was still in the cemetery, and the greatest
silence prevailed around.

Do you mark them all three,— their eyes red with tears, their
breath choked by the agony of grief, approaching a mound of
newly dug-up earth? There rests the man who did good by
stealth. Oh, say not that virtue is not rewarded, not honored!
The tears of these people weigh thousands in the scales of the
heavenly Judge.

Look! the women are kneeling on the mound. They clasp
their hands and bend their heads over the grave; their lips
move. Is theirs a set speech? are their words studied, measured,
written down, in order that they may remember them? Oh no!
They know only one prayer, which the Lord himself has taught

them: they say the Lord's prayer over and over again. Their voices become clearer whilst they pray:—"Forgive us our debts as we forgive our debtors! Holy Mary, Mother of the Lord, pray for us miserable sinners, now and in the hour of death. Amen." Their sobs, their tears, their sighs tell the rest:—"Sleep in peace, kind-hearted friend! we plant no flowers on thy grave; they are not everlasting as the memory of thy countless charities. May thy soul receive in the bosom of thy Maker a reward which the world cannot give!"

And why does not Frank also kneel on the ground? Why? He is absorbed in grief; he feels no life in him, he has forgotten where he is. Look! there he stands like a statue, his head dropping on his breast, his hand pressed to his forehead. How the streaming tears sparkle which burst from his eyes! Unfortunate youth! who could describe the mortal despair which weighs on thy bursting heart!

Awake! seest thou not that the cold ground will injure the health of thy grandmother? Remove her from the grave, else the evening will perhaps still find her kneeling and weeping here. Take courage! return to thy home.

On the following day Frank said in a sorrowful tone to his parents, "We are unfortunate and poor—I am the cause of your sorrow, I know I am. But let me now put a question to you, and answer it candidly! Can we still hold out for three months without earning any money?"

The question remained long unanswered. The mother went up to the invalid husband, and after a long serious conversation with him said, "Three months with the utmost stretch, but no longer." "Well then," said Frank, "I shall make a last attempt. One picture I will paint still—one only, and if I do not sell it soon, then I shall turn sign-painter."

It gave him evident pain to utter this last word; there was a spasm in his throat,—yet he soon composed himself, and asked once more whether they would let him work for three months without trouble or molestation. This his parents readily promised him. Frank then went to Mr. Wappers and received the last twenty-five francs which his generous patron had left for him. With part of this money he purchased colors, and on the following day he shut himself up in the loft where he used to work, and sketched the first outline of the picture which he intended to execute.

It was the churchyard of Hemixem, with a newly thrown-up grave, on which two women were kneeling in prayer; behind them stood a young man weeping and absorbed in the deepest grief; on the side were the walls of the chapel, and in the background a rich landscape. During two months and a half Frank worked without intermission; he went out to the churchyard in order to draw from nature, and made his mother and grandmother sit to him for models.

Never perhaps had an artist worked with more enthusiasm, with more love and industry, at a picture. His soul was full of his subject, and during all the time he was employed in his work his head burnt feverishly. Could this picture turn out ill? No, it must necessarily bear the stamp of inspiration. And so it was.

Frank got on credit an appropriate frame for the exhibition. But this time another thought struck him: he sent his picture to Germany to the exhibition at Cologne. Will he be more successful there? Yet the picture was gone, and stayed away without any news of it whatever.

Poverty, greater than they had ever felt, now broke in upon the longing family. They ate black bread, and were as if crushed by the awaking to the dreadful reality. The good old grandmother showed the greatest courage; she carried quietly her best habiliments and her few trinkets to the pawnbroker's, and consoled the others. But matters could not thus last long. The clothes of Frank and of the mother must at last also be pawned; even the prize medals and other honorable decorations went to the baker as pledges for a little bread. They had already run up an account with the butcher and the grocer — the baker would let them have no more — none would trust the *wretched artist*, as Frank was nicknamed in the neighborhood; the weekly house-rent was unpaid during a whole month, and the landlord had even sent the bailiff to exact payment.

One afternoon in the month of September the destitution of these people reached its height. None of them had tasted a morsel since the preceding evening. The bailiff had just left them with the warning that he would return at six o'clock, and if they did not then pay their rent they would be turned into the street.

Grandmother held Frank's hand in hers, and sought to console him; the mother shed silent tears; the father, who still wore his arm in a sling, sat at the chimney and stared gloomily into the chamber. All at once he burst into a flood of tears and sobbed aloud.

Frank had never seen his father weep: this was the first time in his life; it struck him like a thunderbolt. A shriek of terror burst from him, and he fell on his knees before his father. "Father," he cried, "father, you weep — you! Oh, be at ease; to-morrow I shall turn sign-painter; then I shall at least earn sixpence a day."

The workman raised his son from the floor, and pressed him with his left arm to his heart. "Frank, my boy," he said, "I don't lay blame on you; but we are so wretched. I weep because I am in despair that I cannot work. We are starving, and craving hunger is gnawing at our hearts. Who will give us to eat before the night falls in? Where shall we go when they turn us out to-morrow? Is it not sufficient to turn my brain, or to make me —"

Frank pressed him forcibly to his bosom, and cut short his awful speech by a tender embrace.

Whilst father and son were thus clasped in each other's arms, the door opened, and a man with a leather bag strapped over his shoulder stretched out his hand with a letter in it. With a sudden start Frank disengaged himself from the arm of his father, and attempted to seize the letter; but the postman drew it back and said dryly, "A letter from Germany — two francs!"

Two francs! Where is such a treasure secreted in this poor dwelling? Two francs from people who are starving! Who could describe the tortures and sorrows of this family? The letter contains perhaps what may put an end to their distress; perhaps it would dry up their tears, satisfy their hunger, and protect them from ejectment. And alas! whilst they are staring with beating heart at the letter, and long so ardently to open it, the postman is turning to go off with it and to rob them of all their hopes. It is as if the ground was burning beneath their feet; they stamp the floor from impatience and tear their hair.

Now the mother kneels down before the postman; she raises her hands imploringly! Ha! he weeps — his heart is not of stone. "Here" — he hands the letter to Frank — "take it; I am a poor man too, but I can't stand this any longer." Frank opens the letter slowly with a trembling hand, cautiously undoing each and every fold: but scarcely had he cast his eyes upon the contents, when the muscles of his face began to tremble convulsively; he grows deadly pale, and a strange scream escapes his breast. He supports himself upon the table, and the letter drops from his hands on the floor. The room rings with lamentations, the grandmother raises her hands to heaven, the mother sinks backward from her chair as if paralyzed. Frank was struggling to speak. It was evident he wanted to say something, but he could not make it pass his trembling lips. At last his speech burst forth — "Grandmother, mother, father, I *am* a painter! Five hundred francs for my picture!"

ROSE TERRY COOKE

(1827–1892)

OSE TERRY was born in Hartford, Connecticut, in 1827, of an old and well-known family, and there nearly all the first half of her life was passed. After that she was little there, spending a number of years with her married sister in Collinsville, and, for fifteen years following her own marriage, in Winsted, Connecticut. The last five years of her life were passed in Pittsfield, Massachusetts, where she died in 1892.

An uneventful life, it might be said; but she had the temperament that makes events. Intensity was the keynote of her nature, the source of her gifts and of her defects. In appearance she was tall and slight, with dark hair, and large dark eyes that dominated her slender oval face, and melted or sparkled with the mood or the occasion. This versatility of temper was deeply founded in her, and is manifest in her work, as in the deep overflowing sentiment of her poems and the almost rollicking humor of her stories, or the tenderness suddenly giving way to bitterness.

Her first literary work was in verse; her earliest venture, before she was twelve years old, being some verses sent privately to the Hartford Courant, and appearing there to the great awe and delight of the little author. As time went on, the creative impulse strengthened and took shape, and she became known as a writer of true poetic feeling and fine rhythmical instinct. In 1860 she gathered her poems into a little volume, which won for her a wider recognition. Quite late in life, in 1888, a complete collection of her poems was made; but she had hardly surpassed that earlier work, which included such gems as 'Then,' 'Trailing Arbutus,' 'The Fishing Song.' Besides these, 'The Two Villages' and 'Nounettes' should be named, as having found their way into many hearts, and as being very perfect specimens of her poetic gift. But it was in her stories that all her rich powers were enlisted. She was one of the first to open by the story-teller's art New England life to the reading public. This field has since been worked to a finer culture, but she brought to the opening of the ground a racy vigor and freshness, a spontaneity, a sparkle, that we could ill spare for the sake of a more delicate finish, and that make her characters stand out with an almost internal force. Among the best of her stories are 'Freedom Wheeler's Controversy

with Providence,' 'The Deacon's Week,' 'Polly Mariner,' 'A Town
Mouse and a Country Mouse,' and 'Odd Miss Todd.' But it is hard
to make an exclusive choice among them. 'The Deacon's Week,'
which she esteemed the best thing she ever did, has had a world-
wide fame and usefulness, having been translated into as many as
four languages, and widely distributed as a tract. Between the years
1881 and 1891 she gathered her stories into book form, under these
titles: 'Somebody's Neighbors,' 'Root-Bound,' 'The Sphinx's Children,' 'Happy Dodd,' 'Huckleberries.' In 1889 appeared her one
novel, 'Steadfast,' an interesting story with much fine character-
drawing. But it is as a writer of short stories of New England life
and of some lovely poems that Rose Terry Cooke will live.

THE REVEREND THOMAS TUCKER AS A PARSON

From 'Some Account of Thomas Tucker'

THE social duties of a settled clergyman might have pressed on
him onerously; but as if Providence saw that he was best
fitted for a life of solitude, just as the Green Street Church
had listened to their learned and pious pastor for the first time
after his installation in their pulpit, Keziah, his sister, was seized
with a sudden and dangerous illness. The kind women of the
church rallied around Thomas Tucker in this hour of his need,
and nursed Keziah with unremitting kindness; but all in vain.
She dropped out of life as silently and patiently as she had
endured living, and it remained only to say that the place which
knew her should now know her no more; for she left behind
her no dear friend but her brother, and not an enemy. Even
Thomas missed her rather as a convenience than a companion;
profiting in a certain sense by her death, as it aroused keenly
the sympathy of the church for his loss and loneliness, and
attached them to him by those links of pity that are proverbially almost as strong as love. In any other circumstances the
Green Street Church would no doubt have discovered, early in
their relation, that Mr. Tucker was as unfit for any pastoral
position as he had been for that post in the college chapel; but
much was forgiven him out of his people's abundant kindness,
and their respect for his learning, his simplicity, and his sincere
piety, forbade their objecting at first to his great deficiencies in
those things considered quite as needful to pulpit success as the

power of preaching and the abundance of knowledge. It happened, soon after Keziah's death, that Mr. Tucker was called to officiate at the funeral of one of his wealthiest parishioners, a man who had just come back from Europe, and been killed in a railroad accident on the way to his home in Deerford. He was personally unknown to Thomas Tucker, but his character was notorious. He went to church, and bought an expensive pew there, merely as a business speculation; it gave him weight in the eyes of his fellows to be outwardly respectable as well as rich; but he was niggardly to his family, ostentatious, overreaching, and cruel as death to the poor and struggling who crossed his path or came into his employ.

The Reverend Mr. Tucker improved the occasion. He took for the text of that funeral address, "What shall it profit a man if he gain the whole world and lose his own soul?" and after a pungent comparison between the goods of this world and the tortures of a future state, he laid down his spectacles and wound up with, "And now, beloved, I have laid before you the two conditions. Think ye that to-day he whose mortal part lieth before you would not utter a loud Amen to my statement? Yea, if there be truth in the Word of God, he who hath left behind him the gain of life and greed is now crying aloud for a drop of water to cool his parched tongue, and longing for an hour of probation wherein to cast off the fetters of ill-gotten gold and sit with Lazarus gathering crumbs in the company of dogs. Wherefore, seeing that God hath spoken sharply to you all in the sudden requirement of this rich man's soul, let his admonition sink into your souls; seek ye first the kingdom of God, and cast in your lot with the poor of this world, rich in faith, and be ready to answer joyfully when the Master calls."

Of course the community was outraged; but for a few kindly souls who stood by the poor parson, and insisted that Keziah's death had unsettled his mind, and not a few who felt that he had manfully told the truth without fear or favor, and could not help feeling a certain respect for him, he would have been asked, forcibly, to resign that very week. As it was, the indignant widow went over to another denomination without delay. "I will never set foot in that church again!" she said. "How can one be safe where a man is allowed to say whatever he chooses in the pulpit? A ritual never can be personal or insulting. I shall abide by the Prayer-Book hereafter."

In due time this matter faded out of the popular mind, as all things do in course of time, and nothing came between pastor and people except a gradual sense on their part that Solomon was right when he said, "Much study is a weariness to the flesh;" not only the student's flesh, but also theirs who have to hear reiterated all the dry outcome of such study.

But Parson Tucker's career was not to be monotonous. His next astonishing performance was at a wedding. A very pretty young girl, an orphan, living in the house of a relative, equally poor but grasping and ambitious, was about to marry a young man of great wealth and thoroughly bad character; a man whom all men knew to be a drunkard, a gambler, and a dissolute fellow, though the only son of a cultivated and very aristocratic family. Poor Emily Manning had suffered all those deprivations and mortifications which result from living in a dependent condition, aware that her presence was irksome and unwelcome, while her delicate organization was overtaxed with work whose limits were as indefinite as the food and clothing which were its only reward. She had entered into this engagement in a sort of desperation, goaded on by the widowed sister-in-law with whom she lived, and feeling that nothing could be much worse than her present position. Parson Tucker knew nothing of this, but he did know the character of Royal Van Wyck; and when he saw the pallid, delicate, shrinking girl beside this already worn-out, debased, bestial creature, ready to put herself into his hands for life, the "daimon" laid hold upon him and spake again. He opened the service, as was customary in Hartland, with a short address; but surely never did such a bridal exhortation enter the ears of man and woman before.

"My friends," he began, "matrimony is not to be lightly undertaken, as the matter of a day; it is an awful compact for life and death that ye enter into here. Young man, if thou hast not within thyself the full purpose to treat this woman with pure respect, loyal service, and tender care; to guard her soul's innocence as well as her bodily welfare; to cleave to her only, and keep thyself from evil thoughts and base indulgences for her sake,—if thou art not fit, as well as willing, to be priest and king of a clean household, standing unto her in character and act in God's stead so far as man may, draw back even now from thine intent; for a lesser purpose is sacrilege here, and will be damnable infamy hereafter."

Royal Van Wyck opened his sallow green eyes with an insolent stare. He would have sworn roundly had not some poor
instinct of propriety restrained him; as it was, he did not speak
but looked away. He could not bear the keen deep-set eyes
fixed upon him, and a certain gaunt majesty in the parson's
outstretched arm and severe countenance daunted him for the
moment. But Thomas Tucker saw that he had no intention of
accepting this good advice, so he turned to Emily.

"Daughter," he said, "if thou art about to enter into this
solemn relation, pause and consider. If thou hast not such confidence in this man that thy heart faileth not an iota at the
prospect of a lifelong companionship with him; if thou canst not
trust him utterly, respect him as thy lord and head, yield him
an obedience joyful and secure next to that thou givest to God;
if he is not to thee the one desirable friend and lover; if thou
hast a thought so free of him that it is possible for thee to
imagine another man in his place without a shudder; if thou art
not willing to give thyself to him in the bonds of a lifelong,
inevitable covenant of love and service; if it is not the best and
sweetest thing earth can offer thee to be his wife and the mother
of his children,—stop now; stop at the very horns of the altar,
lest thou commit the worst sin of woman, sell thy birthright for
a mess of pottage, and find no place for repentance, though thou
seek it carefully and with tears."

Carried away with his zeal for truth and righteousness, speaking as with the sudden inspiration of a prophet, Parson Tucker
did not see the terror and the paleness deepening, as he spoke,
on the bride's fair countenance. As he extended his hand toward
her she fell in a dead faint at his feet. All was confusion in an
instant. The bridegroom swore and Mrs. Manning screamed,
while the relations crowded about the insensible girl and tried to
revive her. She was taken at once up-stairs to her room, and the
wedding put off till the next day, as Mrs. Manning announced.

"And you won't officiate at it, old fellow! I'll swear to that!"
roared the baffled bridgroom with a volley of profane epithets,
shaking his fist in the parson's calm face.

"Having taken the sword, I am content to perish thereby,
even as Scripture saith," answered Thomas Tucker, stalking out
of the door.

That night as he sat in his study, the door opened softly, and
Emily Manning came in and knelt at the side of the parson's

chair. "I have no place to go to, sir," she whispered, with trembling lips. "You saved me to-day; will you help me now? I was going to sin, but I didn't know it till you told me."

"Then it was not sin, my child," said Parson Tucker gently. "Sin is conscious transgression, and from that thou hast instantly departed."

"But what could I do?" she asked, her eyes full of tears. "I have no home. Marcia is tired of me, and I have no other friends. I wanted a home so much. Oh, I was wrong, for I did not love him. And now I have run away from Marcia,— she was so dreadful,— and what shall I do?"

"Poor child!" he said tenderly. "Sit here. I will help. My old woman, in the kitchen below, shall fetch thee to a chamber. Keziah brought her with us; she is kind, and will care for thee, while I go to bring a friend." So saying, the parson rung his bell for old Jane, gave the girl over to her care, and set out himself for President Winthrop's house.

"I have brought you a good work," he said abruptly to Mrs. Winthrop. "Come with me; there is a soul in need at my house."

Mrs. Winthrop was used to this sort of summons from the parson. They had been good friends ever since the eccentric interview brought about by Jack Mason's valentine, and when charity was needed Eleanor Winthrop's heart and hand were always ready for service. She put on hat and shawl, and went with the parson to his house, hearing on the way all the story.

"Mr. Tucker," she said, as he finished the recital, "aren't you going to make much trouble for yourself by your aggressive honesty?"

Thomas looked at her, bewildered.

"But the truth is to be spoken!" he replied, as if that were the end of the controversy. And she was silent, recognizing the fact that here conventions were useless, and self-preservation not the first law of grace, if it is of nature.

All Mrs. Winthrop's kindliness was aroused by the pitiful condition of Emily Manning. She consoled and counseled her like a mother, and soon after took her into her household as governess to the little girls whom Mr. Winthrop's first wife had left him; making for the grateful girl a happy home, which in after years she left to become the wife of a good man, toward whom she felt all that Parson Tucker had required of her on that painful day which she hated now to remember.   And as the parson performed this ceremony he turned after the benediction to Eleanor Winthrop, and said with a beam of noble triumph on his hollow visage, "Blessed be the Lord! I have saved a soul alive!"

But long before this happy sequel came about, he had other opportunities to distinguish himself.   There came a Sunday when the service of infant baptism was to be performed; and when the fair sweet babes, who had behaved with unusual decorum, were returned to their mothers' arms, and the parson according to order said, "Let us pray," he certainly offered the most peculiar petition ever heard in the Green Street Church.   After expressing the usual desire that the baptized children might grow up in the nurture and admonition of the Lord, he went on: — "But if it please thee, O Father, to recall these little ones to thyself in the innocence of their infancy, we will rejoice and give thanks, and sound thy praises upon the harp and timbrel. Yea! with the whole heart we will praise thee; for we know the tribulations and snares, the evil and folly and anguish, of this life below; and we know that not one child of Adam, coming to man's estate, is spared that bitter and woful cup that is pressed out from the fruit of the knowledge of good and evil, which our progenitors ate of in thy garden of Paradise, and thereby sinned and fell, and bequeathed to us their evil longings and habitual transgression.   They are the blessed who are taken away in their infancy, and lie forever by green pastures and still waters in the fields of heaven.   We ask of thee no greater or better gift for these lambs than early to be folded where none shall hurt or destroy in all thy holy mountain, and the love that is above all mother's love shall cradle them throughout eternity.   Amen!"

Not a mother in that congregation failed to shiver and tremble at this prayer, and tears fell fast and thick on the babes who slumbered softly in the tender arms that had gathered them home, after consecrating them to that God who yet they were so unwilling should literally accept their offering.   Fifty pairs of eyes were turned on Parson Tucker with the look of a bear robbed of its cubs; but far more were drowned in tears of memory and regret, poignant still, but strangely soothed by this vivid presentation of the blessedness wherein their loved and lost were safely abiding.

Much comment was exchanged in the church porch, after
service, on the parson's prayer.

"We ought to hold a special meeting to pray that the Lord
will not answer such a petition!" cried one indignant mother,
whose little flock were clinging about her skirts, and who had
left twin babies, yet unbaptized, at home.

"It *is* rather hard on you, aunty!" said the graceless Jack
Mason, the speaker's nephew, now transformed into an unprom-
ising young lawyer in Hartland. "You'd rather have your babies
sin and suffer with you than have 'em safe in their little graves,
hadn't you? I don't go with the parson myself. I didn't so
much mind his funeral gymnastic over old Baker, and his disposition of that party's soul in Hades, because I never before supposed Roosevelt Baker had a soul, and it was quite reassuring to
be certain he met with his dues somewhere; but he's worse than
Herod about the babies!"

However, the parson did not hear or know what was said of
him, and in an ignorance that was indeed bliss continued to
preach and minister to his people in strict accordance with his
own views of duty. His next essay was a pastoral visit to one
of his flock, recently a widow, a woman weak in body and mind
both; desirous above all things to be proper and like other
people, to weep where she must, smile when she ought, wear
clothes like the advance-guard of fashion, and do "the thing"
to be done always, whether it was the right and true thing
or not.

Her husband had spent all her fortune in speculation, taken
to drink as a refuge from folly and reproach at home, and
under the influence of the consoling fluid had turned his wife
out-of-doors whenever he felt in the mood; kicked her, beaten
her, and forced her, in fear of her life, over and over to steal
from her own house and take refuge with the neighbors, and
ask from them the food she was not allowed at home. At last
the end came. Parson Tucker was sent for to see the widow
and arrange for funeral services. She had not been present at
the Baker funeral, or indeed been in Deerford for some years
after that occasion, so she adhered to the conventions; and when
Parson Tucker reached the house he was shown into a darkened room, where the disconsolate woman sat posed already in
deep mourning, a widow's cap perched upon her small head.
A woman would have inferred at once that Mrs. Spring had

anticipated the end of Joe's last attack of *mania à potu*, and prepared these funeral garments beforehand; but Thomas Tucker drew no such conclusions. He sat down silently and grimly, after shaking hands with Mrs. Spring, and said nothing. She began the conversation: —

« This is a dreadful affliction, Mr. Tucker. I don't know how I shall live through it. »

« It is terrible, indeed, » said the parson. « I do not wonder, madam, that you mourn to see your partner cut off in his sins, without time for repentance; but no doubt you feel with gratitude the goodness which hath delivered you from so sore a burden. »

« What? » screamed the widow.

« I speak of God's mercy in removing from your house one who made your life a terror, and your days full of fear and suffering; you might have been as others, bereaved and desolate, and mourning to your life's end. »

« I don't know what you mean, Parson Tucker, » said Mrs. Spring sharply, removing a dry handkerchief from unwet eyes. « Poor dear Joseph is taken away from me, and I'm left a desolate widow, and you talk in this way! I'm sure he had the best of hearts that ever was; it was only, as you may say, accidental to him to be a little overcome at times, and I'm — I'm — o — h! »

Here she gave a little hysterical scream, and did some well-executed sobbing; but the parson did not mind it. He rose up before her, gaunt and gray. « Madam, did not this man beat, and abuse, and insult, and starve you, when he was living? Or have I been misinformed? »

« Well — oh dear, what dreadful questions! »

« Did he? » thundered the parson.

« He didn't mean to; he was excited, Mr. Tucker. He — »

« He was drunk. And is that excuse? Not so, madam. You know, and I know, that his death is a relief and a release to you. I cannot condole with you on that which is not a sorrow; » and he walked rigidly out of the door.

Is it necessary to say that Mr. Spring's funeral did not take place in Deerford? His widow suddenly remembered that he had been born in a small town among the hills of West Massachusetts, and she took his body thither, to be "laid beside his dear payrents," as she expressed it.

Things had now come to a bad pass for Parson Tucker. The church committee had held more than one conference over their duty toward him. It was obvious that they had no real reason for dismissing him but his ghastly honesty, and that hardly offers a decent excuse to depose a minister of the gospel. They hardly knew how to face the matter, and were in this state of perplexity when Mr. Tucker announced, one Sunday, after the sermon, that he would like to see the church committee at his study on Tuesday night; and accordingly they assembled there and found President Winthrop with the parson.

"Brethren," said Thomas Tucker, after the preliminary welcome had passed, "I have sent for you to-night to say, that having now been settled over your church eight years, I have found the salary you paid me so much more than was needed for my bodily support that I have laid by each year as the surplus came to hand, that I might restore to you your goods. The sum is now something over eight thousand dollars, and is placed to the credit of your chairman, in the First Deerford Bank." The committee stared at each other as if each one were trying to arouse himself from sleep. The chairman at last spoke: —

"But Mr. Tucker, this is unheard-of! The salary is yours; we do not desire to take it back; we can't do it."

"That which I have not earned, Brother Street, is not mine. I am a solitary man; my expenses are light. It must be as I said. Moreover, I have to say that I hereby withdraw from your pulpit, of necessity. I have dealt with our best physicians concerning a certain anguish of the breast which seizes me at times unawares, and they all concur that an evil disease lieth upon me. I have not much time to live, and I would fain withdraw from activities and duties that are external, and prepare for the day that is at hand."

The committee were pained as well as shocked. They felt guilty to think how they had plotted this very thing among themselves; and they felt too a certain awe and deep respect for this simple unworldly nature, this supernatural integrity. Mr. Street spoke again; his voice was husky: —

"If this is so, Mr. Tucker, we must of course accept your resignation; but my dear pastor, keep the money! You will need care and comforts, now this trouble has come on you. We can't take it back."

Parson Tucker looked at him with a grave sweet smile. "I thank you, brother, but I have a private store. My sister left her worldly goods to me, and there is enough and to spare for my short sojourn," he answered.

"But it isn't according to the fitness of things that we should take your salary back, Parson Tucker," put in bustling Mr. Taylor. "What upon earth should we do with it?"

"Friend," said the parson, "the eternal fitness of things is but the outcome of their eternal verity. I have not, as I said, earned that wage, and I must restore it: it is for you to decide what end it shall serve in the church."

A few more words passed between them, and then each wrung the parson's hand and left him, not all with unmoved hearts or dry eyes.

"I don't wonder he's going to die!" exclaimed Mr. Street, as the committee separated at a street corner. "He's altogether too honest to live!"

From that day Thomas Tucker sank quietly toward his grave. Friends swarmed about him, and if delicacies of food could have saved him, the dainty stores poured in upon him would have renewed his youth; but all was in vain.

President Winthrop sat by him one summer day, and seeing a sad gleam in his sunken eye, asked gently, "You are ready and willing to go, Brother Tucker?" nothing doubting a glad assent.

But the parson was honest to the last. "No," he said, "I do not want to die; I am afraid. I do not like strange and new things. I do not want to leave my books and my study."

"But, dear brother," broke in the astonished president, "it is a going home to your Father's house!"

"I know not what a home is, friend, in the sense of regret or longing for one. My early home was but as the egg to the bird, a prison wherein I was born, from which I fled; nor was my knowledge of a father one that commends itself as a type of good. I trust, indeed, that the Master will take me by the hand, even as he did Peter upon the water; but the utterance of my secret soul is even that of the apostle with the keys: 'Lord, save, or I perish!'"

"But you have been a power for good, and a close follower of Peter's Lord," said Mr. Winthrop, altogether at a loss for the proper thing to say to this peculiar man.

"One thing alone have I been enabled to do, Brother Winthrop, for which I can with heart and soul thank God, even at this hour. Yea, I thank him that I have been enabled to speak the truth even in the face of lies and deceptions, through his upholding." A smile of unearthly triumph filled every line of the wasted face, and lit his eyes with a flash of divine light as he said this. He grasped close the friendly hand he was holding, turned his cheek to the pillow, and closed his eyes, passing into that life of truth and love that awaited him, even as a child that lies down in the darkness, trembling, fearful, and weary, but awakes, in the dawn of a new day, in the heart of home.

"Still," said President Winthrop to his wife, as they walked home after the funeral, "I believe in the good old proverb, Eleanor, that 'the truth is not to be spoken at all times.'"

"And I never believed in it so little!" she cried, indignantly. "Think what a record he has left; what respect hangs about his memory! Do we know how many weak souls have relied on his example, and held to the truth when it was hard, because he did and could? It is something to be heroic in these days, even if it is unpopular!"

The president shrugged his shoulders.

From 'The Sphinx's Children and Other People's': copyrighted 1886, by Ticknor and Company

JAMES FENIMORE COOPER.

JAMES FENIMORE COOPER

(1789–1851)

BY JULIAN HAWTHORNE

ORE than a century ago, in the town of Burlington, New Jersey, was born a man destined to become one of the best known figures of his time. He was as devout an American as ever lived, for he could arraign the shortcomings of his countrymen as stanchly as he could defend and glorify their ideals. He entered fearlessly and passionately into the life around him, seeing intensely, yet sometimes blind; feeling ardently, yet not always aright; acting with might and conviction, yet not seldom amiss. He loved and revered good, scorned and hated evil, and with the strength and straightforwardness of a bull championed the one and gored the other. He worshiped justice, but lacked judgment; his brain, stubborn and logical, was incongruously mated with a deep and tender heart. A brave and burly backwoods gentleman was he, with a smattering of the humanities from Yale, and a dogged precision of principle and conduct from six years in the navy. He had the iron memory proper to a vigorous organization and a serious, observant mind; he was tirelessly industrious — in nine-and-twenty years he published thirty-two novels, many of them of prodigious length, besides producing much matter never brought to light. His birth fell at a noble period of our history, and his surroundings fostered true and generous manhood. Doubtless many of his contemporaries were as true men as he: but to Cooper in addition was vouchsafed the gift of genius; and that magic quality dominated and transfigured his else rugged and intractable nature, and made his name known and loved over all the earth. No author has been more widely read than he; no American author has won even a tithe of his honorable popularity.

Though Jersey may claim his birthplace, Cooper's childhood from his second to his fourteenth year was passed on the then frontiers of civilization, at Cooperstown on the Susquehanna. There in the primeval forest, hard by the broad Lake Otsego and the wide-flowing river, the old Judge built his house and laid out his town. Trees, mountains, wild animals, and wild men nursed the child, and implanted in him seeds of poetry and wrought into the sturdy fibres of his mind golden threads of creative imagination. Then round about the hearth at night, men of pith and character told tales of the Revolution, of battle, adventure, and endurance, which the child, hearing, fed upon with his soul, and grew strong in patriotism and independence. Nobility was innate in him; he conceived lofty and sweet ideals of human nature and conduct, and was never false to them thereafter. The ideal Man—the ideal Woman—he believed in them to the end. And more than twice or thrice in his fictions we find personages like Harvey Birch, Leatherstocking, Long Tom Coffin, the jailer's daughter in 'The Bravo,' and Mabel Dunham and Dew-of-June in 'The Pathfinder,' which give adequate embodiment to his exalted conception of the possibilities of his fellow creatures. For though portrayal of character in the ultra-refined modern sense of the term was impossible to Cooper, yet he perceived and could impressively present certain broad qualities of human nature, and combine them in consistent and memorable figures. Criticism may smile now and then, and psychology arch her eyebrows, but the figures live, and bid fair to be lusty long after present fashions have been forgotten.

But of the making of books, Cooper, during the first three decades of his life, had no thought at all. He looked forward to a career of action; and after Yale College had given him a glimpse of the range of knowledge, he joined a vessel as midshipman, with the prospect of an admiral's cocked hat and glory in the distance. The glory, however, with which the ocean was to crown him, was destined to be gained through the pen and not the sword, when at the age of five-and-thirty he should have published 'The Pilot.' As a naval officer, he might have helped to whip the English in the War of 1812; but as author of the best sea story in the language he conquered all the world of readers unaided. Meanwhile, when he was twenty-one years old he married a Miss Delancey, whose goodness (according to one of his biographers) was no less eminent than his genius, and who died but a short time before him. The joys of wedded life in a home of his own outweighed with him the chances of warlike distinction, and he resigned his commission and took command of a farm in Westchester County; and a gentleman farmer, either there or at his boyhood's home in Cooperstown, he remained till the end, with the exception of his seven-years' sojourn in Europe.

His was a bodily frame built to endure a hundred years, and the robustness of his intelligence and the vivacity of his feelings would have kept him young throughout; yet he died of a dropsy, at the prime of his powers, in 1851, heartily mourned by innumerable friends, and having already outlived all his enmities. He died, too, the unquestioned chief of American novelists; and however superior to his may have been the genius of his contemporary Walter Scott, the latter can hardly be said to have rivaled him in breadth of dominion over readers of all nationalities. Cooper was a household name from New York to Ispahan, from St. Petersburg to Rio Janeiro; and the copyright on his works in various languages would to-day amount to a large fortune every year. Three generations have passed since with 'The Spy' he won the sympathies of mankind; and he holds them still. It is an enviable record. And although in respect of actual quality of work produced there have been many geniuses greater than he, yet it is fair to remember that Cooper's genius had a great deal of stubborn raw material to subdue before it could proceed to produce anything. It started handicapped. As it was, the man wasted years of time and an immensity of effort in doing, or trying to do, things he had no business with. He would be a political reformer, a critic of society, an interpreter of law, even a master grammarian. He would fight to the finish all who differed from him in opinion; he fought and — incredible as it may seem — he actually conquered the American press. He published reams of stuff which no one now reads and which was never worth reading, to enforce his views and prove that he was right and others wrong. All this power was misdirected; it might have been applied to producing more and better Leatherstockings and Pilots. Perhaps he hardly appreciated at its value that one immortal thing about him, — his genius, — and was too much concerned about his dogmatic and bull-headed Self. Unless the world confessed his infallibility, he could not be quite at peace with it. Such an attitude arouses one's sense of humor; it would never have existed had Cooper possessed a spark of humor himself. But he was uncompromisingly serious on all subjects, or if at times he tried to be playful, we shudder and avert our faces. It is too like Juggernaut dancing a jig. And he gave too much weight to the verdict of the moment, and not enough to that judgment of posterity to which the great Verulam was content to submit his fame. Who cares to-day, or how are we the better or the worse, if Cooper were right or wrong in his various convictions? What concerns us is that he wrote delightful stories of the forest and the sea; it is in those stories, and not in his controversial or didactic homilies, that we choose to discover his faith in good and ire against evil. Cooper, in short, had his limitations; but with all his errors, we may take him and be thankful.

Moreover, his essential largeness appears in the fact that in the midst of his bitterest conflicts, at the very moment when his pamphlets and "satires" were heating the printing-presses and people's tempers, a novel of his would be issued, redolent with pure and serene imagination, telling of the prairies and the woods, of deer and panther, of noble redskins and heroic trappers. It is another world, harmonious and calm; no echo of the petty tumults in which its author seemed to live is audible therein. But it is a world of that author's imagination, and its existence proves that he was greater and wiser than the man of troubles and grievances who so noisily solicits our attention. The surface truculence which fought and wrangled was distinct from the interior energy which created and harmonized, and acted perhaps as the safety-valve to relieve the inward region from disturbance.

The anecdote of how Cooper happened to adopt literature as a calling is somewhat musty, and its only significant feature is the characteristic self-confidence of his exclamation, on laying down a stupid English novel which he had been reading to his wife, « I could write as well as that myself!» Also in point is the fact that the thing he wrote, 'Precaution,' is a story of English life, whereof at that time he had had no personal experience. One would like to know the name of the novel which touched him off; if it was stupider and more turgid than 'Precaution' it must have been a curiosity. Cooper may have thought otherwise, or he may have been stimulated by recognition of his failure, as a good warrior by the discovery that his adversary is a more redoubtable fighter than he had gauged him to be. At all events, he lost no time in engaging once more, and this time he routed his foe, horse and foot. One is reminded of the exclamation of his own Paul Jones, when requested to surrender — «I haven't begun to fight!» 'The Spy' is not a perfect work of art, but it is a story of adventure and character such as the world loves and will never tire of. 'Precaution' had showed not even talent; 'The Spy' revealed unquestionable genius. This is not to say that its merit was actually unquestioned at the time it came out; our native critics hesitated to commit themselves, and awaited English verdicts. But the nation's criticism was to buy the book and read it, and they and other nations have been so doing ever since. Nothing in literature lasts longer, or may be oftener re-read with pleasure, than a good tale of adventure. The incidents are so many and the complications so ingenious that one forgets the detail after a few years, and comes to the perusal with fresh appetite. Cooper's best books are epics, possessing an almost Homeric vitality. The hero is what the reader would like to be, and the latter thrills with his perils and triumphs in his success. Ulysses is Mankind, making sweet uses of adversity, and regenerate at last; and Harvey Birch, Leatherstocking, and the rest are congenial types of Man, acting up to high standards in given circumstances.

But oh! the remorseless tracts of verbiage in these books, the long toiling through endless preliminaries, as of a too unwieldy army marching and marshaling for battle! It is Cooper's way; he must

warm to his work gradually, or his strength cannot declare itself.
His beginnings abound in seemingly profitless detail, as if he must
needs plot his every footstep on the map ere trusting himself to take
the next. Balzac's method is similar, but possesses a spiritual charm
lacking in the American's. The modern ability of Stevenson and
Kipling to plunge into the thick of it in the first paragraph was
impossible to this ponderous pioneer. Yet when at length he does
begin to move, the impetus and majesty of his advance are tremendous; as in the avalanche, every added particular of passive preparation adds weight and power to the final action. Cooper teaches
us, Wellington-like, "what long-enduring hearts can do!" Doubtless,
therefore, any attempt to improve him by blue-penciling his tediousness would result in spoiling him altogether. We must accept him
as he is. Dullness past furnishes fire to present excitement. It is a
mistake to "skip" in reading Cooper; if we have not leisure to read
him as he stands, let us wait until we have.

'Precaution' and 'The Spy' both appeared in 1821, when the
author was about thirty-two years old. Two years passed before the
production of 'The Pioneers,' wherein Cooper draws upon memory
no less than upon imagination, and in which Leatherstocking first
makes our acquaintance. As a rule (proved by exceptions), the best
novels of great novelists have their scene in surroundings with which
the writer's boyhood was familiar. 'The Pioneers' and the ensuing
series of Leatherstocking tales are placed in the neighborhood of the
lake and river which Cooper, as a child, had so lovingly learned by
heart. Time had supplied the requisite atmosphere for the pictures
that he drew, while the accuracy of his memory and the minuteness
of his observation assured ample realism. In the course of the narrative the whole mode of life of a frontier settlement from season to
season appears before us, and the typical figures which constitute it.
It is history, illuminated by romance and uplifted by poetic imagination. One of our greatest poets, speaking after the second-thought
of thirty years, declared Cooper to be a greater poet than Hesiod or
Theocritus. But between a poet and a prose-writer capable of poetic
feeling there is perhaps both a distinction and a difference.

The birth-year of the 'Pioneers' and of the 'Pilot' are again the
same. Now Cooper leaves, for the time, the backwoods, and em-
barks upon the sea. He is as great upon one element as upon the
other: of whom else can that be affirmed? We might adapt the
apophthegm on Washington to him: he was "first on land, first
on sea, and first in the hearts of his readers." In 'The Pilot' the
resources of the writer's invention first appear in full development.
His personal experience of the vicissitudes and perils of a seaman's
life stood him in good stead here, and may indeed have served him

well in the construction of all his fictions.   Fertility in incident and
the element of suspense are valuable parts of a story-teller's outfit,
and Cooper excelled in both; he might have been less adequately
furnished in these respects had he never served on a man-of-war.
Be that as it may, 'The Pilot' is generally accepted as the best sea
story ever written.   Herman Melville and his disciple Clark Russell
have both written lovingly and thrillingly of the sea and seamen,
but neither of them has rivaled their common original.   Long Tom
Coffin is the peer of Leatherstocking himself, and might have been
made the central figure of as many and as excellent tales.   The
three books—'The Spy,' 'The Pioneers,' and 'The Pilot'—form a
trilogy of itself more than sufficient to support a mighty reputation;
and they were all written before Cooper was thirty-five years old.
Indeed, his subsequent works did not importantly add to his fame;
and many of them of course might better never have been written.
'Lionel Lincoln,' in 1825, fell far short of the level of the previous
romances; but 'The Last of the Mohicans,' in the year following, is
again as good as the best, and the great figure of Leatherstocking
even gains in solidity and charm.   As a structure, the story is easily
criticized, but the texture is so sound and the spirit so stirring that
only the cooler after-thought finds fault.   Faults which would shipwreck a lesser man leave this leviathan almost unscathed.

At this juncture occurred the unfortunate episode in Cooper's
career.   His fame having spread over two continents, he felt a
natural desire to visit the scene of his foreign empire and make
acquaintance with his subjects there; it seemed an act of expedi-
ency too to get local color for romances which should appeal more
directly to these friends across the sea.   Upon these pretexts he set
forth, and in due season arrived in Paris.   Here however he chanced
to read a newspaper criticism of the United States government;
and true to his conviction that he was the heaven-appointed agent
to correct and castigate the world, he sat down and wrote a sharp
rejoinder.   He was well furnished with facts, and he exhibited
plenty of acumen in his statement of them; though his cumbrous and
pompous style, as of a schoolmaster laying down the law, was not
calculated to fascinate the lectured ones.   In the controversy which
ensued he found himself arrayed against the aristocratic party,
with only the aged Lafayette to afford him moral support; his arguments were not refuted, but this rendered him only the more
obnoxious to his hosts, who finally informed him that his room was
more desirable than his company.   As a Parthian shaft, our redoubtable champion launched a missile in the shape of a romance of
ancient Venice ('The Bravo'), in which he showed how the perversion of institutions devised to insure freedom, inevitably brings to

pass freedom's opposite. It is a capital novel, worthy of Cooper's fame; but it neither convinced nor pleased the effete monarchists whom it arraigned. In the end accordingly he returned home, with the consciousness of having vindicated his countrymen, but of having antagonized all Europe in the process. It may be possible to win the affection of a people while proving to them that they are fools and worse; but if so, Cooper was not the man to accomplish the feat. It should be premised here that during his residence abroad he had written, in addition to 'The Bravo,' three novels which may be placed among his better works; and one, 'The Wept of Wish-ton-Wish,' whose lovely title is its only recommendation. 'The Red Rover' was by some held to be superior even to 'The Pilot'; and 'Heidenhauer' and 'The Headsman of Berne' attempt, not with entire success, to repeat the excellence of 'The Bravo.' He had also published a volume of letters critical of national features, entitled 'Notions of the Americans,' which may have flattered his countrymen's susceptibilities, but did nothing to assuage the wounded feelings of those with whom he contrasted them.

Now, when a warrior returns home after having manfully supported his country's cause against odds, and at the cost of his own popularity, he feels justified in anticipating a cordial reception. What then must be his feelings on finding himself actually given the cold shoulder by those he had defended, on the plea that his defense was impolitic and discourteous? In such circumstances there is one course which no wise man will pursue, and that is to treat his aspersers with anything else than silent disdain. Cooper was far from being thus wise: he lectured his fellow-citizens with quite as much asperity as he had erewhile lectured the tyrants of the Old World; with as much justice too, and with an effect even more embroiling. In 'A Letter to his Countrymen,' 'Monikins,' 'Homeward Bound,' and 'Home as Found,' he admonished and satirized them with characteristic vigor. The last-named of these books brings us to the year 1838, and of Cooper's life the fiftieth. He seemed in a fair way to become a universal Ishmael. Yet once more he had only begun to fight. In 1838 he commenced action against a New York newspaper for slander, and for five years thereafter the courts of his country resounded with the cries and thwackings of the combatants. But Cooper could find no adversary really worthy of his steel, and in 1843 he was able to write to a friend, "I have beaten every man I have sued who has not retracted his libels!" He had beaten them fairly, and one fancies that even he must at last have become weary of his favorite passion of proving himself in the right. Howbeit, peace was declared over the corpse of the last of his opponents, and the victor in so many fields could now apply himself undisturbedly to the vocations from which war had partially distracted him,— only partially, for in 1840, in the heat of the newspaper fray, he astonished the public by producing one of the loveliest of his romances and perhaps the very best of the Leatherstocking series, 'The Pathfinder.' William Cullen Bryant holds this to be "a glorious work," and speaks of its moral beauty, the vividness and force of its delineations, and the unspoiled love of nature and fresh and warm emotions which give life to the narrative and dialogue. Yet Cooper was at that time over fifty years of age.

Nevertheless, so far as his abilities both mental and physical were concerned, the mighty man was still in the prime of his manhood, if not of his youth. During the seven or eight years yet to elapse, after the close of his slander suits in 1843, before his unexpected death in 1851, he wrote not less than twelve new novels, several of them touching the high-water mark of his genius. Of them may be specially mentioned 'Two Admirals' and 'Wing-and-Wing,' 'Wyandotte,' and 'Jack Tier.' Besides all this long list of his works, he published 'Sketches of Switzerland' in 1836; 'Gleanings in Europe,' in a series of eight volumes, beginning 1837; a 'Naval History of the United States' in two octavo volumes; and wrote three or four other books which seem to have remained in manuscript. Altogether it was a gigantic life-work, worthy of the giant who achieved it.

Cooper was hated as well as loved during his lifetime, but at his death the love had quenched the hate, and there are none but lovers of him now. He was manly, sincere, sensitive, independent; rough without but sweet within. He sought the good of others, he devoutly believed in God, and if he was always ready to take his own part in a fight, he never forgot his own self-respect or forfeited other men's. But above all he was a great novelist, original and irresistible. America has produced no other man built on a scale so continental.

Julian Hawthorne

THE PRIVATEER

From 'The Water-Witch'

THE exploits, the mysterious character, and the daring of the Water-Witch and of him who sailed her, were in that day the frequent subjects of anger, admiration, and surprise. Those who found pleasure in the marvelous listened to the wonders that were recounted of her speed and boldness with pleasure; they who had been so often foiled in their attempts to arrest the hardy dealers in contraband reddened at her name; and all wondered at the success and intelligence with which her movements were controlled. It will therefore create no astonishment when we say that Ludlow and the patroon drew near to the light and graceful fabric with an interest that deepened at each stroke of the oars. So much of a profession which, in that age, was particularly marked and apart from the rest of mankind in habits and opinions, had been interwoven into the character of the former, that he could not see the just proportions, the graceful outlines of the hull, or the exquisite symmetry and neatness of the spars and rigging, without experiencing a feeling somewhat allied to that which undeniable superiority excites in the heart of even a rival. There was also a taste in the style of the merely ornamental parts of the delicate machine, which caused as much surprise as her model and rig.

Seamen, in all ages and in every state of their art, have been ambitious of bestowing on their floating habitations a style of decoration which while appropriate to their element, should be thought somewhat analogous to the architectural ornaments of the land. Piety, superstition, and national usages affect these characteristic ornaments, which are still seen, in different quarters of the world, to occasion broad distinctions between the appearances of vessels. In one, the rudder-head is carved with the resemblance of some hideous monster; another shows goggling eyes and lolling tongues from its cat-heads; this has the patron saint, or the ever-kind Marie, embossed upon its moldings or bows; while that is covered with the allegorical emblems of country and duty. Few of these efforts of nautical art are successful, though a better taste appears to be gradually redeeming even this branch of human industry from the rubbish of barbarism, and to be elevating it to a state which shall do no violence to the more fastidious opinions of the age. But the vessel of which we write, though constructed at so remote a period, would have done credit to the improvements of our own time.

It has been said that the hull of this celebrated smuggler was low, dark, molded with exquisite art, and so justly balanced as to ride upon its element like a sea-fowl. For a little distance above the water it showed a blue that vied with the color of the deep ocean, the use of copper being then unknown; while the more superior parts were of a jet black delicately relieved by two lines of a straw color, that were drawn with mathematical accuracy, paralleled to the plane of her upper works, and consequently converging slightly toward the sea beneath her counter. Glossy hammock-cloths concealed the persons of those who were on the deck, while the close bulwarks gave the brigantine the air of a vessel equipped for war. Still the eye of Ludlow ran curiously along the whole extent of the two straw-colored lines, seeking in vain some evidence of the weight and force of her armament. If she had ports at all, they were so ingeniously concealed as to escape the keenest of his glances. The nature of the rig has been already described. Partaking of the double character of brig and schooner, the sails and spars of the forward-mast being of the former, while those of the after-mast were of the latter construction, seamen have given to this class of shipping the familiar name of hermaphrodites. But though there might be fancied, by this term, some want of the proportions that constitute seemliness, it will be remembered that the departure was only from some former rule of art, and that no violence had been done to those universal and permanent laws which constitute the charm of nature. The models of glass which are seen representing the machinery of a ship, are not more exact or just in their lines than were the cordage and spars of this brigantine. Not a rope varied from its true direction; not a sail but it resembled the neat folds of some prudent housewife; not a mast or a yard was there but it rose into the air, or stretched its arms, with the most fastidious attention to symmetry. All was airy, fanciful, and full of grace, seeming to lend to the fabric a character of unreal lightness and speed. As the boat drew near her side, a change of the air caused the buoyant bark to turn like a vane in its current; and as all the long and pointed proportions of her head-gear came into view,

Ludlow saw beneath the bowsprit an image that might be supposed to make, by means of allegory, some obvious allusions to
the character of the vessel. A female form, fashioned with the
carver's best skill, stood on the projection of the cutwater. The
figure rested lightly on the ball of one foot, while the other was
suspended in an easy attitude resembling the airy posture of the
famous Mercury of the Bolognese. The drapery was fluttering,
scanty, and of a light sea-green tint, as if it had imbibed a hue
from the element beneath. The face was of that dark bronzed
color which human ingenuity has from time immemorial adopted
as the best medium to portray a superhuman expression. The
locks were disheveled, wild, and rich; the eye full of such a
meaning as might be fancied to glitter in the organs of a sorceress; while a smile so strangely meaning and malign played
about the mouth, that the young sailor started when it first met
his view, as if a living thing had returned his look.

"Witchcraft and necromancy!" grumbled the alderman, as this
extraordinary image came suddenly on his vision also. "Here
is a brazen-looking hussy! and one who might rob the queen's
treasury itself, without remorse! Your eyes are young, patroon:
what is that the minx holds so impudently above her head?"

"It seems an open book, with letters of red written on its
pages. One need not be a conjurer to divine it is no extract
from the Bible."

"Nor from the statute books of Queen Anne. I warrant me
'tis a ledger of profit gained in her many wanderings. Goggling
and leers! the bold air of the confident creature is enough to put
an honest man out of countenance!"

"Wilt read the motto of the witch?" demanded he of the
India shawl, whose eye had been studying the detail of the brigantine's equipment, rather than attending to the object which so
much attracted the looks of his companions. "The night air has
tautened the cordage of that flying jib-boom, fellows, until it
begins to lift its nose like a squeamish cockney when he holds
it over salt water! See to it, and bring the spar in line; else
we shall have a reproof from the sorceress, who little likes to
have any of her limbs deranged. Here, gentlemen, the opinions
of the lady may be read as clearly as a woman's mind can ever
be fathomed."

While speaking to his crew, Tiller had changed the direction
of the boat; and it was soon lying, in obedience to a motion of

his hand, directly beneath the wild and significant-looking image just described. The letters in red were now distinctly visible; and when Alderman Van Beverout had adjusted his spectacles, each of the party read the following sentence:—

> "Albeit I never lend nor borrow,
> By taking, nor by giving of excess,
> Yet to supply the ripe wants of my friend,
> I'll break a custom."— 'MERCHANT OF VENICE.'

"The brazen!" exclaimed Myndert, when he had gone through this quotation from the immortal bard. "Ripe or green, one could not wish to be the friend of so impudent a thing; and then to impute such sentiments to any respectable commercial man, whether of Venice or Amsterdam! Let us board the brigantine, friend mariner, and end the connection ere foul mouths begin to traduce our motives for the visit."

"The overdriven ship plows the seas too deep for speed; we shall get into port in better season without this haste. Wilt take another look into the lady's pages? A woman's mind is never known at the first answer."

The speaker raised the rattan he still carried, and caused a page of painted metal to turn on hinges that were so artfully concealed as not to be visible. A new surface, with another extract, was seen.

"What is it, what is it, patroon?" demanded the burgher, who appeared greatly to distrust the discretion of the sorceress. "Follies and rhymes! but this is the way of the whole sex; when nature has denied them tongues, they invent other means of speech."

> "Porters of the sea and land
> Thus do go about, about;
> Thrice to thine, and thrice to thine;
> And thrice again to make up nine."

"Rank nonsense!" continued the burgher. "It is well for those who can, to add thrice and thrice to their stores; but look you, patroon — it is a thriving trade that can double the value of the adventure, and that with reasonable risks and months of patient watching."

"We have other pages," resumed Tiller, "but our affairs drag for want of attending to them. One may read much good matter

in the book of the sorceress, when there is leisure and opportunity. I often take occasion, in the calms, to look into her
volume; and it is rare to find the same moral twice told, as these
brave seamen can swear." . . .

If the exterior of the brigantine was so graceful in form and
so singular in arrangement, the interior was still more worthy of
observation. There were two small cabins beneath the main
deck, one on each side of, and immediately adjoining, the limited
space that was destined to receive her light but valuable cargoes.
It was into one of these that Tiller had descended like a man
who freely entered into his own apartment; but partly above and
nearer to the stern was a suite of little rooms that were fitted
and finished in a style altogether different. The equipments were
those of a yacht, rather than those which might be supposed
suited to the pleasures of even the most successful dealer in
contraband.

The principal deck had been sunk several feet, commencing
at the aftermost bulkhead of the cabins of the subordinate officers, in a manner to give the necessary height, without interfering with the line of the brigantine's shear. The arrangement
was consequently not to be seen by an observer who was not
admitted into the vessel itself. A descent of a step or two,
however, brought the visitors to the level of the cabin floor,
and into an ante-room that was evidently fitted for the convenience of the domestic. A small silver hand-bell lay on a table,
and Tiller rang it lightly, like one whose ordinary manner was
restrained by respect. It was answered by the appearance of a
boy, whose years could not exceed ten, and whose attire was so
whimsical as to merit description.

The material of the dress of this young servitor of Neptune
was a light rose-colored silk, cut in a fashion to resemble the
habits formerly worn by pages of the great. His body was
belted by a band of gold, a collar of fine thread lace floated on
his neck and shoulders, and even his feet were clad in a sort
of buskins, that were ornamented with fringes of real lace and
tassels of bullion. The form and features of the child were
delicate, and his air as unlike as possible to the coarse and
brusque manner of a vulgar ship-boy.

"Waste and prodigality!" muttered the alderman, when this
extraordinary little usher presented himself in answer to the
summons of Tiller. "This is the very wantonness of cheap

goods and an unfettered commerce! There is enough of Mech-
lin, patroon, on the shoulders of that urchin, to deck the
stomacher of the Queen. 'Fore George, goods were cheap in the
market when the young scoundrel had his livery!»

The surprise was not confined, however, to the observant and
frugal burgher. Ludlow and Van Staats of Kinderhook manifested equal amazement, though their wonder was exhibited in a
less characteristic manner. The former turned short to demand
the meaning of this masquerade, when he perceived that the hero
of the India shawl had disappeared. They were then alone with
the fantastic page, and it became necessary to trust to his
intelligence for directions how to proceed.

«Who art thou, child? — and who has sent thee hither?»
demanded Ludlow. The boy raised a cap of the same rose-
colored silk, and pointed to an image of a female, with a swarthy
face and a malign smile, painted with exceeding art on its
front.

«I serve the sea-green lady, with the others of the brigantine.»

«And who is this lady of the color of shallow water, and
whence come you in particular?»

«This is her likeness: if you would speak with her, she
stands on the cutwater, and rarely refuses an answer.»

«'Tis odd that a form of wood should have the gift of
speech!»

«Dost think her, then, of wood?» returned the child, looking
timidly and yet curiously up into the face of Ludlow. «Others
have said the same; but those who know best, deny it. She
does not answer with a tongue, but the book has always something to say.»

«Here is a grievous deception practiced on the superstition
of this boy: I have read the book, and can make but little of its
meaning.»

«Then read again. 'Tis by many reaches that the leeward
vessel gains upon the wind. My master has bid me bring you
in —»

«Hold — thou hast both master and mistress? You have told
us the latter, but we would know something of the former. Who
is thy master?»

The boy smiled and looked aside, as if he hesitated to
answer.

"Nay, refuse not to reply. I come with the authority of the Queen."

"He tells us that the sea-green lady is our queen, and that we have no other."

"Rashness and rebellion!" muttered Myndert; "but this fool-hardiness will one day bring as pretty a brigantine as ever sailed in the narrow seas to condemnation; and then will there be rumors abroad, and characters cracked, till every lover of gossip in the Americas shall be tired of defamation."

"It is a bold subject that dares say this!" rejoined Ludlow, who heeded not the by-play of the alderman: "your master has a name?"

"We never hear it. When Neptune boards us, under the tropics, he always hails the Skimmer of the Seas, and then they answer. The old god knows us well, for we pass his latitude oftener than other ships, they say."

"You are then a cruiser of some service in the brigantine? no doubt you have trod many distant shores, belonging to so swift a craft?"

"I!—I never was on the land!" returned the boy, thought-fully. "It must be droll to be there: they say one can hardly walk, it is so steady! I put a question to the sea-green lady before we came to the narrow inlet, to know when I was to go ashore."

"And she answered?"

"It was some time first. Two watches were passed before a word was to be seen; at last I got the lines. I believe she mocked me, though I have never dared show it to my master, that he might say."

"Hast the words here?—perhaps we might assist thee, as there are some among us who know most of the sea paths."

The boy looked timidly and suspiciously round; then thrusting a hand hurriedly into a pocket, he drew forth two bits of paper, each of which contained a scrawl, and both of which had evidently been much thumbed and studied.

"Here," he said, in a voice that was suppressed nearly to a whisper. "This was on the first page. I was so frightened lest the lady should be angry, that I did not look again till the next watch; and then," turning the leaf, "I found this."

Ludlow took the bit of paper first offered, and read, written in a child's hand, the following extract:—

> "I pray thee
> Remember, I have done thee worthy service;
> Told thee no lies, made no mistakings, served
> Without or grudge or grumblings."

"I thought that 'twas in mockery," continued the boy, when he saw by the eye of the young captain that he had read the quotation; "for 'twas very like, though more prettily worded than that which I had said myself!"

"And what was the second answer?"

"This was found in the first morning watch," the child returned, reading the second extract himself:—

> "'Thou think'st
> It much to tread the ooze of the salt deep,
> And run upon the sharp wind of the north!'

"I never dared to ask again. But what matters that? They say the ground is rough and difficult to walk on; that earthquakes shake it, and make holes to swallow cities; that men slay each other on the highways for money, and that the houses I see on the hills must always remain in the same spot. It must be very melancholy to live always in the same spot; but then it must be odd never to feel a motion—"

"Except the occasional rocking of an earthquake. Thou art better afloat, child—but thy master, the Skimmer of the Seas—"

"Hist!" whispered the boy, raising a finger for silence. "He has come up into the great cabin. In a moment we shall have his signal to enter."

A few light touches on the strings of a guitar followed, and then a symphony was rapidly and beautifully executed by one in the adjoining apartment.

"Alida herself is not more nimble-fingered," whispered the alderman; "and I never heard the girl touch the Dutch lute that cost a hundred Holland guilders, with a livelier movement!"

Ludlow signed for silence. A fine manly voice, of great richness and depth, was soon heard, singing to an accompaniment on the same instrument. The air was grave, and altogether unusual for the social character of one who dwelt upon the ocean, being chiefly in recitation. The words, as near as might be distinguished, ran as follows:—

lighted with a smile that seemed to betray melancholy no less than courtesy. At the same time he raised his cap, and stood in the rich jet-black locks with which nature had so exuberantly shaded his forehead.

The manner of the visitors was less easy. The deep anxiety with which both Ludlow and the patroon had undertaken to board the notorious smuggler had given place to an amazement and a curiosity that caused them nearly to forget their errand; while Alderman Van Beverout appeared shy and suspicious, manifestly thinking less of his niece than of the consequences of so remarkable an interview. They all returned the salutation of their host, though each waited for him to speak.

THE BRIGANTINE'S ESCAPE THROUGH HELL–GATE

From ‹ The Water-Witch ›

AT such moments of intense anxiety, the human mind is wont to seek support in the opinions of others. Notwithstanding the increasing velocity and the critical condition of his own vessel, Ludlow cast a glance in order to ascertain the determination of the "Skimmer of the Seas." Blackwell's was already behind them, and as the two currents were again united, the brigantine had luffed up into the entrance of the dangerous passage, and now followed within two hundred feet of the Coquette, directly in her wake. The bold and manly-looking mariner who controlled her stood between the knight-heads, just above the image of his pretended mistress, where he examined the foaming reefs, the whirling eddies, and the varying currents, with folded arms and a riveted eye. A glance was exchanged between the two officers, and the free-trader raised his sea-cap. Ludlow was too courteous not to return the salutation; then all his senses were engrossed by the care of his ship. A rock lay before them, over which the water broke in a loud and unceasing roar. For an instant it seemed that the vessel could not avoid the danger; then it was already past.

"Brace up!" said Ludlow, in the calm tones that denote a forced tranquillity.

"Luff!" called out the Skimmer, so quickly as to show that he took the movements of the cruiser for his guide. The ship came closer to the wind, but the sudden bend in the stream no longer permitted her to steer in a direct line with its course. Though drifting to windward with vast rapidity, her way through the water, which was greatly increased by the contrary actions of the wind and tide, caused the cruiser to shoot across the current; while a reef, over which the water madly tumbled, lay immediately in her course. The danger seemed too imminent for the observances of nautical etiquette, and Trysail called aloud that the ship must be thrown aback, or she was lost.

"Hard-a-lee!" shouted Ludlow, in the strong voice of authority. "Up with everything — tacks and sheets! — main-top-sail haul!"

The ship seemed as conscious of her danger as any on her decks. The bows whirled away from the foaming reef, and as the sails caught the breeze on their opposite surfaces, they aided in bringing her head in the contrary direction. A minute had scarcely passed ere she was aback, and in the next she was about and full again. The intensity of the brief exertion kept Trysail fully employed; but no sooner had he leisure to look ahead than he again called aloud: —

"Here is another roarer under her bows. Luff, sir, luff, or we are upon it!"

"Hard down your helm!" once again came in deep tones from Ludlow. "Let fly your sheets — throw all aback, forward and aft — away with the yards, with a will, men!"

There was need for all of these precautions. Though the ship had so happily escaped the dangers of the first reef, a turbulent and roaring caldron in the water which as representing the element in ebullition is called "the Pot," lay so directly before her as to render the danger apparently inevitable. But the power of the canvas was not lost on this trying occasion. The forward motion of the ship diminished, and as the current still swept her swiftly to windward, her bows did not enter the rolling waters until the hidden rocks which caused the commotion had been passed. The yielding vessel rose and fell in the agitated water, as if in homage to the whirlpool; but the deep keel was unharmed.

"If the ship shoot ahead twice her length more, her bows will touch the eddy," exclaimed the vigilant master.

Ludlow looked around him for a single moment in indecision. The waters were whirling and roaring on every side, and the sails began to lose their power as the ship drew near the bluff which forms the second angle in this critical pass. He saw by objects on the land that he still approached the shore, and he had recourse to the seaman's last expedient.

"Let go both anchors!" was the final order.

The fall of the massive iron into the water was succeeded by the rumbling of the cable. The first effort to check the progress of the vessel appeared to threaten dissolution to the whole fabric, which trembled under the shock from its mastheads to the keel. But the enormous rope again yielded, and smoke was seen rising round the wood which held it. The ship whirled with the sudden check, and sheered wildly in toward the shore. Met by the helm, and again checked by the efforts of the crew, she threatened to defy restraint. There was an instant when all on board expected to hear the cable snap; but the upper sails filled, and as the wind was now brought over the taffrail, the force of the current was in a great degree met by that of the breeze.

The ship answered her helm and became stationary, while the water foamed against her cutwater as if she were driven ahead with the power of a brisk breeze.

The time from the moment when the Coquette entered the Gate to that when she anchored below "the Pot," though the distance was nearly a mile, seemed but a minute. Certain however that his ship was now checked, the thoughts of Ludlow returned to their other duties with the quickness of lightning.

"Clear away the grapnels," he eagerly cried; "stand by to heave, and haul in!—heave!"

But that the reader may better comprehend the motive of this sudden order, he must consent to return to the entrance of the dangerous passage, and accompany the Water-Witch also in her hazardous experiment to get through without a pilot.

The abortive attempt of the brigantine to stem the tide at the western end of Blackwell's will be remembered. It had no other effect than to place her pursuer more in advance, and to convince her own commander that he had now no other resource than to continue his course; for had he anchored, boats would have insured his capture. When the two vessels appeared off the eastern end of the island, the Coquette was ahead — a fact that the experienced free-trader did not at all regret. He profited by the circumstance to follow her movements, and to make a favorable entrance into the uncertain currents. To him, Hell-Gate was known only by its fearful reputation among mariners; and unless he might avail himself of the presence of the cruiser, he had no other guide than his own general knowledge of the power of the element.

When the Coquette had tacked, the calm and observant Skimmer was satisfied with throwing his head-sails flat to the mast. From that instant the brigantine lay floating in the current, neither advancing nor receding a foot, and always keeping her position at a safe distance from the ship, that was so adroitly made to answer the purposes of a beacon. The sails were watched with the closest care; and so nicely was the delicate machine tended, that it would have been at any moment in her people's power to have lessened her way by turning to the stream. The Coquette was followed till she anchored, and the call on board the cruiser to heave the grapnels had been given, because the brigantine was apparently floating directly down on her broadside.

When the grapnels were hove from the royal cruiser, the free-trader stood on the low poop of his little vessel, within fifty feet of him who had issued the order. There was a smile of indifference on his firm mouth, while he silently waved a hand to his own crew. The signal was obeyed by bracing round their yards, and suffering all the canvas to fill. The brigantine shot quickly ahead, and the useless irons fell heavily into the water.

"Many thanks for your pilotage, Captain Ludlow!" cried the daring and successful mariner of the shawl, as his vessel, borne on by wind and current, receded rapidly from the cruiser. "You will find me off Montauk; for affairs still keep us on the coast. Our lady has however put on the blue mantle, and ere many settings of the sun we shall look for deep water. Take good care of her Majesty's ship, I pray thee, for she has neither a more beautiful nor a faster."

One thought succeeded another with the tumult of a torrent in the mind of Ludlow. As the brigantine lay directly under his broadside, the first impulse was to use his guns; at the next moment he was conscious that before they could be cleared, distance would render them useless. His lips had nearly parted with intent to order the cables cut, but he remembered the speed of the brigantine, and hesitated. A sudden freshening of the breeze decided his course. Finding that the ship was enabled to keep her station, he ordered the crew to thrust the whole of the enormous ropes through the hawse-holes; and freed from the restraint, he abandoned the anchors until an opportunity to reclaim them should offer.

The operation of slipping the cables consumed several minutes; and when the Coquette, with everything set, was again steering in pursuit, the Water-Witch was already beyond the reach of her guns. Both vessels however held on their way, keeping as near as possible to the centre of the stream, and trusting more to fortune than to any knowledge of the channel for safety.

When passing the two small islands that lie at no great distance from the Gate, a boat was seen moving toward the royal cruiser. A man in it pointed to the signal, which was still flying, and offered his services.

"Tell me," demanded Ludlow eagerly, "has yonder brigantine taken a pilot?"

"By her movements, I judge not. She brushed the sunken rock off the mouth of Flushing Bay; and as she passed, I heard the song of the lead. I should have gone on board myself, but the fellow rather flies than sails; and as for signals, he seems to mind none but his own!"

"Bring us up with him, and fifty guineas is thy reward!"

The slow-moving pilot, who in truth had just awakened from a refreshing sleep, opened his eyes, and seemed to gather a new impulse from the promise. When his questions were asked and answered, he began deliberately to count on his fingers all the chances that still existed of a vessel, whose crew was ignorant of the navigation, falling into their hands.

"Admitting that by keeping mid-channel she goes clear of White Stone and Frogs," he said, giving to Throgmorton's its vulgar name, "he must be a wizard to know that the Stepping-Stones lie directly across his course, and that a vessel must steer away northerly or bring up on rocks that will as surely hold him as if he were built there. Then he runs his chance for the Executioners, which are as prettily placed as needs be to make our trade flourish; besides the Middle Ground farther east, though I count but little on that, having often tried to find it myself, without success. Courage, noble captain! if the fellow be the man you say, we shall get a nearer look at him before the sun sets; for certainly he who has run the Gate without a

pilot in safety, has had as much good luck as can fall to his
share in one day."

The opinion of the East River Branch proved erroneous.
Notwithstanding the hidden perils by which she was environed,
the Water-Witch continued her course, with a speed that increased as the wind rose with the sun, and with an impunity
from harm that amazed all who were in the secret of her situation.   Off Throgmorton's there was, in truth, a danger that
might even have baffled the sagacity of the followers of the mysterious lady, had they not been aided by accident.   This is the
point where the straitened arm of the sea expands into the basin
of the sound.   A broad and inviting passage lies directly before
the navigator, while, like the flattering prospects of life, numberless hidden obstacles are in wait to arrest the unheeding and
ignorant.

The "Skimmer of the Seas" was deeply practiced in all the
intricacies and dangers of shoals and rocks.   Most of his life had
been passed in threading the one or in avoiding the other.   So
keen and quick had his eye become in detecting the presence of
any of those signs which forewarn the mariner of danger, that a
ripple on the surface, or a deeper shade in the color of the
water, rarely escaped his vigilance.   Seated on the topsail-yard
of his brigantine, he had overlooked the passage from the moment
they were through the Gate, and issued his mandates to those
below with a precision and promptitude that were not surpassed
by the trained conductor of the Coquette himself.   But when his
sight embraced the wide reach of water that lay in front, as his
little vessel swept round the headland of Throgmorton, he
believed there no longer existed a reason for so much care.   Still
there was a motive for hesitation.   A heavily molded and dull-
sailing coaster was going eastward not a league ahead of the
brigantine, while one of the light sloops of those waters was
coming westward still farther in the distance.   Notwithstanding
the wind was favorable to each alike, both vessels had deviated
from the direct line and were steering toward a common centre,
near an island that was placed more than a mile to the northward of the straight course.   A mariner like him of the India
shawl could not overlook so obvious an intimation of a change
in the channel.   The Water-Witch was kept away, and her
lighter sails were lowered, in order to allow the royal cruiser,
whose lofty canvas was plainly visible above the land, to draw

near. When the Coquette was seen also to diverge, there no longer remained a doubt of the direction necessary to be taken; and everything was quickly set upon the brigantine, even to her studding-sails. Long ere she reached the island the two coasters had met, and each again changed its course, reversing that on which the other had just been sailing. There was in these movements as plain an explanation as a seaman could desire, that the pursued were right. On reaching the island, therefore, they again luffed into the wake of the schooner; and having nearly crossed the sheet of water, they passed the coaster, receiving an assurance in words that all was now plain sailing before them.

Such was the famous passage of the "Skimmer of the Seas" through the multiplied and hidden dangers of the eastern channel. To those who have thus accompanied him, step by step, through its intricacies and alarms, there may seem nothing extraordinary in the event; but coupled as it was with the character previously earned by that bold mariner, and occurring as it did in the age when men were more disposed than at present to put faith in the marvelous, the reader will not be surprised to learn that it greatly increased his reputation for daring, and had no small influence on an opinion which was by no means uncommon, that the dealers in contraband were singularly favored by a power which greatly exceeded that of Queen Anne and all her servants.

THE DOOM OF ABIRAM WHITE

From 'The Prairie'

ABIRAM gave his downcast partner a glance of his eye, and withdrew towards a distant roll of the land which bounded the view towards the east. The meeting of the pair in this naked spot was like an interview held above the grave of their murdered son. Ishmael signed to his wife to take a seat beside him on a fragment of rock, and then followed a space during which neither seemed disposed to speak.

"We have journeyed together long, through good and bad," Ishmael at length commenced: "much have we had to try us, and some bitter cups have we been made to swallow, my

woman; but nothing like this has ever before lain in my
path."

"It is a heavy cross for a poor, misguided, and sinful woman
to bear!" returned Esther, bowing her head to her knees, and
partly concealing her face in her dress. "A heavy and a burdensome weight is this to be laid upon the shoulders of a sister
and a mother!"

"Ay; therein lies the hardship of the case. I had brought
my mind to the punishment of that houseless trapper with no
great strivings, for the man had done me few favors, and God
forgive me if I suspected him wrongfully of much evil! This
is, however, bringing shame in at one door of my cabin in order
to drive it out at the other. But shall a son of mine be murdered, and he who did it go at large?—the boy would never
rest!"

"Oh, Ishmael, we pushed the matter far! Had little been
said, who would have been the wiser? Our consciences might
then have been quiet."

"Esther," said the husband, turning on her a reproachful but
still a dull regard, "the hour has been, my woman, when you
thought another hand had done this wickedness."

"I did, I did! the Lord gave me the feeling as a punishment
for my sins! but his mercy was not slow in lifting the veil; I
looked into the Book, Ishmael, and there I found the words of
comfort."

"Have you that book at hand, woman? it may happen to
advise in such a dreary business."

Esther fumbled in her pocket, and was not long in producing
the fragment of a Bible which had been thumbed and smoke-
dried till the print was nearly illegible. It was the only article
in the nature of a book that was to be found among the chattels
of the squatter, and it had been preserved by his wife as a melancholy relic of more prosperous, and possibly of more innocent
days. She had long been in the habit of resorting to it under
the pressure of such circumstances as were palpably beyond
human redress, though her spirit and resolution rarely needed
support under those that admitted of reparation through any of
the ordinary means of reprisal. In this manner Esther had
made a sort of convenient ally of the Word of God; rarely
troubling it for counsel, however, except when her own incom-
petency to avert an evil was too apparent to be disputed. We

shall leave casuists to determine how far she resembled any other believers in this particular, and proceed directly with the matter before us.

"There are many awful passages in these pages, Ishmael," she said, when the volume was opened and the leaves were slowly turning under her finger, "and some there ar' that teach the rules of punishment."

Her husband made a gesture for her to find one of those brief rules of conduct which have been received among all Christian nations as the direct mandates of the Creator, and which have been found so just that even they who deny their high authority admit their wisdom. Ishmael listened with grave attention as his companion read all those verses which her memory suggested, and which were thought applicable to the situation in which they found themselves. He made her show him the words, which he regarded with a sort of strange reverence. A resolution once taken was usually irrevocable in one who was moved with so much difficulty. He put his hand upon the book and closed the pages himself, as much as to apprise his wife that he was satisfied. Esther, who so well knew his character, trembled at the action, and casting a glance at his ready eye, she said:—

"And yet, Ishmael, my blood and the blood of my children is in his veins! Cannot mercy be shown?"

"Woman," he answered, sternly, "when we believed that miserable old trapper had done this deed, nothing was said of mercy!"

Esther made no reply, but folding her arms upon her breast she sat silent and thoughtful for many minutes. Then she once more turned her anxious gaze upon the countenance of her husband, where she found all passion and care apparently buried in the coldest apathy. Satisfied now that the fate of her brother was sealed, and possibly conscious how well he merited the punishment that was meditated, she no longer thought of mediation. No more words passed between them. Their eyes met for an instant, and then both arose and walked in profound silence towards the encampment.

The squatter found his children expecting his return in the usual listless manner with which they awaited all coming events. The cattle were already herded, and the horses in their gears in readiness to proceed, so soon as he should indicate that such was his pleasure. The children were already in their proper vehicle, and in short, nothing delayed the departure but the absence of the parents of the wild brood.

"Abner," said the father, with the deliberation with which all his proceedings were characterized, "take the brother of your mother from the wagon, and let him stand on the 'arth."

Abiram issued from his place of concealment, trembling, it is true, but far from destitute of hopes as to his final success in appeasing the just resentment of his kinsman. After throwing a glance around him with the vain wish of finding a single countenance in which he might detect a solitary gleam of sympathy, he endeavored to smother those apprehensions that were by this time reviving in their original violence, by forcing a sort of friendly communication between himself and the squatter:—

"The beasts are getting jaded, brother," he said; "and as we have made so good a march already, is it not time to camp? To my eye you may go far before a better place than this is found to pass the night in."

"'Tis well you like it. Your tarry here ar' likely to be long. My sons, draw nigh and listen. Abiram White," he added, lifting his cap, and speaking with a solemnity and steadiness that rendered even his dull mien imposing, "you have slain my firstborn, and according to the laws of God and man must you die!"

The kidnapper started at this terrible and sudden sentence, with the terror that one would exhibit who unexpectedly found himself in the grasp of a monster from whose power there was no retreat. Although filled with the most serious forebodings of what might be his lot, his courage had not been equal to look his danger in the face, and with the deceitful consolation with which timid tempers are apt to conceal their desperate condition from themselves, he had rather courted a treacherous relief in his cunning, than prepared himself for the worst.

"Die!" he repeated, in a voice that scarcely issued from his chest; "a man is surely safe among his kinsmen?"

"So thought my boy," returned the squatter, motioning for the team that contained his wife and the girls to proceed, as he very coolly examined the priming of his piece. "By the rifle did you destroy my son; it is fit and just that you meet your end by the same weapon."

Abiram stared about him with a gaze that bespoke an unsettled reason. He even laughed, as if he would not only persuade himself but others that what he heard was some pleasantry intended to try his nerves. But nowhere did his frightful merriment meet with an answering echo. All around was solemn and still. The visages of his nephews were excited, but cold towards him, and that of his former confederate frightfully determined. This very steadiness of mien was a thousand times more alarming and hopeless than any violence could have proved. The latter might possibly have touched his spirit and awakened resistance, but the former threw him entirely on the feeble resources of himself.

"Brother," he said, in a hurried unnatural whisper, "did I hear you?"

"My words are plain, Abiram White: thou hast done murder, and for the same must thou die!"

"Esther! sister, sister! will you leave me? O sister! do you hear my call?"

"I hear one speak from the grave!" returned the husky tones of Esther, as the wagon passed the spot where the criminal stood. "It is the voice of my first-born calling aloud for justice! God have mercy, God have mercy on your soul!"

The team slowly pursued its route, and the deserted Abiram now found himself deprived of the smallest vestige of hope. Still he could not summon fortitude to meet his death, and had not his limbs refused to aid him he would yet have attempted to fly. Then by a sudden revolution from hope to utter despair he fell upon his knees and commenced a prayer, in which cries for mercy to God and to his kinsman were wildly and blasphemously mingled. The sons of Ishmael turned away in horror at the disgusting spectacle, and even the stern nature of the squatter began to bend before so abject misery.

"May that which you ask of him be granted," he said; "but a father can never forget a murdered child."

He was answered by the most humble appeals for time. A week, a day, an hour, were each implored with an earnestness commensurate to the value they receive when a whole life is compressed into their short duration. The squatter was troubled, and at length he yielded in part to the petitions of the criminal. His final purpose was not altered, though he changed the means. "Abner," he said, "mount the rock and look on every side that we may be sure none are nigh."

While his nephew was obeying this order, gleams of reviving hope were seen shooting across the quivering features of the kidnapper. The report was favorable; nothing having life, the retiring teams excepted, was to be seen. A messenger was however coming from the latter in great apparent haste. Ishmael awaited its arrival. He received from the hands of one of his wondering and frighted girls a fragment of that Book which Esther had preserved with so much care. The squatter beckoned his child away, and placed the leaves in the hands of the criminal.

"Esther has sent you this," he said, "that in your last moments you may remember God."

"Bless her, bless her! a good and kind sister has she been to me! But time must be given that I may read; time, my brother, time!"

"Time shall not be wanting. You shall be your own executioner, and this miserable office shall pass away from my hands."

Ishmael proceeded to put his new resolution in force. The immediate apprehensions of the kidnapper were quieted by an assurance that he might yet live for days, though his punishment was inevitable. A reprieve to one abject and wretched as Abiram temporarily produced the same effects as a pardon. He was even foremost in assisting in the appalling arrangements; and of all the actors in that solemn tragedy, his voice alone was facetious and jocular.

A thin shelf of the rock projected beneath one of the ragged arms of the willow. It was many feet from the ground, and admirably adapted to the purpose which in fact its appearance had suggested. On this little platform the criminal was placed, his arms bound at the elbows behind his back, beyond the possibility of liberation, with a proper cord leading from his neck to the limb of the tree. The latter was so placed that when suspended the body could find no foot-hold. The fragment of the Bible was placed in his hands, and he was left to seek his consolation as he might from its pages.

"And now, Abiram White," said the squatter, when his sons had descended from completing this arrangement, "I give you a last and solemn asking. Death is before you in two shapes. With this rifle can your misery be cut short, or by that cord, sooner or later, must you meet your end."

"Let me yet live! O Ishmael, you know not how sweet life is when the last moment draws so nigh!"

"'Tis done," said the squatter, motioning for his assistants to follow the herds and teams. "And now, miserable man, that it may prove a consolation to your end, I forgive you my wrongs and leave you to your God."

Ishmael turned and pursued his way across the plain at his ordinary sluggish and ponderous gait. Though his head was bent a little towards the earth, his inactive mind did not prompt him to cast a look behind. Once indeed he thought he heard his name called in tones that were a little smothered, but they failed to make him pause.

At the spot where he and Esther had conferred he reached the boundary of the visible horizon from the rock. Here he stopped, and ventured a glance in the direction of the place he had just quitted. The sun was near dipping into the plains beyond, and its last rays lighted the naked branches of the willow. He saw the ragged outline of the whole drawn against the glowing heavens, and he even traced the still upright form of the being he had left to his misery. Turning the roll of the swell, he proceeded with the feelings of one who had been suddenly and violently separated from a recent confederate forever.

Within a mile the squatter overtook his teams. His sons had found a place suited to the encampment for the night, and merely awaited his approach to confirm their choice. Few words were necessary to express his acquiescence. Everything passed in a silence more general and remarkable than ever. The chidings of Esther were not heard among her young, or if heard, they were more in the tones of softened admonition than in her usual upbraiding key.

No questions nor explanations passed between the husband and his wife. It was only as the latter was about to withdraw among her children for the night, that the former saw her taking a furtive look at the pan of his rifle. Ishmael bade his sons seek their rest, announcing his intention to look to the safety of the camp in person. When all was still, he walked out upon the prairie with a sort of sensation that he found his breathing among the tents too straitened. The night was well adapted to heighten the feelings which had been created by the events of the day.

The wind had risen with the moon, and it was occasionally sweeping over the plain in a manner that made it not difficult for the sentinel to imagine strange and unearthly sounds were mingling in the blasts. Yielding to the extraordinary impulses of which he was the subject, he cast a glance around to see that all were slumbering in security, and then he strayed towards the swell of land already mentioned. Here the squatter found himself at a point that commanded a view to the east and to the west. Light fleecy clouds were driving before the moon, which was cold and watery, though there were moments when its placid rays were shed from clear blue fields, seeming to soften objects to its own mild loveliness.

For the first time, in a life of so much wild adventure, Ishmael felt a keen sense of solitude. The naked prairies began to assume the forms of illimitable and dreary wastes, and the rushing of the wind sounded like the whisperings of the dead. It was not long before he thought a shriek was borne past him on a blast. It did not sound like a call from earth, but it swept frightfully through the upper air, mingled with the hoarse accompaniment of the wind. The teeth of the squatter were compressed and his huge hand grasped the rifle, as if it would crush the metal. Then came a lull, a fresher blast, and a cry of horror that seemed to have been uttered at the very portals of his ears. A sort of echo burst involuntarily from his own lips, as men shout under unnatural excitement, and throwing his rifle across his shoulder, he proceeded towards the rock with the strides of a giant.

It was not often that the blood of Ishmael moved at the rate with which the fluid circulates in the veins of ordinary men; but now he felt it ready to gush from every pore in his body. The animal was aroused, in his most latent energies. Ever as he advanced he heard those shrieks, which sometimes seemed ringing among the clouds, and sometimes passed so nigh as to appear to brush the earth. At length there came a cry in which there could be no delusion, or to which the imagination could lend no horror. It appeared to fill each cranny of the air, as the visible horizon is often charged to fullness by one dazzling flash of the electric fluid. The name of God was distinctly audible, but it was awfully and blasphemously blended with sounds that may not be repeated. The squatter stopped, and for a moment he covered his ears with his hands. When he withdrew the latter, a low and husky voice at his elbow asked in smothered tones: —

"Ishmael, my man, heard ye nothing?"

"Hist!" returned the husband, laying a powerful arm on Esther, without manifesting the smallest surprise at the unlooked-for presence of his wife. "Hist, woman! if you have the fear of Heaven, be still!"

A profound silence succeeded. Though the wind rose and fell as before, its rushing was no longer mingled with those fearful cries. The sounds were imposing and solemn, but it was the solemnity and majesty of nature.

"Let us go on," said Esther; "all is hushed."

"Woman, what has brought you here?" demanded her husband, whose blood had returned into its former channels, and whose thoughts had already lost a portion of their excitement.

"Ishmael, he murdered our first-born: but it is not meet that the son of my mother should lie upon the ground like the carrion of a dog."

"Follow!" returned the squatter, again grasping his rifle and striding towards the rock. The distance was still considerable; and their approach, as they drew nigh the place of execution, was moderated by awe. Many minutes had passed before they reached a spot where they might distinguish the outlines of the dusky objects.

"Where have you put the body?" whispered Esther. "See, here are pick and spade, that a brother of mine may sleep in the bosom of the earth!"

The moon broke from behind a mass of clouds, and the eye of the woman was enabled to follow the finger of Ishmael. It pointed to a human form swinging in the wind, beneath the ragged and shining arm of the willow. Esther bent her head and veiled her eyes from the sight. But Ishmael drew nigher, and long contemplated his work in awe, though not in compunction. The leaves of the sacred book were scattered on the ground, and even a fragment of the shelf had been displaced by the kidnapper in his agony. But all was now in the stillness of death. The grim and convulsed countenance of the victim was at times brought full into the light of the moon, and again, as the wind lulled, the fatal rope drew a dark line across its bright disk. The squatter raised his rifle with extreme care, and fired. The cord was cut, and the body came lumbering to the earth, a heavy and insensible mass.

Until now Esther had not moved nor spoken. But her hand was not slow to assist in the labor of the hour. The grave was soon dug. It was instantly made to receive its miserable tenant. As the lifeless form descended, Esther, who sustained the head, looked up into the face of her husband with an expression of anguish, and said:—

"Ishmael, my man, it is very terrible! I cannot kiss the corpse of my father's child!"

The squatter laid his broad hand on the bosom of the dead, and said:—

"Abiram White, we all have need of mercy; from my soul do I forgive you! May God in heaven have pity on your sins!"

The woman bowed her face, and imprinted her lips long and fervently on the pallid forehead of her brother. After this came the falling clods and all the solemn sounds of filling a grave. Esther lingered on her knees, and Ishmael stood uncovered while the woman muttered a prayer. All was then finished.

On the following morning the teams and herds of the squatter were seen pursuing their course towards the settlements. As they approached the confines of society the train was blended among a thousand others. Though some of the numerous descendants of this peculiar pair were reclaimed from their lawless and semi-barbarous lives, the principals of the family themselves were never heard of more.

THE BISON STAMPEDE

From 'The Prairie'

THE warrior suddenly paused and bent his face aside, like one who listened with all his faculties absorbed in the act. Then turning the head of his horse, he rode to the nearest angle of the thicket, and looked intently across the bleak prairie in a direction opposite to the side on which the party stood. Returning slowly from this unaccountable, and, to his observers, startling procedure, he riveted his eyes on Inez, and paced back and forth several times with the air of one who maintained a warm struggle on some difficult point in the recesses of his own thoughts. He had drawn the reins of his impatient steed, and was seemingly about to speak when his head again sank on his chest, and he resumed his former attitude of attention. Galloping like a deer to the place of his former observations, he rode for a moment swiftly in short and rapid circles as if still uncertain of his course, and then darted away like a bird that had been fluttering around its nest before it takes a distant flight. After scouring the plain for a minute he was lost to the eye behind a swell of the land.

The hounds, who had also manifested great uneasiness for some time, followed him for a little distance, and then terminated their chase by seating themselves on the ground and raising their usual low, whining, and warning howls.

These movements had passed in so short a space of time that the old man, while he neglected not to note the smallest incident, had no opportunity of expressing his opinion concerning the stranger's motives. After the Pawnee had disappeared, however, he shook his head and muttered, while he walked slowly to the angle of the thicket that the Indian had just quitted:—

"There are both scents and sounds in the air, though my miserable senses are not good enough to hear the one or to catch the taint of the other."

"There is nothing to be seen," cried Middleton, who kept close at his side. "My ears and my eyes are good, and yet I can assure you that I neither hear nor see anything."

"Your eyes are good! and you are not deaf!" returned the other, with a slight air of contempt; "no, lad, no; they may be good to see across a church, or to hear a town bell, but afore you had passed a year in these prairies you would find yourself taking a turkey for a buffalo, or conceiving fifty times that the roar of a buffalo bull was the thunder of the Lord! There is a deception of natur' in these naked plains in which the air throws up the images like water, and then it is hard to tell the prairies from a sea. But yonder is a sign that a hunter never fails to know."

The trapper pointed to a flight of vultures that were sailing over the plain at no great distance, and apparently in the direction in which the Pawnee had riveted his eyes. At first Middleton could not distinguish the small dark objects that were dotting the dusky clouds; but as they came swiftly onward, first their forms and then their heavy waving wings became distinctly visible.

"Listen!" said the trapper, when he had succeeded in making Middleton see the moving column of birds. "Now you hear the buffaloes, or bisons, as your knowing Doctor sees fit to call them; though buffaloes is their name among all the hunters of these regions. And I conclude that a hunter is a better judge

of a beast and of its name," he added, winking at the young
soldier, "than any man who has turned over the leaves of a
book instead of traveling over the face of the 'arth, in order to
find out the natur's of its inhabitants."

"Of their habits, I will grant you," cried the naturalist, who
rarely missed an opportunity to agitate any disputed point in his
favorite studies. "That is, provided always deference is had to
the proper use of definitions, and that they are contemplated
with scientific eyes."

"Eyes of a mole! as if any man's eyes were not as good for
names as the eyes of any other creatur'! Who named the works
of His hand? can you tell me that, with your book and college
wisdom? Was it not the first man in the Garden, and is it not
a plain consequence that his children inherit his gifts?"

"That is certainly the Mosaic account of the event," said the
Doctor; "though your reading is by far too literal!"

"My reading! nay, if you suppose that I have wasted my
time in schools, you do such a wrong to my knowledge as one
mortal should never lay to the door of another without sufficient
reason. If I have ever craved the art of reading, it has been
that I might better know the sayings of the book you name, for
it is a book which speaks in every line according to human
feelings, and therein according to reason."

"And do you then believe," said the Doctor, a little provoked
by the dogmatism of his stubborn adversary, and perhaps secretly
too confident in his own more liberal, though scarcely as profitable attainments, "do you then believe that all these beasts were
literally collected in a garden to be enrolled in the nomenclature
of the first man?"

"Why not? I understand your meaning; for it is not needful
to live in towns to hear all the devilish devices that the conceit
of man can invent to upset his own happiness. What does it
prove, except indeed it may be said to prove that the garden He
made was not after the miserable fashions of our times, thereby
directly giving the lie to what the world calls its civilizing?
No, no, the garden of the Lord was the forest then, and is the
forest now, where the fruits do grow and the birds do sing,
according to his own wise ordering. Now, lady, you may see
the mystery of the vultures! There come the buffaloes themselves, and a noble herd it is! I warrant me that Pawnee has
a troop of his people in some of the hollows nigh by; and as he

has gone scampering after them, you are about to see a glorious chase. It will serve to keep the squatter and his brood under cover, and for ourselves there is little reason to fear. A Pawnee is not apt to be a malicious savage."

Every eye was now drawn to the striking spectacle that succeeded. Even the timid Inez hastened to the side of Middleton to gaze at the sight, and Paul summoned Ellen from her culinary labors to become a witness of the lively scene.

Throughout the whole of those moving events which it has been our duty to record, the prairies had lain in the majesty of perfect solitude. The heavens had been blackened with the passage of the migratory birds, it is true; but the dogs of the party and the ass of the Doctor were the only quadrupeds that had enlivened the broad surface of the waste beneath. There was now a sudden exhibition of animal life which changed the scene, as it were by magic, to the very opposite extreme.

A few enormous bison bulls were first observed scouring along the most distant roll of the prairie, and then succeeded long files of single beasts, which in their turns were followed by a dark mass of bodies, until the dun-colored herbage of the plain was entirely lost in the deeper hue of their shaggy coats. The herd, as the column spread and thickened, was like the endless flocks of the smaller birds whose extended flanks are so often seen to heave up out of the abyss of the heavens, until they appear as countless as the leaves in those forests over which they wing their endless flight. Clouds of dust shot up in little columns from the centre of the mass, as some animal, more furious than the rest, plowed the plain with his horns; and from time to time a deep hollow bellowing was borne along on the wind, as if a thousand throats vented their plaints in a discordant murmuring.

A long and musing silence reigned in the party as they gazed on this spectacle of wild and peculiar grandeur. It was at length broken by the trapper, who, having been long accustomed to similar sights, felt less of its influence, or rather felt it in a less thrilling and absorbing manner, than those to whom the scene was more novel.

"There go ten thousand oxen in one drove, without keeper or master, except Him who made them and gave them these open plains for their pasture! Ay, it is here that man may see the proofs of his wantonness and folly! Can the proudest governor

in all the States go into his fields and slaughter a nobler bullock
than is here offered to the meanest hand; and when he has gotten his sirloin or his steak, can he eat it with as good a relish
as he who has sweetened his food with wholesome toil, and
earned it according to the law of natur', by honestly mastering
that which the Lord hath put before him?»

"If the prairie platter is smoking with a buffalo's hump, I
answer no," interrupted the luxurious bee-hunter.

"Ay, boy, you have tasted, and you feel the genuine reasoning of the thing! But the herd is heading a little this-away,
and it behooves us to make ready for their visit. If we hide
ourselves altogether, the horned brutes will break through the
place and trample us beneath their feet like so many creeping
worms; so we will just put the weak ones apart, and take post,
as becomes men and hunters, in the van."

As there was but little time to make the necessary arrangements, the whole party set about them in good earnest. Inez
and Ellen were placed in the edge of the thicket on the side
furthest from the approaching herd. Asinus was posted in the
centre, in consideration of his nerves; and then the old man
with his three male companions divided themselves in such a
manner as they thought would enable them to turn the head of
the rushing column, should it chance to approach too nigh their
position. By the vacillating movements of some fifty or a hundred bulls that led the advance, it remained questionable for
many moments what course they intended to pursue. But a
tremendous and painful roar which came from behind the cloud
of dust that rose in the centre of the herd, and which was hor-
ridly answered by the screams of the carrion-birds that were
greedily sailing directly above the flying drove, appeared to give
a new impulse to their flight and at once to remove every symptom of indecision. As if glad to seek the smallest signs of the
forest, the whole of the affrighted herd became steady in its
direction, rushing in a straight line toward the little cover of
bushes which has already been so often named.

The appearance of danger was now in reality of a character
to try the stoutest nerves. The flanks of the dark moving mass
were advanced in such a manner as to make a concave line of
the front; and every fierce eye that was glaring from the shaggy
wilderness of hair in which the entire heads of the males were
enveloped, was riveted with mad anxiety on the thicket. It

seemed as if each beast strove to outstrip his neighbor in gaining this desired cover; and as thousands in the rear pressed
blindly on those in front, there was the appearance of an imminent risk that the leaders of the herd would be precipitated on
the concealed party, in which case the destruction of every one of
them was certain.   Each of our adventurers felt the danger of
his situation in a manner peculiar to his individual character
and circumstances.

Middleton wavered.   At times he felt inclined to rush through
the bushes, and seizing Inez, attempt to fly.   Then recollecting the impossibility of outstripping the furious speed of an
alarmed bison, he felt for his arms, determined to make head
against the countless drove.   The faculties of Dr. Battius were
quickly wrought up to the very summit of mental delusion.   The
dark forms of the herd lost their distinctness, and then the naturalist began to fancy he beheld a wild collection of all the
creatures of the world rushing upon him in a body, as if to
revenge the various injuries which, in the course of a life of
indefatigable labor in behalf of the natural sciences, he had
inflicted on their several genera.   The paralysis it occasioned in
his system was like the effect of the incubus.   Equally unable to
fly or to advance, he stood riveted to the spot, until the infatuation became so complete that the worthy naturalist was beginning, by a desperate effort of scientific resolution, even to class
the different specimens.   On the other hand, Paul shouted, and
called on Ellen to come and assist him in shouting, but his voice
was lost in the bellowings and trampling of the herd.   Furious,
and yet strangely excited by the obstinacy of the brutes and the
wildness of the sight, and nearly maddened by sympathy and a
species of unconscious apprehension in which the claims of nature
were singularly mingled with concern for his mistress, he nearly
split his throat in exhorting his aged friend to interfere.

"Come forth, old trapper," he shouted, "with your prairie
inventions! or we shall be all smothered under a mountain of
buffalo humps!"

The old man, who had stood all this while leaning on his
rifle and regarding the movements of the herd with a steady
eye, now deemed it time to strike his blow.   Leveling his piece
at the foremost bull, with an agility that would have done credit
to his youth, he fired.   The animal received the bullet on the
matted hair between his horns, and fell to his knees; but shaking

his head he instantly arose, the very shock seeming to increase
his exertions. There was now no longer time to hesitate.
Throwing down his rifle, the trapper stretched forth his arms,
and advanced from the cover with naked hands directly towards
the rushing column of the beasts.

The figure of a man, when sustained by the firmness and
steadiness that intellect can only impart, rarely fails of commanding respect from all the inferior animals of the creation.
The leading bulls recoiled, and for a single instant there was a
sudden stop to their speed, a dense mass of bodies rolling up in
front until hundreds were seen floundering and tumbling on the
plain. Then came another of those hollow bellowings from the
rear, and set the herd again in motion. The head of the column, however, divided, the immovable form of the trapper
cutting it as it were into two gliding streams of life. Middleton and Paul instantly profited by his example, and extended the
feeble barrier by a similar exhibition of their own persons.

For a few moments the new impulse given to the animals in
front served to protect the thicket. But as the body of the
herd pressed more and more upon the open line of its defenders,
and the dust thickened so as to obscure their persons, there
was at each instant a renewed danger of the beasts breaking
through. It became necessary for the trapper and his companions to become still more and more alert; and they were gradually yielding before the headlong multitude, when a furious bull
darted by Middleton so near as to brush his person, and at the
next instant swept through the thicket with the velocity of the
wind.

"Close, and die for the ground," shouted the old man, "or a
thousand of the devils will be at his heels!"

All their efforts would have proved fruitless however against
the living torrent, had not Asinus, whose domains had just been
so rudely entered, lifted his voice in the midst of the uproar.
The most sturdy and furious of the bulls trembled at the alarming and unknown cry, and then each individual brute was seen
madly pressing from that very thicket which the moment before
he had endeavored to reach, with the eagerness with which the
murderer seeks the sanctuary.

As the stream divided the place became clear; the two dark
columns moving obliquely from the copse, to unite again at the
distance of a mile, on its opposite side. The instant the old

man saw the sudden effect which the voice of Asinus had produced, he coolly commenced reloading his rifle, indulging at
the same time in a heartfelt fit of his silent and peculiar merriment.

"There they go, like dogs with so many half-filled shot-
pouches dangling at their tails, and no fear of their breaking
their order; for what the brutes in the rear didn't hear with
their own ears, they'll conceit they did: besides, if they change
their minds, it may be no hard matter to get the jack to sing
the rest of his tune!"

"The ass has spoken, but Balaam is silent!" cried the bee-
hunter, catching his breath after a repeated burst of noisy mirth,
that might possibly have added to the panic of the buffaloes by
its vociferation. "The man is as completely dumfounded as if
a swarm of young bees had settled on the end of his tongue,
and he not willing to speak for fear of their answer."

"How now, friend," continued the trapper, addressing the
still motionless and entranced naturalist; "how now, friend; are
you, who make your livelihood by booking the names and natur's
of the beasts of the fields and the fowls of the air, frightened at
a herd of scampering buffaloes? Though perhaps you are ready
to dispute my right to call them by a word that is in the mouth
of every hunter and trader on the frontier!"

The old man was however mistaken in supposing he could
excite the benumbed faculties of the Doctor by provoking a discussion. From that time henceforth he was never known,
except on one occasion, to utter a word that indicated either the
species or the genus of the animal. He obstinately refused the
nutritious food of the whole ox family; and even to the present
hour, now that he is established in all the scientific dignity and
security of a savant in one of the maritime towns, he turns his
back with a shudder on those delicious and unrivaled viands that
are so often seen at the suppers of the craft, and which are
unequaled by anything that is served under the same name at
the boasted chop-houses of London or at the most renowned of
the Parisian restaurants.

RUNNING THE GAUNTLET

From 'The Last of the Mohicans'

THERE yet lingered sufficient light in the heavens to exhibit those bright openings among the tree-tops where different paths left the clearing to enter the depths of the wilderness. Beneath one of them, a line of warriors issued from the woods and advanced slowly toward the dwellings. One in front bore a short pole, on which, as it afterward appeared, were suspended several human scalps. The startling sounds that Duncan had heard were what the whites have not inappropriately called the "death-hallo"; and each repetition of the cry was intended to announce to the tribe the fate of an enemy. Thus far the knowledge of Heyward assisted him in the explanation; and as he knew that the interruption was caused by the unlooked-for return of a successful war-party, every disagreeable sensation was quieted in inward congratulations for the opportune relief and insignificance it conferred on himself.

When at the distance of a few hundred feet from the lodges, the newly arrived warriors halted. The plaintive and terrific cry which was intended to represent equally the wailings of the dead and the triumph of the victors, had entirely ceased. One of their number now called aloud, in words that were far from appalling, though not more intelligible to those for whose ears they were intended than their expressive yells. It would be difficult to convey a suitable idea of the savage ecstasy with which the news thus imparted was received. The whole encampment in a moment became a scene of the most violent bustle and commotion. The warriors drew their knives, and flourishing them, they arranged themselves in two lines, forming a lane that extended from the war-party to the lodges. The squaws seized clubs, axes, or whatever weapon of offense first offered itself to their hands, and rushed eagerly to act their part in the cruel game that was at hand. Even the children would not be excluded; but boys, little able to wield the instruments, tore the tomahawks from the belts of their fathers, and stole into the ranks, apt imitators of the savage traits exhibited by their parents.

Large piles of brush lay scattered about the clearing, and a wary and aged squaw was occupied firing as many as might

serve to light the coming exhibition. As the flame arose, its
power exceeded that of the parting day, and assisted to render
objects at the same time more distinct and more hideous. The
whole scene formed a striking picture, whose frame was composed of the dark and tall border of pines. The warriors just
arrived were the most distant figures. A little in advance stood
two men, who were apparently selected from the rest as the
principal actors in what was to follow. The light was not strong
enough to render their features distinct, though it was quite evident that they were governed by very different emotions. While
one stood erect and firm, prepared to meet his fate like a hero,
the other bowed his head, as if palsied by terror or stricken
with shame. The high-spirited Duncan felt a powerful impulse
of admiration and pity toward the former, though no opportunity
could offer to exhibit his generous emotions. He watched his
slightest movement, however, with eager eyes; and as he traced
the fine outline of his admirably proportioned and active frame,
he endeavored to persuade himself that if the powers of man,
seconded by such noble resolution, could bear one harmless
through so severe a trial, the youthful captive before him might
hope for success in the hazardous race he was about to run.
Insensibly the young man drew nigher to the swarthy lines of
the Hurons, and scarcely breathed, so intense became his interest in the spectacle. Just then the signal yell was given, and
the momentary quiet which had preceded it was broken by a
burst of cries that far exceeded any before heard. The most
abject of the two victims continued motionless; but the other
bounded from the place at the cry, with the activity and swiftness of a deer. Instead of rushing through the hostile lines as
had been expected, he just entered the dangerous defile, and
before time was given for a single blow, turned short, and leap-
ing the heads of a row of children, he gained at once the
exterior and safer side of the formidable array. The artifice
was answered by a hundred voices raised in imprecations, and
the whole of the excited multitude broke from their order and
spread themselves about the place in wild confusion.

A dozen blazing piles now shed their lurid brightness on the
place, which resembled some unhallowed and supernatural arena
in which malicious demons had assembled to act their bloody
and lawless rites. The forms in the background looked like unearthly beings gliding before the eye and cleaving the air with

frantic and unmeaning gestures; while the savage passions of such as passed the flames were rendered fearfully distinct by the gleams that shot athwart their inflamed visages.

It will easily be understood that amid such a concourse of vindictive enemies, no breathing-time was allowed the fugitive. There was a single moment when it seemed as if he would have reached the forest; but the whole body of his captors threw themselves before him, and drove him back into the centre of his relentless persecutors. Turning like a headed deer, he shot with the swiftness of an arrow through a pillar of forked flame, and passing the whole multitude harmless he appeared on the opposite side of the clearing. Here too he was met and turned by a few of the older and more subtle of the Hurons. Once more he tried the throng, as if seeking safety in its blindness; and then several moments succeeded, during which Duncan believed the active and courageous young stranger was lost.

Nothing could be distinguished but a dark mass of human forms tossed and involved in inexplicable confusion. Arms, gleaming knives, and formidable clubs appeared above them, but the blows were evidently given at random. The awful effect was heightened by the piercing shrieks of the women and the fierce yells of the warriors. Now and then Duncan caught a glimpse of a light form cleaving the air in some desperate bound, and he rather hoped than believed that the captive yet retained the command of his astonishing powers of activity. Suddenly the multitude rolled backward, and approached the spot where he himself stood. The heavy body in the rear pressed upon the women and children in front, and bore them to the earth. The stranger reappeared in the confusion. Human power could not, however, much longer endure so severe a trial. Of this the captive seemed conscious. Profiting by the momentary opening, he darted from among the warriors, and made a desperate, and what seemed to Duncan a final, effort to gain the wood. As if aware that no danger was to be apprehended from the young soldier, the fugitive nearly brushed his person in his flight. A tall and powerful Huron, who had husbanded his forces, pressed close upon his heels, and with an uplifted arm menaced a fatal blow. Duncan thrust forth a foot, and the shock precipitated the eager savage headlong, many feet in advance of his intended victim. Thought itself is not quicker than was the motion with which the latter profited by the advantage;

he turned, gleamed like a meteor again before the eyes of Duncan, and at the next moment, when the latter recovered his recollection and gazed around in quest of the captive, he saw him quietly leaning against a small painted post which stood before the door of the principal lodge.

Apprehensive that the part he had taken in the escape might prove fatal to himself, Duncan left the place without delay. He followed the crowd which drew nigh the lodges, gloomy and sullen, like any other multitude that had been disappointed in an execution. Curiosity, or perhaps a better feeling, induced him to approach the stranger. He found him standing with one arm cast about the protecting post, and breathing thick and hard after his exertions, but disdaining to permit a single sign of suffering to escape. His person was now protected by immemorial and sacred usage, until the tribe in council had deliberated and determined on his fate. It was not difficult, however, to foretell the result, if any presage could be drawn from the feelings of those who crowded the place.

There was no term of abuse known to the Huron vocabulary that the disappointed women did not lavishly expend on the successful stranger. They flouted at his efforts and told him with bitter scoffs that his feet were better than his hands, and that he merited wings, while he knew not the use of an arrow or a knife. To all this the captive made no reply, but was content to preserve an attitude in which dignity was singularly blended with disdain. Exasperated as much by his composure as by his good fortune, their words became unintelligible, and were succeeded by shrill piercing yells. Just then the crafty squaw who had taken the necessary precautions to fire the piles made her way through the throng, and cleared a place for herself in front of the captive. The squalid and withered person of this hag might well have obtained for her the character of possessing more than human cunning. Throwing back her light vestment, she stretched forth her long skinny arm in derision, and using the language of the Lenape, as more intelligible to the subject of her gibes, she commenced aloud:—

"Look you, Delaware," she said, snapping her fingers in his face, "your nation is a race of women, and the hoe is better fitted to your hands than the gun. Your squaws are the mothers of deer; but if a bear or a wild cat or a serpent were born among you, ye would flee. The Huron girls shall make you petticoats, and we will find you a husband."

A burst of savage laughter succeeded this attack, during which the soft and musical merriment of the younger females strangely chimed with the cracked voice of their older and more malignant companion. But the stranger was superior to all their efforts. His head was immovable, nor did he betray the slightest consciousness that any were present, except when his haughty eye rolled toward the dusky forms of the warriors who stalked in the background, silent and sullen observers of the scene.

Infuriated at the self-command of the captive, the woman placed her arms akimbo, and throwing herself into a posture of defiance she broke out anew, in a torrent of words that no art of ours could commit successfully to paper. Her breath was however expended in vain; for although distinguished in her nation as a proficient in the art of abuse, she was permitted to work herself into such a fury as actually to foam at the mouth, without causing a muscle to vibrate in the motionless figure of the stranger. The effect of his indifference began to extend itself to the other spectators, and a youngster who was just quitting the condition of a boy to enter the state of manhood, attempted to assist the termagant by flourishing his tomahawk before their victim and adding his empty boasts to the taunts of the woman. Then indeed the captive turned his face toward the light, and looked down on the stripling with an expression that was superior to contempt. At the next moment he resumed his quiet and reclining attitude against the post. But the change of posture had permitted Duncan to exchange glances with the firm and piercing eyes of Uncas.

Breathless with amazement, and heavily oppressed with the critical situation of his friend, Heyward recoiled before the look, trembling lest its meaning might in some unknown manner hasten the prisoner's fate. There was not, however, any instant cause for such an apprehension. Just then a warrior forced his way into the exasperated crowd. Motioning the women and children aside with a stern gesture, he took Uncas by the arm and led him toward the door of the council lodge. Thither all the chiefs and most of the distinguished warriors followed, among whom the anxious Heyward found means to enter without attracting any dangerous attention to himself.

A few minutes were consumed in disposing of those present in a manner suitable to their rank and influence in the tribe. An order very similar to that adopted in the preceding interview was observed, the aged and superior chiefs occupying the area

of the spacious apartment, within the powerful light of a glaring
torch, while their juniors and inferiors were arranged in the
background, presenting a dark outline of swarthy and marked
visages.   In the very centre of the lodge, immediately under an
opening that admitted the twinkling light of one or two stars,
stood Uncas, calm, elevated, and collected.   His high and haughty
carriage was not lost on his captors, who often bent their looks
on his person with eyes which, while they lost none of their
inflexibility of purpose, plainly betrayed their admiration of the
stranger's daring.

The case was different with the individual whom Duncan had
observed to stand forth with his friend previously to the desperate trial of speed; and who, instead of joining in the chase,
had remained throughout its turbulent uproar like a cringing
statue, expressive of shame and disgrace.   Though not a hand
had been extended to greet him nor yet an eye had condescended
to watch his movements, he had also entered the lodge, as
though impelled by a fate to whose decrees he submitted, seemingly, without a struggle.   Heyward profited by the first opportunity to gaze in his face, secretly apprehensive he might find
the features of another acquaintance; but they proved to be those
of a stranger, and what was still more inexplicable, of one who
bore all the distinctive marks of a Huron warrior.   Instead of
mingling with his tribe, however, he sat apart, a solitary being
in a multitude, his form shrinking into a crouching and abject
attitude, as if anxious to fill as little space as possible.   When
each individual had taken his proper station, and silence reigned
in the place, the gray-haired chief already introduced to the
reader spoke aloud, in the language of the Lenni Lenape.

"Delaware," he said, "though one of a nation of women, you
have proved yourself a man.   I would give you food; but he
who eats with a Huron should become his friend.   Rest in peace
till the morning sun, when our last words shall be spoken."

"Seven nights and as many summer days have I fasted on
the trail of the Hurons," Uncas coldly replied; "the children of
the Lenape know how to travel the path of the just without
lingering to eat."

"Two of my young men are in pursuit of your companion,"
resumed the other, without appearing to regard the boast of his
captive; "when they get back, then will our wise men say to
you, 'Live or die.'"

"Has a Huron no ears?" scornfully exclaimed Uncas: "twice since he has been your prisoner has the Delaware heard a gun that he knows. Your young men will never come back."

A short and sullen pause succeeded this bold assertion. Duncan, who understood the Mohican to allude to the fatal rifle of the scout, bent forward in earnest observation of the effect it might produce on the conquerors; but the chief was content with simply retorting:—

"If the Lenape are so skillful, why is one of their bravest warriors here?"

"He followed in the steps of a flying coward, and fell into a snare. The cunning beaver may be caught."

As Uncas thus replied, he pointed with his finger toward the solitary Huron, but without deigning to bestow any other notice on so unworthy an object. The words of the answer and the air of the speaker produced a strong sensation among his auditors. Every eye rolled sullenly toward the individual indicated by the simple gesture, and a low threatening murmur passed through the crowd. The ominous sounds reached the outer door, and the women and children pressing into the throng, no gap had been left between shoulder and shoulder that was not now filled with the dark lineaments of some eager and curious human countenance.

In the mean time the more aged chiefs in the centre communed with each other in short and broken sentences. Not a word was uttered that did not convey the meaning of the speaker, in the simplest and most energetic form. Again a long and deeply solemn pause took place. It was known by all present to be the grave precursor of a weighty and important judgment. They who composed the outer circle of faces were on tiptoe to gaze; and even the culprit for an instant forgot his shame in a deeper emotion, and exposed his abject features in order to cast an anxious and troubled glance at the dark assemblage of chiefs. The silence was finally broken by the aged warrior so often named. He arose from the earth, and moving past the immovable form of Uncas, placed himself in a dignified attitude before the offender. At that moment the withered squaw already mentioned moved into the circle in a slow sidling sort of a dance, holding the torch, and muttering the indistinct words of what might have been a species of incantation. Though her presence was altogether an intrusion, it was unheeded.

Approaching Uncas, she held the blazing brand in such a manner as to cast its red glare on his person and to expose the slightest emotion of his countenance. The Mohican maintained his firm and haughty attitude; and his eye, so far from deigning to meet her inquisitive look, dwelt steadily on the distance as though it penetrated the obstacles which impeded the view, and looked into futurity. Satisfied with her examination, she left him, with a slight expression of pleasure, and proceeded to practice the same trying experiment on her delinquent countryman.

The young Huron was in his war-paint, and very little of a finely molded form was concealed by his attire. The light rendered every limb and joint discernible, and Duncan turned away in horror when he saw they were writhing in inexpressible agony. The woman was commencing a low and plaintive howl at the sad and shameful spectacle, when the chief put forth his hand and gently pushed her aside.

"Reed-that-bends," he said, addressing the young culprit by name, and in his proper language, "though the Great Spirit has made you pleasant to the eyes, it would have been better that you had not been born. Your tongue is loud in the village, but in battle it is still. None of my young men strike the tomahawk deeper into the war-post — none of them so lightly on the Yengeese. The enemy know the shape of your back, but they have never seen the color of your eyes. Three times have they called on you to come, and as often did you forget to answer. Your name will never be mentioned again in your tribe — it is already forgotten."

As the chief slowly uttered these words, pausing impressively between each sentence, the culprit raised his face, in deference to the other's rank and years. Shame, horror, and pride struggled in its lineaments. His eye, which was contracted with inward anguish, gleamed on the persons of those whose breath was his fame; and the latter emotion for an instant predominated. He arose to his feet, and baring his bosom, looked steadily on the keen glittering knife that was already upheld by his inexorable judge. As the weapon passed slowly into his heart he even smiled, as if in joy at having found death less dreadful than he anticipated, and fell heavily on his face at the feet of the rigid and unyielding form of Uncas.

The squaw gave a loud and plaintive yell, dashed the torch to the earth, and buried everything in darkness. The whole shuddering group of spectators glided from the lodge like troubled spirits; and Duncan thought that he and the yet throbbing body of the victim of an Indian judgment had now become its only tenants.

THE PRAIRIE FIRE

From 'The Prairie'

"SEE, Middleton," exclaimed Inez in a sudden burst of youthful pleasure, that caused her for a moment to forget her situation, "how lovely is that sky; surely it contains a promise of happier times!"

"It is glorious!" returned her husband. "Glorious and heavenly is that streak of vivid red, and here is a still brighter crimson; rarely have I seen a richer rising of the sun."

"Rising of the sun!" slowly repeated the old man, lifting his tall person from its seat with a deliberate and abstracted air, while he kept his eye riveted on the changing and certainly beautiful tints that were garnishing the vault of heaven. "Rising of the sun! I like not such risings of the sun. Ah's me! the imps have circumvented us with a vengeance. The prairie is on fire!"

"God in heaven protect us!" cried Middleton, catching Inez to his bosom, under the instant impression of the imminence of their danger. "There is no time to lose, old man; each instant is a day; let us fly!"

"Whither?" demanded the trapper, motioning him, with calmness and dignity, to arrest his steps. "In this wilderness of grass and reeds you are like a vessel in the broad lakes without a compass. A single step on the wrong course might prove the destruction of us all. It is seldom danger is so pressing that there is not time enough for reason to do its work, young officer; therefore let us await its biddings."

"For my own part," said Paul Hover, looking about him with no equivocal expression of concern, "I acknowledge that should this dry bed of weeds get fairly in a flame, a bee would have to make a flight higher than common to prevent his wings from scorching. Therefore, old trapper, I agree with the captain, and say, mount and run."

"Ye are wrong — ye are wrong; man is not a beast to follow the gift of instinct, and to snuff up his knowledge by a taint in the air or a rumbling in the sound; but he must see and reason, and then conclude. So follow me a little to the left, where there is a rise in the ground, whence we may make our reconnoitrings."

The old man waved his hand with authority, and led the way without further parlance to the spot he had indicated, followed by the whole of his alarmed companions. An eye less practiced than that of the trapper might have failed in discovering the gentle elevation to which he alluded, and which looked on the surface of the meadow like a growth a little taller than common. When they reached the place, however, the stunted grass itself announced the absence of that moisture which had fed the rank weeds of most of the plain, and furnished a clue to the evidence by which he had judged of the formation of the ground hidden beneath. Here a few minutes were lost in breaking down the tops of the surrounding herbage, which, notwithstanding the advantage of their position, rose even above the heads of Middleton and Paul, and in obtaining a lookout that might command a view of the surrounding sea of fire.

The frightful prospect added nothing to the hopes of those who had so fearful a stake in the result. Although the day was beginning to dawn, the vivid colors of the sky continued to deepen, as if the fierce element were bent on an impious rivalry of the light of the sun. Bright flashes of flame shot up here and there along the margin of the waste, like the nimble coruscations of the North, but far more angry and threatening in their color and changes. The anxiety on the rigid features of the trapper sensibly deepened, as he leisurely traced these evidences of a conflagration, which spread in a broad belt about their place of refuge, until he had encircled the whole horizon.

Shaking his head, as he again turned his face to the point where the danger seemed nighest and most rapidly approaching, the old man said: —

"Now have we been cheating ourselves with the belief that we had thrown these Tetons from our trail, while here is proof enough that they not only know where we lie, but that they intend to smoke us out, like so many skulking beasts of prey. See: they have lighted the fire around the whole bottom at the same moment, and we are as completely hemmed in by the devils as an island by its waters."

"Let us mount and ride!" cried Middleton; "is life not worth a struggle?"

"Whither would ye go? Is a Teton horse a salamander that can walk amid fiery flames unhurt, or do you think the Lord will show his might in your behalf, as in the days of old, and carry you harmless through such a furnace as you may see glowing beneath yonder red sky? There are Sioux too hemming the fire with their arrows and knives on every side of us, or I am no judge of their murderous deviltries."

"We will ride into the centre of the whole tribe," returned the youth fiercely, "and put their manhood to the test."

"Ay, it's well in words, but what would it prove in deeds? Here is a dealer in bees, who can teach you wisdom in a matter like this."

"Now for that matter, old trapper," said Paul, stretching his athletic form like a mastiff conscious of his strength, "I am on the side of the captain, and am clearly for a race against the fire, though it line me into a Teton wigwam. Here is Ellen, who will — "

"Of what use, of what use are your stout hearts, when the element of the Lord is to be conquered as well as human men? Look about you, friends; the wreath of smoke that is rising from the bottoms plainly says that there is no outlet from the spot, without crossing a belt of fire. Look for yourselves, my men; look for yourselves: if you can find a single opening, I will engage to follow."

The examination which his companions so instantly and so intently made, rather served to assure them of their desperate situation than to appease their fears. Huge columns of smoke were rolling up from the plain and thickening in gloomy masses around the horizon; the red glow which gleamed upon their enormous folds, now lighting their volumes with the glare of the conflagration and now flashing to another point as the flame beneath glided ahead, leaving all behind enveloped in awful darkness, and proclaiming louder than words the character of the imminent and approaching danger.

"This is terrible!" exclaimed Middleton, folding the trembling Inez to his heart. "At such a time as this, and in such a manner!"

"The gates of heaven are open to all who truly believe," murmured the pious devotee in his bosom.

"This resignation is maddening! But we are men, and will make a struggle for our lives! How now, my brave and spirited friend, shall we yet mount and push across the flames, or shall we stand here, and see those we most love perish in this frightful manner, without an effort?"

"I am for a swarming time and a flight before the hive is too hot to hold us," said the bee-hunter, to whom it will be at once seen that Middleton addressed himself. "Come, old trapper, you must acknowledge this is but a slow way of getting out of danger. If we tarry here much longer, it will be in the fashion that the bees lie around the straw after the hive has been smoked for its honey. You may hear the fire begin to roar already, and I know by experience that when the flames once get fairly into the prairie grass, it is no sloth that can outrun it."

"Think you," returned the old man, pointing scornfully at the mazes of the dry and matted grass which environed them, "that mortal feet can outstrip the speed of fire on such a path? If I only knew now on which side these miscreants lay!"

"What say you, friend Doctor," cried the bewildered Paul, turning to the naturalist with that sort of helplessness with which the strong are often apt to seek aid of the weak, when human power is baffled by the hand of a mightier Being; "what say you: have you no advice to give away in a case of life and death?"

The naturalist stood, tablets in hand, looking at the awful spectacle with as much composure as if the conflagration had been lighted in order to solve the difficulties of some scientific problem. Aroused by the question of his companion, he turned to his equally calm though differently occupied associate, the trapper, demanding with the most provoking insensibility to the urgent nature of their situation:—

"Venerable hunter, you have often witnessed similar prismatic experiments—"

He was rudely interrupted by Paul, who struck the tablets from his hands with a violence that betrayed the utter intellectual confusion which had overset the equanimity of his mind. Before time was allowed for remonstrance, the old man, who had continued during the whole scene like one much at loss how to proceed, though also like one who was rather perplexed than alarmed, suddenly assumed a decided air, as if he no longer doubted on the course it was most advisable to pursue.

"It is time to be doing," he said, interrupting the controversy that was about to ensue between the naturalist and the bee-hunter; "it is time to leave off books and moanings, and to be doing."

"You have come to your recollections too late, miserable old man," cried Middleton; "the flames are within a quarter of a mile of us, and the wind is bringing them down in this quarter with dreadful rapidity."

"Anan! the flames! I care but little for the flames. If I only knew how to circumvent the cunning of the Tetons as I know how to cheat the fire of its prey, there would be nothing needed but thanks to the Lord for our deliverance. Do you call this a fire? If you had seen what I have witnessed in the eastern hills, when mighty mountains were like the furnace of a smith, you would have known what it was to fear the flames and to be thankful that you were spared! Come, lads, come: 'tis time to be doing now, and to cease talking; for yonder curling flame is truly coming on like a trotting moose. Put hands upon this short and withered grass where we stand, and lay bare the 'arth."

"Would you think to deprive the fire of its victims in this childish manner?" exclaimed Middleton.

A faint but solemn smile passed over the features of the old man as he answered:—

"Your gran'ther would have said that when the enemy was nigh, a soldier could do no better than to obey."

The captain felt the reproof, and instantly began to imitate the industry of Paul, who was tearing the decayed herbage from the ground in a sort of desperate compliance with the trapper's direction. Even Ellen lent her hands to the labor, nor was it long before Inez was seen similarly employed, though none amongst them knew why or wherefore. When life is thought to be the reward of labor, men are wont to be industrious. A very few moments sufficed to lay bare a spot of some twenty feet in diameter. Into one edge of this little area the trapper brought the females, directing Middleton and Paul to cover their light and inflammable dresses with the blankets of the party. So soon as this precaution was observed, the old man approached the opposite margin of the grass which still environed them in a tall and dangerous circle, and selecting a handful of the driest of the herbage, he placed it over the pan of his rifle. The light combustible kindled at the flash. Then he placed the little flame in a bed of the standing fog, and withdrawing from the spot to the centre of the ring, he patiently awaited the result.

The subtle element seized with avidity upon its new fuel, and in a moment forked flames were gliding among the grass, as the tongues of ruminating animals are seen rolling among their food, apparently in quest of its sweetest portions.

"Now," said the old man, holding up a finger, and laughing in his peculiarly silent manner, "you shall see fire fight fire! Ah's me! many is the time I have burnt a smooty path, from wanton laziness to pick my way across a tangled bottom."

"But is this not fatal?" cried the amazed Middleton; "are you not bringing the enemy nigher to us instead of avoiding it?"

"Do you scorch so easily? your gran'ther had a tougher skin. But we shall live to see — we shall all live to see."

The experience of the trapper was in the right. As the fire gained strength and heat, it began to spread on three sides, dying of itself on the fourth for want of aliment. As it increased, and the sullen roaring announced its power, it cleared everything before it, leaving the black and smoking soil far more naked than if the scythe had swept the place. The situation of the fugitives would have still been hazardous, had not the area enlarged as the flame encircled them. But by advancing to the spot where the trapper had kindled the grass, they avoided the heat, and in a very few moments the flames began to recede in every quarter, leaving them enveloped in a cloud of smoke, but perfectly safe from the torrent of fire that was still furiously rolling onwards.

The spectators regarded the simple expedient of the trapper with that species of wonder with which the courtiers of Ferdinand are said to have viewed the manner in which Columbus made his egg stand on its end, though with feelings that were filled with gratitude instead of envy.

COPERNICUS

(1473–1543)

BY EDWARD S. HOLDEN

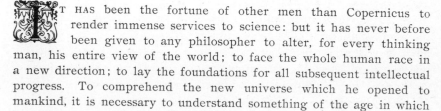T HAS been the fortune of other men than Copernicus to render immense services to science: but it has never before been given to any philosopher to alter, for every thinking man, his entire view of the world; to face the whole human race in a new direction; to lay the foundations for all subsequent intellectual progress. To comprehend the new universe which he opened to mankind, it is necessary to understand something of the age in which he lived, and its critical relations to the past and future.

The life of Copernicus covered the years 1473 to 1543. The astronomy of the Greeks came to its flower with Ptolemy (circa A. D. 150), who was followed by a host of able commentators. Their works were mostly lost in some one of the several destructions of the Alexandrian library. Many important treatises survived, of course, though Grecian science was then dead. Bagdad became the seat of astronomy under the Abbasside Caliphs. It is said that Al Mamun (circa A. D. 827) stipulated in a treaty with the Emperor for copies of the manuscripts of Greek philosophers in the Constantinople libraries, and that these were translated for the benefit of Arabian scholars. The Arabs carried this learning, improved in many details, to the lands they conquered. Bagdad, Cordova, Seville, Tangier, have been successively the homes of exact science. Under the Moguls the seat of astronomy was transferred to Samarkand (1405). It was not firmly rooted in Europe until Tycho Brahe built Uranienborg in Denmark in 1576.

The Arabs touched Europe in Spain (711–1492) and through the Crusaders (1099). The ancient Ptolemaic system of the world, which counted the earth as the centre of the universe, was successively amended by new devices,

> «With centric and eccentric scribbled o'er,
> Cycle and epicycle, orb in orb—»

until it had reached a complexity past belief. King Alfonso X. of Castile expended an enormous sum for the construction of the Alfonsine Tables (1252), which were designed to give, by a comparatively simple calculation, the positions of the sun and planets for past and future epochs,—employing the theories of Ptolemy as a basis.   Alfonso's critical remark upon these theories is well known: to wit, that if he had been present at the creation, he could have given the Creator much good advice.   As the determination of the places of the planets (their latitudes and longitudes) became more exact, it was increasingly difficult to account for their observed movements by the devices introduced by Ptolemy.   New contrivances were required, and each successive epicycle made the system more complex and cumbrous.   It was on the point of breaking by its own weight.

There is hardly a glimmer of scientific light in the darkness of the two centuries following.   From Roger Bacon (1214–94) to the birth of Leonardo da Vinci (1452) there is scarcely a single date to record except that of 1438, when the art of printing was invented — or re-invented — in Europe.

The writings of Purbach (1460) and of Regiomontanus (1471) brought astronomy in Germany to the same level as the Arabian science of five centuries earlier in Spain, and marked the beginning of a new era for Northern lands.   In Italy the impulse was earlier 'felt, though it manifested itself chiefly in literature.   Mathematics was not neglected, however, at the ancient University of Bologna; and it was to Bologna that Copernicus came as a student in 1496.

The voyages of Columbus in 1492 and of Vasco da Gama in 1498 were other signs of the same impulsion which was manifest throughout the Western lands.

Nicolas Copernicus was born in 1473, in the town of Thorn in Poland.   His father was originally from Bohemia, and his mother was the sister of the Bishop of Ermeland.   The father died when the lad was but ten years old, and left him to the care of his uncle.   His studies were prosecuted at the best schools and at the University of Cracow, where he followed the courses in medicine, and became in due time a doctor.   Mathematics and astronomy were ardently studied under learned professors, and the young man also became a skillful artist in painting.   At the termination of his studies he turned his face towards Italy, entered the universities of Padua and Bologna, and finally received the appointment of Professor of Mathematics at Rome in 1499, at the age of twenty-seven years.   Here his duties were to expound the theories of Ptolemy as taught in the 'Almagest,' and he became entirely familiar with their merits and with their deficiencies.

Astronomers everywhere were asking themselves if there might not be simpler methods of accounting for the movements of the planets and of predicting their situations in the sky than the Ptolemaic methods, loaded down as they were with new complexities.

We know that these questions occupied Copernicus during the seven years of his stay in Italy, 1496 to 1502. He made a few astronomical observations then and subsequently, but he was not a born observer like his successor Tycho Brahe. His observations were directed towards determining the positions of the planets, as a test of the tables by which these positions had been predicted; and they were sufficient to show the shortcomings of the accepted Ptolemaic theory. He was a theoretical astronomer, but his theory was controlled by observation.

In 1502 Copernicus returned to his native land and at once entered holy orders. In 1510 he became canon of Frauenburg, a small town not far from Königsberg. Here he divided his time between his religious duties, the practice of medicine, and the study of astronomy —a peaceful life, one would say, and likely to be free from vexations.

It became necessary for the priest to leave his cloister, however, to defend the interests of the Church in a lawsuit against the Knights of the Teutonic Order. The lawsuit was won at last, but Copernicus had raised up powerful enemies. His conclusions with regard to the motion of the earth were not yet published, but it was known that he entertained such opinions. Here was an opportunity for his enemies to bring him to ridicule and to disgrace, which was not neglected. Troupes of strolling players were employed to turn himself and his conclusions into ridicule; and it requires no imagination to conceive that they were perfectly successful before the audiences of the day. But these annoyances fell away in time. The reputation of the good physician and the good priest conquered his townsfolk, while the scholars of Europe were more and more impressed with his learning.

His authority grew apace. He was consulted on practical affairs, such as the financial conduct of the mint. In 1507 he had begun to write a treatise on the motion of the heavenly bodies — 'De Revolutionibus Orbium Cœlestium' — and he appears to have brought it to completion about 1514. It is replete with interest to astronomers, but there are few passages suitable for quotation in a summary like the present. The manuscript was touched and retouched from time to time; and finally in 1541, when he was nearly seventy years of age, he confided it to a disciple in Nuremberg to be printed. In the month of May, 1543, the impression was completed, and the final sheets were sent to the author. They reached him when he was on his death-bed, a few days before he died.

His epitaph is most humble:—"I do not ask the pardon accorded to Paul; I do not hope for the grace given to Peter. I beg only the favor which You have granted to the thief on the cross." His legacy to the world was an upright useful life, and a volume containing an immortal truth: —

The earth is not the centre of the universe; the earth is in motion around the sun.

The conception that the earth might revolve about the sun was no new thing. The ancients had considered this hypothesis among others. Ptolemy made the earth the centre of all the celestial motions. As the motions became more precisely known, Ptolemy's hypothesis required new additions, and it was finally overloaded. It is the merit of Copernicus that he reversed the ancient process of thought and inquired what hypothesis would fit observed facts, and not what additions must be made to an *a priori* assumption to represent observations. He showed clearly and beyond a doubt that the facts were represented far better by the theory that the sun was the centre of motion of the earth, and not only of the earth, but of all the planets. He says: —

«By no other combination have I been able to find so admirable a symmetry in the separate parts of the great whole, so harmonious a union between the motions of the celestial bodies, as by placing the torch of the world — that Sun which governs all the family of the planets in their circular revolutions — on his royal throne, in the midst of Nature's temple.»*

He did not demonstrate this arrangement to be the true one. It was left to Galileo to prove that Venus had phases like our moon, and hence that its light was sunlight, and that its motion was heliocentric. The direct service of Copernicus to pure astronomy lay in his *method*. What theory will best fit the facts? How shall we test the theory by observation? Indirectly he laid the foundations for the reformation of astronomy by Kepler and Galileo; for Newton's working out of the conception of the sun as a centre of force as well as a centre of motion; for the modern ideas of the relations between force and matter.

The Church, which regarded all sciences as derivatives of theology, placed the work of Copernicus on the Index Expurgatorius at Rome, 1616. The Reformation maintained an official silence on the mooted questions. Luther condemned the theory of Copernicus. But the service of Copernicus to mankind was immense, revolutionary,— incalculable. For thousands of years the earth, with its inhabitants, was the centre of a universe created for its benefit. At one step all this was changed, and man took his modest place. He became a creature painfully living on a small planet — one of many — revolving

* Quoted from the French of Flammarion's 'Life of Copernicus,' page 122.

around one of the smaller stars or suns; and that sun was only one of the millions upon millions shining in the stellar vault. Man's position in the universe was destroyed. The loss of kingship would seem to be intolerable, were it not that it was by a man, after all, that Man was dethroned. All our modern thought, feeling, action, is profoundly modified by the consequences of the dictum of Copernicus — " *The earth is not the centre of the universe.*" Mankind was faced in a new direction by that pronouncement. Modern life became possible. Modern views became inevitable. The end is not yet. When in future ages the entire history of the race is written, many names now dear to us will be ignored: they have no vital connection with the progress of the race. But one name is sure of a place of honor: Copernicus will not be forgotten by our remotest descendants.

Edward S. Holden

FRANÇOIS COPPÉE

(1842–)

BY ROBERT SANDERSON

AMONG writers of the present day whose influence on French letters is strongly felt, François Coppée occupies a foremost rank. Indeed, poets of the new generation look up to him as a master and take him for a model. Born in 1842, at the age of twenty-four he first began to draw attention by the publication in 1866 of a number of poems, collected under the name of 'Le Reliquaire' (The Reliquary or Shrine). Since then he has gone on writing poems, plays, and novels; but it is on his work as a poet that his fame will stand. We cannot do better than turn to one of his books, not for his biography alone, but also for the manner of thinking and feeling of this author. 'Toute une Jeunesse' (An Entire Youth) is not strictly an autobiography; but Coppée informs us that the leading character in this work, Amédée Violette, felt life as he felt it when a child and young man.

FRANÇOIS COPPÉE

Here we learn that Coppée's father was a clerk in the War Offices, earning barely enough to keep his family. The boy was of weakly constitution, nervous and sentimental. The mother died; François grew up with his three sisters, two of whom painted for a living, while the third kept house. Then the father died, and his son also obtained employment in the government offices.

François's boyhood and part of his youth were spent in sadness, almost misery; and the shadow cast over his life by this gloomy period of his existence is very perceptible in the poet's writings. It did not however make him a cynic, a pessimist, or a rebel against the existing social conditions. To be sure, his verse is not unfrequently ironical; but it is the irony of fate that the poet makes you keenly feel, although he touches it with a light hand. The recollection of those joyless days filled Coppée with an immense feeling of sadness and sympathy for all who suffer on this earth, especially for those who struggle on, bravely concealing from all eyes their griefs and sorrows. His life, he tells us, was composed of desires and reveries. His only consolation was in his literary work. He felt the inclination and the need of expressing in a way both simple and sincere what passed under his eyes; of extracting what humble ideal there might be in the small folk with whom he had lived, in the melancholy landscapes of the Parisian suburbs where his childhood had been spent,— in short, to paint from nature. He made the attempt, felt that he was successful, and lived then the best and noblest hours of his life; hours in which the artist, already a master of his instrument and having still that abundance and vivacity of sensations of youth, writes the first work that he knows to be good, and writes it with complete disinterestedness, without even thinking that others will see it; working for himself alone, for the sole joy of producing, of pouring out his whole imagination and his whole heart. Hours of pure enthusiasm, Coppée goes on to say, and of perfect happiness, that he will nevermore find when he shall have bitten into the savory fruit of success, when he shall be spurred on by the feverish desire for fame! Delightful and sacred hours, that can be compared only to the rapture of first love!

Rising at six, Coppée would vigorously begin his battle with words, ideas, pictures. At nine he left for his office. There, having blackened with ink a sufficient number of government foolscap sheets, he would find himself with two or three spare hours, which he employed in reading and taking notes. Every night found him up until twelve at his writing-table. The whole of Sunday was given to his favorite occupation of writing verse. Such a continuous effort, he says, kept up in his mind that ardor, spirit, and excitement without which no poetical production is possible.

Such was Coppée's life until, his name becoming known, he earned enough with his pen to give himself up entirely to his art. Then came his success with 'Le Passant' (The Passer-by: 1869), a one-act play; and the following year, the war, the siege of Paris, through which Coppée served in the militia. "Amédée Violette" has now become famous, and his reputation as a poet rests upon the sincerity of his work. He is esteemed for the dignity of his life, wholly taken up with art; and in the world of French letters his place is in the very first rank. He lives out of the world, in the close intimacy of those he loves, and knows nothing of the wretchedness of vanity and ambition. Like many writers and thinkers of the present day, he feels the weariness of life, and finds oblivion in the raptures of poetry and dreams. Such is the man: a wonderfully delicate organization, of a modest shrinking nature, — notice the name of *Violette* he gives himself, —sensitive to a degree of morbidness.

The Academy elected him a member in 1884. Let us now consider the writer. The general character of Coppée's poetry is tender and melancholy, and the greater part of his work may be summed up as the glorification of the lowly, the weak, the ill-favored by nature or fortune; his heroes are chosen by preference among those who fill the humblest stations in life. One naturally associates poetry with a higher order of things than those presented to our eyes by the contemplation of daily events; but Coppée possesses the art of extracting from the humblest creature, from the meanest occupation, the beautiful, the poetic, the ideal. In the treatment in familiar verse of these commonplace subjects, Coppée is an accomplished master; and therein lies his originality, and there also will be found his best work. The poems comprised in the collections called 'Les Humbles,' 'Contes et Poésies,' and certain stanzas of 'Promenades et Intérieurs,' contain the best specimens of this familiar and sympathetic style of poetry.

There is another key that Coppée touches in his poems, with a light and tender hand; a tone difficult to analyze,—the expression of one's inner emotions, especially that of love; a yearning for an ideal affection of woman; the feeling buried in the hearts of all who have lived, loved, and suffered; regret in comparing what is with what might have been: all these varied emotions more easily felt than defined, all that the French sum up by the term *vécu*, have been rendered by Coppée in some of the poems contained in 'Le Reliquaire,' in 'Intimites,' 'Le Cahier Rouge' (The Red Notebook), 'Olivier,' under whose name the poet has portrayed himself; 'L'Exilée'; 'Les Mois' (The Months), in the collection having for title 'Les Récits et les Élégies'; 'Arrière-Saison' (Martinmas, or what in this country might be called Indian Summer).

The patriotic chord resounds in several of Coppée's compositions,—usually straightforward, manly; here and there however with a slight touch of chauvinism. The 'Lettre d'un Mobile Breton,' a letter written by a Breton soldier to his parents during the siege of Paris; 'Plus de Sang!' (No More Blood!) 'Aux Amputés de la Guerre' (To the Maimed in Battle), will serve to illustrate Coppée's treatment of subjects inspired by the events of the war, the siege, and the Commune.

Among the various well-known poems of this writer, the fame of which was increased by their being recited in Parisian salons by skilled artists, should be mentioned 'Les Aïeules' (The Grandmothers); 'La Grève des Forgerons' (The Blacksmiths' Strike); 'Le Naufragé' (The Shipwrecked Sailor); and 'La Bénédiction,' an episode of the taking of Saragossa by the French in 1809.

François Coppée has written for the stage; but he is too elegiac, too sentimental a poet to be a first-class playwright, although some of his plays have met with great success: 'Le Passant' (The Passer-by: 1869), a one-act comedy whose great charm lies in the expression of suffering love; 'Le Luthier de Crémone' (The Musical Instrument Maker of Cremona: 1876), probably the best of his dramatic compositions, a one-act comedy in which the leading character is again one of the humble,—Filippo the hunchback, whose deformity covers a brave heart and a magnanimous spirit; and 'Pour la Couronne' (For the Crown: 1895), a five-act drama with more action than is usually found in Coppée's plays. The scene is laid in the Balkans. The character of Constantine Brancomir, who is falsely accused of selling his country to the Turks and submits to an ignominious punishment to save his father's memory, is a very noble one. With these exceptions, Coppée's plays lack action. Remaining titles are: 'Deux Douleurs' (Two Sorrows), a one-act drama, the story of two women who love the same man, and from being rivals become reconciled at his death; 'Fais ce que Dois' (Do What You Ought), a dramatic episode in one act, of a patriotic nature,—somewhat commonplace, however; 'L'Abandonnée,' a two-act drama presenting the picture of a young girl abandoned by her lover, who meets again with him at her death-bed in a hospital ward; 'Les Bijoux de la Déliverance' (The Jewels of Ransom, Freedom), simply a scene, in which a lady dressed for the ball suddenly reflects that the foreigner is still occupying the territory of France until the payment of the ransom, and removes her glittering jewels to be used for a nobler purpose. Still other plays are 'Le Rendezvous,' 'La Guerre de Cent Ans' (The Hundred Years' War), 'Le Trésor' (The Treasure), 'Madame de Maintenon,' 'Severo Torelli,' 'Les Jacobites'; and 'Le Pater' (The Father), which was prohibited by the French government in 1889.

In common with other modern French writers, with Daudet, Maupassant, and others, Coppée excels in the writing of tales. His prose is remarkable for the same qualities that appear in his poetical works: sympathy, tenderness, marked predilection for the weak, the humble, and especially a masterly treatment of subjects essentially Parisian and modern. These *contes* or tales have been collected under various titles:—'Contes en Prose'; 'Vingt Contes Nouveaux' (Twenty New Tales); 'Longues et Brèves' (Long and Short Ones); 'Contes Tout Simples' (Simple Stories). The following may be mentioned as among some of the best of this writer's prose tales:— 'Le Morceau de Pain' (The Piece of Bread); 'Une Mort Volontaire' (A Voluntary Death); 'Le Pain Bénit' (The Consecrated Bread); 'La Soeur de Lait' (The Foster-Sister); 'Un Accident'; 'Les Vices du Capitaine';

'Les Sabots du Petit Wolff'; 'Mon Ami Meutrier' (My Friend Meutrier).

Coppée's other prose works are 'Une Idylle Pendant le Siége,' 'Henriette,' 'Rivales,' *nouvelles* or novelettes; 'Toute une Jeunesse'; 'Mon Franc-Parler' (Freely Spoken Words), essays on different subjects, books, authors, celebrities, etc.

Robert Sanderson

THE PARRICIDE

From 'For the Crown'

The scene represents a rocky plateau in the Balkans. In the background and centre of the stage, a ruined Roman triumphal arch. A huge signal-pyre is prepared for firing, near the path. Beside it burns a torch, stuck into the rock. On all sides are pine-trees and crags. In the distance are the Balkans, with snowy summits. It is the middle of a fine starlight night. Michael Brancomir, solus:—

I HAVE promised — have sworn. 'Tis the moment, the place —
Michael, naught is left but to hold to thy oath.
   What calm! Far below there, the torrent scarce drips —
Othorgul soon will come: I shall speedily hear
On the old Roman high-road the tramp of his horse;
I shall see him approach, he, the foe, 'neath the arch
Built by Dacia's conqueror, Trajan the Great.
What matters it? Ripe for all daring am I,
Basilide! Ah, thy amorous arms, whence I come,
Have embraces to stifle and smother remorse.
Yes, thy hand have I kissed, pointing out shame's abyss;
With joy throbs my heart that I love thee to crime!
And since crime must ensue that thy pleasure be done,
I feel in such treason an awful content.
Enmeshed in the night of thy locks, I have sworn
That in place of the Turk, should the Prince of the Pit
Rise up with a sneer and stretch forth to my hand
This crown I desire, all with hell-fires aglow,
To thee, Basilide, my seared hand should it bring!
Starry night! All thy splendors undaunted I meet.

[*Perceiving his son* Constantine *suddenly approaching over the rocks at the right hand, exclaims, loud and harshly:* —]

What's there? Do I dream? Near the crag there's a man!
Ho, prowler! stand off, 'tis forbid to approach!
Further back, and at once! The command is most strict.
Further back there, I say!

Constantine [*drawing nearer*] — Fear not, father! 'Tis I.

Michael —
Constantine! Thou, my son!

Constantine — Yes.

Michael — What brings thee here,— say,—
To this waste at this hour of the night? Tell me, too,
Why so trembling thy lip? why so pallid thy face?
What thy errand?

Constantine — Say, rather, what doest *thou* here?

Michael —
First, my answer! My patience thou bring'st to an end!
Say, what brings thee thus here?

Constantine — Duty, father. I *know*.

Michael [*starting back*] —
What "knowest" thou, boy?

Constantine — That the clamor of arms
In the Balkans will rise — the Turk comes — that yon pyre
Has beside it this moment no warder of faith —
That this night, if all Christendom's world shall be saved,
I shall fire yonder signal, in spite even of — you!

Michael [*aside*] —
Just God! To a demon defiance I cast —
And the spirit of hell takes the shape of my son!
[*Aloud.*] What madness inspires thee? What folly, what dream?

Constantine —
Nay, spare thyself, father, the shame of a lie.
Thy bargain is made — thy throne offered — the Turk
Meets thee here. I know all — I have heard *all*, I say!

Michael —
Damnation!

Constantine — — Or no! Let it be, 'tis not true!
Let it be I'm abused — that a horror I dream;
That a madness beset me; that truth is with thee;
That when such a compact of shame thou didst make,
Thy aim was deceiving the traitress, whose kiss
Thou hadst wiped from thy lips, rushing forth into night.
I divine it — thy traitorous part is a ruse!
'Tis alone for thy country, the war for the Cross,

That the mask of disloyalty shadows thy face.
To fire with thine own hand yon signal thou'rt here.
Othorgul in an ambush shall fall and be crushed;
On the Balkans, the girdle of fire — our defense —
Shall flare from Iskren to remote Kilandar —
Ah, I wake! I cast from me this nightmare of shame.
Take the torch, light the pyre — let it burst to its blaze!

Michael —

So suspected I stand? So my son is a spy?
A new order, sooth! What, the heir of my name
Dares to ask to my face if a treason I work!
Since when did a father endure to be told
That his son sets his ears to the cracks of the door?
Say, when did I ask *thy* opinions? Since when
Does the chief take his orderly's counsels in war?
I deign no reply to thy insolent charge.
Thou hast not now to learn that my frown means "Obey."
Hearken then: 'tis my wish to abide here alone
This night at the post. To the fortress at once!
Choose the path the most short! Get thee hence, boy, I
            say.
The signal I light when shall seem to me good.
In the weal of our land I am not to be taught.
I have spoken. Return to thy post, sir. Obey!

Constantine —

It is true, then! No hideous dream of disgrace!
The villainy ripe to its finish! I stay.

Michael —

Thou darest?

Constantine —   Ay, father, thy wrath I can brook.
It is love, yes, the last throbs of love for thyself
That have drawn me to seek thee alone on these heights,
To stand between thee and that hideous crime.
Filial duty? Obedience unto my chief?
To the winds with them both! In my heart rules one
            thought —
I would save thee — to God must I render account —
I must rescue my country, must pluck thee from shame.
Give place there, I say! Stand aside from that torch!
Let the mountain heights glow with their fires!

Michael —   No, by God!

Constantine —

O father, bethink thee! O father, beware!
From above God looks down, and the eyes of the stars.

Of myself I have asked, when thy treason I knew,
What by honor was set?—where lay duty from me?
Alas, it was clear! To denounce to the world
Thy plot—and thyself—and that woman most vile;
To unmask too thy spy. But for thee this means death!
(Death held in reserve through the torture's dread scenes)
—It means in an instant thy glory effaced.
I have pictured thy end at the gibbet, through me.
I could not denounce thee! I held back in dread
From the part of a son who to death yields a sire.
I could not endure that thy name so renowned
Should be scorned—that thy glory should take such dark
              flight.
But at present I act as I must. Time is swift.
I shall kindle yon signal, I say. Give me place!
Calm the woes of thy country!—appease Heaven's wrath!
Think, think, that my silence has turned from thyself
A death on a scaffold, and tortures before.
Think, think that my silence had meant for thee chains,
And the doomsman's dread hand laying clutch upon thee. . .
O father, thou wilt not that I should—regret!

Michael—

Too late. Regret now to have saved thus my life.
O son too devoted, best gained were thy wish
Hadst thou told all—hadst seen me a Judas, disgraced,
Cut down by my soldiers before thine own eyes.
The worse now for thee! Thy heart questions, disputes;
That thing whereon mine is resolved, that I do.
Who has nothing foreseen, he can nothing prevent:
I permit that no hand yonder beacon shall fire.

Constantine—

Thou wouldst yield then, defenseless, our ancient frontier?
Thou wilt suffer the Turk to make Europe his prey,
To all Christendom's ruin—

Michael—   'Tis ingrate to me.

Constantine—

And thy Christ, and thy God?

Michael—   Has God made of me king?
Spite of God, king I would be, will be!

Constantine—   Say—*perhaps*.

Oft a crown is too large for a traitorous head.
It can suddenly prove a garrote—for the stake.

Michael—

Thou insultest! The folly is passing all bounds!

Constantine [*in sudden emotion*] —

    Ah yes, I am wrong! O my father, forgive! —
    What I utter I know not; for aid I must call!
    To my help, then, O memories great of days sped,
    Ye evenings of rapture that followed fights won.
    Come, turmoils of booty, flags snatched as in sheaves,
    Shouts of joy and of pride when from fray I returned
    And felt on my forehead, blood-scarred, his hot kiss! —
    O ye visions like these, of past glory, crowd thick!
    The valor of old years, of old time the deeds,
    Quick, rank yourselves here, face this wretchedest man,
    Bring a blush to his face at his treason so vile!
    Speak, speak to him! Say that at morn, in the town,
    The standards that hang at the gates of his halls
    Will stoop, as he passes, to smite at his face.
    Say, oh say, to this hero become renegade,
    That the soldiers long dead on his battle-fields past
    In this hour know the crime unexampled he plots, —
    That they whisper in dread, 'twixt themselves, 'neath the
        earth,
    And if passes some wanderer to-night by their graves,
    Indignant the murmur is breathed through the grass.
    No, no! to such falsity thou wilt not go;
    Even now you repent — all unwilling to leave
    A name to be cursed in the memories of all!
    Seest thou not, O my father, thy victories come
    Like suppliants imploring, to close round your knees?
    Will you hold them in hate, will you drive them away? —
    The triumphs that all this West-world has acclaimed,
    Will you treat them as prostitutes, bowed, to be scorned?
    No, this crime so debased you will dare not commit!
    It cannot be, father — it never must be!
    See me cast at your feet, in last hope, in last prayer;
    I shall find the lost hero — the father I've lost!
    You will catch up the torch, you will fire yon dry pile:
    With an effort supreme from your heart you will tear
    This project unspeakable, — promise debased;
    You will cast them away to the pyre's fiercest glow
    As one burns into naught some foul herb, root and fruit:
    You will stand purified as by fire, and the wind
    Of the night will bear off on its wings this dark dream
    In a whirlwind uproaring of sparks and of flame.

Michael —

    'Tis enough, I say! Up! By all devils in hell,
    Of the hills and the plains of this land I'll be king!

Ay, and crown my fair queen — be revenged on the priest.
As that sky is unstained, so shall all this be done.
Thy heroics thou wastest — thy insolence too.
Go, dispute with the lion the quarry he holds
When thou seest him tear with his talons the prey.
Of no use all thy menaces — vain sobs, vain prayers:
Be sure once for all that thy childishness fails.
While I live, no man kindles this signal to-night!

Constantine —

While thou *livest!* What word do I catch from thy mouth?
While thou *livest?* O bloody and terrible thought!
In my brain is set loose worse than horror, than death!

Michael —

I guess not thy meaning. Wouldst see me a corpse?

Constantine —

I dream in this moment that one thou — *shouldst* be —
By a doom full of shame, by the traitor's own fate!

Michael —

What dost mean?

Constantine —   Ah, I think, while we parley so long,
Othorgul and his Turks in the valleys approach —
Each instant that's spent makes accomplice of — me!
I think of the duty that I must fulfill.

Michael —

What "duty"?

Constantine [*with desperate resolution*] —

                         I say to myself that, unjust,
I have wished from the chastisement — death — thee to save.
Lo, thy life is a menace, escaping the axe,
A menace to all. And I have here my sword!

Michael [*in horror*] —

Thou! Thy sword!

Constantine —   Yes, of old, without blemish, my blade
Has known well how to stand between death and thy brow;
Still witness to that is the wound that I bear —
But since such keen envy, such ignoble love,
Have made of my hero a creature so base,
Since to scorn of all men, toward the Turk thou dost turn,
To beg at his hands for the crown thou usurp'st —
See, my sword, in its honor, leaps out from its sheath
And commands me thy judge and thy doomsman to be.

                              [*He draws his sword.*]

Michael [*drawing his sword in turn*] —

My sword then behold! It is fearless of thine!

Constantine —
　　'Tis my land I defend — Christian Europe I keep,
　　And my duty as soldier, the truth of my line;
　　But you, 'tis for treason alone that you draw.
　　God beholds us. He watches the lists. Let him judge!
　　Traitor, die!

[*Constantine leaps at his father. The swords cross for a moment in quick combat. Then Michael receives a stroke full in the breast, and falls.*]

Michael —　　　　　　Ah!
Constantine —　　　　　　My God! What a deed!
Michael [*on the ground expiring*]　—　　　　　Parricide!
　　Be cursed!　　　　　　　　　　　　[*He dies.*
Constantine —　　First the signal! The fire to the pile!

[*He takes the torch and sets the signal blaze burning, which soon mounts high. Then gradually one sees far along the mountain-chain the other signals flashing out, and alarm-guns begin to be heard below.*]

Constantine —
　　O ye stars, eyes of God! Be the witnesses, ye!
　　But before yonder corpse in the face of that flame,
　　I dare to look up and to show you my soul.
　　My father his country, his faith would betray.
　　I have killed him, O stars! Have I sinned? Ye shall say!

Unrhymed version, in the metre of the original, by E. Irenæus Stevenson.

THE SUBSTITUTE

From 'Ten Tales,' by François Coppée: copyright 1890, by Harper and
Brothers

H E WAS scarcely ten years old when he was first arrested as a
vagabond.
　　He spoke thus to the judge: —
　　"I am called Jean François Leturc, and for six months I was
with the man who sings and plays upon a cord of catgut between
the lanterns at the Place de la Bastille. I sang the refrain with
him, and after that I called, 'Here's all the new songs, ten
centimes two sous!' He was always drunk and used to beat
me. That is why the police picked me up the other night.
Before that I was with the man who sells brushes. My mother
was a laundress; her name was Adèle. At one time she lived

with a man on the ground-floor at Montmartre. She was a good
workwoman and liked me. She made money, because she had
for customers waiters in the cafés, and they use a good deal of
linen. On Sundays she used to put me to bed early, so that she
could go to the ball. On week-days she sent me to Les Frères,
where I learned to read. Well, the sergeant-de-ville whose beat
was in our street used always to stop before our windows to talk
with her — a good-looking chap, with a medal from the Crimea.
They were married, and after that everything went wrong. He
didn't take to me, and turned mother against me. Every one
had a blow for me, and so to get out of the house I spent
whole days in the Place Clichy, where I knew the mountebanks.
My father-in-law lost his place, and my mother her work. She
used to go out washing to take care of him; this gave her a
cough — the steam. . . . She is dead at Lariboisière. She
was a good woman. Since that I have lived with the seller of
brushes and the catgut scraper. Are you going to send me to
prison?"

He said this openly, cynically, like a man. He was a little
ragged street-arab, as tall as a boot, his forehead hidden under a
queer mop of yellow hair.

Nobody claimed him, and they sent him to the Reform School.

Not very intelligent, idle, clumsy with his hands, the only
trade he could learn there was not a good one,— that of reseat-
ing straw chairs. However, he was obedient, naturally quiet and
silent, and he did not seem to be profoundly corrupted by that
school of vice. But when in his seventeenth year he was thrown
out again on the streets of Paris, he unhappily found there his
prison comrades, all great scamps, exercising their dirty professions: teaching dogs to catch rats in the sewers, and blacking
shoes on ball nights in the passage of the Opera; amateur wres-
tlers, who permitted themselves to be thrown by the Hercules of
the booths; or fishing at noontime from rafts: all of these occupations he followed to some extent, and some months after he
came out of the House of Correction, he was arrested again for
a petty theft — a pair of old shoes prigged from a shop window.
Result: a year in the prison of Sainte Pélagie, where he served
as valet to the political prisoners.

He lived in much surprise among this group of prisoners,—
all very young, negligent in dress, who talked in loud voices, and
carried their heads in a very solemn fashion. They used to meet

in the cell of one of the oldest of them, a fellow of some thirty years, already a long time in prison and quite a fixture at Sainte Pélagie; a large cell, the walls covered with colored caricatures, and from the window of which one could see all Paris — its roofs, its spires, and its domes — and far away the distant line of hills, blue and indistinct upon the sky. There were upon the walls some shelves filled with volumes and all the old paraphernalia of a fencing-room: broken masks, rusty foils, breast-plates, and gloves that were losing their tow. It was there that the "politicians" used to dine together, adding to the everlasting "soup and beef," fruit, cheese, and pints of wine which Jean François went out and got by the can; a tumultuous repast, interrupted by violent disputes, and where, during the dessert, the 'Carmagnole' and 'Ça Ira' were sung in full chorus. They assumed, however, an air of great dignity on those days when a newcomer was brought in among them, at first entertaining him gravely as a citizen, but on the morrow using him with affectionate familiarity and calling him by his nickname. Great words were used there: "Corporation," "responsibility," and phrases quite unintelligible to Jean François — such as this, for example, which he once heard imperiously put forth by a frightful little hunchback who blotted some writing-paper every night: —

: is done. This is the composition of the Cabinet: Raymond, the Bureau of Public Instruction; Martial, the Interior; and for Foreign Affairs, myself."

His time done, he wandered again around Paris, watched afar by the police, after the fashion of cockchafers made by cruel children to fly at the end of a string. He became one of those fugitive and timid beings whom the law, with a sort of coquetry, arrests and releases by turn; something like those platonic fishers who, in order that they may not exhaust their fish-pond, throw immediately back in the water the fish which has just come out of the net. Without a suspicion on his part that so much honor had been done to so sorry a subject, he had a special bundle of memoranda in the mysterious portfolios of the Rue de Jérusalem. His name was written in round hand on the gray paper of the cover, and the notes and reports, carefully classified, gave him his successive appellations: "Name, Leturc;" "The prisoner Leturc;" and at last, "The criminal Leturc."

He was two years out of prison, — dining where he could, sleeping in night lodging-houses and sometimes in lime-kilns, and taking part with his fellows in interminable games of pitch-penny on the boulevards near the barriers. He wore a greasy cap on the back of his head, carpet slippers, and a short white blouse. When he had five sous he had his hair curled. He danced at Constant's at Montparnasse; bought for two sous to sell for four at the door of Bobino, the jack of hearts or the ace of clubs serving as a countermark; sometimes opened the door of a carriage; led horses to the horse-market. From the lottery of all sorts of miserable employments he drew a goodly number. Who can say if the atmosphere of honor which one breathes as a soldier, if military discipline might not have saved him? Taken in a cast of the net with some young loafers who robbed drunkards sleeping on the streets, he denied very earnestly having taken part in their expeditions. Perhaps he told the truth, but his antecedents were accepted in lieu of proof, and he was sent for three years to Poissy. There he made coarse playthings for children, was tattooed on the chest, learned thieves' slang and the penal code. A new liberation, and a new plunge into the sink of Paris; but very short this time, for at the end of six months at the most he was again compromised in a night robbery, aggravated by climbing and breaking,— a serious affair, in which he played an obscure rôle, half dupe and half fence. On the whole, his complicity was evident, and he was sent for five years at hard labor. His grief in this adventure was above all in being separated from an old dog which he had found on a dung-heap and cured of the mange. The beast loved him.

Toulon, the ball and chain, the work in the harbor, the blows from a stick, wooden shoes on bare feet, soup of black beans dating from Trafalgar, no tobacco money, and the terrible sleep in a camp swarming with convicts: that was what he experienced for five broiling summers and five winters raw with the Mediterranean wind. He came out from there stunned, was sent under surveillance to Vernon, where he worked some time on the river. Then, an incorrigible vagabond, he broke his exile and came again to Paris. He had his savings,— fifty-six francs, — that is to say, time enough for reflection. During his absence his former wretched companions had dispersed. He was well hidden, and slept in a loft at an old woman's, to whom he represented himself as a sailor, tired of the sea, who had lost his papers in a recent shipwreck, and who wanted to try his hand at something else. His tanned face and his calloused hands, together with some sea phrases which he dropped from time to time, made his tale seem probable enough.

One day when he risked a saunter in the streets, and when chance had led him as far as Montmartre, where he was born, an unexpected memory stopped him before the door of Les Frères, where he had learned to read. As it was very warm, the door was open, and by a single glance the passing outcast was able to recognize the peaceable school-room. Nothing was changed: neither the bright light shining in at the great windows, nor the crucifix over the desk, nor the rows of benches with the tables furnished with inkstands and pencils, nor the table of weights and measures, nor the map where pins stuck in still indicated the operations of some ancient war. Heedlessly and without thinking, Jean François read on the blackboard the words of the Evangelist which had been set there as a copy:—

"Joy shall be in heaven over one sinner that repenteth, more than over ninety-and-nine just persons which need no repentance."

It was undoubtedly the hour for recreation, for the Brother Professor had left his chair, and sitting on the edge of a table, he was telling a story to the boys who surrounded him with eager and attentive eyes. What a bright and innocent face he had, that beardless young man, in his long black gown, and a white necktie, and great ugly shoes, and his badly cut brown hair streaming out behind! All the simple figures of the children of the people who were watching him seemed scarcely less childlike than his; above all when, delighted with some of his own simple and priestly pleasantries, he broke out in an open and frank peal of laughter which showed his white and regular teeth, —a peal so contagious that all the scholars laughed loudly in their turn. It was such a sweet simple group in the bright sunlight, which lighted their dear eyes and their blond curls.

Jean François looked at them for some time in silence, and for the first time in that savage nature, all instinct and appetite, there awoke a mysterious, a tender emotion. His heart, that seared and hardened heart, unmoved when the convict's cudgel or the heavy whip of the watchman fell on his shoulders, beat oppressively. In that sight he saw again his infancy; and closing his eyes sadly, the prey to torturing regret, he walked quickly away.

Then the words written on the blackboard came back to his mind.

"If it wasn't too late, after all!" he murmured; "if I could again, like others, eat honestly my brown bread, and sleep my fill without nightmare! The spy must be sharp who recognizes me. My beard, which I shaved off down there, has grown out thick and strong. One can burrow somewhere in the great ant-hill, and work can be found. Whoever is not worked to death in the hell of the galleys comes out agile and robust, and I learned there to climb ropes with loads upon my back. Building is going on everywhere here, and the masons need helpers. Three francs a day! I never earned so much. Let me be forgotten, and that is all I ask."

He followed his courageous resolution; he was faithful to it, and after three months he was another man. The master for whom he worked called him his best workman. After a long day upon the scaffolding in the hot sun and the dust, constantly bending and raising his back to take the hod from the man at his feet and pass it to the man over his head, he went for his soup to the cook-shop, tired out, his legs aching, his hands burning, his eyelids stuck with plaster, but content with himself and carrying his well-earned money in a knot in his handkerchief. He went out now without fear, since he could not be recognized in his white mask, and since he had noticed that the suspicious glances of the policeman were seldom turned on the tired workman. He was quiet and sober. He slept the sound sleep of fatigue. He was free.

At last — oh supreme recompense! — he had a friend!

He was a fellow-workman like himself, named Savinien, a little peasant with red lips who had come to Paris with his stick over his shoulder and a bundle on the end of it, fleeing from the wine-shops and going to mass every Sunday. Jean François loved him for his piety, for his candor, for his honesty, for all that he himself had lost, and so long ago. It was a passion, profound and unrestrained, which transformed him by fatherly cares and attentions. Savinien, himself of a weak and egotistical nature, let things take their course, satisfied only in finding a companion who shared his horror of the wine-shop. The two friends lived together in a fairly comfortable lodging, but their resources were very limited. They were obliged to take into their room a third companion, an old Auvergnat, gloomy and rapacious, who found it possible out of his meagre salary to save something with which to buy a place in his own country. Jean François and Savinien were always together. On

holidays they together took long walks in the environs of Paris,
and dined under an arbor in one of those small country inns
where there are a great many mushrooms in the sauces and
innocent rebuses on the napkins. There Jean François learned
from his friend all that lore of which they who are born in the
city are ignorant: learned the names of the trees, the flowers
and the plants; the various seasons for harvesting; he heard
eagerly the thousand details of a laborious country life,—the
autumn sowing, the winter chores, the splendid celebrations of
harvest and vintage days, the sound of the mills at the water-
side and the flails striking the ground, the tired horses led to
water and the hunting in the morning mist, and above all the
long evenings, shortened by marvelous stories, around the fire of
vine-shoots. He discovered in himself a source of imagination
before unknown, and found a singular delight in the recital of
events so placid, so calm, so monotonous.

One thing troubled him, however: it was the fear lest Savinien
might learn something of his past. Sometimes there escaped
from him some low word of thieves' slang, a vulgar gesture,—
vestiges of his former horrible existence,—and he felt the pain
one feels when old wounds reopen; the more because he fancied
that he sometimes saw in Savinien the awakening of an
healthy curiosity. When the young man, already temp   by
the pleasures which Paris offers to the poorest, asked him a   ut
the mysteries of the great city, Jean François feigned ignorance
and turned the subject; but he felt a vague inquietude for the
future of his friend.

His uneasiness was not without foundation. Savinien could
not long remain the simple rustic that he was on his arrival in
Paris. If the gross and noisy pleasures of the wine-shop always
repelled him, he was profoundly troubled by other temptations,
full of danger for the inexperience of his twenty years. When
spring came he began to go off alone, and at first he wandered
about the brilliant entrance of some dancing-hall, watching the
young girls who went in with their arms around each others'
waists, talking in low tones. Then one evening, when lilacs
perfumed the air and the call to quadrilles was most captivating,
he crossed the threshold, and from that time Jean François
observed a change, little by little, in his manners and his visage. He became more frivolous, more extravagant. He often
borrowed from his friend his scanty savings, and he forgot to

repay. Jean François, feeling that he was abandoned, jealous and forgiving at the same time, suffered and was silent. He felt that he had no right to reproach him, but with the foresight of affection he indulged in cruel and inevitable presentiments.

One evening, as he was mounting the stairs to his room, absorbed in his thoughts, he heard, as he was about to enter, the sound of angry voices, and he recognized that of the old Auvergnat who lodged with Savinien and himself. An old habit of suspicion made him stop at the landing-place and listen to learn the cause of the trouble.

"Yes," said the Auvergnat angrily, "I am sure that some one has opened my trunk and stolen from it the three louis that I had hidden in a little box; and he who has done this thing must be one of the two companions who sleep here, if it were not the servant Maria. It concerns you as much as it does me, since you are the master of the house, and I will drag you to the courts if you do not let me at once break open the valises of the two masons. My poor gold! It was here yesterday in its place, and I will tell you just what it was, so that if we find it again nobody can accuse me of having lied. Ah, I know them, my three beautiful gold pieces, and I can see them as plainly as I see you! One piece was more worn than the others; it was of greenish gold, with a portrait of the great emperor. The other was a great old fellow with a queue and epaulettes; and the third, which had on it a Philippe with whiskers, I had marked with my teeth. They don't trick me. Do you know that I only wanted two more like that to pay for my vineyard? Come, search these fellows' things with me, or I will call the police! Hurry up!"

"All right," said the voice of the landlord; "we will go and search with Maria. So much the worse for you if we find nothing, and the masons get angry. You have forced me to it."

Jean François's soul was full of fright. He remembered the embarrassed circumstances and the small loans of Savinien, and how sober he had seemed for some days. And yet he could not believe that he was a thief. He heard the Auvergnat panting in his eager search, and he pressed his closed fists against his breast as if to still the furious beating of his heart.

"Here they are!" suddenly shouted the victorious miser. "Here they are, my louis, my dear treasure; and in the Sunday vest of that little hypocrite of Limousin! Look, landlord, they are just as I told you. Here is the Napoleon, the man with a queue, and the Philippe that I have bitten. See the dents? Ah, the little beggar with the sanctified air! I should have much sooner suspected the other. Ah, the wretch! Well, he must go to the convict prison."

At this moment Jean François heard the well-known step of Savinien coming slowly up the stairs.

"He is going to his destruction," thought he. "Three stories. I have time!"

And pushing open the door he entered the room, pale as death, where he saw the landlord and the servant stupefied in a corner, while the Auvergnat, on his knees in the disordered heap of clothes, was kissing the pieces of gold.

"Enough of this," he said, in a thick voice; "I took the money and put it in my comrade's trunk. But that is too bad. I am a thief, but not a Judas. Call the police; I will not try to escape, only I must say a word to Savinien in private. Here he is."

In fact, the little Limousin had just arrived; and seeing his crime discovered, believing himself lost, he stood there, his eyes fixed, his arms hanging.

Jean François seized him forcibly by the neck, as if to embrace him; he put his mouth close to Savinien's ear, and said to him in a low supplicating voice:—

"Keep quiet."

Then turning towards the others:—

"Leave me alone with him. I tell you I won't go away. Lock us in if you wish, but leave us alone."

With a commanding gesture he showed them the door. They went out.

Savinien, broken by grief, was sitting on the bed, and lowered his eyes without understanding anything.

"Listen," said Jean François, who came and took him by the hands, "I understand! You have stolen three gold pieces to buy some trifle for a girl. That costs six months in prison. But one only comes out from there to go back again, and you will become a pillar of police courts and tribunals. I understand it. I have been seven years at the Reform School, a year at Sainte Pélagie, three years at Poissy, five years at Toulon. Now, don't be afraid. Everything is arranged. I have taken it on my shoulders."

"It is dreadful," said Savinien; but hope was springing up again in his cowardly heart.

"When the elder brother is under the flag, the younger one does not go," replied Jean François. "I am your substitute, that's all. You care for me a little, do you not? I am paid. Don't be childish — don't refuse. They would have taken me again one of these days, for I am a runaway from exile. And then, do you see, that life will be less hard for me than for you. I know it all, and I shall not complain if I have not done you this service for nothing, and if you swear to me that you will never do it again. Savinien, I have loved you well, and your friendship has made me happy. It is through it that since I have known you I have been honest and pure, as I might always have been, — perhaps if I had had, like you, a father to put a tool in my hands, a mother to teach me my prayers. It was my sole regret that I was useless to you, and that I deceived you concerning myself. To-day I have unmasked in saving you. It is all right. Do not cry, and embrace me, for already I hear heavy boots on the stairs. They are coming with the *posse*, and we must not seem to know each other so well before those chaps."

He pressed Savinien quickly to his breast, then pushed him from him, when the door was thrown wide open.

It was the landlord and the Auvergnat, who brought the police. Jean François sprang forward to the landing-place, held out his hands for the handcuffs, and said, laughing, "Forward, bad lot!"

To-day he is at Cayenne, condemned for life as an incorrigible.

P. CORNEILLE.

PIERRE CORNEILLE

(1606–1684)

BY FREDERICK MORRIS WARREN

ORNEILLE'S life, apart from the performance and publication of his works, is but imperfectly known, owing to the lack of contemporaneous records and allusions. He was born at Rouen, capital of the old province of Normandy, on June 6th, 1606. At his christening on June 9th he received the name of Pierre, after his father and godfather. He was educated in the Jesuit college (academy) at Rouen, and obtained in 1620 a prize for excellence. Choosing his father's profession, he studied law, and was admitted to the bar on June 18th, 1624. The office of attorney-general in the department of waters and forests was purchased by him on December 16th, 1628. The year following, Mondory, who with a company of actors was probably playing at Rouen, persuaded him to give his (Mondory's) troupe a comedy he had already written; and the season of 1629-30 saw the play produced in Paris, at the newly established Marais Theatre.

The success of this comedy, 'Mélite,' confirmed Corneille in his purpose of writing for the stage and led him to study the principles of dramatic art. While he continued to discharge his legal duties at Rouen, he would frequently visit Paris in order to offer some new play to Mondory, or mingle in the literary society of the capital. So 'Mélite,' made up entirely of conversations where nothing happened, was followed by 'Clitandre,' a tragi-comedy of the popular type, full of bloody episodes. Like 'Mélite,' it was in twelve-syllable verse (Alexandrine) and contained five acts. It also showed Corneille's first attempt to observe unity of time. When it was published in March 1632, a selection of Corneille's poetry, a part of which antedated 'Mélite,' was put with it.

The next two years saw the publication of occasional poems by him in French, and some Latin verse in honor of the King and Richelieu. Before March 1634 he also composed four more comedies: 'The Widow,' a character study, noticeable for the attempt to compromise on unity of time by allowing a day to each act; 'The Gallery of the Palace,' where the action takes place in the fashionable shops of the day, and in which the modern character of the soubrette displaces the traditional nurse of Renaissance comedy, taken by a man in disguise; 'The Lady's Maid,' a study of this successful substitute, where finally Corneille observes both the unities of time and place, and makes his five acts equal, line for line; and 'The Palais Royal,' another topical comedy for Parisians. These four plays are much like their predecessors in lack of action and super-fluity of complimentary talk. The same may be said of Corneille's collaboration on Richelieu's 'Comedy of The Tuileries' (1635). His superiority to his colleagues at this time consisted mainly in his poetic talent and common-sense.

In the season of 1634–35 he tried a tragedy, 'Medea,' patterned after Seneca's Latin drama of that name. It shows an advance on his previous efforts, yet did not come up to his high standard; and he sought a diversion for his disappointment by eulogizing the theatrical profession in a play within a play, 'The Dramatic Illusion,' which he gave to the actors of the Hôtel of Burgundy, probably in 1635.

About this time Corneille's attention was drawn to the Spanish drama, then at its highest point. The storied deeds of Spain's national hero especially appealed to his temperament, and he selected Guillen de Castro's 'First Exploits of the Cid' as a model for his imitation. A year or more he may have been busy in adapting its complexity of scene and character to the orderly, simple require-ments of the French stage. For it was not till the last days of 1636, after unusual preparations in rehearsals and costuming, that Mon-dory's company brought out 'The Cid.' Its success was instantane-ous. The theatre was crowded for many nights. The stage even was filled in with seats for the nobility, to the great annoyance of the actors and the detriment of the scenery. And sixteen years later, Pellisson, the historian of the Academy, could still write:—"It is difficult to conceive the approbation with which this play was re-ceived by the Court and public. People never tired of going to it; you could hear nothing else talked about; everybody knew some part of it by heart; children were made to learn it, and in several places in France it gave rise to the proverb, 'That is as beautiful as The Cid.'"

The history of modern French drama dates from the first perform-ance of 'The Cid.' The theme here selected became the typical one. It shows the struggle between love and honor on the part of the hero, love and duty on the part of the heroine. Jimena's father has insulted Rodrigo's, enfeebled by his advanced years. He calls upon his son to avenge his honor. In spite of his love for Jimena, Rodrigo shows no hesitation. He challenges the Count and kills him. In the lovers' interview which follows, Jimena is more distracted from her duty by her love than Rodrigo was, but yet resolves on vengeance. She demands a champion of the king, who objects that Rodrigo should be pardoned, having just saved the city from the invading Moors. Jimena insists: a champion appears, is overthrown, and is spared by Rodrigo, whereupon the king intervenes and orders the betrothal of the lovers.

Since 'The Cid' ends happily, so far as the hero and heroine are concerned, Corneille first called it a tragi-comedy, but later substituted the title of tragedy. Its general structure is the same as that of his other plays,—five fairly equal acts, subdivided into scenes, with rhymed Alexandrine couplets, excepting in a few lyric strophes. The time of the action is limited to twenty-four hours, but the scene of the action is restricted only by the boundaries of the town (Seville), the different places being marked by a fixed scenery, which presented several localities to the audience at the same time.

His dramatic form and stage properties Corneille had obtained from his French predecessors of the classical school. The mediæval Miracle Plays had practically fallen out of favor nearly a century before 'Mélite,' and had been prohibited in Paris in 1548. But the Fraternity of the Passion still occupied the only theatre in the city, and had a monopoly of all the performances in the city and suburbs. Into its theatre of the Hôtel of Burgundy it had put as much of its old multiplex scenery as it could fit into the new and narrow stage. And while it could no longer act the old Mysteries, still it clung to dramatic stories which knew neither unity of time, place, nor even action.

Outside of these playwrights, however, the Renaissance had created a set of men who looked towards classical antiquity for their literary standards. In 1552 Jodelle and his friends of the Pléiade had appealed to this class by acting in Boncourt College a tragedy modeled on Seneca's Latin dramas. This example was subsequently followed by many writers, who however rarely got their pieces acted, and therefore fell into the way of writing without having the necessities of stage effects in view. Consequently for nearly half a century the best dramatists of France were strangers to the public of the Hôtel of Burgundy, and were drifting more and more from a dramatic conception of the theatre into a lyric one. Long declamatory monologues, acts varying greatly in length and separated by elaborate choruses, were the chief features of this school. Nothing happened on the stage; all was told by messengers.

Yet these dramas, by their very lack of action and scenery, were suited to the limited means of strolling companies of actors; and modifications of them were being played more and more to provincial audiences. Finally in 1599 one of these companies came to Paris, leased the Hôtel of Burgundy from the Fraternity, now tired of its avocation, and laid there the foundations of modern French drama. The purveyor to this troupe was Alexandre Hardy, a man of some education, of considerable theatrical endowments, but lacking in literary taste. True to his classical models so far as the unlettered public of the Hôtel and its scenery would allow, he managed by cutting down the monologues, equalizing the acts, restricting or suppressing the choruses, and leading the dialogue to some climax visible to his audience, to effect a compromise between the partisans of the two schools and educate a new body of theatre-goers. His scenery he could not change, and it still remained a constant temptation to diversity of place and multiplication of episodes. Hardy labored for more than thirty years. It is to his dramatic form, audience, and stage that Corneille succeeded, continuing his work while avoiding his excesses. And aided by the growing taste and intelligence of his public, Corneille could further simplify and refine the style of play in vogue.

Now De Castro's 'Cid' had enjoyed the freedom of the Miracle Plays. It numbered three acts, divided into fifty-three scenes. Its episodes, many of them purely digressive, occupied nearly two years of time and were bounded in place only by the frontiers of Spain. In order to reduce this epic exuberance to the severity of the classical mold, Corneille had to eliminate the digressive episodes, cut down and combine the essential ones, connect the places where the action took place, and lessen the time of its duration. In the French 'Cid,' Rodrigo kills Jimena's father and is betrothed to her in less than twenty-four hours.

This instance alone illustrates the effort Corneille made on himself. It caught also the eye of his rivals and critics. 'The Cid' was fiercely assailed for its "inhumanity" and "improbability," and with the connivance of Richelieu the newly organized Academy was called upon to condemn it. While the opinion of this body was not indeed unfavorable, yet the dispute had so irritated Corneille that he retired to Rouen and for a time renounced his art. When he reappeared, it was as a dramatizer of classical subjects, that dealt with but one episode to a play. But the romantic side still survived in the love affair invariably interwoven with his nobler, sterner theme.

So 'Horace' (1640) treated of the fight of the Horatii and the Curatii, and the immolation of a woman's love to the Roman fatherland. 'Cinna' (1640–41) narrated a conspiracy against Augustus, which was undertaken through love for the heroine, but was pardoned by the Emperor's magnanimity. 'Polyeuctus' (1643) showed how a steadfast Christian husband could preserve his wife's fidelity against the memory of a first love, and how his martyrdom could result in her conversion. 'Pompey' (1643–44) recited the death of that leader and the devotion of Cornelia, his wife, to his memory.

These four plays, tragedies all, represent in their eloquence, their diction, nobility of thought, and lofty aspiration, the highest development of Corneille's dramatic genius.

After this period of serious composition Corneille sought relaxation in comedy, and produced from Spanish models 'The Liar' (1644) and 'The Sequel to the Liar' (1645). Both are superior in dialogue, action, and verse to his earlier plays, and the first remained the best comedy of the new school up to the appearance of Molière. Towards the end of 1645 'Rodogune' was acted, a tragedy to which Corneille was ever partial on account of its highly wrought, exciting solution. 'Théodore' (1646), the fate of another Christian martyr, and 'Heraclius' (1646–47), preceded their author's election to the Academy (January 22d, 1647). The Fronde then intervened, and it was not till 1649 that Corneille's best tragi-comedy, 'Don Sancho,' was performed. A spectacular play or opera, 'Andromeda' (1650), closely followed it. 'Nicomedes' (1651) was a successful tragedy, 'Pertharite' (1652) a failure. Consequently for the next few years Corneille devoted himself to religious poetry and a verse translation of the 'Imitation of Christ.'

But the visit of Molière's company to Rouen in 1658 incited him to write again for the stage. 'Œdipus' (1659), 'Sertorius' (1662), 'Sophonisba' (1663), 'Otho' (1664), 'Agesilas' (1666), and 'Attila' (1667), all tragedies, were the result. Some were successful, but others were not. Molière was now in full career, and Racine was beginning. Corneille's defects were growing. His plays were too much alike, and gallant talk supplied in them the place of deeds. In 1660 a second spectacular drama, 'The Golden Fleece,' had been performed; and the same year he had edited a general edition of his plays, with a critical preface to each play and three essays on the laws and theories of the drama. All this time he had not neglected society and religious verse, and probably in 1662 he had moved from Rouen to Paris.

A retirement of three years followed 'Attila.' Then in 1670 Corneille reappeared with the tragedy 'Titus and Berenice,' neglected by the public for Racine's 'Berenice.' In 1671 he collaborated with Molière and Quinault on a comedy-ballet, 'Psyche.' In 1672 he wrote 'Pulcheria,' a tragi-comedy, and in 1674 gave his last play, the tragedy of 'Surena,' to the stage. Henceforth only supplicatory poems addressed to the King reminded the Parisians of Corneille's existence. In 1682 he published the final revision of his dramas, and in 1684, on the night of September 30th, he passed away. He had married in 1641. Four children survived him.

Corneille's contemporaries complain of his slovenliness, his timidity, quick temper, and wearying conversation. He could never read his own plays successfully, and is even said to have spoken French incorrectly. He was reputed avaricious, but was continually lamenting his poverty, and seems to have died in want. He was quite tall, well set, with large eyes and strongly marked features.

Besides his services to French comedy, Corneille may be said to have established the higher comedy in verse, with its decent manners and self-respecting characters. In this departure he undoubtedly owed much to Plautus and Terence, but probably more to Hardy's tragi-comedies and lighter plays. The chief merit of his style was fine diction, eloquence, and harmony of phrase. His thought was high and noble. As a dramatist he excelled in the invention and variety of his situations. His defects were the reverse of these qualities: rhetoric, subtle sentiment, stiff characters.

The best complete edition of Corneille is Marty-Laveaux's in the Hachette series of 'Les Grands Écrivains de la France' (Great Writers of France), 12 volumes, 1862–68. This edition contains a biographical notice. The most complete bibliography is E. Picot's 'Bibliographie Cornélienne' (Paris, 1865). J. Taschereau's 'Histoire de la Vie et des Œuvres de Corneille' (History of the Life and Works of Corneille) is the best biography (published Paris, 1829: 3d edition, 1869). F. Guizot's 'Corneille and His Times' is the only life that has been translated into English (London, 1857). Of the separate plays, 'The Cid,' 'Horace,' and 'Polyeuctus' have been rendered into English blank verse by W. F. Nokes (Hachette and Company), and these three, together with 'Cinna,' have been literally translated by R. Mongan and D. McRae (London: 1878–86.)

F. M. Warren.

THE LOVERS

From 'The Cid'

The scene is an apartment in the house of Chimène's *father in Seville.* Chimène *and* Elvire *are conversing, after* Chimène *has learned that her father, the* Count de Gormas, *has lost his life in a duel with* Don Rodrigue, *the son of an aged nobleman insulted by* De Gormas.

CHIMÈNE — At stake is my honor; revenge must be mine;
  Whate'er the desire love may flattering stir,
  To the soul nobly born all excuse is disgrace.

Elvire —
> Thou lov'st Don Rodrigue; he can never offend.

Chimène —
> I admit it.

Elvire — Admitting it, how canst thou act?

Chimène —
> By sustaining my honor, by casting my care —
> Pursue him, destroy him, and after him — die.

Don Rodrigue [*entering as she speaks the last words*] —
> 'Tis well! Without taking the pains of pursuit,
> Be secure in the pleasure of ending my days.

Chimène —
> Elvire, oh where are we? What, what do I see?
> Rodrigue in this house! Before me, Rodrigue!

Don Rodrigue —
> Oh, spare not my blood; unresisted, pray taste
> Of my ruin the sweetness, of vengeance the joy.

Chimène —
> Alas!

Don Rodrigue — Hear me, lady!

Chimène — I die!

Don Rodrigue — But one word —

Chimène —
> Go, I say; let me die!

Don Rodrigue — Ah, vouchsafe me a word!
> And once I have spoke, make reply with — this sword.

Chimène —
> What! The sword e'en now red with the blood of my sire!

Don Rodrigue —
> Chimène, my Chimène!

Chimène — Hide that hideous steel,
> That rebuketh my eyes for thy crime and thy life.

Don Rodrigue —
> Nay, rather behold it, thy hate to excite,
> Thy wrath to increase — and my doom so to speed.

Chimène —
> It is tinged with my blood.

Don Rodrigue — Plunge it then into mine,
> That so it may lose the dread tint of thy veins.

Chimène —
> Ah, fate all too cruel! that slays in one day
> The father by steel, and the daughter by sight!
> Take away, as I bid, what I cannot endure;
> Thou will'st that I hearken — and kill'st me meantime!

Don Rodrigue —

What thou wishest I do; but with no less desire
That my life, now deplorable, ends by your hand;
For expect not, I beg, from my passion itself
A coward's repentance of deed so deserved.
From thy father's rash hand came a blow — past recall;
It dishonored my sire in his honored old age.
What are blows to a man of due honor thou knowest.
In the shame I had part, and its author must seek;
Him I saw — both my father and honor I 'venged;
I would do it again, if I had it to do.
Yet think not 'gainst duty to father and self
My love for thee, lady, no contest has made;
Of thy power in this moment do thou be the judge.
Too well might I doubt if such vengeance I dared.
Bound to please thee, Chimène, or to suffer affront,
Too rash seemed my arm — I would fain hold it back;
With a deed all too violent blamed I myself:
Thy beauty had weighed down the balance at last,
Had I not, to thy charms, countervailing, opposed
That a man lost to honor could not thee deserve;
That once having loved me when blameless I lived,
She who cared for me stainless must hate me disgraced;
That to hearken to love, to obey its soft voice,
Was to find myself shameful — thy favor to stain.
Again do I tell thee — and while I shall breathe
Unchanged shall I think and unchanging will say —
I have done thee offense, but I could not halt back,
A disgrace to remove and thyself to deserve.
But now, quits with honor, and quits toward my sire,
'Tis thee, thee alone, I would fain satisfy;
'Tis to proffer my blood that thou seest me here.
I have done what I should — what is left I would do.
Well I know that thy father's death arms thee toward mine;
Not thee have I wished of thy victim to cheat.
Boldly immolate, now, the blood he has spilled —
The being who glories that such was his deed.

Chimène —

Ah, Rodrigue! True it is that though hostile I am,
No blame can I speak that disgrace thou hast fled;
Howe'er from my lips this my dolor break forth,
I dare not accuse thee — I weep for my woes.
I know that thy honor, on insult so deep,
Demanded of ardor a valorous proof.

Thou hast done but the duty enjoined on the brave:
Yet more, in its doing 'tis mine thou hast taught.
By thy courage funest, and thy conquest, I'm schooled;
Thy father avenged and thine honor upheld,
Like care, see, is mine; for to load me with grief,
I must father avenge, *I* must honor uphold!
Alas, 'tis thy part here that brings me despair.
Had aught other misfortune bereft me of sire,
My heart in the joy of beholding thyself
The sole solace that heart could receive would have found
Against my affliction a charm would be strong,
My tears would be dried by the dearest of hands.
But lo! I must lose thee, my father a loss;
And the more that my soul may in torment be thrown,
My star has decreed that I compass thy end.
Expect not, in turn, from the passion I own,
That my hand I shall stay from thy punishment meet;
Thy direful offense makes thee worthy of me;
By thy death I shall show myself worthy of thee.

Unrhymed literal version in the metre of the original, by E. Irenæus
Stevenson.

DON RODRIGUE DESCRIBES TO KING FERNANDO HIS VICTORY OVER THE MOORS

From 'The Cid'

UNDER me, then, the troop made advance,
  With soldierly confidence marked on each brow.
    Five hundred we started, but soon reinforced,
Three thousand we were when the port we had reached;
So much did mere sight of our numbers, our mien,
New courage revive in all timorous hearts.
Two-thirds did I ambush, as soon as arrived,
In the vessels in harbor, that ready were found;
But the others, whose numbers each hour did increase,
With impatience on fire, all about me encamped,
Stretched out on the earth passed the beauteous night.
In the harbor, I order the guards to like watch;
Their concealment my stratagem further assists;—
I dared to declare, Sire, as thine the command
That I so followed out, and enjoined upon all.
In the radiance pallid that fell from the stars,
At last, with the flood-tide we spy thirty sails;

Beneath swells the wave, and in movement therewith,
The sea and the Moors into harbor advance.
We permit them a passage — to them all seemed calm,
Our soldiers unseen, and the walls without ward.
Our silence profound well deluded their wit;
No longer they doubt our surprise is achieved;
Without fear they draw nearer — they anchor — they land —
They run to the hands that are waiting to strike.
Then rise we together, and all in a breath
Utter clamorous shoutings that heavenward rise.
From the ships to such signal our troops make response;
They stand forth in arms, and the Moors are dismayed;
By dread they are seized when but half-disembarked;
Ere the battle's begun they have deemed themselves lost.
They have come but to pillage — 'tis fight that they meet.
We assail them on sea, we assail them on land;
On the ground runs the blood we set flowing in streams
Ere a soul can resist — or fly back to his post.
But soon in our spite the chiefs rallied their host,
Their courage awoke, and their fear was o'ercome:
The shame of their dying without having fought,
Their disorder arrests, and their valor restores.
A firm stand they take, and their swords are unsheathed;
The land and the stream, ay, the fleet and the port,
Are a field where, triumphant o'er carnage, is death.
Oh, many the deeds, the exploits worthy fame,
In that horror of darkness are buried for aye,
When each, the sole witness of blows that he struck,
Could not guess whither Fortune the conflict would steer!
I flew to all sides to encourage our force,
Here to push into action, and there to restrain,
To enrank the newcoming, to spur them in turn,
Yet naught could I know till the breaking of day.
But with dawn and the light, our advantage was plain;
The Moors saw their ruin; their courage declined;
And beholding new succor approach to our side,
Changed their ardor for battle to sheer dread of death.
Their vessels they seek, — every cable is cut;
For farewells to our ears are sent up their wild cries;
Their retreat is a tumult — no man ever heeds
If their princes and kings have made good their escape.
Even duty itself yields to fear so extreme.
On the flood-tide they came, the ebb bears them away;
Meantime their two Kings with our host still engaged,

'Mid a handful of followers, slashed by our blows,
In valiance contending, are selling life dear.
In vain to surrender I beg them — entreat,
With the cimeter gripped, not a word will they hear:
But at sight of their troops falling dead at their feet,
The brave who alone make so vain a defense,
Our chief they demand; and to me they submit.
To you, O my Sire, have I sent them, each one —
And the combatants lacking, the combat was done.

THE WRATH OF CAMILLA

From the 'Horace'

Horatius, *the only survivor of the combat, advances to meet his sister*
Camilla *with* Proculus *at his side, bearing the swords of the three
slain* Curatii — *one of whom was* Camilla's *betrothed.* Camilla *surveys him with horror and disdain as he advances.*

Horatius — Lo, sister, the arm that hath brothers avenged! —
The arm that our fate so contrary has checked,
The arm that makes Alba our own; and to-day
By one deed the lot of two nations hath fixed.
See these tokens of honor — my glory's attest.
Do thou pay the tribute now due to my fame.
Camilla —
Receive then my tears: for my tears are thy due.
Horatius —
Nay, Rome likes them not, after action so bold.
Our brothers, both slain by the combat's dark fate,
Are avenged by this blood — no more weeping demand.
If a loss be so paid, then the loss is no more.
Camilla —
Since thou deemest my brothers by blood so appeased,
I will cease to show sign of my grief for their death;
But who shall avenge me my lover's death, say?
And make me forget in one moment such loss?
Horatius —
What sayest thou, unhappy?
Camilla —

O beloved Curiace!
Horatius —
O boldness disgraceful, from sister disgraced!
The name on thy lips and the love in thy heart
Of the foe of our people, whose conquest is mine!

Thy criminal flame to such vengeance aspires!
Thou darest to utter such thought of thy heart!
Follow passion the less, better rule thy desire:
Make me not so to blush that thy sighs are not hid;
From this moment thou owest to smother thy flame,
Free thy heart from them — dwell on these trophies instead,
And make *them* from this hour thy sole pleasure in life.

Camilla —

Nay, first give me, cruel, a heart hard as thine,
And if thou wilt seek all my spirit to read,
Give me back Curiace, or my passion let glow.
My joy and my grief of his lot are a part;
Him living I loved — him in death I deplore.
No more find me sister — deserted by thee!
Behold in me only a woman outraged,
Who — like to some Fury pursuing thy steps —
Unceasing shall charge thee with trespass so great!
O tiger, blood-gorged, who forbiddest my tears,
Who would see me find joy in this death thou hast wrought,
Who vauntest to Heaven itself such a deed,
Shall I by approval bring death to him — twice?
Misfortunes so dire, may they follow thy life
That thou fallest to envying even my own!
Oh, soon by some cowardice mayest thou blot
This glory thy brutal soul reckons so dear!

Horatius —

O heavens! hath any an equal rage seen?
Dost thou think I could brook, all unmoved, such offense?
That race could endure a dishonor so deep?
Love, love thou the death which means good to thy State,
Prefer to thy passion and thoughts of this man
The sentiment due to a daughter of Rome!

Camilla —

Rome! Object supreme of the wrath that I feel!
This Rome, to whose aid came thy arm — and my loss;
Rome, city that bore thee — by thee so adored!
Rome, hated the more for its honoring thee!
O may each of her neighbors together in league
Sap every foundation, as yet so unsure!
Nay, if Italy be not enough to the fall,
Let the East and the West for her ruin unite;
Let peoples conjoined from the four winds of heaven,
Be met to her downfall; let hills aid, and seas;
O'erthrown on her walls may she prostrate be cast,

Torn out by her own hands, her entrails be strewn!
May the anger of Heaven, here kindled by me,
Rain down on her dwellings a deluge of fire!
O grant that mine own eyes such thunderbolt see!—
See her mansions in ashes, her laurels in dust,
See the latest of Romans yielding his last breath,
I cause of it all — I dying of joy!

[*With the last words* Camilla *rushes from the apartment.* Horace *snatches his sword and pursues her, exclaiming:*—]

Oh too much! Even reason to passion gives place.
Go, weep thou thy lost Curiace in the shades!

[*After an instant is heard behind the scenes the shriek of the wounded* Camilla:—]

Ah, traitor!

Horace [*returning to the stage*]—
Receive thou quick chastisement, due
Whomsoever shall dare Roman foe to lament.

Unrhymed literal version in the metre of the original, by E. Irenæus Stevenson.

PAULINA'S APPEAL TO SEVERUS

From 'Polyeucte'

SEVERUS —   I stand agaze,
Rooted, confounded, in sheer wonderment.
Such blind resolve is so unparalleled,
I scarce may trust the witness of mine ears.
A heart that loves you — and what heart so poor
That knowing, loves you not?— one loved of you,
To leave regretless so much bliss just won!
Nay, more — as though it were a fatal prize —
To his corrival straight to yield it up!
Truly, or wondrous manias Christians have,
Or their self-happiness must be sans bourn,
Since to attain it they will cast away
What others at an empire's cost would win.
For me, had fate, a little sooner kind,
Blessed my true service with your hand's reward,
The glory of your eyes had been my worship;
My twin kings had they reigned — kings? nay, my gods!
To dust, to powder, had I grinded been
E'er I had —

Paulina —   Hold! let me not hear too much;
Let not the smoldering embers of old time

Relume to speech unworthy of us both.
Severus, know Paulina utterly:
His latest hour my Polyeuctus nears;
Nay, scarce a minute has he yet to live.
You all unwittingly have been the cause
Of this his death. I know not if your thoughts,
Their portals opening to your wish's knock,
Have dared to some wild hope give harboring,
Based upon his undoing; but know well,
No death so cruel I would not boldly front,
Hell hath no tortures I would not endure,
Or e'er my stainless honor I would spot,
My hand bestowing upon any man
Who anywise were his death's instrument.
And could you for such madness deem me apt,
Hate would replace my erstwhile tender love.
You're generous — still be so, to the end:
My father fears you; is in mood to grant
All you might ask; ay, I e'en dare aver
That if my husband he do sacrifice,
'Twill be to you. Save then your hapless victim;
Bestir yourself; stretch him your helping hand!
That this is much to claim of you, I know,
But more the effort's great, the more the glory!
To save a rival 'spite of rivalry
Were greatness all particular to you.
And — be that not enough for your renown —
'Twere much to let a woman erst so loved,
And haply who may yet be somewhat dear,
Her greatest treasure owe to your great heart.
In fine, remember that you are Severus!
Adieu! alone determine of your course;
For if you be not all I think you are,
I'd still, not knowing it, believe you such.

English Translation by W. F. Nokes.

VICTOR COUSIN

(1792–1867)

ALL Philosophy, past and present, has been based on the attempt to make abstract ideas clear. The questions Cousin endeavors to answer are:—"Do ideas exist apart from Being and Knowledge; and if so, on what are they founded?" and his answer involves his whole doctrine.

Victor Cousin, the son of a watchmaker of Voltairean principles and of a laundress of strong religious convictions, was born in Paris on November 28th, 1792. But in spite of his humble origin he obtained a brilliant education, and through the force of his genius lived to have precedence at court over his social superiors. The little gamin owed his start in life to Madame Viguier, who placed him at school.

VICTOR COUSIN

On leaving college, from which he was graduated first in his class at the age of eighteen, he could have obtained a position in the Council of State at a yearly salary of five thousand francs; but he preferred to enter the Normal School, then but recently established, with the intention of teaching literature. The impression made upon him by Laromiguière's lectures on philosophy decided him to devote himself to the latter branch of study. Philosophy, to Cousin, was not only a keen delight but a battle as well. Many systems were then arrayed against each other; these in turn fascinated his imagination and excited his enthusiasm,—first the sensual school, then Scottish philosophy as developed by Royer-Collard and Maine de Biran; then Kant, Schelling, Hegel, whose genius he was the first to recognize; and later, Plotinus, Descartes, and Leibnitz. All these doctrines, as he expounded them in his lectures, simmered in his imagination for a while, and unconsciously modifying each other, left a deposit from which arose eclecticism.

There was a dearth of French men of letters when Cousin reached manhood. To become a fashionable lecturer it was only necessary to speak of literature and philosophy in elegant language; and as to these requirements the young orator added a poetic imagination, he became famous at once.

One of Cousin's distinguishing qualities was the impetus he gave to other minds. His lectures created positive fanaticism. But twenty years of age, his delicate face was lighted up with magnificent dark eyes which emitted fire as his own enthusiasm grew. He had a fine voice, was a finished comedian, a poet rather than a deep or original thinker, a preacher rather than a professor, and looked like "a tribune and apostle in one."

It is difficult to understand nowadays the enthusiasm aroused by Cousin's philosophy, or the attacks upon it. He advanced no new truths. No objection could be made to a belief in God, the spirituality and immortality of the soul, and moral liberty. But Cousin went further. He wished to establish philosophy on an independent basis; to found an intermediate school that would not clash with religion, but subsist side by side with, though independent of and in a certain measure controlling it. This aroused the hostility of the Church without satisfying the extremists, who clamored for more radical doctrines. After 1820, when the Normal School was suppressed, Cousin had recourse to private teaching, and devoted his leisure to editing the classics. His edition of Plato occupied him many years. "Every man's life should contain one monument and several episodes," he declared; and his Plato, he believed, was destined to be his "monument."

When Cousin was restored to his chair in 1828, he brought with him a new philosophy which fulfilled the aspirations of the rising generation, whose idol he became. During this course he propounded a few transcendental theories borrowed from Hegel and Schelling, emitted several contestable historical views, and distributed all the doctrines he knew,— and, add his enemies, all those he did not know,— into four divisions. Taken as a whole, Cousin's system has far more in common with Christianity than with pantheism.

During the next three years he made rapid strides in his career. He had taken no part in the July Revolution, but his friends were placed in office by that event, and through their influence he became successively member of the Royal Council of Public Instruction, member of the Academy, and Peer of France.

Cousin was in virtual control of French philosophy when, in 1830, he resigned his chair to become Director of the Sorbonne. To his new task he brought an intelligence matured by time; and the twenty years of his administration were fruitful of good results. He formed a corps of learned professors, perfected the study of French, and placed philosophy on a sound basis. His indefatigable activity, breadth of view, and devotion to teaching made him an admirable director of a school destined to train the professors of a nation. Each one was encouraged to take up an original line of research. He regulated the position of the Sorbonne towards religion, instructing the teachers that belief in God, free-will, and duty was to be inculcated.

Not being of a naturally tender disposition, Cousin may not have loved the students for themselves, but he passionately loved talent, and exerted himself to foster and develop it. Of a disdainful, sarcastic turn of mind, Cousin's mordant wit was well known and greatly feared. His habits were frugal, and though he dressed badly, he was prodigal with regard to books. He nowhere appeared to better advantage than in his library at the Sorbonne, where so many of his books were written. He could talk magnificently on any subject — for an hour; after that, his own eloquence carried him beyond all bounds and he was apt to indulge in paradox. Guizot said of him: "C'est l'esprit qui a le plus besoin de garde-fou." (His is a mind which has the greatest need of restraint.) His voice was wonderfully expressive: witty sayings, comparisons, anecdotes, crowded upon his tongue; as a rule he absorbed the entire conversation and created a sensation, as he loved to do.

Liberal in matters of philosophy rather than in politics, Cousin engaged in a battle with the clergy, to whom however he cheerfully conceded the rights granted by the Charter, and a certain preponderance in the schools. He considered it criminal to attack religion, and required it to be taught in the primary schools, though he excluded it from the University, where it might clash with philosophy. Towards the end of his life he entered into a correspondence with the Pope to prevent 'The True, the Beautiful, the Good' from being placed on the Index Expurgatorius, and obtained his point only after lengthy negotiations.

In the earlier years of his life, Cousin's poetic temperament, aided by youth, carried him towards pure philosophy and German ideas. The word pantheism however grew to be a very abomination to him; but storm and protest as he would, it pursued him all his life; his lyric descriptions of God were rigidly interpreted according to pantheistic formulæ, and hurled at his head until he cried "Enough!" "This is the truth," was answered back, though he had long since erased that compromising indorsement of Schelling's system.

Debarred from both politics and teaching at the age of sixty, with intellect and vitality unimpaired, Cousin devoted the fourteen remaining years of his life to literature; and now that the eclectic philosophy is considered merely a brilliant but fleeting system which has lived its day, we still turn with pleasure to his 'Biographies.'

It was by study of the seventeenth century that Cousin's purely literary career began. He relates facts and penetrates the nature of a school destined to train the professors of a nation. Each one was encouraged to take up an original line of research. He regulated the position of the Sorbonne towards religion, instructing the teachers that belief in God, free-will, and duty was to be inculcated.

Not being of a naturally tender disposition, Cousin may not have loved the students for themselves, but he passionately loved talent, and exerted himself to foster and develop it. Of a disdainful, sarcastic turn of mind, Cousin's mordant wit was well known and greatly feared. His habits were frugal, and though he dressed badly, he was prodigal with regard to books. He nowhere appeared to better advantage than in his library at the Sorbonne, where so many of his books were written. He could talk magnificently on any subject — for an hour; after that, his own eloquence carried him beyond all bounds and he was apt to indulge in paradox. Guizot said of him: «C'est l'esprit qui a le plus besoin de garde-fou.» (His is a mind which has the greatest need of restraint.) His voice was wonderfully expressive: witty sayings, comparisons, anecdotes, crowded upon his tongue; as a rule he absorbed the entire conversation and created a sensation, as he loved to do.

Liberal in matters of philosophy rather than in politics, Cousin engaged in a battle with the clergy, to whom however he cheerfully conceded the rights granted by the Charter, and a certain preponderance in the schools. He considered it criminal to attack religion and required it to be taught in the primary schools, though excluded it from the University, where it might clash with philosophy. Towards the end of his life he entered into a correspondence with the Pope to prevent 'The True, the Beautiful, the Good' from being placed on the Index Expurgatorius, and obtained his point only after lengthy negotiations.

In the earlier years of his life, Cousin's poetic temperament, aided by youth, carried him towards pure philosophy and German ideas. The word pantheism however grew to be a very abomination to him; but storm and protest as he would, it pursued him all his life; his lyric descriptions of God were rigidly interpreted according to pantheistic formulæ, and hurled at his head until he cried "Enough!" "This is the truth," was answered back, though he had long since erased that compromising indorsement of Schelling's system.

Debarred from both politics and teaching at the age of sixty, with intellect and vitality unimpaired, Cousin devoted the fourteen remaining years of his life to literature; and now that the eclectic philosophy is considered merely a brilliant but fleeting system which has lived its day, we still turn with pleasure to his 'Biographies.'

It was by study of the seventeenth century that Cousin's purely literary career began. He relates facts and penetrates the nature of his characters. Taine declares that when at last the lovely face of Madame de Longueville does appear, crash goes a pile of folios to the floor! Nevertheless, strength and energy characterize Cousin's style, and make good his dictum "Style is movement." To the very end, Cousin retained the spontaneous emotion of youth. The quality of vehemence everywhere so apparent in these 'Biographies' presupposes an intense emotion which is communicated from the writer to the reader.

It was a current joke among the professors of the Sorbonne that her biographer was in love with Madame de Longueville. "Every one knows that Cousin is the *chevalier servant* of Madame de Longueville," writes Taine. "This noble lady has had the rare privilege of making post-mortem conquests, and the solid walls of the Sorbonne have not protected M. Cousin from the darts of her beautiful eyes. He is so deeply in love with her that he speaks of Condé (her brother) as a brother-in-law, and of La Rochefoucauld (her lover) as a rival."

Cousin's critics take this retrospective infatuation too seriously. It was merely an "episode" in his life; and when Sainte-Beuve said, "Cousin's bust would one day have engraved beneath it: 'He wished to found a great system of philosophy, and he loved Madame de Longueville,'"— he was more witty than just. It is only fair to add that Sainte-Beuve considered Cousin the most brilliant meteor that had flashed across the sky of the nineteenth century.

In his later years, Cousin recommended 'The True, the Beautiful, the Good' and his 'Philosophy of History' for perusal, in preference to his other books. He was conscious of the drawback attendant upon scattering his doctrines over so many books, and condensed them in the former volume. Composed of brilliant and incomplete fragments, if it does not constitute a systematic whole, the pages relating to God and necessary and universal principles are however full of grandeur, and will always endear it to humanity.

On the 2d of January, 1867, Cousin passed away during his sleep, having been until the last in full possession of the lucidity and vigor which characterized his mind. He left his fine library to the State, with ample funds for its maintenance. He has had the privilege of living in the books of many distinguished men whose minds he trained, whose careers he advanced, and who have recorded in brilliant pages the debt owed him, not by themselves alone, but by all Frenchmen of succeeding generations.

PASCAL'S SKEPTICISM

From 'Les Pensées de Pascal'

Pascal was skeptical of philosophy, not of religion. It is because he is skeptical in philosophical matters, and recognizes the powerlessness of reason and the destruction of natural truth among men, that he clings desperately to religion as the last resource of humanity.

What is philosophical skepticism? It is a philosophical opinion which consists in rejecting philosophy as unfounded, on the ground that man of himself is incapable of reaching any truth, and still less those truths which constitute what philosophy terms natural morals and religion, such as free-will; the law of duty; the distinction between good and evil, the saint and the sinner; the holiness of virtue; the immateriality of the soul; and divine providence. Skepticism is not the enemy of any special school of philosophy, but of all.

Pascal's 'Pensées' are imbued with philosophical skepticism; Pascal is the enemy of all philosophy, which he rejected utterly. He does not admit the possibility of proving God's existence; and to demonstrate the impotence of reason, he invented a desperate argument. We can ignore truth, but we cannot ignore our own interest, the interest of our eternal happiness. According to him, we must weigh the problem of divine Providence from this point of view. If God does not exist, it cannot hurt us to believe in him; but if by chance he should exist, and we do not believe in him, the consequences to us would be terrible.

"Let us examine this point of view and say: God is, or he is not," writes Pascal. "To which belief do we incline? Reason is powerless to solve the question for us. Chaos separates us from its solution. At the extreme end of this infinite distance, a game is being played in which heads or tails will turn up. What do we win in either case? Through the power of mere reason we can neither prove nor disprove God's existence; through the power of reason we can defend neither proposition."

On this foundation, not of truth but of interest, Pascal founds the celebrated calculation to which he applies the law of chance. Here is the conclusion he reaches:— "In the eyes of Reason, to believe or not to believe in God (the for and against, or as I say, the game of 'croix ou pile') is equally without consequence;

but in the eyes of interest the difference is infinite, because the Infinite is to be gained or lost thereby."

Pascal considers skepticism legitimate, because philosophy or natural reason is incapable of attaining to certitude; he affirms "the sole rôle of reason to be the renouncement of reason; that true philosophy consists in despising philosophy."

The God of Abraham, the God of Jacob, not the God of savants and philosophers, is the God of Pascal. He caught a gleam of light, and believed he had found peace in submission to Christ and his confessor. Doubt yielded to grace; but vanquished doubt carried reason and philosophy in its train.

MADAME DE LONGUEVILLE

From the 'Life of Madame de Longueville'

WHAT a number of accomplished women the seventeenth century produced,—women who inspired adoration, drew all hearts towards them, and spread among all ranks the cultus of beauty, termed by Europe, French gallantry! They accompany this great century upon its too rapid flight, and mark its principal moments. Madame de Longueville has her place in the brilliant galaxy of seventeenth-century women by the right of true beauty and rare charm.

Born in 1619, in the prison of Vincennes, during the captivity of her father, Henri de Bourbon,—whose wife, the beautiful Marguerite de Montmorency, shared his imprisonment,—Mademoiselle de Bourbon grew in grace under the care of her mother, dividing her time between the Carmelite Convent and the Hôtel de Rambouillet, nourishing her soul upon pious and romantic books. Married at the age of twenty-three to a man twenty-three years her senior, she found that M. de Longueville, instead of trying by tenderness to make his young wife forget this disparity, followed the triumphal car of the famous Duchesse de Montbazon, the veriest coquette of the century. Insulted by her rival, neglected by her husband, Madame de Longueville yielded by degrees to the contagion in the midst of which she lived, and after having spent some time at the frivolous court of Münster, was fascinated on her return to Paris by the wit, chivalrous appearance, and distinguished manners of the Prince de Marcillac, afterwards Duc de la Rochefoucauld. This intimacy decided her career, the first part of which it closed in 1648.

The vicissitudes of the Fronde; love, as it was understood at the Hôtel Rambouillet,—that is, love *à la Scudéry*, with its enchantments, its sufferings, intermingled with danger and glory, crossed by adventures, triumphant over the greatest tests, yielding finally to its own weakness and exhausting itself,— such is the second period of Madame de Longueville's life, a period so short, and yet so crowded with events, which began in 1648 and ended towards the middle of 1654. After 1654 Madame de Longueville's life was one long repentance, daily growing in austerity; passed first by the bedside of her husband, and then at the Carmelite Convent and at Port-Royal, where she died in 1679.

First, spotless brilliancy; then sin and prompt expiation. Thus is divided the career of Madame de Longueville. A famous beauty, she possessed height and a fine figure. Her eyes were of the tenderest blue; her light-brown hair, of exceptional fineness, fell in abundant curls around the graceful oval of her face and rippled over her shoulders, which were fully exposed in accordance with the fashion of the time. Add to these attractions a complexion whose fairness, delicacy, and soft brilliancy justified its being compared with a pearl. Her charming skin reflected all the emotions of her soul. She spoke in the softest voice; her gestures harmonized with her face and voice, making perfect music. But her greatest charm was a graceful ease of manner, a languor which had brilliant awakenings when she was moved by passion, but which in every-day life gave her an appearance of aristocratic indifference, of indolence, frequently mistaken for ennui or disdain.

Madame de Longueville loved but one person. For his sake she sacrificed repose, interest, duty, and reputation. For his sake she embarked upon the rashest and most contradictory enterprises. La Rochefoucauld drew her into the Fronde; it was he who made her advance or retreat, who separated her from or reconciled her with her family, who controlled her absolutely. In his hands she became a heroic instrument. Passion and pride had their share in the life of adventure she faced so bravely; but what a soul she must have possessed, to find consolation in struggles such as these! And as so often happens, the man for whom she made these sacrifices was unworthy of them. Witty but selfish, he judged others by himself. Subtle in evil as she was in good, full of selfish cunning in the pursuit of his interests, the least chivalrous of men though he affected the semblance of the highest chivalry, when he believed that Madame de Longueville was yielding to the influence of the Duc de Nemours, he turned against her, blackened her reputation, revealed the weaknesses by which he had profited, and when she was struggling to repair her mistakes by the rigid mortification of the cloister, he published those 'Mémoires' in which he tore her to pieces.

La Rochefoucauld made his peace with the court. He even rode in Mazarin's carriages, saying with inimitable aplomb, "Everything comes to pass in France;" he obtained a pension for himself, a fine position for his son; and was worshiped by lovely women, one of whom, Madame de Lafayette, replaced Madame de Longueville and consecrated her life to him.

How different was Madame de Longueville's conduct! Love led her into the Fronde, love kept her there; when love failed her, everything failed her. The proud heroine who waged war against Mazarin, who sold her jewels, braved the ocean, aroused the North and South, and held the royal authority at bay, withdrew from the scene at the age of thirty-five, in the full maturity of her beauty, when her own interest was alone at stake.

To understand Madame de Longueville's character, to exonerate her from the charge of inconsistency or want of purpose, the unity of her life must be sought in her devotion to the man she loved. It is there in its entirety and unchangeableness; at once triumphant, absurd, and pathetic in the midst of the greatest follies. Her recklessness was inspired by the fickle restless mind of La Rochefoucauld. It was he who drifted from one faction to another, moved by his own interest alone. To Madame de Longueville herself belong her courage in the face of danger; a certain secret delight in the extremity of misfortune; and in defeat a pride not inferior to that of De Retz himself. She does not drop her eyes; she directs her gaze towards worthier objects. Once wounded in that which was most precious to her — her love — she bade adieu to the world, without currying favor with the court, and asking pardon of God alone.

MADAME DE CHEVREUSE

From the 'Life of Madame de Chevreuse'

MADAME DE CHEVREUSE was endowed with almost all the qualities constituting political genius. One alone was wanting, and this was precisely the master quality without which all the others lead but to the ruin of their possessor. She was incapable of keeping in view a steady aim, or rather of choosing her own aim; some one else always directed her choice. She had an essentially feminine temperament; therein lay the secret of her strength and weakness. Her spring of action was love, or rather gallantry; and the interest of the man she loved became for the time being her main object in life. This accounts for the wonderful sagacity, subtlety and energy she expended in the pursuit of a chimerical aim which constantly eluded her grasp, and which seemed to charm her by the spell of its difficulty and danger. La Rochefoucauld accuses her of bringing misfortune upon all who loved her. It were more just to say that all whom she loved drew her into foolhardy enterprises.

Richelieu and Mazarin left no stone unturned to attach Madame de Chevreuse to their interests. Richelieu considered her an enemy worthy of his steel; he exiled her several times, and when after his death the doors of France were opened to the men he had proscribed, the Cardinal's implacable resentment survived in the soul of the dying Louis XIII., who closed them to her.

If you turn to Mazarin's confidential letters you will see what intense anxiety this beautiful conspirator caused him in 1643. During the Fronde, he had reason to congratulate himself on having effected a reconciliation with her and followed her wise advice. In 1660, when the victorious Mazarin signed the treaties of Westphalia and the Pyrenees, and Don Luis de Haro congratulated him on the peace which was about to succeed to years of storms, the Cardinal answered that peace was not possible in a country where even women were to be feared. "You Spaniards can speak lightly of such matters, since your women are interested in love alone; but things are different in France, where there are three women quite capable of upsetting the greatest kingdom in the world; namely, the Duchess of Longueville, the Princess Palatine, and the Duchess of Chevreuse."

COMPARISON BETWEEN MADAME DE HAUTEFORT AND MADAME DE CHEVREUSE

From the 'Life of Madame de Chevreuse'

FATE placed them both in the same century, in the same party and in the midst of the same events; but far from resembling each other, they illustrate opposite poles of the character and destiny of women. Both were ravishingly beautiful, brilliantly intelligent, unflinchingly courageous: but one was as pure as she was beautiful, uniting grace with majesty and inspiring respect as well as love. The favorite of a king, not a suspicion touched her; proud to haughtiness with the great and powerful, sweet and compassionate to the oppressed; loving greatness and prizing virtue above the esteem of the world; combining the wit of a précieuse, the daintiness of a fashionable beauty, with the intrepidity of a heroine and the dignity of a great lady,—she left an odor of sanctity behind her.

The other possessed even greater powers of fascination and an irresistible charm. Witty but ignorant; thrown into the midst of party excesses and thinking but little of religion; too great a lady to submit to restraint; bowing only to the dictates of honor; abandoned to gallantry and making light of all else; despising danger and public opinion for the sake of the man she loved; restless rather than ambitious, freely risking her life and that of others; and after spending her youth in intrigues and plots, and strewing her path with victims, traveling through Europe as captive and conqueror and turning the heads of kings; having seen Chalais ascend the scaffold, Châteauneuf dismissed from the ministry, the Duc de Lorraine stripped of his possessions, Buckingham assassinated, the King of Spain launched upon a disastrous war, Queen Anne humiliated, and Richelieu triumphant; defiant to the last, always ready to play a part in that game of politics which had become a passion with her, to descend to the lowest intrigues or to take the most reckless course of action; seeing the weakness of her enemy, and daring enough to undertake his ruin:—Madame de Chevreuse was a devoted friend, an implacable enemy, the most redoubtable adversary of both Richelieu and Mazarin.

ABRAHAM COWLEY

(1618–1667)

BY THOMAS R. LOUNSBURY

ABRAHAM COWLEY, the posthumous son of a citizen and stationer of London, was born in that city in the latter half of 1618. His early education was received at Westminster school. In 1637 he became a scholar of Trinity College, Cambridge, where in 1639 he took the degree of B. A., and in 1642 that of M. A. During the civil commotions that followed, he was ejected from Cambridge University and withdrew to Oxford, which had become for the time being the headquarters of the royalist party. While there he not only continued his studies, but was present and in service in several of King Charles's journeys and expeditions. He finally became secretary to Lord Jermyn, who at the Restoration was created Earl of St. Albans. In this capacity he followed to France the Queen Henrietta Maria, who had left England for that country in 1644, and was there busily engaged in political intrigues to aid the cause of her husband. In her service Cowley was diligently employed, and was dispatched on missions to Jersey, Scotland, Flanders, and Holland. His principal and most absorbing occupation, how-

ABRAHAM COWLEY

ever, was carrying on the cipher correspondence that took place between the King and the Queen. This, and duties allied to this, were so engrossing that according to Sprat, his intimate friend and first biographer, they "for some years together took up all his days and two or three nights every week."

After the execution of Charles, Cowley remained in France until 1656. Then he returned to England, practically to play the part of a spy, if the testimony of the authority already quoted can be trusted. Once there, he was arrested and imprisoned, but subsequently was allowed to go at liberty on bail. After the death of Cromwell he went back to France. He returned at the Restoration, only to meet with the neglect which was incurred by all the followers of the exiled monarch who made the mistake of combining an objectionable sobriety and decency of life with loyalty to the house of Stuart. Furthermore, certain things he had done had made him an object of pretended suspicion. He had been created in 1657 a Doctor of Medicine by the University of Oxford, in obedience to an order of the government. There were passages also in the preface prefixed to the edition of his works published in 1656, which were taken to imply submissive acquiescence on his part in the new order of things. These were satisfactory pretexts for disregarding claims which the self-sacrificing service of years had established. The mastership of the Savoy, which he expected and which he had a right to expect, was given to another. But at last, more fortunate than many of his fellow-sufferers, he received through the influence of the Earl of St. Albans and the Duke of Buckingham a provision sufficient to maintain him in comfort. Withdrawing entirely from public life, he lived successively at Barn Elms and at Chertsey in Sussex. At the latter place he died on July 18th, 1667, and was buried in Westminster Abbey.

Such is a brief outline of the career of the man who during his lifetime was the most popular of English poets. In spite of occasional intervals of good fortune, it is on the whole a melancholy story. Such it seemed to Cowley himself. In the essay entitled 'Of Myself,' quoted below, and in 'The Complaint,' we get not only further details of the author's personal fortunes, but an insight into the feelings of disappointment and dejection which came over him, as he contrasted the difference between what he had hoped and expected and what he had succeeded in achieving or gaining. We learn from the preface to the volume published in 1656, that long before that time he had been eager to withdraw from the harassing occupations in which much of his time had already been wasted, and to spend the remainder of his days in seclusion and study. « My desire,» he then wrote, « has been for some years past (though the execution has been accidentally diverted), and does still vehemently continue, to retire myself to some of our American plantations; not to seek for gold or to enrich myself with the traffic of those parts, which is the end of most men that travel thither, . . . but to forsake this world forever, with all the vanities and vexations of it, and to bury myself in some obscure retreat there, but not without the consolations of letters and philosophy.»

There seems no reason to doubt the genuineness of the feeling thus expressed, and there is little difficulty in tracing it to its cause. Unquestionably the political situation had a good deal to do with its manifestation at that particular time; but the source of his dejection lay deeper than any temporary overthrow of the side with which he sympathized. Cowley's career, however successful, had not fulfilled the extraordinary promise of his youth. He made his appearance as a man of letters long before he became a man, Of all authors in our own tongue, perhaps in any tongue, he was the most precocious. This is not to say that others have not written as early as he, but that no one who wrote so early has written so well. In 1633, when he was but fifteen years old, he brought out a little volume containing over a thousand lines and entitled 'Poetical Blossomes.' It was made up mainly of two productions, entitled respectively 'Constantia and Philautus' and 'Pyramus and Thisbe.' Of this work a second edition appeared in 1636, with a number of additional poems. In the epistle prefixed to this impression, he states that 'Pyramus and Thisbe' was composed at ten years of age and 'Constantia and Philautus' at thirteen. But much more important than either, appeared in this volume of 1636 a poem entitled 'A Vote.' It consists of eleven stanzas, the last three of which, with a few slight verbal alterations, were cited by Cowley in his essay upon himself. This poetry, which he never surpassed, he there tells us was written when he was thirteen years old. The early date given to its composition may have been due to a slip of memory; at any rate it was not until 1636 that the piece appeared in print. But even were it not written till the very year in which it was published, it must be regarded as a marvelous production for a boy, not alone for the poetic ability displayed in it, but for the philosophic view it takes of life.

A third edition of 'Poetical Blossomes' appeared in 1637. In 1638 came out a pastoral comedy, written while he was king's scholar in Westminster School, and called 'Love's Riddle.' During that same year a Latin comedy entitled 'Naufragium Joculare' had been acted by the students of Trinity College, and a little later was published. All the works mentioned, it will be seen, had been produced by him before he had completed, and most of them in fact before he had reached, his twentieth year. For one further dramatic production he is also responsible at a very early age. In 1641, when the King's son Charles (afterwards Charles II.) passed through Cambridge, Cowley "made extempore," as he says, a comedy which was acted, for the entertainment of the Prince, at Trinity College on March 12th. It was called 'The Guardian,' and in 1650 it was published. At a later period it was rewritten by the author, and in 1661 was brought out at the theatre in Lincoln's Inn Fields with a fair degree of success. It was then entitled 'Cutter of Coleman Street.'

From the time of leaving Cambridge, though he did not cease writing, nothing of his was published for a long while, at least under his own name. In 1647 appeared a volume entitled 'The Mistress'; but even this the publisher professed to bring out wholly on his own responsibility. The work consisted entirely of love poems, and the very doubtful assertion is steadily repeated in all notices of Cowley's life that they became the favorite ones of the age. If so, the age must have been peculiarly frigid in its feelings. Whatever excellences these pieces possess, they are not the excellences that characterize love poetry. It is hardly possible to speak of them as the transcript of any personal experiences. They are rather academic exercises, intellectual disquisitions upon the general subject of love, than the impassioned utterances of a man whose feelings have ever been profoundly stirred. The Greek scholar Joshua Barnes, who flourished a little later, declared that in spite of the sentiments expressed in these pieces, and in a subsequent poem called 'The Chronicle,' Cowley was never in love but once in his life. It could not be proved on the evidence of the verses contained in 'The Mistress' that he was ever in love at all. Still, if the poems lack fervor, they often exhibit ingenuity and grace.

On his return to England during the Protectorate he brought out a collected edition of his works in folio. It was published in 1656, and amongst the matter which then appeared for the first time were the odes written in professed imitation of Pindar. The composition of these set a literary fashion which did not die out till the latter half of the next century. To write so-called Pindaric odes became one of the regular duties of all who were in doubt about their poetic inspiration, and felt called upon to convince others as well as themselves of their possession of it. But Cowley introduced the term and not the thing. He seems to have fancied that to produce lines with a different number of feet, and stanzas with a different number of lines, was the proper method of representing the measure. But Pindar's verse, if it can be called irregular at all, was regularly irregular. Cowley's imitation was irregular and nothing else. Still, so great was his influence, that a plentiful crop of these spurious reproductions of an imaginary metrical form sprang up in the literature of the hundred years following the Restoration. Among them can occasionally be found genuine imitations of Pindar's measure, such as are the odes of Congreve and of Gray; but of the countless number of all kinds produced, those of the last-named author are the only ones that can be said still to survive.

Another production that made its first appearance in the folio of 1656 was part of an epic poem, which Cowley had begun while he was at the university. Its subject was the life and exploits of King David, and his intention was to complete it in the orthodox number of twelve books. It would appear from his preface that the theme was chosen from a sense of duty as well as from inclination. Poetry, he there tells us, should no longer be pressed into the service of fable. The Devil had stolen it and alienated it from the service of the Deity; and it was time to recover it out of the tyrant's power and restore it to the kingdom of God. If this doctrine be true, it must be conceded that Cowley's hands were not the ones to effect the restoration. From what he did towards bringing about the result he deemed desirable, it looks rather as if the craft of the great Adversary of mankind had been put forth to defeat the end in view by instigating this particular poet to undertake this particular task. The 'Davideis' is written in rhymed heroic verse, of which Cowley never gained the full mastery. There is nothing in the matter to make amends for the versification, which is rarely well finished and is not unfrequently rough and inharmonious. In truth, the distinguishing characteristic of the work as a whole is its well-sustained tediousness. Fortunately it was not completed beyond the fourth book; it would not have lessened Cowley's reputation if the first had never been begun.

Cowley continued to write after this volume was published; but a good deal of his later production was in the Latin tongue, and has in consequence been condemned to perpetual obscurity. Interest in that could be least expected to survive the general decay of interest which gradually overtook his writings. His fame stood highest in his own century, and he is perhaps as much underestimated now as he was overestimated then. His collected works passed through edition after edition, and by 1681 had reached the seventh. Such a sale in those days of mighty folios and comparatively few readers indicated great and general popularity. But by the end of the century his influence had begun to decline. Dryden at the outset of his literary career had been one of his most fervent admirers; but in the preface to his last book, which appeared in 1700, he censured his faults severely, and declared that he had so sunk in his reputation that for ten impressions which his works had had in so many successive years, scarcely a hundred copies were purchased during a twelvemonth at the time of his writing. This statement reflected more the feelings of the critic than it represented the actual facts, for between 1699 and 1721 four editions of Cowley's works appeared. Still it is none the less true that Cowley's reputation was then steadily sinking, and was destined to sink still lower. In 1737 Pope directly referred to the fact in the following lines, which have been repeatedly quoted in connection with it:—

«Who now reads Cowley? If he pleases yet,
It is his moral pleases, not his wit;
Forgot his epic, nay, Pindaric art,
But still I love the language of his heart.»

Between 1721 indeed and 1802 not a single separate edition of his works was published; though selections were edited by Bishop Hurd in the interval, and of course his poems were included in the great collections of the booksellers, and of Anderson and Chalmers. In 1881 an edition limited to one hundred copies of his works in verse and prose, for the first time completely collected, was brought out by Grosart as a part of the Chertsey Worthies' Library.

The reasons for the decay of Cowley's reputation are not hard to find. It was due to what Pope called his wit, or what more specifically was criticized by Addison in No. 62 of the Spectator as his false wit. "He could never," says Dryden, "forgive any conceit which came in his way, but swept like a drag-net great and small." There are accordingly but few poems of his that can be read with unmixed pleasure. Even when the piece as a whole is admirable, the reader is always in danger of finding somewhat to jar upon his taste in details. A passage containing lofty thoughts nobly expressed is liable to be followed by another, in which forced and unnatural images or far-fetched conceits utterly destroy the impression wrought by the majestic simplicity of what has preceded. This inequality began early to lower him in general esteem. Even as far back as the seventeenth century, Lord Rochester is reported by Dryden as having said of him very pertinently, if somewhat profanely, that "Not being of God, he could not stand."

From this censure, which is too applicable to most of his work, there are portions that are absolutely free. These are his translations and his prose pieces. In the former — especially in his versions of Anacreon — the necessity of adhering to his original rendered it impracticable for him to go straying after these meretricious beauties of style. But for them in the latter he seems never to have had the least inclination. Here his expression never suffered from the perversion of his taste. He preceded Dryden in introducing into our language that simple structure, that easy natural mode of expression which is peculiarly adapted to the genius of our tongue, and forms the greatest possible contrast to the Latinized diction, the involved constructions, the sometimes stately but frequently cumbrous sentences of the men of the former age, like Hooker and Milton. Cowley was in fact the first regular writer of modern prose. In certain particulars his work in that line has rarely been surpassed. It is simple and straightforward, never sinking into commonplace when treating of the common, never lacking in dignity when occasion demands it to rise. The longest and most important of these prose pieces — nearly all of which are interspersed with poetry — is the one entitled 'A Discourse concerning the Government of Oliver Cromwell.' It was written shortly after the Protector's death, though not published until 1661. In spite of the fact that it is mainly an elaborate attack upon that great ruler, the opening pages prove how profound had been the impression produced upon Cowley by the personality of the man.

Cowley is perhaps the chief of the poets who for some inexplicable reason have been termed metaphysical. The peculiarities of style which led to this school being so designated, were exemplified in passages taken from his works, in the elaborate criticism given of him by Dr. Johnson in the biography he prepared. To most persons that account is now better known than the productions of the man who was its subject. It is not to be expected indeed that Cowley will ever again be a popular author. But he will always be a favorite to a certain extent of a small body of cultivated men, who will overlook his faults for the sake of the lofty morality couched in lofty diction that is scattered through his writings, and even more for that undertone of plaintive tenderness which Pope aptly styled "the language of his heart." In literary history he will have a place of his own, as having founded in the so-called Pindaric odes a temporary fashion of writing; and a more exalted position for having been the pioneer in the production of our present prose style.

Thomas R. Lounsbury.

OF MYSELF

IT IS a hard and nice subject for a man to write of himself; it grates his own heart to say anything of disparagement, and the reader's ears to hear anything of praise from him. There is no danger from me of offending him in this kind: neither my mind nor my body nor my fortune allow me any materials for that vanity. It is sufficient for my own contentment that they have preserved me from being scandalous or remarkable on the defective side. But besides that, I shall here speak of myself only in relation to the subject of these precedent discourses, and shall be likelier thereby to fall into the contempt than rise up to the estimation of most people.

As far as my memory can return back into my past life, before I knew, or was capable of guessing, what the world or the glories or business of it were, the natural affections of my soul gave me a secret bent of aversion from them, as some plants are said to turn away from others by an antipathy imperceptible to themselves and inscrutable to man's understanding. Even when I was a very young boy at school, instead of running about on holy-days and playing with my fellows, I was wont to steal from them and walk into the fields, either alone with a book, or with some one companion if I could find any of the same temper. I was then too so much an enemy to all constraint, that my masters could never prevail on me, by any persuasions or encouragements, to learn without book the common rules of grammar; in which they dispensed with me alone, because they found I made a shift to do the usual exercise out of my own reading and observation. That I was then of the same mind as I am now (which I confess I wonder at, myself) may appear by the latter end of an ode which I made when I was but thirteen years old, and which was then printed with many other verses. The beginning of it is boyish; but of this part, which I here set down (if a very little were corrected), I should hardly now be much ashamed.

> THIS only grant me, that my means may lie
> Too low for envy, for contempt too high.
> Some honor I would have,
> Not from great deeds, but good alone;
> The unknown are better, than ill known:
> Rumor can ope the grave.
> Acquaintance I would have, but when't depends
> Not on the number, but the choice of friends.
>
> Books should, not business, entertain the light,
> And sleep, as undisturbed as death, the night.
> My house a cottage more
> Than palace; and should fitting be
> For all my use, no luxury.
> My garden painted o'er
> With nature's hand, not art's; and pleasures yield,
> Horace might envy in his Sabin field.
>
> Thus would I double my life's fading space;
> For he that runs it well, twice runs his race.
> And in this true delight,
> These unbought sports, this happy state,
> I would not fear, nor wish, my fate;
> But boldly say each night,
> "To-morrow let my sun his beams display,
> Or in clouds hide them; I have lived to-day."

You may see by it, I was even then acquainted with the poets (for the conclusion is taken out of Horace); and perhaps it was the immature and immoderate love of them, which stampt first, or rather engraved, these characters in me: they were like letters cut into the bark of a young tree, which with the tree still grow proportionably. But how this love came to be produced in me so early, is a hard question: I believe I can tell the particular little chance that filled my head first with such chimes of verse as have never since left ringing there: for I remember, when I began to read, and to take some pleasure in it, there was wont to lie in my mother's parlor (I know not by what accident, for she herself never in her life read any book but of devotion),—but there was wont to lie Spenser's works: this I happened to fall upon, and was infinitely delighted with the stories of the knights and giants and monsters and brave houses, which I found everywhere there (though my understanding had little to do with all this); and by degrees with the tinkling of the rhyme and dance of the numbers; so that I think I had read him all over before I was twelve years old, and was thus made a poet as immediately as a child is made an eunuch.

With these affections of mind, and my heart wholly set upon letters, I went to the university; but was soon torn from thence by that violent public storm, which would suffer nothing to stand where it did, but rooted up every plant, even from the princely cedars to me the hyssop. Yet I had as good fortune as could have befallen me in such a tempest; for I was cast by it into the family of one of the best persons, and into the court of one of the best princesses, of the world. Now, though I was here engaged in ways most contrary to the original design of my life,—that is, into much company, and no small business, and into a daily sight of greatness, both militant and triumphant (for that was the state then of the English and French courts), yet all this was so far from altering my opinion, that it only added the confirmation of reason to that which was before but natural inclination. I saw plainly all the paint of that kind of life, the nearer I came to it; and that beauty which I did not fall in love with when for aught I knew it was real, was not like to bewitch or entice me when I saw that it was adulterate. I met with several great persons, whom I liked very well; but could not perceive that any part of their greatness was to be liked or desired, no more than I would be glad or content to be

in a storm, though I saw many ships which rid safely and
bravely in it: a storm would not agree with my stomach, if it
did with my courage. Though I was in a crowd of as good
company as could be found anywhere, though I was in business
of great and honorable trust, though I ate at the best table, and
enjoyed the best conveniences for present subsistence that ought
to be desired by a man of my condition in banishment and public distresses; yet I could not abstain from renewing my old
school-boy's wish, in a copy of verses to the same effect:—

> "Well then, I now do plainly see
> ' This , busy world and I shall ne'er agree," etc.

And I never then proposed to myself any other advantage
from his Majesty's happy Restoration, but the getting into some
moderately convenient retreat in the country; which I thought,
in that case, I might easily have compassed as well as some
others, who with no greater probabilities or pretenses have
arrived to extraordinary fortune: but I had before written a
shrewd prophecy against myself, and I think Apollo inspired me
in the truth though not in the elegance of it:—

> "THOU neither great at court, nor in the war,
> Nor at th' exchange shalt be, nor at the wrangling bar.
>   Content thyself with the small barren praise
>   Which neglected verse does raise."
>   She spake; and all my years to come
>   Took their unlucky doom.
>   Their several ways of life let others chuse,
>   Their several pleasures let them use;
>   But I was born for Love and for a Muse.
>
>   With Fate what boots it to contend?
> Such I began, such am, and so must end.
>   The star that did my being frame
>   Was but a lambent flame,
>   And some small light it did dispense,
>   But neither heat nor influence.
> No matter, Cowley; let proud Fortune see
> That thou canst her despise no less than she does thee.
>
>   Let all her gifts the portion be
>   Of folly, lust, and flattery,
>   Fraud, extortion, calumny,

Murder, infidelity,
Rebellion and hypocrisy.
Do thou nor grieve nor blush to be,
As all th' inspired tuneful men,
And all thy great forefathers were, from Homer down to Ben.

However, by the failing of the forces which I had expected, I did not quit the design which I had resolved on; I cast myself into it *à corps perdu*, without making capitulations, or taking counsel of fortune. But God laughs at a man who says to his soul, "Take thy ease." I met presently not only with many little incumbrances and impediments, but with so much sickness (a new misfortune to me) as would have spoiled the happiness of an emperor as well as mine; yet I do neither repent nor alter my course. "Non ego perfidum dixi sacramentum;" nothing shall separate me from a mistress which I have loved so long and have now at last married; though she neither has brought me a rich portion, nor lived yet so quietly with me as I hoped from her:—

"Nec vos, dulcissima mundi
Nomina, vos Musæ, Libertas, Otia, Libri,
Hortique Sylvæque, anima remanente, relinquam,"

(Nor by me e'er shall you,
You, of all names the sweetest and the best,
You, Muses, books, and liberty, and rest;
You, gardens, fields, and woods, forsaken be,
As long as life itself forsakes not me.)

But this is a very pretty ejaculation; because I have concluded all the other chapters with a copy of verses, I will maintain the humor to the last.

ON THE DEATH OF CRASHAW

POET and Saint! to thee alone are given
The two most sacred names of earth and heaven;
The hard and rarest union which can be,
Next that of Godhead with humanity.
Long did the Muses banished slaves abide,
And build vain pyramids to mortal pride;
Like Moses, thou (though spells and charms withstand)
Hast brought them nobly home back to their holy land.

Ah, wretched we, poets of earth! but thou
Wert, living, the same poet which thou'rt now;
Whilst angels sing to thee their airs divine,
And joy in an applause so great as thine.
Equal society with them to hold,
Thou need'st not make new songs, but say the old;
And they, kind spirits! shall all rejoice, to see
How little less than they exalted man may be.

Still the old heathen gods in numbers dwell;
The heavenliest thing on earth still keeps up hell;
Nor have we yet quite purged the Christian land;
Still idols here, like calves at Bethel, stand.
And though Pan's death long since all oracles broke,
Yet still in rhyme the fiend Apollo spoke:
Nay, with the worst of heathen dotage, we
Vain men! the monster woman deify;
Find stars, and tie our fates there in a face,
And paradise in them, by whom we lost it, place.

What different faults corrupt our Muses thus?
Wanton as girls, as old wives fabulous!
Thy spotless Muse, like Mary, did contain
The boundless Godhead; she did well disdain
That her eternal verse employed should be
On a less subject than eternity;
And for a sacred mistress scorned to take
But her, whom God himself scorned not his spouse to make.

It (in a kind) her miracle did do;
A fruitful mother was, and virgin too.
How well, blest swan, did Fate contrive thy death,
And make thee render up thy tuneful breath
In thy great mistress's arms, thou most divine
And richest offering of Loretto's shrine!
Where, like some holy sacrifice t' expire,
A fever burns thee, and Love lights the fire.
Angels, they say, brought the famed Chapel there,
And bore the sacred load in triumph through the air:
'Tis surer much they brought thee there; and they,
And thou their charge, went singing all the way.

Pardon, my Mother-Church, if I consent
That angels led him when from thee he went;
For ev'n in error seen no danger is,
When joined with so much piety as his.

Ah, mighty God! with shame I speak't, and grief;
Ah, that our greatest faults were in belief!
And our weak reason were ev'n weaker yet,
Rather than thus our wills too strong for it.
His faith, perhaps, in some nice tenets might
Be wrong; his life, I'm sure, was in the right;
And I myself a Catholic will be,
So far at least, great Saint, to pray to thee.

Hail, bard triumphant, and some care bestow
On us, the poets militant below!
Oppressed by our old enemy, adverse chance,
Attacked by envy and by ignorance;
Enchained by beauty, tortured by desires,
Exposed by tyrant Love to savage beasts and fires.
Thou from low earth in nobler flames didst rise,
And like Elijah, mount alive the skies.
Elisha-like, but with a wish much less,
More fit thy greatness and my littleness,
Lo! here I beg — I, whom thou once didst prove
So humble to esteem, so good to love —
Not that thy spirit might on me doubled be,
I ask but half thy mighty spirit for me:
And when my muse soars with so strong a wing,
'Twill learn of things divine, and first of thee, to sing.

ON THE DEATH OF MR. WILLIAM HERVEY

IT WAS a dismal and a fearful night;
    Scarce could the moon disk on th' unwilling light,
        When sleep, death's image, left my troubled breast,
            By something liker death possest.
My eyes with tears did uncommanded flow,
            And on my soul hung the dull weight
            Of some intolerable fate.
What bell was that? ah me! too much I know.

My sweet companion and my gentle peer,
Why hast thou left me thus unkindly here,
Thy end forever, and my life to moan?
            Oh, thou hast left me all alone!
Thy soul and body, where death's agony
            Besieged around thy noble heart,
            Did not with more reluctance part,
Than I, my dearest friend, do part from thee.

My dearest friend, would I had died for thee!
Life and this world henceforth will tedious be;
Nor shall I know hereafter what to do,
       If once my griefs prove tedious too.
Silent and sad I walk about all day,
       As sullen ghosts stalk speechless by,
       Where their hid treasures lie;
Alas! my treasure's gone! why do I stay?

He was my friend, the truest friend on earth;
A strong and mighty influence joined our birth:
Nor did we envy the most sounding name
       By friendship given of old to fame.
None but his brethren he and sisters knew,
       Whom the kind youth preferred to me;
       And ev'n in that we did agree,
For much above myself I loved them too.

Say—for you saw us, ye immortal lights—
How oft unwearied have we spent the nights,
Till the Ledæan stars, so famed for love,
       Wondered at us from above!
We spent them not in toys, in lusts, or wine;
       But search of deep philosophy,
       Wit, eloquence and poetry;
Arts which I loved, for they, my friend, were thine.

Ye fields of Cambridge, our dear Cambridge, say
Have ye not seen us walking every day?
Was there a tree about which did not know
       The love betwixt us two?
Henceforth, ye gentle trees, forever fade;
       Or your sad branches thicker join,
       And into darksome shades combine,
Dark as the grave wherein my friend is laid!
Henceforth, no learnèd youths beneath you sing,
Till all the tuneful birds to your boughs they bring;
No tuneful birds play with their wonted cheer,
       And call the learned youths to hear;
No whistling winds through the glad branches fly:
       But all, with sad solemnity,
       Mute and unmovèd be,
Mute as the grave wherein my friend does lie.

To him my muse made haste with every strain,
Whilst it was new and warm yet from the brain:

He loved my worthless rhymes, and like a friend,
    Would find out something to commend.
Hence now, my Muse! thou canst not me delight:
    Be this my latest verse,
    With which I now adorn his hearse;
And this my grief, without thy help, shall write.

Had I a wreath of bays about my brow,
I should contemn that flourishing honor now,
Condemn it to the fire, and joy to hear
    It rage and crackle there.
Instead of bays, crown with sad cypress me;
    Cypress, which tombs does beautify;
    Not Phœbus grieved so much as I,
For him who first was near that mournful tree.

Large was his soul, as large a soul as e'er
Submitted to inform a body here;
High as the place 'twas shortly in heaven to have,
    But low and humble as his grave:
So high, that all the Virtues there did come,
    As to their chiefest seat,
    Conspicuous and great;
So low, that for me too it made a room.

He scorned this busy world below, and all
That we, mistaken mortals! pleasure call;
Was filled with innocent gallantry and truth,
    Triumphant o'er the sins of youth.
He like the stars, to which he now is gone,
    That shine with beams like flame,
    Yet burn not with the same,
Had all the light of youth, of the fire none.

Knowledge he only sought, and so soon caught,
As if for him knowledge had rather sought:
Nor did more learning ever crowded lie
    In such a short mortality.
Whene'er the skillful youth discoursed or writ,
    Still did the nations throng
    About his eloquent tongue;
Nor could his ink flow faster than his wit.

So strong a wit did nature to him frame,
As all things but his judgment overcame;

His judgment like the heavenly moon did show,
    Tempering that mighty sea below;
Oh! had he lived in learning's world, what bound
    Would have been able to control
    His overpowering soul!
We've lost in him arts that not yet are found.

His mirth was the pure spirits of various wit,
Yet never did his God or friends forget;
And when deep talk and wisdom came in view,
    Retired, and gave to them their due:
For the rich help of books he always took,
    Though his own searching mind before
    Was so with notions written o'er,
As if wise nature had made that her book.

So many virtues joined in him, as we
Can scarce pick here and there in history;
More than old writers' practice e'er could reach;
    As much as they could ever teach.
These did Religion, queen of virtues, sway;
    And all their sacred motions steer,
    Just like the first and highest sphere,
Which wheels about, and turns all heaven one way.

With as much zeal, devotion, piety,
He always lived, as other saints do die.
Still with his soul severe account he kept,
    Wiping all debts out ere he slept:
Then down in peace and innocence he lay,
    Like the sun's laborious light,
    Which still in water sets at night,
Unsullied with his journey of the day.

Wondrous young man! why wert thou made so good,
To be snatched hence ere better understood?
Snatched before half of thee enough was seen!
    Thou ripe, and yet thy life but green!
Nor could thy friends take their last sad farewell;
    But danger and infectious death
    Maliciously seized on that breath
Where life, spirit, pleasure, always used to dwell.

But happy thou, ta'en from this frantic age,
Where ignorance and hypocrisy does rage!

A fitter time for heaven no soul e'er chose,
    The place now only free from those.
There 'mong the blest thou dost forever shine,
      And wheresoe'er thou cast thy view
      Upon that white and radiant crew,
Seest not a soul clothed with more light than thine.

And if the glorious saints cease not to know
Their wretched friends who fight with life below,
Thy flame to me does still the same abide,
    Only more pure and rarefied.
There, whilst immortal hymns thou dost rehearse,
      Thou dost with holy pity see
      Our dull and earthly poesy,
Where grief and misery can be joined with verse.

A SUPPLICATION

AWAKE, awake, my Lyre!
    And tell thy silent master's humble tale
      In sounds that may prevail;
Sounds that gentle thoughts inspire
      Though so exalted she,
      And I so lowly be,
Tell her, such different notes make all thy harmony.

    Hark! how the strings awake;
And though the moving hand approach not near,
      Themselves with awful fear
A kind of numerous trembling make.
      Now all thy forces try,
      Now all thy charms apply;
Revenge upon her ear the conquests of her eye.

    Weak Lyre! thy virtue sure
Is useless here, since thou art only found
      To cure, but not to wound,
And she to wound, but not to cure.
      Too weak, too, wilt thou prove
      My passion to remove;
Physic to other ills, thou'rt nourishment to love.

    Sleep, sleep again, my Lyre!
For thou canst never tell my humble tale
      In sounds that will prevail,

Nor gentle thoughts in her inspire;
　　All thy vain mirth lay by;
　　Bid thy strings silent lie;
Sleep, sleep again, my Lyre, and let thy master die.

EPITAPH ON A LIVING AUTHOR

HERE, passenger, beneath this shed,
　　Lies Cowley, though entombed, not dead;
　　Yet freed from human toil and strife,
And all th' impertinence of life.

Who in his poverty is neat,
And even in retirement great,
With Gold, the people's idol, he
Holds endless war and enmity.

Can you not say, he has resigned
His breath, to this small cell confined?
With this small mansion let him have
The rest and silence of the grave:

Strew roses here as on his hearse,
And reckon this his funeral verse;
With wreaths of fragrant herbs adorn
The yet surviving poet's urn.

WILLIAM COWPER.

WILLIAM COWPER

(1731–1800)

THE poet Cowper, who stands in the gap that separates Pope from Wordsworth, belongs to the group that includes Thomson, Young, Goldsmith, and Crabbe. If he is unimportant to-day in comparison with his importance to his own time, yet his service to English poetry is great, for he dispersed the artificial atmosphere which Pope had thrown around it. His moods and his keys were alike limited, and he was soon overshadowed by Wordsworth. Cowper saw Nature; Wordsworth saw into Nature, and touched chords undreamed of by the gentle poet of rural scenes and fireside pleasures. Cowper's simplicity of diction was in his day almost daring; and he broke away from all the sentimental Arcadian figures with which Thomson's landscapes were peopled. Therefore his value lies in the note of sincerity that he sounded. Singularly enough, he has been admired by French critics. He has been compared to Rousseau, and Sainte-Beuve calls him "the bard of domestic life." His fame as a serious poet rests chiefly on 'The Task,' which Hazlitt calls "a poem which, with its pictures of domestic comfort and social refinement, can hardly be forgotten but with the language itself."

His life is briefly told. He was born at Berkhampstead, England, November 26th, 1731. Through his mother he was descended from the family of the poet John Donne. She died when he was but six years of age, and he was sent to school in Hertfordshire and to Westminster. For three years he studied law at the Temple, but although called to the bar in 1754, he never practiced. As a young man he had an attack of madness, attempted suicide, and was confined at St. Albans for two years. When released he retired to Huntington, where he formed a friendship with the Unwins. On the death of Rev. William Unwin, he and Mrs. Unwin removed to Olney, where most of Cowper's poems were written, and afterward to Weston, where Mrs. Unwin died in 1796. Cowper survived her four years, dying on April 25th, 1800.

At Olney, Cowper lived in seclusion, amusing himself with his garden and greenhouse, raising pineapples, mending windows, writing, reading, and playing with his pets. The chief of them were his three hares, Puss, Tiny, and Bess, which formed the topic of an essay in the Gentleman's Magazine for June, 1784. It is this simple parlor at Olney which Cowper describes in 'The Task,' where he says:—

> « Now stir the fire, and close the shutters fast,
> Let fall the curtains, wheel the sofa round,
> And while the bubbling and loud-hissing urn
> Throws up a steamy column, and the cups
> That cheer, but not inebriate, wait on each,
> So let us welcome peaceful evening in. »

In this retreat from the haunts of the worldly, whom he deemed so trivial and sinful, the poet found happiness in watching the flickering fire and listening to the wild blasts of winter that swept the panes with swirling snow. Here he sat in his easy-chair, while the dog dozed at his feet, the hares gamboled, and the linnets twittered until silenced by a quaint bit of music on the harpsichord. Cowper would twine "silken thread round ivory reels," wind crewels, or read aloud to his two devoted companions as they knitted, or

> « — the well-depicted flower
> Wrought patiently into the snowy lawn. »

The one, Mrs. Unwin, was somewhat prim and puritanical; the other, Lady Austen, a handsome woman of the world, was gay and vivacious, and banished Cowper's dark moods by her grace and charm. To dispel his morbid fancies she told him the old story of the London citizen riding to Edmonton, which, says Hazlitt, "has perhaps given as much pleasure to as many people as anything of the same length that ever was written."

"Lady Austen," says his biographer Wright, "seeing his face brighten, and delighted with her success, wound up the story with all the skill at her command. Cowper could no longer control himself, but burst out into a loud and hearty peal of laughter. The ladies joined in his mirth, and the merriment had scarcely subsided by supper-time. The story made such an impression on his mind that at night he could not sleep; and his thoughts having taken the form of rhyme, he sprang from his bed and committed them to paper, and in the morning brought down to Mrs. Unwin the crude outline of 'John Gilpin.' All that day and for several days he secluded himself in the greenhouse, and went on with the task of polishing and improving what he had written. As he filled his slips of paper, he sent them across the market-place to Mr. Wilson, to the great delight and merriment of that jocular barber, who on several other occasions had been favored with the first sight of some of Cowper's smaller poems."

The portrait of John Gilpin was taken from John Beyer, a linen-draper who lived at No. 3 Cheapside. 'John Gilpin' was published anonymously in the Public Advertiser, and was received with enthusiasm. Printed as a ballad, copies of it, with pictures of John Gilpin flying past the "Bell" at Edmonton, were sold by hundreds; but Cowper did not acknowledge the poem until 1785, when he brought out 'The Task.'

This was also suggested by Lady Austen, who asked him to write something in blank verse. Cowper replied that he lacked a subject. "Subject—nonsense!" she said: "you can write on anything. Take this sofa for a subject." Following her command, the poet named the first book of 'The Task' 'The Sofa.' She suggested also the verses on 'The Loss of the Royal George.'

At Weston Cowper appears to have enjoyed the society of the county-side. His companions here were Puss, the last surviving hare, and the Spaniel Beau, "a spotted liver-color and white, or rather a chestnut" dog, the subject of several poems.

Cowper never married. His attachment to Theodora—the "Delia" of his verses—the daughter of his uncle, Ashley Cowper, lasted through his life, and her sister, Lady Hesketh, was one of his kindest and best friends. It was she who made for him those peculiar muslin caps which he wears in his portraits. Many short poems addressed to her attest his affection and gratitude for her friendship and ministrations, and to Mrs. Unwin belong the verses and the sonnet inscribed 'To Mary.'

Lives of Cowper are numerous. His old friend, John Newton, attempted one immediately after his death, but this was not completed; and the first to appear was a life by Hayley (1803–6), extended in the 'Life and Letters of Cowper,' by T. S. Grimshawe (1835). There are also Cowper's own 'Memoirs' (a description of his mental derangement and religious experiences), published in 1816; 'Life and Letters of Cowper' by Southey in 1835; and two books by T. Wright, 'The Town of Cowper' (1886); and 'Life of Cowper' (1892). An interesting biography has also been written by Goldwin Smith, in the series of 'English Men of Letters,' in which he says:—

"In all his social judgments Cowper is at a wrong point of view. He is always deluded by the idol of his cave. He writes perpetually on the twofold assumption that a life of retirement is more favorable to virtue than a life of action, and that 'God made the country and man made the town.' . . . His flight from the world was rendered necessary by his malady and respectable by his literary work; but it was a flight and not a victory. His misconception was fostered and partly produced by a religion which was essentially ascetic, and which, while it gave birth to characters of the highest and most energetic beneficence, represented salvation too little as the reward of effort, too much as the reward of passion, belief, and of spiritual emotion."

Yet despite this gloom, Cowper possessed the humor which finds admirable expression in many small poems, in ‹John Gilpin› and in his ‹Letters.› These are the real mirror of his life. Southey considers his letters the most delightful in the language. They contain nothing but the details of his daily life, and such happenings as the flowering of pinks, the singing of birds in the apple-blossoms, the falling of the dew on the grass under his window, the pranks of his pets, the tricks of the Spaniel Beau, the frolics of the tortoise-shell kitten, the flight of his favorite hare, and the excitements of a morning walk when the once nodding grass is "fledged with icy feathers." Their English is so easy and graceful, and their humor so spontaneous, that the reader feels a sense of friendship with the modest poet of ‹The Task,› who, despite his platitudes, wins a certain respectful admiration.

THE CRICKET

LITTLE inmate, full of mirth,
  Chirping on my kitchen hearth,
  Wheresoe'er be thine abode,
Always harbinger of good,
Pay me for thy warm retreat
With a song more soft and sweet;
In return thou shalt receive
Such a strain as I can give.

Thus thy praise shall be expressed,
Inoffensive, welcome guest!
While the rat is on the scout,
And the mouse with curious snout,
With what vermin else infest
Every dish, and spoil the best;
Frisking thus before the fire,
Thou hast all thine heart's desire.

Though in voice and shape they be
Formed as if akin to thee,
Thou surpassest, happier far,
Happiest grasshoppers that are;
Theirs is but a summer song —
Thine endures the winter long,
Unimpaired and shrill and clear,
Melody throughout the year.

THE WINTER WALK AT NOON

From 'The Task'

THE night was winter in his roughest mood;
   The morning sharp and clear. But now at noon
   Upon the southern side of the slant hills,
And where the woods fence off the northern blast,
The season smiles, resigning all its rage,
And has the warmth of May. The vault is blue
Without a cloud, and white without a speck
The dazzling splendor of the scene below.
Again the harmony comes o'er the vale;
And through the trees I view the embattled tower
Whence all the music. I again perceive
The soothing influence of the wafted strains,
And settle in soft musings as I tread
The walk, still verdant, under oaks and elms,
Whose outspread branches overarch the glade.
The roof, though movable through all its length,
As the wind sways it, has yet well sufficed;
And intercepting in their silent fall
The frequent flakes, has kept a path for me.
No noise is here, or none that hinders thought.
The redbreast warbles still, but is content
With slender notes, and more than half suppressed:
Pleased with his solitude, and flitting light
From spray to spray, where'er he rests he shakes
From many a twig the pendent drops of ice
That tinkle in the withered leaves below.
Stillness, accompanied with sounds so soft,
Charms more than silence. Meditation here
May think down hours to moments. Here the heart
May give a useful lesson to the head,
And Learning wiser grow without his books.
Knowledge and Wisdom, far from being one,
Have ofttimes no connection. Knowledge dwells
In heads replete with thoughts of other men;
Wisdom in minds attentive to their own.
Knowledge, a rude unprofitable mass,
The mere materials with which Wisdom builds,
Till smoothed and squared, and fitted to its place,
Does but encumber whom it seems to enrich.
Knowledge is proud that he has learned so much;

Wisdom is humble that he knows no more.
Books are not seldom talismans and spells,
By which the magic art of shrewder wits
Holds an unthinking multitude enthralled.
Some to the fascination of a name
Surrender judgment, hoodwinked. Some the style
Infatuates, and through labyrinths and wilds
Of error leads them, by a tune entranced;
While sloth seduces them, too weak to bear
The insupportable fatigue of thought,
And swallowing therefore without pause or choice
The total grist unsifted, husks and all.
But trees and rivulets, whose rapid course
Defies the check of winter, haunts of deer,
And sheep-walks populous with bleating lambs,
And lanes, in which the primrose ere her time
Peeps through the moss that clothes the hawthorn root,
Deceive no student. Wisdom there, and truth,—
Not shy, as in the world, and to be won
By slow solicitation,—seize at once
The roving thought, and fix it on themselves.

ON THE LOSS OF THE ROYAL GEORGE

Written When the News Arrived

Toll for the brave—
    The brave that are no more!
  All sunk beneath the wave,
    Fast by their native shore!

Eight hundred of the brave,
    Whose courage well was tried,
  Had made the vessel heel,
    And laid her on her side.

A land breeze shook the shrouds,
    And she was overset—
  Down went the Royal George,
    With all her crew complete.

Toll for the brave!
    Brave Kempenfelt is gone;
  His last sea fight is fought,
    His work of glory done.

It was not in the battle;
  No tempest gave the shock;
She sprang no fatal leak;
  She ran upon a rock.

His sword was in its sheath;
  His fingers held the pen,
When Kempenfelt went down
  With twice four hundred men.

Weigh the vessel up,
  Once dreaded by our foes!
And mingle with our cup
  The tear that England owes.

Her timbers yet are sound,
  And she may float again,
Full charged with England's thunder,
  And plow the distant main.

But Kempenfelt is gone —
  His victories are o'er;
And he and his eight hundred
  Shall plow the waves no more.

IMAGINARY VERSES OF ALEXANDER SELKIRK

DURING HIS SOLITARY ABODE ON JUAN FERNANDEZ

I AM monarch of all I survey —
  My right there is none to dispute;
From the centre all round to the sea,
  I am lord of the fowl and the brute.
O Solitude! where are the charms
  That sages have seen in thy face?
Better dwell in the midst of alarms
  Than reign in this horrible place.

I am out of humanity's reach;
  I must finish my journey alone,
Never hear the sweet music of speech —
  I start at the sound of my own.
The beasts that roam over the plain
  My form with indifference see;
They are so unacquainted with man,
  Their tameness is shocking to me.

Society, friendship, and love,
   Divinely bestowed upon man!
O, had I the wings of a dove,
   How soon would I taste you again!
My sorrows I then might assuage
   In the ways of religion and truth —
Might learn from the wisdom of age,
   And be cheered by the sallies of youth.

Religion! What treasure untold
   Resides in that heavenly word! —
More precious than silver and gold,
   Or all that this earth can afford;
But the sound of the church-going bell
   These valleys and rocks never heard,
Never sighed at the sound of a knell,
   Or smiled when the Sabbath appeared.

Ye winds that have made me your sport,
   Convey to this desolate shore
Some cordial endearing report
   Of a land I shall visit no more!
My friends — do they now and then send
   A wish or a thought after me?
Oh tell me I yet have a friend,
   Though a friend I am never to see.

How fleet is the glance of the mind!
   Compared with the speed of its flight,
The tempest itself lags behind,
   And the swift-wingèd arrows of light.
When I think of my own native land,
   In a moment I seem to be there;
But alas! recollection at hand
   Soon hurries me back to despair.

But the sea-fowl has gone to her nest,
   The beast is laid down in his lair;
Even here is a season of rest,
   And I to my cabin repair.
There's mercy in every place,
   And mercy — encouraging thought!
Gives even affliction a grace,
   And reconciles man to his lot.

THE IMMUTABILITY OF HUMAN NATURE
From a Letter to William Unwin (1780)

WHEN we look back upon our forefathers, we seem to look back upon the people of another nation; almost upon creatures of another species. Their vast rambling mansions, spacious halls, and painted casements, the Gothic porch smothered with honeysuckles, their little gardens and high walls, their box-edgings, balls of holly, and yew-tree statues, are become so entirely unfashionable now, that we can hardly believe it possible that a people who resemble us so little in their taste should resemble us in anything else. But in everything else, I suppose, they were our counterparts exactly; and time, that has sewed up a slashed sleeve and reduced the large trunk-hose to a neat pair of silk stockings, has left human nature just where it found it.

The inside of the man at least has undergone no change. His passions, appetites, and aims are just what they ever were. They wear perhaps a handsomer disguise than they did in the days of yore, for philosophy and literature will have their effect upon the exterior; but in every other respect a modern is only an ancient in a different dress.

FROM A LETTER TO REV. JOHN NEWTON

OLNEY, NOVEMBER 30TH, 1783.

My dear Friend:—

I HAVE neither long visits to pay nor to receive, nor ladies to spend hours in telling me that which might be told in five minutes; yet often find myself obliged to be an economist of time, and to make the most of a short opportunity. Let our station be as retired as it may, there is no want of playthings and avocations, nor much need to seek them, in this world of ours. Business, or what presents itself to us under that imposing character, will find us out even in the stillest retreat, and plead its importance, however trivial in reality, as a just demand upon our attention. It is wonderful how by means of such real or seeming necessities my time is stolen away. I have just time to observe that time is short, and by the time I have made the observation, time is gone.

I have wondered in former days at the patience of the ante-diluvian world, that they could endure a life almost millenary, and with so little variety as seems to have fallen to their share. It is probable that they had much fewer employments than we. Their affairs lay in a narrower compass; their libraries were indifferently furnished; philosophical researches were carried on with much less industry and acuteness of penetration, and fiddles perhaps were not even invented. How then could seven or eight hundred years of life be supported? I have asked this question formerly, and been at a loss to resolve it; but I think I can answer it now. I will suppose myself born a thousand years before Noah was born or thought of. I rise with the sun; I worship; I prepare my breakfast; I swallow a bucket of goat's milk and a dozen good sizable cakes. I fasten a new string to my bow, and my youngest boy, a lad of about thirty years of age, having played with my arrows till he has stripped off all the feathers, I find myself obliged to repair them. The morning is thus spent in preparing for the chase, and it is become necessary that I should dine. I dig up my roots; I wash them; boil them; I find them not done enough, I boil them again; my wife is angry; we dispute; we settle the point; but in the mean time the fire goes out, and must be kindled again. All this is very amusing.

I hunt; I bring home the prey; with the skin of it I mend an old coat, or I make a new one. By this time the day is far spent; I feel myself fatigued, and retire to rest. Thus, what with tilling the ground and eating the fruit of it, hunting, and walking, and running, and mending old clothes, and sleeping and rising again, I can suppose an inhabitant of the primeval world so much occupied as to sigh over the shortness of life, and to find, at the end of many centuries, that they had all slipped through his fingers and were passing away like a shadow. What wonder then that I, who live in a day of so much greater refinement, when there is so much more to be wanted and wished, and to be enjoyed, should feel myself now and then pinched in point of opportunity, and at some loss for leisure to fill four sides of a sheet like this?

GEORGE CRABBE

(1754–1832)

EORGE CRABBE was born at Aldborough in Suffolk, the son of a customs officer. He received a fair education for a village lad, and at the age of fourteen was apprenticed to a country surgeon. He early showed an inclination toward letters, versifying much while a schoolboy. In 1778 he abandoned his profession of medicine, in which he was not successful, and came up to London with a few pounds and some manuscript in his pocket, determined to make his way in literature. He met with the usual reverses of a beginner without reputation or patronage, and soon was desperately in need of money. He wrote many letters to well-known people, without response. In his extremity he applied to Burke, who, although a stranger, received him most kindly into his own house, gave him advice and criticism, recommended him to Dodsley the publisher, and introduced him to many notable men of the day, among them Reynolds, Johnson, and Fox.

During this time Crabbe wrote 'The Library' and the 'The Village'; and also at the suggestion of his patron qualified himself for the ministry. He took holy

GEORGE CRABBE

orders in 1782, and became shortly after chaplain to the Duke of Rutland. Subsequently he held a number of small livings, procured for him by his friends. The last of these, the rectory of Trowbridge, given him in 1813, he held until his death in 1832.

'The Village,' published in 1783, made the poet's reputation. His next work, 'The Newspaper,' published two years later, was much inferior. For twenty years thereafter he wrote and destroyed vast quantities of manuscript. Not until 1809 did he publish again. 'The Parish Register,' coming out in that year, was even more successful than his first work. In 1810 appeared 'The Borough,' containing his best work; 'Tales in Verse' following in 1812. With 'Tales of the Hall,' appearing in 1819, he took leave of the public.

Crabbe is an important link in the transition period between the poetry of the eighteenth and the nineteenth centuries. Men were growing tired of the artificiality and the conventional frigidity of the current verse in the hands of the imitators of Pope. A feeling for change was in the air, manifested in the incipient romantic movement and in what is called "the return to nature." Goldsmith was one of the first to lead the way back to simplicity, but he enveloped in a tender, somewhat sentimental idealism whatever he touched. Then came Thomson with his generalizations of nature, Cowper, a more faithful painter of rural scenes, and Burns, who sang of the thought and feeling of the common man. The work of these poets was a reaction against the poetry of town life, too apt to become artificial with its subject. Yet, being poets and singers, they expressed not so much the reality as what lies behind — its beauty and its tenderness. To give the right perspective to this return to nature, there was needed a man who should paint life as it is, in its naked realism, unveiled by the glamour of poetic vision.

Crabbe was this man. The most uncompromising realist, he led poetry back to human life on its stern dark side. Born and bred among the poor, he described, as no one else in the whole range of English verse has done, the sordid existences among which he had grown up. He dispelled all illusions about rural life, and dealt the death-blow to the Corydons and Phillises of pastoral poetry. He showed that the poor man can be more immoral and even more unprincipled than the rich, because his higher spiritual nature is hopelessly dwarfed in the desperate struggle to keep the wolf from the door. He supplied harrowing texts to the social economist. He is a gloomy poet, especially in the first part of his work, for he paints principally the shadows that hang over the lives of the lowly; he does not deal with that life imaginatively as Wordsworth and Burns do, but realistically, narrating with photographic accuracy what he saw. He excels in graphic delineations of external facts, but is also a powerful painter of the passions, especially the more violent ones, such as remorse and despair. 'Sir Eustace Grey' is a masterful portrayal of madness.

Crabbe has at times been denied the name of poet. There is little music in his verse, little of that singing quality that goes with all true poetry. His versification is often slipshod and careless. His lack of taste and artistic feeling shows itself not only in the manner but also in the matter of his work. He dwells by preference on the unlovely; he does not choose his details as an artist would. He is too minute, too like those Dutch painters who bestow as much care on the refuse as on the burnished platters of their interiors. And again he is trivial or too literal. But the steady admiration his poetry has excited in men of the most different tastes for several generations shows that it has deeper qualities. The truth is, that his mean and squalid details are not mere heaps of unrelated things, nor irrelevant to his story; they are not even mere "scenery." They are part of the history, in general the tragedy, of human hearts and souls; and owe their validity as poetic material, and their power of interesting us, to their being part of the influences that bear on the history.

Scott had Crabbe's poems read aloud in his last illness. Horace Smith called him "Pope in worsted stockings." Jane Austen said she "could fancy being Mrs. Crabbe." Cardinal Newman read the 'Tales of the Hall' with extreme delight on their first appearance, and fifty years later still thought well of them. These different opinions testify that whatever the shortcomings of Crabbe as craftsman, the earnestness and the genuineness of his work give him a secure place among English poets.

ISAAC ASHFORD

From 'The Parish Register'

NEXT to these ladies, but in naught allied,
    A noble peasant, Isaac Ashford, died.
      Noble he was, contemning all things mean,
His truth unquestioned and his soul serene:
Of no man's presence Isaac felt afraid;
At no man's question Isaac looked dismayed;
Shame knew he not; he dreaded no disgrace;
Truth, simple truth, was written in his face:
Yet while the serious thought his soul approved,
Cheerful he seemed, and gentleness he loved;
To bliss domestic he his heart resigned,
And with the firmest had the fondest mind.

Were others joyful, he looked smiling on,
And gave allowance where he needed none;
Good he refused with future ill to buy,
Nor knew a joy that caused reflection's sigh;
A friend to virtue, his unclouded breast
No envy stung, no jealousy distressed;
(Bane of the poor! it wounds their weaker mind
To miss one favor which their neighbors find.)
Yet far was he from stoic pride removed;
He felt humanely, and he warmly loved.
I marked his action when his infant died,
And his old neighbor for offense was tried:

The still tears, stealing down that furrowed cheek,
Spoke pity plainer than the tongue can speak.
If pride were his, 'twas not their vulgar pride
Who in their base contempt the great deride;
Nor pride in learning: though my Clerk agreed,
If fate should call him, Ashford might succeed;
Nor pride in rustic skill, although we knew
None his superior, and his equals few:
But if that spirit in his soul had place,
It was the jealous pride that shuns disgrace;
A pride in honest fame, by virtue gained,
In sturdy boys to virtuous labors trained:

Pride in the power that guards his country's coast,
And all that Englishmen enjoy and boast;
Pride in a life that slander's tongue defied —
In fact a noble passion, misnamed Pride.
He had no party's rage, no sectary's whim;
Christian and countryman was all with him:
True to his church he came; no Sunday shower
Kept him at home in that important hour;
Nor his firm feet could one persuading sect
By the strong glare of their new light direct;
«On pe in mine own sober light I gaze,
But uld be blind and lose it, in your blaze.»

In times severe, when many a sturdy swain
Felt it his pride, his comfort, to complain,
Isaac their wants would soothe, his own would hide,
And feel in *that* his comfort and his pride. . . .
I feel his absence in the hours of prayer,
And view his seat, and sigh for Isaac there:
I see no more those white locks thinly spread
Round the bald polish of that honored head;
No more that awful glance on playful wight,
Compelled to kneel and tremble at the sight,
To fold his fingers, all in dread the while,
Till Mr. Ashford softened to a smile:
No more that meek and suppliant look in prayer,
Nor the pure faith (to give it force), are there; —
But he is blest, and I lament no more
A wise, good man, contented to be poor.

THE PARISH WORKHOUSE AND APOTHECARY

From 'The Village'

THEIRS is yon house that holds the parish poor,
 Whose walls of mud scarce bear the broken door;
 There, where the putrid vapors flagging play,
And the dull wheel hums doleful through the day;
There children dwell who know no parents' care;
Parents who know no children's love dwell there;
Heart-broken matrons on their joyless bed,
Forsaken wives, and mothers never wed;
Dejected widows with unheeded tears,
And crippled age with more than childhood-fears;
The lame, the blind, and—far the happiest they!—
The moping idiot and the madman gay.

Here too the sick their final doom receive,
Here brought amid the scenes of grief to grieve,
Where the loud groans from some sad chamber flow,
Mixed with the clamors of the crowd below;
Here, sorrowing, they each kindred sorrow scan,
And the cold charities of man to man:
Whose laws indeed for ruined age provide,
And strong compulsion plucks the scrap from pride;
But still that scrap is bought with many a sigh,
And pride embitters what it can't deny.

Say ye, oppressed by some fantastic woes,
Some jarring nerve that baffles your repose;
Who press the downy couch, while slaves advance
With timid eye, to read the distant glance;
Who with sad prayers the weary doctor tease,
To name the nameless ever-new disease;
Who with mock patience dire complaints endure,
Which real pain and that alone can cure:
How would ye bear in real pain to lie,
Despised, neglected, left alone to die?
How would ye bear to draw your latest breath
Where all that's wretched paves the way for death?

Such is that room which one rude beam divides,
And naked rafters form the sloping sides;
Where the vile bands that bind the thatch are seen,
And lath and mud are all that lie between;

Save one dull pane, that, coarsely patched, gives way
To the rude tempest, yet excludes the day:
Here on a matted flock, with dust o'erspread,
The drooping wretch reclines his languid head;
For him no hand the cordial cup applies,
Or wipes the tear that stagnates in his eyes;
No friends with soft discourse his pain beguile,
Or promise hope till sickness wears a smile.

But soon a loud and hasty summons calls,
Shakes the thin roof, and echoes round the walls.
Anon a figure enters, quaintly neat,
All pride and business, bustle and conceit,
With looks unaltered by these scenes of woe,
With speed that, entering, speaks his haste to go;
He bids the gazing throng around him fly,
And carries fate and physic in his eye:
A potent quack, long versed in human ills,
Who first insults the victim whom he kills;
Whose murderous hand a drowsy bench protect,
And whose most tender mercy is neglect.

Paid by the parish for attendance here,
He wears contempt upon his sapient sneer;
In haste he seeks the bed where misery lies,
Impatience marked in his averted eyes;
And some habitual queries hurried o'er,
Without reply he rushes to the door:
His drooping patient, long inured to pain,
And long unheeded, knows remonstrance vain;
He ceases now the feeble help to crave
Of man; and silent sinks into the grave.

DINAH MARIA MULOCK CRAIK

(1826–1887)

LTHOUGH the daughter of a clergyman of the Established Church, Dinah Mulock was not herself a Churchwoman, and in her earlier works she frequently declares her belief in freedom of religious thought and action. She was led to take this attitude by her conviction that her mother was unkindly treated by her father, who in her opinion did not live up to the principles he professed. In a blaze of youthful indignation she carried her delicate mother and younger brothers away from their home at Stoke-on-Trent, Staffordshire, and undertook to support them all by her pen. 'The Ogilvies,' her first novel, was published in 1849, and her first struggle was successful. But she was soon deprived of the cause which she had gone forth to champion. Her mother and one of her brothers died, and she was left alone with her youngest brother to continue her work. Her loving description of her mother in 'My Mother and I' will be remembered as the picture of a pure, tender, and gentle woman.

DINAH M. M. CRAIK

'Olive' and 'The Head of the Family' soon followed 'The Ogilvies,' and in the second of these stories she showed highly imaginative and dramatic qualities, though the plot is simplicity itself. After 'Agatha's Husband' was issued in 1852, no other work of consequence appeared from her pen until the publication in 1857 of 'John Halifax, Gentleman,' her most popular novel. It was the portraiture of a gentleman by instinct, though not by social position. He is a middle-class business man, an inventor who has solved certain problems of capital and labor, and upholds "a true aristocracy," which he defines as "the best men of the country." "These," he says, "ought to govern and will govern one day, whether their patent of nobility be birth and titles or only honesty and brains."

She always maintained that 'A Life for a Life' was her best book, a judgment shared by many of her friends and critics. 'John Halifax,' however, continues to hold the heart and imagination of the many most strongly; perhaps on account of its democratic principles. Mrs. Craik was an earnest advocate of legalizing marriage with a deceased wife's sister, and 'Hannah,' a strong but painful story, deals with this subject. She published between forty and fifty works,—novels, tales for the young, volumes of travel, and poems. She is a writer of the best sort of English domestic novels, full of strong moral purpose. She avoids over-romantic or over-emotional themes, but the tender and poetical ideals of ordinary womanhood find in her a satisfactory exponent. As a poet her position, though not a high one, is lasting. Her versification is good, and her sentiment is always tender, truthful, and noble. Perhaps her best verses are those given below. In 1865 she made a happy marriage, and as her life grew larger and fuller her home became the centre of a group of affectionate friends,—artists, literary men, musicians, and many others full of intellectual interests and aspirations. She died suddenly but peacefully at her home at Shortlands, Kent, near London, on October 12th, 1887.

THE NIGHT ATTACK

From 'John Halifax, Gentleman'

I COULD not sleep—all my faculties were preternaturally alive; my weak body and timid soul became strong and active, able to compass anything. For that one night at least I felt myself a man.

My father was a very sound sleeper. I knew nothing would disturb him till daylight; therefore my divided duty was at an end. I left him and crept down-stairs into Sally Watkins's kitchen. It was silent; only the faithful warder Jem dozed over the dull fire. I touched him on the shoulder, at which he collared me, and nearly knocked me down.

"Beg pardon, Mr. Phineas—hope I didn't hurt 'ee, sir!" cried he, all but whimpering; for Jem, a big lad of fifteen, was the most tender-hearted fellow imaginable. "I thought it were some of them folk that Mr. Halifax ha' gone among."

"Where is Mr. Halifax?"

"Doan't know, sir; wish I did! wouldn't be long a-finding out, though—on'y he says: 'Jem, you stop here wi' they,'" (pointing his thumb up the staircase). "So, Master Phineas, I stop."

And Jem settled himself, with a doggedly obedient but most dissatisfied air, down by the fireplace. It was evident nothing would move him thence; and he was as safe a guard over my poor old father's slumber as the mastiff in the tan-yard, who was as brave as a lion and as docile as a child. My last lingering hesitation ended.

"Jem, lend me your coat and hat; I'm going out into the town."

Jem was so astonished that he stood with open mouth while I took the said garments from him and unbolted the door. At last it seemed to occur to him that he ought to intercept me.

"But sir, Mr. Halifax said —"

"I am going to look for Mr. Halifax."

And I escaped outside. Anything beyond his literal duty did not strike the faithful Jem. He stood on the doorsill and gazed after me with a hopeless expression.

"I s'pose you mun have your way, sir; but Mr. Halifax said, 'Jem, you stop y'ere,' and y'ere I stop."

He went in, and I heard him bolting the door with a sullen determination, as if he would have kept guard behind it — waiting for John — until doomsday.

I stole along the dark alley into the street. It was very silent — I need not have borrowed Jem's exterior in order to creep through a throng of maddened rioters. There was no sign of any such, except that under one of the three oil-lamps that lit the night-darkness of Norton Bury lay a few smoldering hanks of hemp, well rosined. They then had thought of that dreadful engine of destruction — fire. Had my terrors been true? Our house — and perhaps John within it!

On I ran, speeded by a dull murmur which I fancied I heard; but still there was no one in the street — no one except the abbey watchman, lounging in his box. I roused him and asked if all was safe — where were the rioters?

"What rioters?"

"At Abel Fletcher's mill; they may be at his house now —"

"Ay. I think they be."

"And will not one man in the town help him — no constables, no law?"

"Oh, he's a Quaker; the law don't help Quakers."

That was the truth, in those days. Liberty, justice, were idle names to Nonconformists of every kind; and all they knew of the glorious constitution of English law was when its iron hand was turned against them.

I had forgotten this; bitterly I remembered it now. So, wasting no more words, I flew along the churchyard until I saw, shining against the boles of the chestnut-trees, a red light. It was one of the hempen torches. Now at last I had got in the midst of that small body of men — "the rioters."

A mere handful they were, not above twoscore; apparently the relic of the band which had attacked the mill, joined with a few plow-lads from the country round. But they were desperate; they had come up the Coltham road so quietly that, except this faint murmur, neither I nor any one in the town could have told they were near. Wherever they had been ransacking, as yet they had not attacked my father's house; it stood upon the other side of the road, — barred, black, silent.

I heard a muttering, "Th' old man bean't there" — "Nobody knows where he be." No, thank God!

"Be us all y'ere?" said the man with the torch, holding it up so as to see round him. It was well then that I appeared as Jem Watkins. But no one noticed me, except one man who skulked behind a tree, and of whom I was rather afraid, as he was apparently intent on watching.

"Ready, lads? Now for the rosin! Blaze 'un out!"

But in the eager scuffle the torch, the only one light, was knocked down and trodden out. A volley of oaths arose, though whose fault it was no man seemed to know: but I missed my man from behind the tree — nor found him till after the angry throng had rushed on to the nearest lamp. One of them was left behind, standing close to our own railings. He looked round to see if none were by, and then sprung over the gate. Dark as it was, I thought I recognized him.

"John?"

"Phineas?" He was beside me in a bound. "How could you do—"

"I could do anything to-night. But you are safe — no one has harmed you. Oh, thank God, you are not hurt!"

And I clung to his arm — my friend whom I had missed so long, so sorely.

He held me tight — his heart felt as mine, only more silently; and silent hearts are strong.

"Now, Phineas, we have not a minute's time. I must have you safe — we must get into the house."

"Who is there?"

"Jael; she is as good as a staff of constables; she has braved them once to-night, but they're back again, or will be directly."

"And the mill?"

"Safe, as yet; I have had three of the tan-yard men there since yesterday morning, though your father did not know. I have been going to and fro all night between there and here, waiting till the rioters should come back from the Severn mills. Hist! there they are — I say, Jael."

He tapped at the window. In a few seconds Jael had unbarred the door, let us in, and closed it again securely; mounting guard behind it with something that looked very like my father's pistols, though I would not discredit her among our peaceful society by positively stating the fact.

"Bravo!" said John, when we stood all together in the barricaded house and heard the threatening murmur of voices and feet outside. "Bravo, Jael! The wife of Heber the Kenite was no braver woman than you."

She looked gratified, and followed John obediently from room to room.

"I have done all as thee bade me — thee art a sensible lad, John Halifax. We are secure, I think."

Secure? Bolts and bars secure against fire? For that was threatening us now.

"They can't mean it — surely they can't mean it," repeated John, as the cry of "Burn 'un out!" rose louder and louder.

But they did mean it. From the attic window we watched them light torch after torch, sometimes throwing one at the house — but it fell harmless against the staunch oaken door, and blazed itself out on our stone steps. All it did was to show, more plainly than even daylight had shown, the gaunt ragged forms and pinched faces, furious with famine.

John, as well as I, recoiled at that miserable sight.

"I'll speak to them," he said. "Unbar the window, Jael;" and before I could hinder he was leaning right out. "Halloo, there!"

At his loud and commanding voice a wave of upturned faces surged forward, expectant.

"My men, do you know what you are about? To burn down a gentleman's house is — hanging."

There was a hush, and then a shout of derision.

"Not a Quaker's! Nobody'll get hanged for burning out a Quaker!"

"That be true enough," muttered Jael between her teeth. "We must e'en fight, as Mordecai's people fought, hand to hand, until they slew their enemies."

"Fight!" repeated John half to himself, as he stood at the now closed window, against which more than one blazing torch began to rattle.

"Fight with these?—What are you doing, Jael?" For she had taken down a large book—the last book in the house she would have taken under less critical circumstances, and with it was trying to stop up a broken pane.

"No, my good Jael, not this;" and he carefully put back the volume in its place—that volume, in which he might have read, as day after day, year after year, we Christians generally do read such plain words as these: "Love your enemies;" "Bless them that curse you;" "Pray for them that despitefully use you and persecute you."

A minute or two John stood by the book-shelves, thinking. Then he touched me on the shoulder.

"Phineas, I am going to try a new plan—at least one so old that it is almost new. Whether it succeeds or no, you'll bear me witness to your father that I did it for the best, and did it because I thought it right. Now for it."

To my horror, he threw up the window wide, and leaned out.

"My men, I want to speak to you."

He might as well have spoken to the roaring sea. The only answer was a shower of missiles, which missed their aim. The rioters were too far off—our spiked iron railing, eight feet high or more, being a barrier which none had yet ventured to climb. But at length one random shot hit John on the chest.

I pulled him in; but he declared he was not hurt. Terrified, I implored him not to risk his life.

"Life is not always the first thing to be thought of," said he, gently. "Don't be afraid; I shall come to no harm. But I *must* do what I think right, if it is to be done."

While he spoke, I could hardly hear him for the bellowings outside. More savage still grew the cry:—

"Burn 'em out! burn 'em out! They be only Quakers!"

"There's not a minute to lose. Stop, let me think—Jael, is that a pistol?"

"Loaded," she said, handing it over to him with a kind of stern delight. Certainly Jael was not born to be a Friend.

John ran down-stairs, and before I guessed his purpose had unbolted the hall door, and stood on the top of the flight of steps in full view of the mob.

There was no bringing him back, so of course I followed. A pillar sheltered me; I do not think he saw me, though I stood close behind him.

So sudden had been his act that even the rioters did not seem to have noticed, or clearly understood it till the next lighted torch showed them the young man standing there, with his back to the door—*outside* the door.

The sight fairly confounded them. Even I felt for the moment he was safe. They were awed—nay, paralyzed, by his daring.

But the storm raged too fiercely to be lulled, except for one brief minute. A confusion of voices burst out afresh.

"Who be thee?" "It's one o' the Quakers." "No, he bean't." "Burn 'un anyhow." "Touch 'un, if ye dare!"

There was evidently a division rising. One big man, who had made himself very prominent all along, seemed trying to calm the tumult.

John stood his ground. Once a torch was flung at him he stooped and picked it up. I thought he was going to hurl it back again, but he did not; he only threw it down and stamped it out safely with his foot. This simple action had a wonderful effect on the crowd.

The big fellow advanced to the gate, and called John by his name.

"Is that you, Jacob Baines? I am sorry to see you here."

"Be ye, sir?"

"What do you want?"

"Naught wi' thee. We want Abel Fletcher. Where is 'un?"

"I shall certainly not tell you."

As John said this, again the noise arose, and again Jacob Baines seemed to have power to quiet the rest.

John Halifax never stirred. Evidently he was pretty well known. I caught many a stray sentence, such as "Don't hurt the lad;" "He were kind to my lad, he were;" "He be a real gentleman;" "No, he comed here as poor as us," and the like. At length one voice, sharp and shrill, was heard above the rest.

" I say, young man, didst ever know what it was to be pretty nigh vamished ? "

" Ay, many a time. "

The answer, so brief, so unexpected, struck a great hush into the throng. Then the same voice cried: —

"Speak up, man! we won't hurt 'ee! You be one o' we!"

"No, I am not one of you. I'd be ashamed to come in the night and burn my master's house down."

I expected an outbreak, but none came. They listened, as it were by compulsion, to the clear manly voice, that had not in it one shade of fear.

" What do you do it for ? " John continued. "All because he would not sell you, or give you, his wheat. Even so; it was *his* wheat, not yours. May not a man do what he likes with his own ? "

That argument seemed to strike home. There is always a lurking sense of rude justice in a mob — at least a British mob.

"Don't you see how foolish you were ? You tried threats too. Now, you all know Mr. Fletcher; you are his men — some of you. He is not a man to be threatened."

This seemed to be taken rather angrily; but John went on speaking, as if he did not observe the fact.

"Nor am I one to be threatened, neither. Look here — the first one of you who attempted to break into Mr. Fletcher's house, I should most certainly have shot. But I'd rather not shoot you, poor starving fellows! I know what it is to be hungry. I'm sorry for you — sorry from the bottom of my heart."

There was no mistaking that compassionate accent, nor the murmur which followed it.

"But what must us do, Mr. Halifax ? " cried Jacob Baines. "Us be starved a'most. What's the good o' talking to we ? "

John's countenance relaxed. I saw him lift his head and shake his hair back, with that pleased gesture I remembered so well of old. He went down to the locked gate.

"Suppose I gave you something to eat, would you listen to me afterward ? "

There rose up a frenzied shout of assent. Poor wretches! they were fighting for no principle, true or false, only for bare life. They would have bartered their very souls for a mouthful of bread.

"You must promise to be peaceable," said John again, very resolutely, as soon as he could obtain a hearing. "You are Norton Bury folk. I know you. I could get every one of you hanged, even though Abel Fletcher is a Quaker. Mind, you'll be peaceable?"

"Ay, ay! Some'at to eat; give us some'at to eat."

John Halifax called out to Jael, bade her bring all the food of every kind that there was in the house, and give it to him out of the parlor window. She obeyed — I marvel now to think of it, but she implicitly obeyed. Only I heard her fix the bar to the closed front door, and go back, with a strange sharp sob, to her station at the hall window.

"Now, my lads, come in!" and he unlocked the gate.

They came thronging up the steps, not more than twoscore, I imagined, in spite of the noise they had made. But twoscore of such famished, desperate men, God grant I may never again see!

John divided the food as well as he could among them; they fell to it like wild beasts. Meat, cooked or raw, loaves, vegetables, meal — all came alike, and were clutched, gnawed, and scrambled for in the fierce selfishness of hunger. Afterward there was a call for drink.

"Water, Jael; bring them water."

"Beer!" shouted some.

"Water," repeated John. "Nothing but water. I'll have no drunkards rioting at my master's door."

And either by chance or design, he let them hear the click of his pistol. But it was hardly needed. They were all cowed by a mightier weapon still — the best weapon a man can use — his own firm indomitable will.

At length all the food we had in the house was consumed. John told them so; and they believed him. Little enough, indeed, was sufficient for some of them: wasted with long famine, they turned sick and faint, and dropped down even with bread in their mouths, unable to swallow it. Others gorged themselves to the full, and then lay along the steps, supine as satisfied brutes. Only a few sat and ate like rational human beings; and there was but one, the little shrill-voiced man, who asked me if he might "tak a bit o' bread to the old wench at home!"

John, hearing, turned, and for the first time noticed me.

"Phineas, it was very wrong of you; but there is no danger now."

No, there was none — not even for Abel Fletcher's son. I stood safe by John's side, very happy, very proud.

"Well, my men," he said, looking around with a smile, "have you had enough to eat?"

"Oh, ay!" they all cried.

And one man added, "Thank the Lord!"

"That's right, Jacob Baines. And another time *trust* the Lord. You wouldn't then have been abroad this summer morning"— and he pointed to the dawn just reddening in the sky — "this quiet, blessed summer morning, burning and rioting, bringing yourself to the gallows and your children to starvation."

"They be nigh that a'ready," said Jacob, sullenly. "Us men ha' gotten a meal, thankee for i'; bu' what'll become o' the 'ittle uns a' home? I say, Mr. Halifax," and he seemed waxing desperate again, "we must get food somehow."

John turned away, his countenance very sad. Another of the men plucked at him from behind.

"Sir, when thee was a poor lad, I lent thee a rug to sleep on; I doan't grudge 'ee getting on; you was born for a gentleman, surely. But Master Fletcher be a hard man."

"And a just one," persisted John. "You that work for him, did he ever stint you of a halfpenny? If you had come to him and said, 'Master, times are hard; we can't live upon our wages;' he might — I don't say he would — but he *might* even have given you the food you tried to steal."

"D'ye think he'd give it us now?" And Jacob Baines, the big gaunt savage fellow who had been the ringleader — the same too who had spoken of his "little uns"— came and looked steadily in John's face.

"I knew thee as a lad; thee'rt a young man now, as will be a father some o' these days. Oh! Mr. Halifax, may 'ee ne'er want a meal o' good meat for the missus and the babies at home, if 'ee'll get a bit of bread for our'n this day."

"My man, I'll try."

He called me aside, explained to me, and asked my advice and consent, as Abel Fletcher's son, to a plan that had come into his mind. It was to write orders, which each man presenting at our mill should receive a certain amount of flour.

"Do you think your father would agree?"

"I think he would."

"Yes," John added, pondering, "I am sure he would. And besides, if he does not give some he may lose all. But he would not do it for fear of that. No, he is a just man. I am not afraid. Give me some paper, Jael."

He sat down as composedly as if he had been alone in the counting-house, and wrote. I looked over his shoulder, admiring his clear firm handwriting; the precision, concentrativeness, and quickness with which he first seemed to arrange and then execute his ideas. He possessed to the full that "business" faculty so frequently despised, but which out of very ordinary material often makes a clever man, and without which the cleverest man alive can never be altogether a great man.

When about to sign the orders, John suddenly stopped.

"No; I had better not."

"Why so?"

"I have no right; your father might think it presumption."

"Presumption, after to-night!"

"Oh, that's nothing! Take the pen. It is your part to sign them, Phineas."

I obeyed.

"Isn't this better than hanging?" said John to the men, when he had distributed the little bits of paper, precious as pound-notes, and made them all fully understand the same. "Why, there isn't another gentleman in Norton Bury who, if you had come to burn *his* house down, would not have had the constables or the soldiers shoot down one-half of you like mad dogs, and sent the other half to the county jail. Now, for all your mis-doings, we let you go quietly home, well fed, and with food for your children too. *Why*, think you?"

"I doan't know," said Jacob Baines, humbly.

"I'll tell you. Because Abel Fletcher is a Quaker and a Christian."

"Hurrah for Abel Fletcher! hurrah for the Quakers!" shouted they, waking up the echoes down Norton Bury streets: which of a surety had never echoed to *that* shout before. And so the riot was over.

John Halifax closed the hall door and came in — unsteadily — all but staggering. Jael placed a chair for him — worthy soul! she was wiping her old eyes. He sat down shivering, speechless.

I put my hand on his shoulder; he took it and pressed it hard.

"O Phineas, lad, I'm glad; glad it's safe over."

"Yes, thank God!"

"Ay indeed, thank God!"

He covered his eyes for a minute or two, and then rose up, pale, but quite himself again.

"Now let us go and fetch your father home."

We found him on John's bed, still asleep. But as we entered he woke. The daylight shone on his face — it looked ten years older since yesterday. He stared, bewildered and angry, at John Halifax.

"Eh, young man — oh! I remember. Where is my son — where's my Phineas?"

I fell on his neck as if I had been a child. And almost as if it had been a child's feeble head, mechanically he soothed and patted mine.

"Thee art not hurt? Nor any one?"

"No," John answered; "nor is either the house or tan-yard injured."

He looked amazed. "How has that been?"

"Phineas will tell you. Or stay — better wait till you are at home."

But my father insisted on hearing. I told him the whole without any comments on John's behavior; he would not have liked it, and besides, the facts spoke for themselves. I told the simple plain story — nothing more.

Abel Fletcher listened at first in silence. As I proceeded, he felt about for his hat, put it on, and drew its broad brim down over his eyes. Not even when I told him of the flour we had promised in his name, the giving of which would, as we had calculated, cost him considerable loss, did he utter a word or move a muscle.

John at length asked him if he was satisfied.

"Quite satisfied."

But having said this, he sat so long, his hands locked together on his knees, and his hat drawn down, hiding all the face except the rigid mouth and chin — sat so long, so motionless, that we became uneasy.

John spoke to him gently, almost as a son would have spoken.

"Are you very lame still? Could I help you to walk home?"

My father looked up, and slowly held out his hand.

"Thee hast been a good lad, and a kind lad to us. I thank thee."

There was no answer; none. But all the words in the world could not match that happy silence.

By degrees we got my father home. It was just such another summer morning as the one two years back, when we two had stood, exhausted and trembling, before that sternly bolted door. We both thought of that day; I knew not if my father did also.

He entered, leaning heavily on John. He sat down in the very seat, in the very room where he had so harshly judged us — judged him.

Something perhaps of that bitterness rankled in the young man's spirit now, for he stopped on the threshold.

"Come in," said my father, looking up.

"If I am welcome; not otherwise."

"Thee are welcome."

He came in — I drew him in — and sat down with us. But his manner was irresolute, his fingers closed and unclosed nervously. My father too sat leaning his head on his two hands, not unmoved. I stole up to him, and thanked him softly for the welcome he had given.

"There is nothing to thank me for," said he, with something of his old hardness. "What I once did was only justice, or I then believed so. What I have done, and am about to do, is still mere justice. John, how old art thee now?"

"Twenty."

"Then for one year from this time I will take thee as my 'prentice, though thee knowest already nearly as much of the business as I do. At twenty-one thee wilt be able to set up for thyself, or I may take thee into partnership — we'll see. But" — and he looked at me, then sternly, nay fiercely, into John's steadfast eyes — "remember, thee hast in some measure taken that lad's place. May God deal with thee as thou dealest with my son Phineas — my only son!"

"Amen!" was the solemn answer.

And God, who sees us both now — ay, *now!* and perhaps not so far apart as some may deem — he knows whether or no John Halifax kept that vow.

PHILIP, MY KING

Look at me with thy large brown eyes,
    Philip, my King!
   For round thee the purple shadow lies
Of babyhood's regal dignities.
Lay on my neck thy tiny hand,
   With love's invisible sceptre laden;
I am thine Esther to command,
    Till thou shalt find thy queen-handmaiden,
      Philip, my King!

Oh the day when thou goest a-wooing,
    Philip, my King!
When those beautiful lips are suing,
And some gentle heart's bars undoing,
Thou dost enter, love-crowned, and there
   Sittest all glorified!—Rule kindly,
Tenderly, over thy kingdom fair,
For we that love, ah, we love so blindly,
    Philip, my King!

I gaze from thy sweet mouth up to thy brow,
    Philip, my King:
, there lies the spirit, all sleeping now,
That may rise like a giant, and make men bow
As to one God—throned amidst his peers.
   My Saul, than thy brethren higher and fairer,
Let me behold thee in coming years!
   Yet thy head needeth a circlet rarer,
    Philip, my King!

A wreath, not of gold, but palm. One day,
    Philip, my King,
Thou too must tread, as we tread, a way
Thorny, and bitter, and cold, and gray:
Rebels within thee and foes without
   Will snatch at thy crown. But go on, glorious,
Martyr, yet monarch! till angels shout,
   As thou sittest at the feet of God victorious,—
    "Philip, the King!"

TOO LATE

COULD ye come back to me, Douglas, Douglas,
    In the old likeness that I knew, ·
I would be so faithful, so loving, Douglas,
    Douglas, Douglas, tender and true.

Never a scornful word should grieve ye,
    I'd smile on ye sweet as the angels do:
Sweet as your smile on me shone ever,
    Douglas, Douglas, tender and true.

Oh to call back the days that are not!
    My eyes were blinded, your words were few:
Do you know the truth now, up in heaven,
    Douglas, Douglas, tender and true?

I never was worthy of you, Douglas;
    Not half worthy the like of you;
Now all men beside seem to me like shadows —
    I love *you*, Douglas, tender and true.

Stretch out your hand to me, Douglas, Douglas,
    Drop forgiveness from heaven like dew,
As I lay my heart on your dead heart, Douglas,
    Douglas, Douglas, tender and true.

NOW AND AFTERWARDS

«Two hands upon the breast, and labor is past.»
                   RUSSIAN PROVERB.

«TWO hands upon the breast,
    And labor's done;
    Two pale feet crossed in rest,—
       The race is won;
    Two eyes with coin-weights shut,
       And all tears cease;
    Two lips where grief is mute,
       Anger at peace:»
So pray we oftentimes, mourning our lot;
God in his kindness answereth not.

« Two hands to work addressed
    Aye for his praise;
Two feet that never rest
    Walking his ways;
Two eyes that look above
    Through all their tears;
Two lips still breathing love,
    Not wrath, nor fears:»
So pray we afterwards, low on our knees.
Pardon those erring prayers; Father, hear these!

MADAME AUGUSTUS CRAVEN

(PAULINE DE LA FERRONAYS)

(1820–1891)

ADAME CRAVEN has told the story of her home life in 'Récit d'une Sœur: Souvenirs de Famille' (The Story of a Sister). She has given a charming idyllic picture of a Catholic French family—cultivated, simple-minded, and loving, and all animated by religious fervor. She has depicted with the strength of a personal experience the hopes and fears of those who see their dearest friends dying of consumption. She loves to show the gradual renunciation of life, the ennobling influence of sorrow, the triumph of faith over death and bereavement. Her affectionate nature, full of admiring enthusiasm for those she loved, led her to idealize real people as the characters of her books.

She was born at Paris, but had early advantages of travel unusual for a French girl. Her father was Ambassador to Berlin; the family were in Italy for a time; and after her marriage with Augustus Craven she lived a great deal in his native England. So the titles of her books reflect a certain cosmopolitan spirit. She was interested in English politics, and wrote a number of sketches on the subject. The lives of devout Catholic friends appealed to her strongly, and she wrote that of Sister Nathalie Narishkine of the Charity Saint Vincent de Paul, which was cordially indorsed by Cardinal Newman; and that of Lady Georgiana Fullerton.

Her 'Reminiscences,' recollections of England and Italy, show the same keenly sympathetic power of observation. She also translated from the Italian. But her most popular work has been stories. 'The Story of a Sister' (1866), a collection of memoirs, was enthusiastically admired by Catholic readers, and translated into English, was widely read in England and America. It was followed by several novels, of which the most popular have been 'Anne Séverin,' 'Le Mot de l'Énigme' (The Veil Withdrawn), and 'Fleurange.' These have all been translated into English, and the last especially has continued in favor for twenty years. Here, as in her other books, the author's strongest desire is to bear witness to the helpful discipline of trouble and the satisfactions of religion. She treats simple problems of love and duty, depicts primitive emotion, and deals very little in the complex psychology of later fiction. In a strong, fluent, fervid style she demonstrates that religious ecstasy is the most perfect of all joy, and that in Catholicism alone all difficulties may find solution.

ALBERT'S LAST DAYS

From 'A Sister's Story'

ONE of these latter days, Albert suddenly threw his arm round me and exclaimed: "*I am going to die, and we might have been so happy!*" O my God! I felt then as if my heart would really break.

JUNE 26TH. — Before mass, which was again said at twelve o'clock at night in his room, Albert looked at me a long time, and then said with deep feeling, "God bless you!" Then he made the sign of the cross on my forehead, and added, "And God bless your mother, too." After a while he said, "Good-by." I seemed surprised, and perhaps frightened, and then he said, "Good-night," as if to change the sad meaning of the word he had used. And all the while I wished so much to speak openly to him of his death. It was I perhaps who prevented it, by my fear of exciting him. During that last mass, every time that I looked at him he made me a sign to look at the altar. The window was open, but the night was quite dark. At the moment of communion the Abbé Martin de Noirlieu and Albert's father, who was serving mass, came up to him. The Abbé gave one-half of the sacred Host to him, and the other to me. Even in this solemn moment there was something very sweet to me in this. Albert could not open his lips without much suffering — it was for this reason that the Abbé Martin had divided the Host; but even so, he had some difficulty in swallowing, and they were obliged to give him some water. This disturbed him, but the Abbé Gerbet — who was present — assured him it did not signify. Then Albert exclaimed: "My God! Thy will be done!" O my God! this thanksgiving of his must, I think, have been pleasing to thee!

Before mass he had said to the Abbé Martin, who was speaking to him of his sufferings, "The only thing I ask of God now is strength to fulfill my sacrifice." "You are nailed to the cross with our Lord Jesus Christ," the Abbé said, and Albert answered in a very sweet and humble way, "Ah! but I am such a miserble sinner!" The altar had a blue-silk frontal, and was dressed with flowers. It was Eugénie who had arranged it. The blue silk was one of my trousseau dresses that had never been made up, and now was applied to this use.

JUNE 27TH.— Albert was light-headed; was continually talking of going into the country, and pointing to me, cried, "She is coming with me! She is coming with me!" (I was in the habit of writing down every word he said on these latter days of his life; and these words, "She is coming with me," were the last I wrote.) After dinner that same day we were sitting by his side, without speaking. Eugénie bent over him and gently suggested his receiving extreme unction. His countenance did not change in the least. He said gently and quite quietly, "Will it not be taking advantage of the graces the Church bestows to receive it yet?" He was anointed however that same evening, and during the whole time I was standing near him, with my hand on his right shoulder. Eugénie was on the other side of me.

An explanation of this sacrament, which we had read together in our happy days, made me understand all that was going on. The thought flashed through me with a wild feeling of grief: "What, must his soul be purified even of its ardent love for me? Must that too be destroyed?" But I did not shed a single tear. His own wonderful calm was so holy. When it was over, Albert made a little sign of the cross on the Abbé Dupanloup's forehead, who received it with respect, and affectionately embraced him. Then I approached, feeling that it was my turn to receive that dear sign of the cross, which was a sweet habit of happier days. He kissed me, his parents, Eugénie, Fernand, Montal, and then Julian (his servant), who was weeping bitterly. When it came to that, Albert burst into tears, and that was more than I could bear; but he quickly recovered fortitude when I kissed him again, and beckoned to the Sister, whom he would not leave out in this tender and general leave-taking, but with his delicate sense of what was befitting, and in token of gratitude he kissed the hand which had ministered to him, in spite of her resistance. M. l'Abbé Dupanloup, who gave him extreme unction, had prepared him for his first communion, and never forgot the edification it had given him at that time to find Albert on his knees praying in the same place where he had left him three hours before in the Church of St. Sulpice — that church in which his beloved remains were so soon to be deposited. I sat down by his side. He was asleep, and I held his hand in mine while Eugénie was writing the following lines to Pauline: —

"O Pauline, what a night has this been! and yet not terrible,— no, a most blessed night. Albert has just received extreme unction. What wonderful graces God bestows: but why were you not here to receive that dear angel's blessing, who, fitter for Heaven than ourselves, is going before us there. . . . ?" After relating all that has been mentioned, she adds: "Pauline, I could not have conceived anything more touching, more holy, more soothing, or a more heavenly peace. I bless God that nothing in all this time has troubled my notions of happiness in death."

ALEXANDRINE TO THE ABBÉ GERBET

THE SAME DAY.

I should feel it a great mercy if you could come, but I am however perfectly composed. I entreat you, continue your prayers for me, for I can no longer pray for myself. I can only think of God, and remind him that I asked for faith in exchange for happiness.   ALEXANDRINE.

ALEXANDRINE'S JOURNAL

JUNE 28TH.— To-night I called Albert's attention to the rising moon. I thought it had the lurid aspect which once before I saw at Rome, when I thought he was dying at Civita Vecchia. The window was open. We looked on the fine trees of the Luxembourg, and the perfume of the honeysuckles and many flowers was sometimes almost too powerful on the night air. Montal came in later and brought me Albert's letters to him, which I had asked for. It was as if a dagger had been driven into my heart. Still I immediately began to read those pages, which though heart-rending were very sweet. The Abbé Martin gave Albert absolution and the plenary indulgence for the night. I was kneeling by his side, and said to him afterwards, "Do kiss me." He raised his feeble head, put up his lips, and kissed me. Then I asked him to let me kiss his eyes. He shut them in token of assent. Later still, feeling unable any longer to forbear pouring my whole heart into his, and longing to take advantage of the few moments yet remaining to us of life, I said to him:— "Albert, Montal has brought me your letters. They comfort me very much. . . ." "Stop!" he cried feebly. "Stop! I cannot bear it — it troubles me!" — "O Albert! I *worship* you!" — The cry burst forth in the anguish of not being able to speak to him, for the fear of troubling his soul forced me to be silent; but those were the last words of my love for him that my lips ever uttered, and he heard them, as he had asked — even as he lay dying. O my God! whom alone I now worship, thou hast forgiven me for that rash word which I never again shall use but to thee, but which I cannot help being glad — and thou wilt pardon my weakness — to have said to my poor dying love. I wanted to sit up, but from grief and want of sleep my head was confused, and wandered so much that I thought I was speaking to Fernand at the window when he was not even there. Then I became afraid of losing my senses, and Eugénie forced me to lie down on the bed. I trusted more to her than any one else to waken me in time. Already, once or twice, I had experienced that terrible feeling when roused from sleep, of thinking that the dreadful moment was come. I was resolved at any cost to be there.

At about three o'clock in the morning, the 29th of June, I saw Eugénie at my bedside, and was terrified; but she calmed me, and said that Albert had asked, " Where is Alex ? " " Do you want her ? " Eugénie had said. " Of course I want her," he replied, and then began to wander again. I behaved as if I had lost my senses. I passed twice before Albert's bed, and then went into the next room, not the least knowing what I was about. Eugénie came in, holding clasped in her hands the crucifix indulgenced for the hour of death, which the Abbé Dupanloup had lent her. She appeared then as a meek angel of death, for that crucifix was a sign that the end drew near. Albert saw it, seized it himself, kissed it fervently, and exclaimed, " I thank thee, my God! " After that he became quite calm. They changed his position, and turned his head towards the rising sun. He had fallen into a kind of sleep, with his beloved head resting on my left arm. I was standing, and afraid of slipping from my place. The Sister wanted to relieve me, but Eugénie told her not to do so, and that I was glad to be there. When Albert awoke he spoke in his usual voice, and in quite a natural way, to Fernand. . . .

At six o'clock he was then lying in an arm-chair near the window. I saw and knew that the moment was come. . . . Then I felt so great a strength pass into me that nothing could have driven me from my place as I knelt by his side. My sister Eugénie was close to me. His father was kneeling on the other side. His poor mother stood leaning over him, the Abbé Martin by her side. O my God! No one spoke except his father, and each one of his words were words of blessing, the worthiest that could accompany the dying agony of a son. "My child, who hast never caused us pain,—the very best of sons,—we bless you. Do you hear me still, my child? You are looking at your Alexandrine,"—his dying eyes had turned towards me,—"and you bless her also." The Sister began to say the Litany for the Agonizing. And I—his wife—felt what I could never have conceived; I felt that death was blessed, and I said in my heart: "Now, O Lord Jesus, he is in Paradise!" The Abbé Martin began to give the last absolution, and Albert's soul took flight before it was over.

A GENEROUS ENEMY

From 'Fleurange': by permission of American Publishers' Corporation

As the silence lengthened, and she looked at Vera with everincreasing surprise, a sudden apprehension seized her, and a fugitive and remote glimpse of the truth crossed her mind.

Nothing in the world was more vague than her recollection of the name murmured a single time in her presence; but that once was in a conversation of which Count George was the subject, and she remembered that she had then believed that they were talking of a marriage desired by the Princess for her son.

Was it regretfully now that Vera brought to another this permission to accompany him?

Such was the question that Fleurange asked herself. Then approaching Vera, she said to her gently:—

"If you have been intrusted with a message for me, Mademoiselle, how can I thank you sufficiently for having taken the trouble to bring it to me yourself?"

But Vera hastily withdrew her hand, retreating a few steps as she did so. Then as if she were a prey to some emotion which she could not conquer, she fell back in an arm-chair placed near the table; and for some minutes remained pale, panting for breath, her expression gloomy and wild, from time to time brushing away fiercely the tears that in spite of all her efforts escaped from her eyelids.

Fleurange, motionless with surprise, looked at her with mingled terror and interest; but soon the frank decision of her character conquered her timidity. She went straight to the point.

"Countess Vera," she said, "if I have not conjectured rightly the motive which brings you here, tell me the truth. There is going on between us at this moment something which I do not understand. Be sincere; I will be so too. Let us not remain like this toward one another. Above all, do not look at me as if I were not only a stranger, but an enemy."

At this word Vera raised her head.

"Enemies!" she repeated: "Well, it is true; at this moment we are so!"

What did she mean to say? Fleurange folded her arms, and looked at her attentively, seeking to find an explanation to this enigma of her words; to the still more obscure enigma of her face, which expressed by turns the most conflicting sentiments; to the enigma of her eyes, which now regarded her with hate, now with the gentleness and almost the humility of a suppliant.

At last Vera seemed to decide to go on:—

"Yes, you are right," she said: "I must put an end to your suspense, and explain to you my strange conduct; but I need courage to do it, and to come here as I have done, to address myself to you as I am about to do, there must have been — without my knowing why —"

"Well," Fleurange said with a smile, "what else?"

"There must have been in my heart a secret instinct which assured me that you were good and generous!"

This conclusion, after this beginning, did not clear up the situation,— on the contrary, rendered it more involved than ever.

"This is enough by way of introduction," Fleurange said, with a certain tone of firmness. "Speak clearly, Countess Vera; tell me all without reserve; you may believe me when I beseech you to have no fear. Though your words were to do me a harm which at this moment I can neither foresee nor comprehend, speak; I require it of you; hesitate no longer."

"Well then, — here!" said Vera, throwing suddenly upon the table a paper which till then she had held concealed.

Fleurange took it, looked at it, and at first blushed; then she grew pale.

"My petition!" she said; "you bring it back to me? It has been refused then."

"No, it has not been sent."

"You mean to say that the Empress, after having shown so much kindness towards me, has changed her mind and refused to undertake it?"

"No. She has given orders to me, on the contrary, to send your petition, and to add to it her own recommendation."

"Well?"

"I have disobeyed her orders."

"I await the explanation which you are no doubt intending to give me. Go on without interrupting yourself; I shall listen."

"Well then, first of all, answer me. Did you know that George von Walden was the husband who was promised to me, — for whom my father destined me from childhood?"

"Who was promised you? — from childhood? No, I did not know it. But no matter; go on."

"It is true, it is no matter: this is not the question, although I was obliged to refer to it. It is no longer a question of his misfortune, of his fearful sentence, of that frightful Siberia to which you propose to accompany him — to share a fate which you can neither alleviate, nor, possibly, endure yourself. The question is now, to save him from this destiny; to give back to him life, honor, liberty, all that he has lost. His estates, his fortune, his rank, all may yet be restored to him! This is what I have come to tell you, and to ask you to aid in its accomplishment."

"All this can be restored to him!" said Fleurange, in an altered voice. "By what means? By whose power?"

"That of the Emperor, invoked, and of his clemency obtained through my entreaties; but upon two conditions, one of which is imposed upon George, the other of which depends upon me. To these two conditions is joined a third, and that one rests with you, with you only!"

The great eyes of Fleurange were fixed upon Vera, with an expression of profound astonishment, mingled with anguish.

"Finish, I implore you!" she said. "Finish, if you are not dreaming in saying such words to me, or I in hearing them; — if we are not both mad, you and I!"

Vera clasped her hands together and cried passionately: —

"Oh, I beseech you, have mercy upon him!"

She stopped, suffocated by her emotion.

Fleurange continued to look at her with the same expression, and without speaking made a sign to her to go on.

She seemed to concentrate her attention to understand the words that were said to her.

"I am listening," she said at last; "I am listening quietly and attentively; speak to me with the same composure."

Vera resumed in a calmer tone:—

"This morning, at the moment when I had just read your petition, and learned for the first time who the exile was whom you desired to follow,—at this very moment the Emperor arrived at the palace, and sent for me."

"The Emperor?" said Fleurange, with surprise.

"Yes. And do you know what he wished to say to me? You do not guess what it was, and I can understand readily why you should not, for you do not know with what ardor I have solicited pardon for George, how eagerly I have brought together, to this end, all the facts in the case which might disarm his Sovereign's anger against him. What the Emperor wished to say was this, that he deigned to grant me this favor—to grant it to *me*, Fleurange! do you understand?—but on two conditions."

"His pardon?" cried Fleurange. "Go on, I am listening."

"The first, that he should pass four years on his estates in Livonia, without stirring thence—"

Vera ceased suddenly. Fleurange looked up. "And the second?" she said.

"Then," said Vera, slowly and speaking with difficulty, "that the wish of my father and of his should be fulfilled before his departure."

Fleurange shuddered. An icy chill crept towards her heart, and her head grew dizzy. She remained perfectly motionless, however.

"His pardon is upon that condition?" she said.

"Yes. The Emperor has taken an interest in me from my childhood. He loved my father, and it has pleased him to attach this act of clemency to this fulfillment of my father's wish."

There was a long silence. Vera trembled herself as she saw the pale lips and colorless cheeks of Fleurange, and her eyes gazing fixedly into space.

"And he?" she said at last. "He will accept his pardon with this condition without hesitating, will he not?"

"Without hesitation?" repeated Vera, coloring with a new emotion; "that is what I cannot say; this very doubt humiliates and alarms me; for the Emperor would regard the least hesitation as a new ingratitude, and perhaps might retract this pardon."

"But why should he hesitate?" said Fleurange in a voice scarcely audible.

"Fleurange!" said Vera in the same passionate tone she had used more than once during this interview. "Let us break each other's heart, if we must, but let us go to the very end of this. It has been permitted you to see George since you have been here?"

"No."

"But he is expecting you; he knows that you have come, and what devotion has brought you to him?"

"No; he knows nothing of it as yet, and is not to know until to-morrow."

A flash of joy shone in the black eyes of Vera.

"Then it rests with you that he does not hesitate, that he is saved! Yes, Fleurange, let him never know that you are here, let him never see you — never again," she added, looking at her with a jealous terror that she could not conceal, "and life will once more become for him beautiful, brilliant, happy, — what it was, — what it ought always to be, — and the memory of these few months will fade away like a dream!"

"Like a dream!" — Fleurange repeated mechanically these two words, passing her hand across her forehead as she spoke.

"I have not told you all," Vera said; "I have done you an injury that I understand better than any other person can. But," she continued, in a tone which went to the very depths of her listener's heart, "I wished to save George! I desired him to be restored to me! and I have believed — I know not why, for it seems most unreasonable, and I am ordinarily distrustful — yes, I have believed that you would be willing to aid me, against yourself!"

Fleurange, her hands clasped and resting upon her knees, her eyes gazing steadfastly before her, had seemed for a few moments past not to have heard what was said. She was listening, — but it was to that clear distinct voice that rang so true in her own soul, that voice she had always so well known how to recognize, and to which she had never denied obedience.

If George were free, if he recovered his name, his rank, his former position, would she not at once find herself in the same position toward him which she had formerly occupied?—would it not be treason to avail herself in this case of his mother's permission, and that too to the detriment of her who sat there, the wife chosen for him from his childhood? Would it not, still further, be a treason towards him to present herself before him as a danger, as an obstacle, which might, perhaps at the very moment when he recovered his liberty, cause him to lose it anew, with that momentary favor which had restored it to him!

She laid her cold hand upon the hand of Vera, and lifted to hers her gentle and steady gaze.

"It is enough," she said in a calm voice. "You have done right. Yes, I have understood; be tranquil."

Vera, astonished at the look and tone, gazed at her in wonder.

"Act fearlessly," pursued Fleurange. "Act as if I were far away,—as if I had never come."

And taking the petition which lay upon the table, she tore it across, and threw it into the fire! The paper blazed up for a few seconds, then went out. She watched the cinders fly up the chimney.

Vera with an irresistible impulse seized the hand of Fleurange and raised it to her lips; then she remained silent and abashed. She had come resolved to overpower her rival, to convince her, to struggle against her at every point, if she failed in her first attempt; but her victory had taken a character which she had not at all foreseen.

Certainly it had been an easy victory, and yet Vera understood that it had been a cruel one. She felt at this moment more pain than joy, and her attitude no more expressed triumph than did that of Fleurange express defeat. While the one remained with drooping head and downcast eyes, the other had risen to her feet; a fugitive color lingered in her cheeks,—the effort of the sacrifice had lighted up her face and given it unwonted brilliancy.

"I think," she said, "you have nothing more to say to me."

"No—for what I should like to say I cannot and I dare not."

Vera rose and went towards the door, but a recollection brought her back.

"Pardon my forgetfulness," she said. "Here is your bracelet which you dropped this morning, and which I was desired to return to you."

At sight of the talisman Fleurange started; her unnatural color faded, she became deadly pale, and as she looked at it in silence, a few tears, the only ones which she had shed during that interview, slid down her cheeks. But it was only for an instant. Before Vera could think what she was about to do, Fleurange had attached to the arm of her rival the bracelet which the latter had just restored to her.

"This talisman was a present from the Princess Catherine to her son's betrothed; it would bring happiness, she said. It is mine no longer. I give it up to you; it is yours."

Fleurange held out her hand. "We shall never see each other again," she said. "Let us not remember each other with bitterness."

Vera took the hand without looking up. Never had she felt herself so touched and humiliated, and her very gratitude was a wound to her pride. The grave and sweet voice of Fleurange was however irresistible at this moment, and spoke to her heart in spite of herself. She was hesitating between these two feelings, when Fleurange resumed:—

"You are right. It is not my place to wait for you at this moment, for you have nothing now to forgive,—and as for me, I forgive you all."

And while Vera still stood motionless with bowed head, Fleurange bent towards her and kissed her.

FRANCIS MARION CRAWFORD

(1854–)

NDREW LANG has justly called Crawford the "most versatile and various of modern novelists." Since the appearance of 'Mr. Isaacs' in 1882, he has written nearly thirty novels, distinguished for their variety of subject and treatment. He belongs to the race of cosmopolitan Americans; men who, having no mental boundaries, accept for their literary inheritance the romantic traditions and customs of all nationalities. This natural taste, quickened by European education and extensive travel, has made him swift to comprehend all lands and races, with their types of character developed by social or national conditions. His adaptability of mind is partially explained by him in 'The Three Fates,' supposed to be autobiographic, which describes the career of an author. "The young man's true talent," he says, "lay in his ready power of assimilating unfamiliar knowledge by a process of intuition which escapes methodical learners."

MARION CRAWFORD.

Mr. Crawford was born in Bagni di Lucca, Italy, August 2d, 1854. He is of mingled ancestry. His father, Thomas Crawford the sculptor, was a native of Ireland, and his mother was an American. He spent his early childhood in New York. After studying at Cambridge, Heidelberg, Carlsruhe, and Rome, he went to India in 1879 and edited the Indian Herald at Allahabad. There he became acquainted with a Persian jewel merchant who suggested the mysterious personality of 'Mr. Isaacs.' Returning to America in 1881, he wrote the romance which bears this title. The fantastic creation, with its Oriental flavor, its hints of Anglo-India, the introduction of Ram Lal, the shadowy adept of occultism, and the striking figure of Mr. Isaacs, with his graceful languor, Iranian features, blazing eyes, and luxurious tastes, bestowed immediate celebrity upon its author. This was followed by 'Dr. Claudius,' which, although less romantic, showed increase in constructive skill. This became more marked in 'To Leeward,' the unlovely and tragic story of a wife's infidelity and of society in Rome. The tale of a peasant boy who

became a famous tenor is the theme of 'A Roman Singer,' issued in
1884; and in the same year he published 'An American Politician,'
in which are discussed the party spirit and corruption of American
politics.   In 1885 'Zoroaster' was issued, a story of ancient Persia,
introducing the court of King Darius and the aged prophet Daniel.
After 'A Tale of a Lonely Parish,' a sketch of rural life in England,
one of his most popular books appeared—'Saracinesca,' which with
'Sant' Ilario' and 'Don Orsino' forms a trilogy describing the
history of an Italian noble family of that day, and indeed forms a
complete study of Rome from 1865 to 1887.   Cardinal Antonelli is
brought upon the scene, and the bewildered and stormy period of
the last struggles of the Papacy for temporal power are painted with
vigorous skill and rapid generalization, until at last, as he says in
'Don Orsino,'—

«Old Rome is dead, never to be old Rome again. The last breath has
been breathed, the aged eyes are closed forever; corruption has done its
work, and the grand skeleton lies bleaching upon seven hills, half covered
with the piecemeal stucco of a modern architectural body.»

'Marzio's Crucifix' (1887) is the tale of an atheistic artisan who
carves in silver.   This possesses a psychological interest, and that
element deepens in the 'Witch of Prague' (1892), a bold and thrilling
tale of hypnotism.   'Paul Patoff' (1887) relates personal   ~eriences
of a visit to Turkey; 'With the Immortals' (1888) is an a~ ~pt to
reanimate dead celebrities.   'Greifenstein' is a tragedy which takes
place in the Black Forest, and tells the fortunes of two noble German families.   It is valued for its accurate descriptions of the Korps
Studenten, with their extraordinary ideals of romance and honor,
tempered with foaming beer and sabre-cuts.   'The Cigarette Maker's
Romance' is a pathetic story of the madness of Count Skariatine;
'Khaled' a fanciful tale of a genie, who is promised a soul if he
can gain a woman's love.   From romance and fancy, Mr. Crawford
turns to New York life in 'The Three Fates,' and in 'Katharine
Lauderdale' with its sequel 'The Ralstons.'   'Marion Darche' is
also an American story.   'Adam Johnston's Son' depends upon a
simple tale of love for its interest; in 'Casa Braccio,' 'The Children
of the King,' and his last book 'Taquisara' (1896), the author returns
again to his familiar *milieu*, Italy.
   This is a list of extraordinary variety and voluminousness. Since
1884 Mr. Crawford has lived near Sorrento. Here and in his yacht
he writes his novels. Although he has devoted much time to philology, he never intrudes dialect in his books, which are written
with the idea of pleasing instead of instructing his enormous audience. His works have been translated into various languages. He

has received many honors for his literary achievements. He considers ‘Pietro Ghisleri’ the most realistic of his books. In 1893 Mr. Crawford published a small essay entitled ‘The Novel: What it Is.’ In this he defines the novel as an “intellectual artistic luxury,” a “definition which can be made to include,” he says, “a great deal, but which is in reality a closer one than appears at first sight. It covers the three principal essentials of the novel as it should be, of a story, or romance; which in itself and in the manner of telling it shall appeal to the intellect, shall satisfy the requirements of art, and shall be a luxury, in that it can be of no use to a man when he is at work, but may conduce to a peace of mind and delectation during his hours of idleness.”

Born Aug. 2, 1854 died April 9, 1909, at Sorrento, Italy. His father, Thomas Crawford was sculptor of "Liberty" on dome of Capitol at Washington. His mother was a sister of Mrs. Julia Ward Howe

THE GHOST IN THE BERTH

From ‘The Upper Berth,’ in the ‘Autonym Library’: copyrighted by G. P. Putnam’s Sons

WE PLAYED whist in the evening, and I went to bed late. I will confess now that I felt a disagreeable sensation when I entered my state-room. I could not help thinking of the tall man I had seen on the previous night, who was now dead,—drowned, tossing about in the long swell, two or three hundred miles astern. His face rose very distinctly before me as I undressed, and I even went so far as to draw back the curtains of the upper berth, as though to persuade myself that he was actually gone. I also bolted the door of the stateroom. Suddenly I became aware that the port-hole was open, and fastened back. This was more than I could stand. I hastily threw on my dressing-gown and went in search of Robert, the steward of my passage. I was very angry, I remember, and when I found him I dragged him roughly to the door of one hundred and five, and pushed him towards the open port-hole.

“What the deuce do you mean, you scoundrel, by leaving that port open every night? Don’t you know it is against the regulations? Don’t you know that if the ship heeled and the water began to come in, ten men could not shut it? I will report you to the captain, you blackguard, for endangering the ship!”

I was exceedingly wroth. The man trembled and turned pale, and then began to shut the round glass plate with the heavy brass fittings.

“Why don’t you answer me?” I said roughly.

and a descendant of Gen. Francis Marion — His uncle the celebrated "Sam" Ward induced him to write his first novel "Mr. Isaacs" after hearing him tell a story gathered in his Eastern travels. Written in one month, rejected by two publishers, accepted by the London house of Macmillan.

One of his finest works (historical) Ave Roma Immortalis, 1898.

"If you please, sir," faltered Robert, "there's nobody on board as can keep this 'ere port shut at night. You can try it yourself, sir. I ain't a-going to stop hany longer on board o' this vessel, sir; I ain't indeed. But if I was you, sir, I'd just clear out and go and sleep with the surgeon, or something, I would. Look 'ere, sir, is that fastened what you may call securely, or not, sir? Try it, sir; see if it will move a hinch."

I tried the port, and found it perfectly tight.

"Well, sir," continued Robert, triumphantly, "I wager my reputation as a A1 steward, that in 'arf an hour it will be open again; fastened back too, sir, that's the horful thing — fastened back!"

I examined the great screw and the looped nut that ran on it.

"If I find it open in the night, Robert, I will give you a sovereign. It is not possible. You may go."

"Soverin' did you say, sir? Very good, sir. Thank ye, sir. Good night, sir. Pleasant reepose, sir, and all manner of hin-chantin' dreams, sir."

Robert scuttled away, delighted at being released. Of course I thought he was trying to account for his negligence by a silly story intended to frighten me, and I disbelieved him. The consequence was that he got his sovereign, and I spent a very peculiarly unpleasant night.

I went to bed, and five minutes after I had rolled myself up in my blankets the inexorable Robert extinguished the light that burned steadily behind the ground-glass pane near the door. I lay quite still in the dark trying to go to sleep, but I soon found that impossible. It had been some satisfaction to be angry with the steward, and the diversion had banished that unpleasant sensation I had at first experienced when I thought of the drowned man who had been my chum; but I was no longer sleepy, and I lay awake for some time, occasionally glancing at the porthole, which I could just see from where I lay, and which in the darkness looked like a faintly luminous soup-plate suspended in blackness. I believe I must have lain there for an hour, and, as I remember, I was just dozing into sleep when I was roused by a draught of cold air and by distinctly feeling the spray of the sea blown upon my face. I started to my feet, and not having allowed in the dark for the motion of the ship, I was instantly thrown violently across the state-room upon the couch which was placed beneath the porthole. I recovered myself immediately, however, and climbed upon my knees. The port-hole was again wide open and fastened back!

Now these things are facts. I was wide awake when I got up, and I should certainly have been waked by the fall had I still been dozing. Moreover, I bruised my elbows and knees badly, and the bruises were there on the following morning to testify to the fact, if I myself had doubted it. The port-hole was wide open and fastened back — a thing so unaccountable that I remember very well feeling astonishment rather than fear when I discovered it. I at once closed the plate again and screwed down the looped nut with all my strength. It was very dark in the state-room. I reflected that the port had certainly been opened within an hour after Robert had at first shut it in my presence, and I determined to watch it and see whether it would open again. Those brass fittings are very heavy and by no means easy to move; I could not believe that the clump had been turned by the shaking of the screw. I stood peering out through the thick glass at the alternate white and gray streaks of the sea that foamed beneath the ship's side. I must have remained there a quarter of an hour.

Suddenly, as I stood, I distinctly heard something moving behind me in one of the berths, and a moment afterwards, just as I turned instinctively to look — though I could of course see nothing in the darkness — I heard a very faint groan. I sprang across the state-room and tore the curtains of the upper berth aside, thrusting in my hands to discover if there were any one there. There was some one.

I remember that the sensation as I put my hands forward was as though I were plunging them into the air of a damp cellar, and from behind the curtain came a gust of wind that smelled horribly of stagnant sea-water. I laid hold of something that had the shape of a man's arm, but was smooth and wet and icy cold. But suddenly, as I pulled, the creature sprang violently forward against me, a clammy, oozy mass, as it seemed to me, heavy and wet, yet endowed with a sort of supernatural strength. I reeled across the state-room, and in an instant the door opened and the thing rushed out. I had not had time to be frightened, and quickly recovering myself I sprang through the door and gave chase at the top of my speed; but I was too late. Ten yards before me I could see — I am sure I saw it — a dark shadow moving in the dimly lighted passage, quickly as the shadow of a fast horse thrown before a dog-cart by the lamp on a dark night. But in a moment it had disappeared, and I found myself holding on to the polished rail that ran along the bulkhead where the passage turned towards the companion. My hair stood on end, and the cold perspiration rolled down my face. I am not ashamed of it in the least: I was very badly frightened.

Still I doubted my senses, and pulled myself together. It was absurd, I thought. The Welsh rare-bit I had eaten had disagreed with me. I had been in a nightmare. I made my way back to my state-room, and entered it with an effort. The whole place smelled of stagnant sea-water, as it had when I had waked on the previous evening. It required my utmost strength to go in and grope among my things for a box of wax lights. As I lighted a railway reading lantern which I always carry in case I want to read after the lamps are out, I perceived that the port-hole was again open, and a sort of creeping horror began to take possession of me which I never felt before, nor wish to feel again. But I got a light and proceeded to examine the upper berth, expecting to find it drenched with sea-water.

But I was disappointed. The bed had been slept in, and the smell of the sea was strong; but the bedding was as dry as a bone. I fancied that Robert had not had the courage to make the bed after the accident of the previous night — it had all been a hideous dream. I drew the curtains back as far as I could, and examined the place very carefully. It was perfectly dry. But the port-hole was open again. With a sort of dull bewilderment of horror I closed it and screwed it down, and thrusting my heavy stick through the brass loop, wrenched it with all my might till the thick metal began to bend under the pressure. Then I hooked my reading lantern into the red velvet at the head of the couch, and sat down to recover my senses if I could. I sat there all night, unable to think of rest — hardly able to think at all. But the port-hole remained closed, and I did not believe it would now open again without the application of a considerable force.

The morning dawned at last, and I dressed myself slowly, thinking over all that had happened in the night. It was a beautiful day, and I went on deck, glad to get out in the early pure sunshine, and to smell the breeze from the blue water, so different from the noisome, stagnant odor from my state-room. Instinctively I turned aft, towards the surgeon's cabin. There he stood, with a pipe in his mouth, taking his morning airing precisely as on the preceding day.

"Good-morning," said he, quietly, but looking at me with evident curiosity.

"Doctor, you were quite right," said I. "There is something wrong about that place."

"I thought you would change your mind," he answered, rather triumphantly. "You have had a bad night, eh? Shall I make you a pick-me-up? I have a capital recipe."

"No, thanks," I cried. "But I would like to tell you what happened."

I then tried to explain as clearly as possible precisely what had occurred, not omitting to state that I had been scared as I had never been scared in my whole life before. I dwelt particularly on the phenomenon of the port-hole, which was a fact to which I could testify, even if the rest had been an illusion. I had closed it twice in the night, and the second time I had actually bent the brass in wrenching it with my stick. I believe I insisted a good deal on this point.

"You seem to think I am likely to doubt the story," said the doctor, smiling at the detailed account of the state of the port-hole. "I do not doubt it in the least. I renew my invitation to you. Bring your traps here, and take half my cabin."

"Come and take half of mine for one night," I said. "Help me to get at the bottom of this thing."

"You will get at the bottom of something else if you try," answered the doctor.

"What?" I asked.

"The bottom of the sea. I am going to leave the ship. It is not canny."

"Then you will not help me to find out —"

"Not I," said the doctor, quickly. "It is my business to keep my wits about me — not to go fiddling about with ghosts and things."

"Do you really believe it is a ghost?" I inquired, rather contemptuously. But as I spoke I remembered very well the horrible sensation of the supernatural which had got possession of me during the night. The doctor turned sharply on me.

"Have you any reasonable explanation of these things to offer?" he asked. "No, you have not. Well, you say you will find an explanation. I say that you won't, sir, simply because there is not any."

"But, my dear sir," I retorted, "do you, a man of science, mean to tell me that such things cannot be explained?"

"I do," he answered, stoutly. "And if they could, I would not be concerned in the explanation."

I did not care to spend another night alone in the state-room, and yet I was obstinately determined to get at the root of the disturbances. I do not believe there are many men who would have slept there alone, after passing two such nights. But I made up my mind to try it, if I could not get any one to share a watch with me. The doctor was evidently not inclined for such an experiment. He said he was a surgeon, and that in case any accident occurred on board he must always be in readiness. He could not afford to have his nerves unsettled. Perhaps he was quite right, but I am inclined to think that his precaution was prompted by his inclination. On inquiry, he informed me that there was no one on board who would be likely to join me in my investigations, and after a little more conversation I left him. A little later I met the captain, and told him my story. I said that if no one would spend the night with me I would ask leave to have the light burning all night, and would try it alone.

"Look here," said he, "I will tell you what I will do. I will share your watch myself, and we will see what happens. It is my belief that we can find out between us. There may be some fellow skulking on board, who steals a passage by frightening the passengers. It is just possible that there may be something queer in the carpentering of that berth."

I suggested taking the ship's carpenter below and examining the place; but I was overjoyed at the captain's offer to spend the night with me. He accordingly sent for the workman and ordered him to do anything I required. We went below at once. I had all the bedding cleared out of the upper berth, and we examined the place thoroughly to see if there was a board loose anywhere, or a panel which could be opened or pushed aside. We tried the planks everywhere, tapped the flooring, unscrewed the fittings of the lower berth and took it to pieces: in short, there was not a square inch of the state-room which was not searched and tested. Everything was in perfect order, and we put everything back in its place. As we were finishing our work, Robert came to the door and looked in.

"Well, sir — find anything, sir?" he asked with a ghastly grin.

"You were right about the port-hole, Robert," I said; and I gave him the promised sovereign. The carpenter did his work silently and skillfully, following my directions. When he had done he spoke.

"I'm a plain man, sir," he said. "But it's my belief you had better just turn out your things and let me run half a dozen four-inch screws through the door of this cabin. There's no good never came o' this cabin yet, sir, and that's all about it. There's been four lives lost out o' here to my own remembrance, and that in four trips. Better give it up, sir — better give it up!"

"I will try it for one night more," I said.

"Better give it up, sir — better give it up! It's a precious bad job," repeated the workman, putting his tools in his bag and leaving the cabin.

But my spirits had risen considerably at the prospect of having the captain's company, and I made up my mind not to be prevented from going to the end of the strange business. I abstained from Welsh rare-bits and grog that evening, and did not even join in the customary game of whist. I wanted to be quite sure of my nerves, and my vanity made me anxious to make a good figure in the captain's eyes.

A THWARTED PLAN

From 'Marzio's Crucifix': copyrighted 1887, by F. Marion Crawford, and reproduced by permission of the Macmillan Company, Publishers

MARZIO entered the inner studio when Gianbattista was gone, leaving a boy who was learning to cut little files — the preliminary to the chiseler's profession — in charge of the outer workshop. The artist shut himself in and bolted the door, glad to be alone with the prospect of not being disturbed during the whole afternoon. He seemed not to hesitate about the work he intended to do, for he immediately took in hand the crucifix, laid it upon the table, and began to study it, using a lens from time to time as he scrutinized each detail. His rough hair fell forward over his forehead, and his shoulders rounded themselves till he looked almost deformed.

He had suffered very strong emotions during the last twenty-four hours — enough to have destroyed the steadiness of an ordinary man's hand, but with Marzio manual skill was the first habit of nature, and it would have been hard to find a mental impression which could shake his physical nerves. His mind, however, worked rapidly and almost fiercely, while his eyes searched the minute lines of the work he was examining.

Uppermost in his thoughts was a confused sense of humiliation and of exasperation against his brother. The anger he felt had nearly been expressed in a murderous deed not more than two or three hours earlier, and the wish to strike was still present in his mind. He twisted his lips into an ugly smile as he recalled the scene in every detail; but the determination was different from the reality, and more in accordance with his feelings. He realized again that moment during which he had held the sharp instrument over his brother's head, and the thought which had then passed so rapidly through his brain recurred again with increased clearness. He remembered that beneath the iron-bound box in the corner there was a trap-door which descended to the unused cellar, for his workshop had in former times been a wine-shop, and he had hired the cellar with it. One sharp blow would have done the business. A few quick movements, and Paolo's body would have been thrown down the dark steps beneath, the trap closed again, the safe replaced in its position. It was eleven o'clock then, or thereabouts. He would have sent the workmen to their dinner, and would have returned to the inner studio. They would have supposed afterwards that Don Paolo had left the place with him. He would have gone home and would have said that Paolo had left him — or no — he would have said that Paolo had not been there, for some one might see him leave the workshop alone. In the night he would have returned, his family thinking he had gone to meet his friends, as he often did. When the streets were quiet he would have carried the body away upon the hand-cart that stood in the entry of the outer room. It was not far — scarcely three hundred yards, allowing for the turnings — to the place where the Via Montella ends in a mud bank by the dark river. A deserted neighborhood too — a turn to the left, the low trees of the Piazza de' Branca, the dark, short, straight street to the water. At one o'clock after midnight who was stirring? It would all have been so simple, so terribly effectual.

And then there would have been no more Paolo, no more domestic annoyances, no more of the priest's smooth-faced disapprobation and perpetual opposition in the house. He would have soon brought Maria Luisa and Lucia to reason. What could they do without the support of Paolo? They were only women after all. As for Gianbattista, if once the poisonous influence of Paolo were removed — and how surely removed! Marzio's lips twisted as though he were tasting the sourness of failure, like an acid fruit — if once the priest were gone, Gianbattista would come back to his old ways, to his old scorn of priests in general, of churches, of oppression, of everything that Marzio hated. He might marry Lucia then, and be welcome. After all, he was a finer fellow for the pretty girl than Gasparo Carnesecchi, with his claw fingers and his vinegar salad. That was only a farce, that proposal about the lawyer — the real thing was to get rid of Paolo. There could be no healthy liberty of thought in the house while this fellow was sneaking in and out at all hours. Tumble Paolo into a quiet grave, — into the river with a sackful of old castings at his neck, — there would be peace then, and freedom. Marzio ground his teeth as he thought how nearly he had done the thing, and how miserably he had failed. It had been the inspiration of the moment, and the details had appeared clear at once to his mind. Going over them he found that he had not been mistaken. If Paolo came again, and he had the chance, he would do it. It was perhaps all the better that he had found time to weigh the matter.

But would Paolo come again? Would he ever trust himself alone in the workshop? Had he guessed, when he turned so suddenly and saw the weapon in the air, that the blow was on the very point of descending? Or had he been deceived by the clumsy excuse Marzio had made about the sun shining in his eyes?

He had remained calm, or Marzio tried to think so. But the artist himself had been so much moved during the minutes that followed that he could hardly feel sure of Paolo's behavior. It was a chilling thought, that Paolo might have understood and might have gone away feeling that his life had been saved almost by a miracle. He would not come back, the cunning priest, in that case; he would not risk his precious skin in such company. It was not to be expected — a priest was only human, after all, like any other man. Marzio cursed his ill luck again as he bent over his work. What a moment this would be if Paolo would take it into his head to make another visit! Even the men were gone. He would send the one boy who remained to the church where Gianbattista was working, with a message.

They would be alone then, he and Paolo. The priest might scream and call for help — the thick walls would not let any sound through them. It would be even better than in the morning, when he had lost his opportunity by a moment, by the twinkling of an eye.

"They say hell is paved with good intentions — or lost opportunities," muttered Marzio. "I will send Paolo with the next opportunity to help in the paving."

He laughed softly at his grim joke, and bent lower over the crucifix. By this time he had determined what to do, for his reflections had not interfered with his occupation. Removing two tiny silver screws which fitted with the utmost exactness in the threads, he loosened the figure from the cross, removed the latter to a shelf on the wall, and returning laid the statue on a soft leathern pad, surrounding it with sand-bags till it was propped securely in the position he required. Then he took a very small chisel, adjusted it with the greatest care, and tapped upon it with the round wooden handle of his little hammer. At each touch he examined the surface with his lens to assure himself that he was making the improvement he contemplated. It was very delicate work, and as he did it he felt a certain pride in the reflection that he could not have detected the place where improvement was possible when he had worked upon the piece ten years ago. He found it now, in the infinitesimal touches upon the expression of the face, in the minute increase in the depressions and accentuated lines in the anatomy of the figure. As he went over each portion he became more and more certain that though he could not at present do better in the way of idea and general execution, he had nevertheless gained in subtle knowledge of effects and in skill of handling the chisel upon very delicate points. The certainty gave him the real satisfaction of legitimate pride. He knew that he had reached the zenith of his capacities. His old wish to keep the crucifix for himself began to return.

If he disposed of Paolo he might keep his work. Only Paolo had seen it. The absurd want of logic in the conclusion did not strike him. He had not pledged himself to his brother to give this particular crucifix to the cardinal, and if he had he could easily have found a reason for keeping it back. But he was too much accustomed to think that Paolo was always in the way of his wishes, to look at so simple a matter in such a simple light.

"It is strange," he said to himself. "The smallest things seem to point to it. If he would only come!"

Again his mind returned to the contemplation of the deed, and again he reviewed all the circumstances necessary for its safe execution. What an inspiration, he thought, and what a pity it had not found shape in fact at the very moment it had presented itself! He considered why he had never thought of it before, in all the years, as a means of freeing himself effectually from the despotism he detested. It was a despotism, he reflected, and no other word expressed it. He recalled many scenes in his home, in which Paolo had interfered. He remembered how one Sunday in the afternoon they had all been together before going to walk in the Corso, and how he had undertaken to demonstrate to Maria Luisa and Lucia the folly of wasting time in going to church on Sundays. He had argued gently and reasonably, he thought. But suddenly Paolo had interrupted him, saying that he would not allow Marzio to compare a church to a circus, nor priests to mountebanks and tight-rope dancers. Why not? Then the women had begun to scream and cry, and to talk of his blasphemous language, until he could not hear himself speak. It was Paolo's fault. If Paolo had not been there the women would have listened patiently enough, and would doubtless have reaped some good from his reasonable discourse. On another occasion Marzio had declared that Lucia should never be taught anything about Christianity; that the definition of God was reason; that Garibaldi had baptized one child in the name of Reason and that he, Marzio, could baptize another quite as effectually. Paolo had interfered, and Maria Luisa had screamed. The contest had lasted nearly a month, at the end of which time Marzio had been obliged to abandon the uneven contest, vowing vengeance in some shape for the future.

Many and many such scenes rose to his memory, and in every one Paolo was the opposer, the enemy of his peace, the champion of all that he hated and despised. In great things and small his brother had been his antagonist from his early manhood, through eighteen years of married life to the present day. And yet without Paolo he could hardly have hoped to find himself in his present state of fortune.

This was one of the chief sources of his humiliation in his own eyes. With such a character as his, it is eminently true that it is harder to forgive a benefit than an injury. He might have felt less bitterly against his brother if he had not received at his hands the orders and commissions which had turned into solid money in the bank. It was hard to face Paolo, knowing that he owed two-thirds of his fortune to such a source. If he could get rid of the priest he would be relieved at once from the burden of this annoyance, of this financial subjection, as well of all that embittered his life. He pictured to himself his wife and daughter listening respectfully to his harangues and beginning to practice his principles; Gianbattista an eloquent member of the society in the inner room of the old inn, reformed, purged from his sneaking fondness for Paolo,—since Paolo would not be in the world any longer,—and ultimately married to Lucia; the father of children who should all be baptized in the name of Reason, and the worthy successor of himself, Marzio Pandolfi.

Scrutinizing the statue under his lens, he detected a slight imperfection in the place where one of the sharp thorns touched the silver forehead of the beautiful tortured head. He looked about for a tool fine enough for the work, but none suited his wants. He took up the long fine-pointed punch he had thrown back upon the table after the scene in the morning. It was too long, and over-sharp, but by turning it sideways it would do the work under his dexterous fingers.

"Strange!" he muttered, as he tapped upon the tool. "It is like a consecration!"

When he had made the stroke he dropped the instrument into the pocket of his blouse, as though fearing to lose it. He had no occasion to use it again, though he went on with his work during several hours.

The thoughts which had passed through his brain recurred, and did not diminish in clearness. On the contrary, it was as though the passing impulse of the morning had grown during those short hours into a settled and unchangeable resolution. Once he rose from his stool, and going to the corner dragged away the iron-bound safe from its place. A rusty ring lay flat in a little hollow in the surface of the trap-door. Marzio bent over it with a pale face and gleaming eyes. It seemed to him as though if he looked round he should see Paolo's body lying on the floor, ready to be dropped into the space below. He raised the wood and set the trap back against the wall, peering down into the black depths. A damp smell came up to his nostrils from the moist staircase. He struck a match and held it into the opening, to see in what direction the stairs led down.

Something moved behind him and made a little noise. With a short cry of horror Marzio sprang back from the opening and looked round. It was as though the body of the murdered man had stirred upon the floor. His overstrained imagination terrified him, and his eyes started from his head. He examined the bench and saw the cause of the sound in a moment. The silver Christ, unsteadily propped in the position in which he had just placed it, had fallen upon one side of the pad by its own weight.

Marzio's heart still beat desperately as he went back to the hole and carefully re-closed the trap-door, dragging the heavy safe to its position over the ring. Trembling violently, he sat down upon his stool and wiped the cold perspiration from his forehead. Then, as he laid the figure upon the cushion, he glanced uneasily behind him and at the corner.

With an anxious heart he left the house and crossed the street to the workshop, where the men were already waiting for the carts which were to convey the heavy grating to its destination. The pieces were standing against the walls, wrapped in tow and brown paper, and immense parcels lay tied up upon the benches. It was a great piece of work of the decorative kind, but of the sort for which Marzio cared little. Great brass castings were chiseled and finished according to his designs without his touching them with his hands. Huge twining arabesques of solid metal were prepared in pieces and fitted together with screws that ran easily in the thread, and then were taken apart again. . . . It was slow and troublesome work, and Marzio cared little for it, though his artistic instinct restrained him from allowing it to leave the workshop until it had been perfected to the highest degree.

At present the artist stood in the outer room among the wrapped pieces, his pipe in his mouth and his hands in his pockets. A moment after Gianbattista had entered, two carts rolled up to the door and the loading began.

"Take the drills and some screws to spare," said Marzio, looking into the bag of tools the foreman had prepared. "One can never tell in these monstrous things."

"It will be the first time, if we have to drill a new hole after you have fitted a piece of work, Maestro Marzio," answered the foreman, who had an unlimited admiration for his master's genius and foresight.

"Never mind; do as I tell you. We may all make mistakes in this world," returned the artist, giving utterance to a moral sentiment which did not influence him beyond the precincts of the workshop. The workman obeyed, and added the requisite instruments to the furnishing of his leather bag.

"And be careful, Tista," added Marzio, turning to the apprentice. "Look to the sockets in the marble when you place the large pieces. Measure them with your compass, you know; if they are too loose you have the thin plates of brass to pack them; if they are tight, file away, but finish and smooth it well. Don't leave anything rough."

Gianbattista nodded as he lent a helping hand to the workmen who were carrying the heavy pieces to the carts.

"Will you come to the church before night?" he asked.

"Perhaps. I cannot tell. I am very busy."

In ten minutes the pieces were all piled upon the two vehicles, and Gianbattista strode away on foot with the workmen. He had not thought of changing his dress, and had merely thrown an old overcoat over his gray woolen blouse. For the time, he was an artisan at work. When working hours were over, and on Sundays, he loved to put on the stiff high collar and the checked clothes which suggested the garments of the English tourist. He was then a different person, and in accordance with the change he would smoke a cigarette and pull his cuffs over his hands, like a real gentleman, adjusting the angle of his hat from time to time, and glancing at his reflection in the shop windows as he passed along. But work was work; it was a pity to spoil good clothes with handling tools and castings, and jostling against the men, and moreover the change affected his nature. He could not handle a hammer or a chisel when he felt like a real gentleman, and when he felt like an artisan he must enjoy the liberty of being able to tuck up his sleeves and work with a will. At the present moment, too, he was proud of being in sole charge of the work, and he could not help thinking what a fine thing it would be to be married to Lucia and to be the master of the workshop. With the sanguine enthusiasm of a very young man who loves his occupation, he put his whole soul into what he was to do, assured that every skillful stroke of the hammer, every difficulty overcome, brought him nearer to the woman he loved.

PROSPER JOLYOT CRÉBILLON

(1674–1762)

BY ROBERT SANDERSON

ROSPER JOLYOT, tragic poet, called De Crébillon from the name of the estate his father purchased near Dijon, France, was born in that city January 13th, 1674. The elder Jolyot held an office in the magistracy of the province of Burgundy, and he intended that his son should follow in his footsteps. This the young man did for a time. He was admitted to the bar as advocate to the Parliament of Paris, and at the same time entered the office of a *procureur* (prosecuting magistrate), there to study the forms of procedure and practice of law. This *procureur*, whose name was Prieur, appears to have worked a decisive influence over Jolyot's career, as he was the first to discover in the young man strong aptitudes for tragedy. Being a man of letters, he was struck by the correctness of his clerk's criticisms of some of the French tragic poets, and urged him to try his hand at writing a tragedy himself. This Crébillon did at once, and composed his maiden play, 'La Mort des Enfants de Brute' (The Death of Brutus's Children), a subject more than once treated before. The king's troupe of players refused it, and it was not even printed. Cré-

CRÉBILLON

billon was greatly disappointed, but encouraged by the good Prieur, he very soon conceived and wrote another tragedy, 'Idoménée' (1705), which this time was received and played with some success.

'Idoménée' was followed by 'Atrée et Thyeste' (1707), a play that put Crébillon in the very first rank of tragic poets. Called back to his native place by his father's death, and detained there a long time by a family lawsuit, he brought back from the country his third tragedy, 'Électre' (1708), which was as much admired as the preceding one. 'Rhadamiste et Zénobie,' Crébillon's masterpiece, appeared in 1711. It formed part of the repertoire of the Comédie Française up to the year 1829. 'Xerxès,' played in 1714, met with flat failure; 'Sémiramis' (1717) fared somewhat better. Disgusted with the poor success of his last two tragedies, it was nine years before Crébillon wrote again for the stage. 'Pyrrhus' appeared in 1726, and remained for a long time on the play-bills. Of his last two tragedies 'Catilina' (1748) was for its author a renewal of success, whilst 'Le Triumvirat,' written by Crébillon in his eightieth year, contains here and there fine passages.

Crébillon was elected to the French Academy in 1731. He held several offices during life. He was first receiver of fines, then royal censor, and lastly king's librarian; but neither from these various employments nor from his plays did he derive much profit. The most prosperous epoch of his existence seems to have been about the year 1715, during the brilliant but corrupt time of the *Régence;* part of his life was spent in actual penury, and we find him fifteen years later living in a poor quarter of the capital, having for sole companions of his misery a lot of dogs and cats that he picked up in the streets. However, Louis XV. gave him in his old age a proof of his royal favor. After the representation of 'Catilina,' the King ordered that the poet's complete works be printed at his expense. The edition appeared in 1750, and yielded enough to save Crébillon at least from actual want during his remaining lifetime. It may be easily imagined that in his position of royal censor he incurred the enmity of his colleagues whose plays he refused; and in addition to his pecuniary embarrassments his life was embittered by the attacks of his enemies, among whom Voltaire was not the least conspicuous. Crébillon, who was a man of fine presence and strong constitution, died on June 14th, 1762, in his eighty-ninth year.

Taking the writer's tragedies as they appeared, 'Idoménée,' the first one, is borrowed from Homer's Iliad. It is the story of Idomeneus, King of Crete, who returning from the siege of Troy and being assailed by a frightful tempest, took a vow of sacrificing to Neptune the first human creature he should meet on landing. His own son, Idamantus, was the first person he encountered, and his father at once sacrificed him. Such is the Greek legend; but it being too atrocious in its nature to suit modern taste, in Crébillon's tragedy Idamantus kills himself. We can in a measure understand the terrible struggle going on in the father's breast, obliged by his vow to kill his own child; but only in a measure, for our modern ideas will not admit that under such circumstances a parent should be held to his vow. Nor does it help matters that Idamantus should kill himself to save his father from committing the atrocious deed: the subject is repulsive. The speech of Idomeneus in the first act, recounting the storm scene, is not unfrequently mentioned as a piece of rhetoric.

'Atrée et Thyeste' is far superior to 'Idoménée' both in conception and construction. If the object of tragedy be to excite terror, that condition is certainly fulfilled in 'Atrée et Thyeste.' The subject, taken from Seneca, is well known. Atreus, King of Argos, to avenge the wrong done him by his own brother Thyestes, who had carried off his wife, had the latter's son killed and served to him at a feast. Crébillon carries this fierce cruelty even farther, for in his play he makes Atreus offer his brother a cup filled with the blood of Plisthène, son of Thyestes. On being criticized for this refinement of cruelty the poet bluntly answered, "I never should have believed that in a land where there are so many unfortunate husbands, Atreus would have found so few partisans." The strongest scenes are the closing ones. Although the general opinion at the time was that Crébillon had chosen too horrible a subject, he revealed his power as a tragic poet; and his reputation as such really dates from the production of 'Atrée et Thyeste.'

Crébillon's 'Électre' is in the main the same as that of Sophocles, Euripides, and others. Electra, whose father Agamemnon has been murdered by Ægisthus, induces her brother Orestes to slay the murderer. The change introduced into the plot by the French poet is this one: he makes Electra love the son of her father's slayer, whilst Orestes, who is ignorant of his own birth, loves the daughter. The admirers of the classic models were up in arms at these changes, and 'Électre' was attacked on all sides; but if it had its defects, it had also its merits, and these were finally recognized as being of high order. The scene between Clytemnestra and Electra in the first act, the meeting between Electra and Orestes, and the latter's ravings when he discovers that he has killed his mother, are among the best.

'Rhadamiste et Zénobie' is generally considered Crébillon's masterpiece: it is the only one of his tragedies that contains the romantic element. As narrated in Tacitus, the legend upon which this play is founded runs thus: Rhadamistus, son of Pharasmancs, King of Iberia, had married his cousin Zenobia, daughter of his uncle Mithridates, King of Armenia. The latter was put to death by order of Rhadamistus, who took possession of his uncle's provinces. An insurrection broke out, and Rhadamistus had to flee for his life. He carried off Zenobia with him, but she, owing to her condition, unable to bear the fatigues of the flight, begged her husband to put her to death. After piercing her with his sword and throwing her into the Araxes, he hurriedly made off for his father's kingdom. Zenobia, however, was not dead. She was found on the bank of the river by some shepherds, who carried her to the court of the King Tiridates, who received her kindly and treated her as a queen.

In his tragedy Crébillon makes the husband and wife meet again at the court of Pharasmanes; and Zenobia, believing herself to be a widow, shows her love for Prince Arsames, own brother to Rhadamistus.   This invention is certainly no more improbable than the whole story itself.   The interview between Pharasmanes and his son in the second act, and the meeting between Rhadamistus and Zenobia in the third, are both remarkable, the first for its grandeur, the second for its pathos and passion.

'Xerxès' is an inferior tragedy.   The strongest character in the play is that of the prime minister Artaban, who sows discord between the two sons of Xerxès, intending to seize the throne of Persia for himself.   Inferior also is 'Sémiramis.'   The famous queen is in love with Agénor, who proves to be her own son Ninias; but even after this discovery, Sémiramis perseveres in her passion.   Such a subject can be tolerated on the stage only on condition that the spectator be made to feel the victim's struggle and remorse, as in Racine's 'Phèdre.'

'Pyrrhus' differs from Crébillon's previous tragedies in this one point: no blood is spilled upon the stage; the poet does not rely upon his usual method of striking terror to gain success.   For the first time his characters are heroic and express noble sentiments. Pyrrhus, King of Epirus, has been brought up by his guardian Glaucias under the name of Helenus, and believes himself to be his son.   It is only when the usurper Neoptolemes demands of Glaucias the surrender of Pyrrhus, that the latter discovers the truth.   The courage and magnanimity of Glaucias in refusing to give up his trust; of his son Illyrus in taking the place of Pyrrhus; of Pyrrhus in revealing his true name and offering himself to the usurper, and lastly of Neoptolemes in showing clemency, are worthy of admiration.

Twenty-two years intervene between 'Pyrrhus' and 'Catilina' (1748).   As might be expected in a tragedy having for its principal characters Cicero and Cato, political speeches are plentiful.   The scene between Catiline, Cato, and Cicero, in the fourth act, is perhaps the strongest.   Another interval of six years, and Crébillon wrote his last tragedy 'Le Triumvirat' or 'Le Mort de Cicéron,' which may be termed a rehabilitation of Cicero, who, the critics said, should not have been made a subordinate character to that of Catiline in Crébillon's previous tragedy.   Although written in his eightieth year, it cannot be said that this composition shows any sign of mental decay.

With two such masters as Corneille and Racine towering with their mighty height over all other French dramatic poets, it is often difficult to be just towards the latter.   They must always suffer by comparison; yet all they wrote did not deserve almost entire oblivion. In the case of Crébillon, the only tragedy by which he is now remembered is that of 'Rhadamiste et Zénobie,' and that principally because it is the only one that has in it an element of romance. But his others contain also qualities of their own: grandeur of conception, great force and energy, together with a severe and sober language. As to his defects, they consist in too great a predilection for the horrible, and in a style which at times is inflated. Voltaire, who could brook no superiority or even equality in any line of literature, did not spare Crébillon his sarcasms. The best outcome of this rivalry between the two poets was the emulation it stimulated in Voltaire, causing him to write over five of Crébillon's tragedies— 'Sémiramis,' 'Électre,' 'Catilina,' 'Le Triumvirat,' 'Atrée et Thyeste,'—under the respective names of 'Sémiramis,' 'Oreste,' 'Rome Sauvée,' 'Le Triumvirat,' 'Les Pélopides.'

Robert Sanderson

THE BLOODY BANQUET

From 'Atreus and Thyestes'

ATREUS—Now in this cup, the pledge of brotherhood,
  Behold the sacred earnest of our peace!
  How timely has it come, to still the fears
  That bid thee doubt a brother's bounteous love!
  If dark distrust of Atreus linger still
  Within thy heart—give me the sacred cup.
  That shame may fill Thyestes, to withhold
  His share in this fraternal festival:
  That brothers' hearts, whom love hath set at twain,
  Love's holy bonds may reunite again:
  Give me the cup! that I, in drinking first,
  May drown thy doubts. — Eurysthenes, the cup!

[*He takes the cup from the hand of Eurysthenes, his confidant.*]

Thyestes —
  Have I not said, my lord, thou takest ill
  My groundless doubts and coward quavering fears?
  What henceforth could thy hate deprive me of,
  Since son, and provinces, have been restored?
  Whate'er the cause and meaning of this wrath,

Have I deserved that thou shouldst crown my days,
My wretched days, with kindness such as this?
Nay; first, Eurysthenes, give me the cup.
Let me be first to pledge all gratitude,
And drown my heart's misgivings, that have lain
Like bitter lees within the cup I drain.

[*He takes the cup from the hand of Atreus, saying:* —]

　　　Yet why delays my son?

Atreus [*addressing his guards*]—　　　Give answer, guards!
Has he not yet returned?
[*Addressing Thyestes*]—　　　Be not uneasy.
You soon shall see him, soon to him be joined;
More near and close your union than you dream;
Most sacred pledge, he, of our solemn bond.

Thyestes—

Be thou the voucher, then, of Atreus's faith,
And of Thyestes's safety from his hate,—
Cup of our ancestors! And you, ye gods,
Whom I to witness call! may you strike dead
With swift avenging thunderbolt of wrath
Him who first breaks this pact of peace.— And thou,
Brother as dear as daughter or as son,
Receive this proof of firmest faith.

　　　　　　　　[*He drains the cup, and recoils.*
　　　　　　　　　　Ah, wretch!

What do I see?　G　　gods, 'tis blood, blood, blood!
Ah, horror! Blood!—..　e own runs cold within
My frozen heart, my heart with horror chilled.
The sun grows dim around me; and the cup,
Dyed with such dreadful crimson, seems to shrink
From touch of this my trembling hand.— I die!
'Tis death I feel upon me. O my son!
What has become of thee?

[*Turning to Atreus*]—　　　　My son is dead!
My son is dead, thou cruel one! who offerest
False promises of peace to me bereavèd
In the same instant which has snatched him from me.
And lest this frightful blow should leave me living,
Monster! 'tis wine of blood thy hand is giving!
O Earth! canst thou support us at this moment?
My dream, my ghastly dream returned upon me!
Was it thy blood, my son! they gave thy father?

Atreus—

And canst thou recognize this blood?

Thyestes — My brother
    I recognize.
Atreus — Thou shouldst have recognized him
    And known his nature, in the past, nor wronged him,
    And forced him, ingrate! thus to hurl his vengeance!
Thyestes —
    O mighty gods! what crimes are ye avenging?
    Thou fiend spewed forth by hell to blight the earth,
    More fully spend the rage that fills thy breast;
    Send an unhappy father to his son!
    Give this new victim to his bloody manes,
    Nor stop half-way in thy vile path of crime.
    How canst thou spare me, barbarous wretch! to mourn
    Within a world whence thou hast driven away
    The gods, and even the wholesome light of day?
Atreus —
    Nay; I should wish thee back again to life,
    Which I can stuff so bravely with disasters.
    I know thy grief, I hear it in thy moans,
    I see thy sorrows wound thee as I wished;
    And in thy tears I find fulfilled the hope
    That fast was fading in my heart,— revenge!
    Thou callest on death, and I have left thee life,
    'Tis my revenge.
Thyestes — Ah, vain and flattering hope!
    Thyestes's hand can rob thee of that joy!
                         [*He kills himself.*
Theodamia, daughter of Thyestes —
    Ah, heaven!
Thyestes — Be thou comforted, my daughter;
    Hence, and leave justice to the most high gods,
    Whose hearts your tears will move. Hence! and await
    His punishment, whose perjuries turned pale
    The very gods themselves: they promise it;
    'Tis pledged me in this bloody cup, and now—
    Just gods!—I die!
Atreus — And I accept the omen;
    For thy self-slaying hand hath crowned my wishes,
    And I enjoy at last my crimes' fell fruitage!

MOTHER AND DAUGHTER

From ' Electra '

CLYTEMNESTRA — So! far from answering a mother's kindness.
Thou heap'st defiance on that sacred name!
And when my pity seeks her happiness,
Electra scorns me still. Ay, ay, defy me,
Proud princess, unrelenting! but accuse
None save thyself, that Fate so frowns on thee!
From a great monarch, jealous of his power,
I won a hero-husband for my daughter;
And hasty Hope had shown to me the sceptre
Within our house once more, bought by that union;
Yet she, ungrateful, only seeks our ruin!
But one word more: thou hold'st the heart of Itys,
And this same day shall see your lots united.
Refuse him at thy peril! for Ægisthus
Is weary of the slave within his palace,
Whose tears move men and gods to pity.

Electra —   Pity!
Against so proud a tyrant, O ye heavens,
What weapon? Can he fear my harmless tears,
Who thus defies remorse? Ah, madam,—mother!
Is it for thee to add to my misfortunes?
I, I Ægisthus's slave — alack, how comes it?
Ah, hapless daughter! who such slave has made me?
And say, of whom was this Electra born?
And is it fitting thou shouldst so reproach me?
Mother!— if still that holy name can move thee,—
And if indeed my shame be known to all
Within this palace,— show compassion on me,
And on the griefs thy hand hath heaped upon me;
Speed, speed my death! but think not to unite me
To him, the son of that foul murderer!
That wretch whose fury robbed me of a father,
And still pursues him in his son and daughter,
Usurping even the disposal of my hand!
Canst speak of such a marriage, and not shudder?
Mother! that lovedst me once,—how have I lost it,
Thy tender love? Alas! I cannot hate thee;
Despite the sorrows that have hedged me round,
The bitter tears I shed within this place,
'Tis only for the tyrant I invoke
The high gods' wrath. Ah, if I must forget

That I have lost a father — help me, madam,
To still remember that I have a mother!

Clytemnestra —

What can I do? how act? Naught save thy marriage
Will satisfy the King. I pray thee, yield.
Repine no longer at thy destined lot,
And cease bewailing o'er a dead barbarian
Who — had he found another Ilion —
Thyself full quickly would have made an offering
Upon the altar of his own ambition.
Thus did he dare — oh dark and cruel heart! —
Before mine eyes to sacrifice my daughter!

Electra —

Cruel — ay, madam; yet was he thy husband.
If thus he purchased for him punishment,
What gods or men appointed *thee* avenger?
If Heaven in extremity of harshness
Compelled him, hapless hero! to outpour
His own blood — answer! was it not for Heaven
He spilled it? But thou, most unnatural mother
Of sorrow-scourged Electra and Orestes,
Thou too wouldst spill the last drops of that blood;
Not for high Heaven, jealous of its altars,
But for the vilest mortal. Ah, behold him!
He comes, inhuman wretch! and at the sight
Fierce passions stir within my seething soul.

THE MATRICIDE

From 'Electra'

ORESTES —   Strike, ye gods!
Ye gods all-powerful, summoned by my fury;
Avenging gods! if there be such, then strike!
Since still I live. My crime, my hideous crime,
Is yours alone to reckon, yours to judge.
Has Heaven only gentle torments for me?
Alas! I see what stays your righteous vengeance;
You know not how to punish crime so foul,
Ye horror-stricken gods!

Electra —   Ah, brother, brother!
Calm this blind frenzy; cure thee of this madness;
Have I not weight enough of grief to bear?
Wouldst thou, Orestes, slay me as I stand?

Orestes —

    Hush! utter it no more, that name abhorred.
    And thou who shudderest at my odious presence —
    Nature! so oft, so deeply outraged here —
    I have avenged thee of my murdered father;
    But who my murdered mother shall avenge?
    Speak, Justice! if thine arm have lost its power, —
    Filled with the fury of a just despair,
    Behold, myself will aid it to strike home!
    If man's remorse can move divinity,
    Gods! turn ye to the tears, the blood I spill —
    Ha! seest thou, mother?

    [*He tries to kill himself, but is disarmed by his guardian
                        Palamedes.*]

Palamedes —   O my lord!
Orestes —   Leave, leave me!

    From thee I will have nothing, wretch inhuman!
    Nor from Electra. Was it not your hearts,
    Thirsting for blood and victims, that compelled me
    To stain my hands with guilt unspeakable?
    But how now? whence this mist that darkens round me?
    Thanks be to heaven, the way to hell is opened.
    Let us to hell! there's nothing that affrights me, —
    And in the horror of eternal night,
    Hide and enwrap ourselves! — But what pale light
    Shines on me now? who to this dark abode
    Dares to bring daylight back? What do I see?
    The dead of hell look shuddering upon me!
    Oh hear the moans, the painful cries — "Orestes!"
    Who calls me in this horrible retreat?
    It is Ægisthus! oh, too much, too much!
    And in my wrath — but soft: what sight is here?
    What holds he in his hands? My mother's head!
    Ah, what a gaze! Where shall Orestes flee!
    Atrocious monster! what a spectacle
    Thou venturest to show me! Stay thy fury!
    Behold my sufferings; and that awful head —
    Hide, hide it from these terror-smitten eyes!
    Ah, mother, spare me; spare thy unhappy son!
    Ye shades of Agamemnon, hear my cries;
    Shades of mine honored father, give thine aid;
    Come, shield thy son from the pursuing anger
    Of Clytemnestra! ah, show pity on me!
    What! even into thy protecting arms

She, furious, still pursues me. All is over!
I yield me to the life-consuming torture.
My guiltless heart, that bore nor part nor share
In the black crime committed by my hand,
Is torn with torments. O ye gods! what culprit
Of deepest guilt could bear worse punishment?

THE RECONCILIATION

From 'Rhadamistus and Zenobia'

ZENOBIA —   My lord, a hapless woman
Whom Fate has fastened to a tyrant's yoke,—
Dare she appeal, disgraced in chains of bondage,
To Romans, masters of the universe?
Ah! yet indeed what better part to play,
For these same masters of the universe,
Than to relieve my great misfortunes? Heaven,
That to their august laws subjected all —

Rhadamistus —
What do I see? Ah, wretched man! Those features —
That voice — Just gods! what sight do ye present
Before mine eyes?

Zenobia —   How comes it that your soul,
My gracious lord, so stirs at sight of me?

Rhadamistus —
Had not my hand deprived of life —

Zenobia —   What is it
I see and hear in turn? Sad recollection!
I tremble, shudder! where and what am I?
My strength fast leaves me. Ah, my lord, dispel
My terror and confusion. All my blood
Runs cold to my heart's core.

Rhadamistus —   Ah me! the passion
That fills my being, leaves no further doubt.
Hast thou, my hand, achieved but half thy crime?
Victim of man's conspiring cruelty,
Sad object of a jealous desperate love
Swept on by rage to fiercest violence,—
After such storm of madness, frenzy, fury —
Zenobia, is it thou?

Zenobia —   Zenobia!
Ah, gods! O Rhadamistus, thou my husband,
Cruel but yet beloved — after trials
So many and so bitter, is it thou?

Rhadamistus —

    Can it be possible thine eyes refuse
    To recognize him? Yes, I am that monster,
    That heart inhuman; yes! I am that traitor,
    That murderous husband! Would to highest Heaven
    That when to-day he stood unknown before thee,
    Forgetting him, thou hadst forgot his crimes!
    O gods! who to my mortal grief restore her,
    Why could ye not return to her a husband
    Worthy herself? What happy fate befalls me,
    That Heaven, touched to pity by my torments
    Of sharp regret, hath granted me to gaze
    Once more upon such charms? But yet—alas!
    Can it be, too, that at my father's court
    I find a wife so dear weighed down with chains?
    Gods! have I not bewailed my crimes enow,
    That ye afflict my vision with this sight?
    O all too gentle victim of despair
    Like mine! How all I see but fills afresh
    The measure of thy husband's guilt!—How now:
    Thou weepest!

Zenobia —
                  Wherefore, thou unhappy being,
    Should I not weep, in such a fateful hour?
    Ah, cruel one! would Heaven, thy hand of hatred
    Had only sought to snatch Zenobia's life!
    Then would my heart, unstirred to depths of anger
    At sight of thee, beat quickly on beholding
    My husband; then would love, to honor lifted
    By rage of jealousy, replace thy wife
    Within thine arms, fresh filled with happiness.
    Yet think not that I feel for thee no pity,
    Or turn from thee with loathing.

Rhadamistus —
                     Ye great gods!
    Far from reproaches such as should o'erwhelm me,
    It is Zenobia who fears to hate me,
    And justifies herself! Ah, punish me,
    Rather than this; for in such fatal kindness,
    Such free forgiveness, I am made to taste
    Of mine own cruelty! Spare not my blood,
    Dear object of my love! be just; deprive me
    Of such a bliss as seeing thee again!

                              [He falls at her feet.
    Must I, to urge thee, clasp thy very knees?
    Remember what the price, and whose the blood,

That sealed me as thy spouse! All, even my love,
Demands that I should perish. To leave crime
Unpunished, is to share the culprit's guilt.
Strike! but remember — in my wildest fury
Never wast thou cast down from thy high place
Within my heart; remember, if repentance
Could stand for innocence, I need no longer
Rouse thee to hatred, move thee to revenge.
Ay! and remember too, despite the rage
Which well I know must swell within thy soul,
My greatest passion was my love for thee.

Zenobia —

Arise! it is too much. Since I forgive thee,
What profit in regrets? The gods, believe me,
Deny to us the power of wreaking vengeance
On enemies so dear. But name the land
Where thou wouldst dwell, and I will follow thee
Whithersoe'er thou wilt. Speak! I am ready
To follow, from this moment forth, forever,
Assured that such remorse as fills thy heart
Springs from thy virtues, more than thy misfortunes;
And happy, if Zenobia's love for thee
Could some day serve as pattern to Armenia,
Make her like me thy willing, loyal subject,
And teach her, if no more, to know her duty!

Rhadamistus —

Great Heaven! can it be that lawful bonds
Unite such virtues to so many crimes?
That Hymen to a madman's lot should link
The fairest, the most perfect of all creatures
To whom the gods gave life? Canst look upon me,
After a father's death? My outrages,
My brother's love — that prince so great and generous —
Can they not make thee hate a hapless husband?
And I may tell myself, since thou disdainest
The proffered vows of virtuous Arsames,
Thou to his passion turn'st a heart of ice?
What words are these? too happy might I live
To-day, if duty in that noble heart
Might take for me the place of love!

Zenobia —   Ah, quiet
Within thy soul the groundless doubts that fill it;
Or hide at least thy unworthy jealousy!
Remember that a heart that can forgive thee

Is not a heart to doubt, — no, Rhadamistus,
Not without crime!

Rhadamistus —   O thou dear wife, forgive me
My fatal love; forgive me those suspicions
Which my whole heart abhors.   The more unworthy
Thy inhuman spouse, the less should thy displeasure
Visit his unjust fears.   O dear Zenobia!
Give me thy heart and hand again, and deign
To follow me this day to fair Armenia.
Cæsar hath o'er that province made me monarch;
Come! and behold me henceforth blot my crimes
From thy remembrance with a list of virtues.
Come, here is Hiero, a faithful subject,
Whose zeal we trust to cover o'er our flight.
Soon as the night has veiled the staring sky,
Assured that thou shalt see my face again,
Come and await me in this place.   Farewell!
Let us not linger till a barbarous foe,
When Heaven has reunited us, shall part us
Again forever.   O ye gods, who gave her
Back to my arms in answer to my longings,
Deign, deign to give to me a heart deserving
Your goodness!

S. R. CROCKETT

(1862–)

THAT Samuel Rutherford Crockett was born in Little Duchrae, Galloway, Scotland, in 1862, of a long line of tenant farmers; that, a small white-haired boy, beginning at three and a half years of age, he did his daily work on the farm and walked three miles to the parish school, where, under a master who was "a dungeon of learning," he wrestled with Latin as far as "Omnis Gallia" and through the Greek alphabet till he was fifteen; that he then entered Edinburgh University, where he added to his sparse resources by tutoring and journalistic work; and that after severe theological training he was in 1884 ordained to the ministry of the Free Church of Scotland,—reads like a familiar story which with a few changes, such as dates and identities, might have been told of a host of his distinguished countrymen.

S. R. CROCKETT

Between the covers of his books one may learn all that is essential and characteristic of Mr. Crockett, the most important fact in his literary life being an honorable loyalty to his own home and people and faith. It is his good fortune that that home is in a region of romance and legend and daring adventure; that his people are of an austere race, whose shrewd humor underlies a solemn gravity, whose keenest joy is intellectual controversy, and whose highest ambition is that at least one representative of the whitewashed farm-house shall "wag his head in a pulpit." And fundamentally, for his art's sake, it is his good fortune that his faith is their faith, a stern conviction of a stern creed whose tenderest traditions are fostered by the sight of the Martyrs' Monument on Auchenreoch Muir, and the kirk-yards of Balweary and Nether Dullarg, where under the trees the heroes of Scotland lie as thick as gowans on the lea.

Nor should the influence of the scenery of Galloway be ignored on Mr. Crockett's work. Its trackless moors and lairy coverts, the green woodlands of Earlston and the gray Duchrae craigs, the sleeping pools guarded by dark firs standing bravely like men-at-arms on every rocky knoll, the river Ken flowing silver clear, and the great Kells range, ridge behind ridge of hills "whose very names make a storm of music,"—this is the background of wild deeds and wilder passions, in whose recounting in 'The Raiders' and 'The Men of the Moss-Hags' we have as yet the highest exhibition of his genius.

Construction is not perhaps his strong point, but in these stirring scenes and dramatic situations, chronicled by the hero who creates an atmosphere of fond credulity in his adventures and personality, the author is kept to his work by the stress of hard times. The action is swift, for in 'The Raiders' the hill outlaws come down like the blast of a terrible trumpet; and in 'The Men of the Moss-Hags' Lauderdale and Claverhouse are hunting the Covenanters into the caves of the earth, so that in the rush of events both he who tells the tale and he who listens are hurried along. The feature of these fine romances, especially 'The Raiders,' is their Homeric spirit of generous simplicity and bellicose cheerfulness. Mr. Crockett is a fighter for his loves, his fireside, and his Shorter Catechism. And though there are pathetic passages, the robustness of the men and the heroism of the women remove them from our pity to our proud enthusiasm. Were one to seek the source of Mr. Crockett's inspiration, he would probably find it in the Old Testament.

In this class of novels are included the short, sombre story 'Mad Sir Uchtred' and 'The Gray Man.' Nor are these works lacking in the characteristics of his other manner yet to be spoken of. The long hours in which we ride with John Faa, Lord of Little Egypt, and with Willie Gordon of Earlston, are enlivened with shrewd comment and brilliant narration. Humanity in its least complex aspect, and robust faith in God, transport us to the other and sturdier age in which they dwelt.

The other field in which Mr. Crockett has made a reputation, his earlier field, is his presentment of contemporary Scotch peasant life. Robert Fraser and Janet Balchrystie, in 'The Stickit Minister,' are the descendants of John Faa and May Mischief and of Willie Gordon and Maisie Lenox. They dwell in the same sweet holms and by the levels of the same lochs, bonny and broad, and their faith is nurtured on the rugged Caledonian doctrine for which these, their literary forbears, fought and died. As the shepherd knows his sheep that to us who are not shepherds show so little unlikeness, so Mr. Crockett knows the lines and lineaments of his characters. The pathos of their brave lives is kept in shadow with the fine reserve of one who will not suffer a stranger to intermeddle, but it is felt as we feel that there are dark depths to the sea whose surface waves sparkle in the sun.

In this earlier manner 'A Galloway Herd,' 'The Play-Actress,' and the delicate fantasy 'The Lilac Sunbonnet,' are written. If in 'Cleg Kelly,' the story of an Edinburgh waif, there is a touch of the melodramatic, much may be forgiven an author who with the mastery of subtle peculiarities of individual types combines the power to make a novel vibrate with dramatic action.

ENSAMPLES TO THE FLOCK

From 'The Stickit Minister': the Macmillan Company, Publishers

THE family of the late Tyke M'Lurg consisted of three loons and a lassie. Tyke had never done anything for his children except share with a short-lived and shadowy mother the responsibility of bringing them into the world. The time that he could spare from his profession of poacher he had systematically devoted to neglecting them. Tyke had solved successfully for many years the problem of how to live by the least possible expenditure of labor. Kind ladies had taken him in hand time and again. They had provided clothes for his children, which Tyke had primarily converted into coin of the realm, and indirectly into liquid refreshment, at Lucky Morgan's rag store in Cairn Edward. Work had been found for Tyke, and he had done many half-days of labor in various gardens. Unfortunately, however, before the hour of noon it was Tyke's hard case to be taken with a "grooin' in his inside" of such a nature that he became rapidly incapacitated for further work.

"No, mem, I canna tak' it. It's mony a year since I saw the evil o't. Ye'll hae to excuse me, but I really couldna. Oh, thae pains! O sirce, my inside! Weel, gin ye insist, I'll juist hae to try a toothfu' to obleege ye, like."

But Tyke's toothfu's were over for this world, and his shortcomings were lying under four feet of red mold. Half a dozen kindly folk who pitied his "three loons and a lassie" gathered a few pounds and gave him a decent burial,—not for his own sake, but in order that the four little scarecrows might have a decent start in life. It is the most fatal and indestructible of reproaches in the south of Scotland to have a father buried by the parish.

The lassie was the eldest of the children. She was thirteen, and she hardly remembered what it was to have a mother or a new frock. But ever since she was eleven she had never had a dirty one. The smith's wife had shown her how to wash, and she had learned from the teacher how to mend. "Leeb" had appeared on the books of the school as Elizabeth M'Lurg, and she had attended as often as she could — that is, as often as her father could not prevent her; for Tyke, being an independent man, was down on the compulsory clause of the Education Act, and had more than once got thirty days for assaulting the School Board officer.

When he found out that Leeb was attending school at the village he lay in wait for her on her return, with a stick, and after administering chastisement on general principles he went on to specify his daughter's iniquities: —

"Ye upsettin' blastie, wad ye be for gangin' to their schule, learnin' to look doon on yer ain faither that has been at sic pains to rear ye?"— (a pause for further correction, to which poor Leeb vocalized an accompaniment). "Let me see gin ye can read! Hae, read that!" he said, flinging a tattered lesson-book, which the teacher had given her, to his daughter. Leeb opened the book, and punctuating the lesson with her sobs, she read in the high and level shriek of a locomotive engine, "And so brave Bobby, hav-ing sa-ved the tr-r-r-em-bling child, re-turn-ed with the res-cu-ed one in his mouth to the shore."

"Davert! but ye *can* read!" said her father, snatching the book and tearing it up before her eyes. "Noo, listen; I'll hae nane o' my bairns teached to despise their faither by no Schule Boards. Look you here, Leeb M'Lurg, gin ever I catch you within a mile o' the schule, I'll skin ye!"

But for all this tremendous threat, or maybe all the more because of it, and also because she so much desired to be able to do a white seam, Leeb so arranged it that there were few days when she did not manage to come along the mile and half of lochside road which separated her from the little one-roomed, whitewashed schoolhouse on the face of the brae. She even brought one of the "loons" with her pretty often; but as Jock, Rab, and Benny (otherwise known as Rag, Tag, and Bobtail) got a little older, they more easily accommodated themselves to the wishes of their parent; and in spite of Leeb's blandishments they went into "hidie holes" till the School Board officer had passed by.

M'Lurg's Mill where the children lived was a tumble-down erection, beautiful for situation, set on the side of the long loch of Kenick. The house had once been a little farm-house, its windows brilliant with geraniums and verbenas; but in the latter days of the forlorn M'Lurgs it had become betrampled as to its doorsteps by lean swine, and bespattered as to its broken floor by intrusive hens. It was to M'Lurg's Mill that the children returned after the funeral. Leeb had been arrayed in the hat and dress of a neighbor's daughter for the occasion, but the three loons had played "tig" in the intervals of watching their father's funeral from the broomy knoll behind the mill. Jock, the eldest, was nearly eleven, and had been taken in hand by the kind neighbor wife at the same time as Leeb. At one time he looked as though he would even better repay attention, for he feigned a sleek-faced submission and a ready compliance which put Mistress Auld of the Arkland off her guard. Then as soon as his sister, of whom Jock stood much in awe, was gone out, he snatched up his ragged clothes and fled to the hill. Here he was immediately joined by the other two loons. They caught the Arkland donkey grazing in the field beside the mill-dam, and having made a parcel of the good black trousers and jacket, they tied them to the donkey and drove him homeward with blows and shoutings. A funeral was only a dull procession to them, and the fact that it was their father's made no difference.

Next morning Leeb sat down on the "stoop" or wooden bench by the door, and proceeded to cast up her position. Her assets were not difficult to reckon. A house of two rooms, one devoted to hens and lumber; a mill which had once sawn good timber, but whose great circular saw had stood still for many months; a mill-lade broken down in several places, three or four chairs and a stool, a table, and a wash-tub. When she got so far she paused. It was evident that there could be no more school for her, and the thought struck her that now she must take the responsibility for the boys, and bring them up to be useful and diligent. She did not and could not so express her resolve to herself, but a still and strong determination was in her sore little heart not to let the boys grow up like their father.

Leeb had gone to Sabbath school every week, when she could escape from the tyranny of home, and was therefore well known to the minister, who had often exercised himself in vain on the thick defensive armor of ignorance and stupidity which encompassed the elder M'Lurg. His office-bearers and he had often bemoaned the sad example of this ne'er-do-weel family which had intrenched itself in the midst of so many well-doing people. M'Lurg's Mill was a reproach and an eyesore to the whole parish, and the M'Lurg "weans" a gratuitous insult to every self-respecting mother within miles. For three miles round the children were forbidden to play with, or even to speak to, the four outcasts at the mill. Consequently their society was much sought after.

When Leeb came to set forth her resources, she could not think of any except the four-pound loaf, the dozen hens and a cock, the routing wild Indian of a pig, and the two lean and knobby cows on the hill at the back. It would have been possible to sell all these things, perhaps, but Leeb looked upon herself as the trustee for the rest of the family. She resolved therefore to make what use of them she could, and having most of the property under her eye at the time, there was the less need to indite an inventory of it.

But first she must bring her brothers to a sense of their position. She was a very Napoleon of thirteen, and she knew that now that there was no counter authority to her own, she could bring Jock, Rab, and Benny to their senses very quickly. She therefore selected with some care and attention a hazel stick, using a broken table-knife to cut it with a great deal of deftness. Having trimmed it, she went out to the hill to look for her brothers.

It was not long before she came upon them engaged in the fascinating amusement of rooting for pignuts in a green bankside. The natural Leeb would instantly have thrown down her wand of office and joined them in the search, but the Leeb of to-day was a very different person. Her second thought was to rush among them and deal lusty blows with the stick, but she fortunately remembered that in that case they would scatter, and that by force she could only take home one, or at most two. She therefore called to her assistance the natural guile of her sex.

"Boys, are ye hungry?" she said. "There's sic a graun' big loaf come frae the Arkland!" By this time all her audience were on their feet. "An' I'll milk the kye, an' we'll hae a feast."

"Come on, Jock," said Rab, the second loon, and the leader in mischief, "I'll race ye for the loaf."

"Ye needna do that," said Leeb calmly; "the door's lockit."

So as Leeb went along, she talked to her brothers as soberly as though they were models of good behavior and all the virtues, telling them what she was going to do and how she would expect them to help her. By the time she got them into the mill-yard she had succeeded in stirring their enthusiasm, especially that of Jock, to whom with a natural tact she gave the wand of the office of "sairgint," a rank which on the authority of Sergeant M'Millan, the village pensioner, was understood to be very much higher than that of general. "Sairgint" Jock foresaw much future interest in the disciplining of his brothers, and entered with eagerness into the new ploy. The out-of-doors live stock was also committed to his care. He was to drive the cows along the roadside and allow them to pasture on the sweetest and most succulent grasses, while Rab scouted in the direction of the village for supposititious "poalismen" who were understood to take up and sell for the Queen's benefit all cows found eating grass on the public highway. Immediately after Jock and Rab had received a hunch of the Arkland loaf and their covenanted drink of milk, they went off to drive the cows to the loch road, so that they might at once begin to fill up their lean sides. Benny, the youngest, who was eight past, she reserved for her own assistant. He was a somewhat tearful but willing little fellow, whose voice haunted the precincts of M'Lurg's mill like a wistful ghost. His brothers were constantly running away from him, and he pattering after them as fast as his fat little legs could carry him, roaring with open mouth at their cruelty, the tears making clean watercourses down his grimy cheeks. But Benny soon became a new boy under his sister's exclusive care.

"Noo, Benny," she said, "you an' me's gaun to clean the hoose. Jock an' Rab will no' be kennin' it when they come back!" So, having filled the tub with water from the mill-lade, and carried every movable article of furniture outside, Leeb began to wash out the house and rid it of the accumulated dirt of years. Benny carried small bucketfuls of water to swill over the floor. Gradually the true color of the stones began to shine up, and the black incrustation to retreat towards the outlying corners.

"I'm gaun doon to the village," she said abruptly. "Benny, you keep scrubbin' alang the wa's."

Leeb took her way down rapidly to where Joe Turner, the village mason, was standing by a newly begun pig-stye or swine-ree, stirring a heap of lime and sand.

"G'ye way oot o' that!" he said instantly, with the threatening gesture which every villager except the minister and the mistress of Arkland instinctively made on seeing a M'Lurg. This it is to have a bad name.

But Leeb stood her ground, strong in the consciousness of her good intentions.

"Maister Turner," she said, "could ye let me hae a bucketfu' or twa o' whitewash for the mill kitchen? an' I'll pey ye in hen's eggs. Oor hens are layin' fine, an' your mistress is fond o' an egg in the mornin'."

Joe stopped and scratched his head. This was something new, even in a village where a good deal of business is done according to the rules of truck or barter.

"What are ye gaun to do wi' the whitewash?" he inquired, to get time to think. "There was little whitewash in use about M'Lurg's Mill in yer faither's time!"

"But I'm gaun to bring up the boys as they should," said Leeb, with some natural importance, sketching triangles on the ground with her bare toe.

"An' what's whitewash got to do wi' that?" asked Joe, with some asperity.

Leeb could not just put the matter into words, but she instinctively felt that it had a good deal to do with it. White-wash was her badge of respectability both inside the house and out, in which Leeb was at one with modern science.

"I'll gie three dizzen o' eggs for three bucketfu's," she said.

"An' hoo div I ken that I'll ever see ane o' the eggs?" asked Joe.

"I've brocht a dizzen wi' me noo!" said Leeb, promptly, producing them from under her apron.

Leeb got the whitewash that very night, and the loan of a brush to put it on with. Next morning the farmer of the Crae received a shock. There was something large and white down on the loch-side, where ever since he came to the Crae he had seen naething but the trees which hid M'Lurg's mill.

"I misdoot it's gaun to be terrible weather. I never saw that hoose o' Tyke M'Lurg's aff our hill afore!" he said.

The minister came by that day, and stood perfectly aghast at the new splendors of the M'Lurg mansion. Hitherto when he had strangers staying with him he took them another way, in order that his parish might not be disgraced. Not only were the walls of the house shining with whitewash, but the windows were cleaned, a piece of white muslin curtain was pinned across each, and a jug with a bunch of heather and wild flowers looked out smiling on the passers-by. The minister bent his steps to the open door. He could see the two M'Lurg cows pasturing placidly with much contented head-tossing on the roadside, while a small boy sat above, laboring at the first rounds of a stocking. From the house came the shrill voice of singing. Out of the firwood over the knoll came a still smaller boy, bent double with a load of sticks.

In the window, written with large sprawling capitals on a leaf of a copy-book under the heading "Encourage Earnest Endeavor," appeared the striking legend:—

> SOWING & MENDING DUN
> GOOD COWS MILK
>   STICKS FOR FIREWOOD CHEEP
> NEW LAID EGGS
>   BY ELIZABETH McLURG

The minister stood regarding, amazement on every line of his face. Leeb came out singing, a neatly tied bundle of chips made out of the dry débris of the saw-mill in her hand.

"Elizabeth," said he, "what is the meaning of this?"

"Will ye be pleased to step ben?" said Leeb. The minister did so, and was astonished to find himself sitting down in a spotless kitchen, the walls positively painfully white, the wooden chairs scoured with sand till the very fibre of the wood was blanched, and on a floor so clean that one might have dined off it, the mystic whorls and crosses of whiting which connect all good Galloway housekeepers with Runic times.

Before the minister went out of M'Lurg's Mill he had learned the intentions of Leeb to make men of her brothers. He said, "You are a woman already, before your time, Elizabeth!" which was the speech of all others best fitted to please Leeb M'Lurg. He had also ordered milk and eggs for the manse to be delivered by Benny, and promised that his wife would call upon the little head of the house.

As he went down the road by the loch-side he meditated, and this was the substance of his thought:— "If that girl brings up her brothers like herself, Tyke M'Lurg's children may yet be ensamples to the flock."

But as to this we shall see.

SAWNY BEAN; AND THE CAVE OF DEATH

From 'The Gray Man': copyright 1896, by Harper and Brothers

FOR a moment in the darkness I stood dazed, and my head swam. For I bethought me of the earl's words, and I knew that my fate stood upon tiptoe. For here in the finding of this box lay all my life, and it might be my love also. But again another thought crossed the first, damming back and freezing the current of hot blood which surged to my heart. The caird's words in the Grieve's kitchen came to me:— "You will find the treasure of Kelwood in the cave of Sawny Bean, in the head of Benanback over against Benerard."

If this were to be, there was little doubt that we stood in instant and imminent danger of our lives. Yet I could not bring myself to leave the treasure. Doubtless I ought to have done so, and hastened our escape for the sake of the girls. But I thought it might be possible to convey the chest out, and so bring both our quests to an end at once — that for the treasure by the recovery of the box which had been lost and found and lost upon the Red Moss, and that of vengeance by the certain condemnation of the Auchendraynes upon Marjorie's evidence.

The next moment great fear took hold on me. All that I had heard since my childhood about the Unknown who dwelt upon the shore-side, and lived no man knew how, ran through my mind,— his monstrous form; his cloven feet that made steads on the ground like those of a beast; his huge hairy arms, clawed at the finger-ends like the claws of a bear. I minded me of the fireside tales of the travelers who had lost their way in that fastness, and who, falling into the power of his savage tribe, returned no more to kindlier places. I minded also how none might speak to the prowler by night or get answer from him; how every expedition against him had come to naught, because that he was protected by a power stronger, warned and advised by an intelligence higher than his own. Besides, none had been able to find the abode or enter into the secret defenses where lurked the Man-beast of Benerard.

And it was in this abode of death that I, Launce Kennedy, being as I supposed in my sane mind, had taken refuge with two women, one the dearest to me on earth. The blood ran pingling and pricking in my veins. My heart-cords tightened as though it had been shut in a box and the key turned.

Hastily I slipped down, and upon a pretext took the dominie aside to tell him what it was that I had found.

"Ye have found our dead-warrant, then. I wish we had never seen your treasures and banded boxes!" said he roughly, as if I had done it with intent.

And in truth I began to think he was right. But it was none of my fault, and we had been just as badly off in that place if I had not found it.

After that I went ranging hither and thither among all the passages and twinings of the cave, yet never daring to go very far from the place where we were, lest I should not be able to find my way back. For it was an ill place, where every step that I took something strange swept across my face or slithered clammily along my cheek, making one grue to his bone marrows. I am as fond of a nimble fetch of adventures as any man, as every believing reader of this chronicle kens well by this time. But I want no more such experiences. Specially now that I am become a peaceable man, and no longer so regardlessly forward as I was in thrusting myself into all stirs and quarrels up to the elbows.

Then in a little I went soft-footed to where Marjorie and Nell had bestowed themselves. When I told them how we had run into danger with a folly and senselessness which nothing could have excused, save the great necessity into which by the hellish fury of our enemies we had been driven, it was cheerful to hear their words of trust, and their declaration that they could abide the issue with fortitude.

So we made such preparations as we could — as preparing our pistols and loosening our swords. Yet all had to be done by touch in that abode of darkness and black unchristian deeds.

It was silent and eery in the cave. We heard the water lapping further and further from us as it retreated down the long passage. Now and then we seemed to catch a gliff of the noise of human voices. But again, when we listened, it was naught but the wind blowing every way through the passages and halls of the cave; or the echo of the wing-beatings of uncanny things that battened in the roofs and crevices of the murtherous cavern where we abode, unfathomed, unsounded, and obscure.

But we had not long to wait ere our courage and resolution were tested to the uttermost. For presently there came to us clearly, though faintly at first, the crying and baying of voices, fearful and threatening: yet more like the insensate howling of dogs or shut-up hounds in a kennel than human creatures. Then there was empty silence, through which again the noise came in gusts like the sudden deadly anger of a mob; again more sharp and edged with fear, like the wailing of women led to their unpitied doom. And the sound of this inhuman carnival, approaching, filled the cave.

The direful crying came nearer and nearer, till we all cowered pale-faced together, save Marjorie alone — who, having been as it were in hell itself, feared not the most merciless fiends that had broken loose therefrom. She stood a little apart from us, so far that I had not known her presence but for the draught of air that blew inward, which carried her light robe towards me so that its texture touched my face, and I was aware of the old subtle fragrance which in happy days had turned my head in the gardens of Culzean.

But Nell Kennedy stood close to me — so close that I could hear her heart beating and the little sound of the clasping and unclasping of her hands. Which made me somewhat braver, especially when she put both her hands about my arm and gripped convulsively to me, as the noises of the crying and howling waxed louder and nearer.

"I am vexed that I flouted you, Launce!" she whispered in my ear. "I do not care what you said to Kate Allison. After all, she is not such a truth-telling girl, nor yet very by-ordinary bonny."

I whispered to her that I cared not either, and that I was content to die for her.

  .   .   .   .

Thus we sat waiting. Suddenly there was a pause in the noise which filled the cavern below. I thought they had discovered us. But Marjorie moved her hand a little to bid me keep down. So very carefully I raised my head over the rock, so that through the niche I could, as before, look down upon them.

The water-door of the cave was now entirely filled by a black bulk, in shape like a monstrous ape. Even in the flickering light I knew that I had seen the monster before. A thrill ran through me when I remembered the Man-beast with which I had grappled in the barn of Culzean the night I outfaced the Gray Man. And now by the silence, and the crouching of the horde beneath me, I learned also that their master had come home. The thing stood a moment in the doorway as though angered at something. Then he spoke, in a voice like a beast's growl, things which I could not at all understand. Though it was clear that his progeny did, for there ensued a rushing from side to side. Then Sawny Bean strode into the midst of his den. He stumbled, and set his foot upon a lad of nine or ten, judging by the size of him, who sprawled in the doorway. The imp squirmed round like a serpent and bit Sawny Bean in the leg. Whereat he stooped, and catching the lad by the feet, he dashed his head with a dull crash against the wall, and threw him like a dead rabbit in the corner.

The rest stood for a moment aghast. But in a trice, and without a single one so much as going to see if the boy were dead or only stunned, the whole hornets' byke hummed again, and the place was filled with a stifling smell of burning fat and roasting victual, upon which I dared not let my mind for a moment dwell.

When Sawny Bean came in, he had that which looked like a rich cloth of gold over his arm — the plunder of some poor butchered wretch, belike. He stood with his trophy, examining it, before the fire. Presently he threw it over his shoulders with the arms hanging idly down, and strode about 'most like a play-actor or a mad person, but manifestly to his own great content and to the admiration of his followers, who stood still and gaped after him.

When he had satisfied himself with this, I saw him look towards our place of refuge. A great spasm gulped my heart when I saw him take the first step towards us, for I knew that it was his forbidden treasure-house in which we lurked.

So I thought it had come to the bitter push. But something yet more terrible than the matter of the boy diverted for the moment the monster's attention. The lad whom he had cast to the side had been left alone, none daring to meddle. But now, as he passed him, Sawny Bean gave the body a toss with his foot. At this, quick as a darting falcon on the stoop, a woman sprang at him from a crevice where she had been crouching — at least by her shape she was a woman, with long elf-locks twisting like snakes about her brow. She held an open knife in her hand, and she struck at the chieftain's hairy breast. I heard the knife strike the flesh, and the cry of anger and pain which followed. But the monster caught the woman by the wrist, pulled her over his knee, and bent back her head. It was a horrid thing to see, and there is small wonder that I can see it yet in many a dream of the night. And no doubt also I shall see it till I die — hear it as well.

Then for a long season I could look no more. But when I had recovered me a little, and could again command my heart to look, I saw a great part of the crew swarm like flies, fetching, carrying, and working like bees upon spilled honey, from the corner where had been the bodies of the lad and the woman. But it was not in the ordinary way that they were being prepared for burial. In the centre of the cave was Sawny, with some of the younger sort of the women pawing over him and bandaging his wounded shoulder. He was growling and spitting inarticulately all the time like a wildcat. And every time his shoulder hurt him, as the women worked with it, he would take his other hand and strike one of them down, as though it was to her that he owed the twinge of pain.

Presently the monster arose and took the gold brocade again in his hand. I thought that of a certainty now the time was come. And I looked at Nell Kennedy.

God knows what was in my eyes. My heart was like to break. For the like of this pass was never man in. That I should have to smite my love to the death within an hour of the first kiss and the first owning of her affection!

But she that loved me read my thought in mine eyes.

She bared her neck for me, so that I could see its tender whiteness in the flicker of the fire.

"Strike there," she said, "and let me die in your arms, who are my heart's love, Launcelot Kennedy."

I heard the Beast-man's step on the stair. I looked from Nell's dear neck to her eyes and back again to her bosom. I lifted my hand with the steel in it, and nerved myself for the striking, for

I must make no mistaking. And even in that moment I saw a dagger also in Marjorie's hand.

Suddenly a tremendous rush of sound filled the cave. The dagger fell from my hand, and Nell and I clasped one another. The clamor seemed to be about us and all round us. Roaring echoes came back to us. The bowels of the earth quaked. Yet methought there was something familiar in the sound of it. I turned me about, and there, standing erect with all his little height, was the dominie. His cheeks were distended, and he was blowing upon his great war-pipes such a thunderous pibroch as never had been heard in any land since the pipes skirled on the Red Harlaw.

What possession had come upon his mind I know not. But the effect I can tell. The pack of fiends that caroused and slew beneath stood stricken a moment, in amaze at the dreadful incomprehensible sounds. Then they fled helter-skelter, yelly-hooing with fear, down the narrow sea-way, from which the tide had now fully ebbed. And when I looked over, there was not a soul to be seen. Only over the edge of a caldron the body of the murdered woman, or at least a part of it, lay — a bloody incentive to haste out of this direful Cave of Death.

The dominie stepped down as though he had been leading a march, strutting and passaging like the king's piper marching about the banqueting-table at Holyrood. I declare, the creature seemed fey. He was certainly possessed with a devil. But the fearlessness of the man won into our veins also. For with steel or pistol in each of our hands we marched after him, ready to encounter aught that might come in our way. Aye, and even thus passed out of the cave, hasting down the long passage without a quiver of the heart or a blenching of the cheek, so suddenly and so starkly, by way of sudden hope, had the glorious music brought the hot blood back to our hearts, even as it had stricken our cruel foes with instant terror.

Thus dry-shod we marched out of the cave of Sawny Bean, and not so much as a dog barked at us. But when in the gray of a stormy morning we reached the cliff's edge, we heard inland the wild voices of the gang yelling down the wind, as though the furies of fear were pursuing them and tearing at their vitals. What they expected I know not. But I guess that they must have taken us for whatever particular devil they happened to believe in, come to take them quick to their own place. Which, after all, could not be much worse than the den in which we had seen them at their disport, nor could all the torturing fiends of lowest hell have been their marrows in devilish cruelty.

.   .   .   .

So once more the world was before us, and strangely quiet it seemed, as if we had died in stress and riot and been born again into an uncanny quiet. There remained now for us only the bringing to pass of righteous judgments upon the wicked ones who had compassed and plotted all this terrible tale of evils. These murders without end, the hellish cruelties and death-breeding deceits, must not fall alone on the crazed outlaw and his brood, for the chief criminals were those that were greater than Sawny Bean and his merciless crew.

GEORGE CROLY

(1780–1860)

THE versatile Irishman George Croly turned to literature as his means of livelihood when about thirty years old. He had been educated in his native town of Dublin, where he had graduated from Trinity College when only fifteen. Even thus early he had distinguished himself as a classical student and for grace in extempore speaking. He next studied for the ministry, and in 1804 was ordained, and obtained a small curacy in the North of Ireland.

But George Croly had a great fund of ambition, which kept him dissatisfied in this humble position. Hopes of preferment were several times held out to him, but they all failed; and tired of disappointment, he gave up his curacy in 1810 and moved to London with his mother and sisters. There he soon found an opening in journalism, and became dramatic critic on the New Times, and a regular contributor to the Literary Gazette and Britannia. He also wrote for Blackwood's Magazine, and as fellow contributor met the young lady whom he afterwards married.

In spite of his scholarship and great facility in expression, Croly's cannot be called an original mind. His verse is mostly a reflection of the literary influences he experienced. A certain exaggeration of emotion, the romance of Byron and Moore then in highest favor, appealed to him, and he emulated it in his most ambitious poems. 'Paris' (1815), although much weaker, strongly suggests 'Childe Harold.' Like Moore, his imagination delighted in Oriental color and richness, and he often chose Eastern subjects, as in 'The Angel of the World.'

The 'Traditions of the Rabbins' has been called an imitation of De Quincey, and indeed a portion of it is wrongly included in the collection of De Quincey's works. His 'Life and Times of George IV.' is more valuable as entertaining reading than for historical significance. To religious literature he contributed a 'Commentary on the Apocalypse,' and a book upon 'Divine Providence, or the Three Cycles of Revelation.' But although he loved literature and had read extensively, Croly's appreciation of it seems to have been entirely emotional. He could not analyze his impressions, and his critical work is vague enthusiasm rather than suggestive discrimination.

He essayed drama successfully. 'Catiline,' in spite of bombastic reminiscences of Marlowe, has tragic strength and richly rhythmic verse. 'Pride Shall Have a Fall,' a clever exposure of social weaknesses, was successfully given at the Covent Garden Theatre.

Although happy in authorship, Croly was anxious to resume his clerical profession, and in 1835 gladly accepted the rectorship of St. Stephen's Church, Walbrook, where a fashionable congregation accorded him a great reputation for eloquence. He was less successful in 1847, when appointed afternoon lecturer at the Foundling Hospital. The orphans and servant-maids failed to appreciate his flowery periods and emotional fervors. He was evidently quite beyond them, and soon resigned in disgust at their ingratitude.

Croly's poems and several other works, highly praised when they appeared, have been nearly forgotten. His fame rests now upon his fiction: 'Tales of the Saint Bernard,' 'Marston,' and 'Salathiel the Immortal.' The last especially, with the enduring fascination of the Wandering Jew legend, is always interesting. It has been often said that no one else has told the story so well. All the romance-loving side of Croly's nature comes out in the glowing descriptions of Eastern scenery, and in the appeal to heroic sentiment. The fantastic figure of Nero, ancient passions and vices, a spirit of former barbarity interwoven with ideality, the tragedy of unending human life, are curiously impressed on the picturesque pages.

THE FIRING OF ROME

From 'Salathiel the Immortal'

INTELLIGENCE in a few days arrived from Brundusium of the Emperor's landing, and of his intention to remain at Antium on the road to Rome, until his triumphal entry should be prepared. My fate now hung in the scale. I was ordered to attend the imperial presence. At the vestibule of the Antian palace my careful centurion deposited me in the hands of a senator. As I followed him through the halls, a young female richly attired, and of the most beautiful face and form, crossed us, light and graceful as a dancing nymph. The senator bowed profoundly. She beckoned to him, and they exchanged a few words. I was probably the subject; for her countenance, sparkling with the animation of youth and loveliness, grew pale at once; she clasped both her hands upon her eyes, and rushed into an inner chamber. She knew Nero well; and dearly she was yet to pay for her knowledge. The senator, to my inquiring glance, answered in a whisper, "The Empress Poppæa."

A few steps onward, and I stood in the presence of the most formidable being on earth. Yet whatever might have been the natural agitation of the time, I could scarcely restrain a smile at the first sight of Nero. I saw a pale, undersized, light-haired young man sitting before a table with a lyre on it, a few copies of verses and drawings, and a parrot's cage, to whose inmate he was teaching Greek with great assiduity. But for the regal furniture of the cabinet, I should have supposed myself led by mistake into an interview with some struggling poet. He shot round one quick glance on the opening of the door, and then proceeded to give lessons to his bird. I had leisure to gaze on the tyrant and parricide.

Physiognomy is a true science. The man of profound thought, the man of active ability, and above all the man of genius, has his character stamped on his countenance by nature; the man of violent passions and the voluptuary have it stamped by habit. But the science has its limits: it has no stamp for mere cruelty. The features of the human monster before me were mild and almost handsome; a heavy eye and a figure tending to fullness gave the impression of a quiet mind; and but for an occasional restlessness of brow, and a brief glance from under it, in which the leaden eye darted suspicion, I should have pronounced Nero one of the most indolently tranquil of mankind.

He remanded the parrot to his perch, took up his lyre, and throwing a not unskillful hand over the strings, in the intervals of the performance languidly addressed a broken sentence to me. "You have come, I understand, from Judea;— they tell me that you have been, or are to be, a general of the insurrection;— you must be put to death;— your countrymen give us a great deal of trouble, and I always regret to be troubled with them.— But to send you back would only be encouragement to them, and to keep you here among strangers would only be cruelty to you. — I am charged with cruelty: you see the charge is not true.— I am lampooned every day; I know the scribblers, but they must lampoon or starve. I leave them to do both. Have you brought any news from Judea?— They have not had a true prince there since the first Herod; and he was quite a Greek, a cut-throat, and a man of taste. He understood the arts.— I sent for you to see what sort of animal a Jewish rebel was. Your dress is handsome, but too light for our winters.—You cannot die before sunset, as till then I am engaged with my music master.—We all

must die when our time comes.— Farewell—till sunset may
Jupiter protect you!"

I retired to execution! and before the door closed, heard this
accomplished disposer of life and death preluding upon his lyre
with increased energy.   I was conducted to a turret until the
period in which the Emperor's engagement with his music-
master should leave him at leisure to see me die.   Yet there was
kindness even under the roof of Nero, and a liberal hand had
covered the table in my cell.   The hours passed heavily along,
but they passed; and I was watching the last rays of my last
sun, when I perceived a cloud rise in the direction of Rome.   It
grew broader, deeper, darker, as I gazed; its centre was suddenly
tinged with red; the tinge spread; the whole mass of cloud
became crimson: the sun went down, and another sun seemed to
have risen in his stead.   I heard the clattering of horses' feet in
the courtyards below; trumpets sounded; there was confusion in
the palace; the troops hurried under arms; and I saw a squad-
ron of cavalry set off at full speed.

As I was gazing on the spectacle before me, which perpetually became more menacing, the door of my cell slowly opened,
and a masked figure stood upon the threshold.   I had made up
my mind; and demanding if he was the executioner, I told him
"that I was ready."   The figure paused, listened to the sounds
below, and after looking for a while on the troops in the court-
yard, signified by signs that I had a chance of saving my life.
The love of existence rushed back upon me.   I eagerly inquired
what was to be done.   He drew from under his cloak the dress
of a Roman slave, which I put on, and noiselessly followed his
steps through a long succession of small and strangely intricate
passages.   We found no difficulty from guards or domestics.
The whole palace was in a state of extraordinary confusion.
Every human being was packing up something or other: rich
vases, myrrhine cups, table services, were lying in heaps on the
floors; books, costly dresses, instruments of music, all the append-
ages of luxury, were flung loose in every direction, from the
sudden breaking up of the court.   I might have plundered the
value of a province with impunity.   Still we wound our hurried
way.   In passing along one of the corridors, the voice of complaining struck the ear; the mysterious guide hesitated; I glanced
through the slab of crystal that showed the chamber within.   It
was the one in which I had seen the Emperor, but his place

was now filled by the form of youth and beauty that had crossed me on my arrival. She was weeping bitterly, and reading with strong and sorrowful indignation a long list of names, probably one of those rolls in which Nero registered his intended victims, and which in the confusion of departure he had left open. A second glance saw her tear the paper into a thousand fragments, and scatter them in the fountain that gushed upon the floor.

I left this lovely and unhappy creature, this dove in the vulture's talons, with almost a pang. A few steps more brought us into the open air, but among bowers that covered our path with darkness. At the extremity of the gardens my guide struck with his dagger upon a door; it was opened: we found horses outside; he sprang on one; I sprang on its fellow; and palace, guards, and death, were left far behind.

He galloped so furiously that I found it impossible to speak; and it was not till we had reached an eminence a few miles from Rome, where we breathed our horses, that I could ask to whom I had been indebted for my escape. But I could not extract a word from him. He made signs of silence, and pointed with wild anxiety to the scene that spread below. It was of a grandeur and terror indescribable. Rome was an ocean of flame.

Height and depth were covered with red surges, that rolled before the blast like an endless tide. The billows burst up the sides of the hills, which they turned into instant volcanoes, exploding volumes of smoke and fire; then plunged into the depths in a hundred glowing cataracts, then climbed and consumed again. The distant sound of the city in her convulsion went to the soul. The air was filled with the steady roar of the advancing flame, the crash of falling houses, and the hideous outcry of the myriads flying through the streets, or surrounded and perishing in the conflagration.

Hostile to Rome as I was, I could not restrain the exclamation: — "There goes the fruit of conquest, the glory of ages, the purchase of the blood of millions! Was vanity made for man?" My guide continued looking forward with intense earnestness, as if he were perplexed by what avenue to enter the burning city. I demanded who he was, and whither he would lead me. He returned no answer. A long spire of flame that shot up from a hitherto untouched quarter engrossed all his senses. He struck in the spur, and making a wild gesture to me to follow, darted down the hill. I pursued; we found the Appian choked with

wagons, baggage of every kind, and terrified crowds hurrying
into the open country. To force a way through them was
impossible. All was clamor, violent struggle, and helpless death.
Men and women of the highest rank were on foot, trampled by
the rabble, that had then lost all respect of conditions. One
dense mass of miserable life, irresistible from its weight, crushed
by the narrow streets, and scorched by the flames over their
heads, rolled through the gates like an endless stream of black
lava.

We turned back, and attempted an entrance through the gardens of the same villas that skirted the city wall near the Palatine. All were deserted, and after some dangerous leaps over
the burning ruins we found ourselves in the streets. The fire
had originally broken out upon the Palatine, and hot smoke that
wrapped and half blinded us hung thick as night upon the
wrecks of pavilions and palaces: but the dexterity and knowledge
of my inexplicable guide carried us on. It was in vain that I
insisted upon knowing the purpose of this terrible traverse. He
pressed his hand on his heart in reassurance of his fidelity, and
still spurred on.

We now passed under the shade of an immense range of lofty
buildings, whose gloomy and solid strength seemed to bid
defiance to chance and time. A sudden yell appalled me. A
ring of fire swept round its summit; burning cordage, sheets of
canvas, and a shower of all things combustible, flew into the air
above our heads. An uproar followed, unlike all that I had ever
heard,— a hideous mixture of howls, shrieks, and groans. The
flames rolled down the narrow street before us, and made the
passage next to impossible. While we hesitated, a huge fragment of the building heaved as if in an earthquake, and fortunately for us fell inwards. The whole scene of terror was
then open. The great amphitheatre of Statilius Taurus had
caught fire; the stage with its inflammable furniture was intensely
blazing below. The flames were wheeling up, circle above circle,
through the seventy thousand seats that rose from the ground to
the roof. I stood in unspeakable awe and wonder on the side of
this colossal cavern, this mighty temple of the city of fire. At
length a descending blast cleared away the smoke that covered
the arena. The cause of those horrid cries was now visible.
The wild beasts kept for the games had broken from their dens.
Maddened by affright and pain, lions, tigers, panthers, wolves,

whole herds of the monsters of India and Africa, were inclosed in an impassable barrier of fire. They bounded, they fought, they screamed, they tore; they ran howling round and round the circle; they made desperate leaps upwards through the blaze; they were flung back, and fell only to fasten their fangs in each other, and with their parching jaws bathed in blood, died raging.

I looked anxiously to see whether any human being was involved in this fearful catastrophe. To my great relief I could see none. The keepers and attendants had obviously escaped. As I expressed my gladness I was startled by a loud cry from my guide, the first sound that I had heard him utter. He pointed to the opposite side of the amphitheatre. There indeed sat an object of melancholy interest; a man who had either been unable to escape, or had determined to die. Escape was now impossible. He sat in desperate calmness on his funeral pile. He was a gigantic Ethiopian slave, entirely naked. He had chosen his place, as if in mockery, on the imperial throne; the fire was above him and around him; and under this tremendous canopy he gazed, without the movement of a muscle, on the combat of the wild beasts below: a solitary sovereign with the whole tremendous game played for himself, and inaccessible to the power of man.

I was forced away from this absorbing spectacle, and we once more threaded the long and intricate streets of Rome. As we approached the end of one of these bewildering passages, scarcely wide enough for us to ride abreast, I was startled by the sudden illumination of the sky immediately above; and rendered cautious by the experience of our hazards, called to my companion to return. He pointed behind me, and showed the fire bursting out in the houses by which we had just galloped. I followed on. A crowd that poured from the adjoining streets cut off our retreat. Hundreds rapidly mounted on the houses in front, in the hope by throwing them down to check the conflagration. The obstacle once removed, we saw the source of the light — spectacle of horror! The great prison of Rome was on fire. Never can I forget the sights and sounds — the dismay — the hopeless agony — the fury and frenzy that then overwhelmed the heart. The jailers had been forced to fly before they could loose the fetters or open the cells of the prisoners. We saw those gaunt and woe-begone wretches crowding to their casements, and imploring impossible help; clinging to the heated bars; toiling with their impotent grasp to tear out the massive stones; some wringing their hands; some calling on the terrified spectators by every name of humanity to save them; some venting their despair in execrations and blasphemies that made the blood run cold; others, after many a wild effort to break loose, dashing their heads against the walls, or stabbing themselves. The people gave them outcry for outcry; but the flame forbade approach. Before I could extricate myself from the multitude a whirl of fiery ashes shot upwards from the falling roof; the walls rent into a thousand fragments; and the huge prison with all its miserable inmates was a heap of red embers.

Exhausted as I was by this restless fatigue, and yet more by the melancholy sights that surrounded every step, no fatigue seemed to be felt by the singular being that governed my movements. He sprang through the burning ruins,—he plunged into the sulphurous smoke,—he never lost the direction that he had first taken; and though baffled and forced to turn back a hundred times, he again rushed on his track with the directness of an arrow. For me to make my way back to the gates would be even more difficult than to push forward. My ultimate safety might be in following, and I followed. To stand still and to move were equally perilous. The streets, even with the improvements of Augustus, were still scarcely wider than the breadth of the little Italian carts that crowded them. They were crooked, long, and obstructed by every impediment of a city built in haste, after the burning by the Gauls, and with no other plan than the caprice of its hurried tenantry. The houses were of immense height, chiefly wood, many roofed with thatch, and all covered or cemented with pitch. The true surprise is that it had not been burned once a year from the time of its building.

The memory of Nero, that hereditary concentration of vice, of whose ancestor's yellow beard the Roman orator said, "No wonder that his beard was brass, when his mouth was iron and his heart lead," — the parricide and the poisoner — may yet be fairly exonerated of an act which might have been the deed of a drunken mendicant in any of the fifty thousand hovels of this gigantic aggregate of everything that could turn to flame.

We passed along through all the horrid varieties of misery, guilt, and riot that could find their place in a great public calamity: groups gazing in woe on the wreck of their fortunes,

rushing off to the winds in vapor and fire; groups plundering in
the midst of the flame; groups of rioters, escaped felons, and
murderers, exulting in the public ruin, and dancing and drinking with Bacchanalian uproar; gangs of robbers trampling down
and stabbing the fugitives to strip them of their last means;
revenge, avarice, despair, profligacy, let loose naked; undisguised
demons, to swell the wretchedness of this tremendous infliction
upon a guilty and blood-covered empire.

Still we spurred on, but our jaded horses at length sank
under us; and leaving them to find their way into the fields,
we struggled forward on foot.

A WIFE'S INFLUENCE

From 'Catiline'

AURELIA — One hope there is, worth all the rest — Revenge!
        The time is harassed, poor, and discontent;
        Your spirit practiced, keen, and desperate,—
        The Senate full of feuds,— the city vext
        With petty tyranny — the legions wronged —
Catiline [scornfully] —
        Yet who has stirred? Woman, you paint the air
        With Passion's pencil.
Aurelia —   Were my will a sword!
Catiline — Hear me, bold heart! The whole gross blood of Rome
        Could not atone my wrongs! I'm soul-shrunk, sick,
        Weary of man! And now my mind is fixed
        For Sylla: there to make companionship
        Rather of bear and tiger — of the snake —
        The lion in his hunger — than of man!
Aurelia — I had a father once, who would have plunged
        Rome in the Tiber for an angry look!
        You saw our entrance from the Gaulish war,
        When Sylla fled?
Catiline —   My legion was in Spain.
Aurelia — We crept through Italy, a flood of fire,
        A living lava, rolling straight on Rome.
        For days, before we reached it, the whole road
        Was thronged with suppliants — tribunes, consulars;
        The mightiest names o' the State. Could gold have bribed,
        We might have pitched our tents, and slept on gold;

But we had work to do! Our swords were thirsty.
We entered Rome as conquerors, in arms;
I by my father's side, cuirassed and helmed,
Bellona beside Mars.

Catiline [*with coldness*] —   The world was yours!

Aurelia — Rome was all eyes; the ancient tottered forth;
The cripple propped his limbs beside the wall;
The dying left his bed to look, and die.
The way before us was a sea of heads;
The way behind a torrent of brown spears:
So, on we rode, in fierce and funeral pomp,
Through the long living streets, that sunk in gloom,
As we, like Pluto and Proserpina,
Enthroned, rode on — like twofold destiny!

Catiline [*sternly, interrupting her*] —
Those triumphs are but gewgaws. All the earth, —
What is it? Dust and smoke. I've done with life!

Aurelia [*coming closer and looking steadily upon him*] —
Before that eve, one hundred senators
And fifteen hundred knights had paid in blood
The price of taunts, and treachery, and rebellion!
Were my tongue thunder, I would cry — Revenge!

Catiline [*in sudden wildness*] —
No more of this! In to your chamber, wife!
There is a whirling lightness in my brain,
That will not now bear questioning. — Away!

        [*Aurelia moves slowly towards the door.*

Where are our veterans now? Look on these walls;
I cannot turn their tissues into life.
Where are our revenues — our chosen friends?
Are we not beggars? Where have beggars friends?
I see no swords and bucklers on these floors!
I shake the State! *I* — what have I on earth
But these two hands? Must I not dig or starve? —
Come back! I had forgot. My memory dies,
I think, by the hour. Who sups with us to-night?
Let all be of the rarest, — spare no cost.
If 'tis our last, — it may be, — let us sink
In sumptuous ruin, with wonderers round us, wife!
One funeral pile shall send up amber smoke!
We'll burn in myrrh, or — blood!

                     [*She goes.*

I feel a nameless pressure on my brow,
As if the heavens were thick with sudden gloom;

A shapeless consciousness, as if some blow
Were hanging o'er my head. They say such thoughts
Partake of prophecy.

[He stands at the casement.

The air is living sweetness. Golden sun,
Shall I be like thee yet? The clouds have passed —
And, like some mighty victor, he returns
To his red city in the west, that now
Spreads all her gates, and lights her torches up
In triumph for her glowing conqueror.

THE LILY OF THE VALLEY

WHITE bud, that in meek beauty so dost lean
  Thy cloistered cheek as pale as moonlight snow,
Thou seem'st beneath thy huge high leaf of green,
  An eremite beneath his mountain's brow.

White bud! thou 'rt emblem of a lovelier thing,
  The broken spirit that its anguish bears
To silent shades, and there sits offering
  To Heaven the holy fragrance of its tears.

GEORGE CUPPLES

(1822–1891)

ALTHOUGH the Scotch Lowlands were settled by men of pure Anglican blood, the neighboring Highlands and the original Celtic inhabitants of the locality have contributed a strain from another of the primitive Aryan stocks, to the great enrichment in fervor and emotional expressiveness of the people. The Scotchman retains the energy, perseverance, and executive masterfulness of his brothers in Yorkshire and Northumberland, but has in addition a vein of romantic imagination and a touch of Celtic excitability. He may be "dour and canny," and yet not destitute of an instinct for music and color. His name may contain the Celtic "Mac" or "Col," or the English "ton" or "son," but even when his name comes from one source his genius may derive from the other. Stevenson's name is English; but his literary work has the Celtic vividness, brilliancy, pathos, and sense of congruous form. Carlyle's name is Celtic; but in him lies the grim hardness of the Norse seafarers, and the deification of duty, and the impulse to subordinate form to substance, characteristic of the Saxon.

The Scotchman is born to a rich inheritance of tradition,—English wars, border forays, centuries of turbulent life embalmed in legend and ballad. He lives on the scene of action of historical personages, who become as real to him as Holyrood or Arthur's Seat. Scotch national consciousness lies deep in the soul of Scotchmen, though the kingdom be merged into Great Britain, and gives them an individuality and pride of lineage which colors their literature. They are loyal to the Bruce even when they sing 'God Save the Queen.' Blackwood's of the middle of the century, though reckoning the Englishmen Bulwer-Lytton and De Quincey among its honored contributors, was an intensely Scottish magazine; and its Scottish staff was marked by a distinctive literary tone,—a compound of boyish high spirits and old-fashioned conservatism such as we sometimes notice in the cadets of a noble house, to whom their family traditions are sacred, but the necessity of a decorous bearing before the world not at all apparent. The wit of the 'Noctes' is not very subtle, but it is hearty and clean, though it needs high spirits to make it seem amusing. The scholarship is not very profound, but it reaches back to traditions of gentlemanly culture and thoroughly distrusts modern preciosity. Nothing is literature in the estimation of these writers unless it is classic or Scotch. All of them are marked by a hearty love for outdoor sports, and a patriotism enthusiastic indeed, but rather circumscribed, though perhaps on that very account all the more intense. Professor Wilson is the most typical individual of these writers, and George Cupples of the next generation one of the most interesting, and on the whole the one whose literary gift was the most decided and original.

George Cupples was born at Legerwood, August 2d, 1822, and died October 7th, 1891. His father was a minister of the Free Kirk, and his paternal ancestors had been Calvinistic ministers for at least three generations. It was natural that the young man should be intended for the same profession, but he did not feel drawn to it, and when about seventeen went to sea for two years. Although of a firm physical constitution, the life of the seaman wearied him, and he resumed his education at the University of Edinburgh. He fell naturally into a literary career, and though much of his work was journalistic, he was reckoned in his day a critic of true insight. His novels are his best title to reputation, and show a vein of genuine creative power. Cupples combined some of the sterling and attractive traits of the cultured Scotchman of the period into a genuine, manly, and winning personality. Though slightly whimsical, his peculiarities were of the kind that endear a man to his friends; and Cupples numbered among his, Dr. John Brown, Dr. Stirling, Blackwood, and many others of the cultivated Scotchmen of the period.

'The Green Hand,' which came out in Blackwood from 1848 to 1851, is one of the best sea stories ever written. If we put Stevenson's 'Treasure Island' first for balance of description and narration, and sureness in the character touches, 'The Green Hand' and 'Tom Cringle's Log' are close seconds. Cupples's book is perhaps slightly overloaded with description, and deficient in technical construction as a narrative; but it is nevertheless a story which we read without skipping, for the descriptive pages are highly charged with the poetic element, and bear the unmistakable marks of being based on actual observation. Life in a sailing vessel has closer contact with the elemental moods of nature than in a steamer, where the motive power is a mechanical contrivance with the tiresome quality of regularity. To be in alliance or warfare with the wind, and dependent on its fitful moods, brought an element of variety and interest into the seaman's life which steam navigation, with its steadily revolving screw and patent valves, must always lack. Of this Cupples avails himself to the fullest extent; and it would be difficult to find a better presentation of the mysterious life and vastness of the ocean, and of the subtle impression it makes on those brought in daily contact with it, not excepting Victor Hugo's 'Toilers of the Sea.' This is due to

the fact that he spent two years before the mast when a young man.
Especially noticeable too is his admirable use of adjectives denoting
color, which are descriptive because they image truly the observations
of a man of genius, and are not, as in so much modern writing,
purple patches sewed on without any real feeling for the rich and
subtle scheme of nature. In calling up to the imagination the sounds
of the sea,—the creaking of the blocks, the wind in the rigging, the
wash of the water on the sides, the ripple on the bow, and the
infinite variety of the voice of the waves,—Cupples shows true poetic
power. It is not too much to say that 'The Green Hand' does not
suffer from the fact that one of the parts stands in the magazine in
juxtaposition to De Quincey's 'Vision of Sudden Death.'

'Kyloe Jock and the Weird of Wanton-Walls' is a transcript from
the boy life of the author. It appeared in Macmillan's Magazine, in
the autumn numbers of 1860. It is but a short sketch of a group of
simple people in a secluded border parish, but the quality of the
writer is shown as well in small things as in great ones. In it the
wintry scenes especially are given with broad and sure touches, for
the author is a genuine lover of nature; but the characters of Kirstie
the nurse, and of Kyloe Jock, the half-savage herd-boy who knows
so well the wild creatures of the woods and fields that he has even
given names to the foxes, show the feeling for human nature and the
ability to embody it which marks the artist. Kyloe Jock's Scotch is
said to be an absolutely perfect reproduction of the vernacular; and
it might be said that this book, like some of our modern Scotch
stories, would be better if the dialect were not quite so good.

The peculiar qualities of the author are not seen to such good
advantage in another book of his, 'Scotch Deerhounds and Their
Masters.' He was a breeder and unquestioned authority on the
"Grand Dog," and accumulated a store of curious information on its
origin and history; but his enthusiasm for this noble breed, or
"race" as he loves to call it,—and it certainly is the finest and most
striking of all the varieties of the "friend of man,"—led him into
some strange vagaries. One would almost suspect him of holding
the theory that dogs domesticated man, so high does he rank them
as agents of early civilization. His etymology and his ethnology are
alike erratic. He holds that every ancient people in whose name can
be found the combinations "gal," "alb," or "iber," or any other
syllable of a Celtic word, was of the Celtic family, and that the
Scotch deerhound and the Irish greyhound are descendants of the
primeval Celtic dog. In this way he proves that the Carthaginians
and the shepherd kings of Egypt were undoubtedly Celts, for their
sculpture shows that they hunted with large swift dogs that sprang
at the throat of their prey. On the other hand, every tribe that

owned large clumsy dogs that barked is probably non-Celtic. Mr. Cupples's contempt for such dogs is too intense for definite statement, and he evidently thinks that the tribe that owns them cannot hope to rise very high in the scale of civilization. This is certainly Philo-Celticism run mad, and is the more remarkable because Mr. Cupples could discover no Celtic strain in his own ancestry. He gave his dogs, however, Celtic names, as Luath, Shulach, Maida, Morna, Malvina, Oscar, etc. It would have been quite impossible for him to disgrace one of his "tall, swift, venatic hounds" with so Saxon a name as Rover or Barkis. But his enthusiasm is so genuine, and there is such a wealth of curious information in his pages, that his book has a charm and a substantial value of its own.

The other work of Mr. Cupples was, like that of most of the journalistic men of letters of the period, largely anonymous. His essay on Emerson, contributed to the Douglas Jerrold's Magazine, is very highly spoken of. Personally, Mr. Cupples must have been a man of great simplicity and charm, a happy combination of the genuine and most agreeable traits of that hearty and outspoken variety of man, the literary Scotchman.

IN THE TROPICS
From 'The Green Hand'

I LOOKED up the after-hatchway. It seemed still quite dark; and a patch of the deep dark-blue sky showed high over the square opening, with two or three keen sparks of stars, green ones and blue ones — you'd have thought the ladder, short as it was, went up to somewhere clean above the world. But the moment I got on deck I saw it was really lighter — the heavy fog creeping slowly astern off the ship on both hands; the white mist rolling faster over it before the sea breeze against her bows, which had swung seaward by this time from the tide, that rushed like a mill-stream upon both her tight cables; while the muddy river water, bubbling, eddying, and frothing away past, spread far up in the middle, into the dusk astern. *Such* a jabbering, croaking, hissing, shrieking, and yelling, too, as burst into one's ears out of the dark, as if whole legions of monkeys, bullfrogs, parrots, parrakeets, and what not, were coming together full upon us from both sides, one band nearer than the other; till the heavy boom of the surf round the point, and the roar of the tide coming in over the shallows about the river-mouth, pretty well drowned it. The sudden change was a good

relief,—Babel though it seemed after the closeness below,—
with what had been going on; and I looked ahead toward the
sea, which lay away out off our larboard bow, round the headland, and over the opposite point; a cold watery streak of light
showing it from where the breakers rose plunging and scattering
along the sandy bar, to the steady gray line of horizon, clipped
by one of the two brown chops we had got into. It looked
dreary enough as yet, the mouth of it being wider than I'd
fancied it from seaward at night: though even with full water
over the long spit of sand in the middle, there was no draught
at all for the Indiaman except by the channel betwixt it and the
bold point on our right; and pretty narrow it appeared from our
present berth, heaving as it did with the green swell that set in,
while meantime the mist scudding across the face of the headland let us see but the hard lump of bare black rock underneath.

In less time than I've taken to speak, however, the full space
of sky aloft was turning clear; the sea far away suddenly shone
out blue, with the surges tipped white; you saw a sparkling star
high over it sink slowly in, and the fog spread off the water
near us, till here and there you caught the muffled-up shape of
a big tree or two looming through, not half a mile off our starboard quarter; the mist creeping over the headland till the sharp
peak of it stood out against its shadow on the shoulder of a hill
beyond, and old Bob Martin's single clump of cocoas on the rise,
waving in landward from the brisk sea breeze. One passenger
after another came peeping sleepily out of the companion-hatch,
at the men clearing away the wreck of the spars and swabbing
the quarter-deck down; but scarce had Smith, one of the young
writers, reached the poop, when he gave a shout that covered
both poop ladders in no time, with people scrambling over each
other to get up. Next minute you'd have fancied them a knot
of flamingoes with their wings out, as the bright red daybreak
brought out the edge of the woods far astern, through a hazy
lane in the purple mist, topped so with stray cocoanut-trees and
cabbage-palms, dabbled like brushes in the color, that they
scarce knew them to be woods at all, and not a whole lot of
wild savages fresh from other business of the kind, coming down
with all sorts of queer tools upon us; more especially when one
heard such a chorus of unaccountable cries, whistling, and
screaming, as seemed to struggle with the sound of the sea
ahead of us, and the splash alongside. The huge round sun

struck hot crimson along the far turn of the beach, with all
manner of twisted blots upon him, as it were, and the very
grass and long reeds seemingly rustling into his face, so one
didn't for the moment know *him* either; while the muddy, choco-
late-colored eddies, sweeping and closing beyond the ship's
rudder, glittered and frothed up like blood; and every here and
there, along the streak of light, the head of a log or a long
branch came dipping up terribly plain; no wonder the old Serin-
gapatam had apparently turned tail to it all, ready to bolt if she
could. Almost as soon as you took your hands off your eyes,
though, and could see without a red ball or two before them,
there was the nearest shore growing out toward our starboard
bulwark all along, crowded with wet green woods, up into steaming high ground — all to eastward a dazzle of light, with two or
three faint mountain peaks shooting up far off in it, and a
woody blue hill or so between; while here and there a broad
bright hazy spoke off the sun came cutting down into the forest,
that brought a patch full of long big leaves, ten times greener
than the rest, and let look off the deck into the heart of it
among the stems over the bank. The jabber in the woods had
passed off all at once with the dusk, the water deepening over
the bar, and the tide running slower, so that every one's confused face turned breathless with delight and it grew stiller and
stiller. The whole breadth of the river shone out by this time,
full and smooth, to the opposite shore three times as far away,
where the wood and bulrushes seemed to grow out of the water;
a long thick range of low muddy-looking mangroves, with a
cover of dark green, rounding from the farthest point one saw,
down to some sandy hummocks near the mouth, and a ridge of
the same drifted up by the wind off the beach. Beyond that side
there was nothing apparently but a rolling sweep of long
coarse grass, with a few straggling cocoanut-trees and baobabs
like big swollen logs on end, and taken to sprouting at top;
a dun-colored heave of land in the distance, too, that came out
as it got hotter, in a long, desert-like, red brick-dust sort of a
glare. The sole living things to be seen as yet were some small
birds rising up out of the long grass, and the turkey-buzzards
sailing high over all across, as if on the look-out.

The air was so cool and clear, however, from the tornado
over night, — not a cloud in the sky, and the strange scent of
the land reaching us as the dew rose off it, — you could see far

and wide, with a delicious feeling of it all, that kept every one standing there on the spot where he first gained the deck, even the men looking over their shoulders with the ropes in their fists, and the fresh morning breeze lifting one's hair.

NAPOLEON AT ST. HELENA

From 'The Green Hand'

I HAD to get fairly off the saddle,—rather sore, I must say, with riding up St. Helena roads after so many weeks at sea, —and flung myself down on the grass, with little enough fear of the hungry little beast getting far adrift. This said crag, by the way, drew my eye to it by the queer colors it showed—white, blue, gray, and bright red—in the hot sunlight; and being too far off to make out clearly, I slung off the ship's glass I had across my back, just to overhaul it better. The hue of it was to be seen running all down the deep rift between, that seemingly wound away into some glen toward the coast; while the lot of plants and trailers half covering the steep front of it would no doubt, I thought, have delighted my old friend the Yankee, if he *was* the botanizing gentleman in question. By this time it was a lovely afternoon far and wide to Diana's Peak, the sky glowing clearer deep blue at that height than you'd have thought sky could do, even in the tropics—the very peaks of bare red rock being softened into a purple tint, far off around you. One saw into the rough bottom of the huge Devil's Punch Bowl, and far through without a shadow down the green patches in the little valleys, and over Deadwood Camp,—there was *nothing*, as it were, between the grass, the ground, the stones, and leaves, and the empty hollow of the air; while the sea spread far round underneath, of a softer blue than the sky over you. You'd have thought all the world was shrunk into St. Helena, with the Atlantic lying three-quarters round it in one's sight, like the horns of the bright new moon round the dim old one; which St. Helena pretty much resembled, if what the star-gazers say of its surface be true, all peaks and dry hollows—if indeed you weren't lifting up out of the world, so to speak, when one looked through his fingers right into the keen blue overhead!

If I lived a thousand years I couldn't tell half what I felt lying there; but as you may imagine, it had somewhat in it of the late European war by land and sea. Not that I could have said so at the time, but rather a sort of half-doze, such as I've known one have when a schoolboy, lying on the green grass the same way, with one's face turned up into the hot summer heavens; half of it flying glimpses, as it were, of the French Revolution, the battles we used to hear of when we were children — then the fears about the invasion, with the channel full of British fleets, and Dover Cliffs — Trafalgar and Nelson's death, and the battle of Waterloo, just after we heard *he* had got out of Elba. In the terrible flash of the thing all together, one almost fancied them all gone like smoke; and for a moment I thought I was falling away off, *down* into the wide sky, so up I started to sit. From that, suddenly I took to guessing and puzzling closely again how I should go to work myself, if I were the strange Frenchman I saw in the brig at sea, and wanted to manage Napoleon's escape out of St. Helena. And first, there was how to get into the island and put *him* up to the scheme — why, sure enough, I couldn't have laid it down better than they seemed to have done all along: what could one do but just dodge about that latitude under all sorts of false rig, then catch hold of somebody fit to cover one's landing. No Englishman *would* do it, and no foreigner but would set Sir Hudson Lowe on his guard in a moment. Next we should have to get put on the island — and really a neat enough plan it was, to dog one of the very cruisers themselves, knock up a mess of planks and spars in the night-time, set them all ablaze with tar, and pretend we were fresh from a craft on fire; when even Captain Wallis of the Podargus, as it happened, was too much of a British seaman not to carry us straight to St. Helena! Again, I must say it was a touch beyond me — but to hit the governor's notions of a hobby, and go picking up plants around Longwood, was a likely enough way to get speech of the prisoner, or at least let him see one was there!

How should I set about carrying him off to the coast, though? That was the prime matter. Seeing that even if the schooner — which was no doubt hovering out of sight — were to make a bold dash for the land with the trade-wind, in a night eleven hours long, — there were sentries close round Longwood from sunset, the starlight shining mostly always in the want of a moon; and at any rate there was rock and gully enough betwixt here and the coast to try the surest foot aboard the Hebe, let alone

an emperor. With plenty of woods for a cover, one might steal
up close to Longwood, but the bare rocks showed you off to be
made a mark of. Whew! but why were those same blacks on
the island, I thought: just strip them stark naked, and let them
lie in the Devil's Punch Bowl, or somewhere beyond military
hours, when I warrant me they might slip up, gully by gully,
to the very sentries' backs! Their color wouldn't show them,
and savages as they seemed, couldn't they settle as many sentries as they needed, creep into the very bedchamber where
Bonaparte slept, and manhandle him bodily away down through
some of the nearest hollows, before any one was the wiser? The
point that still bothered me was, why the fourth of the blacks
was wanting at present, unless he had his part to play elsewhere.
If it was chance, then the *whole* might be a notion of mine,
which I knew I was apt to have sometimes. If I could only
make out the fourth black, so as to tally with the scheme, on
the other hand, then I thought it was all sure; but of course
this quite pauled me, and I gave it up, to work out my fancy
case by providing signals betwixt us plotters inside and the
schooner, out of sight from the telegraphs. There was no use
for her to run in and take the risk, without good luck having
turned up on the island; yet any sign she could profit by must
be both sufficient to reach sixty miles or so, and hidden enough
not to alarm the telegraphs or the cruisers. Here was a worse
puzzle than all, and I only guessed at it for my own satisfaction — as a fellow can't help doing when he hears a question
he can't answer — till my eye lighted on Diana's Peak, near
three thousand feet above the sea. There it was, by Jove!
'Twas quite clear at the time; but by nightfall there was always
more or less cloud near the top, and if you set a fire on the
very peak 'twould only be seen leagues off: a notion that
brought to mind a similar thing which I told you saved the
Indiaman from a lee-shore one night on the African coast —
and again, by George! I saw *that* must have been meant at first
by the negroes as a smoke to help the French brig easier in!
Putting that and that together, why it struck me at once what
the fourth black's errand might be — namely, to watch for the
schooner, and kindle his signal as soon as he couldn't see the
island for mist. I was sure of it; and as for a dark night coming on at sea, the freshening of the breeze there promised nothing more likely; a bright white haze was softening out the

horizon already, and here and there the egg of a cloud could be seen to break off the sky to windward, all of which would be better known afloat than here.

The truth was, I was on the point of tripping my anchor to hurry down and get aboard again; but on standing up, the head of a peak fell below the sail I had noticed in the distance, and seeing she loomed large on the stretch of water, I pretty soon found she must be a ship of the line. The telegraph over the Alarm House was hard at work again, so I e'en took down my glass and cleaned it to have a better sight, during which I caught sight, for a minute, of some soldier officer or other on horseback, with a mounted redcoat behind him, riding hastily up the gully a good bit from my back, till they were round the red piece of crag, turning at times as if to watch the vessel. Though I couldn't have a better spy at him for want of my glass, I had no doubt he was the governor himself, for the sentries in the distance took no note of him. There was nobody else visible at the time, and the said cliff stood fair up like a look-out place, so as to shut them out as they went higher. Once or twice after, I fancied I made out a man's head or two lower down the gully than the cliff was; which, it occurred to me, might possibly be the botanists, as they called themselves, busy finding out how long St. Helena had been an island; however, I soon ▯ned the glass before me upon the ship, by this time right opposite the ragged opening of Prosperous Bay, and heading well up about fourteen miles or so off the coast, as I reckoned to make James Town harbor. The moment I had the sight of the glass right for her,—though you'd have thought she stood still on the smooth soft blue water,—I could see her whole beam rise off the swells before me, from the dark side and white band, checkered with a double row of ports, to the hamper of her lofty spars, and the sails braced slant to the breeze; the foam gleaming under her high bows, and her wake running aft in the heave of the sea. She was evidently a seventy-four; I fancied I could make out her men's faces peering over the yards toward the island, as they thought of "Boneypart"; a white rear-admiral's flag was at the mizenroyal masthead, leaving no doubt she was the Conqueror at last, with Admiral Plampin, and in a day or two at farthest the Hebe would be bound for India.

I had just looked over my shoulder toward Longwood, letting the Conqueror sink back again into a thing no bigger than a model on a mantelpiece, when all at once I saw some one standing near the brow of the cliff I mentioned, apparently watching the vessel, with a long glass at his eye like myself. 'Twas farther than I could see to make out anything, save so much; and ere I had screwed the glass for such a near sight, there were seven or eight figures more appearing half over the slope behind; while my hand shook so much with holding the glass so long, that at first I brought it to bear full on the cracks and blocks in the front of the crag, with the large green leaves and trailers on it flickering idly with the sunlight against my eyes, till I could have seen the spiders inside, I daresay. Next I held it too high, where the admiral and Lord Frederick were standing by their horses, a good way back; the governor, as I supposed, sitting on his, and two or three others along the rise. At length, what with kneeling down to rest it on one knee, I had the glass steadily fixed on the brow of the rocks, where I plainly saw a tall dark-whiskered man in a rich French uniform, gazing to seaward. I knew him I sought too well by pictures, however, not to be sadly galled. Suddenly a figure came slowly down from before the rest, with his hands behind his back, and his head a little drooped. The officer at once lowered the telescope and held it to him, stepping upward as if to leave him alone — what dress he had on I scarce noticed; but there he was standing, single in the round bright field of the glass I had hold of like a vise — his head raised, his hands hiding his face, as I kept the telescope fixed fair in front of me — only I saw the smooth broad round of his chin. I knew, as if I'd seen him in the Tuileries at Paris, or known him by sight since I was a boy, — I *knew* it was Napoleon.

During that minute the rest of them were out of sight, so far as the glass went — you'd have supposed there was no one there but himself, as still as a figure in iron; watching the same thing, no doubt, as I'd done myself five minutes before, where the noble seventy-four was beating slowly to windward. When I *did* glance to the knot of officers twenty yards back, 'twas as if one saw a ring of his generals waiting respectfully while he eyed some field of battle or other, with his army at the back of the hill; but next moment the telescope fell in his hands, and his face, as pale as death, with his lip firm under it, seemed near enough for me to touch it — his eyes shot stern into me from below his wide white forehead, and I started, dropping my glass in turn. That instant the whole wild lump of St. Helena, with its ragged brim, the clear blue sky and the sea, swung round about the dwindled figures above the crag, till they were nothing but so many people together against the slope beyond.

'Twas a strange scene to witness, let me tell you; never can I forget the sightless, thinking sort of gaze from that head of his, after the telescope sank from his eye, when the Conqueror must have shot back with all her stately hamper into the floor of the Atlantic again! Once more I brought my spy-glass to bear on the place where he had been, and was almost on the point of calling out to warn him off the edge of the cliff, forgetting the distance I was away. Napoleon had stepped, with one foot before him, on the very brink, his two hands hanging loose by his side with the glass in one of them, till the shadow of his small black cocked hat covered the hollows of his eyes, and he stood as it were looking down past the face of the precipice. What he thought of, no mortal tongue can say: whether he was master at the time over a wilder battle than any he'd ever fought; but just then, what was the surprise it gave me to see the head of a man, with a red tasseled cap on it, raised through among the ivy from below, while he seemed to have his feet on the cracks and juts of the rock, hoisting himself by one hand round the tangled roots till no doubt he must have looked right aloft into the French Emperor's face; and perhaps he whispered something — though for my part it was all dumb show to me, where I knelt peering into the glass. I saw even *him* start at the suddenness of the thing — he raised his head upright, still glancing down over the front of the crag, with the spread hand lifted, and the side of his face half turned toward the party within earshot behind, where the governor and the rest apparently kept together out of respect, no doubt watching both Napoleon's back and the ship of war far beyond. The keen sunlight on the spot brought out every motion of the two in front — the *one* so full in my view, that I could mark his look settle again on the other below, his firm lips parting and his hand out before him like a man seeing a spirit he knew; while a bunch of leaves on the end of a wand came stealing up from the stranger's post to Napoleon's very fingers. The head of the man on the cliff turned round seaward for one moment, ticklish as his footing must have been; then he looked back, pointing with his loose hand to the horizon, — there was one minute between them without a motion, seemingly — the captive Emperor's chin was sunk on his breast, though you'd have said his eyes glanced up out of the shadow on his forehead; and the stranger's red cap hung like a bit of the bright colored cliff, under his two hands holding among the leaves. Then I saw Napoleon lift his hand calmly, he gave a sign with it — it might have been refusing, it might have been agreeing, or it might be farewell, I never expect to know; but he folded his arms across his breast, with the bunch of leaves in his fingers, and stepped slowly back from the brink toward the officers. I was watching the stranger below it, as he swung there for a second or two, in a way like to let him go dash to the bottom; his face sluing wildly seaward again. Short though the glance I had of him was, — his features set hard in some bitter feeling or other, his dress different too, besides the mustache being off, and his complexion no doubt purposely darkened, — it served to prove what I'd suspected: he was no other than the Frenchman I had seen in the brig; and mad or sensible, the very look I caught was more like that he faced the thunder-squall with, than aught beside. Directly after, he was letting himself carefully down with his back to my glass; the party above were moving off over the brow of the crags, and the governor riding round, apparently to come once more down the hollow between us. In fact, the seventy-four had stood by this time so far in that the peaks in the distance shut her out; but I ran the glass carefully along the whole horizon in my view, for signs of the schooner. The haze was too bright, however, to make sure either way; though, dead to windward, there were some streaks of cloud risen with the breeze, where I once or twice fancied I could catch the gleam of a speck in it. The Podargus was to be seen through a notch in the rocks, too, beating out in a different direction, as if the telegraph had signaled her elsewhere; after which you heard the dull rumble of the forts saluting the Conqueror down at James Town as she came in: and being late in the afternoon, it was high time for me to crowd sail downward, to fall in with my shipmates.

GEORGE WILLIAM CURTIS

(1824–1892)

BY EDWARD CARY

GEORGE WILLIAM CURTIS was born in Providence, R. I., February 24th, 1824, of a New England family, his ancestry on the father's side running back in unbroken line to the Massachusetts settlers of the first half of the seventeenth century. Though his home was in New York from early boyhood, he was through life a type—one of the best—of New England manhood. The firm, elastic, sometimes hard, fibre of a steadfast and intense moral sense was always found, occasion requiring, beneath the social grace and charm and the blithe and vivid fancy of the author. His schooling was brief—a few years only before the age of eleven. The rest of his education, which was varied and in some lines thorough, was gained by reading, with private tutors, with his accomplished and gifted stepmother, and—richest of all—alone. In 1842, while yet a lad of eighteen, he went for a couple of years as a boarder to Brook Farm. There, to quote his own words, "were the ripest scholars, men and women of the most æsthetic culture and accomplishment, young farmers, seamstresses, mechanics, preachers, the industrious, the lazy, the con-

GEORGE W. CURTIS

ceited, the sentimental. But they associated in such a spirit and under such conditions that, with some extravagance, the best of everybody appeared." "Compared with other efforts upon which time and money and industry are lavished, measured by Colorado and Nevada speculations, by California gold-washings, by oil-boring and the Stock Exchange, Brook Farm was certainly a very reasonable and practical enterprise, worthy of the hope and aid of generous men and women. The friendships that were formed there were enduring. The devotion to noble endeavor, the sympathy with what is most useful to men, the kind patience and constant charity that were fostered there, have been no more lost than the grain dropped upon the field."

These two years, and one spent on a farm at Concord, Massachusetts, near the homes of Emerson, Hawthorne, Thoreau, were followed by four years in Europe,—in Germany, Italy, France, Egypt;
and in 1851, at the age of twenty-seven, Curtis took up seriously the
work of a writer. Within a year he published two small volumes,
'The Nile Notes of a Howadji,' and 'The Howadji in Syria.' For a
couple of years he was a writer on the New York Tribune, where his
Brook Farm friends, Ripley and Dana, were engaged; and 'Lotus-
Eating' was made up of letters to that paper from the then famous
"watering-places." He dropped newspaper work to become an editor
and writer with Putnam's Magazine, and the 'Potiphar Papers' and
'Prue and I' were written for that periodical. For a time he formed
a connection with the printer of Putnam's in a publishing business;
in which, and through the fault of others, he failed; assuming, quite
beyond the requirements of the law, debts which it took a score of
years to discharge. Finally he found his publishing home with the
house of Harper and Brothers. At first a contributor to the Magazine and the Weekly, he became the editor of the Weekly and the
writer of the "Easy Chair"; and from those two coignes of vantage,
until his death on August 31st, 1892, he did what, apart from his
lectures and addresses, was the work of his life. He made no more
books, save the one not successful novel of 'Trumps,' written as a
serial for the Weekly, and the volumes from the Addresses and the
"Easy Chair" published after his death; yet he fulfilled the prophecy
of Hawthorne on the appearance of the 'Nile Notes'—"I see that
you are forever an author."

It would not be easy, were it worth while, exactly to classify
Curtis; and if in general phrase we say that he was an essayist, that
only betrays how comprehensive a label is needed to cover his work.
Essays, long or short, the greater number of his writings were; each
practically embraced a single subject, and of this presented one
phase, important perhaps and grave, or light, amusing, tender, and
sometimes satiric to the verge of bitterness—though never beyond it.

The Howadji books, which first gave him a name and fairly
launched him as a writer, were a singular and original product,
wholly different from what could have been expected of his training
and associations; a venture in a field which, curiously enough, since
the venture was in every sense more than ordinarily successful, he
promptly and forever abandoned. "I aimed," he says in one of his
private letters, "to represent the essentially sensuous, luxurious,
languid, and sense-satisfied spirit of Eastern life." The style was
adapted with courage, not to say audacity, to the aim. No American
at that time had ever written English so riotously beyond the
accepted conventions, so frankly, almost saucily, limited only by what

the writer chose to say of what he felt or fancied under the inspiration of the East.   Leigh Hunt compared the 'Nile Notes' to 'Eothen' and to 'Hyperion,' but the relation was extravagantly remote.   The Howadji books were as individual as the lavish and brilliant bloom of a plant in the hot rays of the southern spring—and as passing. Once the shining and slightly gaudy flowers were shed, the normal growth proceeded to substantial fruitage.

The 'Potiphar Papers' were like the Eastern books in this, that they were at the time a still more successful venture in a field which, if not wholly abandoned by Curtis, was not continuously cultivated, but was only entered occasionally and never quite in the same spirit.   They were a series of satires, fanciful enough in conception, but serious and almost savage in spirit, on the most conspicuous society of the day: its vulgarity, vanity, shallowness, and stupidity, the qualities inherent in the prevalent rivalry in money-spending.   They were of marked importance at the time, because they were the brilliant and stinging comment of a gentleman and a patriot on a portion of society whose wealth gave dangerous prominence to the false standards set up and followed.   Happily the vices Curtis scourged were those of an over-vigorous and unchastened youth of society, and the chief value of the satire now is as a picture of the past.

'Prue and I' was a series of papers written, as Curtis's letters show, in odd moments and with great rapidity, to meet the exigencies of the magazine.   But the papers survive as an example of the pure literary work of the author.   The opulence and extravagance of the 'Howadji' books disappear; but the rich imagination, the sportive fancy, the warm and life-giving sentiment, the broad philosophy, are expressed in a style of singular beauty, flexibility, and strength.

And it was in this line that the "Easy Chair" essays were continued, forming one of the most remarkable bodies of literary product of the time.   They were written for Harper's Magazine, four or five monthly, equivalent each year to an ordinary duodecimo volume, and the series closed with the death of the writer some thirty-five years from their beginning.   Their variety was very great.   Some of them touched the events and questions of the time, and the time embraced the political contest with slavery, the Civil War, and the marvelously rapid and complex development of the nation after the war.   But when the events or questions of the day were touched, it was at at once lightly and broadly, to illuminate and fix some suggestion of philosophy; through all ran the current of wise and gracious and noble thought or sentiment.   Many of the essays were woven of reminiscence and comment on persons.   In the little volume selected by himself and published shortly before his death, a dozen of the

twenty-seven were of this nature, embracing such varying person-
alities as Edward Everett, Browning, Wendell Phillips, Dickens,
Thoreau, Jenny Lind, Emerson, Joseph Jefferson. Whoever was thus
brought under the clear, soft, penetrating light of Curtis's pen lived
thereafter in the mind of the reader with a character more real and
just. In many of the essays of the "Easy Chair" there was a tone of
gentle satire, but always hopeful and helpful, not bitter or discouraging; as if in "Titbottom's Spectacles," that broke the heart of the
wearer with their revelation of the evil in those who passed before
them, new lenses had been set, revealing the everlasting beauty and
power of the ideal which evil violates, and to whose gracious and
blessing sway the writer, with a kindly smile at the incongruities of
the actual, invited his friend the reader. The very title had a gleam
of this subtle humor, it being well known to the profession, and
established by the experience of successive generations, that in
reality there is no such thing as an "editor's easy-chair." Even if
we allow for the fact that Curtis's seat was in his tranquil library on
Staten Island, remote from the complications and vexations of the
magazine's office, we must still recognize that the ease was not in the
chair, but in that firm high poise of the writer's spirit which enabled
him, with wisdom as unfailing as his gracious cheer, "to Report and
Consider all Matters of What Kind Soever."

Curtis was, perhaps, in his lifetime even more widely known as a
speaker than as a writer. At the very outset of his career he became one of the half-dozen lecturers under the curious and potent
lyceum system, that in the third quarter of the century did so much
to arouse and satisfy a deep interest in t   of the mind in the
widely scattered communities of the American republic. At the
very outset, too, he entered with all his soul into the political agitation against slavery, and became one of the most stirring and most
highly regarded popular orators of the Republican party. Later he
was eagerly sought upon occasions of historical interest and for
memorial addresses. Still later he delivered the remarkable series of
addresses on the reform of the civil service, in what was in effect a
second struggle for political emancipation, waged with as broad a
human purpose, with as high courage, as was the struggle against
slavery, and with even a riper knowledge of the conditions of safety
for the republic. The great body of these addresses, many of the
slightest as well as the more elaborate, were essentially literary.
Most of them were written out and committed to memory, and many
were marked by more of the polish and completeness of the scholar's
conscientious and deliberate work than most of the writing intended
only for publication. But they were still the orator's work, addressed
to the ear, though fitted to bear the test of study, and intended

through the ear to touch the conscience and the heart and sway the will. Apart from the unfailing and lofty moral purpose that pervades them, their lasting charm lies in their music. They were the *emmelia*, the «well-tuned speech,» of the Greeks. But the hidden monitor who kept the orator true to the carefully chosen «pitch» was not the freedman of Gracchus, it was the sensitive and faithful artistic sense of the speaker. A writer lives in the world's literature, necessarily, by those of his writings that find a permanent form in books. Of these Curtis left few. But fairly to judge of his influence on the thought, and so on the life as well as the literature, of his country, we must remember that the unusual gifts and the rare spirit revealed in these few books pervaded also his work in the magazine and the journal; that the fruit of his work would fill a hundred volumes, and that it reached readers by the hundred thousand. Had Curtis sought only the fame of the writer, he could hardly have failed to gain it, and in notable measure. In pursuing the object he did, he might rightly believe at the close of his career — it is doubtful if he ever gave it a thought — that he had rendered to American literature a service unrecognized and untraceable, but singularly, perhaps uniquely, great.

Edward Cary.

THE MIST AT NEWPORT

From 'Lotus Eating.' Copyright, 1852, by Harper & Brothers

I RODE one afternoon with Undine along the southern shore of the Island, by the lonely graves of which I have spoken. We could see only a few feet over the water, but the ocean constantly plunged sullenly out of the heavy fog, which was full of hoarse roars and wailings,— the chaotic sound of the sea. We took the homeward path through the solitary fields, just unfamiliar enough to excite us with a vague sense of going astray. At times, gleams of sunlight, bewildered like ourselves, struggled, surprised, through the mist and disappeared. But strange and beautiful were those estrays; and I well understand why Turner studied vapors so long and carefully.

Two grander figures are not in contemporary biography than that of Coleridge, in Carlyle's 'Sterling,' looking out from Highgate over the mingled smoke and vapor which buries London, as

in lava Pompeii is buried; and that of Turner, in some anonymous but accurate sketches of his latter days, at his cottage on
the edge of London, where, apart from his fame and under a
feigned name, he sat by day and night upon the housetop, watching the sun glorify the vapors and the smoke with the same
splendor that he lavishes upon the evening west, and which we
deemed the special privilege of the sky. Those two men, greatest in their kind among their companions, illustrate with happy
force what Wordsworth sang:—

> « In common things that round us lie,
> 　　Some random truths he can impart,—
> The harvest of a quiet eye
> 　　That broods and sleeps on his own heart. »

Gazing from his Highgate window with " large gray eye," did
Coleridge see more than the image of his own mind and his own
career, in that limitless city, wide-sparkling, many-turreted, fad-
ing and mingling in shining mist,— with strange voices calling
from its clouds,— the solemn peal of cathedral chimes and the
low voice of the vesper bell; and out of that London fog with
its irresistible splendors, and out of the holy vapors which float
serene amid the Alps, has Turner quarried his colossal fame.
There is no grander lesson in any history of any art than the
spectacle of the greatest painter of our time, sitting upon his
house-top, and from the mist which to others was but a clog and
inconvenience, and associated in all men's minds only with link-
boys and lanterns, plucking the heart of its mystery and making
it worshiped and remembered.

NAZARETH

From 'Howadji in Syria.'　Copyright, 1856, by Harper & Brothers

THE traditions which cluster around Nazareth are so tender and
　　domestic that you will willingly believe, or at least you will
　　listen to, the improbable stories of the friars as a father
to the enthusiastic exaggerations of his child. With Jerusalem
and its vicinity the gravity of the doctrine is too intimately
associated to allow the mind to heed the quarrels and theories
about the localities. It is the grandeur of the thought which
commands you. But in Nazareth it is the personality of the
Teacher which interests you. All the tenderness of the story

centers here. The youth of the Madonna and the unrecorded years of the Child belong to Nazareth. Therefore imagination unbends to the sweet associations of domestic life. The little picture in the Uffizi recurs again, and the delicate sketches of Overbeck, illustrating the life of Christ, in which as a blooming boy in his father's shop he saws a bit of wood into the form of a cross, looking up smilingly to the thoughtful Joseph and the yearning Mary, as when he brings her the passion-flower in the pleasant room.

The tranquil afternoon streams up the valley, and your heart is softened as if by that tender smile of Mary; and yielding to soliciting friars, you go quietly and see where Joseph's house stood, and where the Angel Gabriel saluted Mary, and the chimney of the hearth upon which she warmed food for her young child, and baked cakes for Joseph when he came home from work, and the rock whence the Jews wished to cast Jesus, and another rock upon which he ate with his disciples.

You listen quietly to these stories, and look at the sights. The childish effort to give plausible form to the necessary facts of the history of the place is too natural to offend. When the pretense is too transparent you smile, but do not scold. For whether he lived upon this side of the way or upon that, this is the landscape he saw for thirty years. A quiet workman, doubtless, with his father, strolling among the melancholy hills of Galilee, looking down into the lake-like vastness of Esdraëlon, where the great captains of his nation had fought,—hearing the wild winds blow from the sea, watching the stars, and remembering the three days of his childhood when he sat in the temple at Jerusalem.

Walking in the dying day over the same solitary hills, you will see in the sunset but one figure moving along the horizon,— a grave manly form, outlined upon the west.

Here was the true struggle of his life—the resolve to devote himself to the work. These are the exceeding high mountains upon which he was lifted in temptation; here in the fullness of his youth and hope Satan walked with him, seductive. For every sin smiles in the first address, says Jeremy Taylor, and carries light in the face and honey in the lip. Green and flowery as Esdraëlon lay the valleys of ease and reputation at his feet; but sternly precipitous as the heights of Galilee, the cliffs of duty above him buried their heads in heaven.

Here too was he transfigured; and in the light of thought he floats between Moses and Elias, between faith and duty, and the splendor of his devotion so overflows history with glory that men call him God.

AURELIA AS A GRANDMOTHER

From 'Prue and I.' Copyright, 1856, by Harper & Brothers

THERE will be a time when you will no longer go out to dinner; or only very quietly, in the family. I shall be gone then; but other old bookkeepers in white cravats will inherit my tastes, and saunter on summer afternoons to see what I loved to see.

They will not pause, I fear, in buying apples, to look at the old lady in venerable cap who is rolling by in the carriage. They will worship another Aurelia. You will not wear diamonds or opals any more, only one pearl upon your blue-veined finger,— your engagement ring. Grave clergymen and antiquated beaux will hand you down to dinner, and the group of polished youth who gather around the yet unborn Aurelia of that day will look at you, sitting quietly upon the sofa, and say softly, "She must have been very handsome in her time."

All this must be; for consider how few years since it was your grandmother who was the belle, by whose side the handsome young men longed to sit and pass expressive mottoes. Your grandmother was the Aurelia of a half-century ago, although you cannot fancy her young. She is indissolubly associated in your mind with caps and dark dresses. You can believe Mary Queen of Scots, or Nell Gwyn, or Cleopatra, to have been young and blooming, although they belonged to old and dead centuries; but not your grandmother. Think of those who shall believe the same of you — you, who to-day are the very flower of youth.

Might I plead with you, Aurelia, — I, who would be too happy to receive one of those graciously beaming bows that I see you bestow upon young men, in passing,— I would ask you to bear that thought with you always, not to sadden your sunny smile, but to give it a more subtle grace. Wear in your summer garland this little leaf of rue. It will not be the skull at the feast, it will rather be the tender thoughtfulness in the face of the young Madonna.

For the years pass like summer clouds, Aurelia, and the children of yesterday are the wives and mothers of to-day. Even I do sometimes discover the mild eyes of my Prue fixed pensively upon my face, as if searching for the bloom which she remembers there in the days, long ago, when we were young. She will never see it there again, any more than the flowers she held in her hand, in our old spring rambles. Yet the tear that slowly gathers as she gazes is not grief that the bloom has faded from my cheek, but the sweet consciousness that it can never fade from my heart; and as her eyes fall upon her work again, or the children climb her lap to hear the old fairy-tales they already know by heart, my wife Prue is dearer to me than the sweetheart of those days long ago.

PRUE'S MAGNOLIA

From 'Prue and I.' Copyright, 1892, by Harper & Brothers

IF I meet Charles, who is bound for Alabama, or John, who sails for Savannah, with a trunk full of white jackets, I do not say to them, as their other friends say:—

"Happy travelers, who cut March and April out of the dismal year!"

I do not envy them. They will be seasick on the way. The Southern winds will blow all the water out of the rivers; and, desolately stranded upon mud, they will relieve the tedium of the interval by tying with large ropes a young gentleman raving with delirium tremens. They will hurry along, appalled by forests blazing in the windy night; and housed in a bad inn, they will find themselves anxiously asking, "Are the cars punctual in leaving?"—grimly sure that impatient travelers find all conveyances too slow. The travelers are very warm indeed, even in March and April,—but Prue doubts if it is altogether the effect of the Southern climate.

Why should they go to the South? If they only wait a little, the South will come to them. Savannah arrives in April; Florida in May; Cuba and the Gulf come in with June; and the full splendor of the Tropics burns through July and August.

Sitting upon the earth, do we not glide by all the constellations, all the awful stars? Does not the flash of Orion's scimitar dazzle as we pass? Do we not hear, as we gaze in hushed midnights, the music of the Lyre; are we not throned with Cassiopeia; do we not play with the tangles of Berenice's hair, as we sail, as we sail?

When Christopher told me that he was going to Italy, I went into Bourne's conservatory, saw a magnolia, and so reached Italy before him. Can Christopher bring Italy home? But I brought to Prue a branch of magnolia blossoms, with Mr. Bourne's kindest regards, and she put them upon her table, and our little house smelled of Italy for a week afterward. The incident developed Prue's Italian tastes, which I had not suspected to be so strong. I found her looking very often at the magnolias; even holding them in her hand, and standing before the table with a pensive air. I suppose she was thinking of Beatrice Cenci, or of Tasso and Leonora, or of the wife of Marino Faliero, or of some other of those sad old Italian tales of love and woe. So easily Prue went to Italy.

Thus the spring comes in my heart as well as in the air, and leaps along my veins as well as through the trees. I immediately travel. An orange takes me to Sorrento, and roses, when they blow, to Pæstum. The camellias in Aurelia's hair bring Brazil into the happy rooms she treads, and she takes me to South America as she goes to dinner. The pearls upon her neck make me free of the Persian Gulf. Upon her shawl, like the Arabian prince upon his carpet, I am transported to the vales of Cashmere; and thus, as I daily walk in the bright spring days, I go around the world.

But the season wakes a finer longing, a desire that could only be satisfied if the pavilions of the clouds were real, and I could stroll among the towering splendors of a sultry spring evening. Ah! if I could leap those flaming battlements that glow along the west — if I could tread those cool, dewy, serene isles of sunset, and sink with them in the sea of stars.

I say so to Prue, and my wife smiles.

OUR COUSIN THE CURATE

From 'Prue and I.' Copyright, 1856, by Harper & Brothers

WHEN Prue and I are most cheerful, and the world looks fair —we talk of our cousin the curate. When the world seems a little cloudy, and we remember that though we have lived and loved together we may not die together — we talk of our cousin the curate. When we plan little plans for the boys and dream dreams for the girls — we talk of our cousin the curate. When I tell Prue of Aurelia, whose character is every day lovelier — we talk of our cousin the curate. There is no subject which does not seem to lead naturally to our cousin the curate. As the soft air steals in and envelops everything in the world, so that the trees, and the hills, and the rivers, the cities, the crops, and the sea, are made remote and delicate and beautiful by its pure baptism, so over all the events of our little lives — comforting, refining, and elevating — falls like a benediction the remembrance of our cousin the curate.

He was my only early companion. He had no brother, I had none; and we became brothers to each other. He was always beautiful. His face was symmetrical and delicate; his figure was slight and graceful. He looked as the sons of kings ought to look; as I am sure Philip Sidney looked when he was a boy. His eyes were blue, and as you looked at them they seemed to let your gaze out into a June heaven. The blood ran close to the skin, and his complexion had the rich transparency of light. There was nothing gross or heavy in his expression or texture; his soul seemed to have mastered his body. But he had strong passions, for his delicacy was positive, not negative; it was not weakness, but intensity.

There was a patch of ground about the house which we tilled as a garden. I was proud of my morning-glories and sweet-peas; my cousin cultivated roses. One day — and we could scarcely have been more than six years old — we were digging merrily and talking. Suddenly there was some kind of difference; I taunted him, and raising his spade he struck me upon the leg. The blow was heavy for a boy, and the blood trickled from the wound. I burst into indignant tears, and limped toward the house. My cousin turned pale and said nothing; but just as I opened the door he darted by me, and before I could interrupt him he had confessed his crime and asked for punishment.

From that day he conquered himself. He devoted a kind of ascetic energy to subduing his own will, and I remember no other outbreak. But the penalty he paid for conquering his will was a loss of the gushing expression of feeling. My cousin became perfectly gentle in his manner; but there was a want of that pungent excess which is the finest flavor of character. His views were moderate and calm. He was swept away by no boyish extravagance; and even while I wished he would sin only a very little, I still adored him as a saint. The truth is, as I tell Prue, I am so very bad because I have to sin for two — for myself and our cousin the curate. Often, when I returned panting and restless from some frolic which had wasted almost all the night, I was rebuked as I entered the room in which he lay peacefully sleeping. There was something holy in the profound repose of his beauty; and as I stood looking at him, how many a time the tears have dropped from my hot eyes upon his face while I vowed to make myself worthy of such a companion,— for I felt my heart owning its allegiance to that strong and imperial nature.

My cousin was loved by the boys, but the girls worshiped him. His mind, large in grasp and subtle in perception, naturally commanded his companions, while the lustre of his character allured those who could not understand him. The asceticism occasionally showed itself in a vein of hardness, or rather of severity, in his treatment of others. He did what he thought it his duty to do; but he forgot that few could see the right so clearly as he, and very few of those few could so calmly obey the least command of conscience. I confess I was a little afraid of him, for I think I never could be severe.

In the long winter evenings I often read to Prue the story of some old father of the church, or some quaint poem of George Herbert's; and every Christmas Eve I read to her Milton's 'Hymn of the Nativity.' Yet when the saint seems to us most saintly, or the poem most pathetic or sublime, we find ourselves talking of our cousin the curate. I have not seen him for many years; but when we parted, his head had the intellectual symmetry of Milton's, without the Puritanic stoop, and with the stately grace of a Cavalier.

THE CHARM OF PARIS

From 'The Potiphar Papers.' Copyright, 1858, by Harper & Brothers

"YES, my dear Madame," answered the Pacha, "this is indeed
making the best of one's opportunities. This is well
worth coming to Europe for. It is in fact for this that
Europe is chiefly valuable to an American, as the experience of
an observer shows. Paris is notoriously the great centre of
historical and romantic interest. To be sure, Italy, Rome,
Switzerland, and Germany — yes, and even England — have some
few objects of interest and attention; but the really great things
of Europe, the superior interests, are all in Paris. Why, just
reflect. Here is the Café de Paris, the Trois Frères, and the
Maison Dorée. I don't think you can get such dinners elsewhere.
Then there is the Grand Opera, the Comic Opera, and now and
then the Italian — I rather think that is good music. Are there
any such theatres as the Vaudeville, the Variétés, and the
Montansier, where there is the most dexterous balancing on the
edge of decency that ever you saw? and when the balance is
lost, as it always is at least a dozen times every evening, the
applause is tremendous, showing that the audience have such a
subtle sense of propriety that they can detect the slightest devia-
tion from the right line. Is there not the Louvre, where, if
there is not the best picture of a single great artist, there are
good specimens of all? Will you please to show me such a
promenade as the Boulevards, such fêtes as those of the Champs
Elysées, such shops as those of the Passages and the Palais
Royal? Above all, will you indicate to such students of mankind
as Mr. Boosey, Mr. Firkin, and I, a city more abounding in
piquant little women, with eyes, and coiffures and toilettes, and
je ne sais quoi, enough to make Diogenes a dandy, to obtain
their favor? I think, dear madame, you would be troubled to
do it. And while these things are Paris, while we are sure of
an illimitable allowance of all this in the gay capital, we do
right to remain here. Let who will, sadden in moldy old Rome,
or luxuriate in the orange groves of Sorrento and the South, or
wander among the ruins of the most marvelous of empires, and
the monuments of art of the highest human genius, or float about
the canals of Venice, or woo the Venus and the Apollo, and
learn from the silent lips of those teachers a lore sweeter than

the French novelists impart; let who will, climb the tremendous Alps, and feel the sublimity of Switzerland as he rises from the summer of Italian lakes and vineyards into the winter of the glaciers, or makes the tour of all climates in a day by descending those mountains towards the south; let those who care for it, explore in Germany the sources of modern history, and the remote beginnings of the American spirit; — ours be the boulevards, the demoiselles, the operas, and the unequaled dinners. Decency requires that we should see Rome, and climb an Alp. We will devote a summer week to the one, and a winter month to the other. They will restore us, renewed and refreshed, for the manly, generous, noble, and useful life we lead in Paris."

«PHARISAISM OF REFORM»

From 'Orations and Addresses.' Copyright, 1893, by Harper & Brothers

N O AMERICAN, it seems to me, is so unworthy the name as he who attempts to extenuate or defend any national abuse, who denies or tries to hide it, or who derides as pessimists and Pharisees those who indignantly disown it and raise the cry of reform. If a man proposes the redress of any public wrong, he is asked severely whether he considers himself so much wiser and better than other men, that he must disturb the existing order and pose as a saint. If he denounces an evil, he is exhorted to beware of spiritual pride. If he points out a dangerous public tendency or censures the action of a party, he is advised to cultivate good-humor, to look on the bright side, to remember that the world is a very good world, at least the best going, and very much better than it was a hundred years ago.

Undoubtedly it is; but would it have been better if everybody had then insisted that it was the best of all possible worlds, and that we must not despond if sometimes a cloud gathered in the sky, or a Benedict Arnold appeared in the patriot army, or even a Judas Iscariot among the chosen twelve? Christ, I think, did not doubt the beloved disciple nor the coming of his kingdom, although he knew and said that the betrayer sat with him at the table. I believe we do not read that Washington either thought it wiser that Arnold's treachery should be denied or belittled, or that he or any other patriot despaired although the treason was so grave. Julius Cæsar or Marlborough

or Frederick would hardly be called a great general if he had
rebuked the soldier who reported that the lines were beginning
to break. When the sea is pouring into the ship through an
open seam, everybody is aware of it. But then it is too late.
It is the watch who reports the first starting of the seam who
saves the ship.

It is an ill sign when public men find in exposure and
denunciation of public abuses evidence of the pharisaic disposition and a tendency in the critic to think himself holier than
other men. Was Martin Luther, cheerfully defending his faith
against the princes of Christendom, a Pharisee? Were the English Puritans, iconoclasts in Church and State but saviors of
liberty, pessimists? Were Patrick Henry demanding liberty or
death, and Wendell Phillips in the night of slavery murmuring
the music of the morning, birds of ill omen? Was Abraham
Lincoln saying of the American Union, "A house divided with
itself cannot stand," assuming to be holier than other Americans? To win a cheap cheer, I have known even intelligent
men to sneer at the scholar in politics. But in a republic
founded upon the common school, such a sneer seems to me to
show a momentary loss of common-sense. It implies that the
political opinions of educated men are unimportant and that
ignorance is a safer counselor of the republic. If the gentleman
who in this very hall last stooped to that sneer, had asked himself what would have been the fortune of this State and this
country without its educated leadership, from Samuel Adams to
Charles Sumner,— both sons of Massachusetts, both scholars in
politics from Harvard College,— he might have spared his country, his party, and himself, the essential recreancy to America
and to manhood which lies in a sneer at education. To the cant
about the pharisaism of reform there is one short and final
answer. The man who tells the truth *is* a holier man than the
liar. The man who does not steal *is* a better man than the
thief.

THE CALL OF FREEDOM

From 'Orations and Addresses.' Copyright, 1893, by Harper & Brothers

INTO how many homes along this lovely valley came the news
of Lexington and Bunker Hill eighty years ago; and young
men like us, studious, fond of leisure, young lovers, young
husbands, young brothers, and sons, knew that they must forsake
the wooded hillside, the river meadows golden with harvest, the
twilight walk along the river, the summer Sunday in the old
church, parents, wife, child, mistress, and go away to uncertain
war. Putnam heard the call at his plow, and turned to go
without waiting. Wooster heard it, and obeyed.

Not less lovely in those days was this peaceful valley, not
less soft this summer air. Life was as dear and love as beautiful to those young men as to us who stand upon their graves.
Bnt because they were so dear and beautiful, those men went
out bravely to fight for them and fall. Through these very
streets they marched, who never returned. They fell and were
buried; but they never can die. Not sweeter are the flowers
that make your valley fair, not greener are the pines that give
your river its name, than the memory of the brave men who
died for freedom. And yet no victim of those days, sleeping
under the green sod of Connecticut, is more truly a martyr of
Liberty than every murdered man whose bones lie bleaching in
this summer sun upon the silent plains of Kansas.

Gentlemen, while we read history we make history. Because
our fathers fought in this great cause, we must not hope to escape
fighting. Because two thousand years ago Leonidas stood against
Xerxes, we must not suppose that Xerxes was slain, nor, thank
God! that Leonidas is not immortal. Every great crisis of human
history is a pass of Thermopylæ, and there is always a Leonidas
and his three hundred to die in it, if they cannot conquer. And
so long as Liberty has one martyr, so long as one drop of blood
is poured out for her, so long from that single drop of bloody
sweat of the agony of humanity shall spring hosts as countless
as the forest leaves and mighty as the sea.

Brothers! the call has come to us. I bring it to you in these
calm retreats. I summon you to the great fight of Freedom. I
call upon you to say with your voices, whenever the occasion
offers, and with your votes when the day comes, that upon

these fertile fields of Kansas, in the very heart of the continent, the upas-tree of slavery, dripping death-dews upon national prosperity and upon free labor, shall never be planted. I call upon you to plant there the palm of peace, the wine and the olive of a Christian civilization. I call upon you to determine whether this great experiment of human freedom, which has been the scorn of despotism, shall by our failure be also our sin and shame. I call upon you to defend the hope of the world.

The voice of our brothers who are bleeding, no less than our fathers who bled, summons us to this battle. Shall the children of unborn generations, clustering over that vast western empire, rise up and call us blessed or cursed? Here are our Marathon and Lexington; here are our heroic fields. The hearts of all good men beat with us. The fight is fierce — the issue is with God. But God is good.

ROBERT BROWNING IN FLORENCE

From 'The Easy Chair.' Copyright, 1891, by Harper & Brothers

IT IS more than forty years since Margaret Fuller first gave distinction to the literary notices and reviews of the New York Tribune. Miss Fuller was a woman of extraordinary scholarly attainments and intellectual independence, the friend of Emerson and of the "Transcendental" leaders; and her critical papers were the best then published, and were fitly succeeded by those of her scholarly friend, George Ripley. It was her review in the Tribune of Browning's early dramas and the 'Bells and Pomegranates' that introduced him to such general knowledge and appreciation among cultivated readers in this country, that it is not less true of Browning than of Carlyle that he was first better known in America than at home.

It was but about four years before the publication of Miss Fuller's paper that the Boston issue of Tennyson's two volumes had delighted the youth of the time with the consciousness of the appearance of a new English poet. The eagerness and enthusiasm with which Browning was welcomed soon after were more limited in extent, but they were even more ardent; and the devoted zeal of Mr. Levi Thaxter as a Browning missionary and pioneer forecast the interest from which the Browning societies of later days have sprung. When Matthew Arnold was told in a small and remote farming village in New England that there had been a lecture upon Browning in the town the week before, he stopped in amazement, and said, "Well, that is the most surprising and significant fact I have heard in America."

It was in those early days of Browning's fame, and in the studio of the sculptor Powers in Florence, that the youthful Easy Chair took up a visiting-card, and reading the name Mr. Robert Browning, asked with eager earnestness whether it was Browning the poet. Powers turned his large, calm, lustrous eyes upon the youth, and answered, with some surprise at the warmth of the question:—

"It is a young Englishman, recently married, who is here with his wife, an invalid. He often comes to the studio."

"Good Heaven!" exclaimed the youth, "it must be Browning and Elizabeth Barrett."

Powers, with the half-bewildered air of one suddenly made conscious that he had been entertaining angels unawares, said reflectively, "I think we must have them to tea."

The youth begged to take the card which bore the poet's address, and hastening to his room near the Piazza Novella, he wrote a note asking permission for a young American to call and pay his respects to Mr. and Mrs. Browning; but wrote it in terms which, however warm, would yet permit it to be put aside if it seemed impertinent, or if for any reason such a call were not desired. The next morning betimes the note was dispatched, and a half-hour had not passed when there was a brisk rap at the Easy Chair's door. He opened it and saw a young man, who briskly inquired:—

"Is Mr. Easy Chair here?"

"That is my name."

"I am Robert Browning."

Browning shook hands heartily with his young American admirer, and thanked him for his note. The poet was then about thirty-five. His figure was not large, but compact, erect, and active; the face smooth, the hair dark; the aspect that of active intelligence, and of a man of the world. He was in no way eccentric, either in manner or appearance. He talked freely, with great vivacity, and delightfully, rising and walking about the room as his talk sparkled on. He heard with evident pleasure, but with entire simplicity and manliness, of the American interest in his works and in those of Mrs. Browning; and the Easy Chair gave him a copy of Miss Fuller's paper in the Tribune.

It was a bright, and to the Easy Chair a wonderfully happy hour. As he went, the poet said that Mrs. Browning would certainly expect to give Mr. Easy Chair a cup of tea in the evening; and with a brisk and gay good-by, Browning was gone.

The Easy Chair blithely hied him to the Café Doné, and ordered of the flower-girl the most perfect of nosegays, with such fervor that she smiled; and when she brought the flowers in the afternoon, said with sympathy and meaning, "Eccola, signore! per la donna bellissima!"

It was not in the Casa Guidi that the Brownings were then living, but in an apartment in the Via della Scala, not far from the place or square most familiar to strangers in Florence — the Piazza Trinità. Through several rooms the Easy Chair passed, Browning leading the way; until at the end they entered a smaller room arranged with an air of English comfort, where at a table, bending over a tea-urn, sat a slight lady, her long curls drooping forward. "Here," said Browning, addressing her with a tender diminutive, "here is Mr. Easy Chair." And, as the bright eyes but wan face of the lady turned towards him, and she put out her hand, Mr. Easy Chair recalled the first words of her verse he had ever known: —

"'Onora, Onora!' her mother is calling;
  She sits at the lattice, and hears the dew falling,
      Drop after drop from the sycamore laden
  With dew as with blossom, and calls home the maiden:
          'Night cometh, Onora!'"

The most kindly welcome and pleasant chat followed, Browning's gayety dashing and flashing in, with a sense of profuse and bubbling vitality, glancing at a hundred topics; and when there was some allusion to his 'Sordello,' he asked, quickly, with an amused smile, "Have you read it?" The Easy Chair pleaded that he had not seen it. "So much the better. Nobody understands it. Don't read it, except in the revised form, which is coming." The revised form has come long ago, and the Easy Chair has read, and probably supposes that he understands. But Thackeray used to say that he did not read Browning, because he could not comprehend him, adding ruefully, "I have no head above my eyes."

A few days later —

"O gift of God! O perfect day!" —

the Easy Chair went with Mr. and Mrs. Browning to Vallom-brosa, and the one incident most clearly remembered is that of Browning's seating himself at the organ in the chapel, and play-ing, — some Gregorian chant, perhaps, or hymn of Pergolesi's. It was enough to the enchanted eyes of his young companion that they saw him who was already a great English poet sitting at the organ where the young Milton had sat, and touching the very keys which Milton's hand had pressed.

ERNST CURTIUS

(1814–1896)

ERNST CURTIUS, a noted German archæologist and historian, was born at Lübeck September 2d, 1814. He studied philology at Bonn, Göttingen, and Berlin. When in 1837 Christian August Brandis was appointed confidential adviser to Prince Otho of Bavaria, the newly elected king of Greece, Curtius accompanied Brandis's family to Athens as a private tutor. He remained with the Brandises until 1840, when he joined Ottfried Müller's archæological expedition to Delphi. No sooner were the excavations well under way, however, than Müller died. Curtius thereupon returned to Germany, stopping at Rome on the way; and in 1841 took his doctor's degree at Halle.

ERNST CURTIUS

In 1844 he was appointed tutor to the Crown Prince of Prussia (the late Emperor Frederick), being at the same time made a professor extraordinary at the University of Berlin. He held his position as tutor to the Crown Prince until 1850, when the latter matriculated at Bonn. In 1856 he succeeded Hermann as professor of classical philology at Göttingen, but returned some twelve years later to Berlin to occupy the chair of classical archæology and to act as director of the cabinet of antiquities in the Royal Museum.

Curtius also much advanced the study of classical archæology as presiding officer of the Archæological Society, as editor of the Archæological Journal, as perpetual secretary of the Royal Academy, and as the founder of the German Archæological Institute at Athens. He undertook a number of scientific missions in the service of the Prussian government, and in 1874 concluded with the Greek government a convention which secured to the German Empire for a term of years the exclusive right to make excavations in the Greek kingdom. The following year the first excavation was begun at Olympia in Elis, the site of the ancient Olympic games, under the direction of Curtius, who with others published the results in a voluminous and most interesting report.

VII—266

Curtius's chief work is his 'History of Greece,' which appeared in 1867. It was originally published in three volumes as one of a series of manuals for classical students issued by a Berlin house, and was consequently intended for popular use; a circumstance that necessitated the omission of the copious notes in which the text of a German scientific work is commonly lost. It showed a remarkable familiarity with the climate, resources, and physical characteristics of Greece; and interpreted ancient life with much eloquence from the classical literature and from the monuments of ancient art. But the monarchical leaning of the author prevented him from entering fully into and appreciating the public life of the democratic communities which he described; and his enthusiastic temperament led him sometimes to exaggerate and to be too eager a partisan, to accept unproven hypotheses too readily and press them too hard.

Besides his 'History of Greece,' Curtius's most notable works are 'Peloponnesos' (1850–51), which describes in detail the ancient remains on the Peloponnesus; 'Die Stadtgeschichte von Athen' (Municipal History of Athens: 1891), and 'Sieben Karten zur Topographie von Athen nebst erläuterndem Text' (Seven Maps of Athens: 1886). His life was a busy and eminently distinguished one, as an archæologist, historian, and instructor, and his death in the summer of 1896 was generally lamented by his associates.

THE CAUSES OF DISLIKE TOWARD SOCRATES

From the 'History of Greece'

THE Athenians disliked men who wished to be different from every one else; particularly when these eccentrics, instead of quietly pursuing their own path and withdrawing from the world like Timon, forced themselves among their neighbors and assumed towards them the attitude of pedagogues, as Socrates did. For what could be more annoying to an Athenian of repute than to find himself, on his way to the council meeting or the law court, unexpectedly involved in a conversation intended to confuse him, to shake his comfortable self-assurance, and to end by making him ridiculous? In any other city such conversation would have been altogether hard to manage; but at Athens the love of talk was so great that many allowed themselves to be caught, and that gradually the number became very large of those who had been the victims of this inconvenient questioner, and who carried about with them the remembrance of a humiliation inflicted on them by him. And most of all was he hated by those who had allowed themselves to be touched and moved to tears of a bitter recognition of their own selves by his words, but who had afterwards sunk back into their former ways and were now ashamed of their hours of weakness. Thus Socrates had daily to experience that the testing of men was the most ungrateful of tasks which could be pursued at Athens; nor could he, without the sacred resolution of an absolutely unselfish devotion to his mission, have without ceasing obeyed the divine voice which every morning anew bade him go forth among men.

But that there were also more general and deep-seated grounds for the sense of annoyance manifested by the Attic public, is most clearly proved by the attacks of the comic stage. " To me too," it is said in a comedy by Eupolis, " this Socrates is offensive: this beggarly talker, who has considered everything with hair-splitting ingenuity; the only matter which he has left unconsidered is the question how he will get a dinner to-day." Far more serious were the attacks of Aristophanes. His standpoint, as well as that of Eupolis and Cratinus, was the ancient Attic view of life: he regarded the teachers of philosophy, round whom the young men gathered, as the ruin of the State; and although he could not possibly mistake the difference between Socrates and the Sophists,— although moreover he by no means belonged to the personal enemies of Socrates, with whom he rather seems to have enjoyed a certain degree of intimacy,— yet he thought it both his right and his duty, as a poet and a patriot, to combat in Socrates the Sophist, nay, the most dangerous of Sophists. The Athenian of the old school hated these conversations extending through whole hours of the broad daylight, during which the young men were kept away from the *palæstræ;* these painful discussions of topics of morality and politics, as to which it behooved every loyal citizen to have made up his mind once for all. If everything was submitted to examination, everything was also exposed to rejection; and what was to become of the city, if only that was to be allowed as valid which found gracious acceptance at the hands of this or that professor of talk? If everything had to be learnt, if everything was to be acquired by reflection, then there was an end of true civic virtue, which ought to be a thing inborn in a citizen and secured by his training as such. In these days all action and capability of action

was being dissolved into an idle knowledge; the one-sided cultivation of the intellect was loosening the sinews of men, and
making them indifferent to their country and religion. From
this standpoint the poet rejects all such culture of youth as is
founded upon the testing of the mind, and leading it to perfect
knowledge, and lauds those young Athenians who do not care
for wasting their time by sitting and talking with Socrates.

The priestly party, again, was adverse to Socrates, although
the highest authority in religious matters which existed in Hel-
las, and had at all events not been superseded by any other,
had declared in his favor,—at the suggestion of Chærephon,
who from his youth up was attached with devoted affection to
his teacher. His was an enthusiastic nature; and he desired
nothing so ardently as that the beneficent influence which he
had experienced in his own soul might be shared by the largest
possible number of his fellow-citizens. For this reason he was
anxious for an outward recognition of the merits of his so frequently misjudged friend; and he is said to have brought home
from Delphi the oracle which declared Socrates to be the wisest
of all men. Now, although this oracle was incapable of giving
a loftier assurance of his mission to the philosopher himself,
although it could not even remove the antipathy of the public,
yet it might be expected that it would disarm the calumny representing Socrates as a teacher of dangerous heresies; and in
this sense he could not but personally welcome the Delphic
declaration. For it must be remembered that he continued to
regard the oracle as the reverend centre of the nation, as the
symbol of a religious communion among the Hellenes; and in
disallowing all presumptuous meditation on the right way of
venerating the gods, he entirely followed the precedent of the
Delphic oracle, which was in the habit of settling questions of
this kind by the answer that it was according to the usage of
their fathers that men should venerate the gods. At Delphi,
on the other hand, there could be no question as to the importance of one who was leading the revolted world back to reverence for things holy, and who, while his contemporaries were
derisively despising the obsolete ways of the past, and running
after the *ignes fatui* of the wisdom of the day, held up before their eyes the primitive sayings of the temples; a serious
consideration of which he declared to be sufficient to reveal
the treasure of immortal truth contained in them. If it was

confessedly impossible to put an end to the prevailing desire for independent inquiry, then the priests could not but acknowledge that this was the only way by which the old religion could be saved.

Even the recognition by Delphi, however, was unable to protect Socrates against the suspicion of heresy. The fanaticism of the priestly party increased in inverse ratio to its prospects of real success; it regarded any philosophical discussion of religious truths as a desecration, and placed Socrates on the same level as Diagoras. Finally, the democrats, who after the restoration of the constitution were the ruling party, hated philosophy, because out of its school had issued a large proportion of the oligarchs; not only Critias and Theramenes, but also Pythodorus the archon of the days of anarchy, Aristoteles one of the Four Hundred and of the Thirty, Charmides, and others, were known as men of philosophical culture. Philosophy and the tendency towards political reaction accordingly seemed to be necessarily connected with one another. In a word, Socrates found opposition everywhere: some deemed him too conservative and others too liberal; he had against him both the Sophists and the enemies of the Sophists, both rigid orthodoxy and infidelity, both the patriots of the old school and the representatives of the renovated democracy.

Notwithstanding all this hostile feeling, the personal security of Socrates was not endangered, because he pursued his path as a blameless man, and because it was a matter of conscience with him to avoid every offense against the law. But after the restoration of the constitution a variety of circumstances continued to imperil his position at Athens.

SOCRATES AS AN INFLUENCE AND AS A MAN

From the 'History of Greece'

IF WE contemplate Socrates in his whole way of living and being (and in truth no other personage of Greek antiquity is so distinctly brought before our eyes), it seems to us in the first place as if at Athens he were not in his natural place; so foreign to Athens are his ways, and so dissociated from it is his whole individuality. He cannot be fitted into any class of

Athenian civil society, and is to be measured by no such standard as we apply to his fellow-citizens. He is one of the poorest of all the Athenians, and yet he passes with a proud step through the streets of the city and confronts the richest and best born as their equal; his ungainly and neglected exterior makes him an object of public derision, and yet he exercises an unexampled influence upon high and low, upon learned and unlearned alike. He is a master both of thought and of speech, yet at the same time an opponent on principle of those who were the instructors of the Athenians in both; he is a man of free thought, who allows nothing to remain untested, and yet he is more diligent in offering sacrifices than any of his neighbors, he venerates the oracles, and reposes a simple faith in many things which the age laughs at as nursery tales; he blames without reticence the dominion of the multitude, and yet is an adversary of oligarchs. Entirely his own master, he thinks differently from all other Athenians; he goes his own path without troubling himself about public opinion; and so long as he remains in harmony with himself, no contradiction, no hostile attack, no derision vexes his soul. Such a man as this seemed in truth to have been transplanted into the midst of Athens as it were from some other world.

And yet, unique in his kind as this Socrates was, we are unable on closer examination to mistake him for aught but a genuine Athenian. Such he was in his whole intellectual tendency, in his love of talk and skill in talk,—growths impossible in any but Athenian air,—in the delicate wit with which he contrived to combine the serious and the sportive, and in his unflagging search after a deep connection between action and knowledge. He was a genuine Athenian of the ancient stamp, when with inflexible courage he stood forth as the champion of the laws of the State against all arbitrary interference, and in the field shrank from no danger or hardship. He knew and loved the national poets; but above all it is in his indefatigable impulse towards culture that we recognize the true son of his native city. Herein lay a spiritual affinity between him and the noblest among the Athenians, a Solon and a Pericles. Socrates, like Solon, thought that no man is too old to learn; that to learn and to know is not a schooling for life, but life itself, and that which alone gives to life its value. To become by knowledge better from day to day, and to make others better, appeared to both to be the real duty of man. Both found the one true happiness in the health of the soul, whose greatest unhappiness they held to lie in wrong and ignorance.

Thus with all his originality Socrates most decidedly stood on the basis of Attic culture; and if it is taken into consideration that the most celebrated representatives of Sophistry and the tendencies akin to it all came from abroad,— *e. g.*, Protagoras from Abdera, Prodicus from Ceos, Diagoras from Melos,— it may fairly be affirmed that as against these foreign teachers the best principles of Attic wisdom found their representative in Socrates. Far, however, from merely recurring to the ancient foundations of patriotic sentiment,— fallen into neglect to the great loss of the State,— and from opposing himself on an inflexible defensive to the movement of the age, he rather stood in the very midst of it; and merely sought to lead it to other and higher ends. What he desired was not a turning back, but a progress in knowledge beyond that which the most sagacious teachers of wisdom offered. For this reason he was able to unite in himself elements which seemed to others irreconcilably contradictory; and upon this conception was based what most distinguished him above all his fellow countrymen, the lofty freedom and independence of his mind. Thus, without becoming disloyal to his home, he was able to rise above the restrictions of customary ideas; which he most notably achieved by making himself perfectly independent of all external things, in the midst of a people which worshiped the beauty of outward appearance, and by attaching value exclusively to the possessions which are within, and to moral life. For this reason too his personal ugliness — the broad face with the snub nose, thick lips and prominent eyes — was a characteristic feature of his individuality; because it testified against the traditional assumption of a necessary union between physical and intellectual excellence; because it proved that even in a form like that of Silenus there might dwell a spirit like that of Apollo, and thus conduced to a loftier conception of the being of man. Thus he belonged to his people and to his age, but stood above both; and such a man the Athenians needed, in order to find the path whereon it was possible to penetrate through the conflict of opinions to a moral assurance, and to reach a happiness containing its own warrant.

Socrates appears before us as an individuality complete and perfect, of which the gradual development continues to remain

a mystery. Its real germ, however, doubtless lies in the desire
for knowledge, which was innate in him with peculiar strength.
This desire would not allow him to remain under pupilage to
his father: it drove him forth out of the narrow workshop into
the streets and the open places of the city, where in those days
every kind of culture, art, and science, was offered in rich
abundance; for at the time when Socrates was in his twentieth
year, Pericles stood at the height of his splendid activity, which
the son of a sculptor might be supposed to have had occasion
fully to appreciate. The youthful Socrates however brought with
him out of his father's house a certain one-sided and so to
speak *bourgeois* tendency, — *i. e.*, a sober homely sense for the
practically useful, which would not allow itself to be dazzled by
splendor and magnificence. Accordingly he passed by with tolerable indifference the much admired works of art with which
the city was at that time filled; for the ideal efforts of the
Periclean age he lacked comprehension; nor do the tragedies of
a Sophocles appear to have exercised much attraction upon him.
If there was one-sidedness in this, on the other hand it bore
good fruit in so far as it confirmed the independence of his
judgment, and enabled him to recognize and combat the defects
and diseases from which Athens suffered even in the midst of
her glories.

But although the son of Sophroniscus carried the idea of the
practically useful into the domain of science, he gave to it in
this so deep and grand a significance that for him it again
became an impulse towards searching with unflagging zeal for
all real means of culture offered by Athens; for he felt the
impossibility of satisfactorily responding to the moral tasks which
most immediately await man, without the possession of a connected knowledge. Thus he eagerly associated with men and
women esteemed as highly cultured; he listened to the lectures
of the Sophists; acquainted himself with the writings of the
earlier philosophers, which he found to be still of vital effect
upon his contemporaries; thoroughly studied with friends desirous
of self-improvement the works of Heraclitus and Anaxagoras;
and in this constant intercourse he gradually became himself
another man,— *i. e.*, he grew conscious of the unsatisfactory
standpoint of the wisdom of the teachers of the day, as well as
conscious of his own aims and mission. For in putting questions
of a kind which could meet with no reply, and in searching for

deeper things than could be offered to him by his hearers, he gradually became himself the person from whom the impulse proceeded, and from whom in the end was expected an answer to the questions which had remained unsolved. He, the seeker after instruction, became the centre of a circle of younger men who were enthusiastically attached to him. In how high a degree that which he endeavored to supply corresponded to the deeply felt needs of the age, is evident from the fact that men of the most utterly different dispositions and stations in life gave themselves up to him: youths of the highest class of society, full of self-consciousness, buoyancy, and reckless high spirits, such as Alcibiades; and again, men of a melancholy and timid turn of mind, such as the well-known eccentric Apollodorus of Phalerus, who, perpetually discontented with himself and others, led a miserable existence until in Socrates he found the sole individuality appeasing his wants, and in intercourse with him the satisfaction for which he had longed. To him Socrates was all in all, and every hour during which he was away from Socrates he accounted as lost. Thus Socrates was able to re-awaken among the Athenians — among whom personal intercourse between those of the same age, as well as between men and youths, was disturbed or desecrated either by party interests or by impure sensuality — the beneficent power of pure friendship and unselfish devotion. Sober and calm himself, he excited the noblest enthusiasm, and by the simplest means obtained a far-reaching influence such as before him no man had possessed at Athens; even before the Peace of Nicias, when Aristophanes made him the principal character in his 'Clouds,' he was one of the best known and most influential personages at Athens.

As Socrates gradually became a teacher of the people, so his mode and habits of life, too, formed themselves in indissoluble connection with his philosophical development. For this was the most pre-eminent among his qualities: that his life and his teachings were formed in the same mold, and that none of his disciples could say whether he had been more deeply affected by the words or by the example of his master. And this was connected with the fact that from the first his philosophy directed itself to that which might make man better and more pleasing to Heaven, freer and happier at once. To this tendency he could not devote himself without rising in his own consciousness to a continuously loftier clearness and purity, and without subjecting

to reason the elements inborn in him, of sensual impulses, of
inertia and passion. Thus he became a man in whom the
world found much to smile and mock at, but whom even those
who could not stomach his wisdom were obliged to acknowledge
as a morally blameless and just citizen. He was devoted with
absolute loyalty to his native city, and without desiring offices
and dignities, he was from an inner impulse indefatigably active
for her good.

    .   .   .   .   .   .

For the rest, Socrates, with all his dislike of the pursuit of
profit and pleasure, was anything but a morose eccentric like
Euripides; from this he was kept by his love of humankind.
He was merry with the merry, and spoilt no festive banquet to
which he had been bidden. In the friendly circle he sat as a
man brave at his cups, and herein likewise offered an example to
his friends how the truly free can at one time suffer deprivation,
and at another enjoy abundance, without at any time losing his
full self-control. After a night of festivity his consciousness was
as clear and serene as ever; he had after a rare fashion made
his body an ever ready servant of his mind; even physically he
could do things impossible to others, and as if protected by some
magic charm, he passed unhurt through all the pestilences of
Athens without ever timidly keeping out of the way of danger.
Fully assured of the inner mission which animated him, he
allowed nothing to derange or to confound him. Hostile attacks
and derision touched him not; nay, he was known to laugh most
heartily of all the spectators when that sinner Aristophanes
exhibited him as a dreamer, abstracted from the world and hanging in a hammock between heaven and earth; and when the
other comic poets made the public merry with his personal
appearance. For the same reason, lastly, he was inaccessible to
all the offers made to him by foreign princes, who would have
given much to attract the most remarkable man of the age to
their courts. The Thessalian grandees in particular, Scopas at
Crannon and Eurylochus at Larissa, emulated one another in
their endeavors to secure him. But he was no more tempted by
their gold than by that of Archelaus, the splendor of whose
throne, obtained by guile and murder, failed to dazzle Socrates.
He replied with the pride of a genuine republican that it ill
befitted any man to accept benefits which he had no power of
returning.

CUVIER

(1769–1832)

BY SPENCER TROTTER

ODERN zoölogical science is indebted, in a large measure, to the mind and labor of the three French savants — Lamarck, Saint-Hilaire, and Cuvier. Throughout the troubled times of the French Revolution these three friends and co-laborers pursued their studies, arranging and interpreting the facts which they accumulated, and enriching the literature of the science to which they devoted their lives. Of the three, Cuvier stands forth with greatest prominence to-day as the one who by his studies in the structure and classification of animals, and through his reconstruction of the fossil animals of the Paris Basin, has left the most enduring mark upon the literature of the subject.

CUVIER

George Leopold Christian Frederic Dagobert Cuvier was born at Montbéliard in Alsace, on the 23d of August, 1769. His mother devoted herself to the careful training and development of his growing mind, and in very early life he gave evidence of extraordinary intellectual endowment. Naturally in dustrious, and possessed of a remarkable memory and the power of concentration, young Cuvier by the age of fourteen had mastered the rudiments of several languages, both ancient and modern, had acquired a considerable knowledge of mathematics, had read widely in history, and was proficient in drawing. He very early showed a decided bent toward scientific pursuits, and drew his first inspiration from the works of Buffon, who was then at the zenith of his fame. While at school he formed a society among his fellows for the reading and discussion of various subjects of a scientific and literary nature. Cuvier's talents became known to Prince Charles, the reigning Duke of Würtemberg, who gave him a free education in the University of Stuttgart. After completing his university course with honor he sought for a public office under the government of Prince Charles, but his parents' circumstances (his father being a retired officer of a Swiss regiment in the service of France) forced him to abandon this idea, and at the age of nineteen he accepted the position of a tutor in the family of a nobleman who resided at Caen in Normandy.

This proved to be the determining event in Cuvier's life. He found in the mollusk fauna of the near-by sea-coast a fascinating subject for study, and devoted all of his spare time to the investigation of the structure and relations of the various forms that came to his notice. The Abbé Tessier, a member of the Academy of Sciences, who had fled to Normandy from Paris during the Reign of Terror, made the acquaintance of the young naturalist, and introduced him by correspondence to a number of the most eminent scientific men of Paris. One of these men was Geoffroy Saint-Hilaire; and through his influence Cuvier was invited to assist Mertrud, the professor of comparative anatomy in the Museum of Natural History at the Jardin des Plantes. From this time on he threw all the energies of his remarkable mind into the study of animals and the building up of the Museum. The collections which he originated rank among the finest in the world. In 1802 Cuvier was appointed one of six inspector-generals to organize lyceums in a number of the French towns, and ever after gave a great part of his time and thought to the subject of education. The influence of his work in this direction is felt to-day in every institution of public instruction throughout France. On the annexation of Italy he made three different visits to that country in order to reorganize the old academies, and although a Protestant he was intrusted with the organization of the University at Rome. In a similar manner he remodeled the educational systems throughout Holland and Belgium; and his reports on these questions are teeming with interest. Cuvier felt that the strength of a nation lay in the sound education of all classes, the lower as well as the upper; and to his enlightened views may be traced much of the excellent system of primary education that prevails in these countries to-day. Under the bigoted Bourbon government, the despotic rule of Napoleon, and the liberal reign of Louis Philippe, Cuvier maintained his post; and throughout the events of the Hundred Days of 1815 he still held a high position in the Imperial University, of which he had been made a life member of the council at its foundation in 1808. He held a distinguished place as a member of the Council of State, as Minister of the Interior, as Chancellor of the University, and member of the Protestant faculty of theology. Louis Philippe conferred on him the title of Baron. He lived at the Jardin des Plantes, surrounded by his family and friends, and his home was the centre of men of science from all parts of the world. On the 8th of May, 1832, after delivering an unusually eloquent introductory lecture at the College of France, he was stricken with paralysis; and though he rallied sufficiently to preside the next day at the Council of State, he died on the following Sunday.

The chief value of Cuvier's work in general literature lies in the philosophical deductions which he drew from his studies. Lamarck had advanced the theory of the origin of species as a result of the action of the natural conditions of existence impressing and molding the plastic organism. Saint-Hilaire had advanced the doctrine of "homology,"—*i. e.*, the same structure appearing in a different form in different animals as a result of a difference of function. Cuvier opposed both of these theories, holding that each animal was a separate and distinct result of a special creative act, and that each part of its organization was expressly created to meet certain wants. Though the point of view of these three friends differed, yet each held the germ of truth. The action of the environment and the doctrine of homology are vital questions to-day; and Cuvier's deductions are equally pregnant with the truth, only their author viewed the facts as special creative acts of the Divine intelligence. Probably the most wide-reaching effects of Cuvier's work came from his study and restoration of the fossil animals of the Paris Basin, and the consequent recognition of the Tertiary as a distinct geological age. From his investigations in comparative anatomy he proved "that the parts of an animal agree so exactly that from seeing one fragment the whole can be known." This recognition of the *correlation of parts* was one of the grandest achievements of his master mind.

Cuvier's scientific publications were numerous. His best known works are 'Le Règne Animal' (The Animal Kingdom), published in four octavo volumes in 1817, and 'Recherches sur les Ossements Fossiles' (Inquiry Concerning Fossil Bones). This latter work is probably the most enduring monument to his fame, as it laid the basis of the present science of palæontology. The first volume of this work is a masterpiece of scientific literature, and has been widely translated. The English translation by Professor Jameson of Edinburgh, entitled 'Essay on the Theory of the Earth,' has passed through several editions.

OF CHANGES IN THE STRUCTURE OF THE EARTH
From ‹The Theory of the Earth›

THE lowest and most level parts of the earth, when penetrated to a very great depth, exhibit nothing but horizontal strata composed of various substances, and containing almost all of them innumerable marine productions. Similar strata, with the same kind of productions, compose the hills even to a great height. Sometimes the shells are so numerous as to constitute the entire body of the stratum. They are almost everywhere in such a perfect state of preservation that even the smallest of them retain their most delicate parts, their sharpest ridges, and their finest and tenderest processes. They are found in elevations far above the level of every part of the ocean, and in places to which the sea could not be conveyed by any existing cause. They are not only inclosed in loose sand, but are often incrusted and penetrated on all sides by the hardest stones. Every part of the earth, every hemisphere, every continent, every island of any size, exhibits the same phenomenon. We are therefore forcibly led to believe not only that the sea has at one period or another covered all our plains, but that it must have remained there for a long time, and in a state of tranquillity; which circumstance was necessary for the formation of deposits so extensive, so thick, in part so solid, and containing exuviæ so perfectly preserved.

The time is past for ignorance to assert that these remains of organized bodies are mere *lusus naturæ*,— productions generated in the womb of the earth by its own creative powers. A nice and scrupulous comparison of their forms, of their contexture, and frequently even of their composition, cannot detect the slightest difference between these shells and the shells which still inhabit the sea. They have therefore once lived in the sea, and been deposited by it; the sea consequently must have rested in the places where the deposition has taken place. Hence it is evident the basin or reservoir containing the sea has undergone some change at least, either in extent, or in situation, or in both. Such is the result of the very first search, and of the most superficial examination.

The traces of revolutions become still more apparent and decisive when we ascend a little higher, and approach nearer to the foot of the great chains of mountains. There are still found many beds of shells; some of these are even larger and more solid; the shells are quite as numerous and as entirely preserved: but they are not of the same species with those which were found in the less elevated regions. The strata which contain them are not so generally horizontal; they have various degrees of inclination, and are sometimes situated vertically. While in the plains and low hills it was necessary to dig deep in order to detect the succession of the strata, here we perceive them by means of the valleys which time or violence has produced, and which disclose their edges to the eye of the observer. At the bottom of these declivities huge masses of their débris are collected, and form round hills, the height of which is augmented by the operation of every thaw and of every storm.

These inclined or vertical strata, which form the ridges of the secondary mountains, do not rest on the horizontal strata of the hills which are situated at their base and serve as their first steps; but on the contrary are situated underneath them. The latter are placed upon the declivities of the former. When we dig through the horizontal strata in the neighborhood of the inclined strata, the inclined strata are invariably found below. Nay sometimes, when the inclined strata are not too much elevated, their summit is surmounted by horizontal strata. The inclined strata are therefore more ancient than the horizontal strata. And as they must necessarily have been formed in a horizontal position, they have been subsequently shifted into their inclined or vertical position, and that too before the horizontal strata were placed above them.

Thus the sea, previous to the formation of the horizontal strata, had formed others which by some means have been broken, lifted up, and overturned in a thousand ways. There had therefore been also at least one change in the basin of that sea which preceded ours; it had also experienced at least one revolution: and as several of these inclined strata which it had formed first are elevated above the level of the horizontal strata which have succeeded and which surround them, this revolution, while it gave them their present inclination, had also caused them to project above the level of the sea so as to form islands, or at least rocks and inequalities; and this must have happened whether one of their edges was lifted up above the water, or the depression of the opposite edge caused the water to subside.

This is the second result, not less obvious nor less clearly demonstrated than the first, to every one who will take the trouble of studying carefully the remains by which it is illustrated and proved.

If we institute a more detailed comparison between the various strata and those remains of animals which they contain, we shall soon discover still more numerous differences among them, indicating a proportional number of changes in their condition. The sea has not always deposited stony substances of the same kind. It has observed a regular succession as to the nature of its deposits: the more ancient the strata are, so much the more uniform and extensive are they; and the more recent they are, the more limited are they, and the more variation is observed in them at small distances. Thus the great catastrophes which have produced revolutions in the basin of the sea were preceded, accompanied, and followed by changes in the nature of the fluid and of the substances which it held in solution; and when the surface of the seas came to be divided by islands and projecting ridges, different changes took place in every separate basin.

Amidst these changes of the general fluid, it must have been almost impossible for the same kind of animals to continue to live; nor did they do so in fact. Their species, and even their genera, change with the strata: and though the same species occasionally recur at small distances, it is generally the case that the shells of the ancient strata have forms peculiar to themselves; that they gradually disappear, till they are not to be seen at all in the recent strata, still less in the existing seas, in which indeed we never discover their corresponding species, and where several, even of their genera, are not to be found; that on the contrary the shells of the recent strata resemble, as respects the genus, those which still exist in the sea; and that in the last formed and loosest of these strata there are some species which the eye of the most expert naturalists cannot distinguish from those which at present inhabit the ocean.

In animal nature, therefore, there has been a succession of changes corresponding to those which have taken place in the chemical nature of the fluid; and when the sea last receded from our continent, its inhabitants were not very different from those which it still continues to support.

Finally, if we examine with greater care these remains of organized bodies, we shall discover, in the midst even of the

most ancient secondary strata, other strata that are crowded with
animal or vegetable productions, which belong to the land and
to fresh water; and amongst the most recent strata — that is, the
strata which are nearest the surface — there are some of them in
which land animals are buried under heaps of marine productions. Thus the various catastrophes of our planet have not only
caused the different parts of our continent to rise by degrees
from the basin of the sea, but it has also frequently happened
that lands which had been laid dry have been again covered by
the water, in consequence either of these lands sinking down
below the level of the sea, or of the sea being raised above the
level of the lands. The particular portions of the earth also,
which the sea has abandoned by its last retreat, had been laid
dry once before, and had at that time produced quadrupeds,
birds, plants, and all kinds of terrestrial productions; it had then
been inundated by the sea, which has since retired from it and
left it to be occupied by its own proper inhabitants.

The changes which have taken place in the productions of
the shelly strata, therefore, have not been entirely owing to a
gradual and general retreat of the waters, but to successive
irruptions and retreats, the final result of which, however, has
been an universal depression of the level of the sea.

These repeated irruptions and retreats of the sea have been
neither slow nor gradual; most of the catastrophes which have
occasioned them have been sudden: and this is easily proved,
especially with regard to the last of them, the traces of which
are most conspicuous. In the northern regions it has left the
carcasses of some large quadrupeds which the ice had arrested,
and which are preserved even to the present day with their skin,
their hair, and their flesh. If they had not been frozen as soon
as killed, they must quickly have been decomposed by putrefac-
tion. But this eternal frost could not have taken possession of
the regions which these animals inhabited except by the same
cause which destroyed them; this cause therefore must have
been as sudden as its effect. The breaking to pieces and overturnings of the strata, which happened in former catastrophes,
show plainly enough that they were sudden and violent like the
last; and the heaps of débris and rounded pebbles which are
found in various places among the solid strata demonstrate the
vast force of the motions excited in the mass of waters by these
overturnings. Life, therefore, has been often disturbed on this

earth by terrible events: calamities which, at their commencement, have perhaps moved and overturned to a great depth the
entire outer crust of the globe, but which, since these first commotions, have uniformly acted at a less depth and less generally.
Numberless living beings have been the victims of these catastrophes; some have been destroyed by sudden inundations, others
have been laid dry in consequence of the bottom of the seas
being instantaneously elevated. Their races even have become
extinct, and have left no memorial of them except some small
fragment which the naturalist can scarcely recognize.

Such are the conclusions which necessarily result from the
objects that we meet with at every step of our inquiry, and which
we can always verify by examples drawn from almost every
country. Every part of the globe bears the impress of these
great and terrible events so distinctly, that they must be visible
to all who are qualified to read their history in the remains
which they have left behind.

But what is still more astonishing and not less certain, there
have not been always living creatures on the earth, and it is
easy for the observer to discover the period at which animal
productions began to be deposited.

As we ascend to higher points of elevation, and advance
towards the lofty summits of the mountains, the remains of
marine animals — that multitude of shells we have spoken of —
begin very soon to grow rare, and at length disappear altogether.
We arrive at strata of a different nature, which contain no vestige at all of living creatures. Nevertheless their crystallization,
and even the nature of their strata, show that they also have
been formed in a fluid; their inclined position and their slopes
show that they also have been moved and overturned; the oblique
manner in which they sink under the shelly strata shows that
they have been formed before these; and the height to which
their bare and rugged tops are elevated above all the shelly
strata, shows that their summits have never again been covered
by the sea since they were raised up out of its bosom.

Such are those primitive or primordial mountains which traverse our continents in various directions, rising above the clouds,
separating the basins of the rivers from one another, serving by
means of their eternal snows as reservoirs for feeding the springs,
and forming in some measure the skeleton, or as it were the
rough framework of the earth. The sharp peaks and rugged

indentations which mark their summits, and strike the eye at a great distance, are so many proofs of the violent manner in which they have been elevated. Their appearance in this respect is very different from that of the rounded mountains and the hills with flat surfaces, whose recently formed masses have always remained in the situation in which they were quietly deposited by the sea which last covered them.

These proofs become more obvious as we approach. The valleys have no longer those gently sloping sides, or those alternately salient and re-entrant angles opposite to one another, which seem to indicate the beds of ancient streams. They widen and contract without any general rule; their waters sometimes expand into lakes, and sometimes descend in torrents; and here and there the rocks, suddenly approaching from each side, form transverse dikes over which the waters fall in cataracts. The shattered strata of these valleys expose their edges on one side, and present on the other side large portions of their surface lying obliquely; they do not correspond in height, but those which on one side form the summit of the declivity often dip so deep on the other as to be altogether concealed.

Yet amidst all this confusion some naturalists have thought that they perceived a certain degree of order prevailing, and that among these immense beds of rocks, broken and overturned though they be, a regular succession is observed, which is nearly the same in all the different chains of mountains. According to them, the granite, which surmounts every other rock, also dips under every other rock; and is the most ancient of any that has yet been discovered in the place assigned it by nature. The central ridges of most of the mountain chains are composed of it; slaty rocks, such as clay slate, granular quartz (*grès*), and mica slate, rest upon its sides and form lateral chains; granular, foliated limestone or marble, and other calcareous rocks that do not contain shells, rest upon the slate, forming the exterior ranges, and are the last formations by which this ancient uninhabited sea seems to have prepared itself for the production of its beds of shells.

On all occasions, even in districts that lie at a distance from the great mountain chains, where the more recent strata have been digged through and the external covering of the earth penetrated to a considerable depth, nearly the same order of stratification has been found as that already described. The crystallized marbles never cover the shelly strata; the granite in mass never rests upon the crystallized marble, except in a few places where it seems to have been formed of granites of newer epochs. In one word, the foregoing arrangement appears to be general, and must therefore depend upon general causes, which have on all occasions exerted the same influence from one extremity of the earth to the other.

Hence it is impossible to deny that the waters of the sea have formerly, and for a long time, covered those masses of matter which now constitute our highest mountains; and farther, that these waters during a long time did not support any living bodies. Thus it has not been only since the commencement of animal life that these numerous changes and revolutions have taken place in the constitution of the external covering of our globe: for the masses formed previous to that event have suffered changes, as well as those which have been formed since; they have also suffered violent changes in their positions, and a part of these assuredly took place while they existed alone, and before they were covered over by the shelly masses. The proof of this lies in the overturnings, the disruptions, and the fissures which are observable in their strata, as well as in those of more recent formation, which are there even in greater number and better defined.

But these primitive masses have also suffered other revolutions, posterior to the formation of the secondary strata, and have perhaps given rise to, or at least have partaken of, some portion of the revolutions and changes which these latter strata have experienced. There are actually considerable portions of the primitive strata uncovered, although placed in lower situations than many of the secondary strata; and we cannot conceive how it should have so happened, unless the primitive strata in these places had forced themselves into view after the formation of those which are secondary. In some countries we find numerous and prodigiously large blocks of primitive substances scattered over the surface of the secondary strata, and separated by deep valleys from the peaks or ridges whence these blocks must have been derived. It is necessary, therefore, either that these blocks must have been thrown into those situations by means of eruptions, or that the valleys, which otherwise must have stopped their course, did not exist at the time of their being transported to their present sites.

Thus we have a collection of facts, a series of epochs anterior to the present time, and of which the successive steps may be ascertained with perfect certainty, although the periods which intervened cannot be determined with any degree of precision. These epochs form so many fixed points, answering as rules for directing our inquiries respecting this ancient chronology of the earth.

OF THE FABULOUS ANIMALS OF THE ANCIENT WRITERS

PERHAPS some persons may be disposed to employ an opposite train of argument, and to allege that the ancients were not only acquainted with as many large quadrupeds as we are, as has been already shown, but that they actually described several others which we do not now know; that we are rash in considering the accounts of all such animals as fabulous; that we ought to search for them with the utmost care, before concluding that we have acquired a complete knowledge of the existing animal creation; and in fine, that among those animals which we presume to be fabulous we may perhaps discover, when better acquainted with them, the actual originals of the bones of those species which are now unknown. Perhaps some may even conceive that the various monsters, essential ornaments of the history of the heroic ages of almost every nation, are precisely those very species which it was necessary to destroy in order to allow the establishment of civilized societies. Thus Theseus and Bellerophon must have been more fortunate than all the nations of more modern days, who have only been able to drive back the noxious animals into the deserts and ill-peopled regions, but have never yet succeeded in exterminating a single species.

It is easy to reply to the foregoing objections, by examining the descriptions that are left us by the ancients of those unknown animals, and by inquiring into their origins. Now the greater number of those animals have an origin purely mythological, and of this origin the descriptions given of them bear the most unequivocal marks; as in almost all of them we see merely the different parts of known animals united by an unbridled imagination, and in contradiction to every established law of nature. Those which have been invented by the poetical fancy of the

Greeks have at least some grace and elegance in their composition, resembling the fantastic decorations which are still observable on the ruins of some ancient buildings, and which have been multiplied by the fertile genius of Raphael in his paintings. Like these, they unite forms which please the eye by agreeable contours and fanciful combinations, but which are utterly repugnant to nature and reason; being merely the productions of inventive and playful genius, or perhaps meant as emblematical representations of metaphysical or moral propositions, veiled under mystical hieroglyphics after the Oriental manner. Learned men may be permitted to employ their time and ingenuity in attempts to decipher the mystic knowledge concealed under the forms of the Sphinx of Thebes, the Pegasus of Thessaly, the Minotaur of Crete, or the Chimera of Epirus; but it would be folly to expect seriously to find such monsters in nature. We might as well endeavor to find the animals of Daniel, or the beasts of the Apocalypse, in some hitherto unexplored recesses of the globe. Neither can we look for the mythological animals of the Persians,— creatures of a still bolder imagination,— such as the *martichore*, or destroyer of men, having a human head on the body of a lion, and the tail of a scorpion; the *griffin*, or guardian of hidden treasures, half eagle and half lion; or the *cartazonon*, or wild ass, armed with a long horn on its forehead.

Ctesias, who reports these as actual living animals, has been looked upon by some authors as an inventor of fables; whereas he only attributes real existence to hieroglyphical representations. These strange compositions of fancy have been seen in modern times on the ruins of Persepolis. It is probable that their hidden meanings may never be ascertained; but at all events we are quite certain that they were never intended to be representations of real animals.

Agatharcides, another fabricator of animals, drew his information in all probability from a similar source. The ancient monuments of Egypt still furnish us with numerous fantastic representations, in which the parts of different kinds of creatures are strangely combined,— men with the heads of animals, and animals with the heads of men,— which have given rise to cynocephali, satyrs, and sphinxes. The custom of exhibiting in the same sculpture, in bas-relief, men of very different heights, — of making kings and conquerors gigantic while their subjects and vassals are represented as only a fourth or fifth part of their size,— must have given rise to the fable of the pigmies. In some corner of these monuments Agatharcides must have discovered his carnivorous bull, whose mouth, extending from ear to ear, devoured every other animal that came in his way. But scarcely any naturalist will acknowledge the existence of any such animal, since nature has never joined cloven hoofs and horns with teeth adapted for cutting and devouring animal food.

There may have been other figures equally strange with these, either among those monuments of Egypt which have not been able to resist the ravages of time, or in the ancient temples of Ethiopia and Arabia which have been destroyed by the religious zeal of the Abyssinians and Mahometans. The monuments of India teem with such figures; but the combinations in these are so ridiculously extravagant that they have never imposed even upon the most credulous. Monsters with a hundred arms and twenty heads of different kinds are far too absurd to be believed.

Nay, the inhabitants of China and Japan have their imaginary animals, which they represent as real, and that too in their religious books. The Mexicans had them. In short, they are to be found among every people whose idolatry has not yet acquired some degree of refinement. But is there any one who could possibly pretend to discover, amidst the realities of animal nature, what are thus so plainly the production of ignorance and superstition? And yet some travelers, influenced by a desire to make themselves famous, have gone so far as to pretend that they saw these fancied beings; or, deceived by a slight resemblance into which they were too careless to inquire, they have identified these with creatures that actually exist. In their eyes, large baboons or monkeys have become *cynocephali*, and sphinxes real men with long tails. It is thus that St. Augustine imagined he had seen a satyr.

Real animals, observed and described with equal inaccuracy, may have given rise to some of these ideal monsters. Thus we can have no doubt of the existence of the hyena, though the back of this animal is not supported by a single bone, and though it does not change its sex yearly, as alleged by Pliny. Perhaps the carnivorous bull may only have been the two-horned rhinoceros falsely described. M. de Weltheim considers the auriferous ants of Herodotus as the *corsacs* of modern naturalists.

The most famous among these fabulous animals of the ancients was the *unicorn*. Its real existence has been obstinately asserted even in the present day, or at least proofs of its existence have been eagerly sought for. Three several animals are frequently mentioned by the ancients as having only one horn placed on the middle of the forehead. The *oryx* of Africa, having cloven hoofs, the hair placed reversely to that of other animals, its height equal to that of the bull, or even of the rhinoceros, and said to resemble deer and goats in its form; the *Indian ass*, having solid hoofs; and the *monoceros*, properly so called, whose feet are sometimes compared to those of the lion and sometimes to those of the elephant, and is therefore considered as having divided feet. The horse unicorn and the bull unicorn are doubtless both referable to the Indian ass, for even the latter is described as having solid hoofs. We may therefore be fully assured that these animals have never really existed, as no solitary horns have ever found their way into our collections, excepting those of the rhinoceros and narwhal.

After careful consideration, it is impossible that we should give any credit to rude sketches made by savages upon rocks. Entirely ignorant of perspective, and wishing to represent the outlines of a straight-horned antelope in profile, they could only give the figure one horn, and thus they produced an oryx. The oryxes that are seen on the Egyptian monuments, likewise, are probably nothing more than productions of the stiff style imposed on the sculptors of the country by religious prejudices. Several of their profiles of quadrupeds show only one fore and one hinder leg; and it is probable that the same rule led them also to represent only one horn. Perhaps their figures may have been copied after individuals that had lost one of their horns by accident, a circumstance that often happens to the chamois and the saiga, species of the antelope genus; and this would be quite sufficient to establish the error. All the ancients, however, have not represented the oryx as having only one horn. Oppian expressly attributes two to this animal, and Ælian mentions one that had four. Finally, if this animal was ruminant and cloven-footed, we are quite certain that its frontal bone must have been divided longitudinally into two, and that it could not possibly, as it is very justly remarked by Camper, have had a horn placed upon the suture.

It may be asked, however: What two-horned animals could have given an idea of the *oryx* in the forms in which it has been transmitted down to us, even independent of the notion of a single horn? To this I answer, as already done by Pallas, that it was the straight-horned *antelope oryx* of Gmelin, improperly named *pasan* by Buffon. This animal inhabits the deserts of Africa, and must frequently approach the confines of Egypt, and appears to be that which is represented in the hieroglyphics. It equals the ox in height, while the shape of its body approaches to that of a stag, and its straight horns present exceedingly formidable weapons, hard almost as iron, and sharp-pointed like javelins. Its hair is whitish; it has black spots and streaks on its face, and the hair on its back points forward. Such is the description given by naturalists; and the fables of the Egyptian priests, which have occasioned the insertion of its figure among their hieroglyphics, do not require to have been founded in nature. Supposing that an individual of this species may have been seen which had lost one of its horns by some accident, it may have been taken as a representative of the entire race, and erroneously adopted by Aristotle to be copied by all his successors. All this is quite possible and even natural, and gives not the smallest evidence for the existence of a single-horned species of antelope.

In regard to the Indian ass, of the alexipharmic virtues of whose horn the ancients speak, we find the Eastern nations of the present day attributing exactly the same property of counteracting poison to the horn of the rhinoceros. When this horn was first imported into Greece, nothing probably was known respecting the animal to which it belonged; and accordingly it was not known to Aristotle. Agatharcides is the first author by whom it is mentioned. In the same manner, ivory was known to the ancients long before the animal from which it is procured; and perhaps some of their travelers may have given to the rhinoceros the name of *Indian ass*, with as much propriety as the Romans denominated the elephant the *bull of Lucania*. Everything which they relate of the strength, size, and ferocity of their wild ass of India corresponds sufficiently with the rhinoceros. In succeeding times, when the rhinoceros came to be better known to naturalists, finding that former authors mentioned a single-horned animal under the name of Indian ass, they concluded without any examination that it must be quite a distinct creature, having solid hoofs. We have remaining a detailed description of the Indian ass, written by Ctesias; but as we have already seen that this must have been taken from the ruins of Persepolis, it should go for nothing in the real history of the animal.

When there afterwards appeared more exact descriptions of an animal having several toes or hoofs on each foot, the ancients conceived it to be a third species of one-horned animals, to which they gave the name of *monoceros*. These double and even triple references are most frequent among ancient writers, because most of their works which have come down to us were mere compilations; because even Aristotle himself has often mixed borrowed facts with those which had come under his own observation; and because the habit of critically investigating the authorities of previous writers was as little known among ancient naturalists as among their historians.

From all these reasonings and digressions, it may be fairly concluded that the large animals of the ancient continent with which we are now acquainted were known to the ancients; and that all the animals of which the ancients have left descriptions, and which are now unknown, were merely fabulous. It also follows that the large animals of the three anciently known quarters of the world were very soon known to the people who frequented their coasts.

It may also be concluded that no large species remains to be discovered in America, as there is no good reason that can be assigned why any such should exist in that country with which we are unacquainted; and in fact none has been discovered there during the last hundred and fifty years. . . .

From all these considerations it may be safely concluded, as shall be more minutely explained in the sequel,— that none of the large species of quadrupeds, whose remains are now found imbedded in regular rocky strata, are at all similar to any of the known living species; that this circumstance is by no means the mere effect of chance, or because the species to which these fossil bones have belonged are still concealed in the desert and uninhabited parts of the world, and have hitherto escaped the observation of travelers, but — that this astonishing phenomenon has proceeded from general causes, and that the careful investigation of it affords one of the best means for discovering and explaining the nature of these causes.